Study and Solutions Guide for

CALCULUS: Early Transcendental Functions

SECOND EDITION

Larson / Hostetler / Edwards

David E. Heyd
The Pennsylvania State University
The Behrend College

Bruce H. Edwards
Mathematics Department
University of Florida

Houghton Mifflin Company　　Boston　　New York

Sponsoring Editor: Jack Shira
Managing Editor: Cathy Cantin
Senior Associate Editor: Maureen Ross
Associate Editor: Michael J. Richards
Assistant Editor: Carolyn Johnson
Supervising Editor: Karen Carter
Project Editor: Patty Bergin
Editorial Assistant: Christine E. Lee
Art Supervisor: Gary Crespo
Marketing Manager: Ros Kane
Marketing Assistant: Erin Dionne
Design: Henry Rachlin
Composition and Art: Meridian Creative Group

Calculator Key font used with permission of Texas Instruments Incorporated. Copyright 1990, 1993, 1996.

Printed in the U.S.A.

ISBN: 0-395-93323-4

6789-EW-03 02 01

Preface

This *Study and Solutions Guide* is designed as a supplement to *Calculus: Early Transcendental Functions, Second Edition*, by Roland E. Larson, Robert P. Hostetler, and Bruce H. Edwards. All references to chapters, theorems, and exercises relate to the main text. Although this supplement is not a substitute for good study habits, it can be valuable when incorporated into a well-planned course of study. The following suggestions may assist you in the use of the text, your lecture notes, and this *Guide*.

- *Read the section in the text for general content before class.* You will be surprised at how much more you will absorb from the lecture if you are aware of the objectives of the section and the types of problems that will be solved. If you are familiar with the topic, you will understand more of the lecture, and you will be able to take fewer (and better) notes.

- *As soon after class as possible, work problems from the exercise set.* The exercise sets in the text are divided into groups of similar problems and are presented in approximately the same order as the section topics. Try to get an overall picture of the various types of problems in the set. As you work your way through the exercise set, reread your class notes and the portion of the section that covers each type of problem. Pay particular attention to the solved examples.

- *Learning calculus takes practice.* You cannot learn calculus merely by reading, any more than you can learn to play the piano or to bowl merely by reading. Only after you have practiced the techniques of a section and have discovered your weak points can you make good use of the supplementary solutions in this *Guide*.

- *Technology.* Graphing utilities and symbolic algebra systems are now readily available. The computer and calculator are merely tools. Your ability to use these tools effectively requires that you continually sharpen your problem-solving skills and your understanding of fundamental mathematical principles.

During many years of teaching we have found that good study habits are essential for success in mathematics. Our students have found the following additional suggestions to be helpful in making the best use of their time.

- *Write neatly in pencil.* A notebook filled with unorganized scribbling has little value.

- *Work at a deliberate and methodical pace, without skipping steps.* When you hurry through a problem you are more apt to make careless arithmetic or algebraic errors that, in the long run, waste time.

- *Keep up with the work.* This suggestion is crucial because calculus is a very structured topic. If you cannot do the problems in one section, you are not likely to be able to do the problems in the next. The night before a quiz or test is not the time to start working problems. In some instances cramming may help you pass an examination, but it is an inferior way to learn and retain essential concepts.

- After working some of the assigned exercises with access to the examples and answers, *try at least one of each type of exercise with the book closed.* This will increase your confidence on quizzes and tests.

- Do not be overly concerned with finding the most efficient way to solve a problem. *Your first goal is to find one way that works.* Short cuts and clever methods come later.

- If you have trouble with the algebra of calculus, *refer to the algebra review at the beginning of this guide.*

We wish to acknowledge several people whose help and encouragement were invaluable in the production of this *Guide*. First, we are grateful to Roland E. Larson, and Robert P. Hostetler for the privilege of working with them on the main text. We also wish to thank the staffs at Larson Texts, Inc. and Houghton Mifflin Company. We are also grateful to our wives, Jean and Consuela, and our children, Ed, Ruth, Andy, and Lisa for their love and support.

David E. Heyd
Bruce H. Edwards

Preface

Contents

Algebra Review

0.1 Monomial Factors

Factor as indicated:

(a) $3x^4 + 4x^3 - x^2 = x^2(\quad)$

(b) $2\sqrt{x} + 6x^{3/2} = 2\sqrt{x}(\quad)$

(c) $e^{-x} - xe^{-x} + 2x^2e^{-x} = e^{-x}(\quad)$

(d) $x^{-1} - 2 + x = x^{-1} = x^{-1}(\quad)$

(e) $\dfrac{x}{2} - 6x^2 = \dfrac{x}{2}(\quad)$

(f) $\sin x + \tan x = \sin x(\quad)$

(g) $\dfrac{1}{2x^2 + 4x} = \dfrac{1}{2x}(\quad)$

Solution:

(a) $3x^4 + 4x^3 - x^2 = x^2(3x^2 + 4x - 1)$

(b) $2\sqrt{x} + 6x^{3/2} = 2\sqrt{x}(1 + 3x)$

(c) $e^{-x} - xe^{-x} + 2x^2e^{-x} = e^{-x}(1 - x + 2x^2)$

(d) $x^{-1} - 2 + x = x^{-1} = x^{-1}(1 - 2x + x^2)$

(e) $\dfrac{x}{2} - 6x^2 = \dfrac{x}{2}(1 - 12x)$

(f) $\sin x + \tan x = \sin x + \dfrac{\sin x}{\cos x} = \sin x\left(1 + \dfrac{1}{\cos x}\right)$

$$= \sin x(1 + \sec x)$$

(g) $\dfrac{1}{2x^2 + 4x} = \dfrac{1}{2x}\left(\dfrac{1}{x + 2}\right)$

0.2 Binomial Factors

Factor as indicated:

(a) $(x - 1)^2(x) - (x - 1) = (x - 1)(\quad)$

(b) $3(x^2 + 4)(x^2 + 1) + 6(x^2 + 4)^2 = 3(x^2 + 4)(\quad)$

(c) $\sqrt{x^2 + 1} - \dfrac{x^2}{\sqrt{x^2 + 1}} = \dfrac{1}{\sqrt{x^2 + 1}}(\quad)$

(d) $(x - 3)^3(x + 2) - 2(x - 3)^2(x + 2)^2 = (x - 3)^2(x + 2)(\quad)$

(e) $(2x + 1)^{3/2}(x^{1/2}) + (2x + 1)^{5/2}(x^{-1/2}) = (2x + 1)^{3/2}(x^{-1/2})(\quad)$

Solution:

(a) $(x - 1)^2(x) - (x - 1) = (x - 1)[(x - 1)x - 1]$

$$= (x - 1)(x^2 - x - 1)$$

(b) $3(x^2 + 4)(x^2 + 1) + 6(x^2 + 4)^2 = 3(x^2 + 4)[(x^2 + 1) + 2(x^2 + 4)]$

$$= 3(x^2 + 4)(3x^2 + 9)$$

—CONTINUED—

1

—CONTINUED—

(c)
$$\sqrt{x^2 + 1} - \frac{x^2}{\sqrt{x^2 + 1}} = (x^2 + 1)^{1/2} - x^2(x^2 + 1)^{-1/2}$$

$$= (x^2 + 1)^{-1/2}[(x^2 + 1) - x^2]$$

$$= \frac{1}{\sqrt{x^2 + 1}}$$

(d) $(x - 3)^3(x + 2) - 2(x - 3)^2(x + 2)^2 = (x - 3)^2(x + 2)[(x - 3) - 2(x + 2)]$

$$= (x - 3)^2(x + 2)(-x - 7)$$

(e) $(2x + 1)^{3/2}(x^{1/2}) + (2x + 1)^{5/2}(x^{-1/2}) = (2x + 1)^{3/2}(x^{-1/2})[x + (2x + 1)]$

$$= (2x + 1)^{3/2}(x^{-1/2})(3x + 1)$$

0.3   Factoring Quadratic Expressions

Factor as indicated:

(a) $x^2 - 3x + 2 = ($ $)($ $)$

(b) $x^2 - 9 = ($ $)($ $)$

(c) $x^2 + 5x - 6 = ($ $)($ $)$

(d) $x^2 + 5x + 6 = ($ $)($ $)$

(e) $2x^2 + 5x - 3 = ($ $)($ $)$

(f) $e^{2x} + 2 + e^{-2x} = ($ $)^2$

(g) $x^4 - 7x^2 + 12 = ($ $)($ $)($ $)$

(h) $1 - \sin^2 x = ($ $)($ $)$

Solution:

(a) $x^2 - 3x + 2 = (x - 2)(x - 1)$

(b) $x^2 - 9 = (x + 3)(x - 3)$

(c) $x^2 + 5x - 6 = (x + 6)(x - 1)$

(d) $x^2 + 5x + 6 = (x + 2)(x + 3)$

(e) $2x^2 + 5x - 3 = (2x - 1)(x + 3)$

(f) $e^{2x} + 2 + e^{-2x} = (e^x + e^{-x})^2$

(g) $x^4 - 7x^2 + 12 = (x^2 - 3)(x^2 - 4) = (x^2 - 3)(x + 2)(x - 2)$

(h) $1 - \sin^2 x = (1 + \sin x)(1 - \sin x)$

0.4   Cancellation

Reduce each expression to lowest terms:

(a) $\dfrac{3x + 9}{6x}$

(b) $\dfrac{x^2}{x^{1/2}}$

(c) $\dfrac{(x + 1)^3(x - 2) + 3(x + 1)^2}{(x + 1)^4}$

(d) $\dfrac{x^{1/2} - x^{1/3}}{x^{1/6}}$

(e) $\dfrac{\sqrt{x - 1} + (x - 1)^{3/2}}{\sqrt{x - 1}}$

(f) $\dfrac{1 - (\sin x + \cos x)^2}{2 \sin x}$

Solution:

(a) $\dfrac{3x + 9}{6x} = \dfrac{3(x + 3)}{3(2x)} = \dfrac{x + 3}{2x}$

(b) $\dfrac{x^2}{x^{1/2}} = \dfrac{(x^{1/2})(x^{3/2})}{x^{1/2}} = x^{3/2}$

—CONTINUED—

—CONTINUED—

(c) $\dfrac{(x + 1)^3(x - 2) + 3(x + 1)^2}{(x + 1)^4} = \dfrac{(x + 1)^2[(x + 1)(x - 2) + 3]}{(x + 1)^4}$

$$= \dfrac{x^2 - x + 1}{(x + 1)^2}$$

(d) $\dfrac{x^{1/2} - x^{1/3}}{x^{1/6}} = \dfrac{x^{1/6}(x^{2/6} - x^{1/6})}{x^{1/6}} = x^{1/3} - x^{1/6}$

(e) $\dfrac{\sqrt{x - 1} + (x - 1)^{3/2}}{\sqrt{x - 1}} = \dfrac{\sqrt{x - 1}[1 + (x - 1)]}{\sqrt{x - 1}} = x$

(f) $\dfrac{1 - (\sin x + \cos x)^2}{2 \sin x} = \dfrac{1 - (\sin^2 x + 2 \sin x \cos x + \cos^2 x)}{2 \sin x}$

$$= \dfrac{1 - (\sin^2 x + \cos^2 x) - 2 \sin x \cos x}{2 \sin x}$$

$$= \dfrac{1 - 1 - 2 \sin x \cos x}{2 \sin x} = -\cos x$$

0.5   Quadratic Formula

Equation	*Solve for*
(a) $x^2 - 4x - 1 = 0$	x
(b) $2x^2 + x - 3 = 0$	x
(c) $\cos^2 x + 3 \cos x + 2 = 0$	$\cos x$
(d) $x^2 - xy - (1 + y^2) = 0$	x
(e) $x^4 - 4x^2 + 2 = 0$	x^2

Solution:

(a) $x = \dfrac{4 \pm \sqrt{16 + 4}}{2} = \dfrac{4 \pm \sqrt{20}}{2} = \dfrac{4 \pm 2\sqrt{5}}{2} = 2 \pm \sqrt{5}$

(b) $x = \dfrac{-1 \pm \sqrt{1 + 24}}{4} = \dfrac{-1 \pm 5}{4}$

$x = \dfrac{4}{4} = 1$ or $x = -\dfrac{6}{4} = -\dfrac{3}{2}$

(c) $\cos x = \dfrac{-3 \pm \sqrt{9 - 8}}{2} = \dfrac{-3 \pm 1}{2}$

$\cos x = -\dfrac{2}{2} = -1$ or $\cos x = -\dfrac{4}{2} = -2$

(d) $x = \dfrac{y \pm \sqrt{y^2 + 4(1 + y^2)}}{2} = \dfrac{y \pm \sqrt{y^2 + 4 + 4y^2}}{2}$

$$= \dfrac{y \pm \sqrt{5y^2 + 4}}{2}$$

(e) $x^2 = \dfrac{4 \pm \sqrt{16 - 8}}{2} = \dfrac{4 \pm \sqrt{8}}{2} = \dfrac{4 \pm 2\sqrt{2}}{2} = 2 \pm \sqrt{2}$

0.6   Synthetic Division

Using synthetic division to factor as indicated:

(a) $x^3 - 4x^2 + 2x + 1 = (x - 1)(\quad)$

(b) $2x^3 + 5x + 7 = (x + 1)(\quad)$

(c) $x^4 - 3x^3 + x^2 + x + 2 = (x - 2)(\quad)$

(d) $4x^4 + 3x^2 - 1 = (2x - 1)(\quad)$

Solution:

(a) $x^3 - 4x^2 + 2x + 1$

$$
\begin{array}{r|rrrr}
1 & 1 & -4 & 2 & 1 \\
 &   & 1 & -3 & -1 \\
\hline
 & 1 & -3 & -1 & 0
\end{array}
$$

$x^3 - 4x^2 + 2x + 1 = (x - 1)(x^2 - 3x - 1)$

(b) $2x^3 + 5x + 7$

$$
\begin{array}{r|rrrr}
-1 & 2 & 0 & 5 & 7 \\
 &   & -2 & 2 & -7 \\
\hline
 & 2 & -2 & 7 & 0
\end{array}
$$

$2x^3 - 5x + 7 = (x + 1)(2x^2 - 2x + 7)$

(c) $x^4 - 3x^3 + x^2 + x + 2$

$$
\begin{array}{r|rrrrr}
2 & 1 & -3 & 1 & 1 & 2 \\
 &   & 2 & -2 & -2 & -2 \\
\hline
 & 1 & -1 & -1 & -1 & 0
\end{array}
$$

$x^4 - 3x^3 + x^2 + x + 2 = (x - 2)(x^3 - x^2 - x - 1)$

(d) $4x^4 + 3x^2 - 1$

$$
\begin{array}{r|rrrrr}
\frac{1}{2} & 4 & 0 & 3 & 0 & -1 \\
 &   & 2 & 1 & 2 & 1 \\
\hline
 & 4 & 2 & 4 & 2 & 0
\end{array}
$$

$4x^4 + 3x^2 - 1 = \left(x - \dfrac{1}{2}\right)(4x^3 + 2x^2 + 4x + 2)$

$$= (2x - 1)(2x^3 + x^2 + 2x + 1)$$

0.7   Special Products

Factor completely (into linear or irreducible quadratic factors):

(a) $x^3 - 27$

(b) $x^3 - 3x^2 + 3x - 1$

(c) $x^3 + 6x^2 + 12x + 8$

(d) $x^4 - 25$

(e) $x^4 - 8x^3 + 24x^2 - 32x + 16$

Solution:

(a) $x^3 - 27 = (x - 3)(x^2 + 3x + 9)$

(b) $x^3 - 3x^2 + 3x - 1 = (x - 1)^3$

(c) $x^3 + 6x^2 + 12x + 8 = x^3 + 3(2)x^2 + 3(2^2)x + 2^3 = (x + 2)^3$

(d) $x^4 - 25 = (x^2 + 5)(x^2 - 5) = (x^2 + 5)\left(x + \sqrt{5}\right)\left(x - \sqrt{5}\right)$

(e) $x^4 - 8x^3 + 24x^2 - 32x + 16 = x^4 - 4(2)x^3 + 6(2^2)x^2 - 4(2^3)x + 2^4 = (x - 2)^4$

0.8   Factoring by Grouping

Factor completely (into linear or irreducible quadratic factors):

(a) $x^3 + 4x^2 - 2x - 8$

(b) $x^3 + 2x^2 + 3x + 6$

(c) $5\cos^2 x - 5\sin^2 x + \sin x + \cos x$

(d) $\cos^2 x + 4\cos x + 4 - \tan^2 x$

Solution:

(a) $x^3 + 4x^2 - 2x - 8 = x^2(x + 4) - 2(x + 4)$

$$= (x^2 - 2)(x + 4)$$

$$= \left(x + \sqrt{2}\right)\left(x - \sqrt{2}\right)(x + 4)$$

—CONTINUED—

—CONTINUED—

(b) $x^3 + 2x^2 + 3x + 6 = x^2(x + 2) + 3(x + 2)$

$$= (x^2 + 3)(x + 2)$$

(c) $5\cos^2 x - 5\sin^2 x + \sin x + \cos x = 5(\cos^2 x - \sin^2 x) + (\sin x + \cos x)$

$$= 5(\cos x - \sin x)(\cos x - \sin x) + (\cos x + \sin x)$$

$$= (\cos x + \sin x)[5(\cos x - \sin x) + 1]$$

(d) $\cos^2 x + 4\cos x + 4 - \tan^2 x = (\cos x + 2)^2 - \tan^2 x$

$$= (\cos x + 2 + \tan x)(\cos x + 2 - \tan x)$$

0.9 Simplifying

Rewrite each of the following in simplest form:

(a) $\dfrac{(x - 1)(x + 3) - (x + 1)^2}{x + 1}$

(b) $\dfrac{\sqrt{x^2 + 1} - \dfrac{1}{\sqrt{x^2 + 1}}}{x^2 + 1}$

(c) $\dfrac{x^2 - 5x + 6}{x^2 - 4x + 4}$

(d) $\dfrac{1}{x + 1} - \dfrac{1}{x - 1} - \dfrac{2}{x^2 - 1}$

(e) $\dfrac{x(-2x)}{2\sqrt{1 - x^2}} + \sqrt{1 - x^2} + \dfrac{1}{\sqrt{1 - x^2}}$

Solution:

(a) $\dfrac{(x - 1)(x + 3) - (x + 1)^2}{x + 1} = \dfrac{(x^2 + 2x - 3) - (x^2 + 2x + 1)}{x + 1} = \dfrac{-4}{x + 1}$

(b) $\dfrac{\sqrt{x^2 + 1} - \dfrac{1}{\sqrt{x^2 + 1}}}{x^2 + 1} = \dfrac{\dfrac{1}{\sqrt{x^2 + 1}}(x^2 + 1 - 1)}{x^2 + 1} = \dfrac{x^2 + 1 - 1}{\sqrt{x^2 + 1}(x^2 + 1)} = \dfrac{x^2}{(x^2 + 1)^{3/2}}$

(c) $\dfrac{x^2 - 5x + 6}{x^2 - 4x + 4} = \dfrac{(x - 2)(x - 3)}{(x - 2)^2} = \dfrac{x - 3}{x - 2}$

(d) $\dfrac{1}{x + 1} - \dfrac{1}{x - 1} - \dfrac{2}{x^2 - 1} = \dfrac{(x - 1) - (x + 1) - 2}{x^2 - 1} = \dfrac{-4}{x^2 - 1}$

(e) $\dfrac{x(-2x)}{2\sqrt{1 - x^2}} + \sqrt{1 - x^2} + \dfrac{1}{\sqrt{1 - x^2}} = \dfrac{-x^2}{\sqrt{1 - x^2}} + \dfrac{1 - x^2}{\sqrt{1 - x^2}} + \dfrac{1}{\sqrt{1 - x^2}} = \dfrac{2 - 2x^2}{\sqrt{1 - x^2}}$

$$= \dfrac{2(1 - x^2)}{\sqrt{1 - x^2}} = 2\sqrt{1 - x^2}$$

0.10 Rationalizing

Remove the sum or difference from the denominator by multiplying the numerator and denominator by the conjugate of the denominator.

(a) $\dfrac{1}{1 - \cos x}$

(b) $\dfrac{x}{1 - \sqrt{x^2 + 1}}$

(c) $\dfrac{2}{x + \sqrt{x^2 + 1}}$

Solution:

(a) $\dfrac{1}{1 - \cos x} = \left(\dfrac{1}{1 - \cos x}\right)\left(\dfrac{1 + \cos x}{1 + \cos x}\right)$

$$= \dfrac{1 + \cos x}{1 - \cos^2 x} = \dfrac{1 + \cos x}{\sin^2 x}$$

—CONTINUED—

—CONTINUED—

(b) $\left(\dfrac{x}{1 - \sqrt{x^2 + 1}}\right)\left(\dfrac{1 + \sqrt{x^2 + 1}}{1 + \sqrt{x^2 + 1}}\right) = \dfrac{x\left(1 + \sqrt{x^2 + 1}\right)}{1 - (x^2 + 1)}$

$$= \dfrac{x\left(1 + \sqrt{x^2 + 1}\right)}{-x^2} = \dfrac{1 + \sqrt{x^2 + 1}}{-x}$$

(c) $\left(\dfrac{2}{x + \sqrt{x^2 + 1}}\right)\left(\dfrac{x - \sqrt{x^2 + 1}}{x - \sqrt{x^2 + 1}}\right) = \dfrac{2\left(x - \sqrt{x^2 + 1}\right)}{x^2 - (x^2 + 1)} = -2\left(x - \sqrt{x^2 + 1}\right)$

0.11   Algebraic Errors to Avoid

Error	Correct form	Comments
$a - (x - b) \neq a - x - b$	$a - (x - b) = a - x + b$	Change all signs when distribution negative through parentheses.
$(a + b)^2 \neq a^2 + b^2$	$(a + b)^2 = a^2 + 2ab + b^2$	Don't forget middle term when squaring binomials.
$\left(\dfrac{1}{2}a\right)\left(\dfrac{1}{2}b\right) \neq \dfrac{1}{2}ab$	$\left(\dfrac{1}{2}a\right)\left(\dfrac{1}{2}b\right) = \dfrac{1}{4}(ab)$	1/2 occurs twice as a factor.
$\dfrac{a}{x + b} \neq \dfrac{a}{x} + \dfrac{a}{b}$	Leave as $\dfrac{a}{x + b}$	Don't add denominators when adding fractions.
$\dfrac{1}{a} + \dfrac{1}{b} \neq \dfrac{1}{a + b}$	$\dfrac{1}{a} + \dfrac{1}{b} = \dfrac{a + b}{ab}$	Use definition for adding fractions.
$\dfrac{\frac{x}{a}}{b} \neq \dfrac{bx}{a}$	$\dfrac{\frac{x}{a}}{b} = \left(\dfrac{x}{a}\right)\left(\dfrac{1}{b}\right) = \dfrac{x}{ab}$	Multiply by reciprocal of the denominator.
$\dfrac{1}{3x} \neq \dfrac{1}{3}x$	$\dfrac{1}{3x} = \dfrac{1}{3} \cdot \dfrac{1}{x}$	Use definition for multiplying fractions.
$1/x + 2 \neq \dfrac{1}{x + 2}$	$1/x + 2 = \dfrac{1}{x} + 2$	Be careful when using a slash to denote division.
$(x^2)^3 \neq x^5$	$(x^2)^3 = x^{2 \cdot 3} = x^6$	Multiply exponents when an exponential form is raised to a power.
$2x^3 \neq (2x)^3$	$2x^3 = 2(x^3)$	Exponents have priority over coefficients.
$\dfrac{1}{x^2 + x^3} \neq x^{-2} + x^{-3}$	Leave as $\dfrac{1}{x^2 + x^3}$	Don't shift term-by-term from denominator to numerator.
$\sqrt{5x} \neq 5\sqrt{x}$	$\sqrt{5x} = \sqrt{5}\sqrt{x}$	Radicals apply to every factor inside radical.
$\sqrt{x^2 + a^2} \neq x + a$	Leave as $\sqrt{x^2 + a^2}$	Don't apply radicals term-by-term.
$\dfrac{a + bx}{a} \neq 1 + bx$	$\dfrac{a + bx}{a} = 1 + \dfrac{b}{a}x$	Cancel common factor, *not* common terms.
$\dfrac{a + ax}{a} \neq a + x$	$\dfrac{a + ax}{a} = 1 + x$	Factor *before* canceling.

CHAPTER P
Preparation for Calculus

CHAPTER P
Preparation for Calculus

Section P.1   Graphs and Models

Solutions to Exercises

1. $y = -\frac{1}{2}x + 2$

x-intercept: $(4, 0)$

y-intercept: $(0, 2)$

Matches graph (b).

3. $y = 4 - x^2$

x-intercepts: $(2, 0), (-2, 0)$

y-intercept: $(0, 4)$

Matches graph (a).

5. To find the x-intercepts, let $y = 0$. Then

$$x^2 + x - 2 = 0$$

and by factoring (or by the quadratic formula),

$$(x + 2)(x - 1) = 0.$$

Therefore, $y = 0$ when $x = -2$ or $x = 1$ and the x-intercepts are $(-2, 0)$ and $(1, 0)$. To find the y-intercepts, let $x = 0$. Then $y = 0^2 + 0 - 2 = -2$, and the y-intercept is $(0, -2)$.

7. $y = x^2\sqrt{9 - x^2}$

y-intercept: $y = 0^2\sqrt{9 - 0^2}$

$\qquad\qquad\quad y = 0;\ (0, 0)$

x-intercepts: $0 = x^2\sqrt{9 - x^2}$

$\qquad\qquad\quad 0 = x^2\sqrt{(3 - x)(3 + x)}$

$\qquad\qquad\quad x = 0, \pm 3;\ (0, 0), (\pm 3, 0)$

9. To find the x-intercepts you let $y = 0$. Then

$$x^2(0) - x^2 + 4(0) = -x^2 = 0,$$

which implies that $x = 0$. Letting $y = 0$ yields the same result and the only intercept is $(0, 0)$.

11. Symmetric with respect to the y-axis since $y = (-x)^2 - 2 = x^2 - 2$.

13. There is *no symmetry* about the y-axis since replacing x with $-x$ in the equation yields

$$y^2 = (-x)^3 - 4(-x) = -x^3 + 4x$$

which is *not* equivalent to the original equation. There is *symmetry* about the x-axis since replacing y with $-y$ in the equation yields

$$(-y)^2 = x^3 - 4x \quad\text{or}\quad y^2 = x^3 - 4x$$

which *is* equivalent to the original equation. There is *no symmetry* about the origin since replacing x with $-x$ and y with $-y$ in the equation yields

$$(-y)^2 = (-x)^3 - 4(-x) \quad\text{or}\quad y^2 = -x^3 + 4x$$

which is *not* equivalent to the original equation.

15. Symmetric with respect to the origin since

$$(-y) = (-x)^3 + (-x)$$

$$-y = -x^3 - x$$

$$y = x^3 + x.$$

17. There is *no symmetry* about the y-axis since replacing x with $-x$ in the equation yields

$$y = \frac{-x}{(-x)^2 + 1} = \frac{-x}{x^2 + 1}$$

which is *not* equivalent to the original equation. There is *no symmetry* about the x-axis since replacing y with $-y$ in the equation yields

$$-y = \frac{x}{x^2 + 1}$$

which is *not* equivalent to the original equation. There is *symmetry* with respect to the origin since replacing x with $-x$ and y with $-y$ in the equation yields

$$-y = \frac{-x}{(-x)^2 + 1} \quad \text{or} \quad y = \frac{x}{x^2 + 1}$$

which *is* equivalent to the original equation.

19. $y = -3x + 2$

Intercepts: $\left(\frac{2}{3}, 0\right), (0, 2)$

Symmetry: none

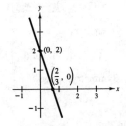

21. $y = \frac{x}{2} - 4$

Intercepts: $(8, 0), (0, -4)$

Symmetry: none

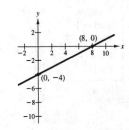

23. To find the x-intercepts, let $y = 0$. Then

$$0 = 1 - x^2$$

and by factoring

$$0 = (1 + x)(1 - x).$$

Therefore, the x-intercepts are $(-1, 0)$ and $(1, 0)$. To find any y-intercept, let $x = 0$. Then $y = 1$ and the y-intercept is $(0, 1)$. There is *symmetry* with respect to the y-axis since replacing x with $-x$ in the equation yields

$$y = 1 - (-x)^2 \quad \text{or} \quad y = 1 - x^2$$

which is equivalent to the original equation. Some solution points are given in the table.

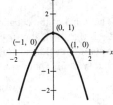

x	0	±1	±2
y	1	0	-3

25. $y = x^3 + 2$

Intercepts: $\left(-\sqrt[3]{2}, 0\right), (0, 2)$

Symmetry: none

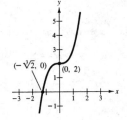

27. $y = (x + 2)^2$

Intercepts: $(-2, 0), (0, 4)$

Symmetry: none

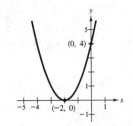

29. The graph has no intercepts since the equation has no solution if either $x = 0$ or $y = 0$. There is *symmetry* with respect to the origin since replacing x with $-x$ and y with $-y$ in the equation yields

$$-y = \frac{1}{-x}$$

which is equivalent to the original equation. Some solution points are given in the table.

x	$\frac{1}{5}$	$\frac{1}{2}$	1	2	3	4	5
y	5	2	1	$\frac{1}{2}$	$\frac{1}{3}$	$\frac{1}{4}$	$\frac{1}{5}$

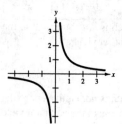

From the table we see that y increases without bound as x approaches 0, and y approaches 0 as x increases without bound. Using this information and symmetry, we obtain the graph in the figure.

31.
```
Xmin = -3
Xmax = 5
Xscl = 1
Ymin = -3
Ymax = 5
Yscl = 1
```

33. $y = -2x^2 + x + 1$

$\qquad = (2x + 1)(-x + 1)$

Intercepts:

$\qquad \left(-\frac{1}{2}, 0\right), (1, 0), (0, 1)$

Symmetry: none

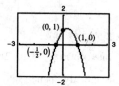

35. $y = \dfrac{5}{x^2 + 1} - 1$

Intercepts:

$\qquad (0, 4), (-2, 0), (2, 0)$

Symmetry: y-axis

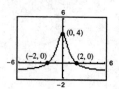

37.

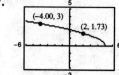

(a) $(2, y) = (2, 1.73)$ $\left(y = \sqrt{5 - 2} = \sqrt{3} \approx 1.73\right)$

(b) $(x, 3) = (-4, 3)$ $\left(3 = \sqrt{5 - (-4)}\right)$

39. The graph of the equation passes through the points $(-2, 0)$, $(4, 0)$, and $(6, 0)$. If the equation is a polynomial equation, then factors of the equation are $(x + 2)$, $(x - 4)$, and $(x - 6)$. Therefore, one possible equation is

$\qquad y = (x + 2)(x - 4)(x - 6) = x^3 - 8x^2 + 4x + 48.$

The graph of the equation is shown in the figure.

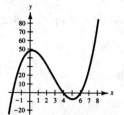

41. Some possible equations:

$\qquad y = x$

$\qquad y = x^3$

$\qquad y = 3x^3 - x$

$\qquad y = \sqrt[3]{x}$

43. $x + y = 2 \Longrightarrow y = 2 - x$

$\qquad 2x - y = 1 \Longrightarrow y = 2x - 1$

$\qquad\qquad 2 - x = 2x - 1$

$\qquad\qquad\quad 3 = 3x$

$\qquad\qquad\quad 1 = x$

The corresponding y-value is $y = 1$.

Point of intersection: $(1, 1)$

45. To solve the two equations

$$x + y = 7$$
$$3x - 2y = 11$$

simultaneously, multiply the first equation by 2 and add. Thus,

$$\begin{aligned} 2x + 2y &= 14 \\ (+)\ 3x - 2y &= 11 \\ \hline 5x\quad\;\; &= 25 \\ x &=\ 5. \end{aligned}$$

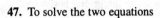

Substituting $x = 5$ into the first equation, we have

$$5 + y = 7 \quad \text{or} \quad y = 2.$$

Thus, the point of intersection is $(5, 2)$.

47. To solve the two equations

$$x^2 + y^2 = 5$$
$$x - y = 1$$

simultaneously, solve the second equation for x and obtain $x = y + 1$. Substituting into the first equation yields

$$(y + 1)^2 + y^2 = 5$$
$$(y^2 + 2y + 1) + y^2 = 5$$
$$2y^2 + 2y - 4 = 0$$
$$2(y + 2)(y - 1) = 0$$

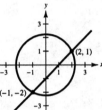

which implies that $y = -2$ or $y = 1$. Therefore,

$$x = (-2) + 1 = -1 \quad \text{or} \quad x = 1 + 1 = 2$$

and the points of intersection are $(-1, -2)$ and $(2, 1)$.

49.

$$y = x^3$$
$$y = x$$
$$x^3 = x$$
$$x^3 - x = 0$$
$$x(x + 1)(x - 1) = 0$$
$$x = 0, x = -1, \text{ or } x = 1$$

The corresponding y-values are $y = 0, y = -1,$ and $y = 1$.

Points of intersection: $(0, 0), (-1, -1), (1, 1)$

51. The graphs are shown in the figure. Equating the two expressions for y yields

$$x^3 - 2x^2 + x - 1 = -x^2 + 3x - 1$$
$$x^3 - 2x^2 + x^2 + x - 3x - 1 + 1 = 0$$
$$x^3 - x^2 - 2x = 0$$
$$x(x - 2)(x + 1) = 0.$$

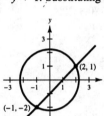

Thus, $x = 0, 2,$ or -1, and substituting these values into the second (or first) equation, we have

$$y = -(0)^2 + 3(0) - 1 = -1$$
$$y = -(2)^2 + 3(2) - 1 = 1$$
$$y = -(-1)^2 + 3(-1) - 1 = -5.$$

Therefore, the points of intersection are $(0, -1), (2, 1),$ and $(-1, -5)$.

53. $5.5\sqrt{x} + 10{,}000 = 3.29x$

$$\left(5.5\sqrt{x}\right)^2 = (3.29x - 10{,}000)^2$$

$$30.25x = 10.8241x^2 - 65{,}800x + 100{,}000{,}000$$

$$0 = 10.8241x^2 - 65{,}830.25x + 100{,}000{,}000 \qquad \text{Use the Quadratic Formula.}$$

$$x \approx 3133 \text{ units}$$

The other root, $x \approx 2949$, does not satisfy the equation $R = C$. This problem can also be solved by using a graphing utility and finding the intersection of the graphs of C and R.

55. (a) Using a graphing utility, you obtain

$$y = 0.0127t^2 + 4.4181t + 36.2896.$$

(b)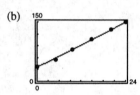

(c) For the year 2000, $t = 30$ and $y \approx 180.3$ CPI.

57. The graph of

$$y = \frac{10{,}770}{x^2} - 0.37$$

for $5 \le x \le 100$ is shown in the figure. If x is replaced by $2x$, we have

$$y = \frac{10{,}770}{(2x)^2} - 0.37 = \frac{10{,}770}{4x^2} - 0.37.$$

Therefore, the resistance is changed by approximately a factor of $1/4$.

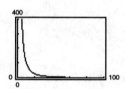

59. False; x-axis symmetry means that if $(1, -2)$ is on the graph, then $(1, 2)$ is also on the graph.

61. True; the x-intercepts are

$$\left(\frac{-b \pm \sqrt{b^2 - 4ac}}{2a}, 0\right).$$

63.   Distance to the origin $= K \times$ Distance to $(2, 0)$

$$\sqrt{x^2 + y^2} = K\sqrt{(x - 2)^2 + y^2}, K \ne 1$$

$$x^2 + y^2 = K^2(x^2 - 4x + 4 + y^2)$$

$$(1 - K^2)x^2 + (1 - K^2)y^2 + 4K^2x - 4K^2 = 0$$

Note: This is the equation of a circle!

Section P.2   Linear Models and Rates of Change

1. $m = 1$

3. $m = 0$

5. $m = -12$

7.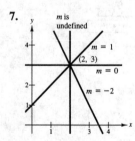

9. Let $(3, -4) = (x_1, y_1)$ and $(5, 2) = (x_2, y_2)$. The slope of the line passing through (x_1, y_1) and (x_2, y_2) is

$$m = \frac{y_2 - y_1}{x_2 - x_1} = \frac{2 - (-4)}{5 - 3} = \frac{6}{2} = 3.$$

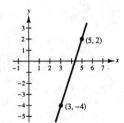

11. $m = \dfrac{4 - 2}{-2 - 1}$

$= -\dfrac{2}{3}$

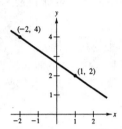

13. Since the slope is 0, the line is horizontal and its equation is $y = 1$. Therefore, three additional points are $(0, 1)$, $(1, 1)$, and $(3, 1)$.

15. Since the slope is -3, it follows that

$$\frac{\Delta y}{\Delta x} = \frac{-3}{1}.$$

Therefore, for each positive one-unit increase in x, y decreases three units. Starting at the point $(1, 7)$, we have

$$(1 + 1, 7 - 3) = (2, 4),$$

$$(2 + 1, 4 - 3) = (3, 1), \quad \text{and}$$

$$(3 + 1, 1 - 3) = (4, -2).$$

Since the slope is -3, it also follows that

$$\frac{\Delta y}{\Delta x} = \frac{3}{-1}.$$

Therefore, for each one-unit decrease in x, y increases three units. Starting at the point $(1, 7)$, we have

$$(1 - 1, 7 + 3) = (0, 10),$$

$$(0 - 1, 10 + 3) = (-1, 13), \quad \text{and}$$

$$(-1 - 1, 13 + 3) = (-2, 16).$$

17. The slopes of the line segments are

$$\frac{1.63 - 1.25}{1} = 0.38$$

$$\frac{2.53 - 1.63}{1} = 0.9$$

$$\frac{2.32 - 2.53}{1} = -0.21$$

$$\frac{2.87 - 2.32}{1} = 0.55$$

$$\frac{2.99 - 2.87}{1} = 0.12$$

$$\frac{3.10 - 2.99}{1} = 0.11$$

$$\frac{2.95 - 3.10}{1} = -0.15.$$

Earnings decreased most rapidly from 1989 to 1990 ($m = -0.21$). Earnings increased most rapidly from 1988 to 1989 ($m = 0.9$).

19. Given a line L, you can use any two distinct points to calculate its slope. Since a line is straight, the ratio of the change in y-values to the change in x-values will always be the same. See Section P.2 Exercise 85 for a proof.

21. $x + 5y = 20$

$$y = -\tfrac{1}{5}x + 4$$

Therefore, the slope is $m = -\tfrac{1}{5}$ and the y-intercept is $(0, 4)$.

23. $x = 4$

The line is vertical. Therefore, the slope is undefined and there is no y-intercept.

25. Let $(2, 1) = (x_1, y_1)$ and $(0, -3) = (x_2, y_2)$. The slope of the line passing through (x_1, y_1) and (x_2, y_2) is

$$m = \frac{y_2 - y_1}{x_2 - x_1} = \frac{-3 - 1}{0 - 2} = 2.$$

Using the point-slope form of the equation of a line, we have

$$y - y_1 = m(x - x_1)$$
$$y - 1 = 2(x - 2)$$
$$y - 1 = 2x - 4$$
$$0 = 2x - y - 3. \qquad \text{General form}$$

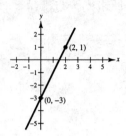

27. $m = \dfrac{3 - 0}{-1 - 0} = -3$

$$y - 0 = -3(x - 0)$$
$$y = -3x$$
$$3x + y = 0$$

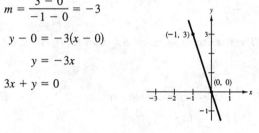

29. $m = 0$

$$y = -2$$
$$y + 2 = 0$$

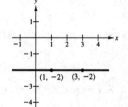

31. Using the slope-intercept form of the equation of a line, we have

$$y = mx + b$$
$$y = \tfrac{3}{4}x + 3$$
$$4y = 3x + 12$$
$$0 = 3x - 4y + 12.$$

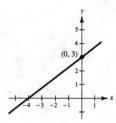

33.
$$y = \tfrac{2}{3}x$$
$$3y = 2x$$
$$2x - 3y = 0$$

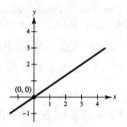

35. $y - 2 = 4(x - 0)$

$$y = 4x + 2$$
$$0 = 4x - y + 2$$

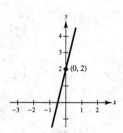

37.
$$x = 3$$
$$x - 3 = 0$$

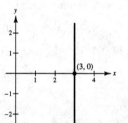

39.
$$\frac{x}{2} + \frac{y}{3} = 1$$
$$3x + 2y - 6 = 0$$

41. $\dfrac{x}{a} + \dfrac{y}{a} = 1$

$$\frac{1}{a} + \frac{2}{a} = 1$$
$$\frac{3}{a} = 1$$
$$a = 3 \Longrightarrow x + y = 3$$
$$x + y - 3 = 0$$

43. The line given by $4x - 2y = 3$ has a slope of 2 since

$$4x - 2y = 3$$
$$-2y = -4x + 3$$
$$y = 2x - \tfrac{3}{2} = mx + b.$$

(a) The line through $(2, 1)$ parallel to $4x - 2y = 3$ must also have a slope of 2. Thus its equation must be

$$y - y_1 = m(x - x_1)$$
$$y - 1 = 2(x - 2)$$
$$-2x + y + 3 = 0$$
$$2x - y - 3 = 0.$$

(b) The line through $(2, 1)$ perpendicular to $4x - 2y = 3$ must have a slope of $m = -\tfrac{1}{2}$. Thus its equation must be

$$y - y_1 = m(x - x_1)$$
$$y - 1 = -\tfrac{1}{2}(x - 2)$$
$$2y - 2 = -x + 2$$
$$x + 2y - 4 = 0.$$

45. $5x + 3y = 0$

$$y = -\tfrac{5}{3}x$$
$$m = -\tfrac{5}{3}$$

(a)

$$y - \tfrac{3}{4} = -\tfrac{5}{3}\left(x - \tfrac{7}{8}\right)$$
$$24y - 18 = -40x + 35$$
$$40x + 24y - 53 = 0$$

(b)

$$y - \tfrac{3}{4} = \tfrac{3}{5}\left(x - \tfrac{7}{8}\right)$$
$$40y - 30 = 24x - 21$$
$$24x - 40y + 9 = 0$$

47. (a) $x = 2 \Longrightarrow x - 2 = 0$

(b) $y = 5 \Longrightarrow y - 5 = 0$

49. $y = -3$

$$y + 3 = 0$$

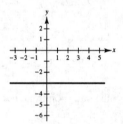

51. Writing the equation in slope-intercept form we have

$$y = 2x - 3.$$

Therefore, the slope is $m = 2$ and the y-intercept is -3. The line passes through the points $(0, 3)$ and $(4, 5)$. Plotting the two points and drawing a line through them yields the line shown in the figure.

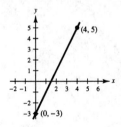

53. $y = -2x + 1$

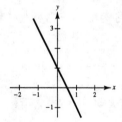

55. $y = 0.5x - 3$. The second viewing rectangle shows the important features of the line (intercepts).

57. The slope is 125. Hence, $V = 125(t - 8) + 2540 = 125t + 1540.$

59. The slope is -2000. Hence, $V = -2000(t - 8) + 20{,}400 = -2000t + 36{,}400.$

61.

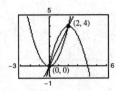

You can use the graphing utility to determine that the points of intersection are $(0, 0)$ and $(2, 4)$. Analytically,

$$x^2 = 4x - x^2$$
$$2x^2 - 4x = 0$$
$$2x(x - 2) = 0$$
$$x = 0 \Rightarrow y = 0 \Rightarrow (0, 0)$$
$$x = 2 \Rightarrow y = 4 \Rightarrow (2, 4).$$

The slope of the line joining $(0, 0)$ and $(2, 4)$ is $m = (4 - 0)/(2 - 0) = 2$. Hence, an equation of the line is

$$y - 0 = 2(x - 0)$$
$$y = 2x.$$

63. Let $(-2, 1) = (x_1, y_1)$, $(-1, 0) = (x_2, y_2)$, and $(2, -2) = (x, y)$. The point (x, y) lies on the line passing through (x_1, y_1) and (x_2, y_2) if and only if

$$\frac{y - y_1}{x - x_1} = m = \frac{y - y_2}{x - x_2}.$$

Since

$$\frac{-2 - 1}{2 - (-2)} = -\frac{3}{4} \neq -\frac{2}{3} = \frac{-2 - 0}{2 - (-1)},$$

the three points are *not* collinear.

65. Equations of perpendicular bisectors:

$$y - \frac{c}{2} = \frac{a - b}{c}\left(x - \frac{a + b}{2}\right)$$

$$y - \frac{c}{2} = \frac{a + b}{-c}\left(x - \frac{b - a}{2}\right)$$

Letting $x = 0$ in either equation gives the point of intersection:

$$\left(0, \frac{-a^2 + b^2 + c^2}{2c}\right).$$

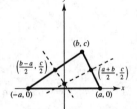

67. Equations of altitudes:

$$y = \frac{a - b}{c}(x + a)$$

$$x = b$$

$$y = -\frac{a + b}{c}(x - a)$$

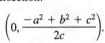

Solving simultaneously, the point of intersection is

$$\left(b, \frac{a^2 - b^2}{c}\right).$$

69. Find the equation of the line through the points $(0, 32)$ and $(100, 212)$.

$$m = \frac{180}{100} = \frac{9}{5}$$

$$F - 32 = \frac{9}{5}(C - 0)$$

$$F = \frac{9}{5}C + 32$$

$$5F - 9C - 160 = 0$$

For $F = 72°$, $C \approx 22.2°$.

71. (a) $W_1 = 0.75x + 12.50$

$W_2 = 1.30x + 9.20$

(c) Both jobs pay \$17 per hour if 6 units are produced. For someone who can produce more than 6 units per hour, the second offer would pay more. For a worker who produces less than 6 units per hour, the first offer pays more.

(b)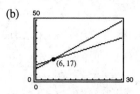

Using a graphing utility, the point of intersection is approximately (6, 17). Analytically,

$$0.75x + 12.50 = 1.30x + 9.20$$

$$3.3 = 0.55x \Rightarrow x = 6$$

$$y = 0.75(6) + 12.50 = 17.$$

73. (a) Two solution points to the linear equation are $(x_1 p_1) = (50, 580)$ and $(x_2, p_2) = (47, 625)$. Therefore, the slope is

$$m = \frac{625 - 580}{47 - 50} = -15,$$

and the equation of the line is

$$p - 580 = -15(x - 50)$$

$$p = -15x + 1330 \text{ or } x = \frac{1}{15}(1330 - p).$$

(b) The graph of the line is shown in the figure.

When $p = \$655$, $x = \frac{1}{15}(1330 - 655) = 45$ units.

(c) When $p = \$595$, $x = \frac{1}{15}(1330 - 595) = 49$ units.

75.
$$4x + 3y - 10 = 0 \Rightarrow d = \frac{|4(0) + 3(0) - 10|}{\sqrt{4^2 + 3^2}} = \frac{10}{5} = 2$$

77. $x - y - 2 = 0 \Rightarrow d = \dfrac{|1(-2) + (-1)(1) - 2|}{\sqrt{1^2 + 1^2}} = \dfrac{5}{\sqrt{2}} = \dfrac{5\sqrt{2}}{2}$

79. A point on the line $x + y = 1$ is $(2, -1)$. The distance between the given parallel lines is equal to the distance from $(2, -1)$ to the line $x + y = 5$. Letting $(2, -1) = (x_1, y_1)$ and $x + y - 5 = Ax + By + C = 0$, we have

$$d = \frac{|Ax_1 + By_1 + C|}{\sqrt{A^2 + B^2}} = \frac{|1(2) + 1(-1) - 5|}{\sqrt{1^2 + 1^2}} = \frac{|-4|}{\sqrt{2}} = \frac{4}{\sqrt{2}} = 2\sqrt{2}.$$

81. If $A = 0$, then $By + C = 0$ is the horizontal line $y = -C/B$. The distance to (x_1, y_1) is

$$d = \left| y_1 - \left(\frac{-C}{B} \right) \right| = \frac{|By_1 + C|}{|B|} = \frac{|Ax_1 + By_1 + C|}{\sqrt{A^2 + B^2}}.$$

If $B = 0$, then $Ax + C = 0$ is the vertical line $x = -C/A$. The distance to (x_1, y_1) is

$$d = \left| x_1 - \left(\frac{-C}{A} \right) \right| = \frac{|Ax_1 + C|}{|A|} = \frac{|Ax_1 + By_1 + C|}{\sqrt{A^2 + B^2}}.$$

(Note that A and B cannot both be zero.)

—CONTINUED—

81. —CONTINUED—

The slope of the line $Ax + By + C = 0$ is $-A/B$. The equation of the line through (x_1, y_1) perpendicular to $Ax + By + C = 0$ is:

$$y - y_1 = \frac{B}{A}(x - x_1)$$

$$Ay - Ay_1 = Bx - Bx_1$$

$$Bx_1 - Ay_1 = Bx - Ay$$

The point of intersection of these two lines is:

$$Ax + By = -C \quad \Rightarrow \quad A^2x + ABy = -AC \qquad (1)$$

$$Bx - Ay = Bx_1 - Ay_1 \Rightarrow \quad B^2x - ABy = B^2x_1 - ABy_1 \qquad (2)$$

$$(A^2 + B^2)x = -AC + B^2x_1 - ABy_1 \quad \text{(By adding equations (1) and (2))}$$

$$x = \frac{-AC + B^2x_1 - ABy_1}{A^2 + B^2}$$

$$Ax + By = -C \quad \Rightarrow \quad ABx + B^2y = -BC \qquad (3)$$

$$Bx - Ay = Bx_1 - Ay_1 \Rightarrow -ABx + A^2y = -ABx_1 + A^2y_1 \qquad (4)$$

$$(A^2 + B^2)y = -BC - ABx_1 + A^2y_1 \quad \text{(By adding equations (3) and (4))}$$

$$y = \frac{-BC - ABx_1 + A^2y_1}{A^2 + B^2}$$

$$\left(\frac{-AC + B^2x_1 - ABy_1}{A^2 + B^2}, \frac{-BC - ABx_1 + A^2y_1}{A^2 + B^2} \right) \quad \text{point of intersection}$$

The distance between (x_1, y_1) and this point gives us the distance between (x_1, y_1) and the line $Ax + By + C = 0$.

$$d = \sqrt{\left[\frac{-AC + B^2x_1 - ABy_1}{A^2 + B^2} - x_1 \right]^2 + \left[\frac{-BC - ABx_1 + A^2y_1}{A^2 + B^2} - y_1 \right]^2}$$

$$= \sqrt{\left[\frac{-AC - ABy_1 - A^2x_1}{A^2 + B^2} \right]^2 + \left[\frac{-BC - ABx_1 - B^2y_1}{A^2 + B^2} \right]^2}$$

$$= \sqrt{\left[\frac{-A(C + By_1 + Ax_1)}{A^2 + B^2} \right]^2 + \left[\frac{-B(C + Ax_1 + By_1)}{A^2 + B^2} \right]^2}$$

$$= \sqrt{\frac{(A^2 + B^2)(C + Ax_1 + By_1)^2}{(A^2 + B^2)^2}}$$

$$= \frac{|Ax_1 + By_1 + C|}{\sqrt{A^2 + B^2}}$$

83. For simplicity, let the vertices of the rhombus be $(0, 0)$, $(a, 0)$, (b, c), and $(a + b, c)$, as shown in the figure. The slopes of the diagonals are then

$$m_1 = \frac{c}{a + b} \text{ and } m_2 = \frac{c}{b - a}.$$

Since the sides of the rhombus are equal, $a^2 = b^2 + c^2$, and we have

$$m_1 m_2 = \frac{c}{a + b} \cdot \frac{c}{b - a} = \frac{c^2}{b^2 - a^2} = \frac{c^2}{-c^2} = -1.$$

Therefore, the diagonals are perpendicular.

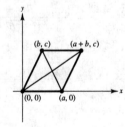

85. Consider the figure below in which the four points are collinear. Since the triangles are similar, the result immediately follows.

$$\frac{y_2^{*} - y_1^{*}}{x_2^{*} - x_1^{*}} = \frac{y_2 - y_1}{x_2 - x_1}$$

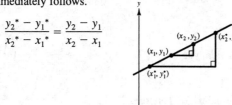

87. True

$$ax + by = c_1 \Rightarrow y = -\frac{a}{b}x + \frac{c_1}{b} \Rightarrow m_1 = -\frac{a}{b}$$

$$bx - ay = c_2 \Rightarrow y = \frac{b}{a}x - \frac{c_2}{a} \Rightarrow m_2 = \frac{b}{a}$$

$$m_2 = -\frac{1}{m_1}$$

Section P.3   Functions and Their Graphs

1. (a) $f(0) = 2(0) - 3 = -3$

(b) $f(-3) = 2(-3) - 3 = -9$

(c) $f(b) = 2b - 3$

(d) $f(x - 1) = 2(x - 1) - 3 = 2x - 5$

3. $f(x) = \begin{cases} 2x + 1, & x < 0 \\ 2x + 2, & x \geq 0 \end{cases}$

(a) $f(-1) = 2(-1) + 1 = -1$

(b) $f(0) = 2(0) + 2 = 2$

(c) $f(2) = 2(2) + 2 = 6$

(d) Since $t^2 + 1 > 0$, we have

$$f(t^2 + 1) = 2(t^2 + 1) + 2 = 2t^2 + 4.$$

5. (a) $f(0) = \cos(2(0)) = \cos 0 = 1$

(b) $f\left(-\frac{\pi}{4}\right) = \cos\left(2\left(-\frac{\pi}{4}\right)\right) = \cos\left(-\frac{\pi}{2}\right) = 0$

(c) $f\left(\frac{\pi}{3}\right) = \cos\left(2\left(\frac{\pi}{3}\right)\right) = \cos\frac{2\pi}{3} = -\frac{1}{2}$

7. $f(x) = x^3$

$$\frac{f(x + \Delta x) - f(x)}{\Delta x} = \frac{(x + \Delta x)^3 - x^3}{\Delta x}$$

$$= \frac{x^3 + 3x^2\Delta x + 3x(\Delta x)^2 + (\Delta x)^3 - x^3}{\Delta x}$$

$$= \frac{\Delta x[3x^2 + 3x\Delta x + (\Delta x)^2]}{\Delta x}$$

$$= 3x^2 + 3x\Delta x + (\Delta x)^2$$

9. $\dfrac{f(x) - f(2)}{x - 2} = \dfrac{(1/\sqrt{x - 1} - 1)}{x - 2}$

$$= \frac{1 - \sqrt{x - 1}}{(x - 2)\sqrt{x - 1}} \cdot \frac{1 + \sqrt{x - 1}}{1 + \sqrt{x - 1}} = \frac{2 - x}{(x - 2)\sqrt{x - 1}(1 + \sqrt{x - 1})} = \frac{-1}{\sqrt{x - 1}(1 + \sqrt{x - 1})}, x \neq 2$$

11. $f(x) = 4 - x$

Domain: $(-\infty, \infty)$

Range: $(-\infty, \infty)$

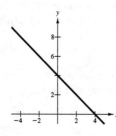

13. $h(x) = \sqrt{x - 1}$

Domain: $[1, \infty)$

Range: $[0, \infty)$

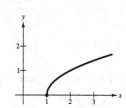

15. $f(x) = \sqrt{9 - x^2}$

Since $9 - x^2$ must be nonnegative ($9 - x^2 \geq 0$), the domain is $[-3, 3]$. The range is $[0, 3]$. There is symmetry with respect to the y-axis since

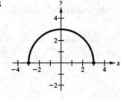

$$y = \sqrt{9 - (-x)^2} = \sqrt{9 - x^2}$$

is equivalent to the original equation. Squaring both members of the equation, you have

$$y^2 = 9 - x^2 \quad \text{or} \quad x^2 + y^2 = 3^2.$$

This is the standard form of an equation of a circle with center $(0, 0)$ and radius 3. Therefore, the graph of $f(x) = \sqrt{9 - x^2}$ is a semicircle in the first and second quadrants with center $(0, 0)$ and radius 3.

17. $g(t) = 2 \sin \pi t$

Domain: $(-\infty, \infty)$

Range: $[-2, 2]$

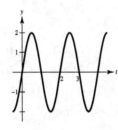

19. $x - y^2 = 0 \Rightarrow y = \pm\sqrt{x}$

y is not a function of x.

21. $f(x) = |x| + |x - 2|$

If $x < 0$, then

$$f(x) = -x - (x - 2) = -2x + 2 = 2(1 - x).$$

If $0 \leq x < 2$, then $f(x) = x - (x - 2) = 2$.

If $x \geq 2$, then $f(x) = x + (x - 2) = 2x - 2 = 2(x - 1)$.

Thus, $f(x) = \begin{cases} 2(1 - x), & x < 0 \\ 2, & 0 \leq x < 2. \\ 2(x - 1), & x \geq 2. \end{cases}$

23. $x^2 + y^2 = 4 \Rightarrow y = \pm\sqrt{4 - x^2}$

y is not a function of x since there are two values of y for some x.

25. Solving the equation for y, yields

$$y^2 = x^2 - 1$$

$$y = \pm\sqrt{x^2 - 1}, \ |x| \geq 1.$$

For each value of the independent variable x such that $|x| > 1$, there corresponds two values of the dependent variable y. Therefore, y is not a function of x.

27. No, the relation is not a function. The element "National League" in the domain corresponds to more than one team name.

29. The function is $g(x) = cx^2$. Since $(1, -2)$ satisfies the equation, $c = -2$. Thus, $g(x) = -2x^2$.

31. The function is $r(x) = c/x$, since it must be undefined at $x = 0$. Since $(1, 32)$ satisfies the equation, $c = 32$. Thus, $r(x) = 32/x$.

33. (a) For each time t, there corresponds a depth d.

(b) Domain: $0 \leq t \leq 5$; range: $0 \leq d \leq 30$

(c)

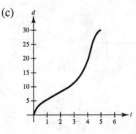

35. By trying each viewing rectangle, you see that the third viewing rectangle is best.

37. The graph of $f(x) = \sqrt{x}$ is shown in the figure.

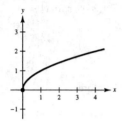

(a) The graph of $y = \sqrt{x} + 2$ is a vertical shift of f 2 units upward.

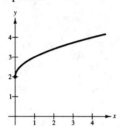

(b) The graph of $y = -\sqrt{x}$ is a reflection of f in the x-axis.

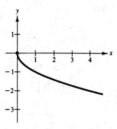

(c) The graph of $y = \sqrt{x - 2}$ is a horizontal shift of f 2 units to the right.

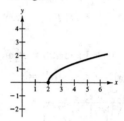

39. (a) $T(4) = 16°, T(15) \approx 23°$

    (b) If $H(t) = T(t - 1)$, then the program would turn on (and off) one hour later.

    (c) If $H(t) = T(t) - 1$, then the overall temperature would be reduced 1 degree.

41. Given the functions $f(x) = x^2$ and $g(x) = \sqrt{x}$, we have

$$(f \circ g)(x) = f[g(x)] = f(\sqrt{x}) = (\sqrt{x})^2 = x \quad \text{and} \quad (g \circ f)(x) = g[f(x)] = g(x^2) = \sqrt{x^2} = |x|.$$

The domain of $(f \circ g)$ is $[0, \infty)$ and the domain of $(g \circ f)$ is $(-\infty, \infty)$. If $x \geq 0$, then $(f \circ g) = (g \circ f)$.

43. $(f \circ g)(x) = f(x^2 + 1) = \dfrac{1}{x^2 + 1}$

Domain: $(-\infty, \infty)$

$(g \circ f)(x) = g\left(\dfrac{1}{x}\right) = \left(\dfrac{1}{x}\right)^2 + 1$

Domain: $(-\infty, 0), (0, \infty)$

The composite functions are not equal.

45. $(A \circ r)(t) = A(r(t)) = A(0.6t) = \pi(0.6t)^2 = 0.36\pi t^2$

$(A \circ r)(t)$ represents the area of the circle at time t.

47. $f(-x) = 4 - (-x)^2 = 4 - x^2 = f(x)$

Even

49. Since $\cos(-x) = \cos x$, we have

$$f(-x) = (-x)\cos(-x) = -x \cos x = -f(x).$$

Therefore, f is an odd function. The graph is shown in the figure.

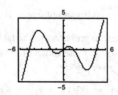

51. (a) If f is even, then $\left(\frac{3}{2}, 4\right)$ is on the graph.

(b) If f is odd, then $\left(\frac{3}{2}, -4\right)$ is on the graph.

53. $f(-x) = a_{2n+1}(-x)^{2n+1} + \cdots + a_3(-x)^3 + a_1(-x)$

$= -[a_{2n+1}x^{2n+1} + \cdots + a_3x^3 + a_1x]$

$= -f(x)$

Odd

55. Let $F(x) = f(x)g(x)$ where f and g are even functions. Thus, $f(-x) = f(x)$ and $g(-x) = g(x)$. Therefore,

$F(-x) = f(-x)g(-x) = f(x)g(x) = F(x)$

which implies that F is an even function.

Let $F(x) = f(x)g(x)$ where f and g are odd functions. Therefore, $f(-x) = -f(x)$ and $g(-x) = -g(x)$. Hence,

$F(-x) = f(-x)g(-x) = [-f(x)][-g(x)] = f(x)g(x) = F(x)$

which implies that F is an even function.

57. $f(x) = x^2 + 1$ and $g(x) = x^4$ are even.

$f(x)g(x) = (x^2 + 1)(x^4) = x^6 + x^4$ is even.

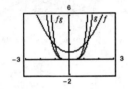

$f(x) = x^3 - x$ is odd and $g(x) = x^2$ is even.

$f(x)g(x) = (x^3 - x)(x^2) = x^5 - x^3$ is odd.

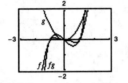

59. (a)

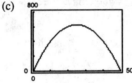

100 = perimeter

(b) $A = x(50 - x) = 50x - x^2$

(c)

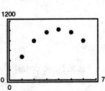

Domain: $0 < x < 50$

(d) The area is maximum when $x = 25$ (a square!).

61. (a) Using the table feature of a graphing utility yields the following.

Height, x	Length and width	Volume, V
1	$24 - 2(1)$	$1[24 - 2(1)]^2 = 484$
2	$24 - 2(2)$	$2[24 - 2(2)]^2 = 800$
3	$24 - 2(3)$	$3[24 - 2(3)]^2 = 972$
4	$24 - 2(4)$	$4[24 - 2(4)]^2 = 1024$
5	$24 - 2(5)$	$5[24 - 2(5)]^2 = 980$
6	$24 - 2(6)$	$6[24 - 2(6)]^2 = 864$

The estimate of the maximum volume is 1024 cubic centimeters.

(c) Using the form of the expressions in the table of part (a) and the variables assigned to the dimensions of the box shown in the text, the volume is given by

$V = x(24 - 2x)^2 = x[2(12 - x)]^2 = 4x(12 - x)^2.$

The size of the material for constructing the box constrains the values of x to the domain $(0, 12)$.

(b) For each value of x there corresponds exactly one value of V. Therefore, V is a function of x. The graph of the points (x, V) are shown in the figure.

(d) The graph of the function for the volume is given in the figure. The volume is maximum when $x \approx 4$. Therefore, the approximate dimensions of the box are $4 \times 16 \times 16$ centimeters.

63. False; let $f(x) = x^2$.

Then $f(-3) = f(3) = 9$, but $-3 \neq 3$.

65. True, the function is even.

Section P.4   Fitting Models to Data

1. Quadratic function

3. Linear function

5. (a)

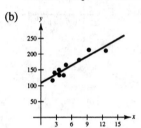

Yes. The cancer mortality increases linearly with increased exposure to the carcinogenic substance.

(b)

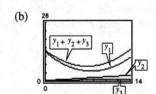

(c) If $x = 3$, then $y \approx 136$.

7. (a) $d = 0.066F$ or $F = 15.1d + 0.1$

(b)

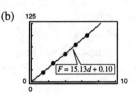

$$\boxed{F = 15.13d + 0.10}$$

The model fits well.

(c) If $F = 55$, then $d \approx 0.066(55) = 3.63$ cm.

9. (a) Begin by entering the data in the statistics lists of your graphing utility. Access the statistic calculation menu and select linear regression ($y = ax + b$). Fitting the linear model to the data yields

$$y = 2.62x + 2.66.$$

(b) Enter the regression model in the $\boxed{Y=}$ screen, and turn on the statistical plot capabilities. The plot of the data and the graph of the model are shown in the figure.

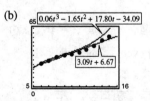

(c) The slope of the model indicates that the per capita gross national product increases an average of \$2620 for each 1000 kilograms of coal equivalent per capita energy consumption. Denmark, Finland, France, Italy, and Japan appear to not follow the linear pattern. Their per capita gross national product appears above average for the amount of energy usage.

11. (a) $y_1 = 0.16t^2 - 2.43t + 13.96$

$y_2 = 0.17t + 0.38$

$y_3 = 0.04t + 0.44$

(b)

(c) For 1998, $t = 18$ and $y_1 + y_2 + y_3 \approx 26.66$ cents/mile.

13. (a) $y_1 = 3.09t + 6.67$

$y_2 = 0.06t^3 - 1.65t^2 + 17.80t - 34.09$

(b)

(c) The cubic model is better.

(d) $y_3 = 0.17t^2 - 0.44t + 23.82$

(e) The slope represents the average increase per year in the number of people in HMO's.

(f) For $t = 10$, $y_1 = 68.5$ (linear) and $y_2 = 141.9$ (cubic).

15. (a) $y = -1.81x^3 + 14.58x^2 + 16.39x + 10$

(b)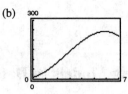

(c) If $x = 4.5$, $y \approx 214$ horsepower.

17. (a) y is a function of t since there corresponds one and only one value of y for each value of t.

(b) The average of the y-values at the maximum displacements from equilibrium is

$$\frac{2.35 + 1.65}{2} = 2.$$

Therefore, the weight is at equilibrium when $y = 2$. The amplitude is the maximum displacement from equilibrium which is 0.35. The period p is twice the distance between the t-values for the consecutive maximum displacements from equilibrium shown in the figure. Thus,

$$p = 2(0.375 - 0.125) = 0.5.$$

(c) Using the model $y = a \sin(bt) + c$, we have $a = 0.35$, $c = 2$, and $0.5 = 2\pi/b$ or $b = 4\pi$. Therefore,

$$y = 0.35 \sin(4\pi t) + 2.$$

(d) The graph of the model is shown in the figure.

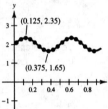

Section P.5 Inverse Functions

1. (a) $f(x) = 5x + 1$

$g(x) = \dfrac{x - 1}{5}$

$f(g(x)) = f\left(\dfrac{x - 1}{5}\right) = 5\left(\dfrac{x - 1}{5}\right) + 1 = x$

$g(f(x)) = g(5x + 1) = \dfrac{(5x + 1) - 1}{5} = x$

(b)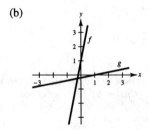

3. (a) $f(x) = x^3$

$g(x) = \sqrt[3]{x}$

$f(g(x)) = f(\sqrt[3]{x}) = (\sqrt[3]{x})^3 = x$

$g(f(x)) = g(x^3) = \sqrt[3]{x^3} = x$

(b)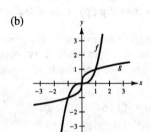

5. (a) $f(x) = \sqrt{x - 4}$ and $g(x) = x^2 + 4$ $(x \ge 0)$

The composite of f with g is given by

$f(g(x)) = f(x^2 + 4)$

$= \sqrt{(x^2 + 4) - 4} = \sqrt{x^2} = x.$

The composite of g with f is given by

$g(f(x)) = g(\sqrt{x - 4})$

$= (\sqrt{x - 4})^2 + 4 = x - 4 + 4 = x.$

Since $f(g(x)) = g(f(x)) = x$, we can conclude that f and g are inverses of each other.

(b) The graphs of f and g are shown in the figure. Note that the graph of g is a reflection of the graph of f in the line $y = x$.

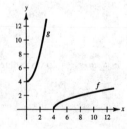

7. (a) $f(x) = \dfrac{1}{x}$

$\quad\quad\quad g(x) = \dfrac{1}{x}$

$\quad\quad\quad f(g(x)) = \dfrac{1}{1/x} = x$

$\quad\quad\quad g(f(x)) = \dfrac{1}{1/x} = x$

(b)

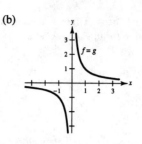

9. Matches (c)

11. Matches (a)

13. The function has an inverse because it is increasing on its entire domain. To find an equation for the inverse, let $y = f(x)$ and solve for x in terms of y.

$\quad\quad 2x - 3 = y$

$\quad\quad\quad x = \dfrac{y + 3}{2}$

$\quad\quad f^{-1}(y) = \dfrac{y + 3}{2}$

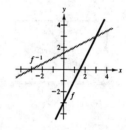

Interchanging x and y yields $f^{-1}(x) = \dfrac{x + 3}{2}$. Remember that any variable can be used to represent the independent variable. Thus,

$$f^{-1}(y) = \dfrac{y + 3}{2}, \; f^{-1}(x) = \dfrac{x + 3}{2}, \text{ and } f^{-1}(t) = \dfrac{t + 3}{2}$$

represent the same function. The graph of f^{-1} is a reflection of the graph of f in the line $y = x$.

15. $f(x) = x^5 = y$

$\quad\quad\quad x = \sqrt[5]{y}$

$\quad\quad\quad y = \sqrt[5]{x}$

$\quad\quad f^{-1}(x) = \sqrt[5]{x} = x^{1/5}$

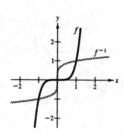

17. $f(x) = \sqrt{x} = y$

$\quad\quad\quad x = y^2$

$\quad\quad\quad y = x^2$

$\quad\quad f^{-1}(x) = x^2, \; x \geq 0$

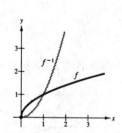

19. $f(x) = \sqrt{4 - x^2} = y, \; 0 \leq x \leq 2$

$\quad\quad\quad x = \sqrt{4 - y^2}$

$\quad\quad\quad y = \sqrt{4 - x^2}$

$\quad\quad f^{-1}(x) = \sqrt{4 - x^2}, \, 0 \leq x \leq 2$

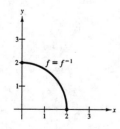

21. $f(x) = \sqrt[3]{x - 1} = y$

$\quad\quad\quad x = y^3 + 1$

$\quad\quad\quad y = x^3 + 1$

$\quad\quad f^{-1}(x) = x^3 + 1$

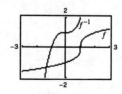

The graphs of f and f^{-1} are reflections of each other across the line $y = x$.

23. The function has an inverse because it is increasing on $[0, \infty)$. To find an equation for the inverse, let $y = f(x)$ and solve for x in terms of y.

$$x^{2/3} = y \qquad x \geq 0$$

$$x = y^{3/2} \qquad y \geq 0$$

$$f^{-1}(y) = y^{3/2} \qquad y \geq 0$$

Finally, using x as the independent variable yields

$$f^{-1}(x) = x^{3/2} \qquad x \geq 0.$$

The graph of f^{-1} is a reflection of the graph of f in the line $y = x$.

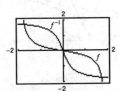

25. $f(x) = \dfrac{x}{\sqrt{x^2 + 7}} = y$

$$x = \frac{\sqrt{7}y}{\sqrt{1 - y^2}}$$

$$y = \frac{\sqrt{7}x}{\sqrt{1 - x^2}}$$

$$f^{-1}(x) = \frac{\sqrt{7}x}{\sqrt{1 - x^2}}, \quad -1 < x < 1$$

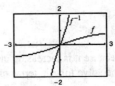

The graphs of f and f^{-1} are reflections of each other across the line $y = x$.

27. $f(x) = \dfrac{x}{x^2 - 4} = y$ on $(-2, 2)$

$$x^2 y - 4y = x$$

$$x^2 y - x - 4y = 0$$

$$a = y, b = -1, c = -4y$$

$$x = \frac{1 \pm \sqrt{1 - 4(y)(-4y)}}{2y} = \frac{1 \pm \sqrt{1 + 16y^2}}{2y}$$

$$y = f^{-1}(x) = \begin{cases} (1 - \sqrt{1 + 16x^2})/2x, & \text{if } x \neq 0 \\ 0, & \text{if } x = 0 \end{cases}$$

Domain: all x; range: $-2 < y < 2$

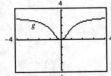

The graphs of f and f^{-1} are reflections of each other across the line $y = x$.

29. (a)

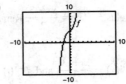

(b)

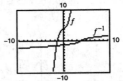

(c) Yes, f is one-to-one and has an inverse. The inverse relation is an inverse function.

31. (a)

(b)

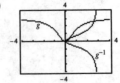

(c) g is not one-to-one and does not have an inverse. The inverse relation is not an inverse function.

33. The function f passes through the points $(0, 1)$, $(1, 2)$, $(2, 3)$, and $(4, 4)$. From the reflective property of inverses, we know the graph of f contains the point (a, b) if and only if the graph f^{-1} contains the point (b, a). Therefore, we obtain the required table by interchanging the x and y coordinates of the preceding points.

x	1	2	3	4
$f^{-1}(x)$	0	1	2	4

The graph of f^{-1} is shown in the figure.

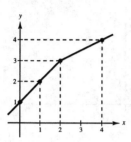 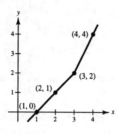

37. $f(x) = \frac{3}{4}x + 6$

One-to-one; has an inverse

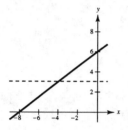

41. The graph of h is shown in the figure. Since h is strictly monotonic (decreasing) on its entire domain, it is one-to-one and, hence, possesses an inverse.

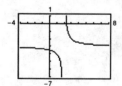

45. $g(x) = (x + 5)^3$

One-to-one; has an inverse

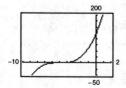

35. (a) Let x be the number of pounds of the commodity costing 1.25 per pound. Since there are 50 pounds total, the amount of the second commodity is $50 - x$. The total cost is

$$y = 1.25x + 1.60(50 - x)$$
$$= -0.35x + 80 \qquad 0 \le x \le 50.$$

(b) We find the inverse of the original function:

$$y = -0.35x + 80$$
$$0.35x = 80 - y$$
$$x = \tfrac{100}{35}(80 - y)$$

Inverse: $y = \frac{100}{35}(80 - x) = \frac{20}{7}(80 - x)$.

x represents cost and y represents pounds.

(c) Domain of inverse is $62.5 \le x \le 80$.

(d) If $x = 73$ in the inverse function,
$y = \frac{100}{35}(80 - 73) = \frac{100}{5} = 20$ pounds.

39. $f(\theta) = \sin \theta$

Not one-to-one; does not have an inverse

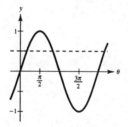

43. $f(x) = \dfrac{1}{1 + x^2}$

Not one-to-one; does not have an inverse

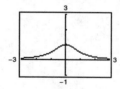

47. $f(x) = (x + a)^3 + b$

f is one-to-one; has an inverse

49. $f(x) = \dfrac{x^4}{4} - 2x^2$

Not one-to-one; f does not have an inverse.

51. $f(x) = 2 - x - x^3$

One-to-one; has an inverse

53. $f(x) = (x - 4)^2$ on $[4, \infty)$

f passes the horizontal line test on $[4, \infty)$; hence, one-to-one

55. A function f is one-to-one if, for a and b in its domain, $f(a) = f(b)$ implies that $a = b$. Let a and b be real numbers in the domain of f such that $f(a) = f(b)$. Then

$$\frac{4}{a^2} = \frac{4}{b^2}$$

$$a^2 = b^2.$$

Since $a > 0$ and $b > 0$, it follows that $a = b$ and the function is one-to-one on the specified domain. Therefore, f has an inverse on the indicated interval.

(*Note:* From the accompanying graph it follows that the graph of f passes the horizontal line test and therefore, f has an inverse on the indicated interval.)

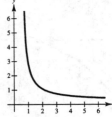

57. $f(x) = \cos x$ on $[0, \pi]$

f passes horizontal line test on $[0, \pi]$; hence, one-to-one

59. $f(x) = \sqrt{x - 2}$, Domain: $x \geq 2$

f is one-to-one; has an inverse

$$\sqrt{x - 2} = y$$

$$x - 2 = y^2$$

$$x = y^2 + 2$$

$$y = x^2 + 2$$

$$f^{-1}(x) = x^2 + 2, x \geq 0$$

61. $f(x) = |x - 2|, x \leq 2$

$$= -(x - 2)$$

$$= 2 - x$$

f is one-to-one; has an inverse

$$2 - x = y$$

$$2 - y = x$$

$$f^{-1}(x) = 2 - x, \ x \geq 0$$

63. One solution is to delete the part of the graph when $x < 3$. The remaining part of the graph is strictly increasing and has an inverse.

$$f(x) = (x - 3)^2, \quad x \geq 3$$

$$y = (x - 3)^2$$

$$\pm\sqrt{y} = x - 3$$

$$x = 3 \pm \sqrt{y}$$

$$y = 3 \pm \sqrt{x}, \quad \text{Interchange } x \text{ and } y$$

Because of the restriction that $x \geq 3$, the inverse must have the positive square root in the equation above.

$$f^{-1}(x) = 3 + \sqrt{x}, \ x \geq 0.$$

The graph of f with the restricted domain and f^{-1} are shown in the figure. (*Note:* If the part of the graph is deleted where $x > 3$, then the inverse function would be

$$f^{-1}(x) = 3 - \sqrt{x}, \ x \geq 0.)$$

65. $f(x) = |x + 3|$ is one-to-one for $x \geq -3$.

$$x + 3 = y$$

$$x = y - 3$$

$$y = x - 3$$

$$f^{-1}(x) = x - 3, \ x \geq 0$$

67.
$$f(x) = 2$$

$$x^3 + 2x - 1 = 2$$

$$x^3 + 2x - 3 = 0$$

$$(x - 1)(x^2 + x + 3) = 0$$

Since $f(1) = 2$, it follows that $f^{-1}(2) = 1$.

69. $f(x) = \sin x$

$$f\left(\frac{\pi}{6}\right) = \frac{1}{2} = a \Rightarrow f^{-1}\left(\frac{1}{2}\right) = \frac{\pi}{6}$$

71. $f(x) = x^3 - \dfrac{4}{x}$

$$f(2) = 6 = a \Rightarrow f^{-1}(6) = 2$$

73. $(f^{-1} \circ g^{-1})(1) = f^{-1}(g^{-1}(1)) = f^{-1}(1) = 32$

75. $(f^{-1} \circ f^{-1})(6) = f^{-1}(f^{-1}(6)) = f^{-1}(72) = 600$

In Exercises 77 and 79, use the following.

$$f(x) = x + 4 \text{ and } g(x) = 2x - 5$$

$$f^{-1}(x) = x - 4 \text{ and } g^{-1}(x) = \frac{x + 5}{2}$$

77.
$$f(x) = x + 4 \ \Rightarrow f^{-1}(x) = x - 4$$

$$g(x) = 2x - 5 \ \Rightarrow g^{-1}(x) = \frac{x + 5}{2}$$

$$(g^{-1} \circ f^{-1}) = g^{-1}(f^{-1}(x))$$

$$= f^{-1}(x - 4) = \frac{(x - 4) + 5}{2} = \frac{x + 1}{2}$$

79. $(f \circ g)^{-1} = [f(g(x))]^{-1}$

$$= [f(2x - 5)]^{-1}$$

$$= [2x - 1]^{-1}$$

$$= \frac{x + 1}{2}$$

81. $y = \arcsin x$

(a)

x	-1	-0.8	-0.6	-0.4	-0.2	0	0.2	0.4	0.6	0.8	1
y	-1.571	-0.927	-0.644	-0.412	-0.201	0	0.201	0.412	0.644	0.927	1.571

(b)

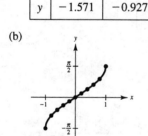

(c)

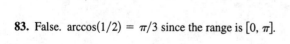

(d) Symmetric about origin:
$$\arcsin(-x) = -\arcsin x$$

Intercept: $(0, 0)$

83. False. $\arccos(1/2) = \pi/3$ since the range is $[0, \pi]$.

85. $\arcsin \dfrac{1}{2} = \dfrac{\pi}{6}$

87. Since $y = \arccos(1/2)$ if and only if $\cos y = 1/2$, then $y = \pi/3$ in the interval $[0, \pi]$. Thus, $\arccos(1/2) = \pi/3$.

89. $\arctan \dfrac{\sqrt{3}}{3} = \dfrac{\pi}{6}$

91. $\operatorname{arccsc}\left(-\sqrt{2}\right) = -\dfrac{\pi}{4}$

93. $\arccos(-0.8) \approx 2.50$

95. $\arcsec(1.269) = \arccos\left(\dfrac{1}{1.269}\right) \approx 0.66$

97. $\arctan 0 = 0$; π is not in the range of $y = \arctan x$.

99. $f(x) = \tan x$

$g(x) = \arctan x$

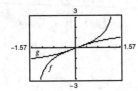

101. $\cos[\arccos(-0.1)] = -0.1$

103. (a) $\sin\left(\arcsin \dfrac{1}{2}\right) = \sin\left(\dfrac{\pi}{6}\right) = \dfrac{1}{2}$

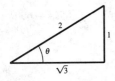

(b) $\cos\left(\arcsin \dfrac{1}{2}\right) = \cos\left(\dfrac{\pi}{6}\right) = \dfrac{\sqrt{3}}{2}$

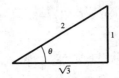

105. (a) Begin by sketching a triangle to represent θ, "the angle whose tangent is $\frac{3}{4}$." Then

$\theta = \arctan \frac{3}{4}$ and $\sin\left(\arctan \frac{3}{4}\right) = \sin\theta = \frac{3}{5}$.

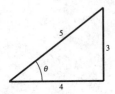

(b) Begin by sketching a triangle to represent θ, "the angle whose sine is $\frac{4}{5}$." Then

$\theta = \arcsin \frac{4}{5}$ and $\sec\left(\arcsin \frac{4}{5}\right) = \sec\theta = \frac{5}{3}$.

107. (a) $\cot\left[\arcsin\left(-\dfrac{1}{2}\right)\right] = \cot\left(-\dfrac{\pi}{6}\right) = -\sqrt{3}$

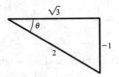

(b) $\csc\left[\arctan\left(-\dfrac{5}{12}\right)\right] = -\dfrac{13}{5}$

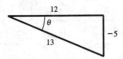

109. $y = \tan(\arctan x)$

$\theta = \arctan x$

$y = \tan\theta = x$

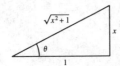

111. $y = \cos(\arcsin 2x)$

$\theta = \arcsin 2x$

$y = \cos\theta = \sqrt{1 - 4x^2}$

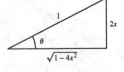

113. Begin by sketching a triangle to represent θ, "the angle whose secant is x." Then $\theta = \arcsec x$ and

$\sin(\arcsec x) = \sin\theta = \dfrac{\sqrt{x^2 - 1}}{x}$.

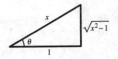

115. $y = \tan\left(\arcsec \dfrac{x}{3}\right)$

$\theta = \arcsec \dfrac{x}{3}$

$y = \tan\theta = \dfrac{\sqrt{x^2 - 9}}{3}$

117. Begin by sketching a triangle to represent θ, "the angle whose tangent is $x/\sqrt{2}$." Then

$$\theta = \arctan\frac{x}{\sqrt{2}}$$

and

$$\csc\left(\arctan\frac{x}{\sqrt{2}}\right) = \csc\theta = \frac{\sqrt{x^2+2}}{x}.$$

119. $\arctan\dfrac{9}{x} = \arcsin\dfrac{9}{\sqrt{x^2+81}}$

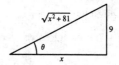

121. (a) $\operatorname{arccsc} x = \arcsin\dfrac{1}{x}, \ |x| \geq 1$

Let $y = \operatorname{arccsc} x$.

Then for $-\dfrac{\pi}{2} \leq y < 0$ and $0 < y \leq \dfrac{\pi}{2}$,

$$\csc y = x \implies \sin y = \frac{1}{x}.$$

Thus, $y = \arcsin\left(\dfrac{1}{x}\right)$. Therefore,

$$\operatorname{arccsc} x = \arcsin\left(\frac{1}{x}\right).$$

(b) $\arctan x + \arctan\dfrac{1}{x} = \dfrac{\pi}{2}, \ x > 0$

Let $y = \arctan x + \arctan\dfrac{1}{x}$. Then

$$\tan y = \frac{\tan(\arctan x) + \tan[\arctan(1/x)]}{1 - \tan(\arctan x)\tan[\arctan(1/x)]}$$

$$= \frac{x + (1/x)}{1 - x(1/x)} = \frac{x + (1/x)}{0}$$

which is undefined.

Thus, $y = \dfrac{\pi}{2}$. Therefore,

$$\arctan x + \arctan\left(\frac{1}{x}\right) = \frac{\pi}{2}.$$

123. $f(x) = \arcsin(x - 1)$

$x - 1 = \sin y$

$x = 1 + \sin y$

Domain: $[0, 2]$

Range: $[-\pi/2, \pi/2]$

$f(x)$ is the graph of $\arcsin x$ shifted right 1 unit.

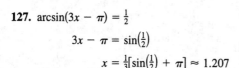

125. $f(x) = \operatorname{arcsec} 2x$

$2x = \sec y$

$x = \dfrac{1}{2}\sec y$

Domain: $\left(-\infty, -\dfrac{1}{2}\right], \left[\dfrac{1}{2}, \infty\right)$

Range: $\left[0, \dfrac{\pi}{2}\right), \left(\dfrac{\pi}{2}, \pi\right]$

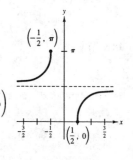

127. $\arcsin(3x - \pi) = \dfrac{1}{2}$

$3x - \pi = \sin\left(\dfrac{1}{2}\right)$

$x = \dfrac{1}{3}\left[\sin\left(\dfrac{1}{2}\right) + \pi\right] \approx 1.207$

129. Taking the sine of each member of the equation, yields

$$\sin\left(\arcsin\sqrt{2x}\right) = \sin\left(\arccos\sqrt{x}\right)$$

$$\sqrt{2x} = \sqrt{1 - x} \quad \text{(see figure)}$$

$$2x = 1 - x$$

$$3x = 1 \implies x = \tfrac{1}{3}.$$

131. $y = \arccos x$

$y = \arctan x$

The point of intersection is given by

$f(x) = \arccos x - \arctan x = 0, \quad \cos(\arccos x) = \cos(\arctan x).$

$$x = \frac{1}{\sqrt{1 + x^2}}$$

$x^2(1 + x^2) = 1$

$x^4 + x^2 - 1 = 0$ when $x^2 = \dfrac{-1 + \sqrt{5}}{2}.$

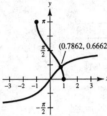

Therefore, $x = \pm \sqrt{\dfrac{-1 + \sqrt{5}}{2}} \approx \pm 0.7862.$

Point of intersection: $(0.7862, 0.6662)$ $[$Since $f(-0.7862) = \pi \neq 0.]$

133. Let $(f \circ g)(x) = y$ then $x = (f \circ g)^{-1}(y)$. Also,

$(f \circ g)(x) = y$

$f(g(x)) = y$

$g(x) = f^{-1}(y)$

$x = g^{-1}(f^{-1}(y))$

$= (g^{-1} \circ f^{-1})(y)$

Since f and g are one-to-one functions,
$(f \circ g)^{-1} = g^{-1} \circ f^{-1}.$

135. Suppose $g(x)$ and $h(x)$ are both inverses of $f(x)$. Then the graph of $f(x)$ contains the point (a, b) if and only if the graphs of $g(x)$ and $h(x)$ contain the point (b, a). Since the graphs of $g(x)$ and $h(x)$ are the same, $g(x) = h(x)$. Therefore, the inverse of $f(x)$ is unique.

137. False

Let $f(x) = x^2.$

139. False

$$\arcsin^2 0 + \arccos^2 0 = 0 + \left(\frac{\pi}{2}\right)^2 \neq 1$$

141. True

143. $\tan(\arctan x + \arctan y) = \dfrac{\tan(\arctan x) + \tan(\arctan y)}{1 - \tan(\arctan x)\tan(\arctan y)} = \dfrac{x + y}{1 - xy}, \quad xy \neq 1$

Therefore, $\arctan x + \arctan y = \arctan\left(\dfrac{x + y}{1 - xy}\right), \quad xy \neq 1.$

Let $x = \dfrac{1}{2}$ and $y = \dfrac{1}{3}.$

$$\arctan\left(\frac{1}{2}\right) + \arctan\left(\frac{1}{3}\right) = \arctan\frac{(1/2) + (1/3)}{1 - [(1/2) \cdot (1/3)]} = \arctan\frac{5/6}{1 - (1/6)} = \arctan\frac{5/6}{5/6} = \arctan 1 = \frac{\pi}{4}$$

Section P.6   Exponential and Logarithmic Functions

1. (a) $25^{3/2} = 5^3 = 125$

   (b) $81^{1/2} = 9$

   (c) $3^{-2} = \dfrac{1}{3^2} = \dfrac{1}{9}$

   (d) $27^{-1/3} = \dfrac{1}{27^{1/3}} = \dfrac{1}{3}$

3. (a) $(5^2)(5^3) = 5^{2+3} = 5^5 = 3125$

   (b) $(5^2)(5^{-3}) = 5^{2-3} = 5^{-1} = \dfrac{1}{5}$

   (c) $\dfrac{5^3}{25^2} = \dfrac{5^3}{5^4} = \dfrac{1}{5}$

   (d) $\left(\dfrac{1}{4}\right)^2 2^6 = \dfrac{2^6}{2^4} = 2^2 = 4$

5. (a) $e^2(e^4) = e^6$

(b) $(e^3)^4 = e^{12}$

(c) $(e^3)^{-2} = e^{-6} = \dfrac{1}{e^6}$

(d) $\dfrac{e^5}{e^3} = e^2$

7. $3^x = 81 \Rightarrow x = 4$

9. Using the properties of exponents, you have:

$$\left(\tfrac{1}{3}\right)^{x-1} = 27$$
$$(3^{-1})^{x-1} = 3^3$$
$$3^{-(x-1)} = 3^3$$
$$-(x-1) = 3$$
$$x - 1 = -3 \Rightarrow x = -2$$

11. $4^3 = (x+2)^3 \Rightarrow 4 = x+2 \Rightarrow x = 2$

13. $x^{3/4} = 8 \Rightarrow x = 8^{4/3} = 2^4 = 16$

15. $e^{-2x} = e^5 \Rightarrow -2x = 5 \Rightarrow x = -\tfrac{5}{2}$

17. $\left(1 + \dfrac{1}{1,000,000}\right)^{1,000,000} \approx 2.718280469$

$$e \approx 2.718281828$$

$$e > \left(1 + \dfrac{1}{1,000,000}\right)^{1,000,000}$$

19. $y = 3^x$

x	-2	-1	0	1	2
y	$\frac{1}{9}$	$\frac{1}{3}$	1	3	9

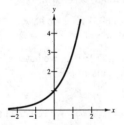

21. $y = \left(\tfrac{1}{3}\right)^x = 3^{-x}$

x	-2	-1	0	1	2
y	9	3	1	$\frac{1}{3}$	$\frac{1}{9}$

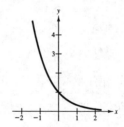

23. $f(x) = 3^{-x^2}$

x	0	± 1	± 2
y	1	$\frac{1}{3}$	0.0123

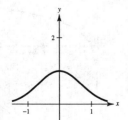

25. $h(x) = e^{x-2}$

x	0	1	2	3	4
y	e^{-2}	e^{-1}	1	e	e^2

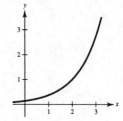

27. The graph is symmetric with respect to the y-axis since

$$y = e^{-(-x)^2} = e^{-x^2}.$$

The y-intercept is $(0, 1)$. The x-axis is a horizontal asymptote since

$$\lim_{x \to \infty} e^{-x^2} = \lim_{x \to \infty} \frac{1}{e^{x^2}} = 0.$$

The graph lies entirely above the x-axis, since for all x

$$0 < e^{-x^2}.$$

The table shows solution points of the equation. By plotting these points and using the information given above we have the graph shown in the figure.

x	0	0.5	1	2
y	1	0.607	0.368	0.135

29. (a)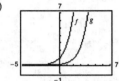

Horizontal shift 2 units to the right

(b)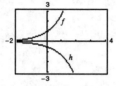

A reflection in the x-axis and a vertical shrink

(c)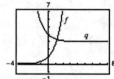

Vertical shift 3 units upward and a reflection in the y-axis

31. $y = Ce^{ax}$

Matches (c)

33. $y = C(1 - e^{-ax})$

Vertical shift C units

Reflection in both the x- and y-axes

Matches (a)

35. (a) $e^0 = 1$

$\ln 1 = 0$

(b) $e^2 = 7.389 \ldots$

$\ln 7.389 \ldots = 2$

37. By definition, $\ln x = b$ if and only if $e^b = x$.

(a) Letting $x = 2$ and $b = 0.6931 \ldots$, we have
$\ln 2 = 0.6931 \ldots$ if and only if $e^{0.6931 \cdots} = 2$.

(b) Letting $x = 8.4$ and $b = 2.128 \ldots$, we have
$\ln 8.4 = 2.128 \ldots$ if and only if $e^{2.128 \cdots} = 8.4$.

39. $f(x) = 3 \ln x$

Domain: $x > 0$

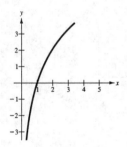

41. The domain of $f(x) = \ln 2x$ is $(0, \infty)$. We construct a table of values for f.

x	$\frac{1}{4}$	$\frac{1}{2}$	1	2	4	6
$f(x)$	-0.6931	0	0.6931	1.3863	2.0794	2.4849

By plotting these points and connecting them with a smooth curve, we obtain the graph of $f(x)$.

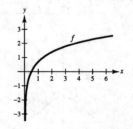

43. $f(x) = \ln(x - 1)$

Domain: $x > 1$

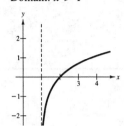

45. $f(x) = e^{2x}$

$g(x) = \ln\sqrt{x} = \frac{1}{2}\ln x$

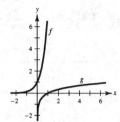

47. $f(x) = e^{x-1}$

$g(x) = 1 + \ln x$

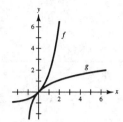

49. $\ln e^{x^2} = x^2$

51. $e^{\ln(5x+2)} = 5x + 2$

53. $e^{\ln\sqrt{x}} = \sqrt{x}$

55. (a) $\ln 6 = \ln(2 \cdot 3)$

$= \ln 2 + \ln 3 \approx 0.6931 + 1.0986 = 1.7917$

(b) $\ln\frac{2}{3} = \ln 2 - \ln 3 \approx 0.6931 - 1.0986 = -0.4055$

(c) $\ln 81 = \ln(3^4) = 4\ln 3 \approx 4(1.0986) = 4.3944$

(d) $\ln\sqrt{3} = \ln(3^{1/2}) = \frac{1}{2}\ln 3 \approx \frac{1}{2}(1.0986) = 0.5493$

57. $\ln\frac{2}{3} = \ln 2 - \ln 3$

59. $\ln\frac{xy}{z} = \ln x + \ln y - \ln z$

61. $\ln\sqrt{2^3} = \ln 2^{3/2} = \frac{3}{2}\ln 2$

63. $\ln\left(\frac{x^2 - 1}{x^3}\right)^3 = 3[\ln(x^2 - 1) - \ln x^3]$

$= 3[\ln[(x + 1)(x - 1)] - 3\ln x]$

$= 3[\ln(x + 1) + \ln(x - 1) - 3\ln x]$

65. $\ln z(z - 1)^2 = \ln z + \ln(z - 1)^2$

$= \ln z + 2\ln(z - 1)$

67. $\ln(x - 2) - \ln(x + 2) = \ln\frac{x - 2}{x + 2}$

69. $\frac{1}{3}[2\ln(x + 3) + \ln x - \ln(x^2 - 1)] = \frac{1}{3}[\ln(x + 3)^2 + \ln x - \ln(x^2 - 1)]$

$= \frac{1}{3}[\ln[x(x + 3)^2] - \ln(x^2 - 1)]$

$= \frac{1}{3}\ln\frac{x(x + 3)^2}{x^2 - 1} = \ln\left(\frac{x(x + 3)^2}{x^2 - 1}\right)^{1/3} = \ln\sqrt[3]{\frac{x(x + 3)^2}{x^2 - 1}}$

71. $2\ln 3 - \frac{1}{2}\ln(x^2 + 1) = \ln\frac{9}{\sqrt{x^2 + 1}}$

73. (a) $e^{\ln x} = 4$

$x = 4$

(b) $\ln e^{2x} = 3$

$2x = 3$

$x = \frac{3}{2}$

75. (a) $\ln x = 2$

$x = e^2 \approx 7.3891$

(b) $e^x = 4$

$x = \ln 4 \approx 1.3863$

77.

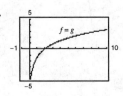

79. $\ln x = \ln\left[\left(\frac{x}{y}\right)y\right]$

$= \ln\frac{x}{y} + \ln y \Rightarrow \ln\frac{x}{y} = \ln x - \ln y$

C H A P T E R 1
Limits and Their Properties

CHAPTER 1
Limits and Their Properties

Section 1.1   A Preview of Calculus

Solutions to Exercises

1. Precalculus: $(20 \text{ ft/sec})(15 \text{ seconds}) = 300 \text{ feet}$

3. Calculus required: slope of tangent line at $x = 2$ is rate of change, and equals about 0.16.

5. The shaded region is a triangle with base 5 units and height 3 units. From the precalculus formula for the area of a triangle we have

$$A = \tfrac{1}{2}bh = \tfrac{1}{2}(5)(3) = \tfrac{15}{2}.$$

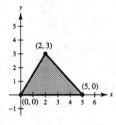

7. Precalculus: Volume $= (2)(4)(3) = 24$

9. (a)

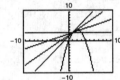

(b) The graphs of y_2 are approximations to the tangent line to y_1 at $x = 1$.

(c) The slope is approximately 2. For a better approximation make the list numbers smaller:

$$\{0.2, 0.1, 0.01, 0.001\}$$

11. (a) Using the Distance Formula to find the straight line distance between the points $(1, 5)$ and $(5, 1)$, we have the following approximation of the length L of the curve.

$$L \approx \sqrt{(5 - 1)^2 + (1 - 5)^2} = \sqrt{32} = 4\sqrt{2} \approx 5.66$$

(b) The intermediate points on the graph of the function are $\left(2, \tfrac{5}{2}\right)$, $\left(3, \tfrac{5}{3}\right)$, and $\left(4, \tfrac{5}{4}\right)$. Therefore, an approximation of the length L of the curve is given by the sum of the lengths of four line segments.

$$L \approx \sqrt{(2 - 1)^2 + \left(\tfrac{5}{2} - 5\right)^2} + \sqrt{(3 - 2)^2 + \left(\tfrac{5}{3} - \tfrac{5}{2}\right)^2} + \sqrt{(4 - 3)^2 + \left(\tfrac{5}{4} - \tfrac{5}{3}\right)^2} + \sqrt{(5 - 4)^2 + \left(1 - \tfrac{5}{4}\right)^2} \approx 6.11$$

(c) To improve the accuracy of the approximation increase the number of line segments. In Section 6.4, we will use calculus to find that the length of the curve (accurate to two decimal places) is 6.14.

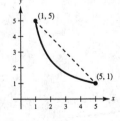
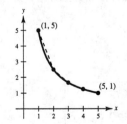

Section 1.2 Finding Limits Graphically and Numerically

1. $C(t) = 0.75 - 0.50[\![-(t-1)]\!]$

(a)

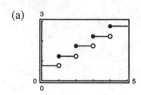

(b)

t	3	3.3	3.4	3.5	3.6	3.7	4
C	1.75	2.25	2.25	2.25	2.25	2.25	2.25

$$\lim_{t \to 3.5} C(t) = 2.25$$

(c)

t	2	2.5	2.9	3	3.1	3.5	4
C	1.25	1.75	1.75	1.75	2.25	2.25	2.25

$\lim_{t \to 3} C(t)$ does not exist. The values of C jump from 1.75 to 2.25 at $t = 3$.

3.

x	1.9	1.99	1.999	2.001	2.01	2.1
$f(x)$	0.3448	0.3344	0.3334	0.3332	0.3322	0.3226

$$\lim_{x \to 2} \frac{x-2}{x^2-x-2} \approx 0.3333 \quad \left(\text{Actual limit is } \tfrac{1}{3}.\right)$$

5. The table lists values of $f(x) = \dfrac{(1/x+1)-(1/4)}{x-3}$ at several x-values near 3.

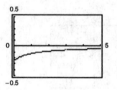

x	2.9	2.99	2.999	3.001	3.01	3.1
$f(x)$	-0.0641	-0.0627	-0.0625	-0.0625	-0.0623	-0.0610

As x approaches 3 from the left and from the right $f(x)$ approaches -0.0625. Therefore, we estimate the limit to be $-\tfrac{1}{16}$.

7.

x	-0.1	-0.01	-0.001	0.001	0.01	0.1
$f(x)$	0.9516	0.9950	0.9995	1.0005	1.0050	1.0517

$$\lim_{x \to 0} \frac{e^x - 1}{x} = 1$$

9.

x	-0.1	-0.01	-0.001	0.001	0.01	0.1
$f(x)$	0.9983	0.99998	1.0000	1.0000	0.99998	0.9983

$$\lim_{x \to 0} \frac{\sin x}{x} \approx 1.0000 \quad \text{(Actual limit is 1.) (Make sure you use radian mode.)}$$

11. The table lists values of $f(x) = \dfrac{\ln(x+1)}{x}$ at several x-values near 0.

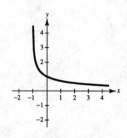

x	-0.1	-0.01	-0.001	0.001	0.01	0.1
$f(x)$	1.0536	1.0050	1.0005	0.9995	0.9950	0.9531

As x approaches 0 from the left and from the right, $f(x)$ approaches 1.
Therefore, we estimate the limit to be 1.

13. $\lim\limits_{x \to 3} (4 - x) = 1$

15. $\lim\limits_{x \to 2} f(x) = \lim\limits_{x \to 2} (4 - x) = 2$

17. $\lim\limits_{x \to 1} \sqrt[3]{x} \ln|x - 2| = 0$

19. From the graph we observe that as x approaches $\pi/2$ from the left, $f(x)$ increases without bound, and as x approaches $\pi/2$ from the right, $f(x)$ decreases without bound. Since $f(x)$ is not approaching a real number L as x approaches $\pi/2$, we say that the limit does *not* exist.

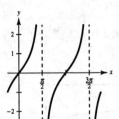

21. $\lim\limits_{x \to 5} \dfrac{|x - 5|}{x - 5}$ does not exist. For values of x to the left of 5, $|x - 5|/(x - 5)$ equals -1, whereas for values of x to the right of 5, $|x - 5|/(x - 5)$ equals 1.

23. We use the definition of limit to verify that

$$\lim\limits_{x \to 2} (3x + 2) = 8.$$

We are required to show that there exists a δ such that $|f(x) - L| < 0.01$ whenever $0 < |x - 2| < \delta$.

$$|f(x) - L| < 0.01$$
$$|(3x + 2) - 8| < 0.01$$
$$|3x - 6| < 0.01$$
$$3|x - 2| < 0.01$$
$$0 < |x - 2| < \frac{0.01}{3}$$

Therefore, $\delta = 0.01/3$.

25. $\lim\limits_{x \to 2} (x^2 - 3) = 1 = L$

$$|(x^2 - 3) - 1| < 0.01$$
$$|x^2 - 4| < 0.01$$
$$|(x + 2)(x - 2)| < 0.01$$
$$|x + 2|\,|x - 2| < 0.01$$
$$|x - 2| < \frac{0.01}{|x + 2|}$$

If we assume $1 < x < 3$, then $\delta = 0.01/5 = 0.002$.

27. $\lim\limits_{x \to 2} (x + 3) = 5$

Given $\epsilon > 0$:

$$|(x + 3) - 5| < \epsilon$$
$$|x - 2| < \epsilon = \delta$$

Hence, let $\delta = \epsilon$.

29. $\lim\limits_{x \to -4} \left(\tfrac{1}{2}x - 1\right) = \tfrac{1}{2}(-4) - 1 = -3$

Given $\epsilon > 0$:

$$\left|\left(\tfrac{1}{2}x - 1\right) - (-3)\right| < \epsilon$$
$$\left|\tfrac{1}{2}x + 2\right| < \epsilon$$
$$\tfrac{1}{2}|x - (-4)| < \epsilon$$
$$|x - (-4)| < 2\epsilon$$

Hence, let $\delta = 2\epsilon$.

31. $\lim\limits_{x \to 6} 3 = 3$

Given $\epsilon > 0$:

$$|3 - 3| < \epsilon$$
$$0 < \epsilon$$

Hence, any $\delta > 0$ will work.

33. We use the definition of limit to verify that

$$\lim\limits_{x \to 0} \sqrt[3]{x} = 0.$$

Given $\epsilon > 0$,

$$\left|\sqrt[3]{x} - 0\right| < \epsilon$$
$$\left(\left|\sqrt[3]{x}\right|\right)^3 < \epsilon^3$$
$$|x| < \epsilon^3 = \delta$$

35. $\lim\limits_{x \to -2} |x - 2| = |(-2) - 2| = 4$

Given $\epsilon > 0$:

$$||x - 2| - 4| < \epsilon$$
$$|-(x - 2) - 4| < \epsilon \quad (x - 2 < 0)$$
$$|-x - 2| = |x + 2| = |x - (-2)| < \epsilon$$

Hence, $\delta = \epsilon$.

37. $\lim\limits_{x \to 1} (x^2 + 1) = 2$

Given $\epsilon > 0$:

$$|(x^2 + 1) - 2| < \epsilon$$
$$|x^2 - 1| < \epsilon$$
$$|(x + 1)(x - 1)| < \epsilon$$
$$|x - 1| < \frac{\epsilon}{|x + 1|}$$

If we assume $0 < x < 2$, then $\delta = \epsilon/3$.

39. $f(x) = \dfrac{\sqrt{x + 5} - 3}{x - 4}$

$\lim\limits_{x \to 4} f(x) = \dfrac{1}{6}$

The domain is $[-5, 4) \cup (4, \infty)$. The graphing utility does not show the hole at $\left(4, \frac{1}{6}\right)$.

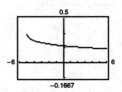

41. The graph of

$$f(x) = \frac{x - 9}{\sqrt{x} - 3}$$

is shown in the figure. From the graph it appears as though the limit exists, and $\lim\limits_{x \to 9} f(x) = 6$.

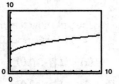

The domain of the function is $[0, 9) \cup (9, \infty)$. The graph generated by the graphing utility does not show that the function is indeterminate at $x = 9$. Therefore, it is important to analyze a function analytically as well as graphically.

43.

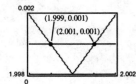

Using the zoom and trace feature, $\delta = 0.001$. That is, for

$$0 < |x - 2| < 0.001, \left|\frac{x^2 - 4}{x - 2} - 4\right| < 0.001.$$

45. False; $f(x) = (\sin x)/x$ is undefined when $x = 0$. From Exercise 9, we have

$$\lim_{x \to 0} \frac{\sin x}{x} = 1.$$

47. False; let

$$f(x) = \begin{cases} x^2 - 4x, & x \neq 4 \\ 10, & x = 4 \end{cases}.$$

$f(4) = 10$

$\lim\limits_{x \to 4} f(x) = \lim\limits_{x \to 4} (x^2 - 4x) = 0 \neq 10$

49. Answers will vary.

51. If $\lim\limits_{x \to c} f(x) = L_1$ and $\lim\limits_{x \to c} f(x) = L_2$, then for every $\epsilon > 0$, there exists $\delta_1 > 0$ and $\delta_2 > 0$ such that

$$|x - c| < \delta_1 \Rightarrow |f(x) - L_1| < \epsilon$$

and

$$|x - c| < \delta_2 \Rightarrow |f(x) - L_2| < \epsilon.$$

Let δ equal the smaller of δ_1 and δ_2. Then for $|x - c| < \delta$, we have

$$|L_1 - L_2| = |L_1 - f(x) + f(x) - L_2|$$
$$\leq |L_1 - f(x)| + |f(x) - L_2| < \epsilon + \epsilon.$$

Therefore, $|L_1 - L_2| < 2\epsilon$. Since $\epsilon > 0$ is arbitrary, it follows that $L_1 = L_2$.

53. $\lim\limits_{x \to c} [f(x) - L] = 0$ means that for every $\epsilon > 0$ there exists $\delta > 0$ such that if

$$0 < |x - c| < \delta,$$

then

$$|(f(x) - L) - 0| < \epsilon.$$

This means the same as $|f(x) - L| < \epsilon$ when

$$0 < |x - c| < \delta.$$

Thus, $\lim\limits_{x \to c} f(x) = L.$

Section 1.3   Evaluating Limits Analytically

1. (a) $\lim\limits_{x \to 0} f(x) = 1$

   (b) $\lim\limits_{x \to -1} f(x) = 3$

3. (a) $\lim\limits_{x \to 2} f(x) = 0$

   (b) $\lim\limits_{x \to -2} f(x) = 0$

5. (a) $\lim\limits_{x \to \pi/3} g(x) = \dfrac{\sqrt{3}}{2} \approx 0.866$

   (b) $\lim\limits_{x \to \pi/2} g(x) = 1$

7.

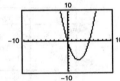

$h(x) = x^2 - 5x$

   (a) $\lim\limits_{x \to 5} h(x) = 0$

   (b) $\lim\limits_{x \to -1} h(x) = 6$

9. The graph of the function

$$f(x) = x \cos x$$

is shown in the figure. From the figure we estimate the limits.

   (a) $\lim\limits_{x \to 0} f(x) \approx 0$ (b) $\lim\limits_{x \to \pi/3} f(x) \approx 0.52$

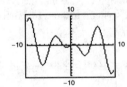

11. $\lim\limits_{x \to 4} x^2 = 4^2 = 16$

13. $\lim\limits_{x \to 0} (2x - 1) = 2(0) - 1 = -1$

15. $\lim\limits_{x \to 2} (-x^2 + x - 2) = -(2)^2 + (2) - 2 = -4$

17. $\lim\limits_{x \to 3} \sqrt{x + 1} = \sqrt{3 + 1} = \sqrt{4} = 2$

19. $\lim\limits_{x \to -4} (x + 3)^2 = (-4 + 3)^2 = 1$

21. $\lim\limits_{x \to 2} \dfrac{1}{x} = \dfrac{1}{2}$

23. $\lim\limits_{x \to -1} \dfrac{x^2 + 1}{x} = \dfrac{(-1)^2 + 1}{-1} = -2$

25. $\lim\limits_{x \to \pi/2} \sin x = \sin \dfrac{\pi}{2} = 1$

27. $\lim\limits_{x \to 1} \cos \pi x = \cos \pi = -1$

29. $\lim\limits_{x \to 0} \sec 2x = \sec 0 = 1$

31. $\lim\limits_{x \to 5\pi/6} \sin x = \sin \dfrac{5\pi}{6} = \dfrac{1}{2}$

33. $\lim\limits_{x \to 3} \tan \dfrac{\pi x}{4} = \tan \dfrac{3\pi}{4} = -1$

35. $\lim\limits_{x \to 0} e^x \cos 2x = e^0 \cos 0 = 1$

37. $\lim\limits_{x \to 1} (\ln 3x + e^x) = \lim\limits_{x \to 1} \ln 3x + \lim\limits_{x \to 1} e^x$
$$= \ln 3(1) + e^1 = \ln 3 + e \approx 3.817$$

39. (a) $\lim\limits_{x \to c} [5g(x)] = 5 \lim\limits_{x \to c} g(x) = 5(3) = 15$

(b) $\lim\limits_{x \to c} [f(x) + g(x)] = \lim\limits_{x \to c} f(x) + \lim\limits_{x \to c} g(x) = 2 + 3 = 5$

(c) $\lim\limits_{x \to c} [f(x)g(x)] = \left[\lim\limits_{x \to c} f(x)\right]\left[\lim\limits_{x \to c} g(x)\right] = (2)(3) = 6$

(d) $\lim\limits_{x \to c} \dfrac{f(x)}{g(x)} = \dfrac{\lim\limits_{x \to c} f(x)}{\lim\limits_{x \to c} g(x)} = \dfrac{2}{3}$

41. (a) $\lim\limits_{x \to c} [f(x)]^3 = \left[\lim\limits_{x \to c} f(x)\right]^3 = 4^3 = 64$

(b) $\lim\limits_{x \to c} \sqrt{f(x)} = \sqrt{\lim\limits_{x \to c} f(x)} = \sqrt{4} = 2$

(c) $\lim\limits_{x \to c} [3f(x)] = 3 \lim\limits_{x \to c} f(x) = 3(4) = 12$

(d) $\lim\limits_{x \to c} [f(x)]^{3/2} = \left[\lim\limits_{x \to c} f(x)\right]^{3/2} = (4)^{3/2} = 8$

43. $f(x) = -2x + 1$ and $g(x) = \dfrac{-2x^2 + x}{x}$ agree except at $x = 0$.

(a) $\lim\limits_{x \to 0} g(x) = \lim\limits_{x \to 0} f(x) = 1$

(b) $\lim\limits_{x \to -1} g(x) = \lim\limits_{x \to -1} f(x) = 3$

45. $f(x) = x(x + 1)$ and $g(x) = \dfrac{x^3 - x}{x - 1}$ agree except at $x = 1$.

(a) $\lim\limits_{x \to 1} g(x) = \lim\limits_{x \to 1} f(x) = 2$

(b) $\lim\limits_{x \to -1} g(x) = \lim\limits_{x \to -1} f(x) = 0$

47. Simplification of the given function yields

$$\dfrac{x^2 - 1}{x + 1} = \dfrac{(x + 1)(x - 1)}{x + 1} = x - 1.$$

If we let $f(x) = (x^2 - 1)/(x + 1)$ and $g(x) = x - 1$, then $f = g$ for all $x \neq -1$. Therefore,

$$\lim\limits_{x \to -1} f(x) = \lim\limits_{x \to -1} g(x) = -2.$$

The graph of f is given in the figure. Note that the graph generated by the graphing utility does not show that f is indeterminate at $x = -1$. Therefore, it is important to analyze a function analytically as well as graphically.

49. $f(x) = \dfrac{x^3 + 8}{x + 2}$ and $g(x) = x^2 - 2x + 4$ agree except at $x = -2$.

$$\lim\limits_{x \to -2} f(x) = \lim\limits_{x \to -2} g(x) = 12$$

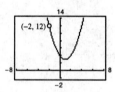

51. $f(x) = \dfrac{(x + 4)\ln(x + 6)}{x^2 - 16}$ and $g(x) = \dfrac{\ln(x + 6)}{x - 4}$

$$\lim\limits_{x \to -4} f(x) = \lim\limits_{x \to -4} g(x) = \dfrac{\ln 2}{-8} \approx -0.0866$$

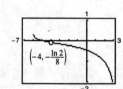

53. $\lim\limits_{x \to 5} \dfrac{x - 5}{x^2 - 25} = \lim\limits_{x \to 5} \dfrac{x - 5}{(x + 5)(x - 5)} = \lim\limits_{x \to 5} \dfrac{1}{x + 5} = \dfrac{1}{10}$ $\qquad$ **55.** $\lim\limits_{x \to 1} \dfrac{x^2 + x - 2}{x^2 - 1} = \lim\limits_{x \to 1} \dfrac{(x + 2)(x - 1)}{(x + 1)(x - 1)} = \lim\limits_{x1} \dfrac{x + 2}{x + 1} = \dfrac{3}{2}$

57. $\lim\limits_{x \to 0} \dfrac{\sqrt{3 + x} - \sqrt{3}}{x} = \lim\limits_{x \to 0} \dfrac{\sqrt{3 + x} - \sqrt{3}}{x} \cdot \dfrac{\sqrt{3 + x} + \sqrt{3}}{\sqrt{3 + x} + \sqrt{3}}$

$$= \lim\limits_{x \to 0} \dfrac{3 + x - 3}{\left(\sqrt{3 + x} + \sqrt{3}\right)x} = \lim\limits_{x \to 0} \dfrac{1}{\left(\sqrt{3 + x} + \sqrt{3}\right)} = \dfrac{1}{2\sqrt{3}} = \dfrac{\sqrt{3}}{6}$$

59. $\lim\limits_{x \to 0} \dfrac{\dfrac{1}{2 + x} - \dfrac{1}{2}}{x} = \lim\limits_{x \to 0} \dfrac{\dfrac{2 - (2 + x)}{2(2 + x)}}{x} = \lim\limits_{x \to 0} \dfrac{-x}{x(2)(2 + x)} = \lim\limits_{x \to 0} \dfrac{-1}{2(2 + x)} = -\dfrac{1}{4}$

61. $\lim\limits_{\Delta x \to 0} \dfrac{2(x + \Delta x) - 2x}{\Delta x} = \lim\limits_{\Delta x \to 0} \dfrac{2x + 2\Delta x - 2x}{\Delta x} = \lim\limits_{\Delta x \to 0} 2 = 2$

63. $\lim\limits_{\Delta x \to 0} \dfrac{(x + \Delta x)^2 - 2(x + \Delta x) + 1 - (x^2 - 2x + 1)}{\Delta x} = \lim\limits_{\Delta x \to 0} \dfrac{x^2 + 2x\Delta x + (\Delta x)^2 - 2x - 2\Delta x + 1 - x^2 + 2x - 1}{\Delta x}$

$$= \lim\limits_{\Delta x \to 0} \dfrac{2x\Delta x + (\Delta x)^2 - 2\Delta x}{\Delta x}$$

$$= \lim\limits_{\Delta x \to 0} \dfrac{\Delta x(2x + \Delta x - 2)}{\Delta x}$$

$$= \lim\limits_{\Delta x \to 0} (2x + \Delta x - 2) = 2x - 2$$

65. The graph of

$$f(x) = \dfrac{\sqrt{x + 2} - \sqrt{2}}{x}$$

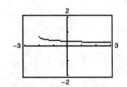

is shown in the figure. From the graph we estimate the limit to be 0.35. The table lists values of $f(x)$ at several x-values near 0.

x	-0.1	-0.01	-0.001	0.001	0.01	0.1
$f(x)$	0.3581	0.3540	0.3536	0.3535	0.3531	0.3492

As x approaches 0 from the left and from the right, $f(x)$ approached 0.35. Finding the limit analytically, we have the following.

$$\lim\limits_{x \to 0} \dfrac{\sqrt{x + 2} - \sqrt{2}}{x} = \lim\limits_{x \to 0} \left(\dfrac{\sqrt{x + 2} - \sqrt{2}}{x}\right)\left(\dfrac{\sqrt{x + 2} + \sqrt{2}}{\sqrt{x + 2} + \sqrt{2}}\right)$$

$$= \lim\limits_{x \to 0} \dfrac{x + 2 - 2}{x\left(\sqrt{x + 2} + \sqrt{2}\right)}$$

$$= \lim\limits_{x \to 0} \dfrac{1}{\sqrt{x + 2} + \sqrt{2}} = \dfrac{1}{2\sqrt{2}} = \dfrac{\sqrt{2}}{4}$$

67. $\lim\limits_{x \to 0} \dfrac{\dfrac{1}{2 + x} - \dfrac{1}{2}}{x} = -\dfrac{1}{4}$

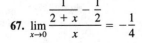

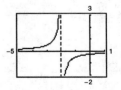

x	-0.1	-0.01	-0.001	0	0.001	0.01	0.1
$f(x)$	-0.263	-0.251	-0.250	?	-0.250	-0.249	-0.238

Analytically, $\lim\limits_{x \to 0} \dfrac{\dfrac{1}{2 + x} - \dfrac{1}{2}}{x} = \lim\limits_{x \to 0} \dfrac{2 - (2 + x)}{2(2 + x)} \cdot \dfrac{1}{x} = \lim\limits_{x \to 0} \dfrac{-x}{2(2 + x)} \cdot \dfrac{1}{x} = \lim\limits_{x \to 0} \dfrac{-1}{2(2 + x)} = -\dfrac{1}{4}.$

69. $\lim\limits_{x \to \pi/2} \dfrac{\sin x}{5x} = \lim\limits_{x \to \pi/2} \left[\left(\dfrac{1}{5}\right)\left(\dfrac{\sin x}{x}\right) \right] = \left(\dfrac{1}{5}\right)1 = \dfrac{1}{5}$

71. $\lim\limits_{\theta \to 0} \dfrac{\sec \theta - 1}{\theta \sec \theta} = \lim\limits_{\theta \to 0} \dfrac{1 - \cos \theta}{\theta} = 0$

73. $\lim\limits_{x \to 0} \dfrac{\sin^2 x}{x} = \lim\limits_{x \to 0} \left[\dfrac{\sin x}{x} \sin x \right] = (1)\sin 0 = 0$

75. $\lim\limits_{x \to 0} \dfrac{1 - e^{-x}}{e^x - 1} = \lim\limits_{x \to 0} \left(\dfrac{1 - e^{-x}}{e^x - 1} \cdot \dfrac{e^x}{e^x} \right)$

$= \lim\limits_{x \to 0} \dfrac{e^x - 1}{e^x(e^x - 1)} = \lim\limits_{x \to 0} \dfrac{1}{e^x} = 1$

77. $\lim\limits_{x \to \pi/2} \dfrac{\cos x}{\cot x} = \lim\limits_{x \to \pi/2} \dfrac{\cos x}{\cos x / \sin x}$

$= \lim\limits_{x \to \pi/2} \sin x = 1$

79. $\lim\limits_{h \to 0} \dfrac{(1 - \cos h)^2}{h} = \lim\limits_{h \to 0} \left[\dfrac{1 - \cos h}{h}(1 - \cos h) \right]$

$= (0)(0) = 0$

81. $\lim\limits_{x \to 6} \dfrac{\ln(x - 5)}{\ln(x - 5)^2} = \lim\limits_{x \to 6} \dfrac{\ln(x - 5)}{2\ln(x - 5)} = \lim\limits_{x \to 6} \dfrac{1}{2} = \dfrac{1}{2}$

83. $\lim\limits_{t \to 0} \dfrac{\sin^2 t}{t^2} = \lim\limits_{t \to 0} \left(\dfrac{\sin t}{t} \right)^2 = (1)^2 = 1$

85. $f(t) = \dfrac{\sin 3t}{t}$

t	-0.1	-0.01	-0.001	0	0.001	0.01	0.1
$f(t)$	2.96	2.9996	3	?	3	2.9996	2.96

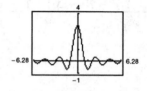

The limit appears to equal 3.

Analytically, $\lim\limits_{t \to 0} \dfrac{\sin 3t}{t} = \lim\limits_{t \to 0} 3\left(\dfrac{\sin 3t}{3t} \right) = 3(1) = 3.$

87. $f(x) = \dfrac{\ln x}{x - 1}$

x	0.5	0.9	0.99	1.01	1.1	1.5
$f(x)$	1.3863	1.0536	1.0050	0.9950	0.9531	0.8109

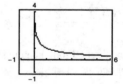

$\lim\limits_{x \to 1} \dfrac{\ln x}{x - 1} = 1$

89. $f(x) = \dfrac{\sin x^2}{x}$

x	-0.1	-0.01	-0.001	0	0.001	0.01	0.1
$f(x)$	-0.099998	-0.01	-0.001	?	0.001	0.01	0.099998

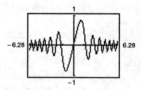

The limit appears to equal 0.

Analytically, $\lim\limits_{x \to 0} \dfrac{\sin x^2}{x} = \lim\limits_{x \to 0} x\left(\dfrac{\sin x^2}{x^2} \right) = 0(1) = 0.$

91. $\lim\limits_{h \to 0} \dfrac{f(x + h) - f(x)}{h} = \lim\limits_{h \to 0} \dfrac{2(x + h) + 3 - (2x + 3)}{h} = \lim\limits_{h \to 0} \dfrac{2x + 2h + 3 - 2x - 3}{h} = \lim\limits_{h \to 0} \dfrac{2h}{h} = 2$

93. $\lim\limits_{h \to 0} \dfrac{f(x + h) - f(x)}{h} = \lim\limits_{h \to 0} \dfrac{\sqrt{x + h} - \sqrt{x}}{h} = \lim\limits_{h \to 0} \dfrac{\sqrt{x + h} - \sqrt{x}}{h} \cdot \dfrac{\sqrt{x + h} + \sqrt{x}}{\sqrt{x + h} + \sqrt{x}}$

$= \lim\limits_{h \to 0} \dfrac{x + h - x}{h\left(\sqrt{x + h} + \sqrt{x}\right)} = \lim\limits_{h \to 0} \dfrac{1}{\sqrt{x + h} + \sqrt{x}} = \dfrac{1}{2\sqrt{x}}$

95. $\displaystyle\lim_{h\to 0}\frac{f(x+h)-f(x)}{h}=\lim_{h\to 0}\frac{\dfrac{4}{x+h}-\dfrac{4}{x}}{h}$

$$=\lim_{h\to 0}\left[\frac{\dfrac{4}{x+h}-\dfrac{4}{x}}{h}\cdot\frac{x(x+h)}{x(x+h)}\right]$$

$$=\lim_{h\to 0}\frac{4x-4(x+h)}{hx(x+h)}$$

$$=\lim_{h\to 0}\frac{-4h}{hx(x+h)}$$

$$=\lim_{h\to 0}\frac{-4}{x(x+h)}=-\frac{4}{x^2}$$

97. $\displaystyle\lim_{h\to 0}\frac{f(x+h)-f(x)}{h}=\lim_{h\to 0}\frac{(x+h)^2-4(x+h)-(x^2-4x)}{h}=\lim_{h\to 0}\frac{x^2+2xh+h^2-4x-4h-x^2+4x}{h}$

$$=\lim_{h\to 0}\frac{h(2x+h-4)}{h}=\lim_{h\to 0}(2x+h-4)=2x-4$$

99. $\displaystyle\lim_{x\to 0}(4-x^2)\le\lim_{x\to 0}f(x)\le\lim_{x\to 0}(4+x^2)$

$$4\le\lim_{x\to 0}f(x)\le 4$$

Therefore, $\displaystyle\lim_{x\to 0}f(x)=4$.

101. $f(x)=x\cos x$

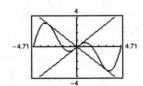

$$\lim_{x\to 0}(x\cos x)=0$$

103. $f(x)=|x|\sin x$

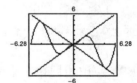

$$\lim_{x\to 0}|x|\sin x=0$$

105. The graphs of $y=x$, $y=-x$, and $y=x\sin(1/x)$ are shown in the figure. What follows is a direct application of the Squeeze Theorem to find the required limit. Since

$$\lim_{x\to 0}(-|x|)=0\quad\text{and}\quad\lim_{x\to 0}|x|=0\quad\text{and}\quad-|x|\le x\sin\frac{1}{x}\le|x|,$$

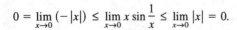

we have

$$0=\lim_{x\to 0}(-|x|)\le\lim_{x\to 0}x\sin\frac{1}{x}\le\lim_{x\to 0}|x|=0.$$

Therefore, by the Squeeze Theorem $\displaystyle\lim_{x\to 0}x\sin\frac{1}{x}=0$.

107. $f(x)=x,\ g(x)=\sin x,\ h(x)=\dfrac{\sin x}{x}$

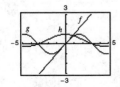

When you are "close to" 0 the magnitude of f is approximately equal to the magnitude of g. Thus, $|g|/|f|\approx 1$ when x is "close to" 0.

109. $s(t) = -16t^2 + 1000$

$$\lim_{t \to 5} \frac{s(5) - s(t)}{5 - t} = \lim_{t \to 5} \frac{600 - (-16t^2 + 1000)}{5 - t} = \lim_{t \to 5} \frac{16(t + 5)(t - 5)}{-(t - 5)} = \lim_{t \to 5} -16(t + 5) = -160 \text{ ft/sec}$$

111. $\lim_{t \to 3} \dfrac{s(3) - s(t)}{3 - t} = \lim_{t \to 3} \dfrac{105.9 - (-4.9t^2 + 150)}{3 - t} = \lim_{t \to 3} \dfrac{4.9t^2 - 44.1}{3 - t} = \lim_{t \to 3} \dfrac{-4.9(3 + t)(3 - t)}{3 - t} = \lim_{x \to 3} \left[-4.9(3 + t) \right]$

$$= -29.4 \text{ meters per second}$$

113. (a)

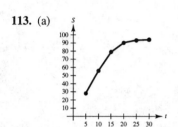

(b) Yes. As time increases, the typing speed seems to approach 95 or 100. The rate of increase is decreasing.

115. Suppose, on the contrary, that $\lim_{x \to c} g(x)$ exists. Then, since $\lim_{x \to c} f(x)$ exists, so would $\lim_{x \to c} [f(x) + g(x)]$, which is a contradiction. Hence, $\lim_{x \to c} g(x)$ does not exist.

117. Given $f(x) = x^n$, n is a positive integer, then

$$\lim_{x \to c} x^n = \lim_{x \to c} (xx^{n-1}) = \left[\lim_{x \to c} x \right]\left[\lim_{x \to c} x^{n-1} \right]$$

$$= c\left[\lim_{x \to c} (xx^{n-2}) \right] = c\left[\lim_{x \to c} x \right]\left[\lim_{x \to c} x^{n-2} \right]$$

$$= c(c)\lim_{x \to c} (xx^{n-3}) = \cdots = c^n.$$

119. False. Let $f(x) = \frac{1}{2}x^2$ and $g(x) = x^2$. Then $f(x) < g(x)$ for all $x \neq 0$. But $\lim_{x \to 0} f(x) = \lim_{x \to 0} g(x) = 0$.

121. $-M|f(x)| \le f(x)g(x) \le M|f(x)|$

$$\lim_{x \to c} (-M|f(x)|) \le \lim_{x \to c} f(x)g(x) \le \lim_{x \to c} (M|f(x)|)$$

$$-M(0) \le \lim_{x \to c} f(x)g(x) \le M(0)$$

$$0 \le \lim_{x \to c} f(x)g(x) \le 0$$

Therefore, $\lim_{x \to c} f(x)g(x) = 0$.

123. Given $\lim_{x \to c} f(x) = L$:

For every $\epsilon > 0$, there exists $\delta > 0$ such that $|f(x) - L| < \epsilon$ whenever $0 < |x - c| < \delta$. Since $||f(x)| - |L|| \le |f(x) - L| < \epsilon$ for $|x - c| < \delta$, then $\lim_{x \to c} |f(x)| = |L|$.

125. $\lim_{x \to 0} \dfrac{1 - \cos x}{x} = \lim_{x \to 0} \dfrac{1 - \cos x}{x} \cdot \dfrac{1 + \cos x}{1 + \cos x}$

$$= \lim_{x \to 0} \frac{1 - \cos^2 x}{x(1 + \cos x)} = \lim_{x \to 0} \frac{\sin^2 x}{x(1 + \cos x)}$$

$$= \lim_{x \to 0} \frac{\sin x}{x} \cdot \frac{\sin x}{1 + \cos x}$$

$$= \left[\lim_{x \to 0} \frac{\sin x}{x} \right]\left[\lim_{x \to 0} \frac{\sin x}{1 + \cos x} \right]$$

$$= (1)(0) = 0$$

127. $f(x) = \dfrac{\sec x - 1}{x^2}$

(a) The domain of f is all $x \neq 0,\ \pi/2 + n\pi$.

(b)

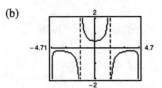

The domain is not obvious. The hole at $x = 0$ is not apparent.

(c) $\displaystyle\lim_{x \to 0} f(x) = \dfrac{1}{2}$

(d) $\dfrac{\sec x - 1}{x^2} = \dfrac{\sec x - 1}{x^2} \cdot \dfrac{\sec x + 1}{\sec x + 1} = \dfrac{\sec^2 x - 1}{x^2(\sec x + 1)}$

$$= \dfrac{\tan^2 x}{x^2(\sec x + 1)} = \dfrac{1}{\cos^2 x}\left(\dfrac{\sin^2 x}{x^2}\right)\dfrac{1}{\sec x + 1}$$

Hence, $\displaystyle\lim_{x \to 0} \dfrac{\sec x - 1}{x^2} = \lim_{x \to 0} \dfrac{1}{\cos^2 x}\left(\dfrac{\sin^2 x}{x^2}\right)\dfrac{1}{\sec x + 1}$

$$= 1(1)\left(\dfrac{1}{2}\right) = \dfrac{1}{2}.$$

129. Two functions agree at all but one point means that the functions are identical for all x in their domain, except possibly at one value of x.

Section 1.4   Continuity and One-Sided Limits

1. (a) The limit does not exist at $x = c$.

(b) The function is not defined at $x = c$.

(c) The limit exists at $x = c$, but it is not equal to the value of the function at $x = c$.

(d) The limit does not exist at $x = c$.

3.

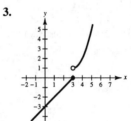

The function is not continuous at $x = 3$ because $\displaystyle\lim_{x \to 3^+} f(x) = 1 \neq 0 = \lim_{x \to 3^-} f(x)$.

5. (a) $\displaystyle\lim_{x \to 3^+} f(x) = 1$

(b) $\displaystyle\lim_{x \to 3^-} f(x) = 1$

(c) $\displaystyle\lim_{x \to 3} f(x) = 1$

7. (a) $\displaystyle\lim_{x \to c^+} f(x) = 0$

(b) $\displaystyle\lim_{x \to c^-} f(x) = 0$

(c) Since

$$\lim_{x \to c^+} f(x) = 0 = \lim_{x \to c^-} f(x),$$

$\displaystyle\lim_{x \to c} f(x) = 0$. [Note that $f(c) \neq \lim_{x \to c} f(x)$.]

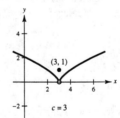

9. (a) $\displaystyle\lim_{x \to 3^+} f(x) = 3$

(b) $\displaystyle\lim_{x \to 3^-} f(x) = -3$

(c) $\displaystyle\lim_{x \to 3} f(x)$ does not exist.

11. $\displaystyle\lim_{x \to 5^+} \dfrac{x - 5}{x^2 - 25} = \lim_{x \to 5^+} \dfrac{1}{x + 5} = \dfrac{1}{10}$

13. $\lim\limits_{x\to 2^+} \dfrac{x}{\sqrt{x^2-4}}$ does not exist since $\dfrac{x}{\sqrt{x^2-4}}$ grows

without bound as $x \to 2^+$.

15. $\lim\limits_{x\to 0^+} \dfrac{|x|}{x} = \lim\limits_{x\to 0^+} \dfrac{x}{x} = 1$

$$\lim\limits_{x\to 0^-} \dfrac{|x|}{x} = \lim\limits_{x\to 0^-} \dfrac{-x}{x} = -1$$

Since the limit from the left is *not equal* to the limit from the right, the limit does *not* exist.

17. $\lim\limits_{\Delta x\to 0^-} \dfrac{\dfrac{1}{x+\Delta x} - \dfrac{1}{x}}{\Delta x} = \lim\limits_{\Delta x\to 0^-} \dfrac{x-(x+\Delta x)}{x(x+\Delta x)} \cdot \dfrac{1}{\Delta x} = \lim\limits_{\Delta x\to 0^-} \dfrac{-\Delta x}{x(x+\Delta x)} \cdot \dfrac{1}{\Delta x}$

$$= \lim\limits_{\Delta x\to 0^-} \dfrac{-1}{x(x+\Delta x)}$$

$$= \dfrac{-1}{x(x+0)} = -\dfrac{1}{x^2}$$

19. $\lim\limits_{x\to 3^-} f(x) = \lim\limits_{x\to 3^-} \dfrac{x+2}{5} = \dfrac{5}{2}$

$$\lim\limits_{x\to 3^+} f(x) = \lim\limits_{x\to 3^+} \dfrac{12-2x}{3} = 2$$

Since the limit from the left is *not equal* to the limit from the right, the limit does *not* exist.

21. $\lim\limits_{x\to 1^-} f(x) = \lim\limits_{x\to 1^-} (x^3+1) = 2$

$$\lim\limits_{x\to 1^+} f(x) = \lim\limits_{x\to 1^+} (x+1) = 2$$

Since the limit from the left is *equal* to the limit from the right, we have $\lim\limits_{x\to 1} f(x) = 2$.

23. $\lim\limits_{x\to 3^+} \ln(x-3) = \ln 0$ does not exist.

25. $\lim\limits_{x\to 2^-} \ln[x^2(3-x)] = \ln[4(1)] = \ln 4$

27. $\lim\limits_{x\to \pi} \cot x$ does not exist since

$$\lim\limits_{x\to \pi^+} \cot x \text{ and } \lim\limits_{x\to \pi^-} \cot x \text{ do not exist.}$$

29. $\lim\limits_{x\to 3^-} (2[\![x]\!] - 1) = 2(2) - 1 = 3$

$([\![x]\!] = 2 \text{ for } 2 < x < 3)$

31. $f(x) = \dfrac{1}{x^2-4}$

has discontinuities at $x = -2$ and $x = 2$ since $f(-2)$ and $f(2)$ are not defined.

33. As shown in the figure, the limit as x approaches a given integer from the left and from the right are not equal because of the greatest integer function. For any integer n, we have the following limits.

$$\lim\limits_{x\to n^+} \left(\tfrac{1}{2}[\![x]\!] + x\right) = \tfrac{1}{2}(n) + n = \tfrac{3}{2}n$$

$$\lim\limits_{x\to n^-} \left(\tfrac{1}{2}[\![x]\!] + x\right) = \tfrac{1}{2}(n-1) + n = \tfrac{3}{2}n - \tfrac{1}{2}$$

Therefore, f has a nonremovable discontinuity at any integer n.

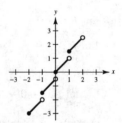

35. $f(x) = x^2 - 2x + 1$ is continuous for all real x.

37. $f(x) = x + \sin x$ is continuous for all real x.

39. From Theorem 1.11 we know that

$$f(x) = \dfrac{1}{x-1}$$

is continuous for all x other than $x = 1$. At $x = 1$ the function is discontinuous and the discontinuity is nonremovable since

$$\lim\limits_{x\to 1^-} \dfrac{1}{x-1} = -\infty \quad \text{and} \quad \lim\limits_{x\to 1^+} \dfrac{1}{x-1} = \infty.$$

41. $f(x) = \dfrac{x}{x^2 + 1}$ is continuous for all real x.

43. Since $x^2 - 3x - 10 = (x - 5)(x + 2)$, $x = 5$, and $x = -2$ are not in the domain of

$$f(x) = \frac{x + 2}{x^2 - 3x - 10}.$$

By Theorem 1.11, f is continuous for all x other than $x = 5$ or $x = -2$. At $x = 5$ the function is discontinuous and the discontinuity is nonremovable since

$$\lim_{x \to 5^-} \frac{x + 2}{(x - 5)(x + 2)} = \lim_{x \to 5^-} \frac{1}{x - 5} = -\infty$$

$$\lim_{x \to 5^+} \frac{x + 2}{(x - 5)(x + 2)} = \lim_{x \to 5^+} \frac{1}{x - 5} = \infty.$$

At $x = -2$ the function is discontinuous but it is removable since

$$\lim_{x \to -2} \frac{x + 2}{x^2 - 3x - 10} = \lim_{x \to -2} \frac{1}{x - 5} = -\frac{1}{7}.$$

45. $f(x) = \dfrac{|x + 2|}{x + 2}$

has a nonremovable discontinuity at $x = -2$ since $\lim\limits_{x \to -2} f(x)$ does not exist.

47. $f(x) = \begin{cases} x, & x \le 1 \\ x^2, & x > 1 \end{cases}$

has a **possible** discontinuity at $x = 1$.

1. $f(1) = 1$

2. $\left.\begin{array}{l} \lim\limits_{x \to 1^-} f(x) = \lim\limits_{x \to 1^-} x = 1 \\ \lim\limits_{x \to 1^+} f(x) = \lim\limits_{x \to 1^+} x^2 = 1 \end{array}\right\} \lim\limits_{x \to 1} f(x) = 1$

3. $f(1) = \lim\limits_{x \to 1} f(x)$

f is continuous at $x = 1$, therefore, f is continuous for all real x.

49. Since f is linear to the right and left of $x = 2$, it is continuous for all x other than possibly at $x = 2$. At $x = 2$,

$$\lim_{x \to 2^-} f(x) = \lim_{x \to 2^-} \left(\frac{x}{2} + 1\right) = 2$$

$$\lim_{x \to 2^+} f(x) = \lim_{x \to 2^+} (3 - x) = 1$$

Thus, f is discontinuous at $x = 2$ and this discontinuity is nonremovable since the limit from the left is *not equal* to the limit from the right.

51. $f(x) = \begin{cases} \csc \dfrac{\pi x}{6}, & |x - 3| \le 2 \\ 2, & |x - 3| > 2 \end{cases} = \begin{cases} \csc \dfrac{\pi x}{6}, & 1 \le x \le 5 \\ 2, & x < 1 \text{ or } x > 5 \end{cases}$ has **possible** discontinuities at $x = 1$, $x = 5$.

1. $f(1) = \csc \dfrac{\pi}{6} = 2 \qquad f(5) = \csc \dfrac{5\pi}{6} = 2$

2. $\lim\limits_{x \to 1} f(x) = 2 \qquad\qquad \lim\limits_{x \to 5} f(x) = 2$

3. $f(1) = \lim\limits_{x \to 1} f(x) \qquad\quad f(5) = \lim\limits_{x \to 5} f(x)$

f is continuous at $x = 1$ and $x = 5$, therefore, f is continuous for all real x.

53. The function f is continuous for all x other than possibly at $x = 0$. At $x = 0$,

$$\lim_{x \to 0^-} f(x) = \lim_{x \to 0^-} (1 - x^2) = 1$$
$$\lim_{x \to 0^+} f(x) = \lim_{x \to 0^+} \ln(x + 1) = 0.$$

Thus, f is discontinuous at $x = 0$ and this discontinuity is nonremovable since the limit from the left is *not equal* to the limit from the right.

55. $f(x) = \csc 2x$ has nonremovable discontinuities at integer multiples of $\pi/2$.

57. $f(x) = [\![x - 1]\!]$ has nonremovable discontinuities at each integer k.

59. $\lim_{x \to 0^+} f(x) = 0$

$\lim_{x \to 0} f(x) = 0$

f is not continuous at $x = -2$.

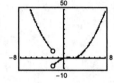

61. Since each part of the piecewise-defined function is a polynomial, f is continuous except possibly at $x = 2$. Since $f(2) = 8$, find a so that

$$\lim_{x \to 2^+} ax^2 = 8.$$

$$\lim_{x \to 2^+} ax^2 = a(2^2) = 8 \implies a = \frac{8}{2^2} = 2$$

63. Find a and b such that $\lim_{x \to -1^+} (ax + b) = -a + b = 2$ and $\lim_{x \to 3^-} (ax + b) = 3a + b = -2$.

$$a - b = -2$$
$$\underline{(+)\ 3a + b = -2}$$
$$4a \quad\ = -4$$
$$a = -1$$
$$b = \ 2 + (-1) = 1$$

$$f(x) = \begin{cases} 2, & x \le -1 \\ -x + 1, & -1 < x < 3 \\ -2, & x \ge 3 \end{cases}$$

65. $f(g(x)) = (x - 1)^2$

Continuous for all real x

67. $f(g(x)) = \dfrac{1}{(x^2 + 5) - 6} = \dfrac{1}{x^2 - 1}$

Nonremovable discontinuities at $x = \pm 1$

69. $y = [\![x]\!] - x$

Nonremovable discontinuity at each integer

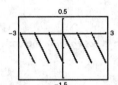

71. Since each part of the piecewise-defined function is a polynomial, f is continuous except possibly at $x = 3$. The graph of f is shown in the figure. From the graph, we see that

$$\lim_{x \to 3^-} f(x) \ne \lim_{x \to 3^+} f(x).$$

Therefore, f has a nonremovable discontinuity at $x = 3$.

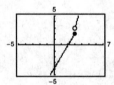

73. $f(x) = \dfrac{x}{x^2 + 1}$

Continuous on $(-\infty, \infty)$

75. $f(x) = \csc \dfrac{x}{2}$

Continuous on: $\ldots, (-2\pi, 0), (0, 2\pi), (2\pi, 4\pi), \ldots$

77. The graph of the function

$$f(x) = \frac{\sin x}{x}$$

over the interval $[-4, 4]$ is shown in the figure. The graph was produced by a graphing utility and appears continuous. Since $f(0)$ is not defined, the function is not continuous at $x = 0$. This example shows that a removable continuity usually cannot be observed on a graph produced by a graphing utility. Therefore, it is important to examine a function analytically as well as graphically.

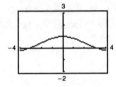

79. $f(x) = \dfrac{\ln(x^2 + 1)}{x}$

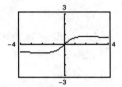

The graph **appears** to be continuous on the interval $[-4, 4]$. Since $f(0)$ is not defined, it is discontinuous there. Removable discontinuities do not always show up.

81. $f(x) = x^2 - 4x + 3$

$f(x)$ is continuous on $[2, 4]$.

$f(2) = -1$ and $f(4) = 3$

By the Intermediate Value Theorem, $f(c) = 0$ for at least one value of c between 2 and 4.

83. h is continuous on $\left[0, \dfrac{\pi}{2}\right]$.

$h(0) = -2 < 0$ and $h\left(\dfrac{\pi}{2}\right) \approx 0.91 > 0$.

By the Intermediate Value Theorem, $h(c) = 0$ for at least one value of c between 0 and $\dfrac{\pi}{2}$.

85. $g(t) = 2 \cos t - 3t$

g is continuous on $[0, 1]$.

$g(0) = 2 > 0$ and $g(1) \approx -1.9 < 0$.

By the Intermediate Value Theorem, $g(t) = 0$ for at least one value of t between 0 and 1. Using a graphing utility, we find that $t \approx 0.5636$.

87. $f(x) = x^3 + x - 1$

$f(x)$ is continuous on $[0, 1]$.

$f(0) = -1$ and $f(1) = 1$.

By the Intermediate Value Theorem, $f(x) = 0$ for at least one value of x between 0 and 1. Using a graphing utility, we find that $x \approx 0.6823$.

89. $f(x) = x^2 + x - 1$

f is continuous on $[0, 5]$.

$f(0) = -1$ and $f(5) = 29$.

$-1 < 11 < 29$

The Intermediate Value Theorem applies.

$$x^2 + x - 1 = 11$$
$$x^2 + x - 12 = 0$$
$$(x + 4)(x - 3) = 0$$
$$x = -4 \text{ or } x = 3$$
$$x = 3 \ (x = -4 \text{ is not in the interval.})$$

Thus, $f(3) = 11$, and $c = 3$.

91. Since

$$f(x) = x^3 - x^2 + x - 2$$

is a polynomial function, it is continuous on the entire real line and in particular on the interval $[0, 3]$. Also,

$$f(0) = -2 < 19 = f(3).$$

Hence, the Intermediate Value Theorem applies. To find c, we solve the following equation.

$$x^3 - x^2 + x - 2 = 4$$
$$x^3 - x^2 + x - 6 = 0$$
$$(x - 2)(x^2 + x + 3) = 0$$

Since $x^2 + x + 3 = 0$ has no real solution, the only real solution is $x = 2$ and it is in the specified interval $[0, 3]$. Therefore, $c = 2$ and $f(2) = 4$.

93. Let $V = \frac{4}{3}\pi r^3$ be the volume of a sphere of radius r.

$V(1) = \frac{4}{3}\pi \approx 4.19$

$V(5) = \frac{4}{3}\pi(5^3) \approx 523.6$

Since $4.19 < 275 < 523.6$, the Intermediate Value Theorem implies that there is at least one value r between 1 and 5 such that $V(r) = 275$. (In fact, $r \approx 4.0341$.)

95. Since the number of units in inventory is given by

$$N(t) = 25\left(2\left[\!\left[\frac{t+2}{2}\right]\!\right] - t\right) = 25\left(2\left[\!\left[\frac{t}{2} + 1\right]\!\right] - t\right),$$

we observe that the greatest integer function is discontinuous at every positive even integer. Therefore, $N(t)$ is discontinuous at every positive even integer. We demonstrate this by evaluating the function for several values of t and plotting the points to generate the figure.

$N(0) = 25(2[\![1]\!] - 0) = 25[2(1) - 0] = 50$

$N(1) = 25(2[\![1.5]\!] - 1) = 25[2(1) - 1] = 25$

$N(1.8) = 25(2[\![1.9]\!] - 1.8) = 25[2(1) - 1.8] = 5$

$N(2) = 25(2[\![2]\!] - 2) = 25[2(2) - 2] = 50$

$N(3) = 25(2[\![2.5]\!] - 3) = 25[2(2) - 3] = 25$

$N(3.8) = 25(2[\![2.9]\!] - 3.8) = 25[2(2) - 3.8] = 5$

$N(4) = 25(2[\![3]\!] - 4) = 25[2(3) - 4] = 50$

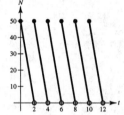

The company must replenish his inventory every two months.

97. $S = 28{,}500(1.09)^{[\![t]\!]}$

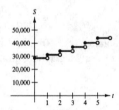

S is discontinuous at every positive integer.

99. Suppose there exists x_1 in $[a, b]$ such that $f(x_1) > 0$ and there exists x_2 in $[a, b]$ such that $f(x_2) < 0$. Then by the Intermediate Value Theorem, $f(x)$ must equal zero for some value of x in $[x_1, x_2]$ (or $[x_2, x_1]$ if $x_2 < x_1$). Thus, f would have a zero in $[a, b]$, which is a contradiction. Therefore, $f(x) > 0$ for all x in $[a, b]$ or $f(x) < 0$ for all x in $[a, b]$.

101. If $x = 0$, then $f(0) = 0$ and $\lim_{x \to 0} f(x) = 0$. Hence, f is continuous at $x = 0$.

If $x \neq 0$, then $\lim_{t \to x} f(t) = 0$ for x rational, whereas $\lim_{t \to x} f(t) = \lim_{t \to x} kt = kx \neq 0$ for x irrational. Hence, f is not continuous for all $x \neq 0$.

103. True

1. $f(c) = L$ is defined.

2. $\lim_{x \to c} f(x) = L$ exists.

3. $f(c) = \lim_{x \to c} f(x)$

All of the conditions for continuity are met.

105. False; a rational function can be written as $P(x)/Q(x)$ where P and Q are polynomials of degree m and n, respectively. It can have, at most, n discontinuities.

107. (a)

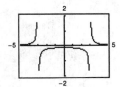

(b) There appears to be a limiting speed and a possible cause is air resistance.

109. Let y be a real number. If $y = 0$, then $x = 0$. If $y > 0$, then let $0 < x_0 < \pi/2$ such that $M = \tan x_0 > y$ (this is possible since the tangent function increases without bound on $[0, \pi/2)$). By the Intermediate Value Theorem, $f(x) = \tan x$ is continuous on $[0, x_0]$ and $0 < y < M$, which implies that there exists x between 0 and x_0 such that $\tan x = y$. The argument is similar if $y < 0$.

111. To find the domain begin by observing that f is indeterminate at $x = 0$. It is also necessary that $x + c^2$ be nonnegative which implies that $x \geq -c^2$. Therefore, the domain is $[-c^2, 0) \cup (0, \infty)$.

$$\lim_{x \to 0} \frac{\sqrt{x + c^2} - c}{x} = \lim_{x \to 0} \left[\frac{\sqrt{x + c^2} - c}{x} \cdot \frac{\sqrt{x + c^2} + c}{\sqrt{x + c^2} + c} \right]$$

$$= \lim_{x \to 0} \frac{(x + c^2) - c^2}{x\left[\sqrt{x + x^2} + c \right]}$$

$$= \lim_{x \to 0} \frac{1}{\sqrt{x + c^2} + c} = \frac{1}{2c}$$

Define $f(0) = 1/(2c)$ to make f continuous at $x = 0$.

Section 1.5   Infinite Limits

1. $\displaystyle\lim_{x \to -2^+} \frac{1}{(x + 2)^2} = \infty$

$\displaystyle\lim_{x \to -2^-} \frac{1}{(x + 2)^2} = \infty$

3. $\displaystyle\lim_{x \to -2^+} \tan \frac{\pi x}{4} = -\infty$

$\displaystyle\lim_{x \to -2^-} \tan \frac{\pi x}{4} = \infty$

5. When $x = 3$, the values of the numerator and denominator of the function

$$f(x) = \frac{1}{x^2 - 9}$$

are 1 and 0, respectively. Therefore, $x = -3$ is a vertical asymptote. The behavior of f and x approaches -3 from the left and from the right can be seen from the table:

x	-3.5	-3.1	-3.01	-3.001	-2.999	-2.99	-2.9	-2.5
$f(x)$	0.31	1.64	16.64	166.64	-166.69	-16.69	-1.69	-0.36

Therefore,

$$\lim_{x \to -3^-} \frac{1}{x^2 - 9} = \infty \quad \text{or} \quad \lim_{x \to -3^+} \frac{1}{x^2 - 9} = -\infty. \text{ The graph is shown in the figure.}$$

7. $f(x) = \dfrac{x^2}{x^2 - 9}$

x	-3.5	-3.1	-3.01	-3.001	-2.999	-2.99	-2.9	-2.5
$f(x)$	3.769	15.75	150.8	1501	-1499	-149.3	-14.25	-2.273

$\displaystyle \lim_{x \to -3^-} f(x) = \infty$

$\displaystyle \lim_{x \to -3^+} f(x) = -\infty$

9. $\displaystyle \lim_{x \to 0^+} \frac{1}{x^2} = \infty = \lim_{x \to 0^-} \frac{1}{x^2}$

Therefore, $x = 0$ is a vertical asymptote.

11. $\displaystyle \lim_{x \to 2^+} \frac{x^2 - 2}{(x - 2)(x + 1)} = \infty$

$\displaystyle \lim_{x \to 2^-} \frac{x^2 - 2}{(x - 2)(x + 1)} = -\infty$

Therefore, $x = 2$ is a vertical asymptote.

$\displaystyle \lim_{x \to -1^+} \frac{x^2 - 2}{(x - 2)(x + 1)} = \infty$

$\displaystyle \lim_{x \to -1^-} \frac{x^2 - 2}{(x - 2)(x + 1)} = -\infty$

Therefore, $x = -1$ is a vertical asymptote.

13. $\displaystyle \lim_{x \to -1^+} \frac{x^3}{x^2 - 1} = \infty$

$\displaystyle \lim_{x \to -1^-} \frac{x^3}{x^2 - 1} = -\infty$

Therefore, $x = -1$ is a vertical asymptote.

$\displaystyle \lim_{x \to 1^+} \frac{x^3}{x^2 - 1} = \infty$

$\displaystyle \lim_{x \to 1^-} \frac{x^3}{x^2 - 1} = -\infty$

Therefore, $x = 1$ is a vertical asymptote.

15. $f(x) = \dfrac{e^{-2x}}{x - 1}.$ $x = 1$ is a vertical asymptote.

17. By rewriting the equation for this function as the ratio of two polynomials, we have

$$T(t) = 1 - \frac{4}{t^2} = \frac{t^2 - 4}{t^2}$$

When $t = 0$, the values of the numerator and denominator of the function are -4 and 0, respectively. Therefore, $t = 0$ is the only vertical asymptote.

19. By factoring the denominator we have

$$f(x) = \frac{x}{x^2 + x - 2} = \frac{x}{(x - 1)(x + 2)}.$$

Therefore, the function has two vertical asymptotes, and they are $x = 1$ and $x = -2$.

21. $f(x) = \tan 2x = \dfrac{\sin 2x}{\cos 2x}$ has vertical asymptotes at

$$x = \frac{(2n + 1)\pi}{4} = \frac{\pi}{4} + \frac{n\pi}{2}, n \text{ any integer.}$$

23. $h(t) = \dfrac{\ln(t^2 + 1)}{t + 2}.$ $t = -2$ is a vertical asymptote.

25. $f(x) = \dfrac{1}{e^x - 1}$

When $x = 0$, the denominator is 0 and the numerator is not 0. Hence, by Theorem 1.14 we can conclude that $x = 0$ is a vertical asymptote.

27. $f(x) = \dfrac{x^3 + 1}{x + 1} = \dfrac{(x + 1)(x^2 - x + 1)}{x + 1}$

has no vertical asymptote since

$$\lim_{x \to -1} f(x) = \lim_{x \to -1} (x^2 - x + 1) = 3,$$

not infinity.

29. $s(t) = \dfrac{t}{\sin t}$ has vertical asymptotes at $t = n\pi$, n

a nonzero integer. There is no vertical asymptote at $t = 0$ since

$$\lim_{t \to 0} \frac{t}{\sin t} = 1.$$

31. $\displaystyle\lim_{x \to -1} \frac{x^2 - 1}{x + 1} = \lim_{x \to -1} (x - 1) = -2$

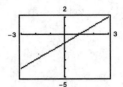

Removable discontinuity at $x = -1$

33. At $x = -1$ the numerator of the function is not zero and the denominator is equal to zero. Therefore, the graph of f has a vertical asymptote at $x = -1$. This result is also verified by the following one-sided limits.

$$\lim_{x \to -1^+} \frac{x^2 + 1}{x + 1} = \infty$$

$$\lim_{x \to -1^-} \frac{x^2 + 1}{x + 1} = -\infty$$

The graph of the function is shown in the figure.

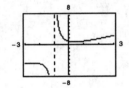

35. $f(x) = \dfrac{e^{2(x+1)} - 1}{e^{x+1} - 1} = \dfrac{(e^{x+1} - 1)(e^{x+1} + 1)}{e^{x+1} - 1} = e^{x+1}$,

$x \neq -1$

Removable discontinuity at $x = -1$

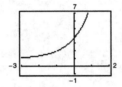

37. $\displaystyle\lim_{x \to 2^+} \frac{x - 3}{x - 2} = -\infty$

39. $\displaystyle\lim_{x \to 4^+} \frac{x^2}{x^2 - 16} = \infty$

41. $\displaystyle\lim_{x \to -3^-} \frac{x^2 + 2x - 3}{x^2 + x - 6} = \lim_{x \to -3^-} \frac{x - 1}{x - 2} = \frac{4}{5}$

43. $\displaystyle\lim_{x \to (\pi/2)^-} \ln|\cos x| = \ln\left|\cos \frac{\pi}{2}\right| = \ln 0 = -\infty$

45. Since

$$\lim_{x \to 0^+} 2 = 2 \quad \text{or} \quad \lim_{x \to 0^+} \sin x = 0,$$

it follows that

$$\lim_{x \to 0^+} \frac{2}{\sin x} = \infty.$$

47. $\displaystyle\lim_{x \to 1} \frac{x^2 - x}{(x^2 + 1)(x - 1)} = \lim_{x \to 1} \frac{x}{x^2 + 1} = \frac{1}{2}$

49. $\displaystyle\lim_{x \to 0^-} \left(1 + \frac{1}{x}\right) = -\infty$

51. $f(x) = \dfrac{x^2 + x + 1}{x^3 - 1}$

$$\lim_{x \to 1^+} f(x) = \lim_{x \to 1^+} \frac{1}{x - 1} = \infty$$

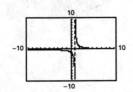

53. $f(x) = \dfrac{1}{x^2 - 25}$

$$\lim_{x \to 5^-} f(x) = -\infty$$

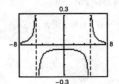

55. $S = \dfrac{k}{1-r}$, $0 < |r| < 1$. Assume $k \neq 0$.

$$\lim_{r \to 1^-} S = \lim_{r \to 1^-} \frac{k}{1-r} = \infty \quad (\text{or } -\infty \text{ if } k < 0)$$

57. (a) When $x = 7$, we have

$$r = \frac{2(7)}{\sqrt{625 - 7^2}} = \frac{14}{\sqrt{576}} = \frac{7}{12} \text{ feet per second.}$$

(b) When $x = 15$, we have

$$r = \frac{2(15)}{\sqrt{625 - 15^2}} = \frac{30}{\sqrt{400}} = \frac{3}{2} \text{ feet per second.}$$

(c) As x approaches 25 from the left, we have

$$\lim_{x \to 25^-} \frac{2x}{\sqrt{625 - x^2}} = \infty.$$

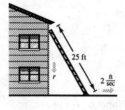

25 ft

r

$2 \frac{\text{ft}}{\text{sec}}$

59. $C = \dfrac{528x}{100 - x}$, $0 \le x < 100$

(a) $C(25) = \$176$ million

(b) $C(50) = \$528$ million

(c) $C(75) = \$1584$ million

(d) $\displaystyle \lim_{x \to 100^-} \frac{528}{100 - x} = \infty$ Thus, it is not possible.

61. $m = \dfrac{m_0}{\sqrt{1 - (v^2/c^2)}}$

$$\lim_{v \to c^-} m = \lim_{v \to c^-} \frac{m_0}{\sqrt{1 - (v^2/c^2)}} = \infty$$

63. (a) The linear velocities of the two pulleys must be the same. Linear velocity is given by $v = r\omega$ where r is the radius of a pulley and ω is its angular velocity in radians per unit time. Letting R be the number of revolutions per minute of the saw, we have the following.

$$10\left(\frac{1700}{2\pi}\right) = 20\left(\frac{R}{2\pi}\right)$$

The solution of the equation is $R = 850$ revolutions per minute.

(b) The direction of rotation of the saw is reversed.

(c) Observe the figure for the assignment of the variables x and y to the straight sections of the belt and for the magnitudes of the angles required in the following calculations.

Begin by recalling that the length of an arc of a circle is $s = r\theta$ where r is the radius of the circle and θ is magnitude of the central angle. Therefore, the lengths of the belt in contact with the pulleys are the following.

Small pulley: $10(\pi + 2\phi)$

Large pulley: $20(\pi + 2\phi)$

The lengths x and y of the straight sections of the belt are the following.

$$\cot \phi = \frac{y}{10} \implies y = 10 \cot \phi$$

$$\cot \phi = \frac{x}{20} \implies x = 20 \cos \phi$$

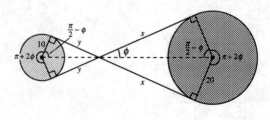

Therefore, the total length L of the belt is

$$L = 2x + 2y + 10(\pi + 2\phi) + 20(\pi + 2\phi)$$

$$= 60 \cot \phi + 30(\pi + 2\phi).$$

The domain of the function is $\left(0, \dfrac{\pi}{2}\right)$.

–**(CONTINUED)**–

63. —(CONTINUED)—

(d)

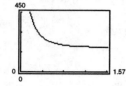

ϕ	0.3	0.6	0.9	1.2	1.5
L	306.2	217.9	195.9	189.6	188.5

(e) The graph of L is shown in the figure.

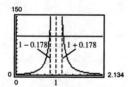

(f) $\displaystyle\lim_{\phi\to(\pi/2)^-} L = 60\cot\frac{\pi}{2} + 30\left(\pi + 2\cdot\frac{\pi}{2}\right)$

$$= 0 + 60\pi = 60\pi$$

As ϕ approaches $\pi/2$ from the left, the distance between the pulleys decreases and the belt tends to wrap farther around each pulley. Therefore, the length of the belt approaches the sum of the two circumferences of the pulleys.

(g) $\displaystyle\lim_{\phi\to0^+} L = \infty$.

65. False; for instance, let

$$f(x) = \frac{x^2 - 1}{x - 1}.$$

The graph of f has a hole at $(1, 2)$, not a vertical asymptote.

67. True

69. Let $f(x) = \dfrac{1}{x^2}$ and $g(x) = \dfrac{1}{x^4}$, and $c = 0$.

$\displaystyle\lim_{x\to0}\frac{1}{x^2} = \infty$ and $\displaystyle\lim_{x\to0}\frac{1}{x^4} = \infty$, but

$$\lim_{x\to0}\left(\frac{1}{x^2} - \frac{1}{x^4}\right) = \lim_{x\to0}\left(\frac{x^2 - 1}{x^4}\right) = -\infty \ne 0.$$

71. Given $\displaystyle\lim_{x\to c} f(x) = \infty$, let $g(x) = 1$. Then

$$\lim_{x\to c}\frac{g(x)}{f(x)} = \lim_{x\to c}\frac{1}{f(x)} = 0$$

by Theorem 1.15.

73. $f(x) = \dfrac{x + 2}{(x - 1)^2}$

(a) $\delta \approx 0.178$ for $M = 100$.

(b) $\delta \approx 0.055$ for $M = 1000$.

(c) As M increases, δ decreases.

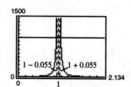

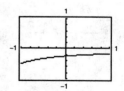

Review Exercises for Chapter 1

1. Calculus required. Using a graphing utility, you can estimate the length to be 8.3. Or, the length is slightly longer than the distance between the two points, 8.25.

3.

x	-0.1	-0.01	-0.001	0.001	0.01	0.1
$f(x)$	-0.26	-0.25	-0.250	-0.2499	-0.249	-0.24

$\displaystyle\lim_{x\to0} f(x) \approx -0.25$

5. The table lists values of $f(x) = \dfrac{20(e^{x/2} - 1)}{x - 1}$ at several x-values near 0.

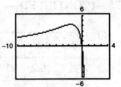

x	-0.1	-0.01	-0.001	0.001	0.01	0.1
$f(x)$	0.8867	0.0988	0.0100	-0.0100	-0.1013	-1.1393

As x approaches 0 from the left and from the right, $f(x)$ approaches 0. Therefore, we estimate the limit to be 0.

7. $h(x) = \dfrac{x^2 - 2x}{x}$

   (a) $\lim\limits_{x \to 0} h(x) = -2$

   (b) $\lim\limits_{x \to -1} h(x) = -3$

9. (a) $\lim\limits_{x \to -3} g(x) = -1$

   (b) $\lim\limits_{x \to -2} g(x)$ does not exist.

11. (a) $\lim\limits_{x \to 0} f(x) = 2$

   (b) $\lim\limits_{x \to 1} f(x) = 3$

13. (a) $\lim\limits_{t \to 0} f(t)$ does not exist.

   (b) $\lim\limits_{t \to -1} f(t) = 0$

15. $\lim\limits_{x \to 2} (5x - 3) = 5(2) - 3 = 7$

17. $\lim\limits_{x \to 2} (5x - 3)(3x + 5) = [5(2) - 3][3(2) + 5]$

$$= 7 \cdot 11 = 77$$

19. $\lim\limits_{t \to 3} \dfrac{t^2 + 1}{t} = \dfrac{3^2 + 1}{3} = \dfrac{10}{3}$

21. $\lim\limits_{t \to -2} \dfrac{t + 2}{t^2 - 4} = \lim\limits_{t \to -2} \dfrac{1}{t - 2} = -\dfrac{1}{4}$

23. $\lim\limits_{x \to 0} \dfrac{\dfrac{1}{x + 1} - 1}{x} = \lim\limits_{x \to 0} \dfrac{\dfrac{1 - (x + 1)}{x + 1}}{x}$

$$= \lim\limits_{x \to 0} \dfrac{1 - x - 1}{x(x + 1)}$$

$$= \lim\limits_{x \to 0} \dfrac{-1}{x + 1} = -1$$

25. $\lim\limits_{x \to -5} \dfrac{x^3 + 125}{x + 5} = \lim\limits_{x \to -5} \dfrac{(x + 5)(x^2 - 5x + 25)}{x + 5}$

$$= \lim\limits_{x \to -5} (x^2 - 5x + 25)$$

$$= 75$$

27. $\lim\limits_{x \to 0^+} \left(x - \dfrac{1}{x^3} \right) = -\infty$

29. Since

$$\sin\left(\dfrac{\pi}{6} + \Delta x \right) = \sin \dfrac{\pi}{6} \cos \Delta x + \cos \dfrac{\pi}{6} \sin \Delta x,$$

we have

$$\lim\limits_{\Delta x \to 0} \dfrac{\sin\left(\dfrac{\pi}{6} + \Delta x \right) - \dfrac{1}{2}}{\Delta x} = \lim\limits_{\Delta x \to 0} \dfrac{\dfrac{1}{2} \cos \Delta x + \dfrac{\sqrt{3}}{2} \sin \Delta x - \dfrac{1}{2}}{\Delta x}$$

$$= \lim\limits_{\Delta x \to 0} \left[\dfrac{\sqrt{3} \sin \Delta x}{2 \Delta x} + \dfrac{1}{2}\left(\dfrac{\cos \Delta x - 1}{\Delta x} \right) \right]$$

$$= \dfrac{\sqrt{3}}{2}.$$

31. $\lim\limits_{x\to 1} e^{x-1}\sin\dfrac{\pi x}{2} = e^0\sin\dfrac{\pi}{2} = 1$

33. $\lim\limits_{x\to -2^-}\dfrac{2x^2 + x + 1}{x + 2} = -\infty$

35. $\lim\limits_{x\to -1^+}\dfrac{x + 1}{x^3 + 1} = \lim\limits_{x\to -1^+}\dfrac{x + 1}{(x + 1)(x^2 - x + 1)}$

$\qquad = \lim\limits_{x\to -1^+}\dfrac{1}{x^2 - x + 1} = \dfrac{1}{3}$

37. $\lim\limits_{x\to 1^-}\dfrac{x^2 + 2x + 1}{x - 1} = -\infty$

39. $\lim\limits_{x\to 0^+}\dfrac{\sin 4x}{5x} = \lim\limits_{x\to 0^+}\left[\dfrac{4}{5}\left(\dfrac{\sin 4x}{4x}\right)\right] = \dfrac{4}{5}$

41. $\lim\limits_{x\to 0^+}\dfrac{\csc 2x}{x} = \lim\limits_{x\to 0^+}\dfrac{1}{x\sin 2x} = \infty$

43. $\lim\limits_{x\to 0^+}\ln(\sin x) = -\infty$

45. $f(x) = \dfrac{\sqrt{2x + 1} - \sqrt{3}}{x - 1}$

(a)

x	1.1	1.01	1.001	1.0001
$f(x)$	0.5680	0.5764	0.5773	0.5773

$\lim\limits_{x\to 1^+}\dfrac{\sqrt{2x + 1} - \sqrt{3}}{x - 1} \approx 0.577$ $\left(\text{Actual limit is }\sqrt{3}/3.\right)$

(b)

(c) $\lim\limits_{x\to 1^+}\dfrac{\sqrt{2x + 1} - \sqrt{3}}{x - 1} = \lim\limits_{x\to 1^+}\dfrac{\sqrt{2x + 1} - \sqrt{3}}{x - 1}\cdot\dfrac{\sqrt{2x + 1} + \sqrt{3}}{\sqrt{2x + 1} + \sqrt{3}}$

$\qquad = \lim\limits_{x\to 1^+}\dfrac{(2x + 1) - 3}{(x - 1)\left(\sqrt{2x + 1} + \sqrt{3}\right)}$

$\qquad = \lim\limits_{x\to 1^+}\dfrac{2}{\sqrt{2x + 1} + \sqrt{3}}$

$\qquad = \dfrac{2}{2\sqrt{3}} = \dfrac{1}{\sqrt{3}} = \dfrac{\sqrt{3}}{3}$

47. $\lim\limits_{x\to k^+}[\![x + 3]\!] = k + 3$ where k is an integer.

$\lim\limits_{x\to k^-}[\![x + 3]\!] = k + 2$ where k is an integer.

Therefore, $f(x) = [\![x + 3]\!]$ has a nonremovable discontinuity at each integer k, and is continuous on $(k, k + 1)$ for all integers k.

49. $f(x) = \begin{cases}\dfrac{3x^2 - x - 2}{x - 1}, & x \neq 1 \\ 0, & x = 1\end{cases}$

$\lim\limits_{x\to 1} f(x) = \lim\limits_{x\to 1}\dfrac{3x^2 - x - 2}{x - 1}$

$\qquad = \lim\limits_{x\to 1}(3x + 2) = 5 \neq 0$

Removable discontinuity at $x = 1$

Continuous on $(-\infty, 1)\cup(1, \infty)$

51. $f(x) = \dfrac{1}{(x - 2)^2}$

$\lim\limits_{x\to 2}\dfrac{1}{(x - 2)^2} = \infty$

Nonremovable discontinuity at $x = 2$

Continuous on $(-\infty, 2)\cup(2, \infty)$

53. $g(x) = 2e^{[\![x]\!]/4}$ is continuous on all intervals $(n, n + 1)$, where n is an integer. g has nonremovable discontinuities at each n.

55. $f(x) = \csc \dfrac{\pi x}{2}$

Nonremovable discontinuities at each even integer.
Continuous on

$$(2k, 2k + 2)$$

for all integers k.

57. $f(x) = \dfrac{3}{x + 1}$

$\lim\limits_{x \to 1^-} f(x) = -\infty$

$\lim\limits_{x \to 1^+} f(x) = \infty$

Nonremovable discontinuity at $x = -1$

Continuous on $(-\infty, -1) \cup (-1, \infty)$

59. $f(x) = \begin{cases} x + 3, & x \le 2 \\ cx + 6, & x > 2 \end{cases}$

Since f is linear to the right and left of 2, it is continuous for all values of x other than possibly at $x = 2$. Furthermore, since $f(2) = 2 + 3 = 5$, we can make f continuous at $x = 2$ by finding c such that

$$c(2) + 6 = 5$$

$$2c = -1$$

$$c = -\frac{1}{2}$$

Now we have

$$\lim_{x \to 2^-} f(x) = \lim_{x \to 2^-} (x + 3) = 2 + 3 = 5$$

and

$$\lim_{x \to 2^+} f(x) = \lim_{x \to 2^+} \left(-\frac{x}{2} + 6\right) = -1 + 6 = 5.$$

Thus, for $c = -1/2$, f is continuous at $x = 2$ and consequently f is continuous for all x.

61. $A = 5000(1.06)^{[2t]}$

Nonremovable discontinuity every 6 months

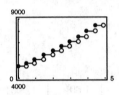

63. $g(x) = 1 + \dfrac{2}{x}$

Vertical asymptote at $x = 0$

65. $f(x) = \dfrac{8}{(x - 10)^2}$

Vertical asymptote at $x = 10$

67. The domain of $g(x) = \ln(9 - x^2)$ is $(-3, 3)$. From the one-sided limits

$$\lim_{x \to -0^+} g(x) = \lim_{x \to -3^+} \ln(9 - x^2) = -\infty$$

$$\lim_{x \to 3^-} g(x) = \lim_{x \to 3^-} \ln(9 - x^2) = -\infty,$$

it follows that $x = -3$ and $x = 3$ are vertical asymptotes.

69. $C = \dfrac{80,000p}{100 - p}$, $0 \le p < 100$

(a) $C(15) \approx \$14,117.65$ (b) $C(50) = \$80,000$

(c) $C(90) = \$720,000$ (d) $\lim\limits_{p \to 100^-} \dfrac{80,000p}{100 - p} = \infty$

71. $\lim\limits_{t a} \dfrac{s(a) - s(t)}{a - t} = \lim\limits_{t 4} \dfrac{[-4.9(4)^2 + 200] - (-4.9t^2 + 200)}{4 - t}$

$$= \lim_{t \to 4} \frac{4.9(t - 4)(t + 4)}{4 - t}$$

$$= \lim_{t \to 4} -4.9(t + 4) = -39.2 \text{ m/sec}$$

73. $\displaystyle\lim_{x\to 0^+}\frac{|x|}{x}=\lim_{x\to 0^+}\frac{x}{x}=\lim_{x\to 0^+}1=1$

$\displaystyle\lim_{x\to 0^-}\frac{|x|}{x}=\lim_{x\to 0^-}\frac{-x}{x}=\lim_{x\to 0^-}(-1)=-1$

Since the limit from the right and the limit from the left are *not* equal, the limit does *not* exist and the given statement is false.

75. True; see Theorem 1.7.

77. True

79. $\displaystyle\lim_{x\to 3}f(x)=1$ is true since

$\displaystyle\lim_{x\to 3^-}(x-2)=1$ and $\displaystyle\lim_{x\to 3^+}(-x^2+8x-14)=1.$

81. $f(x)=\sqrt{(x-1)x}$

Domain: $(-\infty,0]\cup[1,\infty)$

$\displaystyle\lim_{x\to 0^-}f(x)=0$

$\displaystyle\lim_{x\to 1^+}f(x)=0$

CHAPTER 2
Differentiation

C H A P T E R 2
Differentiation

Section 2.1   The Derivative and the Tangent Line Problem
Solutions to Exercises

1. (a) $m = 0$

(b) $m = -3$

3. (a), (b)

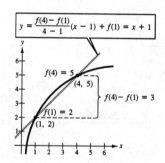

(c) $y = \dfrac{f(4) - f(1)}{4 - 1}(x - 1) + f(1)$

$$= \frac{3}{3}(x - 1) + 2$$

$$= 1(x - 1) + 2$$

$$= x + 1$$

5. $f(x) = 3$

$$f'(x) = \lim_{\Delta x \to 0} \frac{f(x + \Delta x) - f(x)}{\Delta x}$$

$$= \lim_{\Delta x \to 0} \frac{3 - 3}{\Delta x}$$

$$= \lim_{\Delta x \to 0} 0 = 0$$

7. $f(x) = -5x$

$$f'(x) = \lim_{\Delta x \to 0} \frac{f(x + \Delta x) - f(x)}{\Delta x}$$

$$= \lim_{\Delta x \to 0} \frac{-5(x + \Delta x) - (-5x)}{\Delta x}$$

$$= \lim_{\Delta x \to 0} -5 = -5$$

9. $f'(x) = \lim_{\Delta x \to 0} \dfrac{f(x + \Delta x) - f(x)}{\Delta x}$

$$= \lim_{\Delta x \to 0} \frac{2(x + \Delta x)^2 + (x + \Delta x) - 1 - (2x^2 + x - 1)}{\Delta x}$$

$$= \lim_{\Delta x \to 0} \frac{2x^2 + 4x\Delta x + 2(\Delta x)^2 + x + \Delta x - 1 - 2x^2 - x + 1}{\Delta x}$$

$$= \lim_{\Delta x \to 0} \frac{\Delta x(4x + 2\Delta x + 1)}{\Delta x} = \lim_{\Delta x \to 0} (4x + 2\Delta x + 1) = 4x + 1$$

11. $f(x) = x^3 - 12x$

$$f'(x) = \lim_{\Delta x \to 0} \frac{f(x + \Delta x) - f(x)}{\Delta x} = \lim_{\Delta x \to 0} \frac{[(x + \Delta x)^3 - 12(x + \Delta x)] - [x^3 - 12x]}{\Delta x}$$

$$= \lim_{\Delta x \to 0} \frac{x^3 + 3x^2\Delta x + 3x(\Delta x)^2 + (\Delta x)^3 - 12x - 12\Delta x - x^3 + 12x}{\Delta x}$$

$$= \lim_{\Delta x \to 0} \frac{3x^2\Delta x + 3x(\Delta x)^2 + (\Delta x)^3 - 12\Delta x}{\Delta x} = \lim_{\Delta x \to 0} (3x^2 + 3x\Delta x + (\Delta x)^2 - 12) = 3x^3 - 12$$

13. $f'(x) = \lim\limits_{\Delta x \to 0} \dfrac{f(x + \Delta x) - f(x)}{\Delta x} = \lim\limits_{\Delta x \to 0} \dfrac{\dfrac{1}{(x + \Delta x - 1)} - \dfrac{1}{x - 1}}{\Delta x}$

$\qquad = \lim\limits_{\Delta x \to 0} \dfrac{x - 1 - (x + \Delta x - 1)}{\Delta x (x + \Delta x - 1)(x - 1)} = \lim\limits_{\Delta x \to 0} \dfrac{-\Delta x}{\Delta x (x + \Delta x - 1)(x - 1)}$

$\qquad = \lim\limits_{\Delta x \to 0} \dfrac{-1}{(x + \Delta x - 1)(x - 1)} = \dfrac{-1}{(x - 1)(x - 1)} = \dfrac{-1}{(x - 1)^2}$

15. $f(x) = \sqrt{x - 4}$

$\quad f'(x) = \lim\limits_{\Delta x \to 0} \dfrac{f(x + \Delta x) - f(x)}{\Delta x} = \lim\limits_{\Delta x \to 0} \dfrac{\sqrt{x + \Delta x - 4} - \sqrt{x - 4}}{\Delta x} \cdot \dfrac{\sqrt{x + \Delta x - 4} + \sqrt{x - 4}}{\sqrt{x + \Delta x - 4} + \sqrt{x - 4}}$

$\qquad = \lim\limits_{\Delta x \to 0} \dfrac{(x + \Delta x - 4) - (x - 4)}{\Delta x [\sqrt{x + \Delta x - 4} + \sqrt{x - 4}]} = \lim\limits_{\Delta x \to 0} \dfrac{1}{\sqrt{x + \Delta x - 4} + \sqrt{x - 4}} = \dfrac{1}{2\sqrt{x - 4}}$

17. (a) $f(x) = x^2 + 1$

$\qquad f'(x) = \lim\limits_{\Delta x \to 0} \dfrac{f(x + \Delta x) - f(x)}{\Delta x}$

$\qquad\qquad = \lim\limits_{\Delta x \to 0} \dfrac{[(x + \Delta x)^2 + 1] - [x^2 + 1]}{\Delta x}$

$\qquad\qquad = \lim\limits_{\Delta x \to 0} \dfrac{2x\Delta x + (\Delta x)^2}{\Delta x}$

$\qquad\qquad = \lim\limits_{\Delta x \to 0} (2x + \Delta x) = 2x$

At $(2, 5)$, the slope of the tangent line is
$m = 2(2) = 4$. The equation of the tangent line is

$\qquad y - 5 = 4(x - 2)$

$\qquad y - 5 = 4x - 8$

$\qquad\qquad y = 4x - 3.$

(b)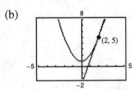

19. $f'(x) = \lim\limits_{\Delta x \to 0} \dfrac{f(x + \Delta x) - f(x)}{\Delta x}$

$\qquad = \lim\limits_{\Delta x \to 0} \dfrac{(x + \Delta x)^3 - x^3}{\Delta x}$

$\qquad = \lim\limits_{\Delta x \to 0} \dfrac{x^3 + 3x^2\Delta x + 3x(\Delta x)^2 + (\Delta x)^3 - x^3}{\Delta x}$

$\qquad = \lim\limits_{\Delta x \to 0} \dfrac{\Delta x[3x^2 + 3x\Delta x + (\Delta x)^2]}{\Delta x}$

$\qquad = \lim\limits_{\Delta x \to 0} [3x^2 + 3x\Delta x + (\Delta x)^2]$

$\qquad = 3x^2$

Thus, $f'(x) = 3x^2$ and the slope of the tangent line at $(2, 8)$ is $f'(2) = 3(2)^2 = 12$. Finally, by the point-slope form of the equation of a line, we have

$\qquad y - y_1 = m(x - x_1)$

$\qquad y - 8 = 12(x - 2)$

$\qquad\qquad y = 12x - 16.$

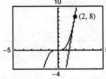

21. (a) $f(x) = x + \dfrac{1}{x}$

$$f'(x) = \lim_{\Delta x \to 0} \frac{f(x + \Delta x) - f(x)}{\Delta x}$$

$$= \lim_{\Delta x \to 0} \frac{\left[(x + \Delta x) + \dfrac{1}{x + \Delta x}\right] - \left[x + \dfrac{1}{x}\right]}{\Delta x}$$

$$= \lim_{\Delta x \to 0} \frac{\Delta x + \dfrac{x - (x + \Delta x)}{(x + \Delta x)x}}{\Delta x}$$

$$= \lim_{\Delta x \to 0} \left[1 + \frac{-\Delta x}{\Delta x(x + \Delta x)x}\right]$$

$$= \lim_{\Delta x \to 0} \left[1 - \frac{1}{(x + \Delta x)x}\right]$$

$$= 1 - \frac{1}{x^2}$$

At $(1, 2)$, the slope of the tangent line is

$$m = 1 - \frac{1}{1^2} = 0.$$

The equation of the tangent line is

$$y - 2 = 0(x - 1)$$

$$y = 2.$$

(b)

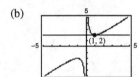

23. The slope of the line given by $3x - y + 1 = 0$ is 3 since

$$3x - y + 1 = 0$$

$$y = 3x + 1 = mx + b$$

Thus, it is necessary to find a point (or points) on the graph of $y = x^3$ such that the tangent line at that point has a slope of 3. From Exercise 19, we know that $dy/dx = 3x^2$ is the slope at any point on the graph of $y = x^3$. Therefore,

$$\frac{dy}{dx} = 3x^2 = 3$$

$$x^2 = 1 \quad \text{or} \quad x = \pm 1.$$

Finally, we conclude that the slope of the graph of $y = x^3$ is 3 at the points $(1, 1)$ and $(-1, -1)$. The tangent lines at these two points are:

$$y - 1 = 3(x - 1) \qquad y - (-1) = 3[x - (-1)]$$

$$y = 3x - 2 \qquad\qquad y = 3x + 2$$

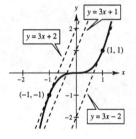

25. To begin, find $f'(x)$ as follows:

$$f'(x) = \lim_{\Delta x \to 0} \frac{f(x + \Delta x) - f(x)}{\Delta x}$$

$$= \lim_{\Delta x \to 0} \frac{4(x + \Delta x) - (x + \Delta x)^2 - (4x - x^2)}{\Delta x}$$

$$= \lim_{\Delta x \to 0} \frac{4x + 4\Delta x - x^2 - 2x\Delta x - (\Delta x)^2 - 4x + x^2}{\Delta x}$$

$$= \lim_{\Delta x \to 0} \frac{\Delta x(4 - 2x - \Delta x)}{\Delta x}$$

$$= \lim_{\Delta x \to 0} (4 - 2x - \Delta x)$$

$$= 4 - 2x$$

Now let (x, y) be a point on the graph of $y = 4x - x^2$. Since $dy/dx = 4 - 2x$, the slope of the tangent line at (x, y) is $m = 4 - 2x$. On the other hand, if the tangent line at (x, y) passes through the point $(2, 5)$, then its slope must be

$$m = \frac{y - 5}{x - 2} = \frac{4x - x^2 - 5}{x - 2}.$$

—CONTINUED—

25. —CONTINUED—

Equating these two expressions for m, we have

$$\frac{4x - x^2 - 5}{x - 2} = 4 - 2x$$

$$4x - x^2 - 5 = (4 - 2x)(x - 2)$$

$$4x - x^2 - 5 = 4x - 2x^2 - 8 + 4x$$

$$x^2 - 4x + 3 = 0$$

$$(x - 3)(x - 1) = 0$$

$$x = 3 \quad \text{or} \quad x = 1.$$

If $x = 3$, then $y = 4(3) - 3^2 = 3$ and $m = 4 - 2(3) = -2$. Therefore,

$$y - 3 = -2(x - 3) \quad \text{or} \quad y = -2x + 9.$$

If $x = 1$, then $y = 4(1) - 1^2 = 3$ and $m = 4 - 2(1) = 2$. Therefore,

$$y - 3 = 2(x - 1) \quad \text{or} \quad y = 2x + 1.$$

27. $f(x) = x$

$f'(x) = 1$

Matches graph (b).

29. $f(x) = x^3$

$f'(x) = 3x^2$

Matches graph (h).

31. $f(x) = |x| = \begin{cases} x, & \text{if } x \geq 0 \\ -x, & \text{if } x < 0 \end{cases}$

$f'(x) = \begin{cases} 1, & \text{if } x > 0 \\ -1, & \text{if } x < 0 \end{cases}$

Matches graph (f).

33. $f(x) = \ln x$. The slope tends to 0 as $x \to \infty$.

Matches graph (c).

35. (a) $g'(0) = -3$

(b) $g'(3) = 0$

(c) Since $g'(1) = -\frac{8}{3}$, the slope of the tangent line to the graph of g is $-\frac{8}{3}$ when $x = 1$. This means the graph is moving downward to the right when $x = 1$.

(d) Since $g'(-4) = \frac{7}{3}$, the slope of the tangent line to the graph of g is $\frac{7}{3}$ when $x = -4$. This means the graph is moving upward to the right when $x = -4$.

(e) Since $g'(x) > 0$ on the interval $[3, 6]$, the graph of g is moving upward to the right for all x in the interval. Therefore, $g(6) > g(4)$ and $g(6) - g(4) > 0$.

(f) No. Knowing only $g'(2)$ is not sufficient information for finding $g(2)$. $g'(2)$ remains the same for any vertical translation of the graph of g.

37.

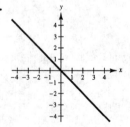

$y = -x$ is one possible answer. (slope is -1)

39. $f(x) = \frac{1}{4}x^3$

By the limit definition of the derivative we have $f'(x) = \frac{3}{4}x^2$.

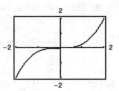

x	-2	-1.5	-1	-0.5	0	0.5	1	1.5	2
$f(x)$	-2	$-\frac{27}{32}$	$-\frac{1}{4}$	$-\frac{1}{32}$	0	$\frac{1}{32}$	$\frac{1}{4}$	$\frac{27}{32}$	2
$f'(x)$	3	$\frac{27}{16}$	$\frac{3}{4}$	$\frac{3}{16}$	0	$\frac{3}{16}$	$\frac{3}{4}$	$\frac{27}{16}$	3

41. $f(x) = 2x - x^2$, $g(x) = \dfrac{f(x + 0.01) - f(x)}{0.01}$

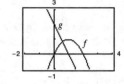

The graphs of f and g are shown in the figure. For any real number x, the difference quotient g gives the slope of the secant line through the points $(x, f(x))$ and $(x + 0.01, f(x + 0.01))$ on the graph of f. Since the two points are "close" to each other, the secant line approximates the slope of the tangent line to the graph of f at $(x, f(x))$. Therefore $g(x) \approx f'(x)$.

43. $f(x) = \dfrac{1}{\sqrt{x}}$ and $f'(x) = \dfrac{-1}{2x^{3/2}}$.

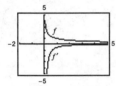

45. $f(x) = 4 - (x - 3)^2$

$$S_{\Delta x}(x) = \frac{f(2 + \Delta x) - f(2)}{\Delta x}(x - 2) + f(2)$$

$$= \frac{4 - (2 + \Delta x - 3)^2 - 3}{\Delta x}(x - 2) + 3 = \frac{1 - (\Delta x - 1)^2}{\Delta x}(x - 2) + 3 = (-\Delta x + 2)(x - 2) + 3$$

(a) $\Delta x = 1$: $S_{\Delta x} = (x - 2) + 3 = x + 1$

$\Delta x = 0.5$: $S_{\Delta x} = \left(\dfrac{3}{2}\right)(x - 2) + 3 = \dfrac{3}{2}x$

$\Delta x = 0.1$: $S_{\Delta x} = \left(\dfrac{19}{10}\right)(x - 2) + 3 = \dfrac{19}{10}x - \dfrac{4}{5}$

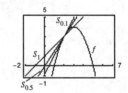

(b) As $\Delta x \to 0$, the line approaches the tangent line to f at $(2, 3)$.

47. $f(x) = x^2 - 1$, $c = 2$

$$f'(2) = \lim_{x \to 2} \frac{f(x) - f(2)}{x - 2}$$

$$= \lim_{x \to 2} \frac{(x^2 - 1) - 3}{x - 2}$$

$$= \lim_{x \to 2} \frac{(x - 2)(x + 2)}{x - 2}$$

$$= \lim_{x \to 2} (x + 2) = 4$$

49. $f'(-2) = \lim_{x \to -2} \dfrac{f(x) - f(-2)}{x - (-2)}$

$$= \lim_{x \to -2} \frac{(x^3 + 2x^2 + 1) - 1}{x + 2}$$

$$= \lim_{x \to -2} \frac{x^2(x + 2)}{x + 2}$$

$$= \lim_{x \to -2} x^2 = 4$$

51. $f(x) = (x - 1)^{2/3}$, $c = 1$

$$f'(1) = \lim_{x \to 1} \frac{f(x) - f(1)}{x - 1} = \lim_{x \to 1} \frac{(x - 1)^{2/3} - 0}{x - 1} = \lim_{x \to 1} \frac{1}{(x - 1)^{1/3}}$$

The limit does not exist. Thus, f is not differentiable at $x = 1$.

53. $f(x)$ is differentiable everywhere except at $x = -3$. (Sharp turn in the graph.)

55. $f(x)$ is differentiable everywhere except at $x = -1$. (Discontinuity)

57. The graph of $f(x) = (x - 3)^{2/3}$ is continuous at $x = 3$. However, the one-sided limits

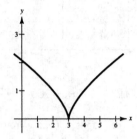

$$\lim_{x \to 3^+} \frac{f(x) - f(3)}{x - 3} = \lim_{x \to 3^+} \frac{(x - 3)^{2/3}}{x - 3} = \lim_{x \to 3^+} \frac{1}{(x - 3)^{1/3}} = \infty$$

$$\lim_{x \to 3^-} \frac{f(x) - f(3)}{x - 3} = \lim_{x \to 3^-} \frac{(x - 3)^{2/3}}{x - 3} = \lim_{x \to 3^-} \frac{1}{(x - 3)^{1/3}} = -\infty$$

are not equal. Therefore, f is not differentiable at $x = 3$ and the point $(3, 0)$ is called a **cusp.** Hence, f is differentiable in the intervals $(-\infty, 3)$ and $(3, \infty)$.

59. $f(x)$ is differentiable on the interval $(1, \infty)$. (At $x = 1$ the tangent line is vertical.)

61. $f(x)$ is differentiable everywhere except at $x = 0$. (Discontinuity)

63. $f(x) = |x - 1|$

The derivative from the left is $\displaystyle\lim_{x \to 1^-} \frac{f(x) - f(1)}{x - 1} = \lim_{x \to 1^-} \frac{|x - 1| - 0}{x - 1} = -1$.

The derivative from the right is $\displaystyle\lim_{x \to 1^+} \frac{f(x) - f(1)}{x - 1} = \lim_{x \to 1^+} \frac{|x - 1| - 0}{x - 1} = 1$.

The one-sided limits are not equal. Therefore, f is not differentiable at $x = 1$.

65. $f(x) = \begin{cases} (x - 1)^3, & x \le 1 \\ (x - 1)^2, & x > 1 \end{cases}$

The derivative from the left is

$$\lim_{x \to 1^-} \frac{f(x) - f(1)}{x - 1} = \lim_{x \to 1^-} \frac{(x - 1)^3 - 0}{x - 1} = \lim_{x \to 1^-} (x - 1)^2 = 0.$$

The derivative from the right is

$$\lim_{x \to 1^+} = \frac{f(x) - f(1)}{x - 1} = \lim_{x \to 1^+} \frac{(x - 1)^2 - 0}{x - 1} = \lim_{x \to 1^+} (x - 1) = 0.$$

These one-sided limits are equal. Therefore, f is differentiable at $x = 1$. ($f'(1) = 0$)

67. The derivative from the left is

$$\lim_{x \to 2^-} \frac{f(x) - f(2)}{x - 2} = \lim_{x \to 2^-} \frac{(x^2 + 1) - 5}{x - 2}$$

$$= \lim_{x \to 2^-} \frac{x^2 - 4}{x - 2}$$

$$= \lim_{x \to 2^-} (x + 2) = 4.$$

The derivative from the right is

$$\lim_{x \to 2^+} \frac{f(x) - f(2)}{x - 2} = \lim_{x \to 2^+} \frac{(4x - 3) - 5}{x - 2}$$

$$= \lim_{x \to 2^+} \frac{4x - 8}{x - 2}$$

$$= \lim_{x \to 2^+} 4 = 4.$$

The one-sided limits are equal. Thus, f is differentiable at $x = 2$ and $f'(2) = 4$.

69. (a) The distance from $(3, 1)$ to the line $mx - y + 4 = 0$ is

(b)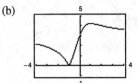

$$d = \frac{|Ax_1 + By_1 + C|}{\sqrt{A^2 + B^2}}$$

$$= \frac{|m(3) - 1(1) + 4|}{\sqrt{m^2 + 1}} = \frac{|3m + 3|}{\sqrt{m^2 + 1}}.$$

The function d is not differentiable at $m = -1$. This corresponds to the line $y = -x + 4$, which passes through the point $(3, 1)$.

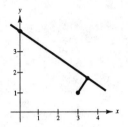

73. True—see Theorem 2.1.

71. False. $y = |x - 2|$ is continuous at $x = 2$, but is not differentiable at $x = 2$. (Sharp turn in the graph)

75. $f(x) = \begin{cases} x \sin(1/x), & x \neq 0 \\ 0, & x = 0 \end{cases}$

Using the Squeeze Theorem, we have $-|x| \leq x \sin(1/x) \leq |x|, \ x \neq 0$. Thus, $\lim\limits_{x \to 0} x \sin(1/x) = 0 = f(0)$ and f is continuous at $x = 0$. Using the alternative form of the derivative we have

$$\lim_{x \to 0} \frac{f(x) - f(0)}{x - 0} = \lim_{x \to 0} \frac{x \sin(1/x) - 0}{x - 0} = \lim_{x \to 0} \left(\sin \frac{1}{x} \right).$$

Since this limit does not exist (it oscillates between -1 and 1), the function is not differentiable at $x = 0$.

$$g(x) = \begin{cases} x^2 \sin(1/x), & x \neq 0 \\ 0, & x = 0 \end{cases}$$

Using the Squeeze Theorem again we have $-x^2 \leq x^2 \sin(1/x) \leq x^2, x \neq 0$. Thus, $\lim\limits_{x \to 0} x^2 \sin(1/x) = 0 = f(0)$ and f is continuous at $x = 0$. Using the alternative form of the derivative again we have

$$\lim_{x \to 0} \frac{f(x) - f(0)}{x - 0} = \lim_{x \to 0} \frac{x^2 \sin(1/x) - 0}{x - 0} = \lim_{x \to 0} x \sin \frac{1}{x} = 0.$$

Therefore, g is differentiable at $x = 0$, $g'(0) = 0$.

Section 2.2   Basic Differentiation Rules and Rates of Change

1. (a) $y = x^{1/2}$

$y' = \frac{1}{2} x^{-1/2}$

$y'(1) = \frac{1}{2}$

(b) $y = x^{3/2}$

$y' = \frac{3}{2} x^{1/2}$

$y'(1) = \frac{3}{2}$

(c) $y = x^2$

$y' = 2x$

$y'(1) = 2$

(d) $y = x^3$

$y' = 3x^2$

$y'(1) = 3$

3. $y = 3$

$y' = 0$

5. $f(x) = x + 1$

$f'(x) = 1$

7. $g(x) = x^2 + 4$

$g'(x) = 2x$

9. $f(t) = -2t^2 + 3t - 6$

$f'(t) = -4t + 3$

11. $s(t) = t^3 - 2t + 4$

$s'(t) = 3t^2 - 2$

13. $f(x) = 6x - 5e^x$

$f'(x) = 6 - 5e^x$

15. $y = \dfrac{1}{x} - 3 \sin x = x^{-1} - 3 \sin x$

$\quad y' = -x^{-2} - 3 \cos x$

$\quad\quad = -\dfrac{1}{x^2} - 3 \cos x$

17. $y = x^2 - \dfrac{1}{2} \cos x$

$\quad y' = 2x + \dfrac{1}{2} \sin x$

19. $g(t) = \frac{1}{2}e^t - 4 \cos t$

$\quad g'(t) = \frac{1}{2}e^t + 4 \sin t$

Function	*Rewrite*	*Differentiate*	*Simplify*
21. $y = \dfrac{1}{3x^3}$	$y = \dfrac{1}{3}x^{-3}$	$y' = -x^{-4}$	$y' = -\dfrac{1}{x^4}$
23. $y = \dfrac{1}{(3x)^3}$	$y = \dfrac{1}{27}x^{-3}$	$y' = -\dfrac{1}{9}x^{-4}$	$y' = -\dfrac{1}{9x^4}$

25.   Function: $f(x) = \dfrac{\sqrt{x}}{x}$

$\quad$ Rewrite: $f(x) = \dfrac{x^{1/2}}{x} = x^{-1/2}$

$\quad$ Derivative: $f'(x) = -\dfrac{1}{2}x^{-3/2}$

$\quad$ Simplify: $f'(x) = -\dfrac{1}{2x^{3/2}}$

27. $f(x) = \dfrac{1}{x}$, $(1, 1)$

$\quad f'(x) = -\dfrac{1}{x^2}$

$\quad f'(1) = -1$

29. $f(t) = \frac{3}{4}e^t$

$\quad f'(t) = \frac{3}{4}e^t$

$\quad$ At the point $\left(0, \frac{3}{4}\right)$ the derivative is

$\quad\quad f'(0) = \frac{3}{4}e^0 = \frac{3}{4}.$

31. $y = (2x + 1)^2 = 4x^2 + 4x + 1$

$\quad y' = 8x + 4$

$\quad$ At the point $(0, 1)$ the derivative is

$\quad\quad y' = 8(0) + 4 = 4.$

33. $f(x) = -\dfrac{1}{2} + \dfrac{7}{5}x^3$, $\left(0, -\dfrac{1}{2}\right)$

$\quad f'(x) = \dfrac{21}{5}x^2$

$\quad f'(0) = 0$

35. $f(\theta) = 4 \sin \theta - \theta$, $(0, 0)$

$\quad f'(\theta) = 4 \cos \theta - 1$

$\quad f'(0) = 4(1) - 1 = 3$

37. $f(x) = x^3 - 3x - 2x^{-4}$

$\quad f'(x) = 3x^2 - 3 + 8x^{-5}$

$\quad\quad = 3x^2 - 3 + \dfrac{8}{x^5}$

39. $g(t) = t^2 - \dfrac{4}{t} = t^2 - 4t^{-1}$

$\quad g'(t) = 2t - (-1)4t^{-2} = 2t + \dfrac{4}{t^2}$

41. $f(x) = \dfrac{x^3 - 3x^2 + 4}{x^2} = \dfrac{x^3}{x^2} - \dfrac{3x^2}{x^2} + \dfrac{4}{x^2} = x - 3 + 4x^{-2}$

$\quad f'(x) = 1 + 4(-2)x^{-3} = 1 - \dfrac{8}{x^3} = \dfrac{x^3 - 8}{x^3}$

43. $f(x) = x^2 - 2e^x$

$\quad f'(x) = 2x - 2e^x$

45. $h(s) = s^{4/5}$

$$h'(s) = \frac{4}{5}s^{-1/5} = \frac{4}{5s^{1/5}}$$

47. $f(x) = 4\sqrt{x} + 3\cos x = 4x^{1/2} + 3\cos x$

$$f'(x) = 4\left(\frac{1}{2}\right)x^{-1/2} + 3(-\sin x) = \frac{2}{\sqrt{x}} - 3\sin x$$

49. $y = x(x^2 + 1) = x^3 + x$

$$y' = 3x^2 + 1$$

51. (a) $y = x^4 - 3x^2 + 2$

$$y' = 4x^3 - 6x$$

Thus the slope of the tangent line at $(1, 0)$ is

$$y' = 4(1)^3 - 6(1) = 4 - 6 = -2.$$

The equation of the tangent line at $(1, 0)$ is

$$y - y_1 = m(x - x_1)$$
$$y - 0 = -2(x - 1)$$
$$2x + y - 2 = 0$$

(b) The graph is shown in the figure.

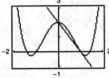

53. (a) $f(x) = \frac{1}{\sqrt[3]{x^2}} = x^{-2/3}$

$$f'(x) = -\frac{2}{3}x^{-5/3} = -\frac{2}{3\sqrt[3]{x^5}}$$

At $\left(8, \frac{1}{4}\right)$: $y' = -\frac{2}{3\left(\sqrt[3]{8}\right)^5} = -\frac{1}{48}.$

Tangent line: $y - \frac{1}{4} = -\frac{1}{48}(x - 8)$

$$-48y + 12 = x - 8$$
$$0 = x + 48y - 20$$

(b)

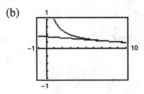

55. (a) $g(x) = x + e^x$

$$g'(x) = 1 + e^x$$

At $(0, 1)$: $g'(0) = 1 + 1 = 2$

Tangent line: $y - 1 = 2(x - 0)$

$$y = 2x + 1$$

(b)

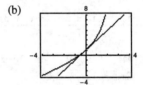

57. A tangent line is horizontal if the derivative (the slope) at the point of tangency is zero. Since $y' = 4x^3 - 16x = 4x(x^2 - 4)$, we must find all values of x that satisfy the equation $y' = 4x(x^2 - 4) = 4x(x + 2)(x - 2) = 0$. The solutions to this equation are $x = -2$, $x = 0$, and $x = 2$. At $x = \pm 2$, we have

$$y = (\pm 2)^4 - 8(\pm 2)^2 + 2 = -14.$$

At $x = 0$, we have $y = 2$. Thus, the points of horizontal tangency are:

$$(-2, -14), (0, 2), \text{ and } (2, -14)$$

59. $y = \frac{1}{x^2} = x^{-2}$

$$y' = -2x^{-3} = \frac{-2}{x^3} \text{ cannot equal zero.}$$

Therefore, there are no horizontal tangents.

61. $y = x + \sin x, 0 \le x < 2\pi$

$$y' = 1 + \cos x = 0$$

$$\cos x = -1 \implies x = \pi$$

At $x = \pi, y = \pi.$

Horizontal tangent: (π, π)

63. $y = -4x + e^x$

$y' = -4 + e^x = 0$

$e^x = 4$

$x = \ln 4$

$(\ln 4, -4 \ln 4 + 4)$

65.

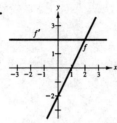

If f is linear then its derivative is a constant function.

$$f(x) = ax + b$$

$$f'(x) = a$$

67. Let (x_1, y_1) and (x_2, y_2) be the points of tangency on the graphs of $y = x^2$ and $y = -x^2 + 6x - 5$, respectively. We know that $y_1 = x_1^2$ and $y_2 = -x_2^2 + 6x_2 - 5$. Let m be the slope of the tangent line. Since the line passes through (x_1, y_1) and (x_2, y_2), it follows that

(1) $m = \dfrac{y_2 - y_1}{x_2 - x_1} = \dfrac{-x_2^2 + 6x_2 - 5 - x_1^2}{x_2 - x_1}$.

Since the line is tangent to $y = x^2$ at (x_1, y_1) and the derivative of this curve is $y' = 2x$, it follows that $m = 2x_1$.

Since the line is tangent to $y = -x^2 + 6x - 5$ at (x_2, y_2) and the derivative of this curve is $y' = -2x + 6$, it follows that

(2) $m = -2x_2 + 6$.

Thus, from the preceding two equations, we have: $m = 2x_1 = -2x_2 + 6$

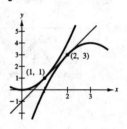

(3) $x_1 = -x_2 + 3$.

Using equations (1), (2), and (3) yields

$$m = -2x_2 + 6 = \frac{-x_2^2 + 6x_2 - 5 - x_1^2}{x_2 - x_1}$$

$$-2x_2 + 6 = \frac{-x_2^2 + 6x_2 - 5 - (-x_2 + 3)^2}{x_2 - (-x_2 + 3)}$$

$$(2x_2 - 3)(-2x_2 + 6) = -x_2^2 + 6x_2 - 5 - (x_2^2 - 6x_2 + 9)$$

$$-4x_2^2 + 18x_2 - 18 = -2x_2^2 + 12x_2 - 14$$

$$-2x_2^2 + 6x_2 - 4 = 0$$

$$x_2^2 - 3x_2 + 2 = 0$$

$$(x_2 - 2)(x_2 - 1) = 0$$

$$x_2 = 1 \quad \text{or} \quad x_2 = 2.$$

If $x_2 = 1$, then $y_2 = -1^2 + 6(1) - 5 = 0$, $x_1 = -1 + 3 = 2$, and $y_1 = 2^2 = 4$. Thus the line containing $(1, 0)$ and $(2, 4)$ is tangent to both curves. The equation of this line is

$$y - 0 = \left(\frac{4 - 0}{2 - 1}\right)(x - 1) \quad \text{or} \quad y = 4x - 4.$$

If $x_2 = 2$, then $y_2 = -2^2 + 6(2) - 5 = -4 + 12 - 5 = 3$, $x_1 = -2 + 3 = 1$, and $y_1 = 1^2 = 1$. Thus the line containing $(2, 3)$ and $(1, 1)$ is tangent to both curves. The equation of this line is

$$y - 1 = \left(\frac{3 - 1}{2 - 1}\right)(x - 1) = 2x - 2$$

$$y = 2x - 1.$$

69. From the figure we observe that the slope of the tangent line can be determined by the derivative of f and by the two-point formula for the slope of the line. Therefore,

$$f'(x) = \frac{y_0 - y}{x_0 - x}.$$

Since $f(x) = \sqrt{x}, f'(x) = 1/(2\sqrt{x})$, $y = \sqrt{x}$, $x_0 = -4$, and $y_0 = 0$, we have the following.

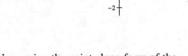

$$f'(x) = \frac{y_0 - y}{x_0 - x}$$

$$\frac{1}{2\sqrt{x}} = \frac{0 - \sqrt{x}}{-4 - x}$$

$$\frac{1}{2\sqrt{x}} = \frac{\sqrt{x}}{4 + x}$$

$$4 + x = 2x \implies x = 4$$

Hence the point of tangency is $(4, 2)$ and the slope of the tangent line is $f'(4) = \frac{1}{4}$. Now, using the point-slope form of the equation of a line, we can write

$$y - 2 = \frac{1}{4}(x - 4)$$

$$4y - 8 = x - 4$$

$$0 = x - 4y + 4.$$

71. (a) One possible secant is between $(3.9, 7.7019)$ and $(4, 8)$:

$$y - 8 = \frac{8 - 7.7019}{4 - 3.9}(x - 4)$$

$$y - 8 = 2.981(x - 4)$$

$$y = S(x) = 2.981x - 3.924$$

(b) $f'(x) = \frac{3}{2}x^{1/2} \implies f'(4) = \frac{3}{2}(2) = 3$

$$T(x) = 3(x - 4) + 8 = 3x - 4$$

$S(x)$ is an approximation of the tangent line $T(x)$.

(c) As you move further away from $(4, 8)$, the accuracy of the approximation T gets worse.

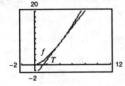

(d)

Δx	-3	-2	-1	-0.5	-0.1	0	0.1	0.5	1	2	3
$f(x)$	1	2.828	5.196	6.548	7.702	8	8.302	9.546	11.180	14.697	18.520
$T(x)$	-1	2	5	6.5	7.7	8	8.3	9.5	11	14	17

73. False. Let $f(x) = x^2$ and $g(x) = x^2 + 4$. Then $f'(x) = g'(x) = 2x$, but $f(x) \neq g(x)$.

75. False. If $y = \pi^2$, then $dy/dx = 0$. (π^2 is a constant.)

77. $f(t) = 2t + 7, [1, 2]$

$f'(t) = 2$

Instantaneous rate of change is the constant 2.
Average rate of change:

$$\frac{f(2) - f(1)}{2 - 1} = \frac{[2(2) + 7] - [2(1) + 7]}{1} = 2$$

(These are the same because f is a line of slope 2.)

81. $g(x) = x^2 + e^x, \quad [0, 1]$

$g'(x) = 2x + e^x$

Instantaneous rate of change:

$(0, 1): \quad g'(0) = 1$

$(1, 1 + e): \quad 2 + e \approx 4.718$

Average rate of change:

$$\frac{g(1) - g(0)}{1 - 0} = \frac{(1 + e) - (1)}{1} = e \approx 2.718$$

85. (a) Since the initial height of the coin is $s_0 = 1362$ feet and the initial velocity is $v_0 = 0$, we have

$$s(t) = -\frac{1}{2}gt^2 + v_0 t + s_0 = -16t^2 + 1362$$

and

$$v(t) = s'(t) = -32t.$$

(b) The average velocity on the interval $[1, 2]$ is

$$\frac{s(2) - s(1)}{2 - 1} = 1298 - 1346 = -48 \text{ ft/sec.}$$

(c) Since $v(t) = -32t$, the instantaneous velocity at time $t = 1$ is

$$s'(1) = -32(1) = -32 \text{ ft/sec}$$

and at time $t = 2$ is $s'(2) = -32(2) = -64$ ft/sec.

79. The average rate of change is given by

$$\frac{\Delta y}{\Delta x} = \frac{f(2) - f(1)}{2 - 1} = \frac{-\frac{1}{2} - (-1)}{2 - 1} = \frac{1}{2}.$$

To find the instantaneous rate of change we first find $f'(x)$.

$$f(x) = -\frac{1}{x} = -x^{-1}$$

$$f'(x) = -(-1)x^{-2} = \frac{1}{x^2}$$

The instantaneous rate of change when $x = 1$ is

$$f'(1) = \frac{1}{1^2} = 1.$$

and the instantaneous rate of change when $x = 2$ is

$$f'(2) = \frac{1}{2^2} = \frac{1}{4}.$$

83.

(a) The slope appears to be steepest between A and B.

(b) The average rate of change between A and B is **greater** than the instantaneous rate of change at B.

(c)

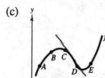

(d) The average rates of change are approximately equal between B and C, and between D and E.

(d) The dollar will reach ground level when

$$s(t) = -16t^2 + 1362 = 0$$

$$t^2 = \frac{1362}{16}$$

$$t = \frac{1}{4}\sqrt{1362}$$

$$= \frac{15}{4} \approx 9.2 \text{ sec}$$

(e) The velocity just before it hits the ground is

$$v\left(\frac{1}{4}\sqrt{1362}\right) = -32\left(\frac{1}{4}\sqrt{1362}\right) = -8\sqrt{1362}$$

$$\approx -295.2 \text{ ft/sec.}$$

87. $s(t) = -4.9t^2 + v_0t + s_0$

$\quad = -4.9t^2 + 120t$

$v(t) = -9.8t + 120$

$v(5) = -9.8(5) + 120 = 71 \text{ m/sec}$

$v(10) = -9.8(10) + 120 = 22 \text{ m/sec}$

89.

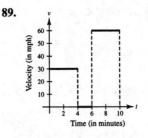

Time (in minutes)

(The velocity has been converted to miles per hour.)

91. $v = 40 \text{ mph} = \frac{2}{3} \text{ mi/min}$

$\left(\frac{2}{3} \text{ mi/min}\right)(6 \text{ min}) = 4 \text{ mi}$

$v = 0 \text{ mph} = 0 \text{ mi/min}$

$(0 \text{ mi/min})(2 \text{ min}) = 0 \text{ mi}$

$v = 60 \text{ mph} = 1 \text{mi/min}$

$(1 \text{ mi/min})(2 \text{ min}) = 2 \text{ mi}$

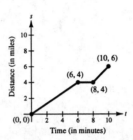

93. (a) Begin by entering the data in the statistics lists of your graphing utility. Access the statistics calculation menu and select linear regression ($y = ax + b$). Fitting this linear model to the data yields

$\quad R(v) = 0.167v - 0.02.$

(b) Access the statistics calculation menu and select quadratic regression. Fitting this quadratic model to the data yields

$\quad B(v) = 0.006v^2 - 0.024v + 0.460.$

(c) $T(v) = R(v) + B(v)$

$\quad = (0.167v - 0.02) + (0.006v^2 - 0.024v + 0.460)$

$\quad = 0.006v^2 + 0.143v + 0.440$

(d) The graphs of the specified functions are shown in the figure

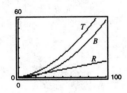

(e) $\quad T(v) = 0.006v^2 + 0.143v + 0.440$

$\quad T'(v) = 0.012v + 0.143$

$\quad T'(40) = 0.012(40) + 0.143 = 0.623 \text{ m/km/hr}$

$\quad T'(80) = 0.012(80) + 0.143 = 1.103 \text{ m/km/hr}$

$\quad T'(100) = 0.012(100) + 0.143 = 1.343 \text{ m/km/hr}$

(f) As the speed increases the total stopping distance increases at an increasing rate.

95. $A = s^2, \dfrac{dA}{ds} = 2s$

When $s = 4$ m, $\dfrac{dA}{ds} = 8 \text{ m}^2.$

97. $\qquad C = \dfrac{1,008,000}{Q} + 6.3Q$

$\dfrac{dC}{dQ} = -\dfrac{1,008,000}{Q^2} + 6.3$

$C(351) - C(350) \approx 5083.095 - 5085 \approx -\$1.91$

When $Q = 350, \dfrac{dC}{dQ} \approx -\$1.93.$

99. The runner was safe. Explanations will vary.

101. The parabola passes through the points $(0, 1)$ and $(1, 0)$ which implies that these points are solution points of the equation $y = ax^2 + bx + c$. By substitution we have

$\quad (0, 1): \ 1 = a(0)^2 + b(0) + c \Rightarrow c = 1$

$\quad (1, 0): \ 0 = a(1)^2 + b(1) + c \Rightarrow b = -a - c = -a - 1.$

The tangent line $y = x - 1$ has slope 1 which must equal the value of the derivative of the quadratic function at $x = 1$. Therefore, at $x = 1$ we have the following.

$\quad y = ax^2 + (-a - 1)x + 1$

$\quad y' = 2ax + (-a - 1)$

$\quad 1 = 2a(1) + (-a - 1)$

$\quad 1 = a - 1 \Rightarrow a = 2$

Hence, $a = 2$, $b = -a - 1 = -3$, $c = 1$, and $y = 2x^2 - 3x + 1$.

103. $y = x^3 - 9x$

$\quad y' = 3x^2 - 9$

Tangent lines through $(1, -9)$:

$\quad\quad y + 9 = (3x^2 - 9)(x - 1)$

$\quad (x^3 - 9x) + 9 = 3x^3 - 3x^2 - 9x + 9$

$\quad\quad\quad 0 = 2x^3 - 3x^2 = x^2(2x - 3)$

$\quad\quad\quad x = 0 \ \text{ or } \ x = \frac{3}{2}$

The points of tangency are $(0, 0)$ and $\left(\frac{3}{2}, -\frac{81}{8}\right)$. At $(0, 0)$ the slope is $y'(0) = -9$. At $\left(\frac{3}{2}, -\frac{81}{8}\right)$ the slope is $y'\left(\frac{3}{2}\right) = -\frac{9}{4}$.

Tangent lines:

$\quad y - 0 = -9(x - 0) \quad\text{and}\quad\quad\quad y + \frac{81}{8} = -\frac{9}{4}\left(x - \frac{3}{2}\right)$

$\quad\quad\quad y = -9x \quad\quad\quad\quad\quad\quad\quad\quad\quad y = -\frac{9}{4}x - \frac{27}{4}$

$\quad\quad 9x + y = 0 \quad\quad\quad\quad\quad\quad 9x + 4y + 27 = 0$

105. $f(x) = \begin{cases} ax^3, & x \le 2 \\ x^2 + b, & x > 2 \end{cases}$

f must be continuous at $x = 2$ to be differentiable at $x = 2$.

$\quad \left. \begin{array}{l} \lim\limits_{x \to 2^-} f(x) = \lim\limits_{x \to 2^-} ax^3 = 8a \\[2mm] \lim\limits_{x \to 2^+} f(x) = \lim\limits_{x \to 2^+} (x^2 + b) = 4 + b \end{array} \right\} \quad \begin{array}{l} 8a = 4 + b \\[2mm] 8a - 4 = b \end{array}$

$\quad f'(x) = \begin{cases} 3ax^2, & x < 2 \\ 2x, & x > 2 \end{cases}$

For f to be differentiable at $x = 2$, the left derivative must equal the right derivative.

$\quad 3a(2)^2 = 2(2)$

$\quad\quad 12a = 4$

$\quad\quad\quad a = \frac{1}{3}$

$\quad\quad\quad b = 8a - 4 = -\frac{4}{3}$

107. Let $f(x) = \cos x$.

$$f'(x) = \lim_{\Delta x \to 0} \frac{f(x + \Delta x) - f(x)}{\Delta x}$$

$$= \lim_{\Delta x \to 0} \frac{\cos x \cos \Delta x - \sin x \sin \Delta x - \cos x}{\Delta x}$$

$$= \lim_{\Delta x \to 0} \frac{\cos x(\cos \Delta x - 1)}{\Delta x} - \lim_{\Delta x \to 0} \sin x\left(\frac{\sin \Delta x}{\Delta x}\right)$$

$$= 0 - \sin x(1) = -\sin x$$

Section 2.3   The Product and Quotient Rules and Higher-Order Derivatives

1. $f(x) = \frac{1}{3}(2x^3 - 4)$

$f'(x) = \frac{1}{3}(6x^2) = 2x^2$

$f'(0) = 0$

3. $f(x) = (x^3 - 3x)(2x^2 + 3x + 5)$

$f'(x) = (x^3 - 3x)(4x + 3) + (2x^2 + 3x + 5)(3x^2 - 3)$

$\quad = 4x^4 + 3x^3 - 12x^2 - 9x + 6x^4 - 6x^2 + 9x^3 - 9x + 15x^2 - 15$

$\quad = 10x^4 + 12x^3 - 3x^2 - 18x - 15$

$f'(0) = -15$

5. $f(x) = e^x \sin x$

$f'(x) = e^x \cos x + e^x \sin x = e^x(\cos x + \sin x)$

$f'(0) = 1$

7. $f(x) = x \cos x$

$f'(x) = (x)(-\sin x) + (\cos x)(1)$

$\quad = \cos x - x \sin x$

$f'\left(\frac{\pi}{4}\right) = \frac{\sqrt{2}}{2} - \frac{\pi}{4}\left(\frac{\sqrt{2}}{2}\right)$

$\quad = \frac{\sqrt{2}}{8}(4 - \pi)$

Function	*Rewrite*	*Differentiate*	*Simplify*
9. $y = \dfrac{x^2 + 2x}{x}$	$y = x + 2, \ x \neq 0$	$y' = 1$	$y' = 1$
11. $y = \dfrac{7}{3x^3}$	$y = \dfrac{7}{3}x^{-3}$	$y' = -3\left(\dfrac{7}{3}\right)x^{-4}$	$y' = -\dfrac{7}{x^4}$
13. $y = \dfrac{3x^2 - 5}{7}$	$y = \dfrac{1}{7}(3x^2 - 5)$	$y' = \dfrac{1}{7}(6x)$	$y' = \dfrac{6x}{7}$

15. $f(x) = \dfrac{3x - 2}{2x - 3}$

$f'(x) = \dfrac{(2x - 3)(3) - (3x - 2)(2)}{(2x - 3)^2}$

$\quad = \dfrac{-5}{(2x - 3)^2}$

17. $f(x) = \dfrac{3 - 2x - x^2}{x^2 - 1}$

$\quad = -\dfrac{x^2 + 2x - 3}{x^2 - 1} = -\dfrac{(x + 3)(x - 1)}{(x + 1)(x - 1)} = -\dfrac{x + 3}{x + 1}$

$f'(x) = -\dfrac{(x + 1)(1) - (x + 3)(1)}{(x + 1)^2} = \dfrac{2}{(x + 1)^2}, x \neq -1$

19. $f(x) = \dfrac{x + 1}{\sqrt{x}}$

$$f'(x) = \frac{\sqrt{x}(1) - (x + 1)\left[1/(2\sqrt{x})\right]}{x}$$

$$= \frac{x - 1}{2x^{3/2}}$$

Alternate solution:

$$f(x) = \frac{x + 1}{\sqrt{x}} = x^{1/2} + x^{-1/2}$$

$$f'(x) = \frac{1}{2}x^{-1/2} - \frac{1}{2}x^{-3/2}$$

$$= \frac{1}{2x^{1/2}} - \frac{1}{2x^{3/2}}$$

$$= \frac{x - 1}{2x^{3/2}}$$

21. $h(s) = (s^3 - 2)^2 = s^6 - 4s^3 + 4$

$\qquad h'(s) = 6s^5 - 12s^2 = 6s^2(s^3 - 2)$

23. $h(t) = \dfrac{t + 1}{t^2 + 2t + 2}$

$$h'(t) = \frac{(t^2 + 2t + 2)(1) - (t + 1)(2t + 2)}{(t^2 + 2t + 2)^2}$$

$$= \frac{-t^2 - 2t}{(t^2 + 2t + 2)^2}$$

25. We begin by using the Associative Law to group the first two factors and then use the Product Rule twice.

$$f(x) = [(3x^3 + 4x)(x - 5)](x + 1)$$

$$f'(x) = [(3x^3 + 4x)(x - 5)](1) + (x + 1)[(3x^3 + 4x)(1) + (x - 5)(9x^2 + 4)]$$

$$= (3x^3 + 4x)(x - 5) + (x + 1)(3x^3 + 4x) + (x + 1)(x - 5)(9x^2 + 4)$$

$$= 15x^4 - 48x^3 - 33x^2 - 32x - 20$$

27. $f(x) = \dfrac{x^2 + c^2}{x^2 - c^2}$

$$f'(x) = \frac{(x^2 - c^2)(2x) - (x^2 + c^2)(2x)}{(x^2 - c^2)^2}$$

$$= \frac{-4xc^2}{(x^2 - c^2)^2}$$

29. $f(t) = t^2 \sin t$

$\qquad f'(t) = t^2 \cos t + 2t \sin t$

$\qquad\qquad = t(t \cos t + 2 \sin t)$

31. $f(t) = \dfrac{\cos t}{t}$

$$f'(t) = \frac{t(-\sin t) - (\cos t)(1)}{t^2} = \frac{-(t \sin t + \cos t)}{t^2}$$

33. $f(x) = -e^x + \tan x$

$\qquad f'(x) = -e^x + \sec^2 x$

35. $g(t) = \sqrt{t} + 4 \sec t$

$\qquad g'(t) = \dfrac{1}{2}t^{-1/2} + 4 \sec t \tan t$

$\qquad\qquad = \dfrac{1}{2\sqrt{t}} + 4 \sec t \tan t$

37. $y = 5x \csc x$

$\qquad y' = -5x \csc x \cot x + 5 \csc x$

$\qquad\quad = 5 \csc x(-x \cot x + 1)$

$\qquad\quad = 5 \csc x(1 - x \cot x)$

39. $y = -\csc x - \sin x$

$$y' = -(-\csc x \cot x) - \cos x = \frac{1}{\sin x}\left(\frac{\cos x}{\sin x}\right) - \cos x$$

$$= \cos x\left(\frac{1}{\sin^2 x} - 1\right) = \frac{\cos x}{\sin^2 x}(1 - \sin^2 x) = \cos x \cot^2 x$$

41. $f(x) = x^2 \tan x$

$$f'(x) = x^2 \sec^2 x + (\tan x)(2x) = x(x \sec^2 x + 2 \tan x)$$

43. $y = x^2 e^x + 2x \cos x$

$$y' = (2xe^x + x^2 e^x) + (2 \cos x - 2x \sin x)$$

$$= e^x(x^2 + 2x) + 2 \cos x - 2x \sin x$$

45. $y = \dfrac{e^x}{4\sqrt{x}} = \left(\dfrac{1}{4}\right)\dfrac{e^x}{x^{1/2}}$

$$\frac{dy}{dx} = \left(\frac{1}{4}\right)\frac{x^{1/2}\dfrac{d}{dx}[e^x] - e^x\dfrac{d}{dx}[x^{1/2}]}{(x^{1/2})^2}$$

$$= \frac{x^{1/2}e^x - e^x\left(\dfrac{1}{2}x^{-1/2}\right)}{4x} = \frac{e^x\left(\sqrt{x} - \dfrac{1}{2\sqrt{x}}\right)}{4x}$$

$$= \frac{e^x(2x - 1)}{8x^{3/2}}$$

47. $g(x) = \left(\dfrac{x + 1}{x + 2}\right)(2x - 5)$

$$g'(x) = \frac{2x^2 + 8x - 1}{(x + 2)^2} \quad \text{(form of answer may vary)}$$

49. $g(\theta) = \dfrac{\theta}{1 - \sin \theta}$

$$g'(\theta) = \frac{1 - \sin \theta + \theta \cos \theta}{(\sin \theta - 1)^2} \quad \text{(form of answer may vary)}$$

51. $y = \dfrac{1 + \csc x}{1 - \csc x}$

$$y' = \frac{(1 - \csc x)(-\csc x \cot x) - (1 + \csc x)(\csc x \cot x)}{(1 - \csc x)^2} = \frac{-2 \csc x \cot x}{(1 - \csc x)^2}$$

$$y\left(\frac{\pi}{6}\right) = \frac{-2(2)(\sqrt{3})}{(1 - 2)^2} = -4\sqrt{3}$$

53. $h(t) = \dfrac{\sec t}{t}$

$$h'(t) = \frac{t(\sec t \tan t) - (\sec t)(1)}{t^2} = \frac{\sec t(t \tan t - 1)}{t^2}$$

$$h'(\pi) = \frac{\sec \pi(\pi \tan \pi - 1)}{\pi^2} = \frac{1}{\pi^2}$$

55. (a) $f(x) = \dfrac{x}{x - 1}$

$$f'(x) = \frac{(x - 1)(1) - (x)(1)}{(x - 1)^2} = \frac{x - 1 - x}{(x - 1)^2} = \frac{-1}{(x - 1)^2}$$

Therefore, the slope of the tangent line at $(2, 2)$ is $f'(2) = -1/(2 - 1)^2 = -1$ and an equation of the tangent line at $(2, 2)$ is

$$y - 2 = -1(x - 2)$$

$$= -x + 2$$

$$y = -x + 4.$$

(b) The graphs are shown in the figure.

57. (a) $f(x) = (x^3 - 3x + 1)(x + 2), \quad (1, -3)$

$f'(x) = (x^3 - 3x + 1)(1) + (x + 2)(3x^2 - 3)$

$\quad = 4x^3 + 6x^2 - 6x - 5$

$f'(1) = -1 = $ slope at $(1, -3)$

Tangent line: $y + 3 = -1(x - 1) \Rightarrow y = -x - 2$

(b)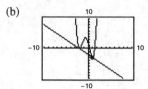

59. (a) $f(x) = \tan x, \quad \left(\dfrac{\pi}{4}, 1\right)$

$f'(x) = \sec^2 x$

$f'\left(\dfrac{\pi}{4}\right) = 2 = $ slope at $\left(\dfrac{\pi}{4}, 1\right)$

Tangent line:

$$y - 1 = 2\left(x - \dfrac{\pi}{4}\right)$$

$$y - 1 = 2x - \dfrac{\pi}{2}$$

$$4x - 2y - \pi + 2 = 0$$

(b)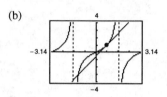

61. (a) $f(x) = (x - 1)e^x$

$f'(x) = (x - 1)e^x + e^x = e^x$

At $(1, 0), f'(1) = e$

Tangent line: $y - 0 = e(x - 1)$

$\qquad\qquad\qquad y = e(x - 1)$

(b)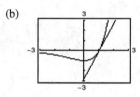

63. Any horizontal tangents to the graph of f will occur where $f'(x) = 0$.

$f(x) = \dfrac{x^2}{x - 1}$

$f'(x) = \dfrac{(x - 1)(2x) - x^2(1)}{(x - 1)^2}$

$\quad = \dfrac{x^2 - 2x}{(x - 1)^2} = \dfrac{x(x - 2)}{(x - 1)^2}$

Therefore, $f'(x) = 0$ when $x = 0$ or $x = 2$. Since $f(0) = 0$ and $f(2) = 4$, the points of horizontal tangency are $(0, 0)$ and $(2, 4)$.

65. $g(x) = \dfrac{8(x - 2)}{e^x}$

$g'(x) = \dfrac{e^x(8) - 8(x - 2)e^x}{e^{2x}} = \dfrac{24 - 8x}{e^x}$

$g'(x) = 0$ when $x = 3$.

Horizontal tangent at $(3, 8e^{-3})$

67. $f(x) = e^x \sin x, \quad 0 \leq x \leq \pi$

$f'(x) = e^x \cos x + e^x \sin x = e^x(\cos x + \sin x)$

$f'(x) = 0$ when $\cos x = -\sin x \Rightarrow x = \dfrac{3\pi}{4}$.

Horizontal tangent at $\left(\dfrac{3\pi}{4}, \dfrac{\sqrt{2}}{2}e^{3\pi/4}\right)$

69. $f(x) = 2g(x) + h(x)$

$f'(x) = 2g'(x) + h'(x)$

$f'(2) = 2g'(2) + h'(2)$

$\quad = 2(-2) + 4$

$\quad = 0$

71. $f(x) = \dfrac{g(x)}{h(x)}$

$f'(x) = \dfrac{h(x)g'(x) - g(x)h'(x)}{[h(x)]^2}$

$f'(2) = \dfrac{h(2)g'(2) - g(2)h'(2)}{[h(2)]^2}$

$\quad = \dfrac{(-1)(-2) - (3)(4)}{(-1)^2}$

$\quad = -10$

73. $f(x) = x^n \sin x$

$f'(x) = x^n \cos x + nx^{n-1} \sin x$

$\qquad = x^{n-1}(x \cos x + n \sin x)$

When $n = 1$: $f'(x) = x \cos x + \sin x$.

When $n = 2$: $f'(x) = x(x \cos x + 2 \sin x)$.

When $n = 3$: $f'(x) = x^2(x \cos x + 3 \sin x)$.

When $n = 4$: $f'(x) = x^3(x \cos x + 4 \sin x)$.

For general n, $f'(x) = x^{n-1}(x \cos x + n \sin x)$.

75. $C = 100\left(\dfrac{200}{x^2} + \dfrac{x}{x + 30}\right), \quad 1 \le x$

$\dfrac{dC}{dx} = 100\left(-\dfrac{400}{x^3} + \dfrac{30}{(x + 30)^2}\right)$

(a) When $x = 10$: $\dfrac{dC}{dx} = -\$38.13$.

(b) When $x = 15$: $\dfrac{dC}{dx} = -\$10.37$.

(c) When $x = 20$: $\dfrac{dC}{dx} = -\$3.80$.

As the order size increases, the cost per item decreases.

77. $P(t) = 500\left(1 + \dfrac{4t}{50 + t^2}\right)$

$P'(t) = 500\left[\dfrac{(50 + t^2)(4) - (4t)(2t)}{(50 + t^2)^2}\right]$

$\qquad = \dfrac{500(200 + 4t^2 - 8t^2)}{(50 + t^2)^2} = \dfrac{2000(50 - t^2)}{(50 + t^2)^2}$

Therefore, the rate of population growth when $t = 2$ is

$P'(2) = \dfrac{2000(50 - 4)}{(50 + 4)^2} \approx 31.55$ bacteria/hr.

79. (a) $\sec x = \dfrac{1}{\cos x}$

$\dfrac{d}{dx}[\sec x] = \dfrac{d}{dx}\left[\dfrac{1}{\cos x}\right] = \dfrac{(\cos x)(0) - (1)(-\sin x)}{(\cos x)^2} = \dfrac{\sin x}{\cos x \cos x} = \dfrac{1}{\cos x} \cdot \dfrac{\sin x}{\cos x} = \sec x \tan x$

(b) $\csc x = \dfrac{1}{\sin x}$

$\dfrac{d}{dx}[\csc x] = \dfrac{d}{dx}\left[\dfrac{1}{\sin x}\right] = \dfrac{(\sin x)(0) - (1)(\cos x)}{(\sin x)^2} = -\dfrac{\cos x}{\sin x \sin x} = -\dfrac{1}{\sin x} \cdot \dfrac{\cos x}{\sin x} = -\csc x \cot x$

(c) $\cot x = \dfrac{\cos x}{\sin x}$

$\dfrac{d}{dx}[\cot x] = \dfrac{d}{dx}\left[\dfrac{\cos x}{\sin x}\right] = \dfrac{\sin x(-\sin x) - (\cos x)(\cos x)}{(\sin x)^2} = -\dfrac{\sin^2 x + \cos^2 x}{\sin^2 x} = -\dfrac{1}{\sin^2 x} = -\csc^2 x$

81.

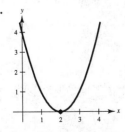

$f(2) = 0$

One such function is $f(x) = (x - 2)^2$.

83. $f(x) = 4x^{3/2}$

$f'(x) = 6x^{1/2}$

$f''(x) = 3x^{-1/2} = \dfrac{3}{\sqrt{x}}$

85. The first derivative of $f(x) = \dfrac{x}{x-1}$ was found in Exercise 55.

$$f'(x) = \frac{-1}{(x-1)^2} = \frac{-1}{x^2 - 2x + 1}$$

$$f''(x) = \frac{(x^2 - 2x + 1)(0) - (-1)(2x - 2)}{(x^2 - 2x + 1)^2}$$

$$= \frac{2(x - 1)}{[(x-1)^2]^2} = \frac{2}{(x-1)^3}$$

87. $g(x) = \dfrac{e^x}{x}$

$$g'(x) = \frac{xe^x - e^x \cdot 1}{x^2} = \frac{e^x(x-1)}{x^2}$$

Note that it is necessary to use both the Quotient Rule and Product Rule when finding the second derivative.

$$g''(x) = \frac{x^2[e^x + (x-1)e^x] - e^x(x-1)(2x)}{x^4}$$

$$= \frac{xe^x[x + x(x-1) - 2(x-1)]}{x^4} = \frac{e^x(x^2 - 2x + 2)}{x^3}$$

89. $f(x) = 3\sin x$

$f'(x) = 3\cos x$

$f''(x) = -3\sin x$

91. $f'(x) = x^2$

$f''(x) = 2x$

93. $f'''(x) = 2\sqrt{x}$

$$f^{(4)}(x) = \frac{1}{2}(2)x^{-1/2} = \frac{1}{\sqrt{x}}$$

95.

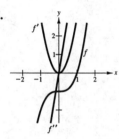

It appears that f is cubic; so f' would be quadratic and f'' would be linear.

97. $f(x) = g(x)h(x)$

(a)
$$f'(x) = g(x)h'(x) + h(x)g'(x)$$

$$f''(x) = g(x)h''(x) + g'(x)h'(x) + h(x)g''(x) + h'(x)g'(x)$$

$$= g(x)h''(x) + 2g'(x)h'(x) + h(x)g''(x)$$

$$f'''(x) = g(x)h'''(x) + g'(x)h''(x) + 2g'(x)h''(x) + 2g''(x)h'(x) + h(x)g'''(x) + h'(x)g''(x)$$

$$= g(x)h'''(x) + 3g'(x)h''(x) + 3g''(x)h'(x) + g'''(x)h(x)$$

$$f^{(4)}(x) = g(x)h^{(4)}(x) + g'(x)h'''(x) + 3g'(x)h'''(x) + 3g''(x)h''(x) + 3g''(x)h''(x) + 3g'''(x)h'(x) + g'''(x)h'(x) + g^{(4)}(x)h(x)$$

$$= g(x)h^{(4)}(x) + 4g'(x)h'''(x) + 6g''(x)h''(x) + 4g'''(x)h'(x) + g^{(4)}(x)h(x)$$

(b) $f^{(n)}(x) = g(x)h^{(n)}(x) + \dfrac{n(n-1)(n-2)\cdots(2)(1)}{1[(n-1)(n-2)\cdots(2)(1)]}g'(x)h^{(n-1)}(x) + \dfrac{n(n-1)(n-2)\cdots(2)(1)}{(2)(1)[(n-2)(n-3)\cdots(2)(1)]}g''(x)h^{(n-2)}(x)$

$$+ \frac{n(n-1)(n-2)\cdots(2)(1)}{(3)(2)(1)[(n-3)(n-4)\cdots(2)(1)]}g'''(x)h^{(n-3)}(x) + \cdots$$

$$+ \frac{n(n-1)(n-2)\cdots(2)(1)}{[(n-1)(n-2)\cdots(2)(1)](1)}g^{(n-1)}(x)h'(x) + g^{(n)}(x)h(x)$$

$$= g(x)h^{(n)}(x) + \frac{n!}{1!(n-1)!}g'(x)h^{(n-1)}(x) + \frac{n!}{2!(n-2)!}g''(x)h^{(n-2)}(x) + \cdots + \frac{n!}{(n-1)!1!}g^{(n-1)}(x)h'(x) + g^{(n)}(x)h(x)$$

Note: For a definition of $n!$ (read "n factorial"), see Section 8.1 of the text.

99. $v(t) = 36 - t^2$, $0 \le t \le 6$

$a(t) = -2t$

$v(3) = 27$ m/sec

$a(3) = -6$ m/sec

The speed of the object is decreasing, but the rate of the decrease is increasing.

101. $s(t) = -8.25t^2 + 66t$

$v(t) = -16.50t + 66$

$a(t) = -16.50$

t(sec)	0	1	2	3	4
$s(t)$ (ft)	0	57.75	99	123.75	132
$v(t) = s'(t)$ (ft/sec)	66	49.5	33	16.5	0
$a(t) = v'(t)$ (ft/sec²)	-16.5	-16.5	-16.5	-16.5	-16.5

Average velocity on:

$[0, 1]$ is $\dfrac{57.75 - 0}{1 - 0} = 57.75.$

$[1, 2]$ is $\dfrac{99 - 57.75}{2 - 1} = 41.25.$

$[2, 3]$ is $\dfrac{123.75 - 99}{3 - 2} = 24.75.$

$[3, 4]$ is $\dfrac{132 - 123.75}{4 - 3} = 8.25.$

103. (a) $f(x) = \cos x$ $\qquad f\left(\dfrac{\pi}{3}\right) = \dfrac{1}{2}$

$f'(x) = -\sin x \qquad f'\left(\dfrac{\pi}{3}\right) = -\dfrac{\sqrt{3}}{2}$

$f''(x) = -\cos x \qquad f''(x)\left(\dfrac{\pi}{3}\right) = -\dfrac{1}{2}$

$P_1(x) = f'(a)(x - a) + f(a)$

$\quad = -\dfrac{\sqrt{3}}{2}\left(x - \dfrac{\pi}{3}\right) + \dfrac{1}{2}$

$P_2(x) = \dfrac{1}{2}f''(a)(x - a)^2 + f'(a)(x - a) + f(a)$

$\quad = -\dfrac{1}{4}\left(x - \dfrac{\pi}{3}\right)^2 - \dfrac{\sqrt{3}}{2}\left(x - \dfrac{\pi}{3}\right) + \dfrac{1}{2}$

(b) The graphs for f, P_1, and P_2 are shown in the figure.

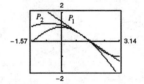

(c) P_2 is a better approximation.

(d) P_1 and P_2 become less accurate for values of x farther from $x = a$.

105. False. If $y = f(x)g(x)$, then

$\dfrac{dy}{dx} = f(x)g'(x) + g(x)f'(x).$

107. True

$h'(c) = f(c)g'(c) + g(c)f'(c)$

$\quad = f(c)(0) + g(c)(0)$

$\quad = 0$

109. True

111. (a) $(fg' - f'g)' = fg'' + f'g' - f'g' - f''g$

$\qquad\qquad = fg'' - f''g \qquad$ True

(b) $(fg)'' = (fg' + f'g)'$

$\qquad = fg'' + f'g' + f'g' + f''g$

$\qquad = fg'' + 2f'g' + f''g$

$\qquad \ne fg'' + f''g \qquad$ False

Section 2.4   The Chain Rule

$y = f(g(x))$	$u = g(x)$	$y = f(u)$
1. $y = (6x - 5)^4$	$u = 6x - 5$	$y = u^4$
3. $y = \sqrt{x^2 - 1}$	$u = x^2 - 1$	$y = \sqrt{u}$
5. $y = \csc^3 x$	$u = \csc x$	$y = u^3$
7. $y = e^{-2x}$	$u = -2x$	$y = e^u$

9. $y = (2x - 7)^3$

$y' = 3(2x - 7)^2(2) = 6(2x - 7)^2$

11. $g(x) = 3(4 - 9x)^4$

$g'(x) = 12(4 - 9x)^3(-9) = -108(4 - 9x)^3$

13. $f(x) = (9 - x^2)^{2/3}$

$f'(x) = \dfrac{2}{3}(9 - x^2)^{-1/3}(-2x) = -\dfrac{4x}{3(9 - x^2)^{1/3}}$

15. $f(t) = (1 - t)^{1/2}$

$f'(t) = \dfrac{1}{2}(1 - t)^{-1/2}(-1) = -\dfrac{1}{2\sqrt{1 - t}}$

17. $y = \sqrt[3]{9x^2 + 4} = (9x^2 + 4)^{1/3}$

$\dfrac{dy}{dx} = \overbrace{\left(\dfrac{1}{3}\right)}^{n}\overbrace{(9x^2 + 4)^{-2/3}}^{u^{n-1}}\overbrace{(18x)}^{u'} = \dfrac{6x}{(9x^2 + 4)^{2/3}}$

19. $y = 2(4 - x^2)^{1/2}$

$y' = (4 - x^2)^{-1/2}(-2x) = -\dfrac{2x}{\sqrt{4 - x^2}}$

21. $y = (x - 2)^{-1}$

$y' = -1(x - 2)^{-2}(1) = \dfrac{-1}{(x - 2)^2}$

23. $f(t) = \dfrac{1}{(t - 3)^2} = (t - 3)^{-2}$

$f'(x) = \overbrace{(-2)}^{n}\overbrace{(t - 3)^{-3}}^{u^{n-1}}\overbrace{(1)}^{u'} = \dfrac{-2}{(t - 3)^3}$

25. $y = \dfrac{1}{\sqrt{x + 2}} = (x + 2)^{-1/2}$

$y' = \left(-\dfrac{1}{2}\right)(x + 2)^{-3/2}(1) = \dfrac{-1}{2(x + 2)^{3/2}}$

27. Applying the Product Rule and the General Power Rule produces

$f(x) = x^2(x - 2)^4$

$f'(x) = x^2(4)(x - 2)^3(1) + (x - 2)^4(2x)$

$\qquad = 2x(x - 2)^3(2x + x - 2) = 2x(x - 2)^3(3x - 2).$

29. $y = x\sqrt{1 - x^2} = x(1 - x^2)^{1/2}$

$y' = x\left[\dfrac{1}{2}(1 - x^2)^{-1/2}(-2x)\right] + (1 - x^2)^{1/2}(1)$

$\quad = -x^2(1 - x^2)^{-1/2} + (1 - x^2)^{1/2}$

$\quad = (1 - x^2)^{-1/2}[-x^2 + (1 - x^2)]$

$\quad = \dfrac{1 - 2x^2}{\sqrt{1 - x^2}}$

31. $y = \dfrac{x}{\sqrt{x^2 + 1}} = x(x^2 + 1)^{-1/2}$

$y' = x\left[-\dfrac{1}{2}(x^2 + 1)^{-3/2}(2x)\right] + (x^2 + 1)^{-1/2}(1)$

$\quad = -x^2(x^2 + 1)^{-3/2} + (x^2 + 1)^{-1/2}$

$\quad = (x^2 + 1)^{-3/2}[-x^2 + (x^2 + 1)]$

$\quad = \dfrac{1}{(x^2 + 1)^{3/2}}$

33. $y = \dfrac{\sqrt{x} + 1}{x^2 + 1}$

$y' = \dfrac{1 - 3x^2 - 4x^{3/2}}{2\sqrt{x}(x^2 + 1)^2}$

The zero of y' corresponds to the point on the graph of y where the tangent line is horizontal.

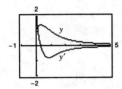

37. $y = \sqrt{\dfrac{x + 1}{x}}$

$y' = -\dfrac{\sqrt{(x + 1)/x}}{2x(x + 1)}$

y' has no zeros.

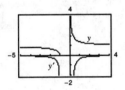

41. $y = \dfrac{\cos \pi x + 1}{x}$

$\dfrac{dy}{dx} = \dfrac{-\pi x \sin \pi x - \cos \pi x - 1}{x^2}$

$= -\dfrac{\pi x \sin \pi x + \cos \pi x + 1}{x^2}$

The zeros of y' correspond to the points on the graph of y where the tangent lines are horizontal.

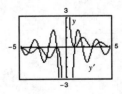

45. $y = \cos 3x$

$\dfrac{dy}{dx} = \overbrace{-\sin 3x}^{-\sin u}\ \overbrace{3}^{u'}$

$= -3 \sin 3x$

35. Using a symbolic differentiation utility, first derivative of the function

$$g(t) = \dfrac{3t^2}{\sqrt{t^2 + 2t - 1}} \text{ is } g'(t) = \dfrac{3t(t^2 + 3t - 2)}{(t^2 + 2t - 1)^{3/2}}.$$

(Your differentiation utility may give the derivative in unsimplified form.) The graphs of the function and its derivative are given in the figure. The zeros of the derivative are approximately $t = -3.56$ and $t = 0.56$. These are the t-coordinates of the points where the graph of $g(t)$ has horizontal tangents.

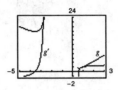

39. $s(t) = \dfrac{-2(2 - t)\sqrt{1 + t}}{3}$

$s'(t) = \dfrac{t}{\sqrt{1 + t}}$

The zero of $s'(t)$ corresponds to the point on the graph of $s(t)$ where the tangent line is horizontal.

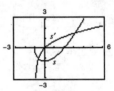

43. (a) $y = \sin x$

$y' = \cos x$

$y'(0) = 1$

1 cycle in $[0, 2\pi]$

(b) $y = \sin 2x$

$y' = 2 \cos 2x$

$y'(0) = 2$

2 cycles in $[0, 2\pi]$

47. $g(x) = 3 \tan 4x$

$g'(x) = 12 \sec^2 4x$

49. $f(\theta) = \frac{1}{4}(\sin 2\theta)^2$

$f'(\theta) = \frac{1}{4}(2)(\sin 2\theta)(\cos 2\theta)(2)$

$\qquad = \frac{1}{2}(2 \sin 2\theta \cos 2\theta) = \frac{1}{2} \sin 4\theta$ Double Angle Identity

51. $y = \sqrt{x} + \frac{1}{4} \sin(2x)^2$

$\qquad = \sqrt{x} + \frac{1}{4} \sin(4x^2)$

$\dfrac{dy}{dx} = \frac{1}{2}x^{-1/2} + \frac{1}{4} \cos(4x^2)(8x)$

$\qquad = \dfrac{1}{2\sqrt{x}} + 2x \cos(2x)^2$

53. $y = \sin(\cos x)$

$\dfrac{dy}{dx} = \cos(\cos x) \cdot (-\sin x)$

$\qquad = -\sin x \cos(\cos x)$

55. $f(x) = e^{2x}$

$f'(x) = 2e^{2x}$

57. $y = e^{\sqrt{x}}$

$\dfrac{dy}{dx} = e^{\sqrt{x}} \dfrac{d}{dx}[\sqrt{x}]$

$\qquad = e^{\sqrt{x}}\left(\dfrac{1}{2\sqrt{x}}\right) = \dfrac{e^{\sqrt{x}}}{2\sqrt{x}}$

59. $g(t) = (e^{-t} + e^t)^3$

$g'(t) = 3(e^{-t} + e^t)^2(e^t - e^{-t})$

61. $y = \dfrac{2}{e^x + e^{-x}} = 2(e^x + e^{-x})^{-1}$

$\dfrac{dy}{dx} = -2(e^x + e^{-x})^{-2}(e^x - e^{-x})$

$\qquad = \dfrac{-2(e^x - e^{-x})}{(e^x + e^{-x})^2}$

63. $y = x^2 e^x - 2xe^x + 2e^x = e^x(x^2 - 2x + 2)$

$\dfrac{dy}{dx} = e^x(2x - 2) + e^x(x^2 - 2x + 2) = x^2 e^x$

65. $g(x) = \ln x^2 = 2 \ln x$

$g'(x) = \dfrac{2}{x}$

67. $y = (\ln x)^4$

$\dfrac{dy}{dx} = 4(\ln x)^3\left(\dfrac{1}{x}\right) = \dfrac{4(\ln x)^3}{x}$

69. $y = \ln(x\sqrt{x^2 - 1}) = \ln x + \ln\sqrt{x^2 - 1}$

$\qquad = \ln x + \frac{1}{2} \ln(x^2 - 1)$

$\dfrac{dy}{dx} = \dfrac{1}{x} + \dfrac{1}{2}\left(\dfrac{1}{x^2 - 1}\right)(2x)$

$\qquad = \dfrac{1}{x} + \dfrac{x}{x^2 - 1} = \dfrac{2x^2 - 1}{x(x^2 - 1)}$

71. $f(x) = \ln \dfrac{x}{x^2 + 1} = \ln x - \ln(x^2 + 1)$

$f'(x) = \dfrac{1}{x} - \dfrac{2x}{x^2 + 1} = \dfrac{1 - x^2}{x(x^2 + 1)}$

73. $y = \ln\sqrt{\dfrac{x + 1}{x - 1}} = \frac{1}{2}[\ln(x + 1) - \ln(x - 1)]$

$\dfrac{dy}{dx} = \dfrac{1}{2}\left[\dfrac{1}{x + 1} - \dfrac{1}{x - 1}\right] = \dfrac{1}{1 - x^2}$

75. $y = \dfrac{-\sqrt{x^2 + 1}}{x} + \ln(x + \sqrt{x^2 + 1})$

$\dfrac{dy}{dx} = -\dfrac{x(1/2)(x^2 + 1)^{-1/2}(2x) - (x^2 + 1)^{1/2}(1)}{x^2} + \dfrac{1}{x + \sqrt{x^2 + 1}}\left[1 + \left(\dfrac{1}{2}\right)(x^2 + 1)^{-1/2}(2x)\right]$

$\qquad = -\dfrac{x^2(x^2 + 1)^{-1/2} - (x^2 + 1)^{1/2}}{x^2} + \left(\dfrac{1}{x + \sqrt{x^2 + 1}}\right)\left(1 + \dfrac{x}{\sqrt{x^2 + 1}}\right)$

$\qquad = \dfrac{-x^2 + (x^2 + 1)}{x^2\sqrt{x^2 + 1}} + \dfrac{1}{\sqrt{x^2 + 1}} = \dfrac{1 + x^2}{x^2\sqrt{x^2 + 1}} = \dfrac{\sqrt{x^2 + 1}}{x^2}$

77. $g(t) = \dfrac{\ln t}{t^2}$

$$g'(x) = \dfrac{(t^2)(1/t) - (\ln t)(2t)}{t^4} = \dfrac{t - 2t \ln t}{t^4} = \dfrac{1 - 2 \ln t}{t^3}$$

79. $y = \ln|\sin x|$

$$\dfrac{dy}{dx} = \dfrac{\cos x}{\sin x} = \cot x$$

81. $y = \ln\left|\dfrac{\cos x}{\cos x - 1}\right| = \ln|\cos x| - \ln|\cos x - 1|$

$$\dfrac{dy}{dx} = \dfrac{1}{\cos x}(-\sin x) - \dfrac{1}{\cos x - 1}(-\sin x)$$

$$= -\tan x + \dfrac{\sin x}{\cos x - 1}$$

83. $y = \ln\left|\dfrac{-1 + \sin x}{2 + \sin x}\right|$

$$= \ln|-1 + \sin x| - \ln|2 + \sin x|$$

$$\dfrac{dy}{dx} = \dfrac{\cos x}{-1 + \sin x} - \dfrac{\cos x}{2 + \sin x}$$

$$= \dfrac{3 \cos x}{(\sin x - 1)(\sin x + 2)}$$

85. Using the inverse relationship between the exponential and logarithmic functions yields

$$y = \ln(e^{x^2}) = x^2 \ln e = x^2.$$

Therefore, $dy/dx = 2x$.

87. $y = e^{-x} \ln x$

$$y' = (e^{-x})\left(\dfrac{1}{x}\right) + (\ln x)(-e^{-x}) = e^{-x}\left(\dfrac{1}{x} - \ln x\right)$$

89. $y = e^x(\sin x + \cos x)$

$$\dfrac{dy}{dx} = e^x(\cos x - \sin x) + (\sin x + \cos x)(e^x)$$

$$= e^x(2 \cos x) = 2e^x \cos x$$

91. $s(t) = (t^2 + 2t + 8)^{1/2}, \quad (2, 4)$

$$s'(t) = \dfrac{1}{2}(t^2 + 2t + 8)^{-1/2}(2t + 2)$$

$$= \dfrac{t + 1}{\sqrt{t^2 + 2t + 8}}$$

$$s'(2) = \dfrac{3}{4}$$

93. $f(x) = \dfrac{3}{x^3 - 4} = 3(x^3 - 4)^{-1}$

$$f'(x) = -3(x^3 - 4)^{-2}(3x^2) = -\dfrac{9x^2}{(x^3 - 4)^2}$$

$$f'(-1) = -\dfrac{9(-1)^2}{[(-1)^3 - 4]^2} = -\dfrac{9}{25}$$

Verify this result by using the numerical differentiation capabilities of your graphing utility.

95. $f(t) = \dfrac{3t + 2}{t - 1}, \quad (0, -2)$

$$f'(t) = \dfrac{(t - 1)(3) - (3t + 2)(1)}{(t - 1)^2} = \dfrac{-5}{(t - 1)^2}$$

$$f'(0) = -5$$

97. $y = 37 - \sec^3(2x), \quad (0, 36)$

$$y' = -3 \sec^2(2x)[2 \sec(2x) \tan(2x)]$$

$$= -6 \sec^3(2x) \tan(2x)$$

$$y'(0) = 0$$

99. (a) $f(x) = \sqrt{3x^2 - 2}, \quad (3, 5)$

$$f'(x) = \dfrac{1}{2}(3x^2 - 2)^{-1/2}(6x) = \dfrac{3x}{\sqrt{3x^2 - 2}}$$

$$f'(3) = \dfrac{9}{5}$$

Tangent line:

$$y - 5 = \dfrac{9}{5}(x - 3) \Longrightarrow 9x - 5y - 2 = 0$$

(b)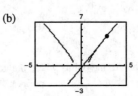

101. (a) $f(x) = \sin 2x$

$f'(x) = (\cos 2x)(2) = 2 \cos 2x$

Therefore, the slope of the tangent line at $(\pi, 0)$ is $f'(\pi) = 2 \cos 2\pi = 2$ and an equation of the tangent line at $(\pi, 0)$ is

$$y - 0 = 2(x - \pi)$$

$$y = 2(x - \pi)$$

$$2x - y - 2\pi = 0$$

(b) The graphs are shown in the figure.

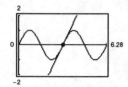

103. (a) $y = 4 - x^2 - \ln\left(\frac{1}{2}x + 1\right)$, $(0, 4)$

$$\frac{dy}{dx} = -2x - \frac{1}{(1/2)x + 1}\left(\frac{1}{2}\right)$$

$$= -2x - \frac{1}{x + 2}$$

When $x = 0$, $\dfrac{dy}{dx} = -\dfrac{1}{2}$.

Tangent line: $y - 4 = -\dfrac{1}{2}(x - 0)$

$$y = -\frac{1}{2}x + 4$$

(b)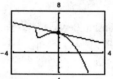

105. $f(x) = 4^x$

$f'(x) = (\ln 4)\, 4^x$

107. $y = 5^{x-2}$

$\dfrac{dy}{dx} = (\ln 5)\, 5^{x-2}$

109. Using the Product Rule and Theorem 2.14 the derivative of the function $g(t) = t^2 2^t$ is

$$g'(t) = t^2(\ln 2)2^t + 2t(2^t) = t(2^t)(t \ln 2 + 2).$$

111. $h(\theta) = 2^{-\theta}\cos \pi\theta$

$h'(\theta) = 2^{-\theta}(-\pi \sin \pi\theta) - (\ln 2)2^{-\theta}\cos \pi\theta$

$$= -2^{-\theta}[(\ln 2)\cos \pi\theta + \pi \sin \pi\theta]$$

115. Begin by rewriting the logarithmic function.

$$f(x) = \log_2 \frac{x^2}{x - 1}$$

$$= \log_2 x^2 - \log_2(x - 1) = 2 \log_2 x - \log_2(x - 1)$$

Using Theorem 2.14, the derivative is

$$f'(x) = \frac{2}{x \ln 2} - \frac{1}{(x - 1)\ln 2} = \frac{x - 2}{(\ln 2)x(x - 1)}.$$

117. Begin by rewriting the logarithmic function.

$$y = \log_5 \sqrt{x^2 - 1}$$

$$= \log_5(x^2 - 1)^{1/2} = \frac{1}{2}\log_5(x^2 - 1)$$

Using Theorem 2.14 the derivative of the function is

$$\frac{dy}{dx} = \left(\frac{1}{2}\right)\frac{1}{(\ln 5)(x^2 - 1)}(2x) = \frac{x}{(x^2 - 1)\ln 5}.$$

119. $g(t) = \dfrac{10 \log_4 t}{t} = \dfrac{10}{\ln 4}\left(\dfrac{\ln t}{t}\right)$

$$g'(t) = \frac{10}{\ln 4}\left[\frac{t(1/t) - \ln t}{t^2}\right] = \frac{10}{t^2 \ln 4}[1 - \ln t] = \frac{5}{t^2 \ln 2}(1 - \ln t)$$

121.

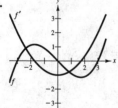

The zeros of f' correspond to the points where the graph of f has horizontal tangents.

123.

The zeros of f' correspond to the points where the graph of f has horizontal tangents.

125. $f(x) = 2(x^2 - 1)^3$

$\qquad f'(x) = 6(x^2 - 1)^2(2x)$

$\qquad\qquad = 12x(x^4 - 2x^2 + 1)$

$\qquad\qquad = 12x^5 - 24x^3 + 12x$

$\qquad f''(x) = 60x^4 - 72x^2 + 12$

$\qquad\qquad = 12(5x^2 - 1)(x^2 - 1)$

129. $f(x) = (3 + 2x)e^{-3x}$

$\qquad f'(x) = (3 + 2x)(-3e^{-3x}) + 2e^{-3x}$

$\qquad\qquad = (-7 - 6x)e^{-3x}$

$\qquad f''(x) = (-7 - 6x)(-3e^{-3x}) - 6e^{-3x}$

$\qquad\qquad = 3(6x + 5)e^{-3x}$

131. (a) $f(x) = g(x)h(x)$

$\qquad\quad f'(x) = g(x)h'(x) + g'(x)h(x)$

$\qquad\quad f'(5) = (-3)(-2) + (6)(3) = 24$

$\qquad$ (b) $f(x) = g(h(x))$

$\qquad\quad f'(x) = g'(h(x))h'(x)$

$\qquad\quad f'(5) = g'(3)(-2) = -2g'(3)$

$\qquad\quad$ Need $g'(3)$ to find $f'(5)$.

133. (a) $f = 132,400(331 - v)^{-1}$

$\qquad\quad f' = (-1)(132,400)(331 - v)^{-2}(-1)$

$\qquad\qquad = \dfrac{132,400}{(331 - v)^2}$

$\qquad\quad$ When $v = 30, f' \approx 1.461$.

$\qquad$ (b) $f = 132,400(331 + v)^{-1}$

$\qquad\quad f' = (-1)(132,400)(331 + v)^{-2}(1)$

$\qquad\qquad = \dfrac{-132,400}{(331 + v)^2}$

$\qquad\quad$ When $v = 30, f' \approx -1.016$.

127. $f(x) = \sin x^2$

$\qquad f'(x) = (\cos x^2)(2x) = 2x \cos x^2$

$\qquad f''(x) = 2[x(-\sin x^2)(2x) + (\cos x^2)(1)]$

$\qquad\qquad = 2(\cos x^2 - 2x^2 \sin x^2)$

(c) $f(x) = \dfrac{g(x)}{h(x)}$

$\qquad f'(x) = \dfrac{h(x)g'(x) - g(x)h'(x)}{[h(x)]^2}$

$\qquad f'(5) = \dfrac{(3)(6) - (-3)(-2)}{(3)^2} = \dfrac{12}{9} = \dfrac{4}{3}$

(d) $f(x) = [g(x)]^3$

$\qquad f'(x) = 3[g(x)]^2 g'(x)$

$\qquad f'(5) = 3(-3)^2(6) = 162$

135. $\theta = 0.2 \cos 8t$

The maximum angular displacement is $\theta = 0.2$ (since $-1 \le \cos 8t \le 1$).

$\qquad \dfrac{d\theta}{dt} = 0.2[-8 \sin 8t] = -1.6 \sin 8t$

When $t = 3$, $d\theta/dt = -1.6 \sin 24 \approx 1.4489$ radians per second.

137. Using the Chain Rule and the fact that r is constant, we have

$\qquad S = C(R^2 - r^2)$

$\qquad \dfrac{dS}{dt} = C\left(2R\dfrac{dR}{dt} - 0\right)$

Substituting the given constants yields

$\qquad \dfrac{dS}{dt} = (1.76 \times 10^5)[2(1.2 \times 10^{-2})(10^{-5})]$

$\qquad\qquad = 4.224 \times 10^{-2}$.

139. (a) $g(x) = f(x) - 2 \Rightarrow g'(x) = f'(x)$

(b) $h(x) = 2f(x) \Rightarrow h'(x) = 2f'(x)$

(c) $r(x) = f(-3x) \Rightarrow r'(x) = f'(-3x)(-3) = -3f'(-3x)$

Hence, you need to know $f'(-3x)$.

$$r'(0) = -3f'(0) = (-3)\left(-\tfrac{1}{3}\right) = 1$$

$$r'(-1) = -3f'(3) = (-3)(-4) = 12$$

(d) $s(x) = f(x + 2) \Rightarrow s'(x) = f'(x + 2)$

Hence, you need to know $f'(x + 2)$.

$$s'(-2) = f'(0) = -\tfrac{1}{3}, \text{ etc.}$$

x	-2	-1	0	1	2	3
$f'(x)$	4	$\frac{2}{3}$	$-\frac{1}{3}$	-1	-2	-4
$g'(x)$	4	$\frac{2}{3}$	$-\frac{1}{3}$	-1	-2	-4
$h'(x)$	8	$\frac{4}{3}$	$-\frac{2}{3}$	-2	-4	-8
$r'(x)$		12	1			
$s'(x)$	$-\frac{1}{3}$	-1	-2	-4		

141. (a) The plot of the data and the graph of the model are given in the figure.

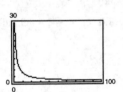

(b) $$T = 87.97 + 34.96 \ln p + 7.91\sqrt{p}$$
$$= 87.97 + 34.96 \ln p + 7.91 p^{1/2}$$

$$T'(p) = 34.96\left(\frac{1}{p}\right) + 7.91\left(\frac{1}{2}\right)p^{-1/2} = \frac{34.96}{p} + \frac{3.955}{\sqrt{p}}$$

$$T'(10) = \frac{34.96}{10} + \frac{3.955}{\sqrt{10}} \approx 4.75°\text{F/lb/sq in.}$$

$$T'(70) = \frac{34.96}{70} + \frac{3.955}{\sqrt{70}} \approx 0.97°\text{F/lb/sq in.}$$

(c) The graph of T' is given in the figure. As the altitude increases, the pressure decreases at a slower rate.

143. (a) $C(t) = 24.95(1.05)^t$

$$C(10) = 24.95(1.05)^{10} \approx \$40.64$$

(b) $C(t) = P(1.05)^t$

$$C'(t) = P \ln(1.05)(1.05)^t$$

$$C'(1) = P \ln(1.05)(1.05)^1 \approx 0.051P$$

$$C'(8) = P \ln(1.05)(1.05)^8 \approx 0.072P$$

(c) $$\frac{dC}{dt} = (\ln 1.05)[P(1.05)^t] = (\ln 1.05)C(t)$$

Therefore, dC/dt is proportional to $C(t)$ and the constant of proportionality is $\ln 1.05$.

145. $f(x + p) = f(x)$ for all x.

(a) Yes, $f'(x + p) = f'(x)$, which shows that f' is periodic as well.

(b) Yes, let $g(x) = f(2x)$, so $g'(x) = 2f'(2x)$. Since f' is periodic, so is g'.

147. $g(x) = \sqrt{x(x + n)}$

$$= \sqrt{x^2 + nx}$$

$$\frac{dg}{dx} = \frac{1}{2}(x^2 + nx)^{-1/2}(2x + n)$$

$$= \frac{2x + n}{2\sqrt{x^2 + nx}}$$

$$= \frac{(2x + n)/2}{\sqrt{x(x + n)}}$$

$$= \frac{[x + (x + n)]/2}{\sqrt{x(x + n)}}$$

$$= \frac{a}{g}$$

149. If $y = |u|$, then

$$\frac{dy}{dx} = u' \frac{u}{|u|}, u \neq 0.$$

Since $g(x) = |u|$ where $u = 2x - 3$ and $u' = 2$, we have the following.

$$g'(x) = 2\left(\frac{2x - 3}{|2x - 3|}\right)$$

151. $h(x) = |x|\cos x$

$$h'(x) = -|x| \sin x + \frac{x}{|x|} \cos x, \quad x \neq 0$$

153. (a) $f(x) = \sin\dfrac{x}{2}$ $\qquad f(\pi) = \sin\dfrac{\pi}{2} = 1$

$f'(x) = \dfrac{1}{2}\cos\dfrac{x}{2}$ $\qquad f'(\pi) = \dfrac{1}{2}\cos\dfrac{\pi}{2} = 0$

$f''(x) = -\dfrac{1}{4}\sin\dfrac{x}{2}$ $\qquad f''(\pi) = -\dfrac{1}{4}\sin\dfrac{\pi}{2} = -\dfrac{1}{4}$

$P_1(x) = f'(\pi)(x - \pi) + f(\pi) = f(\pi) = 1$

$P_2(x) = \dfrac{1}{2}f''(\pi)(x - \pi)^2 + f'(\pi)(x - \pi) + f(\pi)$

$\qquad = \dfrac{1}{2}\left(-\dfrac{1}{4}\right)(x - \pi)^2 + 1 = 1 - \dfrac{1}{8}(x - \pi)^2$

(b)

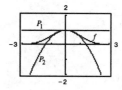

(c) P_2 is a better approximation than P_1.

(d) The accuracy worsens as you move away from $x = \pi$.

155. $f(x) = e^{-x^2/2}, f(0) = 1$

$f'(x) = -xe^{-x^2/2}, f'(0) = 0$

$f''(x) = x^2 e^{-x^2/2} - e^{-x^2/2} = e^{-x^2/2}(x^2 - 1), f''(0) = -1$

$P_1(x) = 1 + 0(x - 0) = 1, P_1(0) = 1$

$P_1'(x) = 0, \ P_1'(0) = 0$

$P_2(x) = 1 + 0(x - 0) - \dfrac{1}{2}(x - 0)^2 = 1 - \dfrac{x^2}{2}, P_2(0) = 1$

$P_2'(x) = -x, P_2'(0) = 0$

$P_2''(x) = -1, P_2''(0) = -1$

The values of f, P_1, P_2 and their first derivatives agree at $x = 0$. The values of the second derivatives of f and P_2 agree at $x = 0$.

157. False. If $y = (1 - x)^{1/2}$, then $y' = \frac{1}{2}(1 - x)^{-1/2}(-1)$.

159. True

Section 2.5   Implicit Differentiation

1. $x^2 + y^2 = 16$

$2x + 2yy' = 0$

$y' = \dfrac{-x}{y}$

3. $x^{1/2} + y^{1/2} = 9$

$\dfrac{1}{2}x^{-1/2} + \dfrac{1}{2}y^{-1/2}y' = 0$

$y' = -\dfrac{x^{-1/2}}{y^{-1/2}} = -\sqrt{\dfrac{y}{x}}$

5. $x^3 - xy + y^2 = 4$

$$\frac{d}{dx}[x^3 - xy + y^2] = \frac{d}{dx}[4]$$

$$\frac{d}{dx}[x^3] - \frac{d}{dx}[xy] + \frac{d}{dx}[y^2] = \frac{d}{dx}[4]$$

$$3x^2 - \left[x\frac{dy}{dx} + y(1)\right] + 2y\frac{dy}{dx} = 0$$

$$3x^2 - x\frac{dy}{dx} - y + 2y\frac{dy}{dx} = 0$$

$$(2y - x)\frac{dy}{dx} = y - 3x^2$$

$$\frac{dy}{dx} = \frac{y - 3x^2}{2y - x}$$

7. $xe^y - 10x + 3y = 0$

$$xe^y\frac{dy}{dx} + e^y - 10 + 3\frac{dy}{dx} = 0$$

$$\frac{dy}{dx}(xe^y + 3) = 10 - e^y$$

$$\frac{dy}{dx} = \frac{10 - e^y}{xe^y + 3}$$

9. $x^3 - 2x^2y + 3xy^2 = 38$

$$3x^2 - 2x^2y' - 4xy + 6xyy' + 3y^2 = 0$$

$$2x(3y - x)y' = 4xy - 3x^2 - 3y^2$$

$$y' = \frac{4xy - 3x^2 - 3y^2}{2x(3y - x)}$$

11. $\sin x + 2\cos 2y = 1$

$$\frac{d}{dx}[\sin x + 2\cos 2y] = \frac{d}{dx}[1]$$

$$\frac{d}{dx}[\sin x] + \frac{d}{dx}[2\cos 2y] = \frac{d}{dx}[1]$$

$$\cos x + 2(-\sin 2y)(2)\frac{dy}{dx} = 0$$

$$\cos x - 4\sin 2y\frac{dy}{dx} = 0$$

$$-4\sin 2y\frac{dy}{dx} = -\cos x$$

$$\frac{dy}{dx} = \frac{\cos x}{4\sin 2y}$$

13. $\sin x = x(1 + \tan y)$

$$\cos x = x(\sec^2 y)y' + (1 + \tan y)(1)$$

$$y' = \frac{\cos x - \tan y - 1}{x\sec^2 y}$$

15. $y = \sin(xy)$

$$y' = [xy' + y]\cos(xy)$$

$$y' - x\cos(xy)y' = y\cos(xy)$$

$$y' = \frac{y\cos(xy)}{1 - x\cos(xy)}$$

17. $x^3y^3 - y - x = 0$

$$3x^3y^2y' + 3x^2y^3 - y' - 1 = 0$$

$$(3x^3y^2 - 1)y' = 1 - 3x^2y^3$$

$$y' = \frac{1 - 3x^2y^3}{3x^3y^2 - 1}$$

19. $x^2 - 3\ln y + y^2 = 10$

$$\frac{d}{dx}[x^2 - 3\ln y + y^2] = \frac{d}{dx}[10]$$

$$2x - 3\left(\frac{1}{y}\right)\frac{dy}{dx} + 2y\frac{dy}{dx} = 0$$

$$\left(-\frac{3}{y} + 2y\right)\frac{dy}{dx} = -2x$$

$$\frac{dy}{dx} = \frac{-2x}{-3/y + 2y} = \frac{2xy}{3 - 2y^2}$$

21. Implicit differentiation of the equation $xy = 4$ yields

$$x\frac{dy}{dx} + y(1) = 0$$

$$x\frac{dy}{dx} = -y$$

$$\frac{dy}{dx} = -\frac{y}{x}$$

At $(-4, -1)$, $\dfrac{dy}{dx} = -\dfrac{-1}{-4} = -\dfrac{1}{4}$.

23. $y^2 = \dfrac{x^2 - 9}{x^2 + 9}$

$$2yy' = \frac{(x^2 + 9)(2x) - (x^2 - 9)2x}{(x^2 + 9)^2}$$

$$y' = \frac{18x}{(x^2 + 9)^2 y}$$

At $(3, 0)$: y' is undefined.

25. Implicit differentiation of the equation $x^{2/3} + y^{2/3} = 5$ yields

$$\frac{2}{3}x^{-1/3} + \frac{2}{3}y^{-1/3}\frac{dy}{dx} = 0$$

$$x^{-1/3} + y^{-1/3}\frac{dy}{dx} = 0$$

$$y^{-1/3}\frac{dy}{dx} = -x^{-1/3}$$

$$\frac{dy}{dx} = -\frac{x^{-1/3}}{y^{-1/3}} = -\sqrt[3]{\frac{y}{x}}$$

At $(8, 1)$, $\dfrac{dy}{dx} = -\sqrt[3]{\dfrac{1}{8}} = -\dfrac{1}{2}$.

27. Implicit differentiation of the equation $\tan(x + y) = x$ yields

$$\sec^2(x + y)\left(1 + \frac{dy}{dx}\right) = 1$$

$$\sec^2(x + y)\frac{dy}{dx} = 1 - \sec^2(x + y)$$

$$\frac{dy}{dx} = \frac{1 - \sec^2(x + y)}{\sec^2(x + y)}$$

$$= \frac{-\tan^2(x + y)}{\tan^2(x + y) + 1} = \frac{-x^2}{x^2 + 1}$$

At $(0, 0)$, $\dfrac{dy}{dx} = \dfrac{0}{1} = 0$.

29. $\qquad 2e^{xy} - x = 0, \qquad (2, 0)$

$$2e^{xy}[xy' + y] - 1 = 0$$

$$2e^{xy}xy' = 1 - 2ye^{xy}$$

$$y' = \frac{1 - 2ye^{xy}}{2xe^{xy}}$$

At $(2, 0)$: $y' = \dfrac{1}{4}$.

31. $\qquad \sqrt{x} + \sqrt{y} = 3$

$$\frac{1}{2}x^{-1/2} + \frac{1}{2}y^{-1/2}y' = 0$$

$$y' = -\frac{(1/2)x^{-1/2}}{(1/2)y^{-1/2}} = -\frac{\sqrt{y}}{\sqrt{x}}$$

At $(4, 1)$: $y' = -\dfrac{1}{2}$.

Tangent line:

$$y - 1 = -\frac{1}{2}(x - 4)$$

$$y = -\frac{1}{2}x + 3$$

$$x + 2y - 6 = 0$$

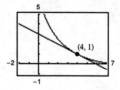

33. $(x^2 + 4)y = 8$

$(x^2 + 4)y' + y(2x) = 0$

$$y' = \frac{-2xy}{x^2 + 4}$$

$$= \frac{-2x[8/(x^2 + 4)]}{x^2 + 4}$$

$$= \frac{-16x}{(x^2 + 4)^2}$$

At $(2, 1)$: $y' = \dfrac{-32}{64} = -\dfrac{1}{2}$.

$\left(\text{Or, you could just solve for } y: \ y = \dfrac{8}{x^2 + 4}\right)$

37. (a) $x^2 + y^2 = 16$

$$y^2 = 16 - x^2$$

$$y = \pm\sqrt{16 - x^2}$$

(b)

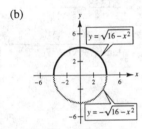

(c) Explicitly:

$$\frac{dy}{dx} = \pm\frac{1}{2}(16 - x^2)^{-1/2}(-2x)$$

$$= \frac{\mp x}{\sqrt{16 - x^2}} = \frac{-x}{\pm\sqrt{16 - x^2}} = \frac{-x}{y}$$

(d) Implicitly:

$$2x + 2yy' = 0$$

$$y' = -\frac{x}{y}$$

35. $(x^2 + y^2)^2 = 4x^2y$

$$2(x^2 + y^2)(2x + 2yy') = 4x^2y' + y(8x)$$

$$4x^3 + 4x^2yy' + 4xy^2 + 4y^3y' = 4x^2y' + 8xy$$

$$4x^2yy' + 4y^3y' - 4x^2y' = 8xy - 4x^3 - 4xy^2$$

$$4y'(x^2y + y^3 - x^2) = 4(2xy - x^3 - xy^2)$$

$$y' = \frac{2xy - x^3 - xy^2}{x^2y + y^3 - x^2}$$

At $(1, 1)$: $y' = 0$.

39. (a) Solving the equation for y, yields

$$9x^2 + 16y^2 = 144$$

$$16y^2 = 144 - 9x^2 = 9(16 - x^2)$$

$$y^2 = \frac{9}{16}(16 - x^2)$$

$$y = \pm\frac{3}{4}\sqrt{16 - x^2}, \quad -4 \le x \le 4$$

(b) The graph is given in the figure.

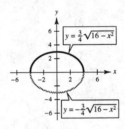

(c) When the explicit functions are differentiated explicitly, we obtain

$$\frac{dy}{dx} = \pm\left(\frac{3}{4}\right)\left(\frac{1}{2}\right)(16 - x^2)^{-1/2}(-2x)$$

$$= \frac{\mp 3x}{4\sqrt{16 - x^2}} = \frac{-3(3x)}{16[\pm(3/4)]\sqrt{16 - x^2}} = \frac{-9x}{16y}$$

(d) Differentiating the equation $9x^2 + 16y^2 = 144$ implicitly yields

$$18x + 32y\frac{dy}{dx} = 0$$

$$\frac{dy}{dx} = \frac{-9x}{16y}$$

41.
$$x^2 + xy = 5$$
$$2x + xy' + y = 0$$
$$y' = \frac{-(2x + y)}{x}$$
$$2 + xy'' + y' + y' = 0$$
$$xy'' = -2(1 + y')$$
$$y'' = \frac{-2[1 - (2x + y)/x]}{x} = \frac{2(x + y)}{x^2}$$
$$y'' = \frac{2(x + y)}{x^2} \cdot \frac{x}{x} = \frac{10}{x^3}$$

(**Note:** You could write $y = (5 - x^2)/x$ and calculate y' and y'' directly.)

45.
$$y^2 = x^3$$
$$2yy' = 3x^2$$
$$y' = \frac{3x^2}{2y} = \frac{3x^2}{2y} \cdot \frac{xy}{xy} = \frac{3y}{2x} \cdot \frac{x^3}{y^2} = \frac{3y}{2x}$$
$$y'' = \frac{2x(3y') - 3y(2)}{4x^2}$$
$$= \frac{2x[3 \cdot (3y/2x)] - 6y}{4x^2}$$
$$= \frac{3y}{4x^2} = \frac{3x}{4y}$$

47. $x^2 + y^2 = 25$
$$y' = \frac{-x}{y}$$
At $(4, 3)$:

Tangent line: $y - 3 = \dfrac{-4}{3}(x - 4) \Longrightarrow 4x + 3y - 25 = 0$

Normal line: $y - 3 = \dfrac{3}{4}(x - 4) \Longrightarrow 3x - 4y = 0$.

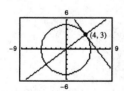

At $(-3, 4)$:

Tangent line: $y - 4 = \dfrac{3}{4}(x + 3) \Longrightarrow 3x - 4y + 25 = 0$

Normal line: $y - 4 = \dfrac{-4}{3}(x + 3) \Longrightarrow 4x + 3y = 0$

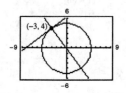

43. $x^2 - y^2 = 16$
$$2x - 2yy' = 0$$
$$-2yy' = -2x$$
$$y' = \frac{x}{y}$$

Differentiating implicitly again yields
$$y'' = \frac{y(1) - (x)y'}{y^2} = \frac{y - x(x/y)}{y^2} = \frac{y^2 - x^2}{y^3} = -\frac{16}{y^3}.$$

49. By implicit differentiation,
$$x^2 + y^2 = r^2$$
$$2x + 2yy' = 0$$
$$y' = -\frac{x}{y}.$$

Thus, if (x, y) is a point on the circle $x^2 + y^2 = r^2$, the slope of the tangent line at (x, y) is $-x/y$. On the other hand, the slope of the line passing through (x, y) and $(0, 0)$ is
$$m = \frac{y - 0}{x - 0} = \frac{y}{x}.$$

Since this slope is the negative reciprocal of y', the line passing through (x, y) and $(0, 0)$ must be perpendicular to the tangent line at (x, y).

51. $25x^2 + 16y^2 + 200x - 160y + 400 = 0$

$$50x + 32yy' + 200 - 160y' = 0$$

$$y' = \frac{200 + 50x}{160 - 32y}$$

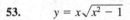

Horizontal tangents occur when $x = -4$:

$$25(16) + 16y^2 + 200(-4) - 160y + 400 = 0$$

$$y(y - 10) = 0 \Rightarrow y = 0, 10$$

Horizontal tangents: $(-4, 0), (-4, 10)$.

Vertical tangents occur when $y = 5$:

$$25x^2 + 400 + 200x - 800 + 400 = 0$$

$$25x(x + 8) = 0 \Rightarrow x = 0, -8$$

Vertical tangents: $(0, 5), (-8, 5)$.

53. $y = x\sqrt{x^2 - 1}$

$$\ln y = \ln x + \frac{1}{2}\ln(x^2 - 1)$$

$$\frac{1}{y}\left(\frac{dy}{dx}\right) = \frac{1}{x} + \frac{x}{x^2 - 1}$$

$$\frac{dy}{dx} = y\left[\frac{2x^2 - 1}{x(x^2 - 1)}\right] = \frac{2x^2 - 1}{\sqrt{x^2 - 1}}$$

55. Begin by taking the natural logarithm of each member of the equation.

$$y = \frac{x^2\sqrt{3x - 2}}{(x - 1)^2}$$

$$\ln y = \ln \frac{x^2\sqrt{3x - 2}}{(x - 1)^2} = 2\ln x + \frac{1}{2}\ln(3x - 2) - 2\ln(x - 1)$$

$$\frac{1}{y}\frac{dy}{dx} = \frac{2}{x} + \left(\frac{1}{2}\right)\frac{3}{3x - 2} - 2\frac{1}{x - 1}$$

$$\frac{dy}{dx} = y\left[\frac{3x^2 - 15x + 8}{2x(3x - 2)(x - 1)}\right]$$

The derivative can be written in terms of x by replacing y with its equivalent in the original equation.

$$y' = \frac{3x^3 - 15x^2 + 8x}{2(x - 1)^3\sqrt{3x - 2}}$$

57. $y = \frac{x(x - 1)^{3/2}}{\sqrt{x + 1}}$

$$\ln y = \ln x + \frac{3}{2}\ln(x - 1) - \frac{1}{2}\ln(x + 1)$$

$$\frac{1}{y}\left(\frac{dy}{dx}\right) = \frac{1}{x} + \frac{3}{2}\left(\frac{1}{x - 1}\right) - \frac{1}{2}\left(\frac{1}{x + 1}\right)$$

$$\frac{dy}{dx} = \frac{y}{2}\left[\frac{2}{x} + \frac{3}{x - 1} - \frac{1}{x + 1}\right]$$

$$= \frac{y}{2}\left[\frac{4x^2 + 4x - 2}{x(x^2 - 1)}\right] = \frac{(2x^2 + 2x - 1)\sqrt{x - 1}}{(x + 1)^{3/2}}$$

59. $y = x^{2/x}$

$$\ln y = \frac{2}{x}\ln x$$

$$\frac{1}{y}\left(\frac{dy}{dx}\right) = \frac{2}{x}\left(\frac{1}{x}\right) + \ln x\left(-\frac{2}{x^2}\right) = \frac{2}{x^2}(1 - \ln x)$$

$$\frac{dy}{dx} = \frac{2y}{x^2}(1 - \ln x) = 2x^{(2/x)-2}(1 - \ln x)$$

61. $y = (x - 2)^{x+1}$

$\ln y = (x + 1) \ln(x - 2)$

$\dfrac{1}{y}\left(\dfrac{dy}{dx}\right) = (x + 1)\left(\dfrac{1}{x - 2}\right) + \ln(x - 2)$

$\dfrac{dy}{dx} = y\left[\dfrac{x + 1}{x - 2} + \ln(x - 2)\right]$

$\qquad = (x - 2)^{x+1}\left[\dfrac{x + 1}{x - 2} + \ln(x - 2)\right]$

63. To find the points of intersection, set $y^2 = 6 - 2x^2$ and $y^2 = 4x$ equal to each other.

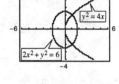

$$4x = 6 - 2x^2$$

$$2x^2 + 4x - 6 = 0$$

$$x^2 + 2x - 3 = 0$$

$$(x + 3)(x - 1) = 0$$

$$x = -3 \quad \text{and} \quad x = 1$$

When $x = 1$, $y = \pm 2$, and when $x = -3$, y is undefined. Thus the two points of intersection are $(1, 2)$ and $(1, -2)$. Differentiating the equation $2x^2 + y^2 = 6$ implicitly yields

$4x + 2yy' = 0$

$y' = -\dfrac{2x}{y}$

and differentiating $y^2 = 4x$ implicitly yields

$2yy' = 4$

$y' = \dfrac{2}{y}.$

Thus at $(1, 2)$ the slopes of the two curves are

$\dfrac{-2(1)}{2} = -1 \qquad \text{and} \qquad \dfrac{2}{2} = 1$

which implies that the tangent lines at this point are perpendicular. Finally, at $(1, -2)$ the slopes of the two curves are

$\dfrac{-2(1)}{-2} = 1 \qquad \text{and} \qquad \dfrac{2}{-2} = -1$

and the tangent lines at this point are also perpendicular

65. $y = -x$ and $x = \sin y$

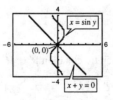

Point of intersection: $(0, 0)$

$y = -x$:	$x = \sin y$:
$y' = -1$	$1 = y' \cos y$
	$y' = \sec y$

At $(0, 0)$, the slopes are:

$y' = -1 \qquad y' = 1.$

Tangents are perpendicular.

67. $xy = C$ $x^2 - y^2 = K$

$xy' + y = 0$ $2x - 2yy' = 0$

$$y' = -\frac{y}{x} \qquad\qquad y' = \frac{x}{y}$$

At any point of intersection (x, y) the product of the slopes is $(-y/x)(x/y) = -1$. The curves are orthogonal.

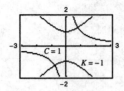 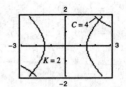

69. $2y^2 - 3x^4 = 0$

(a) $4yy' - 12x^3 = 0$

$4yy' = 12x^3$

$$y' = \frac{12x^3}{4y} = \frac{3x^3}{y}$$

(b) $4y\dfrac{dy}{dt} - 12x^3\dfrac{dx}{dt} = 0$

$$y\frac{dy}{dt} = 3x^3\frac{dx}{dt}$$

71. $\cos \pi y - 3 \sin \pi x = 1$

(a) $-\pi \sin(\pi y)y' - 3\pi \cos \pi x = 0$

$$y' = \frac{-3 \cos \pi x}{\sin \pi y}$$

(b) $-\pi \sin(\pi y)\dfrac{dy}{dt} - 3\pi \cos(\pi x)\dfrac{dx}{dt} = 0$

$$-\sin(\pi y)\frac{dy}{dt} = 3 \cos(\pi x)\frac{dx}{dt}$$

73. (a) The graph of $x^4 = 4(4x^2 - y^2)$ is shown in the figure.

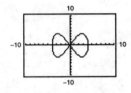

(b) $x^4 = 4(4x^2 - y^2)$

$$4x^3 = 4\left(8x - 2y\frac{dy}{dx}\right)$$

$$2y\frac{dy}{dx} = 8x - x^3$$

$$\frac{dy}{dx} = \frac{x(8 - x^2)}{2y}$$

To find the x-coordinates of the points of tangency when $y = 3$, solve the given equation for x when $y = 3$.

$$x^4 = 4(4x^2 - 3^2)$$

$x^4 - 16x^2 + 36 = 0$

Let $t = x^2$ and obtain the quadratic equation $t^2 - 16t + 36 = 0$. Using the quadratic formula we have the following.

$$t = \frac{16 \pm \sqrt{(-16)^2 - 4(1)(36)}}{2}$$

$$t = x^2 = 2\left(4 \pm \sqrt{7}\right)$$

$$x = \pm\sqrt{2\left(4 \pm \sqrt{7}\right)} = \pm\left(1 \pm \sqrt{7}\right)$$

Therefore, the four points of tangency and the slopes of the slopes of the tangent lines at each point are the following.

—CONTINUED—

73. —CONTINUED—

Point	*Slope*

$$\left(1 + \sqrt{7}, 3\right) \qquad \frac{dy}{dx} = \frac{\left(1 + \sqrt{7}\right)\left[8 - \left(1 + \sqrt{7}\right)^2\right]}{2(3)} = -\frac{1}{3}\left(7 + \sqrt{7}\right)$$

$$\left(1 - \sqrt{7}, 3\right) \qquad \frac{dy}{dx} = \frac{\left(1 - \sqrt{7}\right)\left[8 - \left(1 - \sqrt{7}\right)^2\right]}{2(3)} = -\frac{1}{3}\left(7 - \sqrt{7}\right)$$

$$\left(-1 + \sqrt{7}, 3\right) \qquad \frac{dy}{dx} = \frac{\left(-1 + \sqrt{7}\right)\left[8 - \left(-1 + \sqrt{7}\right)^2\right]}{2(3)} = \frac{1}{3}\left(7 - \sqrt{7}\right)$$

$$\left(-1 - \sqrt{7}, 3\right) \qquad \frac{dy}{dx} = \frac{\left(-1 - \sqrt{7}\right)\left[8 - \left(1 - \sqrt{7}\right)^2\right]}{2(3)} = \frac{1}{3}\left(7 + \sqrt{7}\right)$$

Using each point of tangency and the corresponding slope of the tangent line given above, yields the following equations of the tangent lines.

$$y_1 = -\frac{1}{3}\left[\left(7 + \sqrt{7}\right)x - \left(8\sqrt{7} + 23\right)\right]$$

$$y_2 = -\frac{1}{3}\left[\left(7 - \sqrt{7}\right)x + \left(8\sqrt{7} - 23\right)\right]$$

$$y_3 = \frac{1}{3}\left[\left(7 - \sqrt{7}\right)x - \left(8\sqrt{7} - 23\right)\right]$$

$$y_4 = \frac{1}{3}\left[\left(7 + \sqrt{7}\right)x + \left(8\sqrt{7} + 23\right)\right]$$

The graphs of the tangent lines are shown in the figure.

(c) From the figure in Part (b), we observe that y_1 and y_3 are the two tangent lines with points of tangency in the first quadrant. We now find the point of intersection of these two lines.

$$y_1 = y_3$$

$$-\frac{1}{3}\left[\left(7 + \sqrt{7}\right)x - \left(8\sqrt{7} + 23\right)\right] = \frac{1}{3}\left[\left(7 - \sqrt{7}\right)x - \left(8\sqrt{7} - 23\right)\right]$$

$$-\left(7 + \sqrt{7}\right)x - \left(7 - \sqrt{7}\right)x = -\left(8\sqrt{7} + 23\right) - \left(8\sqrt{7} - 23\right)$$

$$-14x = -16\sqrt{7} \Rightarrow x = \frac{8\sqrt{7}}{7}$$

To find the y-coordinate of the point of intersection substitute this value of x into the equation of one of the two lines. Using y_1 we have the following.

$$y_1 = -\frac{1}{3}\left[\left(7 + \sqrt{7}\right)\left(\frac{8\sqrt{7}}{7}\right) - \left(8\sqrt{7} + 23\right)\right]$$

$$= -\frac{1}{3}\left(8\sqrt{7} + 8 - 8\sqrt{7} - 23\right) = 5$$

Therefore, the point of intersection is $\left(\frac{8\sqrt{7}}{7}, 5\right)$.

75. Let $f(x) = x^n = x^{p/q}$, where p and q are nonzero integers and $q > 0$. First consider the case where $p = 1$. The derivative of $f(x) = x^{1/q}$ is given by

$$\frac{d}{dx}[x^{1/q}] = \lim_{\Delta x \to 0} \frac{f(x + \Delta x) - f(x)}{\Delta x} = \lim_{t \to x} \frac{f(t) - f(x)}{t - x}$$

where $t = x + \Delta x$. Observe that

$$\frac{f(t) - f(x)}{t - x} = \frac{t^{1/q} - x^{1/q}}{t - x} = \frac{t^{1/q} - x^{1/q}}{(t^{1/q})^q - (x^{1/q})^q}$$

$$= \frac{t^{1/q} - x^{1/q}}{(t^{1/q} - x^{1/q})(t^{1-(1/q)} + t^{1-(2/q)}x^{1/q} + \cdots + t^{1/q}x^{1-(2/q)} + x^{1-(1/q)})}$$

$$= \frac{1}{t^{1-(1/q)} + t^{1-(2/q)}x^{1/q} + \cdots + t^{1/q}x^{1-(2/q)} + x^{1-(1/q)}}.$$

As $t \to x$, the denominator approaches $qx^{1-(1/q)}$. That is,

$$\frac{d}{dx}[x^{1/q}] = \frac{1}{qx^{1-(1/q)}} = \frac{1}{q}x^{(1/q)-1}.$$

Now consider $f(x) = x^{p/q} = (x^p)^{1/q}$. From the Chain Rule,

$$f'(x) = \frac{1}{q}(x^p)^{(1/q)-1}\frac{d}{dx}[x^p]$$

$$= \frac{1}{q}(x^p)^{(1/q)-1}px^{p-1} = \frac{p}{q}x^{[(p/q)-p]+(p-1)} = \frac{p}{q}x^{(p/q)-1} = nx^{n-1} \left(n = \frac{p}{q} \right).$$

Section 2.6   Derivatives of Inverse Functions

1. Since $f(1) = 2$, it follows that $f^{-1}(2) = 1$.

$$f(x) = x^3 + 2x - 1$$

$$f'(x) = 3x^2 + 2$$

$$(f^{-1})'(2) = \frac{1}{f'(f^{-1}(2))} \quad \text{Theorem 2.16}$$

$$= \frac{1}{f'(1)} = \frac{1}{3(1)^2 + 2} = \frac{1}{5}$$

3. $f(x) = \sin x, \ f\left(\frac{\pi}{6}\right) = \frac{1}{2} = a$

$$f'(x) = \cos x$$

$$(f^{-1})'\left(\frac{1}{2}\right) = \frac{1}{f'(f^{-1}(1/2))} = \frac{1}{f'(\pi/6)} = \frac{1}{\cos(\pi/6)}$$

$$= \frac{1}{\sqrt{3}/2} = \frac{2\sqrt{3}}{3}$$

5. $f(x) = x^3 - \dfrac{4}{x}, \quad f(2) = 6 = a$

$$f'(x) = 3x^2 + \frac{4}{x^2}$$

$$(f^{-1})'(6) = \frac{1}{f'(f^{-1}(6))} = \frac{1}{f'(2)} = \frac{1}{3(2)^2 + (4/2^2)} = \frac{1}{13}$$

7. $f(x) = x^3, \quad \left(\dfrac{1}{2}, \dfrac{1}{8}\right)$

$$f'(x) = 3x^2$$

$$f'\left(\frac{1}{2}\right) = \frac{3}{4}$$

$$f^{-1}(x) = \sqrt[3]{x}, \quad \left(\frac{1}{8}, \frac{1}{2}\right)$$

$$(f^{-1})'(x) = \frac{1}{3\sqrt[3]{x^2}}$$

$$(f^{-1})'\left(\frac{1}{8}\right) = \frac{4}{3}$$

9. For the function $f(x) = \sqrt{x - 4}$, we have

$$f'(x) = \frac{1}{2\sqrt{x - 4}} \text{ and } f'(5) = \frac{1}{2\sqrt{5 - 4}} = \frac{1}{2}$$

For the function $f^{-1}(x) = x^2 + 4$, we have

$$(f^{-1})'(x) = 2x \text{ and } (f^{-1})'(1) = 2$$

Therefore, $(f^{-1})'(1) = \dfrac{1}{f'(5)}$.

11. $f(x) = 2 \arcsin(x - 1)$

$$f'(x) = 2\frac{1}{\sqrt{1 - (x - 1)^2}}(1) = \frac{2}{\sqrt{2x - x^2}}$$

13. $g(x) = 3 \arccos \dfrac{x}{2}$

$$g'(x) = \frac{-3(1/2)}{\sqrt{1 - (x^2/4)}} = \frac{-3}{\sqrt{4 - x^2}}$$

15. $f(x) = \arctan \dfrac{x}{a}$

$$f'(x) = \frac{1/a}{1 + (x^2/a^2)} = \frac{a}{a^2 + x^2}$$

17. $g(x) = \dfrac{\arcsin 3x}{x}$

$$g'(x) = \frac{x\left(3/\sqrt{1 - 9x^2}\right) - \arcsin 3x}{x^2}$$

$$= \frac{3x - \sqrt{1 - 9x^2}\,\arcsin 3x}{x^2\sqrt{1 - 9x^2}}$$

19. $h(x) = \operatorname{arccot} 6x$

$$h'(x) = \frac{-6}{1 + 36x^2}$$

21. From the figure we know that

$$h(t) = \sin(\arccos t) = \sqrt{1 - t^2}.$$

Therefore,

$$h'(t) = \frac{1}{2}(1 - t^2)^{-1/2}(-2t) = \frac{-t}{\sqrt{1 - t^2}}.$$

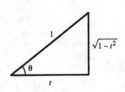

23. $f(x) = \arcsin x + \arccos x = \dfrac{\pi}{2}$

$$f'(x) = 0$$

25. $f(x) = \dfrac{1}{2}\left[\dfrac{1}{2}\ln\left(\dfrac{x + 1}{x - 1}\right) + \arctan x\right] = \dfrac{1}{2}\left[\dfrac{1}{2}\ln(x + 1) - \dfrac{1}{2}\ln(x - 1) + \arctan x\right]$

$$f'(x) = \frac{1}{2}\left[\frac{1}{2(x + 1)} - \frac{1}{2(x - 1)} + \frac{1}{1 + x^2}\right] = \frac{1}{2}\left[\frac{(x - 1) - (x + 1)}{2(x^2 - 1)} + \frac{1}{1 + x^2}\right]$$

$$= \frac{1}{2}\left[\frac{-1}{x^2 - 1} + \frac{1}{1 + x^2}\right] = \frac{1}{2}\left[\frac{1}{1 - x^2} + \frac{1}{1 + x^2}\right] = \frac{1}{2}\left[\frac{1 + x^2 + 1 - x^2}{1 - x^4}\right] = \frac{1}{1 - x^4}$$

27. $f(x) = x \arcsin x + \sqrt{1 - x^2}$

$$f'(x) = x\left(\frac{1}{\sqrt{1 - x^2}}\right) + \arcsin x + \frac{1}{2}(1 - x^2)^{-1/2}(-2x) = \frac{x}{\sqrt{1 - x^2}} + \arcsin x + \frac{-x}{\sqrt{1 - x^2}} = \arcsin x$$

29. $f(x) = \arccos x$

$$f'(x) = \frac{-1}{\sqrt{1 - x^2}} = -2 \text{ when } x = \pm\frac{\sqrt{3}}{2}.$$

When $x = \sqrt{3}/2$, $f(\sqrt{3}/2) = \pi/6$. When $x = -\sqrt{3}/2$, $f(-\sqrt{3}/2) = 5\pi/6$.

Tangent lines: $y - \dfrac{\pi}{6} = -2\left(x - \dfrac{\sqrt{3}}{2}\right) \Rightarrow y = -2x + \left(\dfrac{\pi}{6} + \sqrt{3}\right)$

$$y - \frac{5\pi}{6} = -2\left(x + \frac{\sqrt{3}}{2}\right) \Rightarrow y = -2x + \left(\frac{5\pi}{6} - \sqrt{3}\right)$$

31. Begin by evaluating the function f and its first and second derivatives at $x = 1/2$.

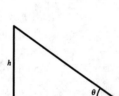

$$f(x) = \arcsin x \qquad f\left(\frac{1}{2}\right) = \frac{\pi}{6}$$

$$f'(x) = \frac{1}{\sqrt{1 - x^2}} \qquad f'\left(\frac{1}{2}\right) = \frac{2\sqrt{3}}{3}$$

$$f''(x) = \frac{x}{(1 - x)^{3/2}} \qquad f''\left(\frac{1}{2}\right) = \frac{4\sqrt{3}}{9}$$

Therefore,

$$P_1(x) = \frac{\pi}{6} + \frac{2\sqrt{3}}{3}\left(x - \frac{1}{2}\right)$$

$$P_2(x) = \frac{\pi}{6} + \frac{2\sqrt{3}}{3}\left(x - \frac{1}{2}\right) + \frac{2\sqrt{3}}{9}\left(x - \frac{1}{2}\right)^2.$$

The graphs of f, P_1, and P_2, produced by a graphing utiltity, are shown in the figure.

33. (a) $h(t) = -16t^2 + 256$

     $-16t^2 + 256 = 0$ when $t = 4$ sec.

(b) $\tan\theta = \dfrac{h}{500} = \dfrac{-16t^2 + 256}{500}$

$$\theta = \arctan\left[\frac{16}{500}(-t^2 + 16)\right]$$

$$\frac{d\theta}{dt} = \frac{-8t/125}{1 + [(4/125)(-t^2 + 16)]^2} = \frac{-1000t}{15{,}625 + 16(16 - t^2)^2}$$

When $t = 1$, $d\theta/dt \approx -0.0520$ rad/sec.

When $t = 2$, $d\theta/dt \approx -0.1116$ rad/sec.

35. (a) Let $y = \arctan u$. Then

$$\tan y = u$$

$$\sec^2 y \frac{dy}{dx} = u'$$

$$\frac{dy}{dx} = \frac{u'}{\sec^2 y} = \frac{u'}{1 + u^2}.$$

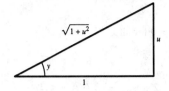

(b) Let $y = \text{arcsec } u$. Then

$$\sec y = u$$

$$\sec y \tan y \frac{dy}{dx} = u'$$

$$\frac{dy}{dx} = \frac{u'}{\sec y \tan y} = \frac{u'}{|u|\sqrt{u^2 - 1}}.$$

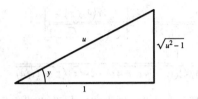

Note: The absolute value sign in the formula for the derivative of arcsec u is necessary because the inverse secant function has a positive slope at every value in its domain.

(c) Let $y = \arccos u$. Then

$$\cos y = u$$

$$-\sin y \frac{dy}{dx} = u'$$

$$\frac{dy}{dx} = -\frac{u'}{\sin y} = -\frac{u'}{\sqrt{1 - u^2}}.$$

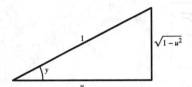

(d) Let $y = \text{arccot } u$. Then

$$\cot y = u$$

$$-\csc^2 y \frac{dy}{dx} = u'$$

$$\frac{dy}{dx} = \frac{u'}{-\csc^2 y} = -\frac{u'}{1 + u^2}.$$

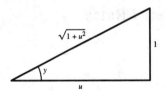

(e) Let $y = \text{arccsc } u$. Then

$$\csc y = u$$

$$-\csc y \cot y \frac{dy}{dx} = u'$$

$$\frac{dy}{dx} = \frac{u'}{-\csc y \cot y} = -\frac{u'}{|u|\sqrt{u^2 - 1}}.$$

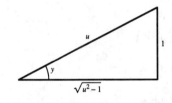

Note: The absolute value sign in the formula for the derivative of arccsc u is necessary because the inverse cosecant function has a negative slope at every value in its domain.

37. $f(x) = \sin x$

$g(x) = \arcsin(\sin x)$

(a) The range of $y = \arcsin x$ is

$$-\pi/2 \le y \le \pi/2.$$

(b) Maximum: $\pi/2$

Minimum: $-\pi/2$

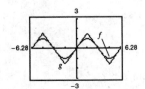

39. $y = 19.14 - 0.18t - 37.10 \text{ arccot } (t)$

(a)

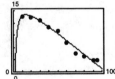

(b) $y' = -0.18 - 37.10 \dfrac{-1}{1 + t^2} = -0.18 + \dfrac{37.10}{1 + t^2}$

$y'(20) \approx -0.087$ million/yr

$y'(60) \approx -0.170$ million/yr

41. True

$$\frac{d}{dx}[\arctan x] = \frac{1}{1 + x^2} > 0 \text{ for all } x$$

43. True

$$\frac{d}{dx}[\arctan(\tan x)] = \frac{\sec^2 x}{1 + \tan^2 x} = \frac{\sec^2 x}{\sec^2 x} = 1$$

45. $f(x) = \arcsin\left(\frac{x-2}{2}\right) - 2\arcsin\frac{\sqrt{x}}{2}, \quad 0 \le x \le 4$

$$f'(x) = \frac{1/2}{\sqrt{1 - [(x-2)/2]^2}} - 2\left[\frac{1/(4\sqrt{x})}{\sqrt{1 - (\sqrt{x}/2)^2}}\right]$$

$$= \frac{1}{2\sqrt{1 - (1/4)(x^2 - 4x + 4)}} - \frac{1}{2\sqrt{x}\sqrt{1 - (x/4)}} = \frac{1}{2\sqrt{x - (x^2/4)}} - \frac{1}{2\sqrt{x - (x^2/4)}} = 0$$

Since the derivative is zero, we conclude that the function is constant. (By letting $x = 0$ in $f(x)$, you can see that the constant is $-\pi/2$.)

47.

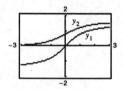

Since $e^x > 0$ for all x, $y_z = \arctan(e^x) > 0$ for all x.

Section 2.7   Related Rates

1. $y = \sqrt{x}$

$$\frac{dy}{dt} = \left(\frac{1}{2\sqrt{x}}\right)\frac{dx}{dt}$$

$$\frac{dx}{dt} = 2\sqrt{x}\frac{dy}{dt}$$

(a) When $x = 4$ and $dx/dt = 3$,

$$\frac{dy}{dt} = \frac{1}{2\sqrt{4}}(3) = \frac{3}{4}.$$

(b) When $x = 25$ and $dy/dt = 2$,

$$\frac{dx}{dt} = 2\sqrt{25}(2) = 20.$$

3. Since x and y are differentiable functions of t, differentiating the equation $xy = 4$ with respect to t yields

$$(1) \quad x\frac{dy}{dt} + y\frac{dx}{dt} = 0.$$

(a) Solving (1) for dy/dt, and substituting $y = 1/2$ and $dx/dt = 10$ when $x = 8$, yields

$$\frac{dy}{dt} = -\frac{y}{x}\frac{dx}{dt} = -\frac{1/2}{8}(10) = -\frac{5}{8}.$$

(b) Solving (1) for dx/dt, and substituting $y = 4$ and $dy/dt = -6$ when $x = 1$, yields

$$\frac{dx}{dt} = -\frac{x}{y}\frac{dy}{dt} = -\frac{1}{4}(-6) = \frac{3}{2}.$$

5. $y = x^2 + 1$

$$\frac{dx}{dt} = 2$$

$$\frac{dy}{dt} = 2x\frac{dx}{dt}$$

(a) When $x = -1$,

$$\frac{dy}{dt} = 2(-1)(2) = -4 \text{ cm/sec.}$$

(b) When $x = 0$,

$$\frac{dy}{dt} = 2(0)(2) = 0 \text{ cm/sec.}$$

(c) When $x = 1$,

$$\frac{dy}{dt} = 2(1)(2) = 4 \text{ cm/sec.}$$

(d) When $x = 3$,

$$\frac{dy}{dt} = 2(3)(2) = 12 \text{ cm/sec.}$$

7. Since x and y are differentiable functions of t, differentiating the equation $y = x \ln x$ with respect to t yields

(1) $\dfrac{dy}{dt} = x\left(\dfrac{1}{x}\right)\dfrac{dx}{dt} + \ln x(1)\dfrac{dx}{dt} = (1 + \ln x)\dfrac{dx}{dt}$

(a) Substituting $x = 1$ and $\dfrac{dx}{dt} = 2$ into (1) yields

$\dfrac{dy}{dt} = (1 + \ln 1)2 = 2.$

(b) Substituting $x = e$ and $\dfrac{dx}{dt} = 2$ in (1) yields

$\dfrac{dy}{dt} = (1 + \ln e)2 = 4.$

9. $y = \tan x$

$\dfrac{dx}{dt} = 2$

$\dfrac{dy}{dt} = \sec^2 x \, \dfrac{dx}{dt}$

(a) When $x = -\pi/3$,

$\dfrac{dy}{dt} = (2)^2(2) = 8 \text{ cm/sec.}$

(b) When $x = -\pi/4$,

$\dfrac{dy}{dt} = \left(\sqrt{2}\right)^2(2) = 4 \text{ cm/sec.}$

(c) When $x = 0$,

$\dfrac{dy}{dt} = (1)^2(2) = 2 \text{ cm/sec.}$

(d) When $x = 1$,

$\dfrac{dy}{dt} = (\sec 1)^2 2 \approx 6.8510 \text{ cm/sec.}$

11. (a) For increasing x, dy/dt decreases.

(b) For increasing y, dx/dt increases.

13. $D = \sqrt{x^2 + y^2} = \sqrt{x^2 + (x^2 + 1)^2} = \sqrt{x^4 + 3x^2 + 1}$

$\dfrac{dx}{dt} = 2$

$\dfrac{dD}{dt} = \dfrac{1}{2}(x^4 + 3x^2 + 1)^{-1/2}(4x^3 + 6x)\dfrac{dx}{dt} = \dfrac{2x^3 + 3x}{\sqrt{x^4 + 3x^2 + 1}}\dfrac{dx}{dt} = \dfrac{4x^3 + 6x}{\sqrt{x^4 + 3x^2 + 1}}$

15. *Area of a circle:* $A = \pi r^2$

Given rate: $\dfrac{dr}{dt} = 2$ centimeters per minute

Find: $\dfrac{dA}{dt}$

Differentiation *with respect to* t of the area formula produces

$\dfrac{dA}{dt} = 2\pi r \dfrac{dr}{dt}.$

(a) When $r = 6$ the rate of change of area is

$\dfrac{dA}{dt} = 2\pi(6)(2) = 24\pi \text{ centimeters per minute.}$

(b) When $r = 24$ the rate of change of area is

$\dfrac{dA}{dt} = 2\pi(24)(2) = 96\pi \text{ centimeters per minute.}$

17. (a) $\sin\dfrac{\theta}{2} = \dfrac{(1/2)b}{s} \Rightarrow b = 2s\sin\dfrac{\theta}{2}$

$\cos\dfrac{\theta}{2} = \dfrac{h}{s} \Rightarrow h = s\cos\dfrac{\theta}{2}$

$A = \dfrac{1}{2}bh = \dfrac{1}{2}\left(2s\sin\dfrac{\theta}{2}\right)\left(s\cos\dfrac{\theta}{2}\right)$

$\qquad = \dfrac{s^2}{2}\left(2\sin\dfrac{\theta}{2}\cos\dfrac{\theta}{2}\right) = \dfrac{s^2}{2}\sin\theta$

(b) $\dfrac{dA}{dt} = \dfrac{s^2}{2}\cos\theta\dfrac{d\theta}{dt}$ where $\dfrac{d\theta}{dt} = \dfrac{1}{2}$ rad/min.

When $\theta = \dfrac{\pi}{6}, \dfrac{dA}{dt} = \dfrac{s^2}{2}\left(\dfrac{\sqrt{3}}{2}\right)\left(\dfrac{1}{2}\right) = \dfrac{\sqrt{3}s^2}{8}$ rad/min.

When $\theta = \dfrac{\pi}{3}, \dfrac{dA}{dt} = \dfrac{s^2}{2}\left(\dfrac{1}{2}\right)\left(\dfrac{1}{2}\right) = \dfrac{s^2}{8}$ rad/min.

(c) If $d\theta/dt$ is constant, dA/dt is proportional to $\cos\theta$.

19. $V = \dfrac{4}{3}\pi r^3, \dfrac{dV}{dt} = 500$

$\dfrac{dV}{dt} = 4\pi r^2\dfrac{dr}{dt}$

$\dfrac{dr}{dt} = \dfrac{1}{4\pi r^2}\left(\dfrac{dV}{dt}\right) = \dfrac{1}{4\pi r^2}(500)$

(a) When $r = 30, \dfrac{dr}{dt} = \dfrac{1}{4\pi(30)^2}(500) = \dfrac{5}{36\pi}$ cm/min.

(b) When $r = 60, \dfrac{dr}{dt} = \dfrac{1}{4\pi(60)^2}(500) = \dfrac{5}{144\pi}$ cm/min.

21. $s = 6x^2$

$\dfrac{dx}{dt} = 3$

$\dfrac{ds}{dt} = 12x\dfrac{dx}{dt}$

(a) When $x = 1$,

$\dfrac{ds}{dt} = 12(1)(3) = 36$ cm^2/sec.

(b) When $x = 10$,

$\dfrac{ds}{dt} = 12(10)(3) = 360$ cm^2/sec.

23. Let V = volume of cone = $\dfrac{1}{3}\pi r^2 h$.

Since the diameter of the base is approximately three times the altitude, we have

$\qquad 2r = 3h \quad$ or $\quad r = \dfrac{3}{2}h$

Therefore,

$\qquad V = \dfrac{1}{3}\pi\left(\dfrac{3}{2}h\right)^2 h = \dfrac{3\pi}{4}h^3.$

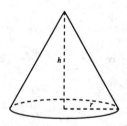

Differentiating with respect to t, yields

$\qquad \dfrac{dV}{dt} = \dfrac{9\pi}{4}h^2\dfrac{dh}{dt} \quad$ or $\quad \dfrac{4(dV/dt)}{9\pi h^2} = \dfrac{dh}{dt}.$

Now, substituting $h = 15$ and $dV/dt = 10$, yields the following rate of change of the height of the conical pile.

$\qquad \dfrac{dh}{dt} = \dfrac{4(10)}{9\pi(15)^2} = \dfrac{8}{405\pi}$ ft/min.

25. From the figure we see that x and y are related by the equation

$$m = \frac{y - 0}{x - 0} = \frac{2 - 0}{12 - 0}$$

$$\frac{y}{x} = \frac{1}{6} \text{ or } x = 6y.$$

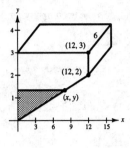

The volume of the inclined portion of the pool is given by the product of the width of the pool and the area of the triangular cross section.

$$V_L = 6\left(\frac{1}{2}\right)xy = 3xy = 3(6y)y = 18y^2$$

When $y = 2$, the inclined portion of the pool has a volume of

$$V_L = 18(2^2) = 72 \text{ cubic meters.}$$

Since the upper rectangular portion of the pool has a volume of

$$V_U = 1(12)(6) = 72 \text{ cubic meters}$$

the total volume of the pool is

$$V = V_L + V_U = 72 + 72 = 144 \text{ cubic meters.}$$

(a) When $y = 1$, the ratio of the filled portion of the pool to the total volume is

$$\frac{18y^2}{V} = \frac{18(1^2)}{144} = 12.5\%.$$

(b) When $y = 1$, we can find dy/dt by differentiating $V_L = 18y^2$ and substituting $dV_L/dt = 1/4$.

$$V_L = 18y^2$$

$$\frac{dV_L}{dt} = 36y\frac{dy}{dt}$$

$$\frac{1}{4} = 36(1)\frac{dy}{dt}$$

$$\frac{dy}{dt} = \frac{1}{4(36)} = \frac{1}{144} \text{ meters per minute}$$

27. (a) From the figure it follows that x and y are related by the equation $x^2 + y^2 = 25^2$. Differentiating this equation with respect to t, yields

$$2x\frac{dx}{dt} + 2y\frac{dy}{dt} = 0$$

$$y\frac{dy}{dt} = -x\frac{dx}{dt}$$

$$\frac{dy}{dt} = -\frac{x}{y}\frac{dx}{dt}$$

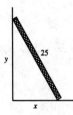

Since $dx/dt = 2$, we have $dy/dt = -2(x/y)$.

When $x = 7$, $y = \sqrt{(25)^2 - 7^2} = \sqrt{576} = 24$.

$$\frac{dy}{dt} = -2\left(\frac{7}{24}\right) = -\frac{7}{12} \approx -0.583 \text{ ft/sec}$$

When $x = 15$, $y = \sqrt{(25)^2 - (15)^2} = \sqrt{400} = 20$.

$$\frac{dy}{dt} = -2\left(\frac{15}{20}\right) = -\frac{3}{2} = -1.5 \text{ ft/sec}$$

When $x = 24$, $y = \sqrt{(25)^2 - (24)^2} = \sqrt{49} = 7$.

$$\frac{dy}{dt} = -2\left(\frac{24}{7}\right) = -\frac{48}{7} \approx -6.857 \text{ ft/sec}$$

—CONTINUED—

27. —CONTINUED—

(b) The area of the triangle in the accompanying figure is

$$A = \frac{1}{2}xy = \frac{1}{2}x\sqrt{625 - x^2}.$$

Differentiating with respect to t yields

$$\frac{dA}{dt} = \frac{1}{2}\left[x\left(\frac{1}{2}\right)(625 - x^2)^{-1/2}\left(-2x\frac{dx}{dt}\right) + \sqrt{625 - x^2}\frac{dx}{dt}\right]$$

$$= \left(\frac{625 - 2x^2}{2\sqrt{625 - x^2}}\right)\frac{dx}{dt}.$$

The rate of change of the area when $x = 7$ and $dx/dt = 2$ is

$$\frac{dA}{dt} = \left(\frac{625 - 2(7)^2}{2\sqrt{625 - (7^2)}}\right)(2) = \frac{527}{24} \text{ ft}^2 \text{ sec}.$$

(c) If θ is the angle between the top of the ladder and the wall of the house, then

$$\sin \theta = \frac{x}{25}$$

$$\cos \theta \frac{d\theta}{dt} = \frac{1}{25}\frac{dx}{dt}$$

$$\frac{d\theta}{dt} = \frac{\sec \theta}{25}\frac{dx}{dt}.$$

When $x = 7$, $\sin \theta = 7/25$ and $\sec \theta = 25/24$.

Since $dx/dt = 2$, the rate of change of the angle θ is

$$\frac{d\theta}{dt} = \frac{25/24}{25}(2) = \frac{1}{12} \text{ rad/sec}.$$

29. When $y = 6$, $x = \sqrt{12^2 - 6^2} = 6\sqrt{3}$, and

$$s = \sqrt{x^2 + (12 - y)^2}$$

$$= \sqrt{108 + 36} = 12.$$

$$x^2 + (12 - y)^2 = s^2$$

$$2x\frac{dx}{dt} + 2(12 - y)(-1)\frac{dy}{dt} = 2s\frac{ds}{dt}$$

$$x\frac{dx}{dt} + (y - 12)\frac{dy}{dt} = s\frac{ds}{dt}$$

Also, $x^2 + y^2 = 12^2$

$$2x\frac{dx}{dt} + 2y\frac{dy}{dt} = 0 \Rightarrow \frac{dy}{dt} = \frac{-x}{y}\frac{dx}{dt}.$$

Thus, $x\dfrac{dx}{dt} + (y - 12)\left(\dfrac{-x}{y}\dfrac{dx}{dt}\right) = s\dfrac{ds}{dt}$

$$\frac{dx}{dt}\left[x - x + \frac{12x}{y}\right] = s\frac{ds}{dt} \Rightarrow \frac{dx}{dt} = \frac{sy}{12x} \cdot \frac{ds}{dt} = \frac{(12)(6)}{(12)(6\sqrt{3})}(-0.2) = \frac{-1}{5\sqrt{3}} = \frac{-\sqrt{3}}{15} \text{ m/sec (horizontal)}$$

$$\frac{dy}{dt} = \frac{-x}{y}\frac{dx}{dt} = \frac{-6\sqrt{3}}{6} \cdot \frac{(-\sqrt{3})}{15} = \frac{1}{5} \text{ m/sec (vertical)}.$$

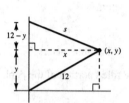

31. (a) $s^2 = x^2 + y^2$

$$\frac{dx}{dt} = -450$$

$$\frac{dy}{dt} = -600$$

$$2s\frac{ds}{dt} = 2x\frac{dx}{dt} + 2y\frac{dy}{dt}$$

$$\frac{ds}{dt} = \frac{x(dx/dt) + y(dy/dt)}{s}$$

When $x = 150$ and $y = 200$, $s = 250$ and

$$\frac{ds}{dt} = \frac{150(-450) + 200(-600)}{250} = -750 \text{ mph}.$$

(b) $t = \dfrac{250}{750} = \dfrac{1}{3} \text{ hr} = 20 \text{ min}$

33. $s^2 = 90^2 + x^2$

$$x = 30$$

$$\frac{dx}{dt} = -28$$

$$2s\frac{ds}{dt} = 2x\frac{dx}{dt} \Rightarrow \frac{ds}{dt} = \frac{x}{s} \cdot \frac{dx}{dt}$$

When $x = 30$,

$$s = \sqrt{90^2 + 30^2} = 30\sqrt{10}$$

$$\frac{ds}{dt} = \frac{30}{30\sqrt{10}}(-28) = \frac{-28}{\sqrt{10}} \approx -8.85 \text{ ft/sec}.$$

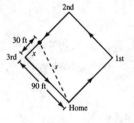

35. From the figure we see that x and s are related by similar triangles in such a way that

$$\frac{s-x}{6} = \frac{s}{15}$$

$$15s - 15x = 6s$$

$$9s = 15x$$

$$s = \frac{5}{3}x.$$

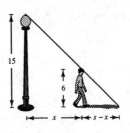

(a) To find ds/dt, given that $dx/dt = 5$, differentiate with respect to t as follows:

$$\frac{ds}{dt} = \frac{5}{3} \cdot \frac{dx}{dt} = \frac{5}{3}(5) = \frac{25}{3} \approx 8.3 \text{ ft/sec}$$

(b) The rate at which the shadow in increasing is

$$\frac{ds}{dt} - \frac{dx}{dt} = \frac{25}{3} - 5 = \frac{10}{3} \approx 3.3 \text{ ft/sec.}$$

(Note: The measurement 10 feet given in this problem is a "red herring" since the distance from the base of the light does not affect ds/dt.)

37. $x(t) = \frac{1}{2} \sin \frac{\pi t}{6}, x^2 + y^2 = 1$

(a) Period: $\dfrac{2\pi}{\pi/6} = 12$ seconds

(b) When $x = \frac{1}{2}, y = \sqrt{1^2 - \left(\frac{1}{2}\right)^2} = \frac{\sqrt{3}}{2}$ m.

Lowest point: $\left(0, \frac{\sqrt{3}}{2}\right)$

(c) When $x = \frac{1}{4}, y = \sqrt{1 - \left(\frac{1}{4}\right)^2} = \frac{\sqrt{15}}{4}$ and $t = 1$

$$\frac{dx}{dt} = \frac{1}{2}\left(\frac{\pi}{6}\right)\cos\frac{\pi t}{6} = \frac{\pi}{12}\cos\frac{\pi t}{6}$$

$$x^2 + y^2 = 1$$

$$2x\frac{dx}{dt} + 2y\frac{dy}{dt} = 0 \Longrightarrow \frac{dy}{dt} = \frac{-x}{y}\frac{dx}{dt}.$$

Thus,

$$\frac{dy}{dt} = -\frac{1/4}{\sqrt{15}/4} \cdot \frac{\pi}{12}\cos\left(\frac{\pi}{6}\right)$$

$$= \frac{-\pi}{\sqrt{15}}\left(\frac{1}{12}\right)\frac{\sqrt{3}}{2} = \frac{-\pi}{24}\frac{1}{\sqrt{5}} = \frac{-\sqrt{5}\pi}{120}$$

$$\text{Speed} = \left|\frac{-\sqrt{5}\pi}{120}\right| = \frac{\sqrt{5}\pi}{120} \text{ m/sec}$$

39. Since the evaporation rate is proportional to the surface area, $dV/dt = k(4\pi r^2)$. However, since $V = (4/3)\pi r^3$, we have

$$\frac{dV}{dt} = 4\pi r^2 \frac{dr}{dt}.$$

Therefore,

$$k(4\pi r^2) = 4\pi r^2 \frac{dr}{dt} \Longrightarrow k = \frac{dr}{dt}.$$

41.
$$pv^{1.3} = k$$

$$1.3\, pv^{0.3}\frac{dv}{dt} + v^{1.3}\frac{dp}{dt} = 0$$

$$v^{0.3}\left(1.3p\frac{dv}{dt} + v\frac{dp}{dt}\right) = 0$$

$$1.3p\frac{dv}{dt} = -v\frac{dp}{dt}$$

43. From the figure it follows that $\tan \theta = h/30$. Differentiating with respect to t yields the following.

$$\tan \theta = \frac{h}{30}$$

$$\sec^2 \theta \frac{d\theta}{dt} = \frac{1}{30} \frac{dh}{dt}$$

$$\frac{d\theta}{dt} = \frac{1}{30} \cos^2 \theta \frac{dh}{dt}$$

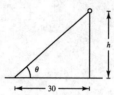

We are given that $dh/dt = 3$ meters per second. Also, when $h = 30$, $\theta = \pi/4$. Substituting into the derivative yields

$$\frac{d\theta}{dt} = \frac{1}{30} \cos^2 \frac{\pi}{4}(3)$$

$$= \frac{1}{10} \cdot \frac{1}{2}$$

$$= \frac{1}{20} \text{ radians per second}$$

$$\approx 2.86 \text{ degrees per second.}$$

45. $\tan \theta = \dfrac{y}{x}, y = 5$

$$\frac{dx}{dt} = -600 \text{ mi/hr}$$

$$(\sec^2 \theta) \frac{d\theta}{dt} = -\frac{5}{x^2} \cdot \frac{dx}{dt}$$

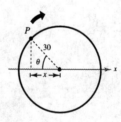

$$\frac{d\theta}{dt} = \cos^2 \theta \left(-\frac{5}{x^2}\right)\frac{dx}{dt} = \frac{x^2}{L^2}\left(-\frac{5}{x^2}\right)\frac{dx}{dt}$$

$$= \left(-\frac{5^2}{L^2}\right)\left(\frac{1}{5}\right)\frac{dx}{dt} = (-\sin^2 \theta)\left(\frac{1}{5}\right)(-600) = 120 \sin^2 \theta$$

(a) When $\theta = 30°$, $\dfrac{d\theta}{dt} = \dfrac{120}{4} = 30 \text{ rad/hr} = \dfrac{1}{2} \text{ rad/min.}$

(b) When $\theta = 60°$, $\dfrac{d\theta}{dt} = 120\left(\dfrac{3}{4}\right) = 90 \text{ rad/hr} = \dfrac{3}{2} \text{ rad/min.}$

(c) When $\theta = 75°$, $\dfrac{d\theta}{dt} = 120 \sin^2 75° \approx 111.96 \text{ rad/hr} \approx 1.87 \text{ rad/min.}$

47. (a) We are given that the wheel rotates at 10 revolutions per second in a clockwise direction. Therefore,

$$\frac{d\theta}{dt} = 10(2\pi) = 20\pi \text{ radians per second.}$$

From the figure we have

$$x = 30 \cos \theta$$

$$\frac{dx}{dt} = -30 \sin \theta \frac{d\theta}{dt}$$

$$= -30 \sin \theta(20\pi) = -600\pi \sin \theta.$$

—CONTINUED—

47. —CONTINUED—

(b) The graph is given in the figure.

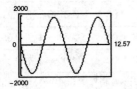

(c) The absolute value of dx/dt is greatest when absolute value of $\sin \theta$ is greatest. This occurs when

$$\theta = (2n - 1)\frac{\pi}{2}, \ n \text{ an integer.}$$

The absolute value of dx/dt is least when $\sin \theta$ is 0. This occurs when

$$\theta = n\pi, \quad n \text{ and integer.}$$

(d) $\theta = 30°$:

$$\frac{dx}{dt} = -600\pi\left(\frac{1}{2}\right) = -300\pi \text{ centimeters per second.}$$

$\theta = 60$:

$$\frac{dx}{dt} = -600\pi\left(\frac{\sqrt{3}}{2}\right) = -300\sqrt{3}\pi \text{ centimeters per second.}$$

49. $\tan\theta = \dfrac{x}{50} \Longrightarrow x = 50 \tan \theta$

$$\frac{dx}{dt} = 50 \sec^2 \theta \ \frac{d\theta}{dt}$$

$$2 = 50 \sec^2 \theta \ \frac{d\theta}{dt}$$

$$\frac{d\theta}{dt} = \frac{1}{25} \cos^2 \theta, \ -\frac{\pi}{4} \le \theta \le \frac{\pi}{4}$$

51. $H = \dfrac{4347}{400,000,000} e^{369,444/(\,50t + 19,793\,)}$

(a) $t = 65° \Longrightarrow H \approx 99.79\%$

$t = 80° \Longrightarrow H \approx 60.20\%$

(b) $H' = H \cdot \left(\dfrac{-369,444(50)}{(50t + 19,793)^2}\right)t'$

At $t = 75$ and $t' = 2, H' \approx -4.7\%$.

53. (a) Using a graphing utility, you obtain

$$m(s) = -1.014s^2 + 31.685s - 214.437.$$

(b) $\dfrac{dm}{dt} = (-2.028s + 31.685)\dfrac{ds}{dt}$

(c) If $\dfrac{ds}{dt} = 1.2$, then $s = 16.5$ in 1995 $(t = 5)$.

Then $\dfrac{dm}{dt} = [-2.028(16.5) + 31.685](1.2) \approx -2.1$.

Section 2.8   Newton's Method

1. $f(x) = x^2 - 3$

$f'(x) = 2x$

$x_1 = 1.7$

n	x_n	$f(x_n)$	$f'(x_n)$	$\dfrac{f(x_n)}{f'(x_n)}$	$x_n - \dfrac{f(x_n)}{f'(x_n)}$
1	1.7000	-0.1100	3.4000	-0.0324	1.7324
2	1.7324	0.0012	3.4648	0.0003	1.7321

3. $f(x) = \sin x$

$f'(x) = \cos x$

$x_1 = 3$

n	x_n	$f(x_n)$	$f'(x_n)$	$\dfrac{f(x_n)}{f'(x_n)}$	$x_n - \dfrac{f(x_n)}{f'(x_n)}$
1	3.0000	0.1411	-0.9900	-0.1425	3.1425
2	3.1425	-0.0009	-1.0000	0.0009	3.1416

5. $f(x) = x^3 + x - 1$

$f'(x) = 3x^2 + 1$

The approximate root is $x = 0.682$.

n	x_n	$f(x_n)$	$f'(x_n)$	$\dfrac{f(x_n)}{f'(x_n)}$	$x_n - \dfrac{f(x_n)}{f'(x_n)}$
1	0.5000	−0.3750	1.7500	−0.2143	0.7143
2	0.7143	0.0787	2.5306	0.0311	0.6832
3	0.6832	0.0021	2.4002	0.0009	0.6823
4	0.6823	0.0000	2.3967	0.0000	0.6823

7. $f(x) = 3\sqrt{x - 1} - x$

$f'(x) = \dfrac{3}{2\sqrt{x - 1}} - 1$

The approximate zero is $x = 1.146$.

n	x_n	$f(x_n)$	$f'(x_n)$	$\dfrac{f(x_n)}{f'(x_n)}$	$x_n - \dfrac{f(x_n)}{f'(x_n)}$
1	1.2000	0.1416	2.3541	0.0602	1.1398
2	1.1398	−0.0180	3.0113	−0.0060	1.1458
3	1.1458	−0.0003	2.9283	−0.0001	1.1459

9. $f(x) = x - e^{-x}$

$f'(x) = 1 + e^{-x}$

$x_1 = 0.5$

n	x_n
1	0.5
2	0.566311
3	0.567143
4	0.567143

Approximate zero: 0.567

11. $f(x) = x^3 - 3.9x^2 + 4.79x - 1.881$

$f'(x) = 3x^2 - 7.8x + 4.79$

n	x_n	$f(x_n)$	$f'(x_n)$	$\dfrac{f(x_n)}{f'(x_n)}$	$x_n - \dfrac{f(x_n)}{f'(x_n)}$
1	0.5000	−0.3360	1.6400	−0.2049	0.7049
2	0.7049	−0.0921	0.7824	−0.1177	0.8226
3	0.8226	−0.0231	0.4037	−0.0573	0.8799
4	0.8799	−0.0045	0.2495	−0.0181	0.8980
5	0.8980	−0.0004	0.2048	−0.0020	0.9000
6	0.9000	0.0000	0.2000	0.0000	0.9000

Approximation of the zero of f is 0.900.

n	x_n	$f(x_n)$	$f'(x_n)$	$\dfrac{f(x_n)}{f'(x_n)}$	$x_n - \dfrac{f(x_n)}{f'(x_n)}$
1	1.1	0.0000	−0.1600	−0.0000	1.1000

Approximation of the zero of f is 1.100.

n	x_n	$f(x_n)$	$f'(x_n)$	$\dfrac{f(x_n)}{f'(x_n)}$	$x_n - \dfrac{f(x_n)}{f'(x_n)}$
1	1.9	0.0000	0.8000	0.0000	1.9000

Approximation of the zero of f is 1.900.

13. $f(x) = x + \sin(x + 1)$

$f'(x) = 1 + \cos(x + 1)$

Approximation of the zero of f is -0.489.

n	x_n	$f(x_n)$	$f'(x_n)$	$\dfrac{f(x_n)}{f'(x_n)}$	$x_n - \dfrac{f(x_n)}{f'(x_n)}$
1	-0.5000	-0.0206	1.8776	-0.0110	-0.4890
2	-0.4890	0.0000	1.8723	0.0000	-0.4890

15. $h(x) = f(x) - g(x) = 2x + 1 - \sqrt{x + 4}$

$h'(x) = 2 - \dfrac{1}{2\sqrt{x + 4}}$

Point of intersection of the graphs of f and g occurs when $x \approx 0.569$.

n	x_n	$h(x_n)$	$h'(x_n)$	$\dfrac{h(x_n)}{h'(x_n)}$	$x_n - \dfrac{h(x_n)}{h'(x_n)}$
1	0.6000	0.0552	1.7669	0.0313	0.5687
2	0.5687	-0.0001	1.7661	0.0000	0.5687

17. To approximate the x-value of the point of intersection of the graphs of $f(x) = x$ and $g(x) = \tan x$, let $x = \tan x$. Since this implies that $x - \tan x = 0$, it is necessary to find the zeros of the function $h(x) = x - \tan x$ where $h'(x) = 1 - \sec^2 x$. The iterative formula for Newton's Method has the form

n	x_n	$h(x_n)$	$h'(x_n)$	$\dfrac{h(x_n)}{h'(x_n)}$	$x_n - \dfrac{h(x_n)}{h'(x_n)}$
1	4.5000	-0.1373	-21.5048	0.0064	4.4936
2	4.4936	-0.0039	-20.2271	0.0002	4.4934

$$x_{n+1} = x_n - \frac{x_n - \tan x_n}{1 - \sec^2 x_n}.$$

The calculations are shown in the table, beginning with an initial guess of $x_n = 4.5$. Therefore, the point of intersection of the graphs of f and g occurs when $x \approx 4.493$.

19. $h(x) = \ln x + x$

$h'(x) = \dfrac{1}{x} + 1$

$x_1 = 0.5$

n	x_n
1	0.5
2	0.564382
3	0.567139
4	0.567143

Approximate intersection at $x \approx 0.567$

21. To approximate the x-value of the point of intersection of the graphs of $f(x) = \arccos x$ and $g(x) = \arctan x$, let $\arccos x = \arctan x$. Since this implies that $\arccos x - \arctan x = 0$, it is necessary to find the zeros of the function $h(x) = \arccos x - \arctan x$ where $h'(x) = -1/\sqrt{1 - x^2} - 1/(1 + x^2)$. The iterative formula for Newton's Method has the form

$$x_{n+1} = x_n - \frac{\arccos x_n - \arctan x_n}{\left(\dfrac{-1}{\sqrt{1 - x_n^2}} - \dfrac{1}{1 + x_n^2} \right)}.$$

The calculations are shown in the table, begininning with an initial guess of $x_n = 0.5$.

n	x_n	$h(x_n)$	$h'(x_n)$	$\dfrac{h(x_n)}{h'(x_n)}$	$x_n - \dfrac{h(x_n)}{h'(x_n)}$
1	0.5	0.5835	-1.9547	-0.2985	0.7985
2	0.7985	-0.0278	-2.2718	0.0122	0.7863
3	0.7863	-0.0003	-2.2365	0.0001	0.7862

Therefore, the point of intersection of the graphs of f and g occures when $x \approx 0.786$.

23. $g(x) = e^{x/10} - x$

n	x_n
1	1.0
2	1.118238
3	1.118326

Approximate fixed point: 1.12

25. Let $g(x) = f(x) - x = \cos x - x$

$g'(x) = -\sin x - 1.$

The fixed point is approximately 0.74.

n	x_n	$g(x_n)$	$g'(x_n)$	$\dfrac{g(x_n)}{g'(x_n)}$	$x_n - \dfrac{g(x_n)}{g'(x_n)}$
1	1.0000	-0.4597	-1.8415	0.2496	0.7504
2	0.7504	-0.0190	-1.6819	0.0113	0.7391
3	0.7391	0.0000	-1.6736	0.0000	0.7391

27. $f(x) = x^3 - 3x^2 + 3, \quad f'(x) = 3x^2 - 6x$

(a)

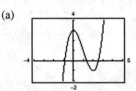

(b) $x_1 = 1$

$x_2 = x_1 - \dfrac{f(x_1)}{f'(x_1)} \approx 1.333$

Continuing, the zero is 1.347.

(c) $x_1 = \dfrac{1}{4}$

$x_2 = x_1 - \dfrac{f(x_1)}{f'(x_1)} \approx 2.405$

Continuing, the zero is 2.532.

(d)

$y = -3x + 4$

$y = -1.313x + 3.156$

The x-intercepts correspond to the values resulting from the first iteration of Newton's Method.

(e) If the initial guess x_1 is not "close to" the desired zero of the function, the x-intercept of the tangent line may approximate another zero of the function.

29. $y = 2x^3 - 6x^2 + 6x - 1 = f(x)$

$y' = 6x^2 - 12x + 6 = f'(x)$

$x_1 = 1$

$f'(x) = 0$; therefore, the method fails.

n	x_n	$f(x_n)$	$f'(x_n)$
1	1	1	0

31. $y = -x^3 + 3x^2 - x + 1 = f(x)$

$y' = -3x^2 + 6x - 1 = f'(x)$

$x_1 = 1$

Fails to converge

n	x_n	$f(x_n)$	$f'(x_n)$	$\dfrac{f(x_n)}{f'(x_n)}$	$x_n - \dfrac{f(x_n)}{f'(x_n)}$
1	1	2	2	1	0
2	0	1	-1	-1	1
3	1	2	2	1	0

33. Let $f(x) = x^2 - a$. Then $f'(x) = 2x$. Since $\sqrt{a}$ is a zero of $f(x) = 0$, we can use Newton's Method to approximate $\sqrt{a}$ as follows:

$$x_{i+1} = x_i - \frac{x_i^2 - a}{2x_i} = \frac{x_i^2 + a}{2x_i}$$

For example, if $a = 2$, and $x_1 = 1$, then we approximate $\sqrt{2}$ as follows:

$$x_1 = 1$$

$$x_2 = \frac{1^2 + 2}{2(1)} = \frac{1 + 2}{2} = 1.5000$$

$$x_3 = \frac{(1.5)^2 + 2}{2(1.5)} = \frac{4.25}{3} = 1.41667$$

$$x_4 = \frac{(1.41667)^2 + 2}{2(1.41667)} = \frac{4.00697}{2.8333} = 1.41421$$

(Note: To five decimal places, $\sqrt{2} = 1.41421$.)

35. $x_{i+1} = \dfrac{x_i^2 + 7}{2x_i}$

i	1	2	3	4	5
x_i	2.0000	2.7500	2.6477	2.6458	2.6458

$\sqrt{7} \approx 2.646$

37. $x_{i+1} = \dfrac{3x_i^4 + 6}{4x_i^3}$

i	1	2	3	4
x_i	1.5000	1.5694	1.5651	1.5651

$\sqrt[4]{6} \approx 1.565$

39. $f(x) = \dfrac{1}{x} - a = 0$

$$f'(x) = -\frac{1}{x^2}$$

$$x_{n+1} = x_n - \frac{(1/x_n) - a}{-1/x_n^2} = x_n + x_n^2\left(\frac{1}{x_n} - a\right) = x_n + x_n - x_n^2 a = 2x_n - x_n^2 a = x_n(2 - ax_n)$$

41. $f(x) = 1 + \cos x$

$f'(x) = -\sin x$

Approximation of the zero: 3.141

n	x_n	$f(x_n)$	$f'(x_n)$	$\dfrac{f(x_n)}{f'(x_n)}$	$x_n - \dfrac{f(x_n)}{f'(x_n)}$
1	3.0000	0.0100	-0.1411	-0.0709	3.0709
2	3.0709	0.0025	-0.0706	-0.0354	3.1063
3	3.1063	0.0006	-0.0353	-0.0176	3.1239
4	3.1239	0.0002	-0.0177	-0.0088	3.1327
5	3.1327	0.0000	-0.0089	-0.0044	3.1371
6	3.1371	0.0000	-0.0045	-0.0022	3.1393
7	3.1393	0.0000	-0.0023	-0.0011	3.1404
8	3.1404	0.0000	-0.0012	-0.0006	3.1410

43.
$$2,500,000 = -76x^3 + 4830x^2 - 320,000$$

$$76x^3 - 4830x^2 + 2,820,000 = 0$$

Let $f(x) = 76x^3 - 4830x^2 + 2,820,000$

$\quad f'(x) = 228x^2 - 9660x.$

From the graph, choose $x_1 = 40$.

n	x_n	$f(x_n)$	$f'(x_n)$	$\dfrac{f(x_n)}{f'(x_n)}$	$x_n - \dfrac{f(x_n)}{f'(x_n)}$
1	40.0000	−44000.0000	−21600.0000	2.0370	37.9630
2	37.9630	17157.6209	−38131.4039	−0.4500	38.4130
3	38.4130	780.0914	−34642.2263	−0.0225	38.4355
4	38.4355	2.6308	−34465.3435	−0.0001	38.4356

The zero occurs when $x \approx 38.4356$ which corresponds to $384,356.

45. False. Let $f(x) = (x^2 - 1)/(x - 1)$. $x = 1$ is a discontinuity. It is not a zero of $f(x)$. This statement would be true if $f(x) = p(x)/q(x)$ is given in **reduced** form.

47. True

49. $f(x) = \frac{1}{4}x^3 - 3x^2 + \frac{3}{4}x - 2$

$\quad f'(x) = \frac{3}{4}x^2 - 6x + \frac{3}{4}$

Let $x_1 = 12$.

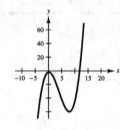

n	x_n	$f(x_n)$	$f'(x_n)$	$\dfrac{f(x_n)}{f'(x_n)}$	$x_n - \dfrac{f(x_n)}{f'(x_n)}$
1	12.0000	7.0000	36.7500	0.1905	11.8095
2	11.8095	0.2151	34.4912	0.0062	11.8033
3	11.8033	0.0015	34.4186	0.0000	11.8033

Approximation: $x \approx 11.803$

Review Exercises for Chapter 2

1. $f(x) = x^2 - 2x + 3$

$$f'(x) = \lim_{\Delta x \to 0} \frac{f(x + \Delta x) - f(x)}{\Delta x}$$

$$= \lim_{\Delta x \to 0} \frac{[(x + \Delta x)^2 - 2(x + \Delta x) + 3] - [x^2 - 2x + 3]}{\Delta x}$$

$$= \lim_{\Delta x \to 0} \frac{(x^2 + 2x(\Delta x) + (\Delta x)^2 - 2x - 2(\Delta x) + 3) - (x^2 - 2x + 3)}{\Delta x}$$

$$= \lim_{\Delta x \to 0} \frac{2x(\Delta x) + (\Delta x)^2 - 2(\Delta x)}{\Delta x} = \lim_{\Delta x \to 0} (2x + \Delta x - 2) = 2x - 2$$

3. (a)

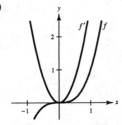

(b)

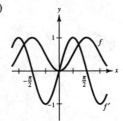

$f' > 0$ where the slopes of tangent lines to the graph of f are positive.

5. f is differentiable for all $x \neq 1$.

7. f is differentiable for $x > -2$.

9. $f(x) = x^3 - 3x^2$

$f'(x) = 3x^2 - 6x = 3x(x - 2)$

11. One method of finding the derivative of f is by rewriting the function prior to taking the derivative.

$$f(x) = \frac{2x^3 - 1}{x^2} = 2x - x^{-2}$$

$$f'(x) = 2 + 2x^{-3}$$

$$= 2\left(1 + \frac{1}{x^3}\right) = \frac{2(x^3 + 1)}{x^3}$$

A second method of finding the derivative is by using the Quotient Rule.

$$f(x) = \frac{2x^3 - 1}{x^2}$$

$$f'(x) = \frac{x^2(6x^2) - (2x^3 - 1)(2x)}{x^4}$$

$$= \frac{6x^4 - 4x^4 + 2x}{x^4}$$

$$= \frac{2x^4 + 2x}{x^4} = \frac{2(x^3 + 1)}{x^3}$$

13. $g(t) = \frac{2}{3}t^{-2}$

$$g'(t) = \frac{-4}{3}t^{-3} = \frac{-4}{3t^3}$$

15. $f(x) = (1 - x^3)^{1/2}$

$$f'(x) = \frac{1}{2}(1 - x^3)^{-1/2}(-3x^2)$$

$$= -\frac{3x^2}{2\sqrt{1 - x^3}}$$

17. $f(x) = (3x^2 + 7)(x^2 - 2x + 3)$

$f'(x) = (3x^2 + 7)(2x - 2) + (x^2 - 2x + 3)(6x)$

$\quad = 6x^3 - 6x^2 + 14x - 14 + 6x^3 - 12x^2 + 18x$

$\quad = 2(6x^3 - 9x^2 + 16x - 7)$

19. $f(x) = \left(x^2 + \frac{1}{x}\right)^5$

$$f'(x) = 5\left(x^2 + \frac{1}{x}\right)^4\left(2x - \frac{1}{x^2}\right)$$

21. $f(x) = \frac{x^2 + x - 1}{x^2 - 1}$

$$f'(x) = \frac{(x^2 - 1)(2x + 1) - (x^2 + x - 1)(2x)}{(x^2 - 1)^2}$$

$$= \frac{2x^3 + x^2 - 2x - 1 - 2x^3 - 2x^2 + 2x}{(x^2 - 1)^2}$$

$$= -\frac{x^2 + 1}{(x^2 - 1)^2}$$

23. $f(x) = (4 - 3x^2)^{-1}$

$$f'(x) = -(4 - 3x^2)^{-2}(-6x) = \frac{6x}{(4 - 3x^2)^2}$$

25. $y = 3\cos(3x + 1)$

$\dfrac{dy}{dx} = 3[-\sin(3x + 1)]\dfrac{d}{dx}[3x + 1]$

$\qquad = -3\sin(3x + 1)(3) = -9\sin(3x + 1)$

27. $y = \dfrac{1}{2}\csc 2x$

$y' = \dfrac{1}{2}(-\csc 2x \cot 2x)(2)$

$\qquad = -\csc 2x \cot 2x$

29. $y = \dfrac{x}{2} - \dfrac{\sin 2x}{4}$

$y' = \dfrac{1}{2} - \dfrac{1}{4}\cos 2x(2)$

$\qquad = \dfrac{1}{2}(1 - \cos 2x) = \sin^2 x$

31. $y = \dfrac{2}{3}\sin^{3/2} x - \dfrac{2}{7}\sin^{7/2}x$

$y' = \sin^{1/2} x \cos x - \sin^{5/2} x \cos x$

$\qquad = (\cos x)\sqrt{\sin x}(1 - \sin^2 x)$

$\qquad = (\cos^3 x)\sqrt{\sin x}$

33. $f(x) = -x\tan x$

$f'(x) = -x\sec^2 x + (\tan x)(-1)$

$\qquad = -(x\sec^2 x + \tan x)$

35. $y = \dfrac{\sin x}{x^2}$

$y' = \dfrac{(x^2)\cos x - (\sin x)(2x)}{x^4} = \dfrac{x\cos x - 2\sin x}{x^3}$

37. Since $g(t) = t^2 e^t$, begin by using the Product Rule.

$g'(t) = t^2 \dfrac{d}{dt}[e^t] + e^t \dfrac{d}{dt}[t^2] = t^2 e^t + e^t(2t) = te^t(t + 2)$

39. $g(x) = \dfrac{x^2}{e^x}$

$g'(x) = \dfrac{e^x(2x) - x^2 e^x}{e^{2x}} = \dfrac{x(2 - x)}{e^x}$

41. $g(x) = \ln\sqrt{x} = \dfrac{1}{2}\ln x$

$g'(x) = \dfrac{1}{2x}$

43. $f(x) = x\sqrt{\ln x}$

$f'(x) = \left(\dfrac{x}{2}\right)(\ln x)^{-1/2}\left(\dfrac{1}{x}\right) + \sqrt{\ln x}$

$\qquad = \dfrac{1}{2\sqrt{\ln x}} + \sqrt{\ln x} = \dfrac{1 + 2\ln x}{2\sqrt{\ln x}}$

45. $f(x) = \ln(e^{-x^2}) = -x^2$

$f'(x) = -2x$

47. $y = \dfrac{1}{b^2}[\ln(a + bx) + a(a + bx)^{-1}]$

$\dfrac{dy}{dx} = \dfrac{1}{b^2}\left[\left(\dfrac{1}{a + bx}\right)(b) + a(-1)(a + bx)^{-2}(b)\right]$

$\qquad = \dfrac{1}{b^2}\left[\dfrac{b}{a + bx} - \dfrac{ab}{(a + bx)^2}\right]$

$\qquad = \dfrac{1}{b^2}\left[\dfrac{b(a + bx) - ab}{(a + bx)^2}\right] = \dfrac{x}{(a + bx)^2}$

49. $y = -\dfrac{1}{a}\ln\left(\dfrac{a + bx}{x}\right) = -\dfrac{1}{a}[\ln(a + bx) - \ln x]$

$\dfrac{dy}{dx} = -\dfrac{1}{a}\left(\dfrac{b}{a + bx} - \dfrac{1}{x}\right) = \dfrac{1}{x(a + bx)}$

51. Begin by sketching a triangle to represent θ, "the angle whose sine is x." This yields

$$\theta = \arcsin x$$

$$y = \tan(\arcsin x) = \tan \theta = \frac{x}{\sqrt{1 - x^2}}.$$

Therefore,

$$\frac{dy}{dx} = \frac{\sqrt{1 - x^2}(1) - x(1/2)(1/\sqrt{1 - x^2})(-2x)}{1 - x^2}$$

$$= \frac{(1 - x^2) + x^2}{(1 - x^2)\sqrt{1 - x^2}} = (1 - x^2)^{-3/2}.$$

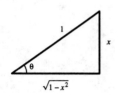

53. $y = x \operatorname{arcsec} x$

$$y' = \frac{x}{|x|\sqrt{x^2 - 1}} + \operatorname{arcsec} x$$

55. $y = x(\arcsin x)^2 - 2x + 2\sqrt{1 - x^2} \arcsin x$

$$y' = \frac{2x \arcsin x}{\sqrt{1 - x^2}} + (\arcsin x)^2 - 2 + \frac{2\sqrt{1 - x^2}}{\sqrt{1 - x^2}} - \frac{2x}{\sqrt{1 - x^2}} \arcsin x = (\arcsin x)^2$$

57. $y = x^{2x+1}$

$$\ln y = (2x + 1) \ln x$$

$$\frac{y'}{y} = \frac{2x + 1}{x} + 2 \ln x$$

$$y' = y\left(\frac{2x + 1}{x} + 2 \ln x\right) = x^{2x+1}\left(\frac{2x + 1}{x} + 2 \ln x\right)$$

59. $g(x) = \log_3(3x + 4)$

$$g'(x) = \frac{1}{\ln 3}\left(\frac{3}{3x + 4}\right)$$

61. $y = \frac{x\sqrt{x^2 + 1}}{x + 4}$

$$\ln y = \ln x + \frac{1}{2}\ln(x^2 + 1) - \ln(x + 4)$$

$$\frac{y'}{y} = \frac{1}{x} + \frac{x}{x^2 + 1} - \frac{1}{x + 4}$$

$$y' = \frac{x\sqrt{x^2 + 1}}{x + 4}\left(\frac{1}{x} + \frac{x}{x^2 + 1} - \frac{1}{x + 4}\right) = \frac{x^3 + 8x^2 + 4}{(x + 4)^2\sqrt{x^2 + 1}}$$

63. Using a symbolic differentiation utility, the first derivative of the function $f(t) = t^2(t - 1)^5$ is

$$f'(t) = t(t - 1)^4(7t - 2).$$

(Your differentiation utility may give the derivative in a different form.) The graphs of f and f' are given in the figure. The zeros of f' correspond to the points on the graph of f where the tangent line is horizontal.

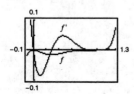

65. $g(x) = 2x(x + 1)^{-1/2}$

$$g'(x) = \frac{x + 2}{(x + 1)^{3/2}}$$

g' does not equal zero for any value of x in the domain. The graph of g has no horizontal tangent lines.

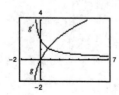

67. $y = x + (2 - x)e^{x-2}$

$y' = 1 + (1 - x)e^{x-2}$

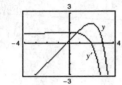

The zeros of y' correspond to the horizontal tangents of y.

69. $y = \tan\sqrt{1 - x}$

$y' = -\dfrac{\sec^2\sqrt{1 - x}}{2\sqrt{1 - x}}$

y' does not equal zero for any x in the domain. The graph has no horizontal tangent lines.

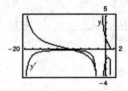

71. $f(t) = (t + 1)^{1/2}(t + 1)^{1/3} = (t + 1)^{5/6}$

$f'(t) = \dfrac{5}{6(t + 1)^{1/6}}$

f' does not equal zero for any x in the domain. The graph of f has no horizontal tangent lines.

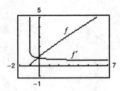

73. $f(x) = \cos\dfrac{\pi x}{2}$

$f'(x) = -\dfrac{\pi}{2}\sin\dfrac{\pi x}{2}$

$f'\left(\dfrac{2}{3}\right) = -\dfrac{\pi}{2} \cdot \dfrac{\sqrt{3}}{2} = -\dfrac{\pi\sqrt{3}}{4}$

75. $f(x) = \sqrt{x}\ln(x - 3)$

$f'(x) = \sqrt{x}\dfrac{1}{x - 3} + \ln(x - 3)\dfrac{1}{2\sqrt{x}}$

$f'(4) = 2 + 0 = 2$

77. $y = 2x^2 + \sin 2x$

$y' = 4x + 2\cos 2x$

$y'' = 4 - 4\sin 2x$

79. $f(x) = \cot x$

$f'(x) = -\csc^2 x$

$f''(x) = -2\csc x(-\csc x \cot x)$

$\qquad = 2\csc^2 x \cot x$

81. $g(x) = x^3 \ln x$

$g'(x) = 3x^2 \ln x + x^3\left(\dfrac{1}{x}\right) = 3x^2 \ln x + x^2$

$g''(x) = 6x \ln x + 3x^2\left(\dfrac{1}{x}\right) + 2x = 5x + 6x \ln x$

83. $f(t) = \dfrac{t}{(1 - t)^2}$

$f'(t) = \dfrac{t + 1}{(1 - t)^3}$

$f''(t) = \dfrac{2(t + 2)}{(1 - t)^4}$

85. $g(x) = x \tan x$

$g'(x) = x \sec^2 x + \tan x$

$g''(x) = 2 \sec^2 x(x \tan x + 1)$

87.
$$x^2 + 3xy + y^3 = 10$$

$$\frac{d}{dx}[x^2 + 3xy + y^3] = \frac{d}{dx}[10]$$

$$\frac{d}{dx}[x^2] + \frac{d}{dx}[3xy] + \frac{d}{dx}[y^3] = \frac{d}{dx}[10]$$

$$2x + 3x\frac{dy}{dx} + 3y + 3y^2\frac{dy}{dx} = 0$$

$$(3x + 3y^2)\frac{dy}{dx} = -2x - 3y$$

$$\frac{dy}{dx} = \frac{-(2x + 3y)}{3(x + y^2)}$$

89.
$$\cos x^2 = xe^y$$

$$-\sin x^2(2x) = xe^y y' + e^y$$

$$xe^y y' = -e^y - 2x\sin x^2$$

$$y' = -\frac{e^y + 2x\sin x^2}{xe^y} = -\frac{1}{x} - 2e^{-y}\sin x^2$$

91.
$$x\sin y = y\cos x$$

$$(x\cos y)y' + \sin y = -y\sin x + y'\cos x$$

$$y'(x\cos y - \cos x) = -y\sin x - \sin y$$

$$y' = \frac{y\sin x + \sin y}{\cos x - x\cos y}$$

93.
$$y\sqrt{x} - x\sqrt{y} = 16$$

$$y\left(\frac{1}{2}x^{-1/2}\right) + x^{1/2}y' - x\left(\frac{1}{2}y^{-1/2}y'\right) - y^{1/2} = 0$$

$$\left(\sqrt{x} - \frac{x}{2\sqrt{y}}\right)y' = \sqrt{y} - \frac{y}{2\sqrt{x}}$$

$$\frac{2\sqrt{xy} - x}{2\sqrt{y}}y' = \frac{2\sqrt{xy} - y}{2\sqrt{x}}$$

$$y' = \frac{2\sqrt{xy} - y}{2\sqrt{x}} \cdot \frac{2\sqrt{y}}{2\sqrt{xy} - x} = \frac{2y\sqrt{x} - y\sqrt{y}}{2x\sqrt{y} - x\sqrt{x}}$$

95.
$$y\ln x + y^2 = 0$$

$$y'\ln x + \frac{y}{x} + 2yy' = 0$$

$$y'(\ln x + 2y) = -\frac{y}{x}$$

$$y' = \frac{-y}{x(\ln x + 2y)}$$

97. $y = (x + 3)^3$

$$y' = 3(x + 3)^2$$

At $(-2, 1)$: $y' = 3$

Tangent line: $y - 1 = 3(x + 2)$

$$3x - y + 7 = 0$$

Normal line: $y - 1 = -\frac{1}{3}(x + 2)$

$$x + 3y - 1 = 0$$

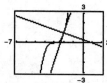

99. $x^2 + y^2 = 20$

$2x + 2yy' = 0$

$$y' = -\frac{x}{y}$$

At $(2, 4)$: $y' = -\frac{1}{2}$

Tangent line: $y - 4 = -\frac{1}{2}(x - 2)$

$$x + 2y - 10 = 0$$

Normal line: $y - 4 = 2(x - 2)$

$$2x - y = 0$$

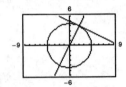

101. $y = \sqrt[3]{(x - 2)^2} = (x - 2)^{2/3}$

$$y' = \left(\frac{2}{3}\right)(x - 2)^{-1/3} = \frac{2}{3(x - 2)^{1/3}}$$

Thus the slope of the tangent line at $(3, 1)$ is

$$y' = \frac{2}{3(3 - 2)^{1/3}} = \frac{2}{3},$$

and the equation of the tangent line at $(3, 1)$ is

$$y - 1 = \frac{2}{3}(x - 3)$$

$$3y - 3 = 2x - 6$$

$$-2x + 3y + 3 = 0$$

Since the slope of the tangent line is 2/3, the slope of the normal line is $-3/2$ and the equation of the normal line is

$$y - 1 = -\frac{3}{2}(x - 3)$$

$$2y - 2 = -3x + 9$$

$$3x + 2y - 11 = 0.$$

The graphs are shown in the figure.

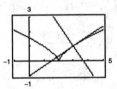

103. $f(x) = \frac{1}{3}x^3 + x^2 - x - 1$

$f'(x) = x^2 + 2x - 1$

(a) $x^2 + 2x - 1 = -1$

$x(x + 2) = 0$

$(0, -1), \left(-2, \frac{7}{3}\right)$

(b) $x^2 + 2x - 1 = 2$

$(x + 3)(x - 1) = 0$

$(-3, 2), \left(1, -\frac{2}{3}\right)$

(c) $x^2 + 2x - 1 = 0$

$(x + 1)^2 = 2$

$x = -1 \pm \sqrt{2}$

$$\left(-1 + \sqrt{2}, \frac{2(1 - 2\sqrt{2})}{3}\right),$$

$$\left(-1 - \sqrt{2}, \frac{2(1 + 2\sqrt{2})}{3}\right)$$

105. $f(x) = 4 - |x - 2|$

(a) Continuous at $x = 2$

(b) Not differentiable at $x = 2$ because of the sharp turn in the graph.

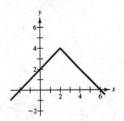

107. Begin by finding the first and second derivatives of the function.

$$y = 2 \sin x + 3 \cos x$$

$$y' = 2 \cos x - 3 \sin x$$

$$y'' = -2 \sin x - 3 \cos x$$

$$y'' + y = (-2 \sin x - 3 \cos x) + (2 \sin x + 3 \cos x)$$

$$= 0$$

109. $y = 2(\ln x) + 3$

$$y' = \frac{2}{x}$$

$$y'' = -\frac{2}{x^2}$$

$$xy'' + y' = x\left(-\frac{2}{x^2}\right) + \frac{2}{x} = 0$$

111. $f(x) = x^3 - 3x - 1$

From the graph you can see that $f(x)$ has three real zeros.

$$f'(x) = 3x^2 - 3$$

n	x_n	$f(x_n)$	$f'(x_n)$	$\dfrac{f(x_n)}{f'(x_n)}$	$x_n - \dfrac{f(x_n)}{f'(x_n)}$
1	-1.5000	0.1250	3.7500	0.0333	-1.5333
2	-1.5333	-0.0049	4.0530	-0.0012	-1.5321

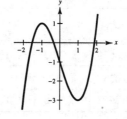

n	x_n	$f(x_n)$	$f'(x_n)$	$\dfrac{f(x_n)}{f'(x_n)}$	$x_n - \dfrac{f(x_n)}{f'(x_n)}$
1	-0.5000	0.3750	-2.2500	-0.1667	-0.3333
2	-0.3333	-0.0371	-2.6667	0.0139	-0.3472
3	-0.3472	-0.0003	-2.6384	0.0001	-0.3473

n	x_n	$f(x_n)$	$f'(x_n)$	$\dfrac{f(x_n)}{f'(x_n)}$	$x_n - \dfrac{f(x_n)}{f'(x_n)}$
1	-1.9000	0.1590	7.8300	0.0203	1.8797
2	1.8797	0.0024	7.5998	0.0003	1.8794

The three real zeros of $f(x)$ are $x \approx -1.532$, $x \approx -0.347$, and $x \approx 1.879$.

113. $f(x) = xe^x - 4$, $f'(x) = e^x(x + 1)$

From the graph, we can see that $f(x)$ has one real zero near $x = 1$. The iterative formula for Newton's Method has the form

$$x_{n+1} = x_n - \frac{x_n e^{x_n} - 4}{e^{x_n}(x_n + 1)}.$$

n	x_n	$f(x_n)$	$f'(x_n)$	$\dfrac{f(x_n)}{f'(x_n)}$	$x_n - \dfrac{f(x_n)}{f'(x_n)}$
1	1	-1.2817	5.4366	-0.2358	1.2358
2	1.2358	0.2525	7.6937	0.0328	1.2030
3	1.2030	0.0061	7.3362	0.0008	1.2022
4	1.2022	0.0002	7.3277	0.0000	1.2022

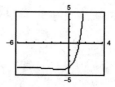

Therefore, $x \approx 1.202$.

115. Find the zeros of $f(x) = x^4 - x - 3$.

$$f'(x) = 4x^3 - 1$$

From the graph you can see that $f(x)$ has two real zeros.

f changes sign in $[-2, -1]$.

n	x_n	$f(x_n)$	$f'(x_n)$	$\dfrac{f(x_n)}{f'(x_n)}$	$x_n - \dfrac{f(x_n)}{f'(x_n)}$
1	-1.2000	0.2736	-7.9120	-0.0346	-1.1654
2	-1.1654	0.0100	-7.3312	-0.0014	-1.1640

On the interval $[-2, -1]$: $x \approx -1.164$.

f changes sign in $[1, 2]$.

n	x_n	$f(x_n)$	$f'(x_n)$	$\dfrac{f(x_n)}{f'(x_n)}$	$x_n - \dfrac{f(x_n)}{f'(x_n)}$
1	1.5000	0.5625	12.5000	0.0450	1.4550
2	1.4550	0.0268	11.3211	0.0024	1.4526
3	1.4526	-0.0003	11.2602	0.0000	1.4526

On the interval $[1, 2]$: $x \approx 1.453$.

117.
$$f(3) = 8 \implies f^{-1}(8) = 3$$
$$f'(x) = 3(x - 1)^2, \quad f'(3) = 12$$
$$(f^{-1})'(8) = \frac{1}{f'(3)} = \frac{1}{12}$$

119.
$$f\left(\frac{\pi}{2}\right) = 0 \implies f^{-1}(0) = \frac{\pi}{2}$$
$$f'(x) = -\sin x, \quad f'\left(\frac{\pi}{2}\right) = -1$$
$$(f^{-1})'(0) = \frac{1}{f'\left(\dfrac{\pi}{2}\right)} = -1$$

121. (a) $y = x^a$

$y' = ax^{a-1}$

(b) $y = a^x$

$y' = (\ln a)a^x$

(c) $y = x^x$

$\ln y = x \ln x$

$\dfrac{1}{y}y' = x \cdot \dfrac{1}{x} + (1) \ln x$

$y' = y(1 + \ln x)$

$y' = x^x(1 + \ln x)$

(d) $y = a^a$

$y' = 0$

123. $T = 700(t^2 + 4t + 10)^{-1}$

$$T' = \frac{-1400(t + 2)}{(t^2 + 4t + 10)^2}$$

(a) When $t = 1$,

$$T' = \frac{-1400(1 + 2)}{(1 + 4 + 10)^2} \approx -18.667 \text{ deg/hr.}$$

(b) When $t = 3$,

$$T' = \frac{-1400(3 + 2)}{(9 + 12 + 10)^2} \approx -7.284 \text{ deg/hr.}$$

(c) When $t = 5$,

$$T' = \frac{-1400(5 + 2)}{(25 + 30 + 10)^2} \approx -3.240 \text{ deg/hr.}$$

(d) When $t = 10$,

$$T' = \frac{-1400(10 + 2)}{(100 + 40 + 10)^2} \approx -0.747 \text{ deg/hr.}$$

125. $F = 200\sqrt{T}$

$$F'(t) = \frac{100}{\sqrt{T}}$$

(a) When $T = 4$, $F'(4) = 50$ vibrations/sec/lb.

(b) When $T = 9$, $F'(9) = 33\frac{1}{3}$ vibrations/sec/lb.

127. We assume that the stone is thrown from an initial height of $s_0 = 0$. Thus the position equation is

$$s = -16t^2 + v_0 t.$$

The maximum value of s occurs when $ds/dt = 0$ and thus we have

$$\frac{ds}{dt} = -32t + v_0 = 0$$

$$-32t = -v_0$$

$$t = \frac{v_0}{32}.$$

This means that the maximum height is

$$s = -16\left(\frac{v_0}{32}\right)^2 + v_0\left(\frac{v_0}{32}\right) = \frac{v_0^2}{64}.$$

If s is to attain a value of 49, we must have

$$\frac{v_0^2}{64} = 49$$

$$v_0^2 = 3136$$

$$v_0 = 56 \text{ ft/sec.}$$

129. (a)

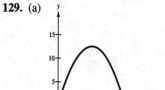

Total horizontal distance: 50

(b) $0 = x - 0.02x^2$

$0 = x\left(x - \dfrac{x}{50}\right)$ implies $x = 50$.

(c) Ball reaches maximum height when $x = 25$.

(d) $y = x - 0.02x^2$

$y' = 1 - 0.04x$

$y'(0) = 1$

$y'(10) = 0.6$

$y'(25) = 0$

$y'(30) = -0.2$

$y'(50) = -1$

(e) $y'(25) = 0$

131. $y = \sqrt{x}$

$L^2 = x^2 + y^2$

$\dfrac{dy}{dt} = 2$ units/sec

$L^2 = y^4 + y^2$

$2L\dfrac{dL}{dt} = (4y^3 + 2y)\dfrac{dy}{dt}$

$\dfrac{dL}{dt} = \dfrac{4y^3 + 2y}{2L}\dfrac{dy}{dt} = \dfrac{4y^3 + 2y}{L} = \dfrac{(4x + 2)\sqrt{x}}{L}$

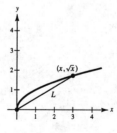

(a) When $x = \dfrac{1}{2}$, $L = \sqrt{\left(\dfrac{1}{2}\right)^2 + \left(\dfrac{1}{\sqrt{2}}\right)^2} = \dfrac{\sqrt{3}}{2}$ and $\dfrac{dL}{dt} = \dfrac{(2 + 2)(1/\sqrt{2})}{\sqrt{3}/2} = \dfrac{8}{\sqrt{6}} = \dfrac{4\sqrt{6}}{3}$ units/sec.

(b) When $x = 1$, $L = \sqrt{(1)^2 + (1)^2} = \sqrt{2}$ and $\dfrac{dL}{dt} = \dfrac{(4 + 2)(1)}{\sqrt{2}} = 3\sqrt{2}$ units/sec.

(c) When $x = 4$, $L = \sqrt{(4)^2 + (2)^2} = 2\sqrt{5}$ and $\dfrac{dL}{dt} = \dfrac{(16 + 2)(2)}{2\sqrt{5}} = \dfrac{18}{\sqrt{5}} = \dfrac{18\sqrt{5}}{5}$ units/sec.

133. The figure is a cross section of the trough when the water is a depth of h meters.

$$\frac{s}{h} = \frac{1/2}{2}$$

$$s = \frac{1}{4}h$$

A = area of cross section of water at depth h

$$= 2h + 2\left(\frac{1}{2}sh\right)$$

$$= 2h + \left(\frac{1}{4}h\right)h = 2h + \frac{1}{4}h^2$$

V = volume of water in trough at depth h

$$= 5A = 5\left(2h + \frac{1}{4}h^2\right)$$

Differentiating with respect to t, yields

$$\frac{dV}{dt} = 5\left(2 + \frac{1}{2}h\right)\frac{dh}{dt} = \frac{5}{2}(4 + h)\frac{dh}{dt}$$

$$\frac{2(dV/dt)}{5(4 + h)} = \frac{dh}{dt}$$

Therefore, when $dV/dt = 1$ and $h = 1$, we have

$$\frac{dh}{dt} = \frac{2(1)}{5(4 + 1)} = \frac{2}{25} \text{ meters per minute}$$

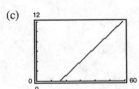

135. $s(t) = 60 - 4.9t^2$

$$s'(t) = -9.8t$$

$$s = 35 = 60 - 4.9t^2$$

$$4.9t^2 = 25$$

$$t = \frac{5}{\sqrt{4.9}}$$

$$\tan 30° = \frac{1}{\sqrt{3}} = \frac{s(t)}{x(t)}$$

$$x(t) = \sqrt{3}\,s(t)$$

$$\frac{dx}{dt} = \sqrt{3}\frac{ds}{dt} = \sqrt{3}(-9.8)\frac{5}{\sqrt{4.9}}$$

$$\approx -38.34 \text{ m/sec}$$

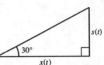

137. (a) $y = 0.14x^2 - 4.43x + 58.4$

(b)

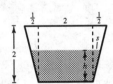

(c)

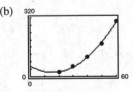

(d) If $x = 65$, $y \approx 362$ feet.

(e) As the speed increases, the stopping distance increases at an increasing rate.

139. (a) You get an error message because $\ln h$ does not exist for $h = 0$.

(b) Reversing the data, you obtain
$$h = 0.8627 - 6.4474 \ln p.$$

(c)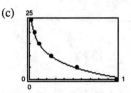

(d) If $p = 0.75$, $h \approx 2.72$ km.

(e) If $h = 13$ km, $p \approx 0.15$ atmosphere.

(f) $h = 0.8627 - 6.4474 \ln p$

$$1 = -6.4474 \frac{1}{p} \frac{dp}{dh} \quad \text{(implicit differentiation)}$$

$$\frac{dp}{dh} = \frac{p}{-6.4474}$$

For $h = 5$, $p = 0.55$ and $dp/dh = -0.0853$ atmos/km.

For $h = 20$, $p = 0.06$ and $dp/dh = -0.00931$ atmos/km.

As the altitude increases, the rate of change of pressure decreases.

141. $y = 10 \ln\!\left(\dfrac{10 + \sqrt{100 - x^2}}{x}\right) - \sqrt{100 - x^2} = 10\left[\ln\!\left(10 + \sqrt{100 - x^2}\right) - \ln x\right] - \sqrt{100 - x^2}$

(a)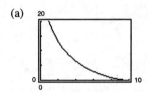

(b) $\dfrac{dy}{dx} = 10\left[\dfrac{-x}{\sqrt{100 - x^2}\left(10 + \sqrt{100 - x^2}\right)} - \dfrac{1}{x}\right] + \dfrac{x}{\sqrt{100 - x^2}}$

$\qquad = \dfrac{x}{\sqrt{100 - x^2}}\left[\dfrac{-10}{10 + \sqrt{100 - x^2}}\right] - \dfrac{10}{x} + \dfrac{x}{\sqrt{100 - x^2}}$

$\qquad = \dfrac{x}{\sqrt{100 - x^2}}\left[\dfrac{-10}{10 + \sqrt{100 - x^2}} + 1\right] - \dfrac{10}{x}$

$\qquad = \dfrac{x}{\sqrt{100 - x^2}}\left[\dfrac{\sqrt{100 - x^2}}{10 + \sqrt{100 - x^2}}\right] - \dfrac{10}{x}$

$\qquad = \dfrac{x}{10 + \sqrt{100 - x^2}} - \dfrac{10}{x}$

$\qquad = \dfrac{x\left(10 - \sqrt{100 - x^2}\right)}{x^2} - \dfrac{10}{x} = -\dfrac{\sqrt{100 - x^2}}{x}$

When $x = 5$, $dy/dx = -\sqrt{3}$. When $x = 9$, $dy/dx = -\sqrt{19}/9$.

(c) $\displaystyle\lim_{x \to 10^-} \frac{dy}{dx} = 0$

CHAPTER 3
Applications of Differentiation

C H A P T E R 3
Applications of Differentiation

Section 3.1   Extrema on an Interval
Solutions to Exercises

1. $f(x) = \dfrac{x^2}{x^2 + 4}$

$f'(x) = \dfrac{(x^2 + 4)(2x) - (x^2)(2x)}{(x^2 + 4)^2} = \dfrac{8x}{(x^2 + 4)^2}$

$f'(0) = 0$

3. $f(x) = x + \dfrac{32}{x^2}$

$f'(x) = 1 - \dfrac{64}{x^3}$

$f'(4) = 0$

5. $f(x) = (x + 2)^{2/3}$

$f'(x) = \dfrac{2}{3}(x + 2)^{-1/3}$

$f'(-2)$ is undefined.

7. Let f be defined at c. If $f'(c) = 0$ or if f' is undefined at c, then c is called a critical number of f. Begin by finding f'.

$f(x) = x^2(x - 3) = x^3 - 3x^2$

$f'(x) = 3x^2 - 6x = 3x(x - 2)$

Since $f'(0) = 0$ and $f'(2) = 0$, $x = 0$ and $x = 2$ are critical numbers. f' is defined for all real numbers x.

9. $g(t) = t\sqrt{4 - t}$

$g'(t) = t\left[\dfrac{1}{2}(4 - t)^{-1/2}(-1)\right] + (4 - t)^{1/2}$

$= \dfrac{1}{2}(4 - t)^{-1/2}[-t + 2(4 - t)] = \dfrac{8 - 3t}{2\sqrt{4 - t}}$

Critical numbers: $t = 4, t = \dfrac{8}{3}$

11. $h(x) = \sin^2 x + \cos x, 0 \le x < 2\pi$

$h'(x) = 2\sin x \cos x - \sin x = \sin x(2\cos x - 1)$

Critical numbers: $x = 0, x = \dfrac{\pi}{3}, x = \pi, x = \dfrac{5\pi}{3}$

13. $f(x) = x^2 \log_2(x^2 + 1) = x^2 \dfrac{\ln(x^2 + 1)}{\ln 2}$

$f'(x) = 2x\dfrac{\ln(x^2 + 1)}{\ln 2} + x^2\dfrac{2x}{\ln 2(x^2 + 1)}$

$= \dfrac{2x}{\ln 2}\left[\ln(x^2 + 1) + \dfrac{x^2}{x^2 + 1}\right] = 0 \Rightarrow x = 0$

Critical number: $x = 0$

15. $f(x) = 2(3 - x), [-1, 2]$

$f'(x) = -2 \Rightarrow$ No critical numbers

Left endpoint: $(-1, 8)$ Maximum

Right endpoint: $(2, 2)$ Minimum

17. $f(x) = -x^2 + 3x$

$f'(x) = -2x + 3 = 0$

Therefore, $x = \dfrac{3}{2}$ is a critical number in $[0, 3]$. We determine the extrema of f by evaluating f at the critical number and at the endpoints of $[0, 3]$.

$\quad f(0) = -0^2 + 3(0) = 0 \qquad$ Minimum

$\quad f\left(\dfrac{3}{2}\right) = -\left(\dfrac{3}{2}\right)^2 + 3\left(\dfrac{3}{2}\right) = \dfrac{9}{4} \qquad$ Maximum

$\quad f(3) = -3^2 + 3(3) = 0 \qquad$ Minimum

19. $f(x) = x^3 - 3x^2, [-1, 3]$

$f'(x) = 3x^2 - 6x = 3x(x - 2)$

Left endpoint: $(-1, -4)$ Minimum

Critical number: $(0, 0)$ Maximum

Critical number: $(2, -4)$ Minimum

Right endpoint: $(3, 0)$ Maximum

21. $f(x) = 3x^{2/3} - 2x$

$f(x) = 2x^{-1/3} - 2$

$= 2\left(\dfrac{1 - \sqrt[3]{x}}{\sqrt[3]{x}}\right)$

Therefore, $x = 1$ and $x = 0$ are critical numbers in the interval $[-1, 1]$. $[f'(0)$ is undefined.$]$

We determine the extrema of f by evaluating f at the critical numbers and at the endpoints of the interval $[-1, 1]$.

$f(-1) = 3(-1)^{2/3} - 2(-1) = 5$ Maximum

$f(0) = 3(0)^{2/3} - 2(0) = 0$ Minimum

$f(1) = 3(1)^{2/3} - 2(1) = 1$

23. $h(t) = 4 - |t - 4|, [1, 6]$

From the graph of the function on the interval $[1, 6]$ you can determine the following.

Left endpoint: $(1, 1)$ Minimum

Critical number: $(4, 4)$ Maximum

Right endpoint: $(6, 2)$

25. $h(s) = \dfrac{1}{s - 2}, [0, 1]$

$h'(s) = \dfrac{-1}{(s - 2)^2}$

Left endpoint: $\left(0, -\dfrac{1}{2}\right)$ Maximum

Right endpoint: $(1, -1)$ Minimum

27. $y = e^x \sin x$

$\dfrac{dy}{dx} = e^x \cos x + e^x \sin x = e^x(\cos x + \sin x)$

Find any critical numbers in the interval $[0, \pi]$ by solving the following equation.

$$\dfrac{dy}{dx} = 0$$

$$\cos x + \sin x = 0$$

$$1 + \tan x = 0$$

$$\tan x = -1 \Longrightarrow x = \dfrac{3\pi}{4}$$

The extrema of y are determined by evaluating y at the critical number and at the endpoints of the interval $[0, \pi]$.

$y(0) = e^0 \sin 0 = 0$ Minimum

$y\left(\dfrac{3\pi}{4}\right) = e^{3\pi/4} \sin \dfrac{3\pi}{4} \approx 7.46$ Maximum

$y(\pi) = e^\pi \sin \pi = 0$ Minimum

29. $f(x) = \cos \pi x$

$f'(x) = -\sin \pi x \dfrac{d}{dx}[\pi x] = -\pi \sin \pi x$

Therefore, $x = 0$ is a critical number in the interval $[0, 1/6]$, and the extrema are at endpoints of the interval.

$f(0) = \cos 0 = 1$ Maximum

$f\left(\dfrac{1}{6}\right) = \cos \dfrac{\pi}{6} = \dfrac{\sqrt{3}}{2}$ Minimum

31. $f(x) = \tan x$

f is continuous on $[0, \pi/4]$ but not on $[0, \pi]$.

$\lim\limits_{x \to \pi/2^-} \tan x = \infty$

33. (a) Yes

(b) No

35. (a) Since f is decreasing in the interval (a, c) and increasing in the interval (c, b), the only possible minimum in the interval (a, b) would occur at $x = c$. However, $f(c)$ is greater than $f(x)$ for x near c. Thus, there is no minimum.

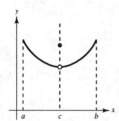

(b) Since $f(c) \leq f(x)$ for all x in (a, b), $f(c)$ is a minimum.

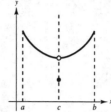

37. (a) Minimum: $(0, -3)$

   Maximum: $(2, 1)$

   (b) Minimum: $(0, -3)$

   (c) Maximum: $(2, 1)$

   (d) No extrema

39. $f(x) = \begin{cases} 2x + 2, & 0 \leq x \leq 1 \\ 4x^2, & 1 < x \leq 3 \end{cases}$

At $x = 1$, the derivative from the left is

$$\lim_{x \to 1^-} \frac{f(x) - f(1)}{x - 1} = \lim_{x \to 1^-} \frac{(2x + 2) - 4}{x - 1}$$

$$= \lim_{x \to 1^-} \frac{2(x - 1)}{x - 1}$$

$$= \lim_{x \to 1^-} 2 = 2.$$

At $x = 1$, the derivative from the right is

$$\lim_{x \to 1^+} \frac{f(x) - f(1)}{x - 1} = \lim_{x \to 1^+} \frac{4x^2 - 4}{x - 1}$$

$$= \lim_{x \to 1^+} \frac{4(x + 1)(x - 1)}{x - 1}$$

$$= \lim_{x \to 1^+} [4(x + 1)] = 8.$$

Since the one-sided limits are unequal, the derivative does not exist at $x = 1$, and $x = 1$ is a critical number. We determine the extrema of f by evaluating f at the critical number and at the endpoints of $[0, 3]$.

$f(0) = 2(0) + 2 = 2$ Minimum

$f(1) = 2(1) + 2 = 4$

$f(3) = 4(3^2) = 36$ Maximum

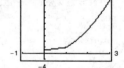

These results agree with the graph shown in the figure.

41. $f(x) = \dfrac{3}{x - 1}, (1, 4]$

Right endpoint: $(4, 1)$ Minimum

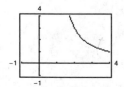

43. (a)

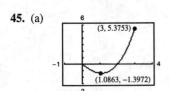

Maximum: $(1, 4.7)$

Minimum: $(0.4398, -1.0613)$

(b)
$$f(x) = 3.2x^5 + 5x^3 - 3.5x, [0, 1]$$
$$f'(x) = 16x^4 + 15x^2 - 3.5$$
$$16x^4 + 15x^2 - 3.5 = 0$$
$$x^2 = \frac{-15 \pm \sqrt{(15)^2 - 4(16)(-3.5)}}{2(16)}$$
$$= \frac{-15 \pm \sqrt{449}}{32}$$
$$x = \sqrt{\frac{-15 + \sqrt{449}}{32}} \approx 0.4398$$
$$f(0) = 0$$
$$f(1) = 4.7 \quad \text{Maximum}$$
$$f\left(\sqrt{\frac{-15 + \sqrt{449}}{32}}\right) \approx -1.0613$$

Minimum: $(0.4398, -1.0613)$

45. (a)

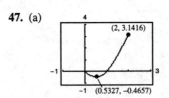

(b) $(1.0863, -1.3972)$ minimum

47. (a)

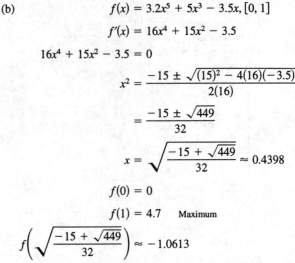

(b) $(0.5327, -0.4657)$ minimum

49. To find the maximum value of $|f''(x)|$ in $[0, 2]$, select the maximum of $|f''(0)|, |f''(2)|,$ and $|f''(c)|,$ where c is any critical number of $f''(x)$ [i.e., $f'''(c) = 0$ or $f'''(c)$ does not exist.] Using a symbolic differentiation utility yields the following derivatives.

$$f(x) = \sqrt{1 + x^3}$$

$$f'(x) = \frac{3x^2}{2\sqrt{1 + x^3}}$$

$$f''(x) = \frac{3x(x^3 + 4)}{4(1 + x^3)^{3/2}}$$

$$f'''(x) = \frac{-3(x^6 + 20x^3 - 8)}{8(1 + x^3)^{5/2}}$$

Therefore, $f'''(x) = 0$ when $x^6 + 20x^3 - 8 = 0$. Solving this equation using the symbolic differentiation utility yields the critical numbers

$$x = \begin{cases} \sqrt[3]{-10 + 6\sqrt{3}} & \approx 0.732 \\ \sqrt[3]{-10 - 6\sqrt{3}} & \approx -2.732 \end{cases}$$

The critical number in the interval $[0, 2]$ is $\sqrt[3]{-10 + 6\sqrt{3}}$. Evaluating the absolute value of the second derivative at the critical number and the endpoints of the interval, yields

$$\left| f''\left(\sqrt[3]{-10 + 6\sqrt{3}}\right) \right| \approx 1.468$$

$$|f''(0)| = 0$$

$$|f''(2)| = \frac{2}{3}.$$

The maximum value of $|f''(x)|$ in $[0, 2]$ is $\left| f''\left(\sqrt[3]{-10 + 6\sqrt{3}}\right) \right| \approx |f''(0.732)| \approx 1.468.$

51. $f(x) = e^{-x^2/2}$, $[0, 1]$

$f'(x) = -xe^{-x^2/2}$

$f''(x) = -x(-xe^{-x^2/2}) - e^{-x^2/2}$

$\quad = e^{-x^2/2}(x^2 - 1)$

$f'''(x) = e^{-x^2/2}(2x) + (x^2 - 1)(-xe^{-x^2/2})$

$\quad = xe^{-x^2/2}(3 - x^2)$

Left endpoint: $f''(0) = -1$

Right endpoint: $f''(1) = 0$

Maximum value of $|f''(x)|$ is 1 on $[0, 1]$.

53. $f(x) = (x + 1)^{2/3}$, $[0, 2]$

$f'(x) = \frac{2}{3}(x + 1)^{-1/3}$

$f''(x) = -\frac{2}{9}(x + 1)^{-4/3}$

$f'''(x) = \frac{8}{27}(x + 1)^{-7/3}$

$f^{(4)}(x) = -\frac{56}{81}(x + 1)^{-10/3}$

$f^{(5)}(x) = \frac{560}{243}(x + 1)^{-13/3}$

$|f^{(4)}(0)| = \frac{56}{81}$ is the maximum value.

55. Since $V = 12$ and $R = 0.5$, you have

$$P = 12I - \frac{1}{2}I^2$$

$$\frac{dP}{dI} = 12 - I.$$

Therefore, $I = 12$ is a critical number on the interval $[0, 15]$. We determine the maximum of P by evaluating P at the critical number and at the endpoints of the interval $[0, 15]$. Since

$$P(0) = 12(0) - \frac{1}{2}(0)^2 = 0$$

$$P(12) = 12(12) - \frac{1}{2}(12)^2 = 72$$

$$P(15) = 12(15) - \frac{1}{2}(15)^2 = 67.5,$$

it follows that the power P is maximum when $I = 12$.

57. $x = \frac{v^2 \sin 2\theta}{32}$, $\frac{\pi}{4} \leq \theta \leq \frac{3\pi}{4}$

$\frac{d\theta}{dt}$ is constant.

$\frac{dx}{dt} = \frac{dx}{d\theta}\frac{d\theta}{dt}$ (by the Chain Rule)

$\quad = \frac{v^2 \cos 2\theta}{16}\frac{d\theta}{dt}$

In the interval $[\pi/4, 3\pi/4]$, $\theta = \pi/4, 3\pi/4$ indicate minimums for dx/dt and $\theta = \pi/2$ indicates a maximum for dx/dt. This implies that the sprinkler waters longest when $\theta = \pi/4$ and $3\pi/4$. Thus, the lawn farthest from the spinkler gets the most water.

59. $\quad S = 6hs + \frac{3s^2}{2}\left(\frac{\sqrt{3} - \cos\theta}{\sin\theta}\right)$, $\frac{\pi}{6} \leq \theta \leq \frac{\pi}{2}$

$\frac{dS}{d\theta} = \frac{3s^2}{2}(-\sqrt{3}\csc\theta\cot\theta + \csc^2\theta)$

$\quad = \frac{3s^2}{2}\csc\theta(-\sqrt{3}\cot\theta + \csc\theta) = 0$

$\csc\theta = \sqrt{3}\cot\theta$

$\sec\theta = \sqrt{3}$

$\theta = \text{arcsec}\sqrt{3} \approx 0.9553$ radians

$S\left(\frac{\pi}{6}\right) = 6hs + \frac{3s^2}{2}(\sqrt{3})$

$S\left(\frac{\pi}{2}\right) = 6hs + \frac{3s^2}{2}(\sqrt{3})$

$S(\text{arcsec}\sqrt{3}) = 6hs + \frac{3s^2}{2}(\sqrt{2})$

S is minimum when $\theta = \text{arcsec}\sqrt{3} \approx 0.9553$ radians.

61. True. See Exercise 17.

63. True.

65. $f(x) = [\![x]\!]$

The derivative of f is undefined at every integer and is zero at any noninteger real number. All real numbers are critical numbers.

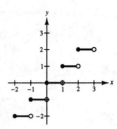

Section 3.2 Rolle's Theorem and the Mean Value Theorem

1. Rolle's Theorem does not apply to $f(x) = 1 - |x - 1|$ over $[0, 2]$ since f is not differentiable at $x = 1$.

3. $f(x) = x^2 - 2x, [0, 2]$

$f(0) = f(2) = 0$

f is continuous on $[0, 2]$. f is differentiable on $(0, 2)$. Rolle's Theorem applies.

$$f'(x) = 2x - 2$$

$$2x - 2 = 0 \Rightarrow x = 1$$

c value: 1

5. Since $f(x) = (x - 1)(x - 2)(x - 3)$ is a polynomial, it is continuous and differentiable for all x. Also, the zeros of f are $x = 1$, $x = 2$, and $x = 3$. Thus, Rolle's Theorem can be applied on the intervals $[1, 2]$ and $[2, 3]$. Setting $f'(x) = 0$ yields

$$f'(x) = 3x^2 - 12x + 11 = 0$$

$$x = \frac{12 \pm \sqrt{144 - 132}}{6} = \frac{12 \pm 2\sqrt{3}}{6} = \frac{6 \pm \sqrt{3}}{3}.$$

Therefore, in the interval $[1, 2]$,

$$f'\left(\frac{6 - \sqrt{3}}{3}\right) = 0 \quad \text{where} \quad c = \frac{6 - \sqrt{3}}{3} \approx 1.423.$$

and in the interval $[2, 3]$,

$$f'\left(\frac{6 + \sqrt{3}}{3}\right) = 0 \quad \text{where} \quad c = \frac{6 + \sqrt{3}}{3} \approx 2.577.$$

7. We first observe that $f(x) = x^{2/3} - 1$ is continuous on the interval $[-8, 8]$. The zeros of f are found by solving the following equation.

$$f(x) = x^{2/3} - 1 = 0$$

$$x^{2/3} = 1$$

$$x^2 = 1 \quad \text{or} \quad x = \pm 1$$

Since

$$f'(x) = \frac{2}{3x^{1/3}},$$

we observe that $f'(0)$ is undefined and therefore, f is not differentiable at $x = 0$. Thus, Rolle's Theorem cannot be applied to this function on the specified interval.

9. $f(x) = \dfrac{x^2 - 2x - 3}{x + 2}, [-1, 3]$

$f(-1) = f(3) = 0$

f is continuous on $[-1, 3]$. (**Note:** The discontinuity, $x = -2$, is not in the interval.) f is differentiable on $(-1, 3)$. Rolle's Theorem applies.

$$f'(x) = \frac{(x + 2)(2x - 2) - (x^2 - 2x - 3)(1)}{(x + 2)^2} = 0$$

$$\frac{x^2 + 4x - 1}{(x + 2)^2} = 0$$

$$x = \frac{-4 \pm 2\sqrt{5}}{2} = -2 \pm \sqrt{5}$$

c value: $-2 + \sqrt{5}$

11. We first observe that $f(x) = (x^2 - 2x)e^x$ is continuous and differentiable for all x. Also, the zeros of f are $x = 0$ and $x = 2$. Thus, Rolle's Theorem applies in the interval $[0, 2]$.

$$f'(x) = (x^2 - 2)e^x$$

Setting $f'(x) = 0$ yields $x = \pm\sqrt{2}$. Therefore, in the interval $[0, 2]$, we have $f'(\sqrt{2}) = 0$ and $c = \sqrt{2} \approx 1.414$.

13. $f(x) = \sin x,\ [0, 2\pi]$

$$f(0) = f(2\pi) = 0$$

f is continuous on $[0, 2\pi]$. f is differentiable on $(0, 2\pi)$. Rolle's Theorem applies.

$$f'(x) = \cos x$$

c values: $\dfrac{\pi}{2}, \dfrac{3\pi}{2}$

15. $f(x) = \sin 2x,\ \left[\dfrac{\pi}{6}, \dfrac{\pi}{3}\right]$

$$f\left(\frac{\pi}{6}\right) = f\left(\frac{\pi}{3}\right) = \frac{\sqrt{3}}{2}$$

f is continuous on $[\pi/6, \pi/3]$. f is differentiable on $(\pi/6, \pi/3)$. Rolle's Theorem applies.

$$f'(x) = 2\cos 2x$$

$$2\cos 2x = 0$$

$$x = \frac{\pi}{4}$$

c value: $\dfrac{\pi}{4}$

17. $f(x) = \tan x,\ [0, \pi]$

$$f(0) = f(\pi) = 0$$

f is not continuous on $[0, \pi]$ since $f(\pi/2)$ does not exist. Rolle's Theorem does not apply.

19. $f(x) = |x| - 1,\ [-1, 1]$

$$f(-1) = f(1) = 0$$

f is continuous on $[-1, 1]$. f is not differentiable on $(-1, 1)$ since $f'(0)$ does not exist. Rolle's Theorem does not apply.

21. f is continuous on $[-(1/4), (1/4)]$ and differentiable on $(-(1/4), (1/4))$. Therefore, Rolle's Theorem applies. Setting $f'(x) = 0$ yields the following.

$$f(x) = 4x - \tan \pi x$$

$$f'(x) = 4 - \pi \sec^2 \pi x$$

$$4 - \pi \sec^2 \pi x = 0$$

$$\sec^2 \pi x = \frac{4}{\pi}$$

$$\sec \pi x = \pm\frac{2}{\sqrt{\pi}}$$

$$x = \pm\frac{1}{\pi} \operatorname{arcsec} \frac{2}{\sqrt{\pi}}$$

$$= \pm\frac{1}{\pi} \arccos \frac{\sqrt{\pi}}{2} \approx \pm 0.1533 \text{ radian}$$

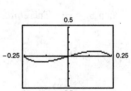

Therefore, $c \approx \pm 0.1433$ radian.

23. $f(x) = 2 + \arcsin(x^2 - 1)$, $[-1, 1]$

$f(-1) = f(1) = 2$

$$f'(x) = \frac{2x}{\sqrt{1 - (x^2 - 1)^2}} = \frac{2x}{\sqrt{2x^2 + x^4}}$$

$f'(0)$ does not exist. Rolle's Theorem does not apply.

25. $f(t) = -16t^2 + 48t + 32$

(a) $f(1) = f(2) = 64$

(b) $v = f'(t)$ must be 0 at some time in $[1, 2]$.

$$f'(t) = -32t + 48 = 0$$

$$t = \tfrac{3}{2} \text{ seconds}$$

27. No. Let $f(x) = x^2$ on $[-1, 2]$.

$$f'(x) = 2x$$

$f'(0) = 0$ and zero is in the interval $(-1, 2)$ but $f(-1) \neq f(2)$.

29. (a) f is continuous on $[-10, 4]$ and changes sign, $(f(-8) > 0, f(3) < 0)$. By the Intermediate Value Theorem, there exists at least one value of x in $[-10, 4]$ satisfying $f(x) = 0$.

(b) There exist real numbers a and b such that $-10 < a < b < 4$ and $f(a) = f(b) = 2$. Therefore, by Rolle's Theorem there exists at least one number c in $(-10, 4)$ such that $f'(c) = 0$. This is called a critical number.

(c)

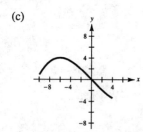

(d)

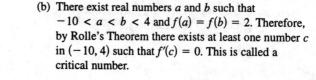

(e) No, f' did not have to be continuous on $[-10, 4]$.

31. $f(x) = x^2$ is continuous on $[-2, 1]$ and differentiable on $(-2, 1)$.

$$\frac{f(1) - f(-2)}{1 - (-2)} = \frac{1 - 4}{3} = -1$$

$f'(x) = 2x = -1$ when $x = -\dfrac{1}{2}$. Therefore,

$$c = -\frac{1}{2}.$$

33. Since $f(x) = x^{2/3}$ is continuous on $[0, 1]$ and differentiable on $(0, 1)$, the Mean Value Theorem can be applied.

$$f(x) = x^{2/3}$$

(1) $$f'(x) = \frac{2}{3}x^{-1/3} = \frac{2}{3\sqrt[3]{x}}$$

(2) $$\frac{f(1) - f(0)}{1 - 0} = \frac{1 - 0}{1 - 0} = 1$$

Equating the right-hand members of the equations (1) and (2) yields

$$\frac{2}{3\sqrt[3]{x}} = 1$$

$$\frac{2}{3} = \sqrt[3]{x}$$

$$\frac{8}{27} = x.$$

Therefore, $c = 8/27$.

35. $f(x) = \sqrt{x-2}$ is continuous on $[2, 6]$ and differentiable on $(2, 6)$.

$$\frac{f(6) - f(2)}{6 - 2} = \frac{2 - 0}{4} = \frac{1}{2}$$

$$f'(x) = \frac{1}{2\sqrt{x-2}} = \frac{1}{2}$$

$$\sqrt{x-2} = 1$$

$$c = 3$$

37. $f(x) = \sin x$ is continuous on $[0, \pi]$ and differentiable on $(0, \pi)$.

$$\frac{f(\pi) - f(0)}{\pi - 0} = \frac{0 - 0}{\pi} = 0$$

$$f'(x) = \cos x = 0$$

$$c = \frac{\pi}{2}$$

39. $f(x) = x \log_2 x = x\dfrac{\ln x}{\ln 2}$

f is continuous on $[1, 2]$ and differentiable on $(1, 2)$.

$$\frac{f(2) - f(1)}{2 - 1} = \frac{2 - 0}{2 - 1} = 2$$

$$f'(x) = x\frac{1}{x \ln 2} + \frac{\ln x}{\ln 2} = 2$$

$$1 + \ln x = 2 \ln 2 = \ln 4$$

$$xe = 4$$

$$x = \frac{4}{e} \Rightarrow c = \frac{4}{e}$$

41. (a) The graph of $f(x) = x/(x + 1)$ on the interval $\left[-\frac{1}{2}, 2\right]$ is shown in the figure.

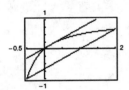

(b) The slope of the required secant line is

$$\frac{f(2) - f(-1/2)}{2 - (-1/2)} = \frac{(2/3) - (-1)}{5/2} = \frac{2}{3}.$$

The secant line passes through the point $\left(-\frac{1}{2}, -1\right)$. The equation of the secant line is

$$y - (-1) = \frac{2}{3}\left[x - \left(-\frac{1}{2}\right)\right]$$

$$y = \frac{2}{3}x - \frac{2}{3}.$$

The graph of the secant line is shown on the graph in part (a).

(c) To find the equation of the tangent line, we need to find the point of tangency where the slope of the tangent line equals $\frac{2}{3}$, the slope of the secant line. We begin by finding the derivative.

$$f(x) = \frac{x}{x + 1}$$

$$f'(x) = \frac{(x + 1)(1) - x(1)}{(x + 1)^2} = \frac{1}{(x + 1)^2}$$

$$\frac{1}{(x + 1)^2} = \frac{2}{3}$$

$$x + 1 = \pm\sqrt{\frac{3}{2}} \Rightarrow x = -1 \pm \frac{\sqrt{6}}{2}$$

Therefore, on the interval $\left[-\frac{1}{2}, 2\right]$, the value of c in the Mean Value Theorem is $c = -1 + \left(\sqrt{6}/2\right)$.

$$f\left(-1 + \frac{\sqrt{6}}{2}\right) = \frac{-1 + \left(\sqrt{6}/2\right)}{\left(-1 + \sqrt{6}/2\right) + 1} = 1 - \frac{\sqrt{6}}{3}$$

Therefore, the point of tangency is

$$\left(-1 + \frac{\sqrt{6}}{2}, 1 - \frac{\sqrt{6}}{3}\right)$$

and the equation of tangent line is

$$y - \left(1 - \frac{\sqrt{6}}{3}\right) = \frac{2}{3}\left[x - \left(-1 + \frac{\sqrt{6}}{2}\right)\right]$$

$$y = \frac{2}{3}x + \frac{1}{3}\left(5 - 2\sqrt{6}\right).$$

The graph of the tangent line is shown on the graph of part (a).

43. $f(x) = \sqrt{x}$, $[1, 9]$

$(1, 1), (9, 3)$

$m = \dfrac{3 - 1}{9 - 1} = \dfrac{1}{4}$

(a)

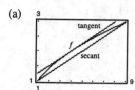

(b) Secant line: $y - 1 = \dfrac{1}{4}(x - 1)$

$y = \dfrac{1}{4}x + \dfrac{3}{4}$

$0 = x - 4y + 3$

(c) $f'(x) = \dfrac{1}{2\sqrt{x}}$

$\dfrac{f(9) - f(1)}{9 - 1} = \dfrac{1}{4}$

$\dfrac{1}{2\sqrt{c}} = \dfrac{1}{4}$

$\sqrt{c} = 2$

$c = 4$

$(c, f(c)) = (4, 2)$

$m = f'(4) = \dfrac{1}{4}$

Tangent line: $y - 2 = \dfrac{1}{4}(x - 4)$

$y = \dfrac{1}{4}x + 1$

$0 = x - 4y + 4$

45. $f(x) = 2e^{x/4} \cos \dfrac{\pi x}{4}$, $0 \le x \le 2$

$f(0) = 2$, $f(2) = 0$

$m = \dfrac{0 - 2}{2 - 0} = -1$

(a)

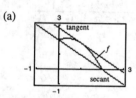

(c) Tangent line: $y - 1.8 = -1(x - 1.0161)$

$y = -x + 2.8161$

(b) Secant line: $y - 2 = -1(x - 0)$

$y = -x + 2$

$f'(x) = 2\left(\dfrac{1}{4}e^{x/4} \cos \dfrac{\pi x}{4}\right) + 2e^{x/4}\left(-\sin \dfrac{\pi x}{4}\right)\dfrac{\pi}{4}$

$= e^{x/4}\left[\dfrac{1}{2} \cos \dfrac{\pi x}{4} - \dfrac{\pi}{2} \sin \dfrac{\pi x}{4}\right]$

$f'(c) = -1 \Rightarrow c \approx 1.0161$, $f(c) \approx 1.8$

47. $f(x) = \dfrac{1}{x - 3}$, $[0, 6]$

f has a discontinuity at $x = 3$.

49. f is continuous on $[-5, 5]$ and does not satisfy the conditions of the Mean Value Theorem.

$\Rightarrow f$ is not differentiable on $(-5, 5)$.

Example: $f(x) = |x|$

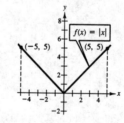

51. (a) The position function is $s(t) = -4.9t^2 + 500$. The average velocity during the first three seconds is

$$\frac{s(3) - s(0)}{3 - 0} = \frac{455.9 - 500}{3} = -\frac{44.1}{3} = -14.7.$$

(b) The instantaneous velocity of the object is given by $s'(t) = -9.8t$. We must find the time t in the interval $[0, 3]$ such that $s'(t) = -14.7$.

$$s'(t) = -14.7$$
$$-9.8t = -14.7 \implies t = 1.5$$

The instantaneous velocity equals the average velocity over the interval $[0, 3]$ when $t = 1.5$ seconds.

53. False. $f(x) = 1/x$ has a discontinuity at $x = 0$.

55. True. A polynomial is continuous and differentiable everywhere.

57. The polynomial $f(x) = x^{2n+1} + ax + b$ is continuous and differentiable for all x. Therefore, by Rolle's Theorem, if $f(x) = 0$ for two distinct values of x, there must be at least one value of x such that $f'(x) = 0$. However,

$$f(x) = x^{2n+1} + ax + b$$
$$f'(x) = (2n + 1)x^{2n} + a = 0$$
$$(x^n)^2 = -\frac{a}{2n + 1}$$

(positive number) = (negative number).

Therefore, $f'(x) = 0$ has no solution and consequently $f(x) = 0$ cannot have two real zeros.

59. If $p(x) = Ax^2 + Bx + C$, then

$$p'(x) = 2Ax + B = \frac{f(b) - f(a)}{b - a} = \frac{(Ab^2 + Bb + C) - (Aa^2 + Ba + C)}{b - a}$$
$$= \frac{A(b^2 - a^2) + B(b - a)}{b - a}$$
$$= \frac{(b - a)[A(b + a) + B]}{b - a}$$
$$= A(b + a) + B.$$

Thus, $2Ax = A(b + a)$ and $x = (b + a)/2$ which is the midpoint of $[a, b]$.

61. $f(x) = \frac{1}{2}\cos x$ is differentiable on $(-\infty, \infty)$.

$$f'(x) = -\frac{1}{2}\sin x$$
$$-\frac{1}{2} \le f'(x) \le \frac{1}{2} \implies f'(x) < 1 \text{ for all real numbers.}$$

Thus, from Exercise 60, f has, at most, one fixed point $(x \approx 0.4502)$.

Section 3.3   Increasing and Decreasing Functions and the First Derivative Test

1. $f(x) = x^2 - 6x + 8$

Increasing on: $(3, \infty)$

Decreasing on: $(-\infty, 3)$

3. $y = \dfrac{x^3}{4} - 3x$

Increasing on: $(-\infty, -2), (2, \infty)$

Decreasing on: $(-2, 2)$

5. $f(x) = \dfrac{1}{x^2}$

Increasing on: $(-\infty, 0)$

Decreasing on: $(0, \infty)$

7. $f(x) = -2x^2 + 4x + 3$

$f'(x) = -4x + 4 = 0$

Critical number: $x = 1$

Test intervals:	$-\infty < x < 1$	$1 < x < \infty$
Sign of $f'(x)$:	$f' > 0$	$f' < 0$
Conclusion:	Increasing	Decreasing

Increasing on: $(-\infty, 1)$

Decreasing on: $(1, \infty)$

Relative maximum: $(1, 5)$

9. $f(x) = x^2 - 6x$

$f'(x) = 2x - 6 = 0$

Critical number: $x = 3$

Test intervals:	$-\infty < x < 3$	$3 < x < \infty$
Sign of $f'(x)$:	$f' < 0$	$f' > 0$
Conclusion:	Decreasing	Increasing

Increasing on: $(3, \infty)$

Decreasing on: $(-\infty, 3)$

Relative minimum: $(3, -9)$

11. $f(x) = 2x^3 + 3x^2 - 12x$

$f'(x) = 6x^2 + 6x - 12 = 6(x + 2)(x - 1)$

Therefore, $f'(x) = 0$ when $x = -2$ or $x = 1$. Since f is a polynomial, it is differentiable for all x and the only critical numbers are $x = -2$ and $x = 1$.

Interval	$-\infty < x < -2$	$-2 < x < 1$	$1 < x < \infty$
Test value	$x = -3$	$x = 0$	$x = 2$
Sign of $f'(x)$	$f'(-3) > 0$	$f'(0) < 0$	$f'(2) > 0$
Conclusion	f is increasing	f is decreasing	f is increasing

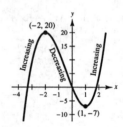

When $x = -2$, we have $f(-2) = 2(-2)^3 + 3(-2)^2 - 12(-2) = 20$. When $x = 1$, we have $f(1) = 2 + 3 - 12 = -7$. Therefore, it follows that $(-2, 20)$ is a relative maximum and $(1, -7)$ is a relative minimum.

13. $f(x) = \dfrac{x^5 - 5x}{5}$

$f'(x) = x^4 - 1$

Test intervals:	$-\infty < x < -1$	$-1 < x < 1$	$1 < x < \infty$
Sign of $f'(x)$:	$f' > 0$	$f' < 0$	$f' > 0$
Conclusion:	Increasing	Decreasing	Increasing

Critical numbers: $x = -1, 1$

Increasing on: $(-\infty, -1), (1, \infty)$

Decreasing on: $(-1, 1)$

Relative maximum: $\left(-1, \dfrac{4}{5}\right)$

Relative minimum: $\left(1, -\dfrac{4}{5}\right)$

15. $f(x) = x^{1/3} + 1$

$f'(x) = \left(\dfrac{1}{3}\right)x^{-2/3} = \dfrac{1}{3x^{2/3}}$

Since f is continuous for all x and differentiable for all x other than $x = 0$, the only critical number is $x = 0$. ($f'(0)$ is undefined.) We also observe that $f'(x) > 0$ for all x not equal to zero. Therefore, it follows that f is increasing for all x and there are no relative extrema.

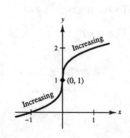

17. $f(x) = 5 - |x - 5|$

$$f'(x) = -\frac{x-5}{|x-5|} = \begin{cases} 1, & x < 5 \\ -1, & x > 5 \end{cases}$$

Critical number: $x = 5$

Test intervals:	$-\infty < x < 5$	$5 < x < \infty$
Sign of $f'(x)$:	$f' > 0$	$f' < 0$
Conclusion:	Increasing	Decreasing

Increasing on: $(-\infty, 5)$

Decreasing on: $(5, \infty)$

Relative maximum: $(5, 5)$

19. $f(x) = \dfrac{x^2}{x^2 - 9}$

$$f'(x) = \frac{(x^2 - 9)(2x) - (x^2)(2x)}{(x^2 - 9)^2} = \frac{-18x}{(x^2 - 9)^2}$$

Critical number: $x = 0$

Discontinuities: $x = -3, 3$

Test intervals:	$-\infty < x < -3$	$-3 < x < 0$	$0 < x < 3$	$3 < x < \infty$
Sign of $f'(x)$:	$f' > 0$	$f' > 0$	$f' < 0$	$f' < 0$
Conclusion:	Increasing	Increasing	Decreasing	Decreasing

Increasing on: $(-\infty, -3), (-3, 0)$

Decreasing on: $(0, 3), (3, \infty)$

Relative maximum: $(0, 0)$

21. $f(x) = x^3 - 6x^2 + 15$

$f'(x) = 3x^2 - 12x = 3x(x - 4) = 0$

Critical numbers: $x = 0, 4$

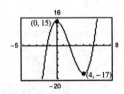

Test intervals:	$-\infty < x < 0$	$0 < x < 4$	$4 < x < \infty$
Sign of $f'(x)$:	$f' > 0$	$f' < 0$	$f' > 0$
Conclusion:	Increasing	Decreasing	Increasing

Increasing on: $(-\infty, 0), (4, \infty)$

Decreasing on: $(0, 4)$

Relative maximum: $(0, 15)$

Relative minimum: $(4, -17)$

23. $f(x) = (x - 1)^{2/3}$

$$f'(x) = \frac{2}{3(x - 1)^{1/3}}$$

Critical number: $x = 1$

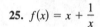

Test intervals:	$-\infty < x < 1$	$1 < x < \infty$
Sign of $f'(x)$:	$f' < 0$	$f' > 0$
Conclusion:	Decreasing	Increasing

Increasing on: $(1, \infty)$

Decreasing on: $(-\infty, 1)$

Relative minimum: $(1, 0)$

25. $f(x) = x + \dfrac{1}{x}$

$$f'(x) = 1 - \frac{1}{x^2} = \frac{x^2 - 1}{x^2}$$

Critical numbers: $x = -1, 1$

Discontinuity: $x = 0$

Test intervals:	$-\infty < x < -1$	$-1 < x < 0$	$0 < x < 1$	$1 < x < \infty$
Sign of $f'(x)$:	$f' > 0$	$f' < 0$	$f' < 0$	$f' > 0$
Conclusion:	Increasing	Decreasing	Decreasing	Increasing

Increasing on: $(-\infty, -1), (1, \infty)$

Decreasing on: $(-1, 0), (0, 1)$

Relative maximum: $(-1, -2)$

Relative minimum: $(1, 2)$

27. The function f is continuous for all x other than $x = -1$. The graph of f has a vertical asymptote at $x = -1$.

$$f(x) = \frac{x^2 - 2x + 1}{x + 1}$$

$$f'(x) = \frac{(x + 1)(2x - 2) - (x^2 - 2x + 1)(1)}{(x + 1)^2} = \frac{(x + 1)(2)(x - 1) - (x - 1)^2}{(x + 1)^2}$$

$$= \frac{(x - 1)(2x + 2 - x + 1)}{(x + 1)^2} = \frac{(x - 1)(x + 3)}{(x + 1)^2}$$

Since f is differentiable for all x other than $x = -1$, the only critical numbers are $x = 1$ and $x = -3$.

Interval	$-\infty < x < -3$	$-3 < x < -1$	$-1 < x < 1$	$1 < x \, \infty$
Test value	$x = -4$	$x = -2$	$x = 0$	$x = 2$
Sign of $f'(x)$	$f'(-4) > 0$	$f'(-2) < 0$	$f'(0) < 0$	$f'(2) > 0$
Conclusion	f is increasing	f is decreasing	f is decreasing	f is increasing

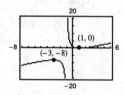

When $x = -3$, we have $f(-3) = (9 + 6 + 1)/(-2) = -8$, and when $x = 1$, we have $f(1) = (1 - 2 + 1)/2 = 0$. Therefore, $(-3, -8)$ is a relative maximum and $(1, 0)$ is a relative minimum. The figure is the graph of f produced by a graphing utility.

29. $f(x) = (3 - x)e^{x-3}$

$f'(x) = (3 - x)e^{x-3} + e^{x-3}(-1) = (2 - x)e^{x-3}$

Since f is differentiable for all x, the only critical number is $x = 2$.

Interval:	$-\infty < x < 2$	$2 < x < \infty$
Test value:	$x = 0$	$x = 3$
Sign of $f'(x)$:	$f'(0) = 2e^{-3} > 0$	$f'(3) = -1 < 0$
Conclusion:	Increasing	Decreasing

When $x = 2$, you have $f(2) = e^{-1}$. Therefore, $(2, e^{-1})$ is a relative maximum. The figure is the graph of f produced by a graphing utility.

31. $f(x) = 4(x - \arcsin x), \quad -1 \le x \le 1$

$f'(x) = 4 - \dfrac{4}{\sqrt{1 - x^2}}$

Critical number: $x = 0$

Test intervals:	$-1 \le x < 0$	$0 < x \le 1$
Sign of $f'(x)$:	$f' < 0$	$f' < 0$
Conclusion:	Decreasing	Decreasing

Decreasing on: $[-1, 1]$

No relative extrema

(Absolute maximum at $x = -1$, absolute minimum at $x = 1$)

33. $f(x) = x - \log_4 x = x - \dfrac{\ln x}{\ln 4}$

$f'(x) = 1 - \dfrac{1}{x \ln 4} = 0 \Rightarrow x \ln 4 = 1 \Rightarrow x = \dfrac{1}{\ln 4} = \dfrac{1}{2 \ln 2}$

Critical number: $x = \dfrac{1}{\ln 4}$

Test intervals:	$0 < x < \dfrac{1}{\ln 4}$	$\dfrac{1}{\ln 4} < x < \infty$
Sign of $f'(x)$:	$f' < 0$	$f' > 0$
Conclusion:	Decreasing	Increasing

Increasing on: $\left(\dfrac{1}{\ln 4}, \infty \right)$

Decreasing on: $\left(0, \dfrac{1}{\ln 4} \right)$

Relative minimum: $\left(\dfrac{1}{\ln 4}, \dfrac{1}{\ln 4} - \log_4\!\left(\dfrac{1}{\ln 4} \right) \right)$

35. $f(x) = \dfrac{x}{2} + \cos x$

$f'(x) = \dfrac{1}{2} - \sin x$

Hence, $f'(x) = 0$ when $x = \pi/6$ or $x = 5\pi/6$. Since f is continuous and differentiable for all x, the only critical numbers are $x = \pi/6$ and $5\pi/6$.

Interval	$0 < x < \pi/6$	$\pi/6 < x < 5\pi/6$	$5\pi/6 < x < 2\pi$
Test value	$x = \pi/12$	$x = \pi/2$	$x = \pi$
Sign of $f'(x)$	$f'(\pi/12) > 0$	$f'(\pi/2) < 0$	$f'(\pi) > 0$
Conclusion	f is increasing	f is decreasing	f is increasing

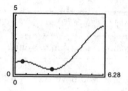

We conclude that a relative maximum occurs at $\left(\dfrac{\pi}{6}, \dfrac{\pi + 6\sqrt{3}}{12}\right)$ and a relative minimum at $\left(\dfrac{5\pi}{6}, \dfrac{5\pi - 6\sqrt{3}}{12}\right)$. The figure is the graph of f produced by a graphing utility.

37. $f(x) = \sin^2 x + \sin x, \, 0 < x < 2\pi$

$f'(x) = 2 \sin x \cos x + \cos x = \cos x (2 \sin x + 1) = 0$

Critical numbers: $x = \dfrac{\pi}{2}, \dfrac{7\pi}{6}, \dfrac{3\pi}{2}, \dfrac{11\pi}{6}$

Test intervals:	$0 < x < \dfrac{\pi}{2}$	$\dfrac{\pi}{2} < x < \dfrac{7\pi}{6}$	$\dfrac{7\pi}{6} < x < \dfrac{3\pi}{2}$	$\dfrac{3\pi}{2} < x < \dfrac{11\pi}{6}$	$\dfrac{11\pi}{6} < x < 2\pi$
Sign of $f'(x)$:	$f' > 0$	$f' < 0$	$f' > 0$	$f' < 0$	$f' > 0$
Conclusion:	Increasing	Decreasing	Increasing	Decreasing	Increasing

Increasing on: $\left(0, \dfrac{\pi}{2}\right), \left(\dfrac{7\pi}{6}, \dfrac{3\pi}{2}\right), \left(\dfrac{11\pi}{6}, 2\pi\right)$

Decreasing on: $\left(\dfrac{\pi}{2}, \dfrac{7\pi}{6}\right), \left(\dfrac{3\pi}{2}, \dfrac{11\pi}{6}\right)$

Relative minima: $\left(\dfrac{7\pi}{6}, -\dfrac{1}{4}\right), \left(\dfrac{11\pi}{6}, -\dfrac{1}{4}\right)$

Relative maxima: $\left(\dfrac{\pi}{2}, 2\right), \left(\dfrac{3\pi}{2}, 0\right)$

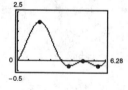

39. $f(x) = 2x\sqrt{9 - x^2}, \, [-3, 3]$

(a) $f'(x) = \dfrac{2(9 - 2x^2)}{\sqrt{9 - x^2}}$

(b)

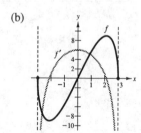

(c) $\dfrac{2(9 - 2x^2)}{\sqrt{9 - x^2}} = 0$

Critical numbers: $x = \pm\dfrac{3}{\sqrt{2}} = \pm\dfrac{3\sqrt{2}}{2}$

(d) Intervals:

$\left(-3, -\dfrac{3\sqrt{2}}{2}\right)$	$\left(-\dfrac{3\sqrt{2}}{2}, \dfrac{3\sqrt{2}}{2}\right)$	$\left(\dfrac{3\sqrt{2}}{2}, 3\right)$
$f'(x) < 0$	$f'(x) > 0$	$f'(x) < 0$
Decreasing	Increasing	Decreasing

f is increasing when f' is positive and decreasing when f' is negative.

41. (a) $f(t) = t^2 \sin t$

$f'(t) = t^2 \cos t + 2t \sin t = t(t \cos t + 2 \sin t)$

(b) The graphs of f and f' are shown in the figure.

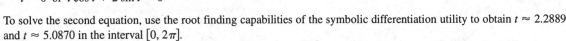

(c) To find the critical numbers, solve the equation $f'(t) = 0$ on the interval $[0, 2\pi]$.

$t(t \cos t + 2 \sin t) = 0$

$t = 0$ or $t \cos t + 2 \sin t = 0$

To solve the second equation, use the root finding capabilities of the symbolic differentiation utility to obtain $t \approx 2.2889$ and $t \approx 5.0870$ in the interval $[0, 2\pi]$.

Interval	$0 < t < 2.2889$	$2.2889 < t < 5.0870$	$5.0870 < t < 2\pi$
Test value	$t = 1$	$t = 3$	$t = 6$
Sign of $f'(x)$	$f'(1) > 0$	$f'(3) < 0$	$f'(6) > 0$
Conclusion	f is increasing	f is decreasing	f is increasing

f is increasing when f' is positive and decreasing when f' is negative.

43. (a) $f(x) = \dfrac{1}{2}(x^2 - \ln x), \quad (0, 3]$

$f'(x) = \dfrac{2x^2 - 1}{2x}$

(c) $f'(x) = 0 \Rightarrow x = \dfrac{1}{\sqrt{2}} = \dfrac{\sqrt{2}}{2}$

(d) $f' > 0$ on $\left(\dfrac{\sqrt{2}}{2}, 3\right]$; $f' < 0$ on $\left(0, \dfrac{\sqrt{2}}{2}\right)$

(b)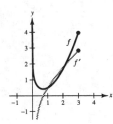

In Exercises 45–49, $f'(x) > 0$ on $(-\infty, -4)$, $f'(x) < 0$ on $(-4, 6)$ and $f'(x) > 0$ on $(6, \infty)$.

45. $g(x) = f(x) + 5$

$g'(x) = f'(x)$

$g'(0) = f'(0) < 0$

47. $g(x) = -f(x)$

$g'(x) = -f'(x)$

$g'(-6) = -f'(-6) < 0$

49. $g(x) = f(x - 10)$

$g'(x) = f'(x - 10)$

$g'(0) = f'(-10) > 0$

51. The graph of f is decreasing in the interval $(-\infty, 2)$, and therefore, f' is negative in this interval. The graph of f is increasing in the interval $(2, \infty)$, and therefore, f' is positive in this interval. The graph of f has a horizontal tangent at $x = 2$, and therefore $f'(2) = 0$. Using this information, we can sketch a possible graph of f' as shown in the figure.

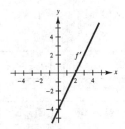

53. f is a 4th degree polynomial $\Rightarrow f'$ is a cubic polynomial.

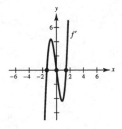

55. $f'(x) = \begin{cases} > 0, & x < 4 \Rightarrow f \text{ is increasing on } (-\infty, 4). \\ \text{undefined}, & x = 4 \\ < 0, & x > 4 \Rightarrow f \text{ is decreasing on } (4, \infty). \end{cases}$

Two possibilities for $f(x)$ are given below.

(a)

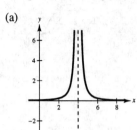

(b)

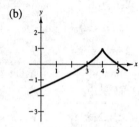

57. The critical numbers are in intervals $(-0.50, -0.25)$ and $(0.25, 0.50)$ since the sign of f' changes in these intervals. f is decreasing on approximately $(-1, -0.40)$, $(0.48, 1)$, and increasing on $(-0.40, 0.48)$.

Relative minimum when $x \approx -0.40$.

Relative maximum when $x \approx 0.48$.

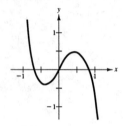

59. $f(x) = x, g(x) = \sin x, 0 < x < \pi$

(a)

x	0.5	1	1.5	2	2.5	3
$f(x)$	0.5	1	1.5	2	2.5	3
$g(x)$	0.479	0.841	0.997	0.909	0.598	0.141

$f(x)$ seems greater than $g(x)$ on $(0, \pi)$.

(b)

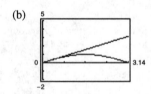

$x > \sin x$ on $(0, \pi)$

(c) Let $h(x) = f(x) - g(x) = x - \sin x$

$h'(x) = 1 - \cos x > 0$ on $(0, \pi)$.

Therefore, $h(x)$ is increasing on $(0, \pi)$. Since $h(0) = 0$, $h(x) > 0$ on $(0, \pi)$. Thus,

$$x - \sin x > 0$$
$$x > \sin x$$
$$f(x) > g(x) \text{ on } (0, \pi).$$

61. $v = k(R - r)r^2 = k(Rr^2 - r^3)$

$\dfrac{dv}{dr} = k(2Rr - 3r^2) = kr(2R - 3r)$

Therefore, $dv/dr = 0$ when $r = 0$ or $r = \frac{2}{3}R$. Since v is continuous and differentiable for all r, the only critical numbers are $r = 0$ and $r = 2R/3$. We conclude that the velocity v is maximum when $r = (2R)/3$.

Interval	$-\infty < r < 0$	$0 < r < \frac{2}{3}R$	$\frac{2}{3}R < r < \infty$
Test value	$r = -R$	$r = \frac{R}{3}$	$r = \frac{4R}{3}$
Sign of $v'(r)$	$v'(-R) < 0$	$v'\left(\frac{R}{3}\right) > 0$	$v'\left(\frac{4R}{3}\right) < 0$
Conclusion	v is decreasing	v is increasing	v is decreasing

63. $P = \dfrac{vR_1R_2}{(R_1 + R_2)^2}$, v and R_1 are constant.

$$\frac{dP}{dR_2} = \frac{(R_1 + R_2)^2(vR_1) - vR_1R_2[2(R_1 + R_2)(1)]}{(R_1 + R_2)^4} = \frac{vR_1(R_1 - R_2)}{(R_1 + R_2)^3} = 0 \Rightarrow R_2 = R_1$$

Maximum when $R_1 = R_2$.

65. (a) Using a graphing utility, you obtain

$$B = -0.1538t^4 + 3.5379t^3 - 19.7537t^2 + 42.3906t + 352.8234.$$

(c) The maximum of the model is $B = 951.5$ at $t = 12.58$.

(b)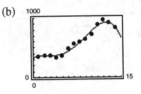

67. (a) Since there are two relative extrema, there are two critical numbers. This implies that the minimum degree of f' is 2. Therefore, the minimum degree of f is 3 and $f(x) = a_3x^3 + a_2x^2 + a_1x + a_0$.

(c) Using a graphing utility to solve the system in part (b) yields $a_3 = -\frac{1}{2}$ and $a_2 = \frac{3}{2}$. The required polynomial function is
$$f(x) = -\tfrac{1}{2}x^3 + \tfrac{3}{2}x^2.$$

(d) The graph of f is shown in the figure.

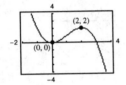

(b) Since $(0, 0)$ and $(2, 2)$ are solution points, we have the following.

$$f(0) = 0 = a_3(0^3) + a_2(0^2) + a_1(0) + a_0$$
$$a_0 = 0$$
$$f(2) = 2 = a_3(2^3) + a_2(2^2) + a_1(2) + a_0$$
$$2 = 8a_3 + 4a_2 + 2a_1 + a_0$$

(1) $\quad 1 = 4a_3 + 2a_2 + a_1$

Since $(0, 0)$ and $(2, 2)$ are extrema, $x = 0$ and $x = 2$ are critical numbers. The derivative of f is

$$f'(x) = 3a_3x^2 + 2a_2x + a_1.$$
$$f'(0) = 0 = 3a_3(0^2) + 2a_2(0) + a_1$$
$$0 = a_1$$
$$f'(2) = 0 = 3a_3(2^2) + 2a_2(2) + a_1$$
$$0 = 12a_3 + 4a_2 + 0$$

(2) $\quad 0 = 3a_3 + a_2$

Hence, $a_0 = a_1 = 0$. To find a_2 and a_3 solve the linear system comprised of equations (1) and (2).

$$4a_3 + 2a_2 = 1$$
$$3a_3 + a_2 = 0$$

(c) The solution is $a_0 = a_1 = 0$, $a_2 = 4$, $a_3 = -2$, $a_4 = \frac{1}{4}$:

$$f(x) = \frac{1}{4}x^4 - 2x^3 + 4x^2$$

(d)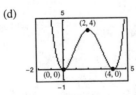

69. (a) Use a fourth degree polynomial
$$f(x) = a_4x^4 + a_3x^3 + a_2x^2 + a_1x + a_0.$$

(b) $f'(x) = 4a_4x^3 + 3a_3x^2 + 2a_2x + a_1$

$(0, 0)$: $0 = a_0$ $\quad (f(0) = 0)$

$\;\; 0 = a_1$ $\quad (f'(0) = 0)$

$(4, 0)$: $0 = 256a_4 + 64a_3 + 16a_2$ $\quad (f(4) = 0)$

$\;\; 0 = 256a_4 + 48a_3 + 8a_2$ $\quad (f'(4) = 0)$

$(2, 4)$: $4 = 16a_4 + 8a_3 + 4a_2$ $\quad (f(2) = 4)$

$\;\; 0 = 32a_4 + 12a_3 + 4a_2$ $\quad (f'(2) = 0)$

71. True

Let $h(x) = f(x) + g(x)$ where f and g are increasing. Then $h'(x) = f'(x) + g'(x) > 0$ since $f'(x) > 0$ and $g'(x) > 0$.

73. False

Let $f(x) = x^3$, then $f'(x) = 3x^2$ and f only has one critical number. Or, let $f(x) = x^3 + 3x + 1$, then $f'(x) = 3(x^2 + 1)$ has no critical numbers.

75. Assume that $f'(x) < 0$ for all x in the interval (a, b) and let $x_1 < x_2$ be any two points in the interval. By the Mean Value Theorem, we know there exists a number c such that $x_1 < c < x_2$, and

$$f'(c) = \frac{f(x_2) - f(x_1)}{x_2 - x_1}.$$

Since $f'(c) < 0$ and $x_2 - x_1 > 0$, then $f(x_2) - f(x_1) < 0$, which implies that $f(x_2) < f(x_1)$. Thus, f is decreasing on the interval.

77. Let $f(x) = (1 + x)^n - nx - 1$. Then

$$f'(x) = n(1 + x)^{n-1} - n$$

$$= n[(1 + x)^{n-1} - 1] > 0 \text{ since } x > 0 \text{ and } n > 1.$$

Thus, $f(x)$ is increasing on $(0, \infty)$. Since $f(0) = 0 \Rightarrow f(x) > 0$ on $(0, \infty)$

$$(1 + x)^n - nx - 1 > 0 \Rightarrow (1 + x)^n > 1 + nx.$$

Section 3.4   Concavity and the Second Derivative Test

1. $y = x^2 - x - 2, y'' = 2$

Concave upward: $(-\infty, \infty)$

3. $f(x) = \dfrac{24}{x^2 + 12}, y'' = \dfrac{-144(4 - x^2)}{(x^2 + 12)^3}$

Concave upward: $(-\infty, -2), (2, \infty)$

Concave downward: $(-2, 2)$

5. $f(x) = \dfrac{x^2 + 1}{x^2 - 1}$

Concave upward: $(-\infty, -1), (1, \infty)$

Concave downward: $(-1, 1)$

7. $f(x) = 6x - x^2$

$f'(x) = 6 - 2x$

$f''(x) = -2$

Critical number: $x = 3$

$f''(3) < 0$

Therefore, $(3, 9)$ is relative maximum.

9. $f(x) = (x - 5)^2$

$f'(x) = 2(x - 5)$

$f''(x) = 2$

Critical number: $x = 5$

$f''(5) > 0$

Therefore, $(5, 0)$ is a relative minimum.

11. $f(x) = x^3 - 3x^2 + 3$

$f'(x) = 3x^2 - 6x = 3x(x - 2)$

$f'(x) = 0$ when $x = 0, 2$

$f''(x) = 6x - 6$

At $x = 0$, we have $f(0) = 3, f'(0) = 0$, and $f''(0) = -6$. Therefore, by the Second Derivative Test, $(0, 3)$ is a relative maximum.

At $x = 2$, we have $f(2) = -1, f'(2) = 0$, and $f''(2) = 6$. Therefore, by the Second Derivative Test, $(2, -1)$ is a relative minimum.

13. $f(x) = x^4 - 4x^3 + 2$

$f'(x) = 4x^3 - 12x^2 = 4x^2(x - 3)$

$f''(x) = 12x^2 - 24x = 12x(x - 2)$

Critical numbers: $x = 0, x = 3$

However, $f''(0) = 0$, so we must use the First Derivative Test. $f'(x) < 0$ on the intervals $(-\infty, 0)$ and $(0, 3)$; hence, $(0, 2)$ is not an extremum. $f''(3) > 0$ so $(3, -25)$ is a relative minimum.

15. $f(x) = x^{2/3} - 3$

$f'(x) = \dfrac{2}{3x^{1/3}}$

$f''(x) = \dfrac{-2}{9x^{4/3}}$

Critical number: $x = 0$

However, $f''(0)$ is undefined, so we must use the First Derivative Test. Since $f'(x) < 0$ on $(-\infty, 0)$ and $f'(x) > 0$ on $(0, \infty)$, $(0, -3)$ is a relative minimum.

17. $f(x) = x + \dfrac{4}{x}$

$f'(x) = 1 - \dfrac{4}{x^2} = \dfrac{x^2 - 4}{x^2}$

$f'(x) = 0$ when $x = \pm 2$

(Note that f' is undefined when $x = 0$. It is **not** a critical number since it is not in the domain of f.)

$$f''(x) = (-4)(-2)x^{-3} = \dfrac{8}{x^3}$$

At $x = -2$, we have $f(-2) = -4, f'(-2) = 0$, and $f''(-2) = -1$. Therefore, by the Second Derivative Test, $(-2, -4)$ is a relative maximum.

Since the graph of f is symmetric to the origin, $(2, 4)$ is a relative minimum.

19. $f(x) = x - \ln x$

$f'(x) = 1 - \dfrac{1}{x}$

$f''(x) = \dfrac{1}{x^2}$

Critical number: $x = 1$

$f''(1) > 0 \Rightarrow (1, 1)$ is a relative minimum.

21. $f(x) = \cos x - x$

$f'(x) = -\sin x - 1$

Therefore, $f'(x) = 0$ when $\sin x = -1$. The critical numbers in the interval $[0, 4\pi]$ are

$$x = \dfrac{3\pi}{2} \quad \text{and} \quad x = \dfrac{7\pi}{2}.$$

However, there are no relative extrema since $f'(x) \le 0$ for all x.

23. $f(x) = x^3 - 12x$

$f'(x) = 3x^2 - 12 = 3(x + 2)(x - 2) = 0$ when $x = \pm 2$.

$f''(x) = 6x$

$f''(-2) = -12 < 0 \Rightarrow (-2, 16)$ is a relative maximum.

$f''(2) = 12 > 0 \Rightarrow (2, -16)$ is a relative minimum.

$f''(x) = 6x = 0$ when $x = 0$.

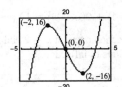

Test interval	$-\infty < x < 0$	$0 < x < \infty$
Sign of $f''(x)$	$f''(x) < 0$	$f''(x) > 0$
Conclusion	Concave downward	Concave upward

Point of inflection: $(0, 0)$

25. $f(x) = x^3 - 6x^2 + 12x$

$f'(x) = 3x^2 - 12x + 12$

$\quad = 3(x - 2)^2 = 0$ when $x = 2$.

$f''(x) = 6(x - 2) = 0$ when $x = 2$.

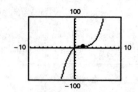

Since $f'(x) > 0$ when $x \ne 2$ and the concavity changes at $x = 2$. $(2, 8)$ is a point of inflection.

27. $f(x) = \dfrac{1}{4}x^4 - 2x^2$

$f'(x) = x^3 - 4x = x(x + 2)(x - 2) = 0$ when $x = 0, \pm 2$.

$f''(x) = 3x^2 - 4$

$f''(-2) = 8 > 0 \Rightarrow (-2, -4)$ is a relative minimum.

$f''(0) = -4 < 0 \Rightarrow (0, 0)$ is a relative maximum.

$f''(2) = 8 > 0 \Rightarrow (2, -4)$ is a relative minimum.

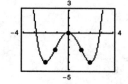

$f''(x) = 3x^2 - 4 = 0$ when $x = \pm\dfrac{2}{\sqrt{3}}$.

Test interval	$-\infty < x < -\dfrac{2}{\sqrt{3}}$	$-\dfrac{2}{\sqrt{3}} < x < \dfrac{2}{\sqrt{3}}$	$\dfrac{2}{\sqrt{3}} < x < \infty$
Sign of $f''(x)$	$f''(x) > 0$	$f''(x) < 0$	$f''(x) > 0$
Conclusion	Concave upward	Concave downward	Concave upward

Points of inflection: $\left(\pm\dfrac{2}{\sqrt{3}}, -\dfrac{20}{9}\right)$

29. $f(x) = x(x - 4)^3$

$f'(x) = x[3(x - 4)^2(1)] + (x - 4)^3(1)$

$\quad = (x - 4)^2[3x + (x - 4)] = 4(x - 4)^2(x - 1)$

$f'(x) = 0$ when $x = 1, 4$

$f''(x) = 4[(x - 4)^2(1) + (x - 1)(2)(x - 4)(1)]$

$\quad = 4(x - 4)[(x - 4) + 2(x - 1)] = 12(x - 4)(x - 2)$

Possible points of inflection occur at $x = 2$ and $x = 4$. By testing the intervals determined by these x-values, we can conclude that they both yield points of inflection.

Interval	$-\infty < x < 2$	$2 < x < 4$	$4 < x < \infty$
Test value	$x = 0$	$x = 3$	$x = 5$
Sign of $f''(x)$	$f''(0) > 0$	$f''(3) < 0$	$f''(5) > 0$
Conclusion	Concave upward	Concave downward	Concave upward

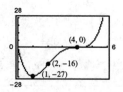

Therefore, $(1, -27)$ is a relative minimum, and $(2, -16)$ and $(4, 0)$ are points of inflection. Note that there is **not** a relative extrema at $(4, 0)$ even though $x = 4$ is a critical number. The first derivative remains nonnegative as x increases through the critical number $x = 4$.

31. $f(x) = x\sqrt{x+3}$

$$f'(x) = x\left(\frac{1}{2}\right)(x+3)^{-1/2}(1) + (x+3)^{1/2}(1)$$

$$= \frac{x}{2\sqrt{x+3}} + \sqrt{x+3}$$

$$= \frac{x + 2(x+3)}{2\sqrt{x+3}} = \frac{3(x+2)}{2\sqrt{x+3}}$$

$f'(x) = 0$ when $x = -2$

$$f''(x) = \frac{3}{2}\left[\frac{\sqrt{x+3}(1) - (x+2)(1/2)(x+3)^{-1/2}(1)}{x+3}\right]$$

$$= \frac{3}{2}\left[\frac{\sqrt{x+3} - (x+2)/(2\sqrt{x+3})}{x+3}\right]$$

$$= \frac{3(x+4)}{4(x+3)^{3/2}} > 0 \text{ for all } x \text{ in } (-3, \infty)$$

Domain: $(-3, \infty)$

We conclude that the graph is concave upward for each x in the domain of f and therefore that $(-2, -2)$ is a relative minimum.

33. $f(x) = x^2 e^{-x}$

$$f'(x) = x^2(-e^{-x}) + e^{-x}(2x) = xe^{-x}(-x+2)$$

$$f''(x) = (xe^{-x})(-1) + (-x+2)[x(-e^{-x}) + e^{-x}(1)]$$

$$= e^{-x}[-x + (-x+2)(-x+1)] = e^{-x}(x^2 - 4x + 2)$$

Intercept: $(0, 0)$

Solving the equation $f' = 0$ yields the critical numbers $x = 0$ and $x = 2$. Solve the equation $x^2 - 4x + 2 = 0$ to determine where $f''(x) = 0$. The solutions of this equation are $x = 2 \pm \sqrt{2}$.

Interval	$f(x)$	$f'(x)$	$f''(x)$	Shape of graph
$-\infty < x < 0$		$-$	$+$	decreasing, concave up
$x = 0$	0	0	$+$	relative minimum
$0 < x < 2 - \sqrt{2}$		$+$	$+$	increasing, concave up
$x = 2 - \sqrt{2}$	0.191	$+$	0	point of inflection
$2 - \sqrt{2} < x < 2$		$+$	$-$	increasing, concave down
$x = 2$	0.541	0	$-$	relative maximum
$2 < x < 2 + \sqrt{2}$		$-$	$-$	decreasing, concave down
$x = 2 + \sqrt{2}$	0.384	$-$	0	point of inflection
$2 + \sqrt{2} < x < \infty$		$-$	$+$	decreasing, concave up

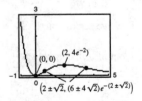

35. $f(x) = \dfrac{e^x + e^{-x}}{2}$

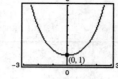

$f'(x) = \dfrac{e^x - e^{-x}}{2} = 0$ when $x = 0$.

$f''(x) = \dfrac{e^x + e^{-x}}{2} > 0$

Relative minimum: $(0, 1)$

37. $y = \dfrac{x^2}{2} - \ln x$

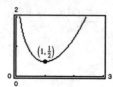

$y' = x - \dfrac{1}{x}$

$y'' = 1 + \dfrac{1}{x^2} > 0$

Domain: $0 < x$

We first observe that $y' = 0$ when $x = \pm 1$. However, $x = -1$ is not in the domain of the function. Since y'' is positive for all x in the domain, the graph is concave up and $\left(1, \frac{1}{2}\right)$ is a relative minimum point. Furthermore, since y'' is never zero, there are no points of inflection. By plotting a few points, we sketch the graph shown in the figure.

x	0.25	0.5	1	1.5	2	3
y	1.418	0.818	0.5	0.720	1.307	3.401

39. $y = \dfrac{x}{\ln x}$

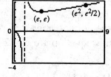

Domain: $0 < x < 1, \; x > 1$

$y' = \dfrac{(\ln x)(1) - (x)(1/x)}{(\ln x)^2} = \dfrac{\ln x - 1}{(\ln x)^2} = 0$ when $x = e$.

$y'' = \dfrac{2 - \ln x}{x(\ln x)^3} = 0$ when $x = e^2$.

Relative minimum: (e, e)

Point of inflection: $\left(e^2, \dfrac{e^2}{2}\right)$

41. $f(x) = 8x(4^{-x})$

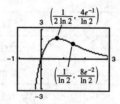

$f'(x) = -8(4^{-x})(x \ln 4 - 1)$

$f''(x) = 8(4^{-x}) \ln 4 (x \ln 4 - 2)$

$f'(x) = 0 \Rightarrow x = \dfrac{1}{\ln 4} = \dfrac{1}{2 \ln 2}$

$f''\left(\dfrac{1}{2 \ln 2}\right) < 0 \Rightarrow$ relative maximum

$f''(x) = 0 \Rightarrow x = \dfrac{2}{\ln 4} = \dfrac{1}{\ln 2}$

Relative maximum: $\left(\dfrac{1}{2 \ln 2}, \dfrac{4e^{-1}}{\ln 2}\right)$

Point of inflection: $\left(\dfrac{1}{\ln 2}, \dfrac{8e^{-2}}{\ln 2}\right)$

43. $f(x) = \sin\left(\dfrac{x}{2}\right), 0 \le x \le 4\pi$

$f'(x) = \dfrac{1}{2}\cos\left(\dfrac{x}{2}\right) = 0$ when $x = \pi, 3\pi$.

$f''(x) = -\dfrac{1}{4}\sin\left(\dfrac{x}{2}\right)$

$f''(\pi) < 0 \Rightarrow (\pi, 1)$ is a relative maximum.

$f''(3\pi) > 0 \Rightarrow (3\pi, -1)$ is a relative minimum.

$f''(x) = 0$ when $x = 0, 2\pi, 4\pi$.

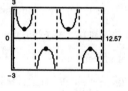

Test interval	$0 < x < 2\pi$	$2\pi < x < 4\pi$
Sign of $f''(x)$	$f'' < 0$	$f'' > 0$
Conclusion	Concave downward	Concave upward

Point of inflection: $(2\pi, 0)$

45. $f(x) = \sec\left(x - \dfrac{\pi}{2}\right), 0 < x < 4\pi$

$f'(x) = \sec\left(x - \dfrac{\pi}{2}\right)\tan\left(x - \dfrac{\pi}{2}\right) = 0$ when $x = \dfrac{\pi}{2}, \dfrac{3\pi}{2}, \dfrac{5\pi}{2}, \dfrac{7\pi}{2}$.

$f''(x) = \sec^3\left(x - \dfrac{\pi}{2}\right) + \sec\left(x - \dfrac{\pi}{2}\right)\tan^2\left(x - \dfrac{\pi}{2}\right) \ne 0$ for any x in the domain of f.

$f''\left(\dfrac{\pi}{2}\right) > 0 \Rightarrow \left(\dfrac{\pi}{2}, 1\right)$ is a relative minimum.

$f''\left(\dfrac{3\pi}{2}\right) < 0 \Rightarrow \left(\dfrac{3\pi}{2}, -1\right)$ is a relative maximum.

$f''\left(\dfrac{5\pi}{2}\right) > 0 \Rightarrow \left(\dfrac{5\pi}{2}, 1\right)$ is a relative minimum.

$f''\left(\dfrac{7\pi}{2}\right) < 0 \Rightarrow \left(\dfrac{7\pi}{2}, -1\right)$ is a relative maximum.

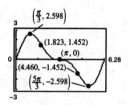

47. $f(x) = 2\sin x + \sin 2x$

$f'(x) = 2\cos x + 2\cos 2x$

$\quad = 2[\cos x + 2\cos^2 x - 1] = 2(2\cos x - 1)(\cos x + 1)$

$f'(x) = 0$ when $x = \dfrac{\pi}{3}, \pi, \dfrac{5\pi}{3}$

$f''(x) = -2\sin x - 4\sin 2x$

$\quad = -2(\sin x + 4\sin x\cos x) = -2\sin x(1 + 4\cos x)$

$f''(x) = 0$ when $x = 0, \pi, \arccos\left(-\dfrac{1}{4}\right), 2\pi - \arccos\dfrac{1}{4}$

Since $f''(\pi/3) < 0$, there is a relative maximum at $(\pi/3, 3\sqrt{3}/2)$, and since $f''(5\pi/3) > 0$, there is a relative minimum at $(5\pi/3, -3\sqrt{3}/2)$. The inflection points are $(\pi, 0)$, $(1.823, 1.452)$, and $(4.460, -1.452)$.

49. $f(x) = \text{arcsec } x - x$, Domain: $(-\infty, -1], [1, \infty)$

$$f'(x) = \frac{1}{|x|\sqrt{x^2 - 1}} = 0$$

$$|x|\sqrt{x^2 - 1} = 1$$

$$x^2(x^2 - 1) = 1$$

$$x^4 - x^2 - 1 = 0 \Rightarrow x^2 = \frac{1 + \sqrt{5}}{2}$$

Therefore, $f'(x) = 0$ when $x = \pm\sqrt{\dfrac{1 + \sqrt{5}}{2}} \approx \pm 1.272$. Note that $f'(x)$ is undefined for $x = \pm 1$.

Interval	$-\infty < x < -1.272$	$-1.272 < x < 1$	$1 < x < 1.272$	$1.272 < x < \infty$
Test value	$x = -2$	$x = -1.1$	$x = 1.1$	$x = 2$
Sign of $f'(x)$	$f'(-2) < 0$	$f'(-1.1) > 0$	$f'(1.1) > 0$	$f'(2) < 0$
Conclusion	f is decreasing.	f is increasing.	f is increasing.	f is decreasing.

We conclude that $(-1.272, 3.747)$ is a relative minimum and $(1.272, -0.606)$ is a relative maximum. There are no points of inflection.

51. $f(x) = 0.2x^2(x - 3)^3, [-1, 4]$

(a) $f'(x) = 0.2x(5x - 6)(x - 3)^2$

$f''(x) = (x - 3)(4x^2 - 9.6x + 3.6)$

$\quad\quad = 0.4(x - 3)(10x^2 - 24x + 9)$

(b) $f''(0) < 0 \Rightarrow (0, 0)$ is a relative maximum.

$f''\left(\frac{6}{5}\right) > 0 \Rightarrow (1.2, -1.6796)$ is a relative minimum.

Points of inflection:

$(3, 0), (0.4652, -0.7049), (1.9348, -0.9049)$

(c)

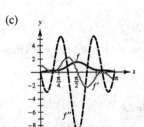

f is increasing when $f' > 0$ and decreasing when $f' < 0$. f is concave upward when $f'' > 0$ and concave downward when $f'' < 0$.

53. $f(x) = \sin x - \frac{1}{3}\sin 3x + \frac{1}{5}\sin 5x, [0, \pi]$

(a) $f'(x) = \cos x - \cos 3x + \cos 5x$

$f'(x) = 0$ when $x = \frac{\pi}{6}, x = \frac{\pi}{2}, x = \frac{5\pi}{6}$.

$f''(x) = -\sin x + 3\sin 3x - 5\sin 5x$

$f''(x) = 0$ when $x = \frac{\pi}{6}, x = \frac{5\pi}{6}, x \approx 1.1731, x \approx 1.9685$

(b) $f''\left(\frac{\pi}{2}\right) < 0 \Rightarrow \left(\frac{\pi}{2}, 1.53333\right)$ is a relative maximum.

Points of inflection: $\left(\frac{\pi}{6}, 0.2667\right)$, $(1.1731, 0.9638)$,

$$(1.9685, 0.9637), \left(\frac{5\pi}{6}, 0.2667\right)$$

Note: $(0, 0)$ and $(\pi, 0)$ are not points of inflection since they are endpoints.

(c)

The graph of f is increasing when $f' > 0$ and decreasing when $f' < 0$. f is concave upward when $f'' > 0$ and concave downward when $f'' < 0$.

55.

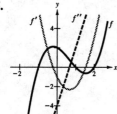

57. Since f' is an increasing function, its derivative f'' is a positive function. Since $f'' > 0$, f is concave upward.

(a) Since $f' < 0$, the function is decreasing. The graph shows a function that is decreasing and concave upward.

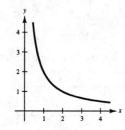

(b) Since $f' > 0$, the function is increasing. The graph shows a function that is increasing and concave upward.

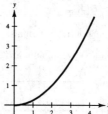

59.

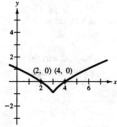

61.

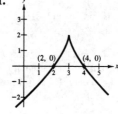

63. $f(x) = ax^3 + bx^2 + cx + d$, $f'(x) = 3ax^2 + 2bx + c$, $f''(x) = 6ax + 2b = 2(3ax + b)$

$f(3) = 3 \implies \quad 27a + 9b + 3c + d = 3 \quad (1)$

$f(4) = 2 \implies \quad 64a + 16b + 4c + d = 2 \quad (2)$

$f(5) = 1 \implies \quad 125a + 25b + 5c + d = 1 \quad (3)$

$f'(3) = 0 \implies \qquad 27a + 6b + c = 0 \quad (4)$

$f'(5) = 0 \implies \qquad 75a + 10b + c = 0 \quad (5)$

$f''(4) = 0 \implies \qquad 2(12a + b) = 0 \quad (6)$

From (6) we get $b = -12a$. Substituting this into (5), we obtain:

$$75a + 10(-12a) + c = 0$$

$$-45a + c = 0$$

$$c = 45a$$

Substitution into (1) and (2) yields

$$27a + 9(-12a) + 3(45a) + d = 3$$

$$54a + d = 3 \quad (7)$$

$$64a + 16(-12a) + 4(45a) + d = 2$$

$$52a + d = 2. \quad (8)$$

To solve simultaneously, subtract (8) from (7) and obtain $2a = 1$, $a = \frac{1}{2}$.

From (7), $d = 3 - 54(\frac{1}{2}) = -24$, $c = 45(\frac{1}{2}) = \frac{45}{2}$, $b = -12(\frac{1}{2}) = -6$.

Therefore, $f(x) = \frac{1}{2}x^3 - 6x^2 + \frac{45}{2}x - 24 = \frac{1}{2}(x^3 - 12x^2 + 45x - 48)$.

65.

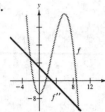

f'' is linear.

f' is quadratic.

f is cubic.

f concave upwards on $(-\infty, 3)$, downwards on $(3, \infty)$.

67. (a) $n = 1$:

$f(x) = x - 2$

$f'(x) = 1$

$f''(x) = 0$

No inflection points

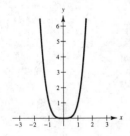

$n = 2$:

$f(x) = (x - 2)^2$

$f'(x) = 2(x - 2)$

$f''(x) = 2$

No inflection points

Relative minimum: $(2, 0)$

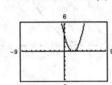

$n = 3$:

$f(x) = (x - 2)^3$

$f'(x) = 3(x - 2)^2$

$f''(x) = 6(x - 2)$

Inflection point: $(2, 0)$

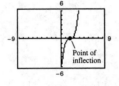

$n = 4$:

$f(x) = (x - 2)^4$

$f'(x) = 4(x - 2)^3$

$f''(x) = 12(x - 2)^2$

No inflection points:

Relative minimum: $(2, 0)$

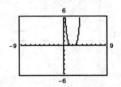

Conclusion: If $n \geq 3$ and n is odd, then $(2, 0)$ is an inflection point. If $n \geq 2$ and n is even, then $(2, 0)$ is a relative minimum.

(b) Let $f(x) = (x - 2)^n$, $f'(x) = n(x - 2)^{n-1}$, $f''(x) = n(n - 1)(x - 2)^{n-2}$. For $n \geq 3$ and odd, $n - 2$ is also odd and the concavity changes at $x = 2$. For $n \geq 4$ and even, $n - 2$ is also even and the concavity does not change at $x = 2$. Thus, $x = 2$ is an inflection point if and only if $n \geq 3$ is odd.

69. (a) The rate of change of sales is increasing.

$S'' > 0$

(b) The rate of change of sales is decreasing.

$S' > 0, S'' < 0$

(c) The rate of change of sales is constant.

$S' = C, S'' = 0$

(d) Sales are steady.

$S = C, S' = 0, S'' = 0$

(e) Sales are declining, but at a lower rate.

$S' < 0, S'' > 0$

(f) Sales have bottomed out and have started to rise.

$S' > 0$

71. $f(x) = ax^3 + bx^2 + cx + d$

Maximum: $(-4, 1)$

Minimum: $(0, 0)$

(a) $f'(x) = 3ax^2 + 2bx + c$, $f''(x) = 6ax + 2b$

$f(0) = 0 \Rightarrow d = 0$

$f(-4) = 1 \Rightarrow -64a + 16b - 4c = 1$

$f'(-4) = 0 \Rightarrow 48a - 8b + c = 0$

$f'(0) = 0 \Rightarrow c = 0$

Solving this system yields $a = \frac{1}{32}$ and $b = 6a = \frac{3}{16}$.

$f(x) = \frac{1}{32}x^3 + \frac{3}{16}x^2$

(b) The plane would be descending at the greatest rate at the point of inflection.

$f''(x) = 6ax + 2b = \frac{3}{16}x + \frac{3}{8} = 0 \Rightarrow x = -2.$

Two miles from touchdown

73. The domain of D is $[0, L]$.

$$D(x) = 2x^4 - 5Lx^3 + 3L^2x^2$$

$$D'(x) = 8x^3 - 15Lx^2 + 6L^2x = x(8x^2 - 15Lx + 6L^2)$$

$$D''(x) = 24x^2 - 30Lx + 6L^2 = 6(4x^2 - 5Lx + L^2)$$

To find the critical numbers, solve the equation $D'(x) = 0$. At the critical number $x = 0$, there is no deflection since $D(0) = 0$. To find additional critical numbers use the Quadratic Formula to solve the equation

$$8x^2 - 15Lx + 6L^2 = 0$$

$$x = \frac{15L \pm \sqrt{(-15L)^2 - 4(8)(6L^2)}}{2(8)}$$

$$= \left(\frac{15 \pm \sqrt{33}}{16}\right)L.$$

The critical number in the domain of the function is

$$x = \left(\frac{15 - \sqrt{33}}{16}\right)L \approx 0.578L.$$

$$D''\left(\frac{15 - \sqrt{33}}{16}\right)L = \frac{3}{16}\left(11 - 5\sqrt{33}\right)L^2 \approx -3.323L^2 < 0.$$

By the Second Derivative Test, the deflection is maximum when

$$x = \left(\frac{15 - \sqrt{33}}{16}\right)L \approx 0.578L.$$

75. $C = 0.5x^2 + 15x + 5000$

$$\overline{C} = \frac{C}{x} = 0.5x + 15 + \frac{5000}{x}$$

$\overline{C}$ = average cost per unit

$$\frac{d\overline{C}}{dx} = 0.5 - \frac{5000}{x^2} = 0 \text{ when } x = 100$$

By the First Derivative Test, $\overline{C}$ is minimized when $x = 100$ units.

77. $v = -2400\pi \sin \theta$

$$\frac{d\theta}{dt} = (200)(2\pi) = 400\pi \text{ rad/min}$$

$$\frac{dv}{dt} = -2400\pi \cos \theta \cdot \frac{d\theta}{dt} = -2400\pi(400\pi) \cos \pi$$

$$= 0 \text{ when } \theta = \frac{(2n+1)\pi}{2} = \frac{\pi}{2} + 2n\pi, n \text{ any integer.}$$

By the First Derivative Test, v is maximum when $\theta = (3\pi/2) + 2n\pi$. The speed $|v|$ is maximum when $\theta = (\pi/2) + 2n\pi$ and $(3\pi/2) + 2n\pi$.

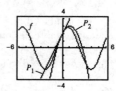

79. $f(x) = 2(\sin x + \cos x),$ $f(0) = 2$

$f'(x) = 2(\cos x - \sin x),$ $f'(0) = 2$

$f''(x) = 2(-\sin x - \cos x),$ $f''(0) = -2$

$P_1(x) = 2 + 2(x - 0) = 2(1 + x)$

$P_1'(x) = 2$

$P_2(x) = 2 + 2(x - 0) + \frac{1}{2}(-2)(x - 0)^2 = 2 + 2x - x^2$

$P_2'(x) = 2 - 2x$

$P_2''(x) = -2$

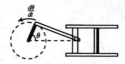

The values of f, P_1, P_2, and their first derivatives are equal at $x = 0$. The values of the second derivatives of f and P_2 are equal at $x = 0$. The approximations worsen as you move away from $x = 0$.

81. We begin by evaluating the function f and its first and second derivatives at $x = \pi/4$.

$$f(x) = 2(\sin x + \cos x) \qquad f'\left(\frac{\pi}{4}\right) = 2\sqrt{2}$$

$$f'(x) = 2(\cos x - \sin x) \qquad f'\left(\frac{\pi}{4}\right) = 0$$

$$f''(x) = -2(\sin x + \cos x) \qquad f''\left(\frac{\pi}{4}\right) = -2\sqrt{2}$$

$$P_1(x) = 2\sqrt{2} + 0\left(x - \frac{\pi}{4}\right) = 2\sqrt{2}$$

$$P_2(x) = 2\sqrt{2} + 0\left(x - \frac{\pi}{4}\right) + \frac{1}{2}(-2\sqrt{2})\left(x - \frac{\pi}{4}\right)^2 = 2\sqrt{2} - \sqrt{2}\left(x - \frac{\pi}{4}\right)^2.$$

The graphs of f, P_1, and P_2 produced by a graphing utility are shown in the figure.

83. $f(x) = x \sin\left(\dfrac{1}{x}\right)$

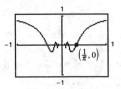

$$f'(x) = x\left[-\frac{1}{x^2}\cos\left(\frac{1}{x}\right)\right] + \sin\left(\frac{1}{x}\right) = -\frac{1}{x}\cos\left(\frac{1}{x}\right) + \sin\left(\frac{1}{x}\right)$$

$$f''(x) = -\frac{1}{x}\left[\frac{1}{x^2}\sin\left(\frac{1}{x}\right)\right] + \frac{1}{x^2}\cos\left(\frac{1}{x}\right) - \frac{1}{x^2}\cos\left(\frac{1}{x}\right) = -\frac{1}{x^3}\sin\left(\frac{1}{x}\right) = 0$$

$$x = \frac{1}{\pi}$$

Point of inflection: $\left(\dfrac{1}{\pi}, 0\right)$

When $x > 1/\pi$, $f'' < 0$, so the graph is concave downward.

85. We assume the three zeros of the cubic are r_1, r_2, and r_3. Then,

$$f(x) = a(x - r_1)(x - r_2)(x - r_3)$$

$$f'(x) = a[x - r_1)(x - r_2) + (x - r_1)(x - r_3) + (x - r_2)(x - r_3)]$$

$$f''(x) = a[(x - r_1) + (x - r_2) + (x - r_1) + (x - r_3) + (x - r_2) + (x - r_3)]$$

$$= a[6x - 2(r_1 + r_2 + r_3)].$$

Consequently, $f''(x) = 0$ if

$$x = \frac{2(r_1 + r_2 + r_3)}{6} = \frac{r_1 + r_2 + r_3}{3} = \text{average of } r_1, r_2, \text{ and } r_3.$$

87. Suppose $y_1 < d < y_2$ and let $g(x) = f(x) - d(x - a)$. g is continuous on $[a, b]$, and therefore, by the Extreme Value Theorem, attains a minimum value at some point c in $[a, b]$. This point c cannot be the endpoints a or b because

$$g'(a) = f'(a) - d = y_1 - d < 0$$

$$g'(b) = f'(b) - d = y_2 - d > 0.$$

Hence, g attains its minimum value at c, $a < c < b$. This implies that $g'(c) = 0$ and $f'(c) = d$. The proof for $y_2 < d < y_1$ is similar.

89. True. Let $y = ax^3 + bx^2 + cx + d, a \neq 0$. Then $y'' = 6ax + 2b = 0$ when $x = -(b/3a)$, and the concavity changes at this point.

91. False

$$f(x) = 3 \sin x + 2 \cos x$$

$$f'(x) = 3 \cos x - 2 \sin x$$

$$3 \cos x - 2 \sin x = 0$$

$$3 \cos x = 2 \sin x$$

$$\tfrac{3}{2} = \tan x$$

Critical number: $x = \tan^{-1}\left(\tfrac{3}{2}\right)$

$f\left(\tan^{-1}\tfrac{3}{2}\right) \approx 3.60555$ is the maximum value of y.

Section 3.5   Limits at Infinity

1. $f(x) = \dfrac{3x^2}{x^2 + 2}$

No vertical asymptotes

Horizontal asymptote: $y = 3$

Matches (f)

3. $f(x) = \dfrac{x}{x^2 + 2}$

No vertical asymptotes

Horizontal asymptote: $y = 0$

Matches (d)

5. $f(x) = \dfrac{4 \sin x}{x^2 + 1}$

No vertical asymptotes

Horizontal asymptotes: $y = 0$

Matches (b)

7. $\displaystyle\lim_{x \to \infty} \frac{2x - 1}{3x + 2} = \lim_{x \to \infty} \frac{2 - (1/x)}{3 + (2/x)} = \frac{2 - 0}{3 + 0} = \frac{2}{3}$

9. Divide both the numerator and denominator by x^2 (the highest power of x in the denominator).

$$\lim_{x \to \infty} \frac{x}{x^2 - 1} = \lim_{x \to \infty} \frac{x/x^2}{(x^2/x^2) - (1/x^2)}$$

$$= \lim_{x \to \infty} \frac{1/x}{1 - (1/x^2)}$$

$$= \frac{0}{1 - 0} = 0$$

(Note that the degree of the numerator is less than the degree of the denominator. See Exercise 87 in this section.)

11. Divide both the numerator and denominator by x (the highest power of x in the denominator). Since

$$\lim_{x \to -\infty} \frac{5x^2}{x + 3} = \lim_{x \to -\infty} \frac{5x^2/x}{(x/x) + (3/x)}$$

$$= \lim_{x \to -\infty} \frac{5x}{1 + (3/x)} = -\infty,$$

the limit does not exist. (Note that the degree of the numerator is greater than the degree of the denominator. See Exercise 87 in this section.)

13. Divide the numerator and denominator of the function by x and note that $x = -\sqrt{x^2}$ when $x < 0$.

$$\lim_{x \to -\infty} \frac{x}{\sqrt{x^2 - x}} = \lim_{x \to -\infty} \frac{x/x}{\sqrt{x^2 - x}/\left(-\sqrt{x^2}\right)}$$

$$= \lim_{x \to -\infty} \frac{1}{-\sqrt{1 - (1/x)}}$$

$$= -\frac{1}{\sqrt{1 + 0}} = -1$$

15. $\displaystyle\lim_{x \to \infty} \frac{2x + 1}{\sqrt{x^2 - x}} = \lim_{x \to \infty} \frac{2 + (1/x)}{\sqrt{1 - (1/x)}} = 2$

17. $\displaystyle\lim_{x \to \infty} (2 - 5e^{-x}) = \lim_{t \to \infty} 2 - 5 \lim_{x \to \infty} e^{-x} = 2 - 5(0) = 2$

19. $\lim\limits_{x \to -\infty} \dfrac{3}{1 + 2e^x} = 3$

21. $\lim\limits_{x \to \infty} \log_{10}(1 + 10^{-x}) = 0$

23. Since $(-1/x) \leq (\sin(2x))/x \leq (1/x)$ for all $x \neq 0$, we have by the Squeeze Theorem,

$$\lim_{x \to \infty} -\frac{1}{x} \leq \lim_{x \to \infty} \frac{\sin(2x)}{x} \leq \lim_{x \to \infty} \frac{1}{x}$$

$$0 \leq \lim_{x \to \infty} \frac{\sin(2x)}{x} \leq 0.$$

Therefore, $\lim\limits_{x \to \infty} \dfrac{\sin(2x)}{x} = 0$.

25. $\lim\limits_{x \to \infty} \dfrac{1}{2x + \sin x} = 0$

27. $\lim\limits_{t \to \infty} \left(\dfrac{5}{t} - \arctan t\right) = 0 - \dfrac{\pi}{2} = -\dfrac{\pi}{2}$

29. If we make the substitution $t = 1/x$, then finding the limit as $t \to 0^+$ in the resulting function is equivalent to finding the limit as $x \to \infty$ in the given function.

$$\lim_{x \to \infty} x \sin \frac{1}{x} = \lim_{t \to 0^+} \frac{1}{t} \sin t$$

$$= \lim_{t \to 0^+} \frac{\sin t}{t} = 1.$$

31. $\lim\limits_{x \to -\infty} \left(x + \sqrt{x^2 + 3}\right) = \lim\limits_{x \to -\infty} \left[\left(x + \sqrt{x^2 + 3}\right) \cdot \dfrac{x - \sqrt{x^2 + 3}}{x - \sqrt{x^2 + 3}}\right] = \lim\limits_{x \to -\infty} \dfrac{-3}{x - \sqrt{x^2 + 3}} = 0$

33. $\lim\limits_{x \to \infty} \left(x - \sqrt{x^2 + x}\right) = \lim\limits_{x \to \infty} \left(x - \sqrt{x^2 + x}\right) \dfrac{x + \sqrt{x^2 + x}}{x + \sqrt{x^2 + x}}$

$$= \lim_{x \to \infty} \frac{x^2 - (x^2 + x)}{x + \sqrt{x^2 + x}}$$

$$= \lim_{x \to \infty} \frac{-x}{x + \sqrt{x^2 + x}}$$

$$= \lim_{x \to \infty} \frac{-x/x}{(x/x) + \sqrt{x^2 + x}/\sqrt{x^2}}$$

$$= \lim_{x \to \infty} \frac{-1}{1 + \sqrt{1 + (1/x)}}$$

$$= \frac{-1}{1 + \sqrt{1 + 0}} = -\frac{1}{2}$$

(**Note:** For $x > 0, x = \sqrt{x^2}$.)

35. $f(x) = \dfrac{4x + 3}{2x - 1}$

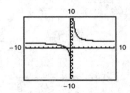

x	10^0	10^1	10^2	10^3	10^4	10^5	10^6
$f(x)$	7	2.26	2.025	2.0025	2.0003	2	2

$\lim\limits_{x \to \infty} f(x) = 2$

37. $f(x) = \dfrac{-6x}{\sqrt{4x^2 + 5}}$

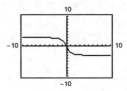

x	10^0	10^1	10^2	10^3	10^4	10^5	10^6
$f(x)$	-2	-2.98	-2.9998	-3	-3	-3	-3

$\lim\limits_{x \to \infty} f(x) = -3$

39.

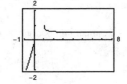

x	10^0	10^1	10^2	10^3	10^4	10^5	10^6
$f(x)$	1	0.513	0.501	0.500	0.500	0.500	0.500

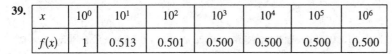

$$\lim_{x \to \infty} \left(x - \sqrt{x(x-1)}\right) = \lim_{x \to \infty} \frac{x - \sqrt{x^2 - x}}{1} \cdot \frac{x + \sqrt{x^2 - x}}{x + \sqrt{x^2 - x}}$$

$$= \lim_{x \to \infty} \frac{x}{x + \sqrt{x^2 - x}}$$

$$= \lim_{x \to \infty} \frac{1}{1 + \sqrt{1 - (1/x)}}$$

$$= \frac{1}{2}$$

41.

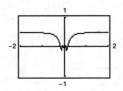

x	10^0	10^1	10^2	10^3	10^4	10^5	10^6
$f(x)$	0.479	0.500	0.500	0.500	0.500	0.500	0.500

Let $x = 1/t$.

$$\lim_{x \to \infty} x \sin\left(\frac{1}{2x}\right) = \lim_{t \to 0^+} \frac{\sin(t/2)}{t} = \lim_{t \to 0^+} \frac{1}{2} \frac{\sin(t/2)}{t/2} = \frac{1}{2}$$

43. If $x = 0$, then $y = 2$ and the y-intercept occurs at $(0, 2)$. If $y = 0$, then $2 + x = 0$, $x = -2$, and the x-intercept is $(-2, 0)$. There is no symmetry with respect to either axis or to the origin. There is a vertical asymptote at $x = 1$. Furthermore,

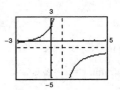

$$\lim_{x \to 1^-} \frac{2 + x}{1 - x} = \infty \quad \text{and} \quad \lim_{x \to 1^+} \frac{2 + x}{1 - x} = -\infty$$

$$\lim_{x \to \pm\infty} \frac{2 + x}{1 - x} = \lim_{x \to \pm\infty} \frac{2/x + x/x}{1/x - x/x} = \lim_{x \to \pm\infty} \frac{(2/x) + 1}{(1/x) - 1} = \frac{0 + 1}{0 - 1} = -1.$$

Therefore, there is a horizontal asymptote (to the right and left) at $y = -1$. Start the graph by plotting the following solution points.

x	-3	-1	0.5	2	3	4
y	-0.25	0.5	5	-4	-2.5	-2

45. $y = \dfrac{x}{x^2 - 4}$

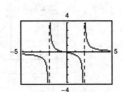

Intercept: $(0, 0)$

Symmetry: origin

Horizontal asymptote: $y = 0$

Vertical asymptote: $x = \pm 2$

47. $y = \dfrac{x^2}{x^2 + 9}$

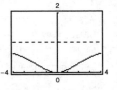

Intercept: $(0, 0)$

Symmetry: y-axis

Horizontal asymptote:
$y = 1$ since

$$\lim_{x \to -\infty} \frac{x^2}{x^2 + 9} = 1 = \lim_{x \to \infty} \frac{x^2}{x^2 + 9}.$$

Relative minimum: $(0, 0)$

49. The intercept is $(0, 0)$ and the graph is symmetric to the y-axis. There are vertical asymptotes at $x = \pm 2$. Since

$$\lim_{x \to \infty} \frac{2x^2}{x^2 - 4} = \lim_{x \to \infty} \frac{2x^2/x^2}{(x^2/x^2) - (4/x^2)} = \lim_{x \to \infty} \frac{2}{1 - (4/x^2)} = 2,$$

there is a horizontal asymptote at $y = 2$.

$$y = \frac{2x^2}{x^2 - 4}$$

$$\frac{dy}{dx} = 2\left[\frac{(x^2 - 4)(2x) - x^2(2x)}{(x^2 - 4)^2}\right] = -\frac{16x}{(x^2 - 4)^2}$$

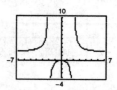

There is a critical number at $x = 0$. We conclude that $(0, 0)$ is a relative maximum since $dy/dx > 0$ for $x < 0$ and $dy/dx < 0$ for $x > 0$.

51. $xy^2 = 4$

Domain: $x > 0$

Intercepts: none

Symmetry: x-axis

Horizontal asymptote: $y = 0$ since

$$\lim_{x \to \infty} \frac{2}{\sqrt{x}} = 0 = \lim_{x \to \infty} -\frac{2}{\sqrt{x}}.$$

Discontinuity: $x = 0$ (Vertical asymptote)

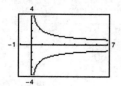

53. $y = \frac{2x}{1 - x}$

Intercept: $(0, 0)$

Symmetry: none

Horizontal asymptote: $y = -2$ since

$$\lim_{x \to -\infty} \frac{2x}{1 - x} = -2 = \lim_{x \to \infty} \frac{2x}{1 - x}.$$

Discontinuity: $x = 1$ (Vertical asymptote)

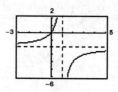

55. $y = 2 - \frac{3}{x^2}$

Intercepts: $\left(\pm\sqrt{3/2}, 0\right)$

Symmetry: y-axis

Horizontal asymptote: $y = 2$ since

$$\lim_{x \to -\infty}\left(2 - \frac{3}{x^2}\right) = 2 = \lim_{x \to \infty}\left(2 - \frac{3}{x^2}\right).$$

Discontinuity: $x = 0$ (Vertical asymptote)

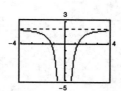

57. $y = 3 + \frac{2}{x}$

Intercept: $y = 0 = 3 + \frac{2}{x} \Longrightarrow \frac{2}{x} = -3 \Longrightarrow x = -\frac{2}{3}$ $\left(-\frac{2}{3}, 0\right)$

Symmetry: none

Horizontal asymptote: $y = 3$

Vertical asymptote: $x = 0$

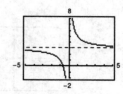

59. Since $x^2 - 4$ must be positive, the domain is $(-\infty, -2)$ and $(2, \infty)$. There is no symmetry with respect to either axis. However, there is symmetry with respect to the origin since

$$(-y) = \frac{(-x)^3}{\sqrt{(-x)^2 - 4}}$$

$$-y = \frac{-x^3}{\sqrt{x^2 - 4}}$$

$$y = \frac{x^3}{\sqrt{x^2 - 4}}$$

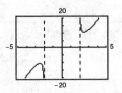

which is equivalent to the original equation. Since the denominator of $x^3/\sqrt{x^2 - 4}$ is zero when $x = 2$ or $x = -2$, there are vertical asymptotes at $x = 2$ and $x = -2$.

x	2.25	2.50	2.75	3.00	4.00
y	11.05	10.45	11.02	12.07	18.48

61. $f(x) = 5 - \dfrac{1}{x^2} = \dfrac{5x^2 - 1}{x^2}$

Domain: $(-\infty, 0), (0, \infty)$

$f'(x) = \dfrac{2}{x^3} \implies$ No relative extrema

$f''(x) = -\dfrac{6}{x^4} \implies$ No points of inflection

Vertical asymptote: $x = 0$

Horizontal asymptote: $y = 5$

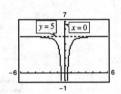

63. $f(x) = \dfrac{x}{x^2 - 4}$

$f'(x) = \dfrac{(x^2 - 4) - x(2x)}{(x^2 - 4)^2}$

$= \dfrac{-(x^2 + 4)}{(x^2 - 4)^2} \neq 0$ for any x in the domain of f.

$f''(x) = \dfrac{(x^2 - 4)^2(-2x) + (x^2 + 4)(2)(x^2 - 4)(2x)}{(x^2 - 4)^2}$

$= \dfrac{2x(x^2 + 12)}{(x^2 - 4)^3} = 0$ when $x = 0$.

Since $f''(x) > 0$ on $(-2, 0)$ and $f''(x) < 0$ on $(0, 2)$, then $(0, 0)$ is a point of inflection.

Vertical asymptotes: $x = \pm 2$

Horizontal asymptote: $y = 0$

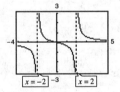

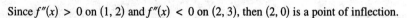

65. $f(x) = \dfrac{x - 2}{x^2 - 4x + 3} = \dfrac{x - 2}{(x - 1)(x - 3)}$

$f'(x) = \dfrac{(x^2 - 4x + 3) - (x - 2)(2x - 4)}{(x^2 - 4x + 3)^2} = \dfrac{-x^2 + 4x - 5}{(x^2 - 4x + 3)^2} \neq 0$

$f''(x) = \dfrac{(x^2 - 4x + 3)^2(-2x + 4) - (-x^2 + 4x - 5)(2)(x^2 - 4x + 3)(2x - 4)}{(x^2 - 4x + 3)^4}$

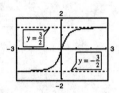

$\qquad = \dfrac{2(x^3 - 6x^2 + 15x - 14)}{(x^2 - 4x + 3)^3} = 0$ when $x = 2$.

Since $f''(x) > 0$ on $(1, 2)$ and $f''(x) < 0$ on $(2, 3)$, then $(2, 0)$ is a point of inflection.

Vertical asymptote: $x = 1, x = 3$

Horizontal asymptote: $y = 0$

67. $f(x) = \dfrac{3x}{\sqrt{4x^2 + 1}}$

$f'(x) = \dfrac{3}{(4x^2 + 1)^{3/2}} \Rightarrow$ No relative extrema

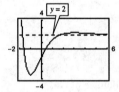

$f''(x) = \dfrac{-36x}{(4x^2 + 1)^{5/2}} = 0$ when $x = 0$.

Point of inflection: $(0, 0)$

Horizontal asymptotes: $y = \pm\dfrac{3}{2}$

No vertical asymptotes

69. $f(x) = 2 + (x^2 - 3)e^{-x}$

$f'(x) = -e^{-x}(x + 1)(x - 3)$

Critical numbers: $x = -1, x = 3$

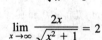

Relative minimum: $(-1, 2 - 2e) \approx (-1, -3.4366)$

Relative maximum: $(3, 2 + 6e^{-3}) \approx (3, 2.2987)$

Horizontal asymptote: $y = 2$

71. (a) $f(x) = \dfrac{|x|}{x + 1}$

$\displaystyle\lim_{x \to \infty} \dfrac{|x|}{x + 1} = 1$

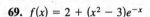

$\displaystyle\lim_{x \to -\infty} \dfrac{|x|}{x + 1} = -1$

Therefore, $y = 1$ and $y = -1$ are both horizontal asymptotes.

(b) $f(x) = \dfrac{2x}{\sqrt{x^2 + 1}}$

$\displaystyle\lim_{x \to \infty} \dfrac{2x}{\sqrt{x^2 + 1}} = 2$

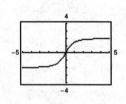

$\displaystyle\lim_{x \to -\infty} \dfrac{2x}{\sqrt{x^2 + 1}} = -2$

Therefore, $y = 2$ and $y = -2$ are both horizontal asymptotes.

73. (a) The figure produced by a graphing utility shows graphically that f and g appear to represent the same function.
Note that $x = 0$ and $x = 3$ are vertical asymptotes.

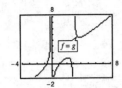

(b) $f(x) = \dfrac{x^3 - 3x^2 + 2}{x(x - 3)}$

$\quad = \dfrac{x(x^2 - 3x) + 2}{x^2 - 3x}$

$\quad = \dfrac{x(x^2 - 3x)}{x^2 - 3x} + \dfrac{2}{x^2 - 3x}$

$\quad = x + \dfrac{2}{x(x - 3)} = g(x)$

(c) When we zoom out sufficiently far on a graphing utility the graph of the function appears as a line. This line is the slant
asymptote $y = x$ and is shown in the figure.

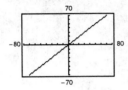

75. (a)

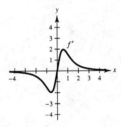

(b) $\displaystyle\lim_{x \to \infty} f(x) = 3, \qquad \lim_{x \to \infty} f'(x) = 0$

(c) Since $\displaystyle\lim_{x \to \infty} f(x) = 3$, the graph approaches that of a
horizontal line, $\displaystyle\lim_{x \to \infty} f'(x) = 0$.

77. $C = 0.5x + 500$

$\overline{C} = \dfrac{C}{x} = \dfrac{0.5x + 500}{x} = 0.5 + \dfrac{500}{x}$

$\displaystyle\lim_{x \to \infty} \overline{C} = \lim_{x \to C} \left(0.5 + \dfrac{500}{x} \right) = 0.5 + 0 = 0.5$

79. (a) $\displaystyle\lim_{t \to \infty} 6.7e^{(-48.1)/t} = 6.7e^0 = 6.7$ million ft^3

(b) $V' = \dfrac{322.27}{t^2} e^{-(48.1)/t}$

$\quad V'(20) \approx 0.073$ million ft^3/yr

$\quad V'(60) \approx 0.040$ million ft^3/yr

81. (a) $T_1(t) = -0.003t^2 + 0.677t + 26.564$

(b)

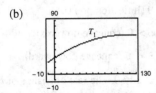

(c)

(d) $T_1(0) \approx 26.6$

$\quad T_2(0) = \dfrac{1451}{58} \approx 25.0$

(e) $\displaystyle\lim_{t \to \infty} T_2 = \dfrac{86}{1} = 86$

(f) The limiting temperature is 86.
T_1 has no horizontal asymptote.

$T_2 = \dfrac{1451 + 86t}{58 + t}$

83. False. Let $f(x) = \dfrac{2x}{\sqrt{x^2 + 2}}$. (See Exercise 2.)

85. $x = 2$ is a critical number.

$f'(x) < 0$ for $x < 2$.

$f'(x) > 0$ for $x > 2$.

$\displaystyle\lim_{x \to -\infty} f(x) = \lim_{x \to \infty} f(x) = 6$

For example, let $f(x) = \dfrac{-6}{0.1(x - 2)^2 + 1} + 6$.

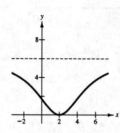

87. $\displaystyle\lim_{x \to \infty} \frac{p(x)}{q(x)} = \lim_{x \to \infty} \frac{a_n x^n + \cdots + a_1 x + a_0}{b_m x^m + \cdots + b_1 x + b_0}$

Divide $p(x)$ and $q(x)$ by x^m.

Case 1: If $n < m$: $\displaystyle\lim_{x \to \infty} \frac{p(x)}{q(x)} = \lim_{x \to \infty} \frac{\dfrac{a_n}{x^{m-n}} + \cdots + \dfrac{a_1}{x^{m-1}} + \dfrac{a_0}{x^m}}{b_m + \cdots + \dfrac{b_1}{x^{m-1}} + \dfrac{b_0}{x^m}} = \frac{0 + \cdots + 0 + 0}{b_m + \cdots + 0 + 0} = \frac{0}{b_m} = 0$

Case 2: If $m = n$: $\displaystyle\lim_{x \to \infty} \frac{p(x)}{q(x)} = \lim_{x \to \infty} \frac{a_n + \cdots + \dfrac{a_1}{x^{m-1}} + \dfrac{a_0}{x^m}}{b_m + \cdots + \dfrac{b_1}{x^{m-1}} + \dfrac{b_0}{x^m}} = \frac{a_n + \cdots + 0 + 0}{b_m + \cdots + 0 + 0} = \frac{a_n}{b_m}.$

Case 3: If $n > m$: $\displaystyle\lim_{x \to \infty} \frac{p(x)}{q(x)} = \lim_{x \to \infty} \frac{a_n x^{n-m} + \cdots + \dfrac{a_1}{x^{m-1}} + \dfrac{a_0}{x^m}}{b_m + \cdots + \dfrac{b_1}{x^{m-1}} + \dfrac{b_0}{x^m}} = \frac{\pm\infty + \cdots + 0}{b_m + \cdots + 0} = \pm\infty.$

Section 3.6   A Summary of Curve Sketching

1. (a) f has constant negative slope. Matches (D)

(c) The slope is periodic, and zero at $x = 0$. Matches (A)

(b) The slope of f approaches ∞ as $x \to 0^-$, and approaches $-\infty$ as $x \to 0^+$. Matches (C)

(d) The slope is positive up to approximately $x = 1.5$. Matches (B)

3. Since $f'(x) = \frac{2}{3}$ for all x, $f(x)$ is a line of slope $\frac{2}{3}$. The y-intercept is $(0, 1)$: $f(x) = \frac{2}{3}x + 1$. Hence, $f(6) = 5$.

5. (a) $f'(x) = 0$ for $x = -2$ and $x = 2$

f' is negative for $-2 < x < 2$ (decreasing function).

f' is positive for $x > 2$ and $x < -2$ (increasing function).

(c) f' is increasing on $(0, \infty)$. $(f'' > 0)$

(b) $f''(x) = 0$ at $x = 0$ (Inflection point).

f'' is positive for $x > 0$ (concave upwards).

f'' is negative for $x < 0$ (concave downward).

(d) $f'(x)$ is minimum at $x = 0$. The rate of change of f at $x = 0$ is less than the rate of change of f for all other values of x.

7. $y = x^3 - 3x^2 + 3$

$y' = 3x^2 - 6x = 3x(x - 2) = 0$ when $x = 0, x = 2$.

$y'' = 6x - 6 = 6(x - 1) = 0$ when $x = 1$.

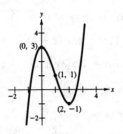

	y	y'	y''	Conclusion
$-\infty < x < 0$		+	−	Increasing, concave down
$x = 0$	3	0	−	Relative maximum
$0 < x < 1$		−	−	Decreasing, concave down
$x = 1$	1	−	0	Point of inflection
$1 < x < 2$		−	+	Decreasing, concave up
$x = 2$	−1	0	+	Relative minimum
$2 < x < \infty$		+	+	Increasing, concave up

9. $y = 2 - x - x^3$

$y' = -1 - 3x^2$

No critical numbers

$y'' = -6x = 0$ when $x = 0$.

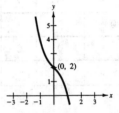

	y	y'	y''	Conclusion
$-\infty < x < 0$		−	+	Decreasing, concave up
$x = 0$	2	−	0	Point of inflection
$0 < x < \infty$		−	−	Decreasing, concave down

11. $f(x) = 3x^3 - 9x + 1$

$f'(x) = 9x^2 - 9 = 9(x^2 - 1) = 0$ when $x = \pm 1$.

$f''(x) = 18x = 0$ when $x = 0$.

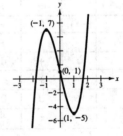

	$f(x)$	$f'(x)$	$f''(x)$	Conclusion
$-\infty < x < -1$		+	−	Increasing, concave down
$x = -1$	7	0	−	Relative maximum
$-1 < x < 0$		−	−	Decreasing, concave down
$x = 0$	1	−	0	Point of inflection
$0 < x < 1$		−	+	Decreasing, concave up
$x = 1$	−5	0	+	Relative minimum
$1 < x < \infty$		+	+	Increasing, concave up

13. $y = 3x^4 + 4x^3 = x^3(3x + 4)$

$y' = 12x^3 + 12x^2 = 12x^2(x + 1)$

$y'' = 36x^2 + 24x = 12x(3x + 2)$

Intercepts: $(0, 0)$, $\left(-\frac{4}{3}, 0\right)$

Critical numbers: $x = 0, x = -1$

Possible inflection points: $\left(-\frac{2}{3}, -\frac{16}{27}\right)$, $(0, 0)$

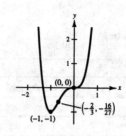

x	y	y'	y''	Shape of graph
$-\infty < x < -1$		$-$	$+$	decreasing, concave up
$x = -1$	-1	0	$+$	relative minimum
$-1 < x < -\frac{2}{3}$		$+$	$+$	increasing, concave up
$x = -\frac{2}{3}$	$-\frac{16}{27}$	$+$	0	point of inflection
$-\frac{2}{3} < x < 0$		$+$	$-$	increasing, concave down
$x = 0$	0	0	0	point of inflection
$0 < x < \infty$		$+$	$+$	increasing, concave up

15. $f(x) = x^4 - 4x^3 + 16x$

$f'(x) = 4x^3 - 12x^2 + 16 = 4(x + 1)(x - 2)^2 = 0$ when $x = -1, x = 2$.

$f''(x) = 12x^2 - 24x = 12x(x - 2) = 0$ when $x = 0, x = 2$.

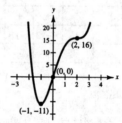

	$f(x)$	$f'(x)$	$f''(x)$	Conclusion
$-\infty < x < -1$		$-$	$+$	Decreasing, concave up
$x = -1$	-11	0	$+$	Relative minimum
$-1 < x < 0$		$+$	$+$	Increasing, concave up
$x = 0$	0	$+$	0	Point of inflection
$0 < x < 2$		$+$	$-$	Increasing, concave down
$x = 2$	16	0	0	Point of inflection
$2 < x < \infty$		$+$	$+$	Increasing, concave up

17. $y = x^5 - 5x$

$y' = 5x^4 - 5 = 5(x^4 - 1) = 0$ when $x = \pm 1$.

$y'' = 20x^3 = 0$ when $x = 0$.

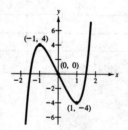

	y	y'	y''	Conclusion
$-\infty < x < -1$		$+$	$-$	Increasing, concave down
$x = -1$	4	0	$-$	Relative maximum
$-1 < x < 0$		$-$	$-$	Decreasing, concave down
$x = 0$	0	$-$	0	Point of inflection
$0 < x < 1$		$-$	$+$	Decreasing, concave up
$x = 1$	-4	0	$+$	Relative minimum
$1 < x < \infty$		$+$	$+$	Increasing, concave up

19. $f(x) = e^{3x}(2 - x)$

$f'(x) = -e^{3x} + 3(2 - x)e^{3x} = e^{3x}(5 - 3x)$

Critical point: $\left(\frac{5}{3}, 49.47\right)$

$f''(x) = -3e^{3x}(-4 + 3x) = 0$ when $x = \frac{4}{3}$.

Relative maximum: $\left(\frac{5}{3}, 49.47\right)$

Inflection point: $\left(\frac{4}{3}, 36.40\right)$

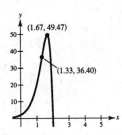

21. $y = (x - 1)\ln(x - 1)$,   Domain: $x > 1$

$y' = 1 + \ln(x - 1)$

$y'' = \dfrac{1}{x - 1}$

Critical number:

$\ln(x - 1) = -1 \Rightarrow (x - 1) = e^{-1} \Rightarrow x = 1 + e^{-1}$

Relative minimum: $(1.3679, -0.3679)$

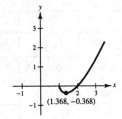

23. $y = |2x - 3|$

$y' = \dfrac{2(2x - 3)}{|2x - 3|}$ undefined at $x = \dfrac{3}{2}$.

$y'' = 0$

	y	y'	Conclusion
$-\infty < x < \frac{3}{2}$		$-$	Decreasing
$x = \frac{3}{2}$	0	Undefined	Relative minimum
$\frac{3}{2} < x < \infty$		$+$	Increasing

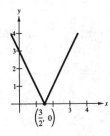

25. $y = x\sqrt{4 - x}$

$y' = x\left(\dfrac{1}{2}\right)(-1)(4 - x)^{-1/2} + (4 - x)^{1/2} = \dfrac{-x}{2\sqrt{4 - x}} + \sqrt{4 - x} = \dfrac{-x + 8 - 2x}{2\sqrt{4 - x}} = \dfrac{-3x + 8}{2\sqrt{4 - x}}$

$y'' = \dfrac{2(4 - x)^{1/2}(-3) - (-3x + 8)(2)(1/2)(-1)(4 - x)^{-1/2}}{4(4 - x)}$

$= \dfrac{-6(4 - x) + (-3x + 8)}{4(4 - x)^{3/2}}$

$= \dfrac{-24 + 6x - 3x + 8}{4(4 - x)^{3/2}} = \dfrac{3x - 16}{4(4 - x)^{3/2}}$

Domain: $x \le 4$

Intercepts: $(0, 0), (4, 0)$

Critical numbers: $\dfrac{8}{3}, 4$

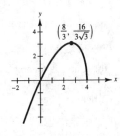

x	y	y'	y''	Shape of graph
$-\infty < x < \frac{8}{3}$		$+$	$-$	increasing, concave down
$x = \frac{8}{3}$	$\frac{16\sqrt{3}}{9}$	0	$-$	relative maximum
$\frac{8}{3} < x < 4$		$-$	$-$	decreasing, concave down
$x = 4$	0	undefined	undefined	

(**Note:** $x = \frac{16}{3}$ is not in the domain of the function.)

27. $y = 3x^{2/3} - 2x = x^{2/3}(3 - 2x^{1/3})$

$y' = 2x^{-1/3} - 2 = \dfrac{2(1 - x^{1/3})}{x^{1/3}}$

$y'' = \left(\dfrac{-1}{3}\right)(2)x^{-4/3} = \dfrac{-2}{3x^{4/3}}$

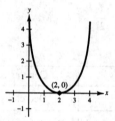

Intercepts: $(0, 0), \left(\dfrac{27}{8}, 0\right)$

Critical numbers: $x = 0, x = 1$

x	y	y'	y''	Shape of graph
$-\infty < x < 0$		$-$	$-$	decreasing, concave down
$x = 0$	0	undefined	undefined	relative minimum
$0 < x < 1$		$+$	$-$	increasing, concave down
$x = 1$	1	0	$-$	relative maximum
$1 < x < \infty$		$-$	$-$	decreasing, concave down

29. $g(x) = 2\arcsin\left(\dfrac{x-2}{2}\right)^2$;   Domain: $[0, 4]$

$g'(x) = \dfrac{4(x-2)}{\sqrt{(4x - x^2)(x^2 - 4x + 8)}}$

$g''(x) = \dfrac{4(x^4 - 8x^3 + 24x^2 - 32x + 32)}{[(4x - x^2)(x^2 - 4x + 8)]^{3/2}}$

Relative minimum: $(2, 0)$

31. $f(x) = \dfrac{x}{2^{x-2}} = x(2^{2-x})$

$f'(x) = x[(\ln 2)2^{2-x}(-1)] + 2^{2-x} = 2^{2-x}(1 - x\ln 2)$

$f''(x) = 2^{2-x}(1 - \ln 2) + (1 - x\ln 2)(\ln 2)2^{2-x}(-1)$

$\quad = 2^{2-x}(\ln 2)(x\ln 2 - 2)$

Intercept: $(0, 0)$

Horizontal asymptote: $y = 0$

Critical number: $x = \dfrac{1}{\ln 2} \approx 1.443$

Possible inflection point: $\left(\dfrac{2}{\ln 2}, \dfrac{8e^{-2}}{\ln 2}\right)$

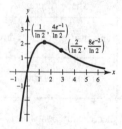

x	$f(x)$	$f'(x)$	$f''(x)$	Shape of graph
$-\infty < x < \dfrac{1}{\ln 2}$		$+$	$-$	increasing, concave down
$x = \dfrac{1}{\ln 2}$	$\dfrac{4e^{-1}}{\ln 2}$	0	$-$	relative maximum
$\dfrac{1}{\ln 2} < x < \dfrac{2}{\ln 2}$		$-$	$-$	decreasing, concave down
$x = \dfrac{2}{\ln 2}$	$\dfrac{8e^{-2}}{\ln 2}$	$-$	0	point of inflection
$\dfrac{2}{\ln 2} < x < \infty$		$-$	$+$	decreasing, concave up

33. $y = \sin x - \dfrac{1}{18}\sin 3x$

$y' = \cos x - \dfrac{1}{6}\cos 3x$

$\quad = \cos x - \dfrac{1}{6}(4\cos^3 x - 3\cos x)$

$\quad = -\dfrac{1}{6}\cos x(4\cos^2 x - 9)$

$y'' = -\dfrac{1}{6}[\cos x(8\cos x)(-\sin x) + (4\cos^2 x - 9)(-\sin x)]$

$\quad = \dfrac{1}{6}\sin x(8\cos^2 x + 4\cos^2 x - 9)$

$\quad = \dfrac{1}{2}\sin x(4\cos^2 x - 3)$

$y'' = 0$ when $x = 0, \dfrac{\pi}{6}, \dfrac{5\pi}{6}, \pi, \dfrac{7\pi}{6}, \dfrac{11\pi}{6}$

Critical numbers: $x = \dfrac{\pi}{2}, \dfrac{3\pi}{2}$

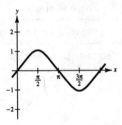

x	y	y'	y''	Shape of graph
$0 < x < \dfrac{\pi}{6}$		$+$	$+$	increasing, concave up
$x = \dfrac{\pi}{6}$	$\dfrac{4}{9}$	$+$	0	point of inflection
$\dfrac{\pi}{6} < x < \dfrac{\pi}{2}$		$+$	$-$	increasing, concave down
$x = \dfrac{\pi}{2}$	$\dfrac{19}{18}$	0	$-$	relative maximum
$\dfrac{\pi}{2} < x < \dfrac{5\pi}{6}$		$-$	$-$	decreasing, concave down
$x = \dfrac{5\pi}{6}$	$\dfrac{4}{9}$	$-$	0	point of inflection
$\dfrac{5\pi}{6} < x < \pi$		$-$	$+$	decreasing, concave up
$x = \pi$	0	$-$	0	point of inflection
$\pi < x < \dfrac{7\pi}{6}$		$-$	$-$	decreasing, concave down
$x = \dfrac{7\pi}{6}$	$-\dfrac{4}{9}$	$-$	0	point of inflection
$\dfrac{7\pi}{6} < x < \dfrac{3\pi}{2}$		$-$	$+$	decreasing, concave up
$x = \dfrac{3\pi}{2}$	$-\dfrac{19}{18}$	0	$+$	relative minimum
$\dfrac{3\pi}{2} < x < \dfrac{11\pi}{6}$		$+$	$+$	increasing, concave up
$x = \dfrac{11\pi}{6}$	$-\dfrac{4}{9}$	$+$	0	point of inflection
$\dfrac{11\pi}{6} < x < 2\pi$		$+$	$-$	increasing, concave down

35. $y = 2x - \tan x, \quad -\dfrac{\pi}{2} < x < \dfrac{\pi}{2}$

$y' = 2 - \sec^2 x = 0$ when $x = \pm\dfrac{\pi}{4}$.

$y'' = -2\sec^2 x \tan x = 0$ when $x = 0$.

Relative maximum: $\left(\dfrac{\pi}{4}, \dfrac{\pi}{2} - 1\right)$

Relative minimum: $\left(-\dfrac{\pi}{4}, 1 - \dfrac{\pi}{2}\right)$

Inflection point: $(0, 0)$

Vertical asymptotes: $x = \pm\dfrac{\pi}{2}$

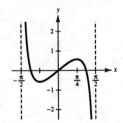

37. $y = \dfrac{x^2}{x^2 + 3}$

$y' = \dfrac{6x}{(x^2 + 3)^2} = 0$ when $x = 0$.

$y'' = \dfrac{18(1 - x^2)}{(x^2 + 3)^3} = 0$ when $x = \pm 1$.

Horizontal asymptote: $y = 1$

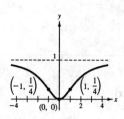

	y	y'	y''	Conclusion
$-\infty < x < -1$		$-$	$-$	decreasing, concave down
$x = -1$	$\frac{1}{4}$	$-$	0	point of inflection
$-1 < x < 0$		$-$	$+$	decreasing, concave up
$x = 0$	0	0	$+$	relative minimum
$0 < x < 1$		$+$	$+$	increasing, concave up
$x = 1$	$\frac{1}{4}$	$+$	0	point of inflection
$1 < x < \infty$		$+$	$-$	increasing, concave down

39. $y = \dfrac{1}{x - 2} - 3$

$\quad = \dfrac{1 - 3(x - 2)}{x - 2}$

$\quad = \dfrac{7 - 3x}{x - 2}$

$y' = \dfrac{-1}{(x - 2)^2}$

$y'' = \dfrac{2}{(x - 2)^3}$

Domain: all $x \ne 2$

Intercepts: $\left(\dfrac{7}{3}, 0\right), \left(0, -\dfrac{7}{2}\right)$

x	y'	y''	Shape of graph
$-\infty < x < 2$	$-$	$-$	decreasing, concave down
$2 < x < \infty$	$-$	$+$	decreasing, concave up

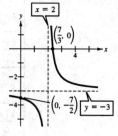

The graph has a vertical asymptote at $x = 2$. Since

$$\lim_{x \to \pm\infty} \left(\dfrac{1}{x - 2} - 3\right) = -3,$$

there is a horizontal asymptote at $y = -3$.

41. $y = \dfrac{2x}{x^2 - 1}$

$y' = \dfrac{-2(x^2 + 1)}{(x^2 - 1)^2} < 0$ if $x \ne \pm 1$.

$y'' = \dfrac{4x(x^2 + 3)}{(x^2 - 1)^3} = 0$ if $x = 0$.

Inflection point: $(0, 0)$

Intercept: $(0, 0)$

Vertical asymptote: $x = \pm 1$

Horizontal asymptote: $y = 0$

Symmetry with respect to the origin

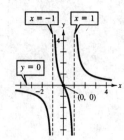

43. $g(x) = x + \dfrac{4}{x^2 + 1}$

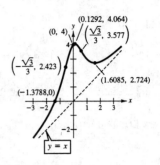

$g'(x) = 1 - \dfrac{8x}{(x^2 + 1)^2} = \dfrac{x^4 + 2x^2 - 8x + 1}{(x^2 + 1)^2} = 0$ when $x \approx 0.1292,\ 1.6085.$

$g''(x) = \dfrac{8(3x^2 - 1)}{(x^2 + 1)^3} = 0$ when $x = \pm\dfrac{\sqrt{3}}{3}.$

$g''(0.1292) < 0,$ therefore, $(0.1292, 4.064)$ is relative maximum.

$g''(1.6085) > 0,$ therefore, $(1.6085, 2.724)$ is a relative minimum.

Points of inflection: $\left(-\dfrac{\sqrt{3}}{3},\ 2.423\right),\ \left(\dfrac{\sqrt{3}}{3},\ 3.577\right)$

Intercepts: $(0, 4),\ (-1.3788, 0)$

Slant asymptote: $y = x$

45. $f(x) = \dfrac{x^2 + 1}{x} = x + \dfrac{1}{x}$

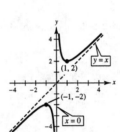

$f'(x) = 1 - \dfrac{1}{x^2} = 0$ when $x = \pm 1.$

$f''(x) = \dfrac{2}{x^3} \neq 0$

Relative maximum: $(-1, -2)$

Relative minimum: $(1, 2)$

Vertical asymptote: $x = 0$

Slant asymptote: $y = x$

47. $y = \dfrac{x^2 - 6x + 12}{x - 4} = x - 2 + \dfrac{4}{x - 4}$

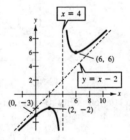

$y' = 1 - \dfrac{4}{(x - 4)^2}$

$\quad = \dfrac{(x - 2)(x - 6)}{(x - 4)^2} = 0$ when $x = 2, 6.$

$y'' = \dfrac{8}{(x - 4)^3}$

$y'' < 0$ when $x = 2.$

Therefore, $(2, -2)$ is a relative maximum.

$y'' > 0$ when $x = 6.$

Therefore, $(6, 6)$ is a relative minimum.

Vertical asymptote: $x = 4$

Slant asymptote: $y = x - 2$

49. $g(t) = \dfrac{10}{1 + 4e^{-t}} = 10(1 + 4e^{-t})^{-1}$

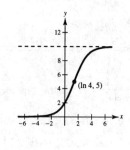

$g'(t) = 10(-1)(1 + 4e^{-t})^{-2}(-4e^{-t}) = \dfrac{40}{(1 + 4e^{-t})^2}$

$g''(t) = 40\left[\dfrac{(1 + 4e^{-t})^2(-e^{-t}) - e^{-t}(2)(1 + 4e^{-t})(-4e^{-t})}{(1 + 4e^{-t})^4}\right]$

$\quad\;\; = 40\left[\dfrac{(1 + 4e^{-t})(-e^{-t}) + 8e^{-t}}{(1 + 4e^{-t})^3}\right]$

$\quad\;\; = \dfrac{40e^{-t}(4e^{-t} - 1)}{(1 + 4e^{-t})^3}$

Observe that $g'(t) > 0$ for all real numbers t. Therefore, g is an increasing function and there are no extrema. Solving the equation $g''(t) = 0$ yields:

$4e^{-t} - 1 = 0$

$\quad 4 - e^{-t} = 0 \Rightarrow t = \ln 4$

Since $g''(t) > 0$ for $t < \ln 4$ and $g''(t) < 0$ for $t > \ln 4$, the point $(\ln 4, 5)$ is a point of inflection. Recall that

$\quad \lim_{t \to \infty} e^{-t} = 0 \quad \text{and} \quad \lim_{t \to -\infty} e^{-t} = \infty.$

Using these limits, it follows that

$\quad \lim_{t \to \infty} \dfrac{10}{1 + 4e^{-t}} = 10$

$\quad \lim_{t \to -\infty} \dfrac{10}{1 + 4e^{-t}} = 0.$

Hence, $y = 0$ and $y = 10$ are horizontal asymptotes.

51. $f(x) = \dfrac{20x}{x^2 + 1} - \dfrac{1}{x} = \dfrac{19x^2 - 1}{x(x^2 + 1)}$

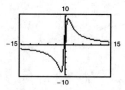

Vertical asymptote: $x = 0$

Horizontal asymptote: $y = 0$

53. Begin by using a symbolic differentiation utility to find f' and f''.

$f(x) = \dfrac{x}{\sqrt{x^2 + 7}}$

$f'(x) = \dfrac{7}{(x^2 + 7)^{3/2}}$

$f''(x) = \dfrac{-21x}{(x^2 + 7)^{5/2}}$

x	$f(x)$	$f'(x)$	$f''(x)$	Shape of graph
$-\infty < x < 0$		$+$	$+$	increasing, concave up
$x = 0$	0	$+$	0	point of inflection
$0 < x < \infty$		$+$	$-$	increasing, concave down

Note that $f'(x) > 0$ for all x and there are no critical numbers. Since $f''(0) = 0$ there is a possible point of inflection at $(0, 0)$.

There are no vertical asymptotes since the function is continuous for all x. To determine if there are horizontal asymptotes, use a symbolic differentiation utility to find the following limits.

$\quad \lim_{x \to \infty} \dfrac{x}{\sqrt{x^2 + 7}} = 1$

$\quad \lim_{x \to -\infty} \dfrac{x}{\sqrt{x^2 + 7}} = -1$

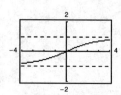

Therefore, $y = 1$ and $y = -1$ are horizontal asymptotes. The graph of f is shown in the figure.

55. $y = \dfrac{x}{2} + \ln\left(\dfrac{x}{x+3}\right)$

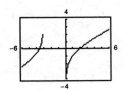

Vertical asymptotes: $x = -3, x = 0$

Slant asymptote: $y = \dfrac{x}{2}$

57. $f(x) = \dfrac{4(x-1)^2}{x^2 - 4x + 5}$

Vertical asymptote: none

Horizontal asymptote: $y = 4$

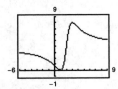

The graph crosses the horizontal asymptote $y = 4$. If a function has a vertical asymptote at $x = c$, the graph would not cross it since $f(c)$ is undefined.

59. $h(x) = \dfrac{6 - 2x}{3 - x}$

$= \dfrac{2(3-x)}{3-x} = \begin{cases} 2, & \text{if } x \neq 3 \\ \text{Undefined}, & \text{if } x = 3 \end{cases}$

The rational function is not reduced to lowest terms.

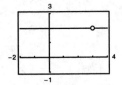

Hole at $(3, 2)$

61. $f(x) = -\dfrac{x^2 - 3x - 1}{x - 2} = -x + 1 + \dfrac{3}{x - 2}$

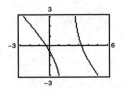

The graph appears to approach the slant asymptote $y = -x + 1$.

63. Vertical asymptote: $x = 5$

Horizontal asymptote: $y = 0$

$$y = \dfrac{1}{x - 5}$$

65. Since $x = 5$ is an asymptote, f is a rational function such that the numerator is not zero and the denominator is zero at $x = 5$. Since $y = 3x + 2$ is a slant asymptote,

$$\lim_{x \to \infty} f(x) = 3x + 2.$$

Therefore,

$$f(x) = 3x + 2 + \dfrac{1}{x - 5} = \dfrac{3x^2 - 13x - 9}{x - 5},$$

is one function that satisfies the requirements.

67. $f(x) = \dfrac{ax}{(x - b)^2}$

(a) The graph has a vertical asymptote at $x = b$. If $a > 0$, the graph approaches ∞ as $x \to b$. If $a < 0$, the graph approaches $-\infty$ as $x \to b$. The graph approaches its vertical asymptote faster as $|a| \to 0$.

(b) As b varies, the position of the vertical asymptote changes: $x = b$. Also, the coordinates of the minimum are changed.

69. $g(x) = \ln f(x),\ f(x) > 0$

$g'(x) = \dfrac{f'(x)}{f(x)}$

(a) Yes. If the graph of g is increasing, then $g'(x) > 0$. Since $f(x) > 0$, you know that $f'(x) = g'(x)f(x)$ and thus, $f'(x) > 0$. Therefore, the graph of f is increasing.

(b) No. Let $f(x) = x^2 + 1$ (positive and concave up). $g(x) = \ln(x^2 + 1)$ is not concave up.

71. (a)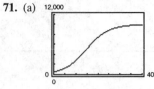

(b) Limiting size: 10,000 fish

(c) $p(t) = \dfrac{10,000}{1 + 19e^{-t/5}}$

$p'(t) = \dfrac{e^{-t/5}}{(1 + 19e^{t/5})^2}\left(\dfrac{19}{5}\right)(10,000) = \dfrac{38,000e^{-t/5}}{(1 + 19e^{-t/5})^2}$

$p'(1) \approx 113.5$ fish/month

$p'(10) \approx 403.2$ fish/month

(d) $p''(t) = -\dfrac{38,000}{5}(e^{-t/5})\left[\dfrac{1 - 19e^{-t/5}}{(1 + 19e^{-t/5})^3}\right] = 0$

$19e^{-t/5} = 1$

$\dfrac{t}{5} = \ln 19$

$t = 5 \ln 19 \approx 14.72$

73. $f'(x) = -(x - 1)(x - 3) = -x^2 + 4x - 3$

Relative minimum when $x = 1$.

Relative maximum when $x = 3$.

$f(x) = -\dfrac{x^3}{3} + 2x^2 - 3x + C, C$ is any constant .

Let $C = 0; f(x) = -\dfrac{x^3}{3} + 2x^2 - 3x$

$f(1) = -\dfrac{4}{3}$

$f(3) = 0.$

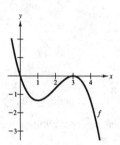

75. $f'(x) = 2$

$f(x) = 2x + C,$
C is any constant.

If $C = 0, f(x) = 2x.$

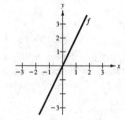

77. f is cubic.

f' is quadratic.

f'' is linear.

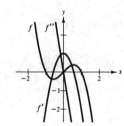

In Exercises 79–83,

$f(x) = ax^3 + bx^2 + cx + d$

$f'(x) = 3ax^2 + 2bx + c$

$f''(x) = 6ax + 2b$

$f'(x) = 0$ when $x = \dfrac{-2b \pm \sqrt{4b^2 - 12ac}}{6a} = \dfrac{-b \pm \sqrt{b^2 - 3ac}}{3a}.$

Furthermore, $\lim\limits_{x \to \infty} f(x) = \infty$ **if and only if** $a > 0,$ **and** $\lim\limits_{x \to \infty} f(x) = -\infty$ **if and only if** $a < 0.$

79. Since $f(x) = ax^3 + bx^2 + cx + d$ and

$\lim\limits_{x \to \infty} f(x) = -\infty, a < 0.$

Also, $f(x)$ is a decreasing function, and therefore $f'(x) = 3ax^2 + 2bx + c < 0$ for all x. Hence, the discriminant must be negative and we have

$(2b)^2 - 4(3a)(c) < 0 \implies 4(b^2 - 3ac) < 0$

$\implies b^2 < 3ac.$

81. Since $\lim_{x \to \infty} f(x) = -\infty, a < 0$. Also, since there is only one critical point, the discriminant is zero.

$$b^2 - 3ac = 0 \Rightarrow b^2 = 3ac$$

83. Since $\lim_{x \to \infty} f(x) = -\infty, a < 0$. Also, since there are two critical points, the discriminant is positive.

$$b^2 - 3ac > 0 \Rightarrow b^2 > 3ac$$

85.

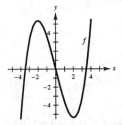

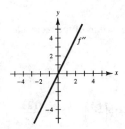

(Any vertical translate of f will do.)

87.

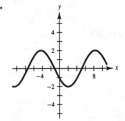

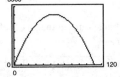

(Any vertical translate of f will do.)

Section 3.7   Optimization Problems

1. (a)

First Number, x	Second Number	Product, P
10	$110 - 10$	$10(110 - 10) = 1000$
20	$110 - 20$	$20(110 - 20) = 1800$
30	$110 - 30$	$30(110 - 30) = 2400$
40	$110 - 40$	$40(110 - 40) = 2800$
50	$110 - 50$	$50(110 - 50) = 3000$
60	$110 - 60$	$60(110 - 60) = 3000$

(b)

First Number, x	Second Number	Product, P
10	$110 - 10$	$10(110 - 10) = 1000$
20	$110 - 20$	$20(110 - 20) = 1800$
30	$110 - 30$	$30(110 - 30) = 2400$
40	$110 - 40$	$40(110 - 40) = 2800$
50	$110 - 50$	$50(110 - 50) = 3000$
60	$110 - 60$	$60(110 - 60) = 3000$
70	$110 - 70$	$70(110 - 70) = 2800$
80	$110 - 80$	$80(110 - 80) = 2400$
90	$110 - 90$	$90(110 - 90) = 1800$
100	$110 - 100$	$100(110 - 100) = 1000$

The maximum is attained near $x = 50$ and 60.

(c) $P = x(110 - x) = 110x - x^2$

(d)

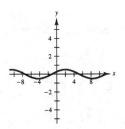

The solution appears to be $x = 55$.

(e) $\dfrac{dP}{dx} = 110 - 2x = 0$ when $x = 55$.

$$\frac{d^2P}{dx^2} = -2 < 0$$

P is a maximum when $x = 110 - x = 55$.

3. Let x and y be two positive numbers such that $xy = 192$.

$$S = x + y = x + \frac{192}{x}$$

$$\frac{dS}{dx} = 1 - \frac{192}{x^2} = 0 \text{ when } x = \sqrt{192}.$$

$$\frac{d^2S}{dx^2} = \frac{384}{x^3} > 0 \text{ when } x = \sqrt{192}.$$

S is a minimum when $x = y = \sqrt{192}$.

5. Let $x =$ first number, $y =$ second number, and $S =$ the sum to be minimized. To minimize S, use the *primary* equation $S = x + y$. Since the second number is the reciprocal of the first, the *secondary* equation is $y = 1/x$, and therefore, $S = x + (1/x)$. Differentiation yields:

$$\frac{dS}{dx} = 1 - \frac{1}{x^2}$$

$$\frac{dS}{dx} = 0 \text{ when } x = \pm 1$$

$$\frac{d^2S}{dx^2} = \frac{2}{x^3}$$

Finally, since the second derivative is positive when $x = 1$, it follows that S is minimum when $x = 1$ and $y = 1$.

7. Let x be the length and y the width of the rectangle.

$$2x + 2y = 100$$

$$y = 50 - x$$

$$A = xy = x(50 - x)$$

$$\frac{dA}{dx} = 50 - 2x = 0 \text{ when } x = 25.$$

$$\frac{d^2A}{dx^2} = -2 < 0 \text{ when } x = 25.$$

A is maximum when $x = y = 25$ meters.

9. Let x be the length and y the width of the rectangle.

$$xy = 64$$

$$y = \frac{64}{x}$$

$$P = 2x + 2y = 2x + 2\left(\frac{64}{x}\right) = 2x + \frac{128}{x}$$

$$\frac{dP}{dx} = 2 - \frac{128}{x^2} = 0 \text{ when } x = 8.$$

$$\frac{d^2P}{dx^2} = \frac{256}{x^3} > 0 \text{ when } x = 8.$$

P is minimum when $x = y = 8$ feet.

11. Let (x, y) to be a point on the graph of $y = \sqrt{x}$. The distance between (x, y) and the point $(4, 0)$ is given by the *primary* equation

$$d(x) = \sqrt{(x - 4)^2 + (y - 0)^2} = [(x - 4)^2 + y^2]^{1/2}.$$

Since $y = \sqrt{x}$, we have $d(x) = [(x - 4)^2 + x]^{1/2}$.

To minimize $d(x)$, solve $d'(x) = 0$ as follows:

$$d'(x) = \frac{1}{2}[(x - 4)^2 + x]^{-1/2}[2(x - 4) + 1]$$

$$= \frac{2(x - 4) + 1}{2\sqrt{(x - 4)^2 + x}} = \frac{2x - 7}{2\sqrt{(x - 4)^2 + x}}$$

We observe that $d'(x) = 0$ when

$$2x - 7 = 0$$

$$x = \frac{7}{2} \quad \text{and} \quad y = \sqrt{\frac{7}{2}}.$$

Therefore, the required point is $\left(\frac{7}{2}, \sqrt{\frac{7}{2}}\right)$.

13. $\dfrac{dQ}{dx} = kx(Q_0 - x) = kQ_0x - kx^2$

$\dfrac{d^2Q}{dx^2} = kQ_0 - 2kx$

$\quad = k(Q_0 - 2x) = 0$ when $x = \dfrac{Q_0}{2}$.

$\dfrac{d^3Q}{dx^3} = -2k < 0$ when $x = \dfrac{Q_0}{2}$.

dQ/dx is maximum when $x = Q_0/2$.

15. $xy = 180,000$ (see figure)

$S = x + 2y = \left(x + \dfrac{360,000}{x} \right)$ where S is the length of fence needed.

$\dfrac{dS}{dx} = 1 - \dfrac{360,000}{x^2} = 0$ when $x = 600$.

$\dfrac{d^2S}{dx^2} = \dfrac{720,000}{x^3} > 0$ when $x = 600$.

S is a minimum when $x = 600$ meters and $y = 300$ meters.

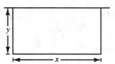

17. (a)

Height, x	Length & Width	Volume
1	$24 - 2(1)$	$1[24 - 2(1)]^2 = 484$
2	$24 - 2(2)$	$2[24 - 2(2)]^2 = 800$
3	$24 - 2(3)$	$3[24 - 2(3)]^2 = 972$
4	$24 - 2(4)$	$4[24 - 2(4)]^2 = 1024$
5	$24 - 2(5)$	$5[24 - 2(5)]^2 = 980$
6	$24 - 2(6)$	$6[24 - 2(6)]^2 = 864$

(b) $V = x(24 - 2x)^2,\ 0 < x < 12$

(c) $\dfrac{dV}{dx} = 2x(24 - 2x)(-2) + (24 - 2x)^2 = (24 - 2x)(24 - 6x)$

$\quad = 12(12 - x)(4 - x) = 0$ when $x = 12, 4$ (12 is not in the domain).

$\dfrac{d^2V}{dx^2} = 12(2x - 16)$

$\dfrac{d^2V}{dx^2} < 0$ when $x = 4$.

When $x = 4$, $V = 1024$ is maximum.

(d)

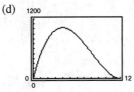

The maximum volume seems to be 1024.

19. The area A of the window is given by the *primary* equation

$$A = xy + \frac{1}{2}\pi r^2 = xy + \frac{1}{2}\pi\left(\frac{x}{2}\right)^2.$$

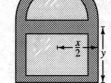

The *secondary* equation is formulated from the known perimeter of the window.

$$2y + x + \pi r = 16$$

$$2y + x + \pi\left(\frac{x}{2}\right) = 16$$

$$4y + 2x + \pi x = 32 \implies y = \frac{32 - 2x - \pi x}{4}$$

Substituting this expression for y into the primary equation and differentiating yields

$$A = x\left(\frac{32 - 2x - \pi x}{4}\right) + \frac{1}{2}\pi\left(\frac{x}{2}\right)^2 = 8x - \frac{1}{2}x^2 - \frac{\pi}{4}x^2 + \frac{\pi}{8}x^2$$

$$\frac{dA}{dx} = 8 - x - \frac{\pi}{2}x + \frac{\pi}{4}x = 8 - \left(1 + \frac{\pi}{4}\right)x$$

$$\frac{d^2A}{dx^2} = -\left(1 + \frac{\pi}{4}\right) < 0.$$

To find any critical numbers solve the equation $dA/dx = 0$.

$$8 - \left(1 + \frac{\pi}{4}\right)x = 0 \implies x = \frac{8}{1 + (\pi/4)} = \frac{32}{4 + \pi}$$

Substituting this value of x into the secondary equation yields

$$y = \frac{32 - 2x - \pi x}{4}$$

$$= \frac{32 - 2\left(\dfrac{32}{4 + \pi}\right) - \pi\left(\dfrac{32}{4 + \pi}\right)}{4} = \frac{16}{4 + \pi}$$

Since $d^2A/dx^2 < 0$, the area is maximum when $x = \dfrac{32}{4 + \pi}$ and $y = \dfrac{16}{4 + \pi}$.

21. $A = 2xy = 2x\sqrt{25 - x^2}$ (see figure)

$$\frac{dA}{dx} = 2x\left(\frac{1}{2}\right)\left(\frac{-2x}{\sqrt{25 - x^2}}\right) + 2\sqrt{25 - x^2} = 2\left(\frac{25 - 2x^2}{\sqrt{25 - x^2}}\right) = 0 \text{ when } x = y = \frac{5\sqrt{2}}{2} \approx 3.54.$$

By the First Derivative Test, the inscribed rectangle of maximum area has vertices

$$\left(\pm\frac{5\sqrt{2}}{2}, 0\right), \left(\pm\frac{5\sqrt{2}}{2}, \frac{5\sqrt{2}}{2}\right).$$

Width: $\dfrac{5\sqrt{2}}{2}$; Length: $5\sqrt{2}$

23. $A = \frac{1}{2}(2r + 2x)\sqrt{r^2 - x^2} = (r + x)\sqrt{r^2 - x^2}$ (see figure)

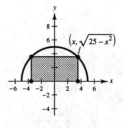

$$\frac{dA}{dx} = (r + x)\left(\frac{1}{2}\right)(r^2 - x^2)^{-1/2}(-2x) + \sqrt{r^2 - x^2}$$

$$= \frac{-x(r + x)}{\sqrt{r^2 - x^2}} + \sqrt{r^2 - x^2} = \frac{r^2 - rx - 2x^2}{\sqrt{r^2 - x^2}}$$

$$= \frac{(r - 2x)(r + x)}{\sqrt{r^2 - x^2}} = 0 \text{ when } x = \frac{r}{2}.$$

By the First Derivative Test, A will be a maximum when the trapezoid bases are r and $2r$, and the altitude is $\left(\sqrt{3}r\right)/2$.

25. (a) See the first six rows of the table in part (b).

(b)

Radius r	Height	Surface Area
0.2	$\dfrac{22}{\pi(0.2)^2}$	$2\pi(0.2)\left[0.2 + \dfrac{22}{\pi(0.2)^2}\right] \approx 220.3$
0.4	$\dfrac{22}{\pi(0.4)^2}$	$2\pi(0.4)\left[0.4 + \dfrac{22}{\pi(0.4)^2}\right] \approx 111.1$
0.6	$\dfrac{22}{\pi(0.6)^2}$	$2\pi(0.6)\left[0.6 + \dfrac{22}{\pi(0.6)^2}\right] \approx 75.6$
0.8	$\dfrac{22}{\pi(0.8)^2}$	$2\pi(0.8)\left[0.8 + \dfrac{22}{\pi(0.8)^2}\right] \approx 59.0$
1.0	$\dfrac{22}{\pi(1.0)^2}$	$2\pi(1.0)\left[1.0 + \dfrac{22}{\pi(1.0)^2}\right] \approx 50.3$
1.2	$\dfrac{22}{\pi(1.2)^2}$	$2\pi(1.2)\left[1.2 + \dfrac{22}{\pi(1.2)^2}\right] \approx 45.7$
1.4	$\dfrac{22}{\pi(1.4)^2}$	$2\pi(1.4)\left[1.4 + \dfrac{22}{\pi(1.4)^2}\right] \approx 43.7$
1.6	$\dfrac{22}{\pi(1.6)^2}$	$2\pi(1.6)\left[1.6 + \dfrac{22}{\pi(1.6)^2}\right] \approx 43.6$
1.8	$\dfrac{22}{\pi(1.8)^2}$	$2\pi(1.8)\left[1.8 + \dfrac{22}{\pi(1.8)^2}\right] \approx 44.8$
2.0	$\dfrac{22}{\pi(2.0)^2}$	$2\pi(2.0)\left[2.0 + \dfrac{22}{\pi(2.0)^2}\right] \approx 47.1$

The estimate of the minimum surface area is 43.6 square inches.

(c) The volume of the right circular cylinder (see figure) is $V = \pi r^2 h$ and its surface area is

$$S = 2(\text{area of base}) + (\text{lateral surface})$$

$$= 2\pi r^2 + 2\pi rh = 2\pi r(r + h).$$

From the formula for the volume it follows that

$h = V/(\pi r^2)$. Since $V = 22$ cubic inches, we have

$$S = 2\pi r\left(r + \frac{22}{\pi r^2}\right) = 2\pi r^2 + \frac{44}{r}.$$

(d) The graph of area function is given in the figure. From the graph, the estimate of the minimum surface area is 43.46 square inches.

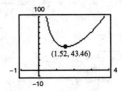

(1.52, 43.46)

(e) $\dfrac{dS}{dr} = 4\pi r - \dfrac{44}{r^2} = 0$

$$2r = \frac{22}{\pi r^2}$$

$$r^3 = \frac{11}{\pi} \text{ or } r = \sqrt[3]{\frac{11}{\pi}}$$

Since

$$\frac{d^2S}{dr^2} = 4\pi + \frac{88}{r^3}$$

is positive at the critical number $r = \sqrt[3]{11/\pi}$, this radius yields the minimum surface area of the cylinder. The corresponding height is

$$h = \frac{22}{\pi r^2} = \frac{22r}{\pi r^3} = \frac{22r}{\pi(11/\pi)} = 2r.$$

Note that the surface area is minimum when the height of the cylinder equals the diameter.

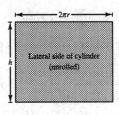

Lateral side of cylinder (unrolled)

27. Let x be the sides of the square ends and y the length of the package.

$$P = 4x + y = 108 \implies y = 108 - 4x$$

$$V = x^2 y = x^2(108 - 4x) = 108x^2 - 4x^3$$

$$\frac{dV}{dx} = 216x - 12x^2$$

$$= 12x(18 - x) = 0 \text{ when } x = 18.$$

$$\frac{d^2V}{dx^2} = 216 - 24x = -216 < 0 \text{ when } x = 18.$$

The volume is maximum when $x = 18$ inches and $y = 108 - 4(18) = 36$ inches.

29. $V = \frac{1}{3}\pi x^2 h = \frac{1}{3}\pi x^2\left(r + \sqrt{r^2 - x^2}\right)$ (see figure)

$$\frac{dV}{dx} = \frac{1}{3}\pi\left[\frac{-x^3}{\sqrt{r^2 - x^2}} + 2x\left(r + \sqrt{r^2 - x^2}\right)\right] = \frac{\pi x}{3\sqrt{r^2 - x^2}}\left(2r^2 + 2r\sqrt{r^2 - x^2} - 3x^2\right) = 0$$

$$2r^2 + 2r\sqrt{r^2 - x^2} - 3x^2 = 0$$

$$2r\sqrt{r^2 - x^2} = 3x^2 - 2r^2$$

$$4r^2(r^2 - x^2) = 9x^4 - 12x^2r^2 + 4r^4$$

$$0 = 9x^4 - 8x^2r^2 = x^2(9x^2 - 8r^2)$$

$$x = 0, \frac{2\sqrt{2}r}{3}$$

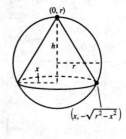

By the First Derivative Test, the volume is a maximum when

$$x = \frac{2\sqrt{2}r}{3} \text{ and } h = r + \sqrt{r^2 - x^2} = \frac{4r}{3}.$$

Thus, the maximum volume is

$$V = \frac{1}{3}\pi\left(\frac{8r^2}{9}\right)\left(\frac{4r}{3}\right) = \frac{32\pi r^3}{81}\text{ cubic units.}$$

31. $V = 12 = \frac{4}{3}\pi r^3 + \pi r^2 h$

$$h = \frac{12 - (4/3)\pi r^3}{\pi r^2} = \frac{12}{\pi r^2} - \frac{4}{3}r$$

$$S = 4\pi r^2 + 2\pi rh = 4\pi r^2 + 2\pi r\left(\frac{12}{\pi r^2} - \frac{4}{3}r\right)$$

$$= 4\pi r^2 + \frac{24}{r} - \frac{8}{3}\pi r^2 = \frac{4}{3}\pi r^2 + \frac{24}{r}$$

$$\frac{dS}{dr} = \frac{8}{3}\pi r - \frac{24}{r^2} = 0 \text{ when } r = \sqrt[3]{9/\pi} \approx 1.42 \text{ cm.}$$

$$\frac{d^2S}{dr^2} = \frac{8}{3}\pi + \frac{48}{r^3} > 0 \text{ when } r = \sqrt[3]{9/\pi} \text{ cm.}$$

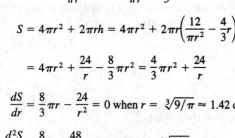

The surface area is minimum when $r = \sqrt[3]{9/\pi}$ cm and $h = 0$. The resulting solid is a sphere of radius $r \approx 1.42$ cm.

33. Let x be the length of a side of the square and y the length of a side of the triangle.

$$4x + 3y = 10$$

$$A = x^2 + \frac{1}{2}y\left(\frac{\sqrt{3}}{2}y\right)$$

$$= \frac{(10 - 3y)^2}{16} + \frac{\sqrt{3}}{4}y^2$$

$$\frac{dA}{dy} = \frac{1}{8}(10 - 3y)(-3) + \frac{\sqrt{3}}{2}y = 0$$

$$-30 + 9y + 4\sqrt{3}y = 0$$

$$y = \frac{30}{9 + 4\sqrt{3}}$$

$$\frac{d^2A}{dy^2} = \frac{9 + 4\sqrt{3}}{8} > 0$$

A is minimum when $y = \frac{30}{9 + 4\sqrt{3}}$ and $x = \frac{10\sqrt{3}}{9 + 4\sqrt{3}}$.

35. Letting S be the strength and k the constant of proportionality, we have $S = kwh^2$. Since $w^2 + h^2 = 24^2$, we have $h^2 = 24^2 - w^2$.

$$S = kw(24^2 - w^2) = k(576w = w^3)$$

Differentiating and solving $dS/dw = 0$, yields

$$\frac{dS}{dw} = k(576 - 3w^2) = 0$$

$$3w^2 = 576$$

$$w^2 = 192$$

$$w = \pm 8\sqrt{3}.$$

Since w is positive, it follows that $w = 8\sqrt{3}$ inches and

$$h = \sqrt{24^2 - \left(8\sqrt{3}\right)^2} = 8\sqrt{6}$$

inches will produce the strongest beam.

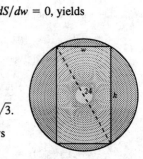

37. $R = \dfrac{v_0^2}{g} \sin 2\theta$

$\dfrac{dR}{d\theta} = \dfrac{2v_0^2}{g} \cos 2\theta = 0$ when $\theta = \dfrac{\pi}{4}, \dfrac{3\pi}{4}$.

$\dfrac{d^2R}{d\theta^2} = -\dfrac{4v_0^2}{g} \sin 2\theta < 0$ when $\theta = \dfrac{\pi}{4}$.

By the Second Derivative Test, R is maximum when $\theta = \pi/4$.

39. $f(x) = \frac{1}{2}x^2$, $g(x) = \frac{1}{16}x^4 - \frac{1}{2}x^2$ on $[0, 4]$

(a)

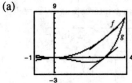

(b) $d(x) = f(x) - g(x) = \frac{1}{2}x^2 - \left(\frac{1}{16}x^4 - \frac{1}{2}x^2\right) = x^2 - \frac{1}{16}x^4$

$d'(x) = 2x - \frac{1}{4}x^3 = 0 \Rightarrow 8x = x^3$

$\Rightarrow x = 0, 2\sqrt{2}$ (in $[0, 4]$)

The maximum distance is $d = 4$ when $x = 2\sqrt{2}$.

(c) $f'(x) = x$, Tangent line at $\left(2\sqrt{2}, 4\right)$ is

$y - 4 = 2\sqrt{2}\left(x - 2\sqrt{2}\right)$

$y = 2\sqrt{2}x - 4$.

$g'(x) = \frac{1}{4}x^3 - x$, Tangent line at $\left(2\sqrt{2}, 0\right)$ is

$y - 0 = \left(\frac{1}{4}(2\sqrt{2})^3 - 2\sqrt{2}\right)\left(x - 2\sqrt{2}\right)$

$y = 2\sqrt{2}x - 8$.

The tangent lines are parallel and 4 vertical units apart.

(d)   The tangent lines will be parallel. If $d(x) = f(x) - g(x)$, then $d'(x) = 0 = f'(x) - g'(x)$ implies that $f'(x) = g'(x)$ at the point x where the distance is maximum.

41.   Let F be the illumination at point P which is x units from Source 1 (see figure).

$F = \dfrac{kI_1}{x^2} + \dfrac{kI_2}{(d - x)^2}$

$\dfrac{dF}{dx} = \dfrac{-2kI_1}{x^3} + \dfrac{2kI_2}{(d - x)^3}$

Find any critical numbers by solving the equation $dF/dx = 0$.

$\dfrac{-2kI_1}{x^3} + \dfrac{2kI_2}{(d - x)^3} = 0$

$\dfrac{2kI_1}{x^3} = \dfrac{2kI_2}{(d - x)^3}$

$\dfrac{\sqrt[3]{I_1}}{\sqrt[3]{I_2}} = \dfrac{x}{d - x}$

$(d - x)\sqrt[3]{I_1} = x\sqrt[3]{I_2}$

$d\sqrt[3]{I_1} = \left(\sqrt[3]{I_1} + \sqrt[3]{I_2}\right)x$

$x = \dfrac{d\sqrt[3]{I_1}}{\sqrt[3]{I_1} + \sqrt[3]{I_2}}$

$\dfrac{d^2F}{dx^2} = \dfrac{6kI_1}{x^4} + \dfrac{6kI_2}{(d - x)^4} > 0$ for all x

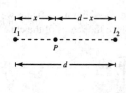

Therefore, the illumination is minimum when $x = \dfrac{d\sqrt[3]{I_1}}{\sqrt[3]{I_1} + \sqrt[3]{I_2}}$.

43. $T = \dfrac{\sqrt{x^2 + 4}}{v_1} + \dfrac{\sqrt{x^2 - 6x + 10}}{v_2}$

$\dfrac{dT}{dx} = \dfrac{x}{v_1\sqrt{x^2 + 4}} + \dfrac{x - 3}{v_2\sqrt{x^2 - 6x + 10}} = 0$

Since

$$\dfrac{x}{\sqrt{x^2 + 4}} = \sin \theta_1 \text{ and } \dfrac{x - 3}{\sqrt{x^2 - 6x + 10}} = -\sin \theta_2$$

we have

$$\dfrac{\sin \theta_1}{v_1} - \dfrac{\sin \theta_2}{v_2} = 0 \Longrightarrow \dfrac{\sin \theta_1}{v_1} = \dfrac{\sin \theta_2}{v_2}.$$

Since

$$\dfrac{d^2T}{dx^2} = \dfrac{4}{v_1(x^2 + 4)^{3/2}} + \dfrac{1}{v_2(x^2 - 6x + 10)^{3/2}} > 0$$

this condition yields a minimum time.

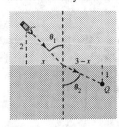

45. $f(x) = 2 - 2 \sin x$

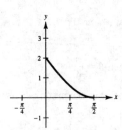

(a) Distance from origin to y-intercept is 2.
Distance from origin to x-intercept is $\pi/2 \approx 1.57$.

(b) $d = \sqrt{x^2 + y^2} = \sqrt{x^2 + (2 - 2 \sin x)^2}$

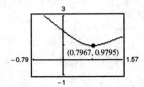

Minimum distance $= 0.9795$ at $x = 0.7967$.

(c) Let $f(x) = d^2(x) = x^2 + (2 - 2 \sin x)^2$.

$f'(x) = 2x + 2(2 - 2 \sin x)(-2 \cos x)$

Setting $f'(x) = 0$, you obtain $x \approx 0.7967$, which corresponds to $d = 0.9795$.

47. We begin by determining the radius of the cone. The circumference of the given circle is $c = 2\pi r = 24\pi$ and the length of the arc of the sector (see figure) removed from the circle is $s = r\theta = 12\theta$. Hence, the circumference of the cone is $C = 24\pi - 12\theta$ and the radius R of the cone is

$$R = \dfrac{C}{2\pi} = \dfrac{24\pi - 12\theta}{2\pi} = \dfrac{6}{\pi}(2\pi - \theta).$$

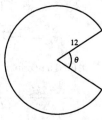

We next find the height of h of the cone. From the figure we observe that the slant height of the cone is the radius of the given circle. Since the radius of the cone has been determined, we find h by the Pythagorean Theorem.

$$h = \sqrt{12^2 - \left[\dfrac{6}{\pi}(2\pi - \theta)\right]^2} = \dfrac{6}{\pi}\sqrt{4\pi^2 - (2\pi - \theta)^2}$$

Therefore, we can determine the volume V of the cone and the value of θ for which V is maximum by solving the equation $dV/d\theta = 0$.

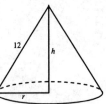

$$V = \dfrac{1}{3}\pi r^2 h = \dfrac{1}{3}\pi\left(\dfrac{6}{\pi}\right)^3(2\pi - \theta)^2\sqrt{4\pi^2 - (2\pi - \theta)^2}$$

$$\dfrac{dV}{d\theta} = \dfrac{1}{3}\pi\left(\dfrac{6}{\pi}\right)^3\left[(2\pi - \theta)^2\dfrac{2\pi - \theta}{\sqrt{4\pi^2 - (2\pi - \theta)^2}} + 2(2\pi - \theta)(-1)\sqrt{4\pi^2 - (2\pi - \theta)^2}\right]$$

$$= \dfrac{1}{3}\pi\left(\dfrac{6}{\pi}\right)^3(2\pi - \theta) \cdot \dfrac{(2\pi - \theta)^2 - 2[4\pi^2 - (2\pi - \theta)^2]}{\sqrt{4\pi^2 - (2\pi - \theta)^2}} = \dfrac{1}{3}\pi\left(\dfrac{6}{\pi}\right)^3\dfrac{2\pi - \theta}{\sqrt{4\pi^2 - (2\pi - \theta)^2}}[3(2\pi - \theta)^2 - 8\pi^2]$$

Therefore, $dV/d\theta = 0$ when

$$3(2\pi - \theta)^2 = 8\pi^2$$

$$2\pi - \theta = \pm\dfrac{2\sqrt{2}\pi}{\sqrt{3}}$$

$$\theta = 2\pi \pm \dfrac{2\sqrt{2}\pi}{\sqrt{3}} = \dfrac{2\pi}{3}(3 \pm \sqrt{6}).$$

The maximum volume of the cone will occur when $\theta = \dfrac{2\pi}{3}(3 - \sqrt{6}) \approx 66°$.

49. $\sin \theta = \dfrac{2}{L_1} \Rightarrow L_1 = \dfrac{2}{\sin \theta}$

$\cos \theta = \dfrac{7}{L_2} \Rightarrow L_2 = \dfrac{7}{\cos \theta}$

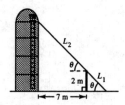

(a)

θ	L_1	L_2	$L_1 + L_2$
0.1	20.0	7.0	27.1
0.2	10.1	7.1	17.2
0.3	6.8	7.3	14.1
0.4	5.1	7.6	12.7
0.5	4.2	8.0	12.1
0.6	3.5	8.5	12.0

(b)

θ	L_1	L_2	$L_1 + L_2$
0.57	3.706	8.315	12.021
0.58	3.650	8.369	12.018
0.59	3.595	8.424	12.019

The minimum length of $L_1 + L_2$ is approximately 12.018 meters.

(c) $L = L_1 + L_2 = \dfrac{2}{\sin \theta} + \dfrac{7}{\cos \theta}$

(d)

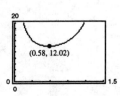

(0.58, 12.02)

The minimum is approximately 12.018 meters.

(e) $L(\theta) = \dfrac{2}{\sin \theta} + \dfrac{7}{\cos \theta} = 2 \csc \theta + 7 \sec \theta$

$L'(\theta) = -2 \csc \theta \cot \theta + 7 \sec \theta \cdot \tan \theta = 0$

$2 \csc \theta \cot \theta = 7 \sec \theta \tan \theta$

$2 \dfrac{\cos \theta}{\sin^2 \theta} = 7 \dfrac{\sin \theta}{\cos^2 \theta}$

$2 \cos^3 \theta = 7 \sin^3 \theta$

$\dfrac{2}{7} = \dfrac{\sin^3 \theta}{\cos^3 \theta} = \tan^3 \theta$

$\tan \theta = \left(\dfrac{2}{7}\right)^{1/3} = \dfrac{\sqrt[3]{98}}{7} \Rightarrow \theta \approx 0.5824$ radians.

$L(0.5824) \approx 12.018$ meters

(f) height $= L \cdot \sin \theta = (12.018)(\sin(0.5824))$

≈ 6.61 meters

51. (a) $\quad f(c) = f(c + x)$

$10ce^{-c} = 10(c + x)e^{-(c+x)}$

$\dfrac{c}{e^c} = \dfrac{c + x}{e^{c+x}}$

$ce^{c+x} = (c + x)e^c$

$ce^x = c + x$

$ce^x - c = x$

$c = \dfrac{x}{e^x - 1}$

(b) $A(x) = xf(c) = x\left[10\left(\dfrac{x}{e^x - 1}\right)e^{-[x/(e^x - 1)]}\right]$

$= \dfrac{10x^2}{e^x - 1}e^{x/(1-e^x)}$

(c) $A(x) = \dfrac{10x^2}{e^x - 1}e^{x/(1-e^x)}$

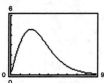

The maximum area is 4.591 for $x = 2.118$ and $f(x) = 2.547$.

(d) $c = \dfrac{x}{e^x - 1}$

$\lim_{x \to 0^+} c = 1, \quad \lim_{x \to \infty} c = 0$

53. $p(t) = \dfrac{250}{1 + 4e^{-t/3}}$

$p'(t) = \dfrac{1000}{3} \dfrac{e^{-t/3}}{(1 + 4e^{-t/3})^2}; \quad p'(2) \approx 18.35$ elk/month

$p''(t) = \dfrac{1000}{9} \dfrac{e^{-t/3}(4e^{-t/3} - 1)}{(1 + 4e^{-t/3})} = 0$ when $t \approx 4.16$ months.

55. The slope of the line is $-\frac{4}{3}$, and the equation is

$$y - 0 = -\frac{4}{3}(x - 3)$$

$$y = -\frac{4}{3}x + 4.$$

For the rectangle, let $(x, y) = (x, -\frac{4}{3}x + 4)$ be the vertex on the line.
Then the area is

$$A = bh = x\left(-\frac{4}{3}x + 4\right) = -\frac{4}{3}x^2 + 4x.$$

$$A'(x) = -\frac{8}{3}x + 4 = 0 \Longrightarrow x = \frac{3}{2} \text{ and } y = 2$$

Base $= \dfrac{3}{2}$, height $= 2$

For the circle, you can use geometry to note that the center of the inscribed
circle is (r, r), and the distance from (r, r) to the line $\frac{4}{3}x + y - 4 = 0$ is also r:

$$\frac{|(4/3)r + r - 4|}{\sqrt{(16/9) + 1}} = r$$

$$|7r - 12| = 5r$$

$$7r - 12 = \pm 5r$$

$$r = 1, 6.$$

Clearly, we must choose $r = 1$ Hence, the center is $(1, 1)$ and the radius is 1.
For the semicircle, observe that the center must be of the form (r, r), and must
lie on the line $y = -\frac{4}{3}x + 4$. Thus,

$$r = \frac{-4}{3}r + 4$$

$$3r = -4r + 12$$

$$7r = 12$$

$$r = \frac{12}{7}.$$

The center is $\left(\frac{12}{7}, \frac{12}{7}\right)$ and the radius is $r = \frac{12}{7}$.

Section 3.8   Differentials

1. $f(x) = x^2$

$f'(x) = 2x$

Tangent line at $(2, 4)$:

$$y - f(2) = f'(2)(x - 2)$$
$$y - 4 = 4(x - 2)$$
$$y = 4x - 4$$

x	1.9	1.99	2	2.01	2.1
$f(x) = x^2$	3.6100	3.9601	4	4.0401	4.4100
$T(x) = 4x - 4$	3.6000	3.9600	4	4.0400	4.4000

3. Given the function $f(x) = x^5, f'(x) = 5x^4$, and $f'(2) = 80$. Therefore, the equation of the tangent line is

$$y - 32 = 80(x - 2)$$
$$y = 80x - 160 + 32$$
$$T(x) = y = 80x - 128.$$

x	1.9	1.99	2	2.01	2.1
$f(x)$	24.761	31.208	32	32.808	40.841
$T(x)$	24.000	31.200	32	32.800	40.000

Notice that the closer x is to 2 the better the linear approximation.

5. $f(x) = \sin x$

$f'(x) = \cos x$

Tangent line at $(2, \sin 2)$:

$$y - f(2) = f'(2)(x - 2)$$
$$y - \sin 2 = (\cos 2)(x - 2)$$
$$y = (\cos 2)(x - 2) + \sin 2$$

x	1.9	1.99	2	2.01	2.1
$f(x) = \sin x$	0.9463	0.9134	0.9093	0.9051	0.8632
$T(x) = (\cos 2)(x - 2) + \sin 2$	0.9509	0.9135	0.9093	0.9051	0.8677

7. $y = f(x) = x^3, f'(x) = 3x^2, x = 1, \Delta x = dx = 0.1$

$\Delta y = f(x + \Delta x) - f(x) = f(1.1) - f(1) = (1.1)^3 - (1)^3 = 0.331$

$dy = f'(x)\, dx = f'(1)(0.1) = 3(0.1) = 0.3$

9. $y = f(x) = x^4 + 1$

$\Delta y = f(x + \Delta x) - f(x)$

$\qquad = f(-1 + 0.01) - f(1)$

$\qquad = f(-0.99) - f(1)$

$\qquad = [(-0.99)^4 + 1] - [(-1)^4 + 1] \approx -0.0394$

Since $f(x) = x^4 + 1, f'(x) = 4x^3$. Therefore,

$\qquad dy = f'(x) \, dx$

$\qquad\qquad = f'(-1)(0.01) = (-4)(0.01) = -0.04.$

The difference between Δy and dy is $\Delta y - dy \approx -0.0394 - (-0.04) = 0.0006.$

11. $y = 3x^2 - 4$

$dy = 6x \, dx$

13. $y = \dfrac{x + 1}{2x - 1}$

$dy = \dfrac{-3}{(2x - 1)^2} \, dx$

15. $y = x\sqrt{1 - x^2}$

$dy = \left[x\left(\dfrac{1}{2}\right)(1 - x^2)^{-1/2}(-2x) + (1 - x^2)^{1/2}(1) \right] dx$

$\quad = \left[\dfrac{-x^2}{\sqrt{1 - x^2}} + \dfrac{1 - x^2}{\sqrt{1 - x^2}} \right] dx = \dfrac{1 - 2x^2}{\sqrt{1 - x^2}} \, dx$

17. $y = \ln\sqrt{4 - x^2} = \dfrac{1}{2}\ln(4 - x^2)$

$dy = \dfrac{1}{2}\dfrac{-2x}{4 - x^2} \, dx = \dfrac{-x}{4 - x^2} \, dx$

19. $y = \dfrac{\sec^2 x}{x^2 + 1}$

$dy = \left[\dfrac{(x^2 + 1)2 \sec^2 x \tan x - \sec^2 x(2x)}{(x^2 + 1)^2} \right] dx$

$\quad = \left[\dfrac{2 \sec^2 x(x^2 \tan x + \tan x - x)}{(x^2 + 1)^2} \right] dx$

21. $y = \dfrac{1}{3}\cos\left(\dfrac{6\pi x - 1}{2}\right)$

$dy = -\pi \sin\left(\dfrac{6\pi x - 1}{2}\right) dx$

23. $y = x \arcsin x$

$dy = \left(x\dfrac{d}{dx}[\arcsin x] + \arcsin x \dfrac{d}{dx}[x] \right)$

$dx = \left(\dfrac{x}{\sqrt{1 - x^2}} + \arcsin x \right) dx$

25. $A = x^2$

$x = 12$

$\Delta x = dx = \pm\dfrac{1}{64}$

$dA = 2x \, dx$

$\Delta A \approx dA = 2(12)\left(\pm\dfrac{1}{64}\right) = \pm\dfrac{3}{8}$ square inches

27. $A = \pi r^2$

$r = 14$

$\Delta r = dr = \pm\dfrac{1}{4}$

$\Delta A \approx dA = 2\pi r \, dr = \pi(28)\left(\pm\dfrac{1}{4}\right)$

$\quad = \pm 7\pi$ square inches

29. (a) $x = 15$ centimeter

$\Delta x = dx = \pm 0.05$ centimeters

$A = x^2$

$dA = 2x \, dx = 2(15)(\pm 0.05) = \pm 1.5$ cm^2

Percentage error: $\dfrac{dA}{A} = \dfrac{\pm 1.5}{(15)^2} = 0.00666\ldots = \dfrac{2}{3}\%$

(b) $\dfrac{dA}{A} = \dfrac{2x \, dx}{x^2} = \dfrac{2 \, dx}{x} \le 0.025$

$\dfrac{dx}{x} \le \dfrac{0.025}{2} = 0.0125 = 1.25\%$

31. The radius of the sphere is $r = 6 \pm 0.02$.

(a) The formula for the volume of the sphere is
$$V = \frac{4}{3}\pi r^3.$$

The approximate ΔV by dV, let $r = 6$ and $dr = \pm 0.02$.

$$dV = \frac{4}{3}\pi(3r^2)\, dr$$

$$dV = 4\pi(36)(\pm 0.02) = \pm 2.88\pi \text{ in}^3$$

(b) The formula for the surface area of the sphere is $S = 4\pi r^2$. To approximate ΔS by dS, let $r = 6$ and $dr = \pm 0.02$.

$$dS = 8\pi r\, dr$$

$$dS = 8\pi(6)(\pm 0.02) = \pm 0.96\pi \text{ in}^2$$

(c) For part (a) the relative error is approximately

$$\frac{dV}{V} = \frac{2.88\pi}{(4/3)\pi(6^3)} = \frac{2.88}{288} = 0.01 = 1\%.$$

For (b) the relative error is approximately

$$\frac{dS}{S} = \frac{0.96\pi}{4\pi(6^2)} = \frac{0.96}{144} = 0.0067 = \frac{2}{3}\%.$$

33. $P = 100xe^{-x/400}$, x changes from 115 to 120.

$$dP = 100\left[e^{-x/400} - \frac{x}{400}e^{-x/400}\right]dx$$

$$= e^{-115/400}\left[100 - \frac{115}{4}\right](120 - 115) \approx 267.24$$

Approximate percentage change:

$$\frac{dP}{P}(100) = \frac{267.24}{8626.57}(100) \approx 3.1\%$$

35. $V = \pi r^2 h = 40\pi r^2$, $r = 5$ cm, $h = 40$ cm, $dr = 0.2$ cm

$$\Delta V \approx dV = 80\pi r\, dr = 80\pi(5)(0.2) = 80\pi \text{ cm}^3$$

37. (a) $T = 2\pi\sqrt{\dfrac{L}{g}}$

$$dT = 2\pi\left(\frac{1}{2}\right)\left(\frac{L}{g}\right)^{-1/2}\left(\frac{1}{g}\right)dL = \frac{\pi}{g\sqrt{L/g}}\, dL$$

$$\frac{dT}{T}(100) = \text{percentage error}$$

$$= \frac{(\pi/g\sqrt{L/g})\, dL}{2\pi\sqrt{L/g}}(100) = \frac{1}{2}\left(\frac{dL}{L}100\right)$$

$$= \frac{1}{2}(\text{percentage change in } L)$$

$$= \frac{1}{2}\left(\frac{1}{2}\right) = \frac{1}{4}\%$$

(b) approximate error $= \left(\dfrac{1}{4}\%\right)(\text{number of seconds per day})$

$$= (0.0025)(60)(60)(24)$$

$$= 216 \text{ seconds} = 3.6 \text{ minutes}$$

39. $E = IR$

$$R = \frac{E}{I}$$

$$dR = -\frac{E}{I^2}dI$$

$$\frac{dR}{R} = \frac{-(E/I^2)dI}{E/I} = -\frac{dI}{I}$$

$$\left|\frac{dR}{R}\right| = \left|-\frac{dI}{I}\right| = \left|\frac{dI}{I}\right|$$

41. $r = \dfrac{v_0^2}{32}(\sin 2\theta)$

$v_0 = 2200$ ft/sec

θ changes from $10°$ to $11°$

$$dr = \frac{(2200)^2}{16}(\cos 2\theta)\, d\theta$$

$$\theta = 10\left(\frac{\pi}{180}\right)$$

$$d\theta = (11 - 10)\frac{\pi}{180}$$

$$\Delta r \approx dr = \frac{(2200)^2}{16}\cos\left(\frac{20\pi}{180}\right)\left(\frac{\pi}{180}\right) \approx 4961 \text{ feet}$$

43. Let $f(x) = \sqrt{x}, x = 100, dx = -0.6$.

$$f(x + \Delta x) \approx f(x) + f'(x)\,dx = \sqrt{x} + \frac{1}{2\sqrt{x}}\,dx$$

$$f(x + \Delta x) = \sqrt{99.4} \approx \sqrt{100} + \frac{1}{2\sqrt{100}}(-0.6) = 9.97$$

Using a calculator: $\sqrt{99.4} \approx 9.96995$

45. Let $f(x) = \sqrt[4]{x}, x = 625$, and $dx = \Delta x = -1$.

$$f(x + \Delta x) = f(x) + \Delta y$$
$$\approx f(x) + dy$$
$$= f(x) + f'(x)\,dx$$
$$= \sqrt[4]{x} + \frac{1}{4\sqrt[4]{x^3}}\,dx$$

$$f(x + \Delta x) = \sqrt[4]{624}$$
$$\approx \sqrt[4]{625} + \frac{1}{4(\sqrt[4]{625})^3}(-1)$$
$$= 5 - \frac{1}{500} = 4.998$$

Using a calculator: $\sqrt[4]{624} \approx 4.9980$.

47. Let $f(x) = x^4, x = 1, dx = -0.01, f'(x) = 4x^3$.

Then

$$f(0.99) \approx f(1) + f'(1)dx$$
$$(0.99)^4 \approx (1)^4 + 4(1)^3(-0.01) = 1 - 4(0.01).$$

49. Let $f(x) = \sec x, x = 0, dx = 0.03, f'(x) = \sec x \tan x$.

Then

$$f(0.03) \approx f(0) + f'(0)\,dx$$
$$\sec 0.03 \approx \sec 0 + (\sec 0 \tan 0)(0.03)$$
$$= 1 + 0(0.03).$$

51. True

53. True

55. $A(x) = x^2$

(a) $dA = 2x\,dx = 2x\,\Delta x$

$\Delta A = (x + \Delta x)^2 - x^2$

$\quad = 2x\,\Delta x + (\Delta x)^2$

(b)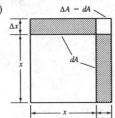

(c) $\Delta A - dA = (\Delta x)^2$

Section 3.9   Business and Economics Applications

1. (a) $C(0)$ represents the fixed costs.

(c) The marginal cost function has a relative minimum. It occurs when production costs are increasing at their slowest rate.

(b)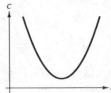

3. $R = 900x - 0.1x^2$

$\dfrac{dR}{dx} = 900 - 0.2x = 0$ when $x = 4500$.

By the First Derivative Test, $x = 4500$ is a maximum.

5. $R = \dfrac{1,000,000x}{0.02x^2 + 1800}$

$\dfrac{dR}{dx} = 1,000,000\left[\dfrac{0.02x^2 + 1800 - x(0.04x)}{(0.02x^2 + 1800)^2}\right]$

$= 0$

$1800 - 0.02x^2 = 0$ when $x = 300$.

By the First Derivative Test, $x = 300$ is a maximum.

7. $C = 0.125x^2 + 20x + 5000$

$$\overline{C} = \frac{C}{x} = 0.125x + 20 + \frac{5000}{x}$$

$$\frac{d\overline{C}}{dx} = 0.125 - \frac{5000}{x^2}$$

$$\frac{d^2\overline{C}}{dx^2} = \frac{10,000}{x^3}$$

To find the critical numbers, solve the following equation.

$$\frac{d\overline{C}}{dx} = 0$$

$$0.125 - \frac{5000}{x^2} = 0$$

$$0.125x^2 - 5000 = 0$$

$$x^2 = 40,000 \implies x = 200$$

Since the second derivative is positive for when $x > 0$, the average cost function is concave upward. By the Second Derivative Test, $x = 200$ yields the minimum average cost.

9. $\overline{C} = 3000 - x(300 - x)^{1/2}$

$$\frac{d\overline{C}}{dx} = -x\left(\frac{1}{2}\right)(300 - x)^{-1/2}(-1) - (300 - x)^{1/2}$$

$$= -\frac{3}{2}(300 - x)^{-1/2}(200 - x)$$

$$= 0 \text{ when } x = 200.$$

By the First Derivative Test, $x = 200$ yields the minimum average cost.

11. $P = 60xe^{-x/5}$

$P' = -12e^{-x/5}(x - 5) = 0$ when $x = 5$.

$x = 5$ is a maximum by the First Derivative Test.

13. The profit is given by

$P = $ (price per unit)(number of units) $-$ (cost)

$\quad = px - C$

$\quad = (90 - x)(x) - (100 + 30x) = -x^2 + 60x - 100$

To maximize P, solve $dP/dx = 0$ as follows:

$$\frac{dP}{dx} = -2x + 60 = 0$$

$$2x = 60 \text{ and } x = 30$$

Therefore, the profit is maximum when the price is $p = 90 - 30 = 60$.

15. $C = 4000 - 40x + 0.02x^2$

$p = 50 - 0.01x$

$P = xp - C = 50x - 0.01x^2 - 4000 + 40x - 0.02x^2$

$\quad = -0.03x^2 + 90x - 4000$

$\dfrac{dP}{dx} = -0.06x + 90 = 0$ when $x = 1500$, so $p = 35$.

By the First Derivative Test, $x = 1500$ is a maximum.

17. $C = 2x^2 + 5x + 18$

Average cost $= \dfrac{C}{x} = \overline{C} = 2x + 5 + \dfrac{18}{x}$

$$\frac{d\overline{C}}{dx} = 2 - \frac{18}{x^2} = 0 \text{ when } x = 3.$$

$$\overline{C}(3) = 6 + 5 + 6 = 17$$

By the First Derivative Test, $x = 3$ is a minimum.

Marginal cost: $\dfrac{dC}{dx} = 4x + 5$

At $x = 3$: $\dfrac{dC}{dx} = 17 = \overline{C}(3)$

19. Average cost: $\overline{C}(x) = \dfrac{C(x)}{x}$

$$\frac{d\overline{C}}{dx} = \frac{xC'(x) - C(x)}{x^2} = 0 \Rightarrow xC'(x) - C(x) = 0 \text{ when } C'(x) = \frac{C(x)}{x} = \overline{C}(x).$$

Marginal cost = average cost

This condition will yield a minimum (if it exists).

21. (a)

Order size, x	Price	Profit
102	$90 - 2(0.15)$	$102[90 - 2(0.15)] - 102(60) = 3029.40$
104	$90 - 4(0.15)$	$104[90 - 4(0.15)] - 104(60) = 3057.60$
106	$90 - 6(0.15)$	$106[90 - 6(0.15)] - 106(60) = 3084.60$
108	$90 - 8(0.15)$	$108[90 - 8(0.15)] - 108(60) = 3110.40$
110	$90 - 10(0.15)$	$110[90 - 10(0.15)] - 110(60) = 3135.00$
112	$90 - 12(0.15)$	$112[90 - 12(0.15)] - 112(60) = 3158.40$

(b)

Order size, x	Profit
148	3374.40
149	3374.90
150	3375.00
151	3374.90
152	3374.40

The maximum profit is 3375.00 for $x = 150$.

(c) $P(x) = x[90 - (x - 100)(0.15)] - 60x$

$\qquad = x(45 - 0.15x),\ x \geq 100$

(d) $\dfrac{dP}{dx} = 45 - 0.30x = 0$ when $x = 150$.

Since $\dfrac{d^2P}{dx^2} < 0$, an order size of $x = 150$ units yields a maximum profit.

(e)

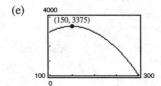

23. Since the speed for the 110-mile is v miles per hour, the total time is $t = 110/v$ hours. Therefore, the total cost is

(Total cost) = (Fuel cost) + (Wages)

$$C = \frac{v^2}{600}\left(\frac{110}{v}\right) + 5\left(\frac{110}{v}\right) = \frac{11}{60}v + 5(110)v^{-1}.$$

To minimize C, solve $dC/dv = 0$ as follows:

$$\frac{dC}{dv} = \frac{11}{60} - 5(110)v^{-2} = 0$$

$$\frac{11}{60} = \frac{5(110)}{v^2}$$

$$v^2 = \frac{5(110)(60)}{11}$$

$$v^2 = 3000$$

$$v = 10\sqrt{30} \approx 54.8 \text{ mi/hr}$$

Thus, a speed 54.8 mi/hr will yield the minimum cost.

25. The total cost $T(x)$ is

$$T(x) = 12(5280)(6 - x) + 16(5280)\sqrt{x^2 + \frac{1}{4}}$$

$$T'(x) = 5280\left[-12 + \frac{16x}{\sqrt{x^2 + (1/4)}}\right] = 0$$

$$12 = \frac{16x}{\sqrt{x^2 + (1/4)}}$$

$$3\sqrt{x^2 + (1/4)} = 4x$$

$$9\left(x^2 + \frac{1}{4}\right) = 16x^2$$

$$\frac{9}{4} = 7x^2 \Longrightarrow x = \frac{3}{2\sqrt{7}} \approx 0.57 \text{ miles.}$$

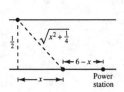

This is a minimum by the First Derivative Test.

27. $S_1 = (4m - 1)^2 + (5m - 6)^2 + (10m - 3)^2$

$$\frac{dS_1}{dm} = 2(4m - 1)(4) + 2(5m - 6)(5) + 2(10m - 3)(10) = 282m - 128 = 0 \text{ when } m = \frac{64}{141}.$$

Line: $y = \dfrac{64}{141}x$

$$S = \left|4\left(\frac{64}{141}\right) - 1\right| + \left|5\left(\frac{64}{141}\right) - 6\right| + \left|10\left(\frac{64}{141}\right) - 3\right| = \left|\frac{256}{141} - 1\right| + \left|\frac{320}{141} - 6\right| + \left|\frac{640}{141} - 3\right| = \frac{858}{141} \approx 6.1 \text{ mi}$$

29. $S_3 = \dfrac{|4m - 1|}{\sqrt{m^2 + 1}} + \dfrac{|5m - 6|}{\sqrt{m^2 + 1}} + \dfrac{|10m - 3|}{\sqrt{m^2 + 1}}$

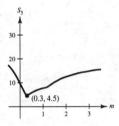

Using a graphing utility, you can see that the minimum occurs when $x \approx 0.3$.

Line: $y \approx 0.3x$

$$S_3 = \frac{|4(0.3) - 1| + |5(0.3) - 6| + |10(0.3) - 3|}{\sqrt{(0.3)^2 + 1}} \approx 4.5 \text{ mi} \approx 4.5 \text{ mi.}$$

31. Let $d =$ amount in the bank, $i =$ interest rate paid by the bank, and $p =$ profit. The bank can take the deposited money d and reinvest to obtain 12% or $(0.12)d$. Since the bank pays out interest to its depositors, its profit is

$$P = (0.12)d - id.$$

Finally, since d is proportional to the square of i, we have

$$d = ki^2.$$

Thus

$$P = (0.12)(ki^2) - i(ki^2) = k[(0.12)i^2 - i^3].$$

To maximize P, solve $dP/di = 0$ as follows:

$$\frac{dP}{di} = k(0.24i - 3i^2) = 0$$

$$ki(0.24 - 3i) = 0$$

(We disregard the critical number $i = 0$.)

$$i = \frac{0.24}{3} = 0.08$$

Thus the bank can maximize its profit by setting $i = 8\%$.

33. $C = 100\left(\dfrac{200}{x^2} + \dfrac{x}{x + 30}\right), \ 1 \le x$

$\dfrac{dC}{dx} = 100\left(-\dfrac{400}{x^3} + \dfrac{30}{(x + 30)^2}\right)$

$= 1000\left[\dfrac{-40(x + 30)^2 + 3x^3}{x^3(x + 30)^2}\right]$

To find the critical number of C use Newton's Method to find the zero of the function $f(x) = -40(x + 30)^2 + 3x^2$ using $x_1 = 30$ as our first estimate.

$f(x) = 3x^3 - 40x^2 - 2400x - 36{,}000 \quad \text{and} \quad f'(x) = 9x^2 - 80x - 2400$

n	x_n	$f(x_n)$	$f'(x_n)$	$\dfrac{f(x_n)}{f'(x_n)}$	$x_n - \dfrac{f(x_n)}{f'(x_n)}$
1	30	$-63{,}000$	3300	-19.091	49.091
2	49.091	104,702	15,362	6.816	42.275
3	42.275	17,712	10,303	1.719	40.556
4	40.556	992.239	9158.622	0.108	40.448

Therefore, it follows that the critical number is $x \approx 40.4$ and the minimum cost occurs when 40 units are ordered.

35. $F = 100{,}000\left(1 + \sin\left[\dfrac{2\pi(t - 60)}{365}\right]\right)$

(a) $\dfrac{dF}{dt} = 100{,}000\left(\dfrac{2\pi}{365}\cos\left[\dfrac{2\pi(t - 60)}{365}\right]\right)$

$= 0$ when $\dfrac{2\pi(t - 60)}{365} = \dfrac{\pi}{2}$ or $\dfrac{3\pi}{2}$.

$t = 151.25$ or 333.75

The maximum occurs when $t = 151.25$ which corresponds to May 31.

(b)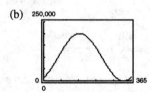

Sales are minimum when $t = 333.75$ which corresponds to November 30.

37. $R = 4.7t^4 - 193.5t^3 + 2941.7t^2 - 19{,}294.7t + 52{,}012$

(a) $R'(t) = 18.8t^3 - 580.5t^2 + 5883.4t - 19{,}294.7 = 0$

The real root is $t = 7.22$ (1987), which yields a minimum.

(b) The maximum occurs at $t = 14$ (1994).

(c) The minimum revenue was 5995 million dollars.

The maximum revenue was 8050.6 million dollars.

(d)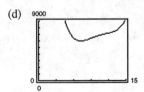

39. Since $p = 400 - 3x, \dfrac{dp}{dx} = -3.$

$\eta = \dfrac{p/x}{dp/dx}$

$= \dfrac{(400 - 3x)/x}{-3} = 1 - \dfrac{400}{3x}$

At $x = 20$, $\eta = 1 - \dfrac{400}{3(20)} = 1 - \dfrac{20}{3} = -\dfrac{17}{3}$. Therefore,

$|\eta| = \dfrac{17}{3} > 1,$

and demand is elastic.

41. $\eta = \dfrac{p/x}{dp/dx} = \dfrac{(400 - 0.5x^2)/x}{-x} = \dfrac{1}{2} - \dfrac{400}{x^2}$

When $x = 20$, we have

$$\eta = \dfrac{1}{2} - \dfrac{400}{(20)^2} = -\dfrac{1}{2}.$$

Since $|\eta| = \frac{1}{2} < 1$, the demand is inelastic.

45. $P = \dfrac{200}{1 + 9e^{-s/5}}$

$P' = \dfrac{360e^{-s/5}}{(1 + 9e^{-s/5})^2}$

$P'' = \dfrac{72e^{-s/5}(9e^{-s/5} - 1)}{(1 + 9e^{-s/5})^3}$

$P'' = 0$ when $x \approx 10.986$ (thousands of dollars).

Review Exercises for Chapter 3

1. A number c in the domain of f is a critical number if $f'(c) = 0$ or f' is undefined at c.

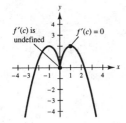

3. $g(x) = 2x + 5 \cos x, [0, 2\pi]$

$g'(x) = 2 - 5 \sin x$

$\qquad = 0$ when $\sin x = \frac{2}{5}$.

Critical numbers: $x \approx 0.41, x \approx 2.73$

Left endpoint: $(0, 5)$

Critical number: $(0.41, 5.41)$

Critical number: $(2.73, 0.88)$ Minimum

Right endpoint: $(2\pi, 17.57)$ Maximum

5. $f(x) = 3 - |x - 4|$

(a)

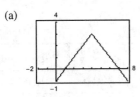

$\qquad f(1) = f(7) = 0$

(b) f is not differentiable at $x = 4$.

7. $\qquad f(x) = x^{2/3}, 1 \le x \le 8$

$\qquad\qquad f'(x) = \dfrac{2}{3}x^{-1/3}$

$\dfrac{f(b) - f(a)}{b - a} = \dfrac{4 - 1}{8 - 1} = \dfrac{3}{7}$

$\qquad\qquad f'(c) = \dfrac{2}{3}c^{-1/3} = \dfrac{3}{7}$

$\qquad\qquad\quad c = \left(\dfrac{14}{9}\right)^3 = \dfrac{2744}{729} \approx 3.764$

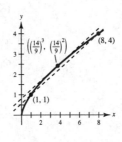

9. Since $f(x) = x - \cos x$ is continuous on $[-\pi/2, \pi/2]$ and differentiable on $(-\pi/2, \pi/2)$, the Mean Value Theorem can be applied.

$$f(x) = x - \cos x$$

(1) $$f'(x) = 1 + \sin x$$

(2) $$\frac{f(b) - f(a)}{b - a} = \frac{(\pi/2) - (-\pi/2)}{(\pi/2) - (-\pi/2)} = 1$$

Equating the right-hand members of the equations (1) and (2) yields

$$1 + \sin x = 1$$

$$\sin x = 0 \implies x = 0.$$

Therefore, $c = 0$ and the point on the graph where the instantaneous rate of change of f equals the average rate of change over the specified interval is $(0, -1)$. This is shown in the figure.

11. Since f is continuous and differentiable for all real x, the Mean Value Theorem can be applied over the specified interval. It is necessary to find all c in $[x_1, x_2]$ such that

$$f'(c) = \frac{f(x_2) - f(x_1)}{x_2 - x_1}.$$

$$f'(x) = 2Ax + B$$

$$f'(c) = 2Ac + B = \frac{f(x_2) - f(x_1)}{x_2 - x_1}$$

$$= \frac{Ax_2^2 + Bx_2 + C - Ax_1^2 - Bx_1 - C}{x_2 - x_1}$$

$$= \frac{A(x_2^2 - x_1^2) + B(x_2 - x_1)}{x_2 - x_1}$$

$$= A(x_2 + x_1) + B$$

$$2c = x_2 + x_1$$

$$c = \frac{x_1 + x_2}{2}$$

For a quadratic function, the required value of c is the average of x_1 and x_2.

13. $f(x) = (x - 1)^2(x - 3)$

$f'(x) = (x - 1)^2(1) + (x - 3)(2)(x - 1)$

$\quad\ = (x - 1)(3x - 7)$

Critical numbers: $x = 1$ and $x = \frac{7}{3}$

Interval	$-\infty < x < 1$	$1 < x < \frac{7}{3}$	$\frac{7}{3} < x < \infty$
Sign of $f'(x)$	$f'(x) > 0$	$f'(x) < 0$	$f'(x) > 0$
Conclusion	Increasing	Decreasing	Increasing

15. $h(x) = \sqrt{x}(x - 3) = x^{3/2} - 3x^{1/2}$

Domain: $[0, \infty)$

$h'(x) = \frac{3}{2}x^{1/2} - \frac{3}{2}x^{-1/2}$

$\quad\ = \frac{3}{2}x^{-1/2}(x - 1) = \frac{3(x - 1)}{2\sqrt{x}}$

Critical numbers: $x = 0, x = 1$

Interval	$0 < x < 1$	$1 < x < \infty$
Sign of $h'(x)$	$h'(x) < 0$	$h'(x) > 0$
Conclusion	Decreasing	Increasing

17. $h(t) = \frac{1}{4}t^4 - 8t$

$h'(t) = t^3 - 8 = (t - 2)(t^2 + 2t + 4)$

Therefore, $h'(t) = 0$ when $t = 2$. Since h is a polynomial, it is differentiable for all t and the only critical number is $t = 2$.

Interval	$-\infty < t < 2$	$2 < t < \infty$
Test Value	$t = 0$	$t = 2$
Sign of $h'(t)$	$h'(0) < 0$	$h'(3) > 0$
Conclusion	h is decreasing	h is increasing

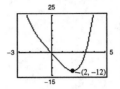

Hence, h has a minimum at $(2, -12)$. The graph of h is shown in the figure.

19. $f(x) = x + \cos x, \ 0 \le x \le 2\pi$

$f'(x) = 1 - \sin x$

$f''(x) = -\cos x = 0$ when $x = \dfrac{\pi}{2}, \dfrac{3\pi}{2}$.

Points of inflection: $\left(\dfrac{\pi}{2}, \dfrac{\pi}{2}\right), \left(\dfrac{3\pi}{2}, \dfrac{3\pi}{2}\right)$

Test Interval	$0 < x < \dfrac{\pi}{2}$	$\dfrac{\pi}{2} < x < \dfrac{3\pi}{2}$	$\dfrac{3\pi}{2} < x < 2\pi$
Sign of $f''(x)$	$f''(x) < 0$	$f''(x) > 0$	$f''(x) < 0$
Conclusion	Concave downward	Concave upward	Concave downward

21. $\displaystyle\lim_{x \to \infty} \frac{2x^2}{3x^2 + 5} = \lim_{x \to \infty} \frac{2}{3 + 5/x^2} = \frac{2}{3}$

23. $\displaystyle\lim_{x \to \infty} \frac{5 \cos x}{x} = 0$, since $|5 \cos x| \le 5$.

25. $h(x) = \dfrac{2x + 3}{x - 4}$

Discontinuity: $x = 4$

$$\lim_{x \to \infty} \frac{2x + 3}{x - 4} = \lim_{x \to \infty} \frac{2 + (3/x)}{1 - (4/x)} = 2$$

Vertical asymptote: $x = 4$

Horizontal asymptote: $y = 2$

27. $f(x) = \dfrac{3}{x} - 2$

Discontinuity: $x = 0$

$$\lim_{x \to \infty} \left(\frac{3}{x} - 2\right) = -2$$

Vertical asymptote: $x = 0$

Horizontal asymptote: $y = -2$

29. $f(x) = \dfrac{5}{3 + 2e^{-x}}$

Since $e^{-x} > 0$ for all x, the denominator of f is always greater than zero. Therefore, the function is continuous for all x and there are no vertical asymptotes. Since

$$\lim_{x \to -\infty} e^{-x} = \infty \quad \text{and} \quad \lim_{x \to \infty} e^{-x} = 0,$$

$$\lim_{x \to -\infty} f(x) = 0 \quad \text{and} \quad \lim_{x \to \infty} f(x) = \frac{5}{3}.$$

Hence, $y = 0$ and $y = \frac{5}{3}$ are horizontal asymptotes.

31. $g(x) = 3 \ln(1 + e^{-x/4})$

Horizontal asymptote: $y = 0$ (to the right)

33. $f(x) = x^3 + \dfrac{243}{x}$

Relative minimum: $(3, 108)$

Relative maximum: $(-3, -108)$

Vertical asymptote: $x = 0$

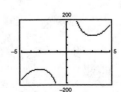

35. $f(x) = \dfrac{x - 1}{1 + 3x^2}$

Relative minimum: $(-0.155, -1.077)$

Relative maximum: $(2.155, 0.077)$

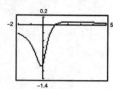

Horizontal asymptote: $y = 0$

37. $f(x) = 4x - x^2 = x(4 - x)$

Domain: $(-\infty, \infty)$

Range: $(-\infty, 4)$

$f'(x) = 4 - 2x$

      $= 0$ when $x = 2$.

$f''(x) = -2$

Therefore, $(2, 4)$ is a relative maximum.

Intercepts: $(0, 0)$, $(4, 0)$

39. The domain of $f(x) = x\sqrt{16 - x^2}$ is all real numbers in the interval $[-4, 4]$ and the graph of f is symmetric to the origin since

$$f(-x) = (-x)\sqrt{16 - (-x)^2} = -x\sqrt{16 - x^2} = -f(x).$$

$$f'(x) = x\left(\frac{1}{2}\right)(16 - x^2)^{-1/2}(-2x) + (16 - x^2)^{1/2} = \frac{16 - 2x^2}{\sqrt{16 - x^2}}$$

$$f''(x) = \frac{\sqrt{16 - x^2}(-4x) - (16 - 2x^2)(1/2)(16 - x^2)^{-1/2}(-2x)}{16 - x^2} = \frac{2x(x^2 - 24)}{(16 - x^2)^{3/2}}$$

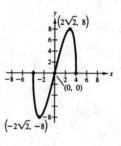

Thus, $f'(x) = 0$ when $x = \pm 2\sqrt{2}$ and undefined when $x = \pm 4$. Since $f''\left(2\sqrt{2}\right) < 0$, the graph is concave downward and $\left(2\sqrt{2}, 8\right)$ is a maximum. By symmetry, $\left(-2\sqrt{2}, -8\right)$ is a minimum. There is a point of inflection at $(0, 0)$.

41. $f(x) = (x - 1)^3(x - 3)^2$

Domain: $(-\infty, \infty)$; Range: $(-\infty, \infty)$

$f'(x) = (x - 1)^2(x - 3)(5x - 11) = 0$ when $x = 1, \dfrac{11}{5}, 3$.

$f''(x) = 4(x - 1)(5x^2 - 22x + 23) = 0$ when $x = 1, \dfrac{11 \pm \sqrt{6}}{5}$.

$f''(3) > 0$

Therefore, $(3, 0)$ is a relative minimum.

$f''\left(\dfrac{11}{5}\right) < 0$

Therefore, $\left(\dfrac{11}{4}, \dfrac{3456}{3125}\right)$ is a relative maximum.

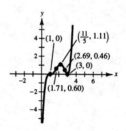

Points of inflection: $(1, 0)$, $\left(\dfrac{11 - \sqrt{6}}{5}, 0.60\right)$, $\left(\dfrac{11 + \sqrt{6}}{5}, 0.46\right)$

Intercepts: $(0, -9)$, $(1, 0)$, $(3, 0)$

43. $f(x) = x^{1/3}(x + 3)^{2/3}$

$$f'(x) = x^{1/3}\left(\frac{2}{3}\right)(x + 3)^{-1/3} + (x + 3)^{2/3}\left(\frac{1}{3}\right)x^{-2/3}$$

$$= \frac{2x^{1/3}}{3(x + 3)^{1/3}} + \frac{(x + 3)^{2/3}}{3x^{2/3}}$$

$$= \frac{2x + x + 3}{3x^{2/3}(x + 3)^{1/3}}$$

$$= \frac{x + 1}{x^{2/3}(x + 3)^{1/3}} = \frac{x + 1}{(x^3 + 3x^2)^{1/3}}$$

$$f''(x) = \frac{(x^3 + 3x^2)^{1/3}(1) - (x + 1)(1/3)(x^3 + 3x^2)^{-2/3}(3x^2 + 6x)}{(x^3 + 3x^2)^{2/3}}$$

$$= \frac{(x^3 + 3x^2) - (x + 1)(x^2 + 2x)}{(x^3 + 3x^2)^{4/3}}$$

$$= \frac{x^3 + 3x^2 - x^3 - 2x^2 - x^2 - 2x}{(x + 3x^4)^{2/3}}$$

$$= \frac{-2x}{(x^3 + 3x^2)^{4/3}} = \frac{-2}{x^{5/3}(x + 3)^{4/3}}$$

Intercepts: $(0, 0), (-3, 0)$

Critical numbers: $x = -1, x = 0, x = -3$

Possible point of inflection: $(0, 0)$

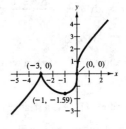

x	$f(x)$	$f'(x)$	$f''(x)$	Shape of graph
$-\infty < x < -3$		+	+	increasing, concave up
$x = -3$	0	undefined	undefined	relative maximum
$-3 < x < -1$		−	+	decreasing, concave up
$x = -1$	$-\sqrt[3]{4}$	0	+	relative minimum
$-1 < x < 0$		+	+	increasing, concave up
$x = 0$	0	undefined	undefined	point of inflection
$0 < x < \infty$		+	−	increasing, concave down

45. $f(x) = \dfrac{x + 1}{x - 1}$

Domain: $(-\infty, 1), (1, \infty)$; Range: $(-\infty, 1), (1, \infty)$

$f'(x) = \dfrac{-2}{(x - 1)^2} < 0$ if $x \neq 1$.

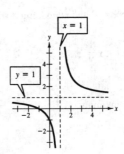

$f''(x) = \dfrac{4}{(x - 1)^3}$

Horizontal asymptote: $y = 1$

Vertical asymptote: $x = 1$

Intercepts: $(-1, 0), (0, -1)$

47. $f(x) = \dfrac{4}{1 + x^2}$

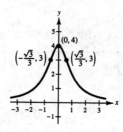

Domain: $(-\infty, \infty)$; Range: $(0, 4]$

$f'(x) = \dfrac{-8x}{(1 + x^2)^2} = 0$ when $x = 0$.

$f''(x) = \dfrac{-8(1 - 3x^2)}{(1 + x^2)^3} = 0$ when $x = \pm\dfrac{\sqrt{3}}{3}$.

$f''(0) < 0$

Therefore, $(0, 4)$ is a relative maximum.

Points of inflection: $\left(\pm\sqrt{3}/3, 3\right)$

Intercept: $(0, 4)$

Symmetric to the y-axis

Horizontal asymptote: $y = 0$

49. $f(x) = x^3 + x + \dfrac{4}{x}$

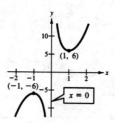

Domain: $(-\infty, 0), (0, \infty)$; Range: $(-\infty, -6], [6, \infty)$

$f'(x) = 3x^2 + 1 - \dfrac{4}{x^2} = \dfrac{3x^4 + x^2 - 4}{x^2} = 0$ when $x = \pm 1$.

$f''(x) = 6x + \dfrac{8}{x^3} = \dfrac{6x^4 + 8}{x^3} \neq 0$

$f''(-1) < 0$

Therefore, $(-1, -6)$ is a relative maximum.

$f''(1) > 0$

Therefore, $(1, 6)$ is a relative minimum.

Vertical asymptote: $x = 0$

Symmetric with respect to origin

51. $f(x) = |x^2 - 9|$

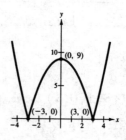

Domain: $(-\infty, \infty)$; Range: $[0, \infty)$

$f'(x) = \dfrac{2x(x^2 - 9)}{|x^2 - 9|} = 0$ when $x = 0$ and is undefined when $x = \pm 3$.

$f''(x) = \dfrac{2(x^2 - 9)}{|x^2 - 9|}$ is undefined at $x = \pm 3$.

$f''(0) < 0$

Therefore, $(0, 9)$ is a relative maximum.

Relative minima: $(\pm 3, 0)$

Points of inflection: $(\pm 3, 0)$

Intercepts: $(\pm 3, 0), (0, 9)$

Symmetric to the y-axis

53. $h(x) = (1 - x)e^x$

$h'(x) = -xe^x$

$h''(x) = -(x + 1)e^x$

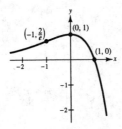

Horizontal asymptote: $y = 0$ (to the left)

Critical point: $(0, 1)$ (relative maximum)

Inflection point: $(-1, 2/e) \approx (-1, 0.736)$

55. $g(x) = (x + 3) \ln(x + 3)$

$g'(x) = \ln(x + 3) + 1$

$g''(x) = \dfrac{1}{x + 3}$

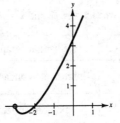

Domain: $x > -3$

Relative minimum: $(-2.632, -0.368)$

Always concave upward

57. $f(x) = \dfrac{10 \log_4 x}{x}$

$f'(x) = 10 \left[\dfrac{x \dfrac{1}{(\ln 4)x} - \log_4 x}{x^2} \right] = \dfrac{10(1 - \ln x)}{x^2(\ln 4)} = \dfrac{5(1 - \ln x)}{x^2 \ln 2} \quad \left(\text{Recall that } \log_4 x = \dfrac{\ln x}{\ln 4}. \right)$

$f''(x) = \dfrac{5}{\ln 2} \left[\dfrac{x^2 \left(-\dfrac{1}{x} \right) - (1 - \ln x)(2x)}{x^4} \right] = \dfrac{5}{\ln 2} \left(\dfrac{2 \ln x - 3}{x^3} \right)$

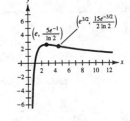

Domain: $(0, \infty)$

Intercept: $(1, 0)$

Horizontal asymptote: $y = 0$

Critical number: $x = e$

Possible inflection point: $\left(e^{3/2}, \dfrac{15e^{-3/2}}{2 \ln 2} \right)$

x	$f(x)$	$f'(x)$	$f''(x)$	Shape of graph
$\infty < x < 2$		$+$	$-$	increasing, concave down
$x = e$	$\dfrac{5e^{-1}}{\ln 2}$	0	$-$	relative maximum
$e < x < e^{3/2}$		$-$	$-$	decreasing, concave down
$x = e^{3/2}$	$\dfrac{15e^{-3/2}}{2 \ln 2}$	$-$	0	point of inflection
$e^{3/2} < x < \infty$		$-$	$+$	decreasing, concave up

59. Domain: $[0, 2\pi]$

Range: $[1, 1 + 2\pi]$

Symmetry: None

Asymptotes: None

Intercepts: $(0, 1)$

$$f(x) = x + \cos x$$

$$f'(x) = 1 - \sin x$$

$$f''(x) = -\cos x$$

Since $f'(x) \geq 0$, f is increasing. $f''(x) = 0$ when $x = \pi/2$ and $x = 3\pi/2$. The graph is shown in the figure.

x	$f(x)$	$f'(x)$	$f''(x)$	Shape of graph
$0 < x < \dfrac{\pi}{2}$		$+$	$-$	increasing, concave down
$x = \dfrac{\pi}{2}$	$\dfrac{\pi}{2}$	$+$	0	point of inflection
$\dfrac{\pi}{2} < x < \dfrac{3\pi}{2}$		$+$	$+$	increasing, concave up
$x = \dfrac{3\pi}{2}$	$\dfrac{3\pi}{2}$	$+$	0	point of inflection
$\dfrac{3\pi}{2} < x < 2\pi$		$+$	$-$	increasing, concave down

61. $y = 4x - 6 \arctan x$

$$y' = 4 - \frac{6}{1 + x^2} = \frac{4x^2 - 2}{1 + x^2}$$

$$y'' = \frac{12x}{(1 + x^2)^2}$$

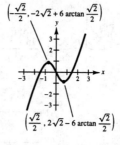

Relative maximum: $\left(-\dfrac{\sqrt{2}}{2}, -2\sqrt{2} + 6 \arctan \dfrac{\sqrt{2}}{2}\right)$

Relative minimum: $\left(\dfrac{\sqrt{2}}{2}, 2\sqrt{2} - 6 \arctan \dfrac{\sqrt{2}}{2}\right)$

Inflection point: $(0, 0)$

63. Let $t = 0$ at noon.

$$L = d^2 = (100 - 12t)^2 + (-10t)^2 = 10,000 - 2400t + 244t^2$$

$$\frac{dL}{dt} = -2400 + 488t = 0 \text{ when } t = \frac{300}{61} \approx 4.92 \text{ hr.}$$

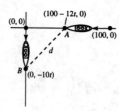

Ship A at $(40.98, 0)$; Ship B at $(0, -49.18)$

$$d^2 = 10,000 - 2400t + 244t^2$$

$$\approx 4098.36 \text{ when } t \approx 4.92 \approx 4:55 \text{ P.M.}$$

$$d \approx 64 \text{ km}$$

65. We have points $(0, y)$, $(x, 0)$, and $(1, 8)$. Thus,

$$m = \frac{y - 8}{0 - 1} = \frac{0 - 8}{x - 1} \text{ or } y = \frac{8x}{x - 1}.$$

Let $f(x) = L^2 = x^2 + \left(\frac{8x}{x - 1}\right)^2$.

$$f'(x) = 2x + 128\left(\frac{x}{x - 1}\right)\left[\frac{(x - 1) - x}{(x - 1)^2}\right] = 0$$

$$x - \frac{64x}{(x - 1)^3} = 0$$

$x[(x - 1)^3 - 64] = 0$ when $x = 0, 5$ (minimum).

Vertices of triangle: $(0, 0)$, $(5, 0)$, $(0, 10)$

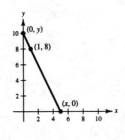

67. $A = $ (Average of bases)(Height)

$$= \left(\frac{x + s}{2}\right)\frac{\sqrt{3s^2 + 2sx - x^2}}{2} \text{ (see figure)}$$

$$\frac{dA}{dx} = \frac{1}{4}\left[\frac{(s - x)(s + x)}{\sqrt{3s^2 + 2sx - x^2}} + \sqrt{3s^2 + 2sx - x^2}\right]$$

$$= \frac{2(2s - x)(s + x)}{4\sqrt{3s^2 + 2sx - x^2}} = 0 \text{ when } x = 2s.$$

A is a maximum when $x = 2s$.

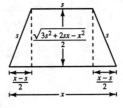

69. The longest pipe that will go around the corner will have a length equal to the minimum length of the hypotenuse [through the point $(4, 6)$] of the triangle whose vertices are $(0, 0)$, $(x, 0)$, and $(0, y)$. Begin by relating x and y as follows.

$$m = \frac{y - 6}{0 - 4} = \frac{6 - 0}{4 - x}$$

$$y - 6 = \frac{-24}{4 - x}$$

$$y = \frac{24}{x - 4} + 6 = \frac{6x}{x - 4}$$

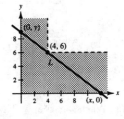

[Note that $dy/dx = -24/(x - 4)^2$.] Now the length of the hypotenuse is given by

$$L = \sqrt{x^2 + y^2}.$$

To minimize L, solve $dL/dx = 0$ as follows.

$$\frac{dL}{dx} = \frac{(1/2)[2x + (2y)(dy/dx)]}{\sqrt{x^2 + y^2}} = 0$$

$$x = -y\frac{dy}{dx} = -\left(\frac{6x}{x - 4}\right)\left[\frac{-24}{(x - 4)^2}\right]$$

$$x(x - 4)^3 = 144x$$

$$(x - 4)^3 = 144$$

$$x - 4 = \sqrt[3]{144}$$

$$x = \sqrt[3]{144} + 4$$

Therefore, the minimum length of L and the maximum length of pipe are given by:

$$L = \sqrt{x^2 + y^2} = \sqrt{x^2 + \frac{36x^2}{(x - 4)^2}} = \frac{x}{x - 4}\sqrt{(x - 4)^2 + 36}$$

$$= \frac{\sqrt[3]{144} + 4}{\sqrt[3]{144}}\sqrt{144^{2/3} + 36} \approx 14.05 \text{ ft}$$

71. From the figure observe that:

$$\csc \theta = \frac{L_1}{6} \quad \text{or} \quad L_1 = 6 \csc \theta$$

$$\csc\left(\frac{\pi}{2} - \theta\right) = \frac{L_2}{9} \quad \text{or} \quad L_2 = 9 \csc\left(\frac{\pi}{2} - \theta\right)$$

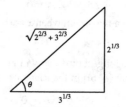

Therefore, the length of the pipe is given by

$$L = L_1 + L_2 = 6 \csc \theta + 9 \csc\left(\frac{\pi}{2} - \theta\right) = 6 \csc \theta + 9 \sec \theta.$$

Note that $\csc[(\pi/2) - \theta] = \sec \theta$. To maximize L, solve $dL/d\theta = 0$ as follows.

$$\frac{dL}{d\theta} = -6 \csc \theta \cot \theta + 9 \sec \theta \tan \theta = 0$$

$$9 \sec \theta \tan \theta = 6 \csc \theta \cot \theta$$

$$\frac{\sec \theta \tan \theta}{\csc \theta \cot \theta} = \frac{6}{9}$$

$$\tan^3 \theta = \frac{2}{3}$$

$$\tan \theta = \frac{2^{1/3}}{3^{1/3}}$$

From the figure observe that:

$$\csc \theta = \frac{\sqrt{2^{2/3} + 3^{2/3}}}{2^{1/3}} \quad \text{and} \quad \sec \theta = \frac{\sqrt{2^{2/3} + 3^{2/3}}}{3^{1/3}}.$$

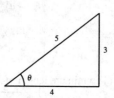

$$L = (6)\left(\frac{\sqrt{2^{2/3} + 3^{2/3}}}{2^{1/3}}\right) + (9)\left(\frac{\sqrt{2^{2/3} + 3^{2/3}}}{2^{1/3}}\right)$$

$$= 3\sqrt{2^{2/3} + 3^{2/3}}(2^{2/3} + 3^{2/3}) = 3(2^{2/3} + 3^{2/3})^{3/2}$$

73. $y = \dfrac{1}{3} \cos 12t - \dfrac{1}{4} \sin 12t$

$v = y' = -4 \sin 12t - 3 \cos 12t$

(a) When $t = \pi/8$, we have $y = \dfrac{1}{3} \cos \dfrac{3\pi}{2} - \dfrac{1}{4} \sin \dfrac{3\pi}{2} = \dfrac{1}{4}$ inch and $v = -4 \sin \dfrac{3\pi}{2} - 3 \cos \dfrac{3\pi}{2} = 4$ inches per second.

(b) The maximum displacement occurs when $y' = v = 0$.

$$-4 \sin(12t) - 3 \cos(12t) = 0$$

$$-4 \sin(12t) = 3 \cos(12t)$$

$$\frac{\sin(12t)}{\cos(12t)} = -\frac{3}{4} \implies \tan(12t) = -\frac{3}{4}$$

From the figure observe that when $\tan \theta = \frac{3}{4}$, $\sin \theta = \frac{3}{5}$, and $\cos \theta = \frac{4}{5}$. Since $\tan(12t)$ is negative, $\sin(12t)$ and $\cos(12t)$ must have opposite signs. If $\sin(12t) = -\frac{3}{5}$ and $\cos(12t) = \frac{4}{5}$, then

$$y = \frac{1}{3}\left(\frac{4}{5}\right) - \frac{1}{4}\left(-\frac{3}{5}\right) = \frac{25}{60} = \frac{5}{12} \text{ inches.}$$

If $\sin(12t) = \frac{3}{5}$ and $\cos(12t) = -\frac{4}{5}$, then

$$y = \frac{1}{3}\left(-\frac{4}{5}\right) - \frac{1}{4}\left(\frac{3}{5}\right) = -\frac{25}{60} = -\frac{5}{12} \text{ inches.}$$

In either case the maximum displacement from equilibrium is $\frac{5}{12}$ inches.

(c) The period of the function is $2\pi/12 = \pi/6$. Since the frequency is the reciprocal of the period, the frequency is $6/\pi$.

75. $t = 50 \log_{10}\left(\dfrac{18{,}000}{18{,}000 - h}\right)$

(a) Domain: $0 \le h < 18{,}000$

(c) $\qquad t = 50 \log_{10}\left(\dfrac{18{,}000}{18{,}000 - h}\right)$

$$10^{t/50} = \frac{18{,}000}{18{,}000 - h}$$

$$18{,}000 - h = 18{,}000(10^{-t/50})$$

$$h = 18{,}000(1 - 10^{-t/50})$$

As $h \to 18{,}000$, $t \to \infty$.

(b)

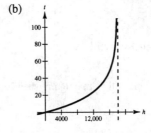

Vertical asymptote: $h = 18{,}000$

(d) $\quad t = 50 \log_{10} 18{,}000 - 50 \log_{10}(18{,}000 - h)$

$$\frac{dt}{dh} = \frac{50}{(\ln 10)(18{,}000 - h)}$$

$$\frac{d^2 t}{dh^2} = \frac{50}{(\ln 10)(18{,}000 - h)^2}$$

No critical numbers

As t increases, the rate of change of the altitude is increasing.

77. $y = x(1 - \cos x) = x - x\cos x$

$$\frac{dy}{dx} = 1 + x\sin x - \cos x$$

$$dy = (1 + x\sin x - \cos x)\,dx$$

79. (a) $S = -0.0810t^3 + 2.9197t^2 - 15.5459t + 92.3247$

(b)

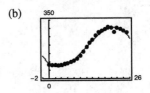

(c) Maximum is $S = 303.3$ at $t = 20.98$ (1990). Note that this is not accurate!

(d) The derivative $S'(t)$ is greatest at $t = 12.0$ (1982).

81. The profit is given by

$$P = (\text{price per unit})(\text{number of units}) - (\text{cost}) = px - C$$

$$= (36 - 4x)(x) - (2x^2 + 6) = 36x - 4x^2 - 2x^2 - 6$$

$$= -6x^2 + 36x - 6.$$

To maximize P, solve $dP/dx = 0$ as follows:

$$\frac{dP}{dx} = -12x + 36 = 0$$

$$12x = 36$$

$$x = 3 \text{ units}$$

Thus the maximum profit is

$$P = -6(3)^2 + 36(3) - 6 = -54 + 108 - 6 = \$48.$$

83. $R = $ (Number of people)(Rate per person)

$\qquad = n[8.00 - 0.05(n - 80)], \; n \geq 80$

$\qquad = 12n - 0.05n^2$

$\dfrac{dR}{dn} = 12 - 0.10n = 0$ when $n = 120$.

$\dfrac{d^2R}{dn^2} = -0.10 < 0 \Rightarrow$ Revenue will be maximum when 120 people go on the bus.

85. $C = \left(\dfrac{Q}{x}\right)s + \left(\dfrac{x}{2}\right)r$

$\dfrac{dC}{dx} = -\dfrac{Qs}{x^2} + \dfrac{r}{2} = 0$

$\dfrac{Qs}{x^2} = \dfrac{r}{2}$

$x^2 = \dfrac{2Qs}{r}$

$x = \sqrt{\dfrac{2Qs}{r}}$

87. False

$\quad$ Let $f(x) = x^3$, $c = 0$.

89. The first derivative is positive and the second derivative is negative. The graph is increasing and is concave down.

C H A P T E R   4
Integration

CHAPTER 4
Integration

Section 4.1 Antiderivatives and Indefinite Integration

Solutions to Exercises

1. $\dfrac{d}{dx}\left(\dfrac{3}{x^3} + C\right) = \dfrac{d}{dx}(3x^{-3} + C) = -9x^{-4} = \dfrac{-9}{x^4}$

3. $\dfrac{d}{dx}\left(\dfrac{1}{3}x^3 - 4x + C\right) = x^2 - 4 = (x-2)(x+2)$

	Given	Rewrite	Integrate	Simplify
5.	$\displaystyle\int \sqrt[3]{x}\,dx$	$\displaystyle\int x^{1/3}\,dx$	$\dfrac{x^{4/3}}{4/3} + C$	$\dfrac{3}{4}x^{4/3} + C$
7.	$\displaystyle\int \dfrac{1}{x\sqrt{x}}\,dx$	$\displaystyle\int x^{-3/2}\,dx$	$\dfrac{x^{-1/2}}{-1/2} + C$	$\dfrac{-2}{\sqrt{x}} + C$
9.	$\displaystyle\int \dfrac{1}{2x^3}\,dx$	$\dfrac{1}{2}\displaystyle\int x^{-3}\,dx$	$\dfrac{1}{2}\left(\dfrac{x^{-2}}{-2}\right) + C$	$-\dfrac{1}{4x^2} + C$

11. $\dfrac{dy}{dt} = 3t^2$

$\quad y = t^3 + C$

$\quad$ **Check:** $\dfrac{d}{dt}[t^3 + C] = 3t^2$

13. $\dfrac{dy}{dx} = x^{3/2}$

$\quad y = \dfrac{2}{5}x^{5/2} + C$

$\quad$ **Check:** $\dfrac{d}{dx}\left[\dfrac{2}{5}x^{5/2} + C\right] = x^{3/2}$

15. $\displaystyle\int (x^3 + 2)\,dx = \dfrac{1}{4}x^4 + 2x + C$

$\quad$ **Check:** $\dfrac{d}{dx}\left(\dfrac{1}{4}x^4 + 2x + C\right) = x^3 + 2$

17. $\displaystyle\int (x^{3/2} + 2x + 1)\,dx = \dfrac{x^{5/2}}{5/2} + 2\left(\dfrac{x^2}{2}\right) + x + C$

$\quad\quad\quad\quad\quad\quad\quad\quad\quad\quad\quad = \dfrac{2x^{5/2}}{5} + x^2 + x + C$

$\quad$ **Check:**

$\quad$ If $y = \dfrac{2x^{5/2}}{5} + x^2 + x + C$, then

$\quad\quad \dfrac{dy}{dx} = \left(\dfrac{2}{5}\right)\left(\dfrac{5}{2}\right)x^{3/2} + 2x + 1 + 0 = x^{3/2} + 2x + 1.$

19. $\displaystyle\int \sqrt[3]{x^2}\,dx = \displaystyle\int x^{2/3}\,dx = \dfrac{x^{5/3}}{5/3} + C = \dfrac{3}{5}x^{5/3} + C$

$\quad$ **Check:** $\dfrac{d}{dx}\left(\dfrac{3}{5}x^{5/3} + C\right) = x^{2/3} = \sqrt[3]{x^2}$

21. $\displaystyle\int \dfrac{1}{x^3}\,dx = \displaystyle\int x^{-3}\,dx = \dfrac{x^{-2}}{-2} + C = -\dfrac{1}{2x^2} + C$

$\quad$ **Check:** $\dfrac{d}{dx}\left(-\dfrac{1}{2x^2} + C\right) = \dfrac{1}{x^3}$

23. $\displaystyle\int \dfrac{x^2 + x + 1}{\sqrt{x}}\,dx = \displaystyle\int (x^{3/2} + x^{1/2} + x^{-1/2})\,dx = \dfrac{2}{5}x^{5/2} + \dfrac{2}{3}x^{3/2} + 2x^{1/2} + C = \dfrac{2}{15}x^{1/2}(3x^2 + 5x + 15) + C$

$\quad$ **Check:** $\dfrac{d}{dx}\left(\dfrac{2}{5}x^{5/2} + \dfrac{2}{3}x^{3/2} + 2x^{1/2} + C\right) = x^{3/2} + x^{1/2} + x^{-1/2} = \dfrac{x^2 + x + 1}{\sqrt{x}}$

25. $\int (x + 1)(3x - 2)\, dx = \int (3x^2 + x - 2)\, dx$

$$= x^3 + \frac{1}{2}x^2 - 2x + C$$

Check:

If $y = x^3 + \frac{1}{2}x^2 - 2x + C$, then

$$\frac{dy}{dx} = 3x^2 + \frac{1}{2}(2x) - 2 + 0$$

$$= 3x^2 + x - 2 = (x + 1)(3x - 2).$$

27. $\int y^2 \sqrt{y}\, dy = \int y^{5/2}\, dy = \frac{2}{7}y^{7/2} + C$

Check: $\frac{d}{dy}\left(\frac{2}{7}y^{7/2} + C\right) = y^{5/2} = y^2\sqrt{y}$

29. $\int dx = \int 1\, dx = x + C$

Check: $\frac{d}{dx}(x + C) = 1$

31. $\int (2 \sin x + 3 \cos x)\, dx = 2\int \sin x\, dx + 3\int \cos x\, dx$

$$= -2 \cos x + 3 \sin x + C$$

Check:

If $y = -2 \cos x + 3 \sin x + C$, then

$$\frac{dy}{dx} = -2(-\sin x) + 3 \cos x + 0 = 2 \sin x + 3 \cos x.$$

33. $\int (1 - \csc t \cot t)\, dt = t + \csc t + C$

Check: $\frac{d}{dt}(t + \csc t + C) = 1 - \csc t \cot t$

35. $\int (2 \sin x - 5e^x)\, dx = -2 \cos x - 5e^x + C$

Check: $\frac{d}{dx}(-2 \cos x - 5e^x + C) = 2 \sin x - 5e^x$

37. $\int (\sec^2 \theta - \sin \theta)\, d\theta = \tan \theta + \cos \theta + C$

Check: $\frac{d}{d\theta}(\tan \theta + \cos \theta + C) = \sec^2 \theta - \sin \theta$

39. $\int (\tan^2 y + 1)\, dy = \int \sec^2 y\, dy = \tan y + C$

Check:

If $f(y) = \tan y + C$, then $f'(y) = \sec^2 y = \tan^2 y + 1$.

41. $\int (2x - 4^x)\, dx = x^2 - \frac{4^x}{\ln 4} + C$

Check: $\frac{d}{dx}\left(x^2 - \frac{4^x}{\ln 4} + C\right) = 2x - 4^x$

43. $\int \left(x - \frac{5}{x}\right) dx = \int x\, dx - 5\int \frac{1}{x}\, dx$

$$= \frac{1}{2}x^2 - 5 \ln|x| + C$$

Check: If $y = \frac{1}{2}x^2 - 5 \ln|x| + C$, then

$$\frac{dy}{dx} = \frac{1}{2}(2x) - 5\left(\frac{1}{x}\right) + 0 = x - \frac{5}{x}.$$

45. $f(x) = \cos x$

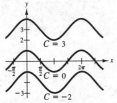

47.

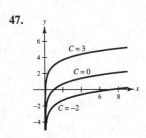

49. $f'(x) = 2$

$f(x) = 2x + C$

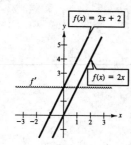

51. $f'(x) = 1 - x^2$

$f(x) = x - \dfrac{x^3}{3} + C$

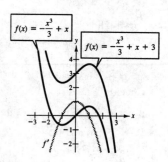

53. $\dfrac{dy}{dx} = 2x - 1$

$y = \displaystyle\int (2x - 1)\, dx = x^2 - x + C$

Substituting the coordinates of the solution point into the antiderivative yields

$y = x^2 - x + C$

$1 = (1)^2 - (1) + C \quad \text{or} \quad C = 1.$

Therefore, the required equation is $y = x^2 - x + 1$.

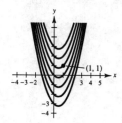

55. $\dfrac{dy}{dx} = \cos x, \ (0, 4)$

$y = \displaystyle\int \cos x\, dx = \sin x + C$

$4 = \sin 0 + C \implies C = 4$

$y = \sin x + 4$

57. (a)

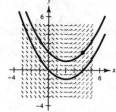

(b) $\dfrac{dy}{dx} = \dfrac{1}{2}x - 1, \ (4, 2)$

$y = \dfrac{x^2}{4} - x + C$

$2 = \dfrac{4^2}{4} - 4 + C$

$2 = C$

$y = \dfrac{x^2}{4} - x + 2$

59. $f''(x) = 2$

$f'(2) = 5$

$f(2) = 10$

$f'(x) = \displaystyle\int 2\, dx = 2x + C_1$

$f'(2) = 4 + C_1 = 5 \implies C_1 = 1$

$f'(x) = 2x + 1$

$f(x) = \displaystyle\int (2x + 1)\, dx = x^2 + x + C_2$

$f(2) = 6 + C_2 = 10 \implies C_2 = 4$

$f(x) = x^2 + x + 4$

61. $f''(x) = x^{-3/2}$

$$f'(x) = \int x^{-3/2} dx$$

$$= \frac{x^{-1/2}}{-1/2} + C_1 = \frac{-2}{\sqrt{x}} + C_1$$

$$f'(4) = \frac{-2}{\sqrt{4}} + C_1 = 2 \Rightarrow C_1 = 3$$

$$f'(x) = -2x^{-1/2} + 3$$

$$f(x) = \int (-2x^{-1/2} + 3)\, dx$$

$$= \frac{(-2)x^{1/2}}{1/2} + 3x + C_2 = -4x^{1/2} + 3x + C_2$$

$$f(0) = -4(0)^{1/2} + 3(0) + C_2 = 0 \Rightarrow C_2 = 0$$

Therefore, $f(x) = -4x^{1/2} + 3x = -4\sqrt{x} + 3x$.

63. $f''(x) = e^x$

$$f'(x) = \int e^x\, dx = e^x + C_1$$

$$f'(0) = 2 = e^0 + C_1 \Rightarrow C_1 = 1$$

$$f(x) = \int (e^x + 1)\, dx = e^x + x + C_2$$

$$f(0) = 5 = e^0 + 0 + C_2 \Rightarrow C_2 = 4$$

$$f(x) = e^x + x + 4$$

65. (a) $h(t) = \int (1.5t + 5)\, dt = 0.75t^2 + 5t + C$

$$h(0) = 0 + 0 + C = 12 \Rightarrow C = 12$$

$$h(t) = 0.75t^2 + 5t + 12$$

(b) $h(6) = 0.75(6)^2 + 5(6) + 12 = 69$ cm

67. $a(t) = -32$ ft/sec^2

$$v(t) = \int -32\, dt = -32t + C_1$$

$$v(0) = 60 = C_1$$

$$v(t) = -32t + 60$$

$$s(t) = \int (-32t + 60)\, dt = -16t^2 + 60t + C_2$$

$$s(0) = 0 = C_2$$

$$s(t) = -16t^2 + 60t$$

The ball reaches its maximum height when

$$v(t) = 0: \ -32t + 60 = 0$$

$$32t = 60$$

$$t = \frac{15}{8}.$$

$$s\left(\frac{15}{8}\right) = -16\left(\frac{15}{8}\right)^2 + 60\left(\frac{15}{8}\right) = 56.26 \text{ feet}$$

69. If $s = f(t)$ is the position of the object at any time t, then $f'(t)$ is its velocity and $f''(t)$ its acceleration. Therefore, $f''(t) = -32$ since -32 ft/sec^2 is the acceleration due to gravity.

$$f'(t) = \int -32\, dt = -32t + C_1 = -32t + v_0$$

where v_0 is the initial velocity. Furthermore,

$$f(t) = \int (-32t + v_0)\, dt = -16t^2 + v_0 t + C_2 = -16t^2 + v_0 t + s_0$$

where $s_0 = 0$ is the initial height. Thus, $s = f(t) = -16t^2 + v_0 t$. Now since s is a maximum when $f'(t) = 0$, we have $-32t + v_0 = 0$ or $t = v_0/32$. Finally, in order for s to attain a height of 550 feet, we have

$$s = -16\left(\frac{v_0}{32}\right)^2 + v_0\left(\frac{v_0}{32}\right) = 550$$

$$\frac{v_0^2}{64} = 550$$

$$v_0^2 = 35,200$$

$$v_0 = \sqrt{35,200} = 40\sqrt{22} \approx 187.617 \text{ ft/sec}$$

71. $a(t) = -9.8$

$$v(t) = \int -9.8 \, dt = -9.8t + C_1$$

$$v(0) = v_0 = C_1 \Rightarrow v(t) = -9.8t + v_0$$

$$f(t) = \int (-9.8t + v_0) \, dt = -4.9t^2 + v_0 t + C_2$$

$$f(0) = s_0 = C_2 \Rightarrow f(t) = -4.9t^2 + v_0 t + C_2$$

73. From Exercise 71, $f(t) = -4.9t^2 + 10t$.

$$v(t) = -9.8t + 10 = 0 \text{ (Maximum height when } v = 0.)$$

$$9.8t = 10$$

$$t = \frac{10}{9.8}$$

$$f\left(\frac{10}{9.8}\right) \approx 5.1 \text{ m}$$

75. $a(t) = -1.6$

$$v(t) = \int (-1.6) \, dt = -1.6t + v_0 = -1.6t$$

Since the stone was dropped, $v_0 = 0$.

$$s(t) = \int (-1.6t) \, dt = -0.8t^2 + s_0$$

Since the stone hit the surface of the moon $t = 20$, we have

$$s(20) = -0.8(20)^2 + s_0$$

$$= -320 + s_0 = 0 \Rightarrow s_0 = 320.$$

Therefore, $s(t) = -0.8t^2 + 320$, and $v(t) = -1.6t$. The stone was dropped from the height $s(0) = 320$ meters, and its velocity at the time of impact was $v(20) = -1.6(20) = -32$ meters per second.

77. $x(t) = t^3 - 6t^2 + 9t - 2 \qquad 0 \le t \le 5$

(a) $v(t) = x'(t) = 3t^2 - 12t + 9$

$$= 3(t^2 - 4t + 3) = 3(t - 1)(t - 3)$$

$a(t) = v'(t) = 6t - 12 = 6(t - 2)$

(b) $v(t) > 0$ when $0 < t < 1$ or $3 < t < 5$.

(c) $a(t) = 6(t - 2) = 0$ when $t = 2$.

$v(2) = 3(1)(-1) = -3$

79. $v(t) = \dfrac{1}{\sqrt{t}} = t^{-1/2} \qquad t > 0$

$$x(t) = \int v(t) \, dt = 2t^{1/2} + C$$

$$x(1) = 4 = 2(1) + C \Rightarrow C = 2$$

$$x(t) = 2t^{1/2} + 2$$

$$a(t) = v'(t) = -\frac{1}{2}t^{-3/2} = \frac{-1}{2t^{3/2}}$$

81. (a) $v(0) = 25 \text{ km/hr} = 25 \cdot \dfrac{1000}{3600} = \dfrac{250}{36} \text{ m/sec}$

$$v(13) = 80 \text{ km/hr} = 80 \cdot \frac{1000}{3600} = \frac{800}{36} \text{ m/sec}$$

$a(t) = a$ (constant acceleration)

$v(t) = at + C$

$$v(0) = \frac{250}{36} \Rightarrow v(t) = at + \frac{250}{36}$$

$$v(13) = \frac{800}{36} = 13a + \frac{250}{36}$$

$$\frac{550}{36} = 13a$$

$$a = \frac{550}{468} = \frac{275}{234} \approx 1.175 \text{ m/sec}^2$$

(b) $s(t) = a\dfrac{t^2}{2} + \dfrac{250}{36}t \qquad (s(0) = 0)$

$$s(13) = \frac{275}{234} \frac{(13)^2}{2} + \frac{250}{36}(13) \approx 189.58 \text{ m}$$

83. Let $T(t)$ and $A(t)$ represent the position functions of the truck and auto. It follows that

$$T'(t) = 30, \quad T(0) = 0$$

$$A''(t) = 6, \quad A'(0) = 0, \quad \text{and} \quad A(0) = 0.$$

For the truck,

$$T(t) = \int 30 \, dt = 30t + C_1$$

$$T(0) = 30(0) + C_1 = 0 \implies C_1 = 0.$$

For the auto,

$$A'(t) = \int 6 \, dt = 6t + C_2$$

$$A'(0) = 6(0) + C_2 = 0 \implies C_2 = 0$$

$$A'(t) = 6t$$

$$A(t) = \int 6t \, dt = 3t^2 + C_3$$

$$A(0) = 3(0)^2 + C_3 = 0 \implies C_3 = 0$$

$$A(t) = 3t^2.$$

Therefore, when the auto catches up with the truck, we have

$$A(t) = T(t)$$

$$3t^2 = 30t$$

$$3t^2 - 30t = 0$$

$$3t(t - 10) = 0$$

$$t = 10 \text{ sec.} \quad \text{We disregard } t = 0.$$

(a) When $t = 10$ sec, the auto will have traveled $A(10) = 3(10^2) = 300$ ft.

(b) It will be traveling

$$A'(10) = 60 \text{ ft/sec} = \frac{60(3600)}{5280} \approx 41 \text{ mi/hr.}$$

85. $a(t) = k$

$v(t) = kt$

$s(t) = \frac{k}{2}t^2$ since $v(0) = s(0) = 0.$

At the time of lift-off, $kt = 160$ and $(k/2)t^2 = 0.7$. Since $(k/2)t^2 = 0.7,$

$$t = \sqrt{\frac{1.4}{k}}$$

$$v\left(\sqrt{\frac{1.4}{k}}\right) = k\sqrt{\frac{1.4}{k}} = 160$$

$$1.4k = 160^2 \implies k = \frac{160^2}{1.4}$$

$$\approx 18{,}285.714 \text{ mi/hr}^2$$

$$\approx 7.45 \text{ ft/sec}^2.$$

87. $\dfrac{dC}{dx} = 2x - 12$

$C(0) = 50$

$C(x) = x^2 - 12x + C$

$C(0) = 0 + C = 50 \implies C = 50$

Cost: $C(x) = x^2 - 12x + 50$

Average cost: $\overline{C}(x) = \dfrac{C(x)}{x} = x - 12 + \dfrac{50}{x}$

89. $\dfrac{dR}{dx} = 100 - 5x$

$$R(x) = \int (100 - 5x)\, dx = 100x - \frac{5}{2}x^2 + C$$

Since there is no revenue generated if no units are sold, $R(0) = 0$. Therefore, $C = 0$ and the revenue function is

$$R(x) = 100x - \frac{5}{2}x^2.$$

The revenue generated is the number of units sold x times the price per unit p.

$$R(x) = xp = 100x - \frac{5}{2}x^2 = x\left(100 - \frac{5}{2}x\right)$$

Thus, the demand function is $\;p = 100 - \frac{5}{2}x.$

91. True

93. True

95. $\dfrac{d}{dx}\big(\ln|Cx|\big) = \dfrac{d}{dx}\big(\ln|C| + \ln|x|\big) = 0 + \dfrac{1}{x} = \dfrac{1}{x}$

97. $f(0) = -4$. Graph of f' is given.

   (a) $f'(4) \approx -1.0$

   (b) No. The slopes of the tangent lines are greater than 2 on $[0, 2]$. Therefore, f must increase more than 4 units on $[0, 4]$.

   (c) No, $f(5) < f(4)$ because f is decreasing on $[4, 5]$.

   (d) f is an maximum at $x = 3.5$ because $f'(3.5) \approx 0$ and the first derivative test.

   (e) f is concave upward when f' is increasing on $(-\infty, 1)$ and $(5, \infty)$. f is concave downward on $(1, 5)$. Points of inflection at $x = 1, 5$.

   (f) f'' is a minimum at $x = 3$.

   (g)

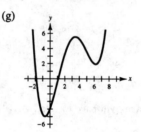

Section 4.2   Area

1. $\displaystyle\sum_{i=1}^{5}(2i + 1) = 2\sum_{i=1}^{5} i + \sum_{i=1}^{5} 1 = 2(1 + 2 + 3 + 4 + 5) + 5 = 35$

3. $\displaystyle\sum_{k=0}^{4}\frac{1}{k^2 + 1} = \frac{1}{0^2 + 1} + \frac{1}{1^2 + 1} + \frac{1}{2^2 + 1} + \frac{1}{3^2 + 1} + \frac{1}{4^2 + 1}$

$$= \frac{1}{1} + \frac{1}{2} + \frac{1}{5} + \frac{1}{10} + \frac{1}{17}$$

$$= \frac{170 + 85 + 34 + 17 + 10}{170}$$

$$= \frac{316}{170} = \frac{158}{85}$$

5. $\displaystyle\sum_{k=1}^{4} c = c + c + c + c = 4c$ **7.** $\displaystyle\sum_{i=1}^{9}\frac{1}{3i}$ **9.** $\displaystyle\sum_{j=1}^{8}\left[2\left(\frac{j}{8}\right) + 3\right]$

11. We begin by noting that the n terms in this sum are each of the form

$$f(i) = \left[\left(\frac{2i}{n}\right)^3 - \frac{2i}{n}\right]\left(\frac{2}{n}\right).$$

Furthermore, observe that in the first term $i = 1$, in the second term $i = 2$, and so on until we reach the nth term. Thus our index i runs from 1 to n, and the sigma notation for the given sum is

$$\sum_{i=1}^{n} f(i) = \sum_{i=1}^{n}\left[\left(\frac{2i}{n}\right)^3 - \frac{2i}{n}\right]\left(\frac{2}{n}\right)$$

$$= \frac{2}{n}\sum_{i=1}^{n}\left[\left(\frac{2i}{n}\right)^3 - \frac{2i}{n}\right].$$

13. $\dfrac{3}{n}\sum_{i=1}^{n}\left[2\left(1 + \dfrac{3i}{n}\right)^2\right]$

15. $\sum_{i=1}^{20} 2i = 2\sum_{i=1}^{20} i = 2\left[\dfrac{20(21)}{2}\right] = 420$

17. $\sum_{i=1}^{20}(i - 1)^2 = \sum_{i=1}^{19} i^2$

$$= \left[\dfrac{19(20)(39)}{6}\right] = 2470$$

19. $\sum_{i=1}^{15} i(i - 1)^2 = \sum_{i=1}^{15}(i^3 - 2i^2 + i)$

$$= \left[\sum_{i=1}^{15} i^3 - 2\sum_{i=1}^{15} i^2 + \sum_{i=1}^{15} i\right]$$

$$= \left[\dfrac{15^2(16)^2}{4} - 2\dfrac{15(16)(31)}{6} + \dfrac{15(16)}{2}\right]$$

$$= 14{,}400 - 2480 + 120 = 12{,}040$$

21. sum seq(x 2 + 3, x, 1, 20, 1) = 2930   *(TI-82)*

$$\sum_{i=1}^{20}(i^2 + 3) = \dfrac{20(20 + 1)[2(20) + 1]}{6} + 3(20)$$

$$= \dfrac{(20)(21)(41)}{6} + 60 = 2930$$

23. $\lim\limits_{n\to\infty}\left[\left(\dfrac{4}{3n^3}\right)(2n^3 + 3n^2 + n)\right] = \lim\limits_{n\to\infty}\left[\dfrac{8}{3} + \dfrac{4}{n} + \dfrac{4}{3n^2}\right] = \dfrac{8}{3}$

25. $\lim\limits_{n\to\infty} s(n) = \lim\limits_{n\to\infty}\dfrac{81}{n^4}\left[\dfrac{n^2(n + 1)^2}{4}\right]$

$$= \lim\limits_{n\to\infty}\dfrac{81}{4}\left(\dfrac{n^4 + 2n^3 + n^2}{n^4}\right)$$

$$= \lim\limits_{n\to\infty}\dfrac{81}{4}\left(1 + \dfrac{2}{n} + \dfrac{1}{n^2}\right) = \dfrac{81}{4}$$

27. $\lim\limits_{n\to\infty}\left[\left(\dfrac{18}{n^2}\right)\dfrac{n(n + 1)}{2}\right] = \dfrac{18}{2}\lim\limits_{n\to\infty}\left[\dfrac{n^2 + n}{n^2}\right] = \dfrac{18}{2}(1) = 9$

29. $\lim\limits_{n\to\infty}\sum_{i=1}^{n}\left(\dfrac{16i}{n^2}\right) = \lim\limits_{n\to\infty}\dfrac{16}{n^2}\sum_{i=1}^{n} i$

$$= \lim\limits_{n\to\infty}\dfrac{16}{n^2}\left(\dfrac{n(n + 1)}{2}\right)$$

$$= \lim\limits_{n\to\infty}\left[8\left(\dfrac{n^2 + n}{n^2}\right)\right]$$

$$= 8\lim\limits_{n\to\infty}\left(1 + \dfrac{1}{n}\right) = 8$$

31. $\sum_{i=1}^{n}\dfrac{1}{n^3}(i - 1)^2 = \dfrac{1}{n^3}\sum_{i=1}^{n}(i^2 - 2i + 1)$

$$= \dfrac{1}{n^3}\left[\sum_{i=1}^{n} i^2 - 2\sum_{i=1}^{n} i + \sum_{i=1}^{n} 1\right]$$

$$= \dfrac{1}{n^3}\left[\dfrac{n(n + 1)(2n + 1)}{6} - 2\dfrac{n(n + 1)}{2} + n\right]$$

$$= \dfrac{1}{n^3}\left(\dfrac{n^3}{3} - \dfrac{n^2}{2} + \dfrac{n}{6}\right)$$

$$= \dfrac{1}{3} - \dfrac{1}{2n} + \dfrac{1}{6n^2}$$

Therefore,

$$\lim\limits_{n\to\infty}\sum_{i=1}^{n}\dfrac{1}{n^3}(i - 1)^2 = \lim\limits_{n\to\infty}\left(\dfrac{1}{3} - \dfrac{1}{2n} + \dfrac{1}{6n^2}\right) = \dfrac{1}{3}.$$

33. $\lim\limits_{n\to\infty} \sum\limits_{i=1}^{n}\left(1 + \dfrac{i}{n}\right)\left(\dfrac{2}{n}\right) = 2\lim\limits_{n\to\infty}\dfrac{1}{n}\left[\sum\limits_{i=1}^{n}1 + \dfrac{1}{n}\sum\limits_{i=1}^{n}i\right] = 2\lim\limits_{n\to\infty}\dfrac{1}{n}\left[n + \dfrac{1}{n}\left(\dfrac{n(n+1)}{2}\right)\right] = 2\lim\limits_{n\to\infty}\left[1 + \dfrac{n^2+n}{2n^2}\right] = 2\left(1 + \dfrac{1}{2}\right) = 3$

35. $S(4) = \sqrt{\dfrac{1}{4}}\left(\dfrac{1}{4}\right) + \sqrt{\dfrac{1}{2}}\left(\dfrac{1}{4}\right) + \sqrt{\dfrac{3}{4}}\left(\dfrac{1}{4}\right) + \sqrt{1}\left(\dfrac{1}{4}\right) = \dfrac{1 + \sqrt{2} + \sqrt{3} + 2}{8} \approx 0.768$

$s(4) = 0\left(\dfrac{1}{4}\right) + \sqrt{\dfrac{1}{4}}\left(\dfrac{1}{4}\right) + \sqrt{\dfrac{1}{2}}\left(\dfrac{1}{4}\right) + \sqrt{\dfrac{3}{4}}\left(\dfrac{1}{4}\right) = \dfrac{1 + \sqrt{2} + \sqrt{3}}{8} \approx 0.518$

37. Dividing the interval into five subintervals of equal width yields

$$x_0 = 1, \quad x_1 = 1.2, \quad x_2 = 1.4, \quad x_3 = 1.6, \quad x_4 = 1.8, \quad x_5 = 2.$$

Since y is decreasing from 1 to 2, the lower sum is obtained by using the *right* endpoints of the five subintervals.

$s = \dfrac{1}{1.2}\left(\dfrac{1}{5}\right) + \dfrac{1}{1.4}\left(\dfrac{1}{5}\right) + \dfrac{1}{1.6}\left(\dfrac{1}{5}\right) + \dfrac{1}{1.8}\left(\dfrac{1}{5}\right) + \dfrac{1}{2}\left(\dfrac{1}{5}\right)$

$= \dfrac{1}{6} + \dfrac{1}{7} + \dfrac{1}{8} + \dfrac{1}{9} + \dfrac{1}{10} \approx 0.646$

Similarly, the upper sum is obtained by using the *left* endpoints of the five subintervals.

$S = 1\left(\dfrac{1}{5}\right) + \dfrac{1}{1.2}\left(\dfrac{1}{5}\right) + \dfrac{1}{1.4}\left(\dfrac{1}{5}\right) + \dfrac{1}{1.6}\left(\dfrac{1}{5}\right) + \dfrac{1}{1.8}\left(\dfrac{1}{5}\right)$

$= \dfrac{1}{5} + \dfrac{1}{6} + \dfrac{1}{7} + \dfrac{1}{8} + \dfrac{1}{9} \approx 0.746$

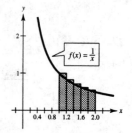

39. (a)

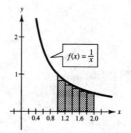

(b) $\Delta x = \dfrac{2-0}{n} = \dfrac{2}{n}$

Endpoints:

$$0 < 1\left(\dfrac{2}{n}\right) < 2\left(\dfrac{2}{n}\right) < \cdots < (n-1)\left(\dfrac{2}{n}\right) < n\left(\dfrac{2}{n}\right) = 2$$

(c) Since $y = x$ is increasing, $f(m_i) = f(x_{i-1})$ on $[x_{i-1}, x_i]$.

$s(n) = \sum\limits_{i=1}^{n} f(x_{i-1})\,\Delta x$

$= \sum\limits_{i=1}^{n} f\left(\dfrac{2i-2}{n}\right)\left(\dfrac{2}{n}\right) = \sum\limits_{i=1}^{n}\left[(i-1)\left(\dfrac{2}{n}\right)\right]\left(\dfrac{2}{n}\right)$

(d) $f(M_i) = f(x_i)$ on $[x_{i-1}, x_i]$

$S(n) = \sum\limits_{i=1}^{n} f(x_i)\,\Delta x = \sum\limits_{i=1}^{n} f\left(\dfrac{2i}{n}\right)\dfrac{2}{n} = \sum\limits_{i=1}^{n}\left[i\left(\dfrac{2}{n}\right)\right]\left(\dfrac{2}{n}\right)$

(e)

x	5	10	50	100
$s(n)$	1.6	1.8	1.96	1.98
$S(n)$	2.4	2.2	2.04	2.02

(f) $\lim\limits_{n\to\infty} \sum\limits_{i=1}^{n}\left[(i-1)\left(\dfrac{2}{n}\right)\right]\left(\dfrac{2}{n}\right) = \lim\limits_{n\to\infty}\dfrac{4}{n^2}\sum\limits_{i=1}^{n}(i-1)$

$= \lim\limits_{n\to\infty}\dfrac{4}{n^2}\left[\dfrac{n(n+1)}{2} - n\right]$

$= \lim\limits_{n\to\infty}\left[\dfrac{2(n+1)}{n} - \dfrac{4}{n}\right] = 2$

$\lim\limits_{n\to\infty} \sum\limits_{i=1}^{n}\left[i\left(\dfrac{2}{n}\right)\right]\left(\dfrac{2}{n}\right) = \lim\limits_{n\to\infty}\dfrac{4}{n^2}\sum\limits_{i=1}^{n} i$

$= \lim\limits_{n\to\infty}\left(\dfrac{4}{n^2}\right)\dfrac{n(n+1)}{2}$

$= \lim\limits_{n\to\infty}\dfrac{2(n+1)}{n} = 2$

41. $y = -2x + 3$ on $[0, 1]$. $\left(\textit{Note: } \Delta x = \dfrac{1 - 0}{n} = \dfrac{1}{n}\right)$

$$s(n) = \sum_{i=1}^{n} f\left(\frac{i}{n}\right)\left(\frac{1}{n}\right) = \sum_{i=1}^{n}\left[-2\left(\frac{i}{n}\right) + 3\right]\left(\frac{1}{n}\right)$$

$$= 3 - \frac{2}{n^2}\sum_{i=1}^{n} i = 3 - \frac{2(n+1)n}{2n^2} = 2 - \frac{1}{n}$$

Area $= \lim_{n \to \infty} s(n) = 2$

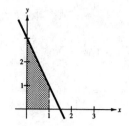

43. $y = x^2 + 2$ on $[0, 1]$. $\left(\textit{Note: } \Delta x = \dfrac{1}{n}\right)$

$$S(n) = \sum_{i=1}^{n} f\left(\frac{i}{n}\right)\left(\frac{1}{n}\right) = \sum_{i=1}^{n}\left[\left(\frac{i}{n}\right)^2 + 2\right]\left(\frac{1}{n}\right)$$

$$= \left[\frac{1}{n^3}\sum_{i=1}^{n} i^2\right] + 2 = \frac{n(n+1)(2n+1)}{6n^3} + 2 = \frac{1}{6}\left(2 + \frac{3}{n} + \frac{1}{n^2}\right) + 2$$

Area $= \lim_{n \to \infty} S(n) = \dfrac{7}{3}$

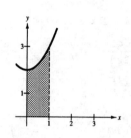

45. $y = 27 - x^3$ on $[1, 3]$. $\left(\textit{Note: } \Delta x = \dfrac{3 - 1}{n} = \dfrac{2}{n}\right)$

$$s(n) = \sum_{i=1}^{n} f\left(1 + \frac{2i}{n}\right)\left(\frac{2}{n}\right) = \sum_{i=1}^{n}\left[27 - \left(1 + \frac{2i}{n}\right)^3\right]\left(\frac{2}{n}\right) = \frac{2}{n}\sum_{i=1}^{n}\left(26 - \frac{6i}{n} - \frac{12i^2}{n^2} - \frac{8i^3}{n^3}\right)$$

$$= \frac{2}{n}\left[26n - \frac{6}{n}\left(\frac{n(n+1)}{2}\right) - \frac{12}{n^2}\left(\frac{n(n+1)(2n+1)}{6}\right) - \frac{8}{n^3}\left(\frac{n^2(n+1)^2}{4}\right)\right]$$

$$= 34 - \frac{26}{n} - \frac{8}{n^2}$$

Area $= \lim_{n \to \infty} s(n) = 34$

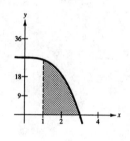

47. Let $\Delta x = [1 - (-1)]/n = 2/n$. Choosing right endpoints, we have

$$c_i = -1 + i\left(\frac{2}{n}\right) = -1 + \frac{2i}{n}.$$

Therefore, for $f(x) = x^2 - x^3$, we have

$$f\left(-1 + \frac{2i}{n}\right)\left(\frac{2}{n}\right).$$

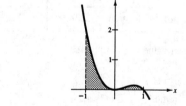

$$\text{Area} = \lim_{n \to \infty}\sum_{i=1}^{n} f\left(-1 + \frac{2i}{n}\right)\left(\frac{2}{n}\right)$$

$$= \lim_{n \to \infty}\frac{2}{n}\sum_{i=1}^{n}\left[\left(-1 + \frac{2i}{n}\right)^2 - \left(-1 + \frac{2i}{n}\right)^3\right]$$

$$= \lim_{n \to \infty}\frac{2}{n}\sum_{i=1}^{n}\left[2 - \frac{10i}{n} + \frac{16i^2}{n^2} - \frac{8i^3}{n^3}\right]$$

$$= \lim_{n \to \infty}\left[\frac{2}{n}\sum_{i=1}^{n} 2 - \frac{20}{n^2}\sum_{i=1}^{n} i + \frac{32}{n^3}\sum_{i=1}^{n} i^2 - \frac{16}{n^4}\sum_{i=1}^{n} i^3\right]$$

$$= \lim_{n \to \infty}\left[\frac{2}{n}(2n) - \left(\frac{20}{n^2}\right)\frac{n(n+1)}{2} + \left(\frac{32}{n^3}\right)\frac{n(n+1)(2n+1)}{6} - \left(\frac{16}{n^4}\right)\frac{n^2(n+1)^2}{4}\right]$$

$$= \lim_{n \to \infty}\left(4 - 10 - \frac{10}{n} + \frac{32}{3} + \frac{16}{n} + \frac{16}{3n^2} - 4 - \frac{8}{n} - \frac{4}{n^2}\right) = 4 - 10 + \frac{32}{3} - 4 = \frac{2}{3}.$$

49. $f(y) = 3y$ on $[0, 2]$. $\left(\textit{Note: } \Delta y = \dfrac{2 - 0}{n} = \dfrac{2}{n}\right)$

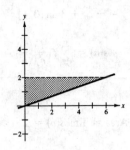

$$S(n) = \sum_{i=1}^{n} f(m_i)\,\Delta y = \sum_{i=1}^{n} f\left(\frac{2i}{n}\right)\left(\frac{2}{n}\right) = \sum_{i=1}^{n} 3\left(\frac{2i}{n}\right)\left(\frac{2}{n}\right)$$

$$= \frac{12}{n^2} \sum_{i=1}^{n} i = \left(\frac{12}{n^2}\right) \cdot \frac{n(n+1)}{2} = \frac{6(n+1)}{n} = 6 + \frac{6}{n}$$

$$\text{Area} = \lim_{n \to \infty} S(n) = \lim_{n \to \infty} \left(6 + \frac{6}{n}\right) = 6$$

51. $f(x) = x^2 + 3$, $0 \le x \le 2$, $n = 4$

Let $c_i = \dfrac{x_i + x_{i-1}}{2}$.

$$\Delta x = \frac{1}{2},\ c_1 = \frac{1}{4},\ c_2 = \frac{3}{4},\ c_3 = \frac{5}{4},\ c_4 = \frac{7}{4}$$

$$\text{Area} \approx \sum_{i=1}^{n} f(c_i)\,\Delta x = \sum_{i=1}^{4} [c_i^2 + 3]\left(\frac{1}{2}\right)$$

$$= \frac{1}{2}\left[\left(\frac{1}{16} + 3\right) + \left(\frac{9}{16} + 3\right) + \left(\frac{25}{16} + 3\right) + \left(\frac{49}{16} + 3\right)\right]$$

$$= \frac{69}{8}$$

53. Consider $f(x) = \tan x$ on the interval $[0, \pi/4]$. Let

$$\Delta x = \frac{\pi/4 - 0}{4} = \frac{\pi}{16}.$$

Dividing the interval into four parts of equal lengths yields endpoints

$$x_0 = 0,\ x_1 = \frac{\pi}{16},\ x_2 = \frac{2\pi}{16},\ x_3 = \frac{3\pi}{16},\ \text{and } x_4 = \frac{4\pi}{16}.$$

The midpoints of these subintervals are

$$\frac{x_0 + x_1}{2} = \frac{\pi}{32},\ \frac{x_1 + x_2}{2} = \frac{3\pi}{32},\ \frac{x_2 + x_3}{2} = \frac{5\pi}{32},\ \text{and}$$

$$\frac{x_3 + x_4}{2} = \frac{7\pi}{32}.$$

$$\text{Area} \approx \sum_{i=1}^{4} f\left(\frac{x_i + x_{i-1}}{2}\right) \Delta x$$

$$= \frac{\pi}{16}\left(\tan\frac{\pi}{32} + \tan\frac{3\pi}{32} + \tan\frac{5\pi}{32} + \tan\frac{7\pi}{32}\right)$$

$$\approx 0.345$$

55. $f(x) = \sqrt{x}$ on $[0, 4]$.

n	4	8	12	16	20
Approximate area	5.3838	5.3523	5.3439	5.3403	5.3384

(Exact value is $16/3$.)

57. $f(x) = \tan\left(\dfrac{\pi x}{8}\right)$ on $[1, 3]$.

n	4	8	12	16	20
Approximate area	2.2223	2.2387	2.2418	2.2430	2.2435

59. $f(x) = \ln x$, $[1, 5]$

n	4	8	12	16	20
Approximate area	4.0786	4.0554	4.0509	4.0493	4.0485

61. (a)

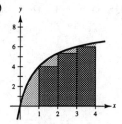

Lower sum:
$$s(4) = 0 + 4 + 5\tfrac{1}{3} + 6 = 15\tfrac{1}{3} = \tfrac{46}{3} \approx 15.333$$

(b)

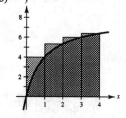

Upper sum:
$$S(4) = 4 + 5\tfrac{1}{3} + 6 + 6\tfrac{2}{5} = 21\tfrac{11}{15} = \tfrac{326}{15} \approx 21.733$$

(c)

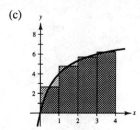

Midpoint Rule:
$$M(4) = 2\tfrac{2}{3} + 4\tfrac{4}{5} + 5\tfrac{5}{7} + 6\tfrac{2}{9} = \tfrac{6112}{315} \approx 19.403$$

(d) In each case, $\Delta x = 4/n$. The lower sum uses left endpoints, $(i - 1)(4/n)$. The upper sum uses right endpoints, $(i)(4/n)$. The Midpoint Rule uses midpoints, $\left(i - \tfrac{1}{2}\right)(4/n)$.

(e)

n	4	8	20	100	200
$s(n)$	15.333	17.368	18.459	18.995	19.06
$S(n)$	21.733	20.568	19.739	19.251	19.188
$M(n)$	19.403	19.201	19.137	19.125	19.125

(f) $s(n)$ increases because the lower sum approaches the exact value as n increases. $S(n)$ decreases because the upper sum approaches the exact value as n increases. Because of the shape of the graph, the lower sum is always smaller than the exact value, whereas the upper sum is always larger.

63. A sketch of the region is given in the figure. Since area is positive, -2 cannot be correct. The area of a rectangle of height 4 over the interval $[0, 2]$ is 8. Thus, the area of the specified region is less than 8 which eliminates 8 and 10 as possible answers. A rectangle of height 3 over the interval $[0, 1]$ has area 3 which appears significantly less than the area of the specified region. It follows that the best approximation of the area is 6 square units given in part (b).

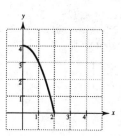

65. True. (Theorem 4.2 (2))

67. $f(x) = \sin x, \ \left[0, \dfrac{\pi}{2}\right]$

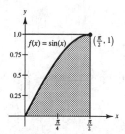

Let A_1 = area bounded by $f(x) = \sin x$, the x-axis, $x = 0$, and $x = \pi/2$. Let A_2 = area of the rectangle bounded by $y = 1$, $y = 0$, $x = 0$, and $x = \pi/2$. Thus, $A_2 = (\pi/2)(1) \approx 1.570796$. In this program, the computer is generating N_2 pairs of random points in the rectangle whose area is represented by A_2. It is keeping track of how many of these points, N_1, lie in the region whose area is represented by A_1. Since the points are randomly generated, we assume that

$$\frac{A_1}{A_2} \approx \frac{N_1}{N_2} \implies A_1 \approx \frac{N_1}{N_2} A_2.$$

The larger N_2 is, the better the approximation to A_1.

69. Suppose there are n rows in the figure. The stars on the left total $1 + 2 + \cdots + n$, as do the stars on the right. There are $n(n + 1)$ stars in total, hence

$$2(1 + 2 + \cdots + n) = n(n + 1)$$

$$1 + 2 + \cdots + n = \tfrac{1}{2}(n)(n + 1).$$

71. (a) $y = (-4.09 \times 10^{-5})x^3 + 0.016x^2 - 2.67x + 452.9$

(b)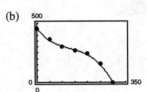

(c) Using the integration capability of a graphing utility, you obtain

$$A \approx 76{,}897.5 \text{ ft}^2.$$

Section 4.3   Riemann Sums and Definite Integrals

1. $\displaystyle\int_0^5 3\, dx$

3. $\displaystyle\int_{-4}^4 (4 - |x|)\, dx$

5. $\displaystyle\int_{-2}^2 (4 - x^2)\, dx$

7. $\displaystyle\int_0^\pi \sin x\, dx$

9. $\displaystyle\int_0^2 y^3\, dy$

11. Rectangle

$A = bh = 3(4)$

$A = \displaystyle\int_0^3 4\, dx = 12$

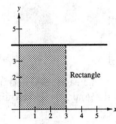

13. Triangle

$A = \dfrac{1}{2}bh = \dfrac{1}{2}(4)(4)$

$A = \displaystyle\int_0^4 x\, dx = 8$

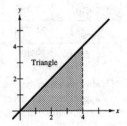

15. The region whose area is given by $\int_0^2 (2x + 5)\, dx$ is shown by the accompanying figure to be a trapezoid. Since the height of the trapezoid is $h = 2$ and the lengths of the two bases are $b_1 = 5$ and $b_2 = 9$, the area of the trapezoid is

$$A = h\left[\frac{b_1 + b_2}{2}\right] = 2\left[\frac{5 + 9}{2}\right] = 14.$$

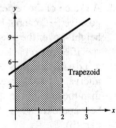

17. Triangle

$A = \dfrac{1}{2}bh = \dfrac{1}{2}(2)(1)$

$A = \displaystyle\int_{-1}^1 (1 - |x|)\, dx = 1$

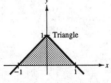

19. Semicircle

$A = \dfrac{1}{2}\pi r^2 = \dfrac{1}{2}\pi(3)^2$

$A = \displaystyle\int_{-3}^3 \sqrt{9 - x^2}\, dx = \dfrac{9\pi}{2}$

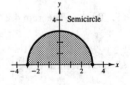

21. (a) $\displaystyle\int_0^7 f(x)\, dx = \int_0^5 f(x)\, dx + \int_5^7 f(x)\, dx = 10 + 3 = 13$

(b) $\displaystyle\int_5^0 f(x)\, dx = -\int_0^5 f(x)\, dx = -10$

(c) $\displaystyle\int_5^5 f(x)\, dx = 0$

(d) $\displaystyle\int_0^5 3f(x)\, dx = 3\int_0^5 f(x)\, dx = 3(10) = 30$

23. (a) $\displaystyle\int_2^6 [f(x) + g(x)]\,dx = \int_2^6 f(x)\,dx + \int_2^6 g(x)\,dx$

$$= 10 + (-2) = 8$$

(b) $\displaystyle\int_2^6 [g(x) - f(x)]\,dx = \int_2^6 g(x)\,dx - \int_2^6 f(x)\,dx$

$$= -2 - 10 = -12$$

(c) $\displaystyle\int_2^6 2g(x)\,dx = 2\int_2^6 g(x)\,dx = 2(-2) = -4$

(d) $\displaystyle\int_2^6 3f(x)\,dx = 3\int_2^6 f(x)\,dx = 3(10) = 30$

25. $y = 6$ on $[4, 10]$. $\left(\text{Note: } \Delta x = \dfrac{10 - 4}{n} = \dfrac{6}{n}, \|\Delta\| \to 0 \text{ as } n \to \infty\right)$

$$\sum_{i=1}^n f(c_i)\,\Delta x_i = \sum_{i=1}^n f\left(4 + \frac{6i}{n}\right)\left(\frac{6}{n}\right) = \sum_{i=1}^n 6\left(\frac{6}{n}\right) = \sum_{i=1}^n \frac{36}{n} = 36$$

$$\int_4^{10} 6\,dx = \lim_{n\to\infty} 36 = 36$$

27. Let $\Delta x = [1 - (-1)]/n = 2/n$. Using right-hand endpoints, we have $c_i = -1 + (2i/n)$, and the definite integral is given by the limit

$$\int_{-1}^1 x^3\,dx = \lim_{n\to\infty} \sum_{i=1}^n \left(-1 + \frac{2i}{n}\right)^3\left(\frac{2}{n}\right)$$

$$= \lim_{n\to\infty} \sum_{i=1}^n \left(\frac{2}{n}\right)\left(-1 + \frac{6i}{n} - \frac{12i^2}{n^2} + \frac{8i^3}{n^3}\right)$$

$$= \lim_{n\to\infty} \left(\frac{2}{n}\right)\left[-\sum_{i=1}^n 1 + \frac{6}{n}\sum_{i=1}^n i - \frac{12}{n^2}\sum_{i=1}^n i^2 + \frac{8}{n^3}\sum_{i=1}^n i^3\right]$$

$$= \lim_{n\to\infty} \left(\frac{2}{n}\right)\left[-n + \frac{6n(n+1)}{2n} - \frac{12n(n+1)(2n+1)}{6n^2} + \frac{8n^2(n+1)^2}{4n^3}\right]$$

$$= \lim_{n\to\infty} \left[\frac{-2n}{n} + \frac{6n(n+1)}{n^2} - \frac{4n(n+1)(2n+1)}{n^3} + \frac{4n^2(n+1)^2}{n^4}\right]$$

$$= -2 + 6 - 8 + 4 = 0.$$

29. $y = x^2 + 1$ on $[1, 2]$. $\left(\text{Note: } \Delta x = \dfrac{2 - 1}{n} = \dfrac{1}{n}, \|\Delta\| \to 0 \text{ as } n \to \infty\right)$

$$\sum_{i=1}^n f(c_i)\,\Delta x_i = \sum_{i=1}^n f\left(1 + \frac{i}{n}\right)\left(\frac{1}{n}\right) = \sum_{i=1}^n \left[\left(1 + \frac{i}{n}\right)^2 + 1\right]\left(\frac{1}{n}\right) = \sum_{i=1}^n \left[1 + \frac{2i}{n} + \frac{i^2}{n^2} + 1\right]\left(\frac{1}{n}\right)$$

$$= 2 + \frac{2}{n^2}\sum_{i=1}^n i + \frac{1}{n^3}\sum_{i=1}^n i^2 = 2 + \left(1 + \frac{1}{n}\right) + \frac{1}{6}\left(2 + \frac{3}{n} + \frac{1}{n^2}\right) = \frac{10}{3} + \frac{3}{2n} + \frac{1}{6n^2}$$

$$\int_1^2 (x^2 + 1)\,dx = \lim_{n\to\infty} \left(\frac{10}{3} + \frac{3}{2n} + \frac{1}{6n^2}\right) = \frac{10}{3}$$

31. $\displaystyle\lim_{\|\Delta\|\to 0} \sum_{i=1}^n (3c_i + 10)\,\Delta x_i = \int_{-1}^5 (3x + 10)\,dx$

on the interval $[-1, 5]$.

33. $\displaystyle\lim_{\|\Delta\|\to 0} \sum_{i=1}^n \sqrt{c_i^2 + 4}\,\Delta x_i = \int_0^3 \sqrt{x^2 + 4}\,dx$

on the interval $[0, 3]$.

35. $\displaystyle\lim_{\|\Delta\|\to 0} \sum_{i=1}^n \left(1 + \frac{3}{c_i}\right)\Delta x_i = \lim_{\|\Delta\|\to 0} \sum_{i=1}^n f(c_i)\Delta x_i = \int_a^b f(x)\,dx$

Therefore, $f(x) = 1 + \dfrac{3}{x}$ and $\displaystyle\lim_{\|\Delta\|\to 0} \sum_{i=1}^n \left(1 + \frac{3}{c_i}\right)\Delta x_i = \int_1^5 \left(1 + \frac{3}{x}\right)dx$ on the interval $[1, 5]$.

37. $\int_0^3 x\sqrt{3-x}\, dx$

n	4	8	12	16	20
$L(n)$	3.6830	3.9956	4.0707	4.1016	4.1177
$M(n)$	4.3082	4.2076	4.1838	4.1740	4.1690
$R(n)$	3.6830	3.9956	4.0707	4.1016	4.1177

39. $f(x) = \dfrac{1}{x}$, $[1, 3]$

n	4	8	12	16	20
$L(n)$	1.2833	1.1865	1.1562	1.1414	1.1327
$M(n)$	1.0898	1.0963	1.0976	1.0980	1.0982
$R(n)$	0.9500	1.0199	1.0451	1.0581	1.0660

41. $\int_0^{\pi/2} \sin^2 x\, dx$

n	4	8	12	16	20
$L(n)$	0.5890	0.6872	0.7199	0.7363	0.7461
$M(n)$	0.7854	0.7854	0.7854	0.7854	0.7854
$R(n)$	0.9817	0.8836	0.8508	0.8345	0.8247

43. Since the function is decreasing and x_i is the left endpoint of the ith subinterval, $f(x_i)\,\Delta x$ represents the area of a circumscribed rectangle extending outside the ith subregion. The sum of the areas of the circumscribed rectangles is greater than the area of the shaded region shown in the figure. Since

$$\int_1^5 f(x)\, dx$$

represents the area of the shaded region, it follows that

$$\sum_{i=1}^n f(x_i)\,\Delta x > \int_1^5 f(x)\, dx.$$

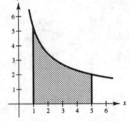

45. Because the curve is concave upward, the midpoint approximation will be less than the actual area: $<$

47. (a) Since f is negative over the interval $[0, 2]$, the definite integral will be negative. The definite integral equals the negative of the area of one-fourth a circle of radius 2. Therefore,

$$\int_0^2 f(x)\, dx = -\frac{1}{4}\pi(2^2) = -\pi.$$

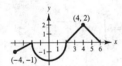

(b) The definite integral over the interval $[2, 6]$ represents the area of a triangle with base 4 and height 2. Therefore,

$$\int_2^6 f(x)\, dx = \frac{1}{2}(4)(2) = 4.$$

(c) Since f is negative over the interval $[-4, 2]$, the definite integral will be negative. The definite integral equals the negative of the combined area of a triangle with base 2 and height 1 and a semicircle of radius 2. Therefore,

$$\int_{-4}^2 f(x)\, dx = -\left(\frac{1}{2}(2)(1) + \frac{1}{2}\pi(2^2)\right) = -(1 + 2\pi).$$

(d) Since

$$\int_{-4}^6 f(x)\, dx = \int_{-4}^2 f(x)\, dx + \int_2^6 f(x)\, dx,$$

it follows from parts (b) and (c) that

$$\int_{-4}^6 f(x)\, dx = -(1 + 2\pi) + 4 = 3 - 2\pi.$$

—CONTINUED—

47. —CONTINUED—

(e) Since

$$\int_{-4}^{6} |f(x)| \, dx = \int_{-4}^{2} |f(x)| \, dx + \int_{2}^{6} f(x) \, dx,$$

it follows from parts (b) and (c) that

$$\int_{-4}^{6} |f(x)| \, dx = |-(1 + 2\pi)| + 4 = 5 + 2\pi.$$

(f) $\int_{-4}^{6} (f(x) + 2) \, dx = \int_{-4}^{6} f(x) \, dx + \int_{-4}^{6} 2 \, dx$

$\int_{-4}^{6} 2 \, dx$ represents the area of a rectangle with base 10 and height 2. Therefore, from part (d) it follows that

$$\int_{-4}^{6} (f(x) + 2) \, dx = (3 - 2\pi) + 20 = 23 - 2\pi.$$

49.

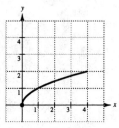

a. $A \approx 5$ square units

51. True

53. True

55. False

$$\int_{0}^{2} (-x) \, dx = -2$$

57. $f(x) = x^2 + 3x, \, [0, 8]$

$x_0 = 0, x_1 = 1, x_2 = 3, x_3 = 7, x_4 = 8$

$\Delta x_1 = 1, \Delta x_2 = 2, \Delta x_3 = 4, \Delta x_4 = 1$

$c_1 = 1, c_2 = 2, c_3 = 5, c_4 = 8$

$$\sum_{i=1}^{4} f(c_i) \, \Delta x = f(1) \, \Delta x_1 + f(2) \, \Delta x_2 + f(5) \, \Delta x_3 + f(8) \, \Delta x_4$$

$$= (4)(1) + (10)(2) + (40)(4) + (88)(1) = 272$$

59. $f(x) = \sqrt{x}, \, y = 0, \, x = 0, \, x = 2, \, c_i = \dfrac{2i^2}{n^2}$

$$\Delta x_i = \frac{2i^2}{n^2} - \frac{2(i-1)^2}{n^2} = \frac{2(2i-1)}{n^2}$$

$$\lim_{n \to \infty} \sum_{i=1}^{n} f(c_i) \, \Delta x_i = \lim_{n \to \infty} \sum_{i=1}^{n} \sqrt{\frac{2i^2}{n^2} \left[\frac{2(2i-1)}{n^2} \right]}$$

$$= \lim_{n \to \infty} \frac{2\sqrt{2}}{n^3} \sum_{i=1}^{n} (2i^2 - i)$$

$$= \lim_{n \to \infty} \frac{2\sqrt{2}}{n^3} \left[2 \left(\frac{n(n+1)(2n+1)}{6} \right) - \frac{n(n+1)}{2} \right]$$

$$= \lim_{n \to \infty} \frac{2\sqrt{2}}{n^3} \left[\frac{4n^3 + 3n^2 - n}{6} \right] = \lim_{n \to \infty} \sqrt{2} \left[\frac{4}{3} + \frac{1}{n} - \frac{2}{n^2} \right] = \frac{4\sqrt{2}}{3}$$

61. The function is not integrable on the specified interval since it has a nonremovable discontinuity at $x = 4$ (see figure).

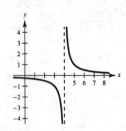

63. $f(x) = |x|/x$ is integrable on $[-1, 1]$, but is not continuous on $[-1, 1]$. There is a discontinuity at $x = 0$. To see that

$$\int_{-1}^{1} \frac{|x|}{x} \, dx$$

is integrable, sketch a graph of the region bounded by $f(x) = |x|/x$ and the x-axis for $-1 \le x \le 1$. You see that the integral equals 0.

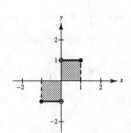

65. $\displaystyle\lim_{n\to\infty} \frac{1}{n^3}[1^2 + 2^2 + 3^2 + \cdots + n^2] = \lim_{n\to\infty} \frac{1}{n^3} \cdot \frac{n(2n + 1)(n + 1)}{6}$

$$= \lim_{n\to\infty} \frac{2n^2 + 3n + 1}{6n^2} = \lim_{n\to\infty} \left(\frac{1}{3} + \frac{1}{2n} + \frac{1}{6n^2}\right) = \frac{1}{3}$$

Let $f(x) = x^2, 0 \le x \le 1$, and $\Delta x_i = 1/n$. The appropriate Riemann Sum is

$$\sum_{i=1}^{n} f(c_i)\Delta x_i = \sum_{i=1}^{n} \left(\frac{i}{n}\right)^2 \frac{1}{n} = \frac{1}{n^3}\sum_{i=1}^{n} i^2.$$

67. Since $-|f(x)| \le f(x) \le |f(x)|$,

$$-\int_a^b |f(x)| \, dx \le \int_a^b f(x) \, dx \le \int_a^b |f(x)| \, dx \implies \left|\int_a^b f(x) \, dx\right| \le \int_a^b |f(x)| \, dx.$$

Section 4.4 The Fundamental Theorem of Calculus

1. $f(x) = \dfrac{4}{x^2 + 1}$

$\displaystyle\int_0^\pi \frac{4}{x^2 + 1} \, dx$ is positive.

3. $f(x) = x\sqrt{x^2 + 1}$

$\displaystyle\int_{-2}^{2} x\sqrt{x^2 + 1} \, dx = 0$

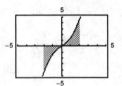

5. $\displaystyle\int_0^1 2x \, dx = \left[x^2\right]_0^1 = 1 - 0 = 1$

7. $\displaystyle\int_{-1}^{0} (x - 2) \, dx = \left[\frac{x^2}{2} - 2x\right]_{-1}^{0} = 0 - \left(\frac{1}{2} + 2\right) = -\frac{5}{2}$

9. $\displaystyle\int_{-1}^{1} (t^2 - 2) \, dt = \left[\frac{t^3}{3} - 2t\right]_{-1}^{1}$

$$= \left(\frac{1}{3} - 2\right) - \left(-\frac{1}{3} + 2\right) = -\frac{10}{3}$$

11. $\displaystyle\int_0^1 (2t - 1)^2 \, dt = \int_0^1 (4t^2 - 4t + 1) \, dt$

$$= \left[\frac{4t^3}{3} - \frac{4t^2}{2} + t\right]_0^1$$

$$= \left(\frac{4}{3} - \frac{4}{2} + 1\right) - (0 - 0 + 0)$$

$$= \frac{4}{3} - \frac{6}{3} + \frac{3}{3} = \frac{1}{3}$$

13. $\displaystyle\int_1^2 \left(\frac{3}{x^2} - 1\right) dx = \left[-\frac{3}{x} - x\right]_1^2 = \left(-\frac{3}{2} - 2\right) - (-3 - 1) = \frac{1}{2}$

15. $\displaystyle\int_1^4 \frac{u-2}{\sqrt{u}}\,du = \int_1^4 (u^{1/2} - 2u^{-1/2})\,du$

$\displaystyle = \left[\frac{2}{3}u^{3/2} - 4u^{1/2}\right]_1^4$

$\displaystyle = \left[\frac{2}{3}(\sqrt{4})^3 - 4\sqrt{4}\right] - \left(\frac{2}{3} - 4\right) = \frac{2}{3}$

17. $\displaystyle\int_{-1}^1 (\sqrt[3]{t} - 2)\,dt = \left[\frac{3}{4}t^{4/3} - 2t\right]_{-1}^1$

$\displaystyle = \left(\frac{3}{4} - 2\right) - \left(\frac{3}{4} + 2\right) = -4$

19. $\displaystyle\int_0^1 \frac{x - \sqrt{x}}{3}\,dx = \frac{1}{3}\int_0^1 (x - x^{1/2})\,dx$

$\displaystyle = \frac{1}{3}\left[\frac{x^2}{2} - \frac{2}{3}x^{3/2}\right]_0^1 = \frac{1}{3}\left(\frac{1}{2} - \frac{2}{3}\right) = -\frac{1}{18}$

21. $\displaystyle\int_{-1}^0 (t^{1/3} - t^{2/3})\,dt = \left[\frac{3}{4}t^{4/3} - \frac{3}{5}t^{5/3}\right]_{-1}^0$

$\displaystyle = 0 - \left(\frac{3}{4} + \frac{3}{5}\right) = -\frac{27}{20}$

23. Since $2x - 3 < 0$ if $x < \frac{3}{2}$, it follows that

$$|2x - 3| = \begin{cases} -(2x - 3), & x < \frac{3}{2} \\ 2x - 3, & x \geq \frac{3}{2} \end{cases}. \qquad \text{(See figure)}$$

$$\int_0^3 |2x - 3|\,dx = \int_0^{3/2} (3 - 2x)\,dx + \int_{3/2}^3 (2x - 3)\,dx$$

$$= 2\int_0^{3/2} (3 - 2x)\,dx \qquad \text{(by symmetry)}$$

$$= 2\left[3x - x^2\right]_0^{3/2} = 2\left(\frac{9}{2} - \frac{9}{4}\right) = \frac{9}{2}$$

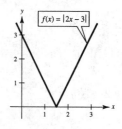

25. $\displaystyle\int_0^\pi (1 + \sin x)\,dx = \left[x - \cos x\right]_0^\pi = (\pi + 1) - (0 - 1) = 2 + \pi$

27. $\displaystyle\int_{-\pi/6}^{\pi/6} \sec^2 x\,dx = \left[\tan x\right]_{-\pi/6}^{\pi/6} = \frac{\sqrt{3}}{3} - \left(-\frac{\sqrt{3}}{3}\right) = \frac{2\sqrt{3}}{3}$

29. $\displaystyle\int_1^e \left(2x - \frac{1}{x}\right)\,dx = \left[x^2 - \ln x\right]_1^e = (e^2 - 1) - (1 - 0) = e^2 - 2$

31. $\displaystyle\int_{-\pi/3}^{\pi/3} 4\sec\theta\tan\theta\,d\theta = \left[4\sec\theta\right]_{-\pi/3}^{\pi/3} = 4\left[\sec\frac{\pi}{3} - \sec\left(-\frac{\pi}{3}\right)\right] = 4[2 - 2] = 0$

33. $\displaystyle\int_0^2 (2^x + 6)\,dx = \left[\left(\frac{1}{\ln 2}\right)2^x + 6x\right]_0^2 = \left[\left(\frac{1}{\ln 2}\right)2^2 + 6(2)\right] - \left[\left(\frac{1}{\ln 2}\right)2^0 + 6(0)\right] = \frac{3}{\ln 2} + 12$

35. $\displaystyle\int_{-1}^1 (e^\theta + \sin\theta)\,d\theta = \left[e^\theta - \cos\theta\right]_{-1}^1$

$= [e^1 - \cos 1] - [e^{-1} - \cos(-1)]$

$= e^1 - e^{-1}$

≈ 2.350

37. $\displaystyle\int_0^3 10{,}000(t - 6)\,dt = 10{,}000\left[\frac{t^2}{2} - 6t\right]_0^3 = -\$135{,}000$

39. $\displaystyle A = \int_0^1 (x - x^2)\,dx = \left[\frac{x^2}{2} - \frac{x^3}{3}\right]_0^1 = \frac{1}{6}$

41. $A = \displaystyle\int_0^3 (3 - x)\sqrt{x}\, dx$

$= \displaystyle\int_0^3 (3x^{1/2} - x^{3/2})\, dx$

$= \left[2x^{3/2} - \dfrac{2}{5}x^{5/2} \right]_0^3$

$= \left[\dfrac{2x\sqrt{x}}{5}(5 - x) \right]_0^3$

$= \dfrac{6\sqrt{3}}{5}(2) - 0 = \dfrac{12\sqrt{3}}{5}$

$y = (3 - x)\sqrt{x}$

43. Since $y \geq 0$ on $[0, 2]$,

$A = \displaystyle\int_0^2 (3x^2 + 1)\, dx = \left[x^3 + x \right]_0^2 = 8 + 2 = 10.$

45. Using the figure we can see that the area of the region is

$\text{Area} = \displaystyle\int_0^2 (x^3 + x)\, dx$

$= \left[\dfrac{1}{4}x^4 + \dfrac{1}{2}x^2 \right]_0^2$

$= (4 + 2) - (0) = 6.$

47. $\displaystyle\int_1^e \dfrac{4}{x}\, dx = 4 \ln x \Big]_1^e = 4 \ln e - 4 \ln 1 = 4$

49. $A = \displaystyle\int_0^{\pi/2} \cos x\, dx = \left[\sin x \right]_0^{\pi/2} = 1$

51. $\displaystyle\int_0^2 (x - 2\sqrt{x})\, dx = \left[\dfrac{x^2}{2} - \dfrac{4x^{3/2}}{3} \right]_0^2 = 2 - \dfrac{8\sqrt{2}}{3}$

$f(c)(2 - 0) = \dfrac{6 - 8\sqrt{2}}{3}$

$c - 2\sqrt{c} = \dfrac{3 - 4\sqrt{2}}{3}$

$c - 2\sqrt{c} + 1 = \dfrac{3 - 4\sqrt{2}}{3} + 1$

$(\sqrt{c} - 1)^2 = \dfrac{6 - 4\sqrt{2}}{3}$

$\sqrt{c} - 1 = \pm\sqrt{\dfrac{6 - 4\sqrt{2}}{3}}$

$c = \left[1 \pm \sqrt{\dfrac{6 - 4\sqrt{2}}{3}} \right]^2$

$c \approx 0.4380 \text{ or } c \approx 1.7908$

53. $\displaystyle\int_{-\pi/4}^{\pi/4} 2 \sec^2 x\, dx = \left[2 \tan x \right]_{-\pi/4}^{\pi/4} = 2(1) - 2(-1) = 4$

$f(c)\left[\dfrac{\pi}{4} - \left(-\dfrac{\pi}{4} \right) \right] = 4$

$2 \sec^2 c = \dfrac{8}{\pi}$

$\sec^2 c = \dfrac{4}{\pi}$

$\sec c = \pm\dfrac{2}{\sqrt{\pi}}$

$c = \pm\text{arcsec}\left(\dfrac{2}{\sqrt{\pi}} \right)$

$= \pm\text{arccos} \dfrac{\sqrt{\pi}}{2} \approx \pm0.4817$

55. $\displaystyle\int_1^4 \left(5 - \dfrac{1}{x} \right) dx = \left[5x - \ln|x| \right]_1^4 = (20 - \ln 4) - (5 - 0) = 15 - \ln 4$

$f(c)(4 - 1) = 15 - \ln 4$

$\left(5 - \dfrac{1}{c} \right)(3) = 15 - \ln 4$

$15 - \dfrac{3}{c} = 15 - \ln 4$

$\dfrac{3}{c} = \ln 4$

$c = \dfrac{3}{\ln 4} \approx 2.1640$

57. The average value is given by

$$\frac{1}{b-a}\int_a^b f(x)\,dx = \frac{1}{2-(-2)}\int_{-2}^{2}(4-x^2)\,dx = \frac{1}{4}\int_{-2}^{2}(4-x^2)\,dx$$

$$= 2\left(\frac{1}{4}\right)\int_0^2(4-x^2)\,dx \quad \text{(by symmetry)}$$

$$= \frac{1}{2}\left[4x - \frac{1}{3}x^3\right]_0^2$$

$$= \frac{1}{2}\left(8 - \frac{8}{3}\right) = \frac{8}{3}.$$

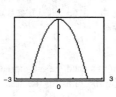

To find the values of x for which $f(x) = 8/3$ in the interval $[-2, 2]$, solve the equation

$$f(x) = 4 - x^2 = \frac{8}{3}$$

$$x^2 = \frac{4}{3}$$

$$x = \pm\frac{2}{\sqrt{3}} = \pm\frac{2\sqrt{3}}{3} \approx \pm1.155.$$

59. $f(x) = 2e^x, \quad [-1, 1]$

$$\text{Average value} = \frac{1}{1-(-1)}\int_{-1}^{1} 2e^x\,dx = \int_{-1}^{1} e^x\,dx$$

$$= e^x\Big]_{-1}^{1} = e - e^{-1} \approx 2.3504$$

$$2e^x = e - e^{-1}$$

$$e^x = \frac{1}{2}(e - e^{-1})$$

$$x = \ln\left(\frac{e - e^{-1}}{2}\right) \approx 0.1614$$

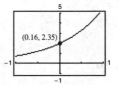

61. $\dfrac{1}{\pi - 0}\displaystyle\int_0^{\pi} \sin x\,dx = \left[-\dfrac{1}{\pi}\cos x\right]_0^{\pi} = \dfrac{2}{\pi}$

$$\text{Average value} = \frac{2}{\pi}$$

$$\sin x = \frac{2}{\pi}$$

$$x \approx 0.690,\ 2.451$$

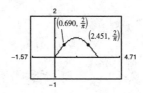

63. $\displaystyle\int_0^2 f(x)\,dx = -(\text{area of region } A) = -1.5$

65. $\displaystyle\int_0^6 |f(x)|\,dx = -\int_0^2 f(x)\,dx + \int_2^6 f(x)\,dx = 1.5 + 5.0 = 6.5$

67. $\displaystyle\int_0^6 [2 + f(x)]\,dx = \int_0^6 2\,dx + \int_0^6 f(x)\,dx$

$$= 12 + 3.5 = 15.5$$

69. (a) Begin by rewriting the given integral as a sum of integrals as follows.

$$\int_1^7 f(x)\,dx = \int_1^2 f(x)\,dx + \int_2^3 f(x)\,dx + \int_3^4 f(x)\,dx + \int_4^7 f(x)\,dx$$

The first three integrals each yield the area of a trapezoid and the fourth yields the area of a rectangle. Using the formulas for the area of trapezoids and rectangles, we have the following.

$$\int_1^7 f(x)\,dx = \frac{1}{2}(3+1) + \frac{1}{2}(1+2) + \frac{1}{2}(2+1) + 3(1) = 8$$

(b) Average value $= \dfrac{\int_1^7 f(x)\,dx}{7-1} = \dfrac{8}{6} = \dfrac{4}{3}$

(c) Since the graph is translated two units upward, it is given by the function $g(x) = f(x) + 2$. Therefore,

$$\int_1^7 g(x)\,dx = \int_1^7 [f(x) + 2]\,dx = \int_1^7 f(x)\,dx + \int_1^7 2\,dx = 8 + 6(2) = 20.$$

The average value of the function is translated 2 units upward. Therefore,

$$\text{Average value} = \frac{4}{3} + 2 = \frac{10}{3}.$$

71. $R = -91.1 - 6.313x + 0.035x^2 + 45.794\sqrt{x},\ 20 \le x \le 60$

(a)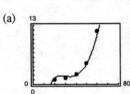

(b) $R'(x) = -6.313 + 0.07x + \dfrac{22.897}{\sqrt{x}}$

$R'(40) \approx 0.12$

$R'(50) \approx 0.43$

(c) $\dfrac{1}{10}\displaystyle\int_{30}^{40} R(x)\,dx \approx 1.80$ \quad (between 30 and 40)

$\dfrac{1}{10}\displaystyle\int_{50}^{60} R(x)\,dx \approx 7.35$ \quad (between 50 and 60)

73. (a) $F(x) = k\sec^2 x$

$F(0) = k\sec^2 0 = k = 500$

$F(x) = 500\sec^2 x,\ \ 0 \le x \le \dfrac{\pi}{3}$

(b) The average force over the interval $[0, \pi/3]$ is

$$\frac{1}{(\pi/3) - 0}\int_0^{\pi/3} 500\sec^2 x\,dx = \frac{1500}{\pi}\int_0^{\pi/3}\sec^2 x\,dx$$

$$= \frac{1500}{\pi}\Big[\tan x\Big]_0^{\pi/3}$$

$$= \frac{1500}{\pi}\left(\sqrt{3}\right)$$

$$\approx 827 \text{ newtons.}$$

75. (a) histogram

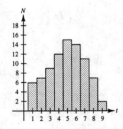

(b) $(6 + 7 + 9 + 12 + 15 + 14 + 11 + 7 + 2)60 = (83)60 = 4980$ customers

—CONTINUED—

75. —CONTINUED—

(c) Using a graphing utility, you obtain

$N(t) = -0.084175t^3 + 0.63492t^2 + 0.79052t + 4.10317.$

(d)

(e) $\int_0^9 N(t)\, dt \approx 85.162$

The estimated number of customers is $(85.162)(60) \approx 5110.$

(f) Between 3 P.M. and 7 P.M., the number of customers is approximately

$\left(\int_3^7 N(t)\, dt \right)(60) \approx (50.28)(60) \approx 3017.$

Hence, $3017/240 \approx 12.6$ customers per minute.

77. (a) $v = -8.61 \times 10^{-4}t^3 + 0.0782t^2 - 0.208t + 0.0952$

(b)

(c) $\int_0^{60} v(t)\, dt = \left[\dfrac{-8.61 \times 10^{-4}t^4}{4} + \dfrac{0.0782t^3}{3} - \dfrac{0.208t^2}{2} + 0.0952t \right]_0^{60} = 2472 \text{ meters}$

79. (a) $\int_0^x (t+2)\, dt = \left[\dfrac{t^2}{2} + 2t \right]_0^x = \dfrac{1}{2}x^2 + 2x$

(b) $\dfrac{d}{dx}\left[\dfrac{1}{2}x^2 + 2x \right] = x + 2$

81. (a) $\int_8^x \sqrt[3]{t}\, dt = \left[\dfrac{3}{4}t^{4/3} \right]_8^x = \dfrac{3}{4}(x^{4/3} - 16) = \dfrac{3}{4}x^{4/3} - 12$

(b) $\dfrac{d}{dx}\left[\dfrac{3}{4}x^{4/3} - 12 \right] = x^{1/3} = \sqrt[3]{x}$

83. (a) $F(x) = \int_{x/4}^x \sec^2 t\, dt = \left[\tan t \right]_{\pi/4}^x = \tan x - 1$

(b) $F'(x) = \dfrac{d}{dx}[\tan x - 1] = \sec^2 x$

85. (a) $F(x) = \int_{-1}^x e^t\, dt = e^t \Big]_{-1}^x = e^x - e^{-1}$

(b) $\dfrac{d}{dx}(e^x - e^{-1}) = e^x$

87. $F(x) = \int_{-2}^x (t^2 - 2t)\, dt$

$F'(x) = x^2 - 2x$

89. $F(x) = \int_{-1}^x \sqrt{t^4 + 1}\, dt$

$F'(x) = \sqrt{x^4 + 1}$

91. $F(x) = \int_0^x t \cos t\, dt$

$F'(x) = x \cos x$

93. $F(x) = \displaystyle\int_{x}^{x+2} (4t + 1)\, dt$

$= \left[2t^2 + t \right]_{x}^{x+2}$

$= [2(x + 2)^2 + (x + 2)] - [2x^2 + x]$

$= 8x + 10$

$F'(x) = 8$

Alternate solution:

$F(x) = \displaystyle\int_{x}^{x+2} (4t + 1)\, dt$

$= \displaystyle\int_{x}^{0} (4t + 1)\, dt + \int_{0}^{x+2} (4t + 1)\, dt$

$= -\displaystyle\int_{0}^{x} (4t + 1)\, dt + \int_{0}^{x+2} (4t + 1)\, dt$

$F'(x) = -(4x + 1) + 4(x + 2) + 1 = 8$

95. Since the function is easily integrated, we can find the derivative as follows.

$F(x) = \displaystyle\int_{0}^{\sin x} \sqrt{t}\, dt = \left[\frac{2}{3} t^{3/2} \right]_{0}^{\sin x} = \frac{2}{3}(\sin x)^{3/2}$

$F'(x) = \frac{2}{3}\left(\frac{3}{2} \right)(\sin x)^{1/2}(\cos x) = \cos x \sqrt{\sin x}$

An alternate method is to use the Second Fundamental Theorem of Calculus and the Chain Rule where $u = \sin x$.

$F'(x) = \dfrac{dF}{du}\dfrac{du}{dx} = \dfrac{d}{du}\left[\displaystyle\int_{0}^{u} \sqrt{t}\, dt \right]\dfrac{du}{dx}$

$= \sqrt{u}(\cos x) = \cos x \sqrt{\sin x}$

97. $F(x) = \displaystyle\int_{0}^{x^3} \sin t^2\, dt$

$F'(x) = \sin(x^3)^2 \cdot 3x^2 = 3x^2 \sin x^6$

99. The extrema of F correspond to the zeros of f and the inflection point of F corresponds to the extrema of f.

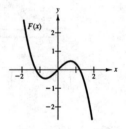

101. (a) $C(x) = 5000\left(25 + 3\displaystyle\int_{0}^{x} t^{1/4} dt \right)$

$= 5000\left(25 + 3\left[\frac{4}{5} t^{5/4} \right]_{0}^{x} \right)$

$= 5000\left(25 + \frac{12}{5} x^{5/4} \right) = 1000(125 + 12x^{5/4})$

(b) $C(1) = 1000[125 + 12(1)^{5/4}] = \$137{,}000$

$C(5) = 1000[125 + 12(5)^{5/4}] \approx \$214{,}721$

$C(10) = 1000[125 + 12(10)^{5/4}] \approx \$338{,}394$

103. True

105. False; $\displaystyle\int_{-1}^{1} x^{-2} dx = \int_{-1}^{0} x^{-2} dx + \int_{0}^{1} x^{-2} dx$

Each of these integrals is infinite. $f(x) = x^{-2}$ has a nonremovable discontinuity at $x = 0$.

107. (a)

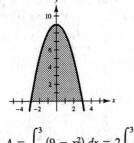

$$A = \int_{-3}^{3} (9 - x^2)\, dx = 2\int_{0}^{3} (9 - x^2)\, dx$$

$$= 2\left[9x - \frac{x^3}{3} \right]_0^3 = 2\left[27 - \frac{27}{3} \right] = 36$$

(b) Base = 6, height = 9, area = $\frac{2}{3}(6)(9) = 36$

(c)

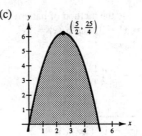

$$A = \int_{0}^{5} (5x - x^2)\, dx = \left[\frac{5}{2}x^2 - \frac{x^3}{3} \right]_0^5 = \frac{125}{2} - \frac{125}{3} = \frac{125}{6}$$

Formula: $A = \frac{2}{3}(5)\left(\frac{25}{4} \right) = \frac{125}{6}$

109. $x(t) = (t - 1)(t - 3)^2 = t^3 - 7t^2 + 15t - 9$

$x'(t) = 3t^2 - 14t + 15$

Using a graphing utility,

Total distance = $\int_{0}^{5} |x'(t)|\, dt \approx 27.37$ units.

Section 4.5   Integration by Substitution

$\int f(g(x))g'(x)\, dx$	$u = g(x)$	$du = g'(x)\, dx$
1. $\int (5x^2 + 1)^2(10x)\, dx$	$5x^2 + 1$	$10x\, dx$
3. $\int \dfrac{x}{\sqrt{x^2 + 1}}\, dx$	$x^2 + 1$	$2x\, dx$
5. $\int \tan^2 x \sec^2 x\, dx$	$\tan x$	$\sec^2 x\, dx$

7. $\int (1 + 2x)^4\, 2\, dx = \dfrac{(1 + 2x)^5}{5} + C$

Check: $\dfrac{d}{dx}\left[\dfrac{(1 + 2x)^5}{5} + C \right] = 2(1 + 2x)^4$

9. $\int (9 - x^2)^{1/2}(-2x)\, dx = \dfrac{(9 - x^2)^{3/2}}{3/2} + C = \dfrac{2}{3}(9 - x^2)^{3/2} + C$

Check: $\dfrac{d}{dx}\left[\dfrac{2}{3}(9 - x^2)^{3/2} + C \right] = \dfrac{2}{3} \cdot \dfrac{3}{2}(9 - x^2)^{1/2}(-2x) = \sqrt{9 - x^2}(-2x)$

11. To evaluate $\int x^2(x^3 - 1)^4 \, dx$, use the method of pattern recognition by letting $g(x) = x^3 - 1$, and $g'(x) = 3x^2$. Thus, by Theorem 4.13, we have

$$\int x^2(x^3 - 1)^4 \, dx = \int (x^3 - 1)^4\left(\frac{1}{3}\right)(3x^2) \, dx$$

$$= \frac{1}{3}\int \overbrace{(x^3 - 1)^4}^{[g(x)]^4} \overbrace{(3x^2)}^{g'(x)} \, dx$$

$$= \frac{1}{3} \frac{[g(x)]^5}{5} + C$$

$$= \left(\frac{1}{3}\right)\left[\frac{(x^3 - 1)^5}{5}\right] + C$$

$$= \frac{1}{15}(x^3 - 1)^5 + C.$$

Check: If $y = \frac{1}{15}(x^3 - 1)^5 + C$, then

$$\frac{dy}{dx} = \frac{1}{15}(5)(x^3 - 1)^4(3x^2) + 0 = x^2(x^3 - 1)^4.$$

13. To evaluate $\int 5x\sqrt[3]{1 - x^2} \, dx$, use the method of pattern recognition by letting $g(x) = 1 - x^2$, and $g'(x) = -2x$.

$$\int 5x\sqrt[3]{1 - x^2} \, dx = -\frac{5}{2}\int \overbrace{(1 - x^2)^{1/3}}^{[g(x)]^{1/3}} \overbrace{(-2x)}^{g'(x)} \, dx$$

$$= -\frac{5}{2}\frac{[g(x)]^{4/3}}{4/3} + C$$

$$= -\left(\frac{5}{2}\right)\left[\frac{(1 - x^2)^{4/3}}{4/3}\right] + C$$

$$= -\frac{15}{8}(1 - x^2)^{4/3} + C$$

Check: If $y = -\frac{15}{8}(1 - x^2)^{4/3} + C$, then

$$\frac{dy}{dx} = -\left(\frac{15}{8}\right)\left(\frac{4}{3}\right)(1 - x^2)^{1/3}(-2x) + 0$$

$$= 5x(1 - x^2)^{1/3}.$$

15. $\int \frac{x^2}{(1 + x^3)^2} \, dx = \frac{1}{3}\int (1 + x^3)^{-2}(3x^2) \, dx = \frac{1}{3}\left[\frac{(1 + x^3)^{-1}}{-1}\right] + C = -\frac{1}{3(1 + x^3)} + C$

Check: $\dfrac{d}{dx}\left[-\dfrac{1}{3(1 + x^3)} + C\right] = -\dfrac{1}{3}(-1)(1 + x^3)^{-2}(3x^2) = \dfrac{x^2}{(1 + x^3)^2}$

17. We evaluate this integral by changing the variable by letting $u = 1 + (1/t)$. Then, $du = -(1/t^2) \, dt$. Therefore,

$$\int \left(1 + \frac{1}{t}\right)^3\left(\frac{1}{t^2}\right) dt = -\int \left(1 + \frac{1}{t}\right)^3\left(\frac{-1}{t^2}\right) dt$$

$$= -\int u^3 \, du$$

$$= -\frac{u^4}{4} + C$$

$$= -\frac{1}{4}\left(1 + \frac{1}{t}\right)^4 + C$$

Check:

If $y = -\dfrac{1}{4}\left(1 + \dfrac{1}{t}\right)^4 + C$, then

$$\frac{dy}{dt} = \left(-\frac{1}{4}\right)(4)\left(1 + \frac{1}{t}\right)^3\left(-\frac{1}{t^2}\right) + 0$$

$$= \left(1 + \frac{1}{t}\right)^3\left(\frac{1}{t^2}\right).$$

19. $\int \dfrac{1}{\sqrt{2x}} \, dx = \int \dfrac{1}{\sqrt{2}\sqrt{x}} \, dx$

$$= \frac{1}{\sqrt{2}}\int x^{-1/2} \, dx$$

$$= \frac{1}{\sqrt{2}}\left(\frac{x^{1/2}}{1/2}\right) + C = \sqrt{2x} + C$$

Check: If $y = \sqrt{2x} + C = (2x)^{1/2} + C$, then

$$\frac{dy}{dx} = \frac{1}{2}(2x)^{-1/2}(2) + 0 = \frac{1}{\sqrt{2x}}.$$

21. $\int \dfrac{x^2 + 3x + 7}{\sqrt{x}} \, dx = \int (x^{3/2} + 3x^{1/2} + 7x^{-1/2}) \, dx = \dfrac{2}{5}x^{5/2} + 2x^{3/2} + 14x^{1/2} + C = \dfrac{2}{5}\sqrt{x}(x^2 + 5x + 35) + C$

Check: $\dfrac{d}{dx}\left[\dfrac{2}{5}x^{5/2} + 2x^{3/2} + 14x^{1/2} + C\right] = \dfrac{x^2 + 3x + 7}{\sqrt{x}}$

23. $\int t^2\left(t - \dfrac{2}{t}\right) dt = \int (t^3 - 2t)\, dt = \dfrac{1}{4}t^4 - t^2 + C$

Check: $\dfrac{d}{dt}\left[\dfrac{1}{4}t^4 - t^2 + C\right] = t^3 - 2t = t^2\left(t - \dfrac{2}{t}\right)$

25. $\int (9 - y)\sqrt{y}\, dy = \int (9y^{1/2} - y^{3/2})\, dy = 9\left(\dfrac{2}{3}y^{3/2}\right) - \dfrac{2}{5}y^{5/2} + C = \dfrac{2}{5}y^{3/2}(15 - y) + C$

Check: $\dfrac{d}{dy}\left[\dfrac{2}{5}y^{3/2}(15 - y) + C\right] = \dfrac{d}{dy}\left[6y^{3/2} - \dfrac{2}{5}y^{5/2} + C\right] = 9y^{1/2} - y^{3/2} = (9 - y)\sqrt{y}$

27. $\dfrac{dy}{dx} = 4x + \dfrac{4x}{\sqrt{16 - x^2}}$

$y = \int\left(4x + \dfrac{4x}{\sqrt{16 - x^2}}\right) dx$

$= 4\int x\, dx + (-2)\int \overbrace{(16 - x^2)^{-1/2}}^{u^{-1/2}}\overbrace{(-2x)\, dx}^{du}$

$= 4\left(\dfrac{x^2}{2}\right) - 2\left[\dfrac{(16 - x^2)^{1/2}}{1/2}\right] + C$

$= 2x^2 - 4\sqrt{16 - x^2} + C$

29. $y = \int \dfrac{x + 1}{(x^2 + 2x - 3)^2}\, dx$

$= \dfrac{1}{2}\int (x^2 + 2x - 3)^{-2}(2x + 2)\, dx$

$= \dfrac{1}{2}\left[\dfrac{(x^2 + 2x - 3)^{-1}}{-1}\right] + C$

$= -\dfrac{1}{2(x^2 + 2x - 3)} + C$

31. $\int \sin 2x\, dx = \dfrac{1}{2}\int (\sin 2x)(2x)\, dx = -\dfrac{1}{2}\cos 2x + C$

33. If we let $u = 1/\theta$, then

$du = -\dfrac{1}{\theta^2}\, d\theta$ and $-du = \dfrac{1}{\theta^2}\, d\theta$.

Therefore,

$\int \dfrac{1}{\theta^2}\cos\dfrac{1}{\theta}\, d\theta = \int \cos\dfrac{1}{\theta}\left(\dfrac{1}{\theta^2}\, d\theta\right) = \int \cos u(-du) = -\int \cos u\, du = -\sin u + C = -\sin\dfrac{1}{\theta} + C.$

35. Let $u = 5x$, $du = 5\, dx$.

$\int e^{5x}5\, dx = e^{5x} + C$

37. If we let $u = -x^3$, then $du = -3x^2\, dx$ and $-\dfrac{1}{3}du = x^2\, dx$. Therefore,

$\int x^2 e^{-x^3}\, dx = \int e^{-x^3}(x^2\, dx) = \int e^u\left(-\dfrac{1}{3}du\right) = -\dfrac{1}{3}\int e^u\, du = -\dfrac{1}{3}e^u + C = -\dfrac{1}{3}e^{-x^3} + C$

39. Using the double angle identity we obtain $2\sin 2x \cos 2x = \sin 4x$. If we let $u = 4x$, then $du = 4\, dx$ and $dx = \dfrac{1}{4}\, du$. Therefore,

$\int \sin 2x \cos 2x\, dx = \dfrac{1}{2}\int \sin 4x\, dx = \dfrac{1}{2}\int \sin u\left(\dfrac{1}{4}\right) du = \dfrac{1}{8}\int \sin u\, du = -\dfrac{1}{8}\cos u + C_1 = -\dfrac{1}{8}\cos 4x + C_1.$

We could also evaluate this integral by letting $u = \sin 2x$. Then $du = 2\cos 2x\, dx$ and $\cos 2x\, dx = \dfrac{1}{2}\, du$. Therefore,

$\int \sin 2x \cos 2x\, dx = \int u\left(\dfrac{1}{2}\right) du = \dfrac{1}{2}\int u\, du = \dfrac{1}{4}u^2 + C_2 = \dfrac{1}{4}\sin^2 2x + C_2.$

Through the use of trigonometric identities it can be proved that the results of the two methods of integration are equivalent. This exercise shows that the method of evaluating an integral may not be unique and the results, even though equivalent, may appear unrelated.

41. $\int \tan^4 x \sec^2 x\, dx = \dfrac{\tan^5 x}{5} + C = \dfrac{1}{5}\tan^5 x + C$

43. $\int \dfrac{\csc^2 x}{\cot^3 x}\, dx = -\int (\cot x)^{-3}(-\csc^2 x)\, dx$

$$= -\dfrac{(\cot x)^{-2}}{-2} + C = \dfrac{1}{2\cot^2 x} + C = \dfrac{1}{2}\tan^2 x + C = \dfrac{1}{2}(\sec^2 x - 1) + C = \dfrac{1}{2}\sec^2 x + C_1$$

45. $\int \cot^2 x\, dx = \int (\csc^2 x - 1)\, dx = -\cot x - x + C$

47. $\int e^x(e^x + 1)^2\, dx = \dfrac{(e^x + 1)^3}{3} + C$

49. If we let $u = 1 - e^x$, then $du = -e^x\, dx$. Therefore,

$$\int e^x\sqrt{1 - e^x}\, dx = -\int (1 - e^x)^{1/2}(-e^x)\, dx$$

$$= -\int u^{1/2}\, du$$

$$= -\dfrac{2}{3}u^{3/2} + C$$

$$= -\dfrac{2}{3}(1 - e^x)^{3/2} + C.$$

51. $\int \dfrac{5 - e^x}{e^{2x}}\, dx = \int 5e^{-2x}\, dx - \int e^{-x}\, dx$

$$= -\dfrac{5}{2}e^{-2x} + e^{-x} + C$$

53. $\int e^{\sin \pi x} \cos \pi x\, dx = \dfrac{1}{\pi}\int e^{\sin \pi x}(\pi \cos \pi x)\, dx$

$$= \dfrac{1}{\pi}e^{\sin \pi x} + C$$

55. If $u = e^{-x}$, then $du = -e^{-x}\, dx$.

$$\int e^{-x}\tan(e^{-x})\, dx = -\int \tan u\, du$$

$$= \ln|\cos u| + C$$

$$= \ln|\cos(e^{-x})| + C$$

57. $\int 3^{x/2}\, dx = 2\int 3^{x/2}\left(\dfrac{1}{2}\right)\, dx = 2\dfrac{3^{x/2}}{\ln 3} + C = \dfrac{2}{\ln 3}3^{x/2} + C$

59. $\int x(5^{-x^2})\, dx = -\dfrac{1}{2}\int 5^{-x^2}(-2x)\, dx$

$$= -\left(\dfrac{1}{2}\right)\dfrac{5^{-x^2}}{\ln 5} + C$$

$$= \dfrac{-1}{2\ln 5}(5^{-x^2}) + C$$

61. $f(x) = \int x\sqrt{4 - x^2}\, dx$

$$= -\dfrac{1}{2}\int (4 - x^2)^{1/2}(-2x)\, dx$$

$$= -\dfrac{1}{2}(4 - x^2)^{3/2}\left(\dfrac{2}{3}\right) + C$$

$$= -\dfrac{1}{3}(4 - x^2)^{3/2} + C$$

$$f(2) = 2 = -\dfrac{1}{3}(0) + C \Rightarrow C = 2$$

$$f(x) = -\dfrac{1}{3}(4 - x^2)^{3/2} + 2$$

63. $f(x) = \int \cos\dfrac{x}{2}\, dx = 2\sin\dfrac{x}{2} + C$

Since $f(0) = 3 = 2\sin 0 + C$, $C = 3$. Thus,

$$f(x) = 2\sin\dfrac{x}{2} + 3.$$

65. $f(x) = \int 2e^{-x/2}\, dx = -4\int e^{-x/2}\left(-\frac{1}{2}\right)dx = -4e^{-x/2} + C$

$f(0) = 1 = -4 + C \Rightarrow C = 5$

$f(x) = -4e^{-x/2} + 5$

67. $f'(x) = \int \frac{1}{2}(e^x + e^{-x})\, dx = \frac{1}{2}(e^x - e^{-x}) + C_1$

$f'(0) = C_1 = 0$

$f(x) = \int \frac{1}{2}(e^x - e^{-x})\, dx = \frac{1}{2}(e^x + e^{-x}) + C_2$

$f(0) = 1 + C_2 = 1 \Rightarrow C_2 = 0$

$f(x) = \frac{1}{2}(e^x + e^{-x})$

69. $u = x + 2, x = u - 2, dx = du$

$\int x\sqrt{x + 2}\, dx = \int (u - 2)\sqrt{u}\, du$

$= \int (u^{3/2} - 2u^{1/2})\, du$

$= \frac{2}{5}u^{5/2} - \frac{4}{3}u^{3/2} + C$

$= \frac{2u^{3/2}}{15}(3u - 10) + C$

$= \frac{2}{15}(x + 2)^{3/2}[3(x + 2) - 10] + C$

$= \frac{2}{15}(x + 2)^{3/2}(3x - 4) + C$

71. Let $u = \sqrt{1 - x}$. Then $u^2 = 1 - x, x = 1 - u^2$, and $dx = -2u\, du$. Thus,

$\int x^2\sqrt{1 - x}\, dx = (1 - u^2)^2\, u(-2u)\, du$

$= -\int (2u^2 - 4u^4 + 2u^6)\, du$

$= -\left(\frac{2u^3}{3} - \frac{4u^5}{5} + \frac{2u^7}{7}\right) + C$

$= \frac{-2u^3}{105}(35 - 42u^2 + 15u^4) + C$

$= \frac{-2}{105}(1 - x)^{3/2}[35 - 42(1 - x) + 15(1 - x)^2] + C$

$= \frac{-2}{105}(1 - x)^{3/2}(15x^2 + 12x + 8) + C.$

73. Let $u = \sqrt{2x - 1}$. Then $u^2 = 2x - 1, x = \dfrac{u^2 + 1}{2}$, and $dx = u\, du$. Thus,

$\int \frac{x^2 - 1}{\sqrt{2x - 1}}\, dx = \int \frac{[(u^2 + 1)/2]^2 - 1}{u}\, (u\, du)$

$= \frac{1}{4}\int (u^4 + 2u^2 - 3)\, du$

$= \frac{1}{4}\left(\frac{u^5}{5} + \frac{2u^3}{3} - 3u\right) + C$

$= \frac{u}{60}(3u^4 + 10u^2 - 45) + C$

$= \frac{1}{60}\sqrt{2x - 1}[3(2x - 1)^2 + 10(2x - 1) - 45] + C$

$= \frac{1}{60}\sqrt{2x - 1}(12x^2 + 8x - 52) + C$

$= \frac{1}{15}\sqrt{2x - 1}(3x^2 + 2x - 13) + C.$

75. $u = x + 1, x = u - 1, dx = du$

$$\int \frac{-x}{(x+1) - \sqrt{x+1}} \, dx = \int \frac{-(u-1)}{u - \sqrt{u}} \, du$$

$$= -\int \frac{(\sqrt{u} + 1)(\sqrt{u} - 1)}{\sqrt{u}(\sqrt{u} - 1)} \, du$$

$$= -\int (1 + u^{-1/2}) \, du$$

$$= -(u + 2u^{1/2}) + C$$

$$= -u - 2\sqrt{u} + C$$

$$= -(x + 1) - 2\sqrt{x+1} + C$$

$$= -x - 2\sqrt{x+1} - 1 + C$$

$$= -(x + 2\sqrt{x+1}) + C_1$$

where $C_1 = -1 + C$.

77. Let $u = x^2 + 1$. Then $du = 2x \, dx$, and $dx = du/2$. Furthermore, when $x = -1$, $u = 2$ and when $x = 1$, $u = 2$. Since the upper and lower limits are equal, we have

$$\int_{-1}^{1} x(x^2 + 1)^3 \, dx = \int_{2}^{2} u^3\left(\frac{1}{2}\right) du = 0.$$

79. Let $u = 2x + 1$, $du = 2 \, dx$.

$$\int_{0}^{4} \frac{1}{\sqrt{2x+1}} \, dx = \frac{1}{2}\int_{0}^{4} (2x+1)^{-1/2}(2) \, dx$$

$$= \left[\sqrt{2x+1}\,\right]_{0}^{4} = \sqrt{9} - \sqrt{1} = 2$$

81.

$$\int_{0}^{1} e^{-2x} \, dx = -\frac{1}{2}\int_{0}^{1} e^{-2x}(-2) \, dx$$

$$= -\frac{1}{2}e^{-2x}\Big]_{0}^{1} = -\frac{1}{2}e^{-2} + \frac{1}{2}$$

83. If $u = 3/x$, then $du = (-3/x^2) \, dx$. When $x = 1$, $u = 3$ and when $x = 3$, $u = 1$. Therefore,

$$\int_{1}^{3} \frac{e^{3/x}}{x^2} \, dx = -\frac{1}{3}\int_{1}^{3} e^{3/x}\left(-\frac{3}{x^2}\right) dx$$

$$= -\frac{1}{3}\int_{3}^{1} e^u \, du$$

$$= -\frac{1}{3}\Big[e^u\Big]_{3}^{1}$$

$$= -\frac{1}{3}(e - e^3)$$

$$= \frac{e}{3}(e^2 - 1).$$

85. Let $u = 1 + \sqrt{x}$. Then $du = 1/(2\sqrt{x}) \, dx$. Furthermore, if $x = 1$, then $u = 2$, and if $x = 9$, then $u = 4$. Hence,

$$\int_{1}^{9} \frac{1}{\sqrt{x}(1 + \sqrt{x})^2} \, dx = 2\int_{1}^{9} \frac{1}{(1 + \sqrt{x})^2}\left(\frac{1}{2\sqrt{x}}\right) dx$$

$$= 2\int_{2}^{4} \frac{1}{u^2} \, du$$

$$= 2\int_{2}^{4} u^{-2} \, du$$

$$= \left[\frac{-2}{u}\right]_{2}^{4}$$

$$= -\frac{1}{2} - (-1) = \frac{1}{2}.$$

87. $u = 2 - x, x = 2 - u, dx = -du$

When $x = 1$, $u = 1$. When $x = 2$, $u = 0$.

$$\int_{1}^{2} (x - 1)\sqrt{2 - x} \, dx = \int_{1}^{0} -[(2 - u) - 1]\sqrt{u} \, du = \int_{1}^{0} (u^{3/2} - u^{1/2}) \, du = \left[\frac{2}{5}u^{5/2} - \frac{2}{3}u^{3/2}\right]_{1}^{0} = -\left[\frac{2}{5} - \frac{2}{3}\right] = \frac{4}{15}$$

89. $\displaystyle\int_{0}^{\pi/2} \cos\left(\frac{2}{3}x\right) dx = \left[\frac{3}{2}\sin\left(\frac{2}{3}x\right)\right]_{0}^{\pi/2} = \frac{3}{2}\left(\frac{\sqrt{3}}{2}\right) = \frac{3\sqrt{3}}{4}$

91. $\displaystyle\int_{-1}^{2} 2^x \, dx = \left[\frac{2^x}{\ln 2}\right]_{-1}^{2}$

$$= \frac{1}{\ln 2}\left[4 - \frac{1}{2}\right]$$

$$= \frac{7}{2\ln 2} = \frac{7}{\ln 4}$$

93. Let $u = \sqrt[3]{x + 1}$. Then $u^3 = x + 1$, $x = u^3 - 1$, and $dx = 3u^2\, du$. Furthermore, if $x = 0$, then $u = 1$, and if $x = 7$, then $u = 2$. Thus,

$$\text{Area} = \int_0^7 x\sqrt[3]{x + 1}\, dx = \int_1^2 (u^3 - 1)(u)(3u^2\, du)$$

$$= 3\int_1^2 (u^6 - u^3)\, du$$

$$= 3\left[\frac{u^7}{7} - \frac{u^4}{4}\right]_1^2$$

$$= 3\left(\frac{128}{7} - \frac{16}{4} - \frac{1}{7} + \frac{1}{4}\right)$$

$$= 3\left(\frac{127}{7} - \frac{15}{4}\right) = 3\left(\frac{508 - 105}{28}\right) = \frac{1209}{28}.$$

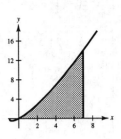

95. $\text{Area} = \displaystyle\int_0^\pi (2 \sin x + \sin 2x)\, dx$

$$= 2\int_0^\pi \sin x\, dx + \frac{1}{2}\int_0^\pi \sin 2x(2)\, dx$$

$$= \left[-2 \cos x - \frac{1}{2} \cos 2x\right]_0^\pi = 4$$

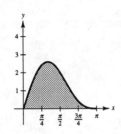

97. $\displaystyle\int_0^4 \frac{x}{\sqrt{2x + 1}}\, dx \approx 3.333 = \frac{10}{3}$

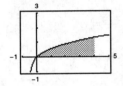

99. $\displaystyle\int_3^7 x\sqrt{x - 3}\, dx \approx 28.8$

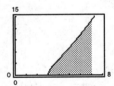

101. $\displaystyle\int_0^3 \left(\theta + \cos \frac{\theta}{6}\right) d\theta \approx 7.377$

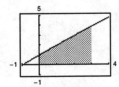

103. $\displaystyle\int_0^{\sqrt{2}} xe^{-(x^2/2)}\, dx = \left[-e^{-(x^2/2)}\right]_0^{\sqrt{2}}$

$$= -e^{-1} + 1 \approx 0.632$$

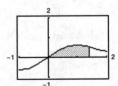

105. Method 1: $\displaystyle\int (2x - 1)^2\, dx = \frac{1}{2}\int (2x - 1)^2(2)\, dx$

$$= \frac{1}{6}(2x - 1)^3 + C_1$$

$$= \frac{4}{3}x^3 - 2x^2 + x - \frac{1}{6} + C_1$$

Method 2: $\displaystyle\int (2x - 1)^2\, dx = \int (4x^2 - 4x + 1)\, dx$

$$= \frac{4}{3}x^3 - 2x^2 + x + C_2$$

The two differ by a constant: $C_2 = C_1 - \dfrac{1}{6}$

107. The function $y = x^2$ is even (see figure).

(a) $\displaystyle\int_{-2}^{0} x^2 \, dx = \int_{0}^{2} x^2 \, dx = \frac{8}{3}$

(b) $\displaystyle\int_{-2}^{2} x^2 \, dx = 2 \int_{0}^{2} x^2 \, dx = \frac{16}{3}$

(c) $\displaystyle\int_{0}^{2} (-x^2) \, dx = -\int_{0}^{2} x^2 \, dx = -\frac{8}{3}$

(d) $\displaystyle\int_{-2}^{0} 3x^2 \, dx = 3 \int_{0}^{2} x^2 \, dx = 8$

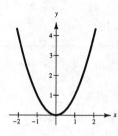

109. $\displaystyle\int_{-4}^{4} (x^3 + 6x^2 - 2x - 3) \, dx = \int_{-4}^{4} (x^3 - 2x) \, dx + \int_{-4}^{4} (6x^2 - 3) \, dx = 0 + 2 \int_{0}^{4} (6x^2 - 3) \, dx = 2 \left[2x^3 - 3x \right]_{0}^{4} = 232$

111. Since the rate of depreciation, dV/dt, is inversely proportional to the square of $t + 1$, it follows that

$$\frac{dV}{dt} = \frac{k}{(t + 1)^2}$$

$$V = \int \frac{k}{(t + 1)^2} \, dt$$

$$= k \int (t + 1)^{-2} \, dt$$

$$= k \int u^{-2} \, du \qquad (u = t + 1, \, du = dt)$$

$$= k \frac{u^{-1}}{-1} + C$$

$$= \frac{-k}{t + 1} + C.$$

Since the initial value of the machine was $500,000, we have

$$V(0) = \frac{-k}{0 + 1} + C = -k + C = 500,000.$$

During the first year the value of the machine decreased $100,000. Therefore,

$$V(1) = \frac{-k}{1 + 1} + C = -\frac{1}{2}k + C = 400,000.$$

Solving the two equations simultaneously yields the solution

$$V(t) = \frac{200,000}{t + 1} + 300,000.$$

The approximate value of the machine after 4 years is

$$V(4) = \frac{200,000}{4 + 1} + 300,000 = \$340,000.$$

Note that according to this model the value of the machine will always be greater than $300,000 since

$$\lim_{t \to \infty} V(t) = 300,000.$$

113. The average sales over the interval of time $a \leq t \leq b$ is

$$\frac{1}{b-a}\int_a^b \left(74.50 + 43.75 \sin \frac{\pi t}{6}\right) dt = \frac{1}{b-a}\left[74.50t - \frac{262.5}{\pi}\cos \frac{\pi t}{6}\right]_a^b.$$

(a) $\dfrac{1}{3}\left[74.50t - \dfrac{262.5}{\pi}\cos \dfrac{\pi t}{6}\right]_0^3 = \dfrac{1}{3}\left(223.5 + \dfrac{262.5}{\pi}\right) \approx 102.352$ thousand units

(b) $\dfrac{1}{3}\left[74.50t - \dfrac{262.5}{\pi}\cos \dfrac{\pi t}{6}\right]_3^6 = \dfrac{1}{3}\left(447 + \dfrac{262.5}{\pi} - 223.5\right) \approx 102.352$ thousand units

(c) $\dfrac{1}{12}\left[74.50t - \dfrac{262.5}{\pi}\cos \dfrac{\pi t}{6}\right]_0^{12} = \dfrac{1}{12}\left(894 - \dfrac{262.5}{\pi} + \dfrac{262.5}{\pi}\right) \approx 74.5$ thousand units

115. $\dfrac{1}{b-a}\displaystyle\int_a^b [2\sin(60\pi t) + \cos(120\pi t)]\, dt = \dfrac{1}{b-a}\left[-\dfrac{1}{30\pi}\cos(60\pi t) + \dfrac{1}{120\pi}\sin(120\pi t)\right]_a^b$

(a) $\dfrac{1}{(1/60) - 0}\left[-\dfrac{1}{30\pi}\cos(60\pi t) + \dfrac{1}{120\pi}\sin(120\pi t)\right]_0^{1/60} = 60\left[\left(\dfrac{1}{30\pi} + 0\right) - \left(-\dfrac{1}{30\pi}\right)\right] = \dfrac{4}{\pi} \approx 1.273$ amps

(b) $\dfrac{1}{(1/240) - 0}\left[-\dfrac{1}{30\pi}\cos(60\pi t) + \dfrac{1}{120\pi}\sin(120\pi t)\right]_0^{1/240} = 240\left[\left(-\dfrac{1}{30\sqrt{2}\pi} + \dfrac{1}{120\pi}\right) - \left(-\dfrac{1}{30\pi}\right)\right]$

$$= \frac{2}{\pi}(5 - 2\sqrt{2}) \approx 1.382 \text{ amps}$$

(c) $\dfrac{1}{(1/30) - 0}\left[-\dfrac{1}{30\pi}\cos(60\pi t) + \dfrac{1}{120\pi}\sin(120\pi t)\right]_0^{1/30} = 30\left[\left(\dfrac{1}{30\pi}\right) - \left(-\dfrac{1}{30\pi}\right)\right] = 0$ amps

117. $0.0665 \displaystyle\int_{48}^{60} e^{-0.0139(t-48)^2}\, dt$

Graphing utility: $0.4772 = 47.72\%$

119. False

$$\int (2x+1)^2\, dx = \frac{1}{2}\int (2x+1)^2\, 2\, dx = \frac{1}{6}(2x+1)^3 + C$$

121. True

$$\int_{-10}^{10} (ax^3 + bx^2 + cx + d)\, dx = \underbrace{\int_{-10}^{10}(ax^3 + cx)\, dx}_{\text{Odd}} + \underbrace{\int_{-10}^{10}(bx^2 + d)\, dx}_{\text{Even}} = 0 + 2\int_0^{10}(bx^2 + d)\, dx$$

123. True

$$4\int \sin x \cos x\, dx = 2\int \sin 2x\, dx = -\cos 2x + C$$

125. Let $u = x + h$, then $du = dx$. When $x = a$, $u = a + h$. When $x = b$, $u = b + h$. Thus,

$$\int_a^b f(x + h)\, dx = \int_{a+h}^{b+h} f(u)\, du = \int_{a+h}^{b+h} f(x)\, dx.$$

Section 4.6   Numerical Integration

1. Exact: $\displaystyle\int_0^2 x^2\,dx = \left[\frac{1}{3}x^3\right]_0^2 = \frac{8}{3} \approx 2.6667$

Trapezoidal: $\displaystyle\int_0^2 x^2\,dx \approx \frac{1}{4}\left[0 + 2\left(\frac{1}{2}\right)^2 + 2(1)^2 + 2\left(\frac{3}{2}\right)^2 + (2)^2\right] = \frac{11}{4} = 2.7500$

Simpson's: $\displaystyle\int_0^2 x^2\,dx \approx \frac{1}{6}\left[0 + 4\left(\frac{1}{2}\right)^2 + 2(1)^2 + 4\left(\frac{3}{2}\right)^2 + (2)^2\right] = \frac{8}{3} \approx 2.6667$

3. Exact: $\displaystyle\int_0^2 x^3\,dx = \left[\frac{x^4}{4}\right]_0^2 = 4.000$

Trapezoidal: $\displaystyle\int_0^2 x^3\,dx \approx \frac{1}{4}\left[0 + 2\left(\frac{1}{2}\right)^3 + 2(1)^3 + 2\left(\frac{3}{2}\right)^3 + (2)^3\right] = \frac{17}{4} = 4.2500$

Simpson's: $\displaystyle\int_0^2 x^3\,dx \approx \frac{1}{6}\left[0 + 4\left(\frac{1}{2}\right)^3 + 2(1)^3 + 4\left(\frac{3}{2}\right)^3 + (2)^3\right] = \frac{24}{6} = 4.0000$

5. Trapezoidal Rule ($n = 8$)

$$\int_0^2 x^3\,dx \approx \frac{2}{2(8)}\left[0 + 2\left(\frac{1}{4}\right)^3 + 2\left(\frac{2}{4}\right)^3 + 2\left(\frac{3}{4}\right)^3 + 2\left(\frac{4}{4}\right)^3 + 2\left(\frac{5}{4}\right)^3 + 2\left(\frac{6}{4}\right)^3 + 2\left(\frac{7}{4}\right)^3 + 2^3\right]$$

$$= \frac{1}{8}\left[\frac{2(1^3 + 2^3 + 3^3 + 4^3 + 5^3 + 6^3 + 7^3)}{4^3} + 8\right]$$

$$= \frac{1}{8}\left[\frac{2(784)}{164} + 8\right] = \frac{65}{16} = 4.0625$$

Simpson's Rule ($n = 8$)

$$\int_0^2 x^3\,dx \approx \frac{2}{3(8)}\left[0 + 4\left(\frac{1}{4}\right)^3 + 2\left(\frac{2}{4}\right)^3 + 4\left(\frac{3}{4}\right)^3 + 2\left(\frac{4}{4}\right)^3 + 4\left(\frac{5}{4}\right)^3 + 2\left(\frac{6}{4}\right)^3 + 4\left(\frac{7}{4}\right)^3 + 2^3\right]$$

$$= \frac{1}{12}\left[\frac{4(1^3 + 3^3 + 5^3 + 7^3) + 2(2^3 + 4^3 + 6^3)}{4^3} + 8\right]$$

$$= \frac{1}{12}\left[\frac{4(496) + 2(288)}{4^3} + 8\right]$$

$$= \frac{1}{12}\left(\frac{2560}{64} + 8\right) = \frac{1}{12}(48) = 4$$

In this particular case, Simpson's Rule is exact since

$$\int_0^2 x^3\,dx = \left[\frac{x^4}{4}\right]_0^2 = \frac{16}{4} = 4.$$

7. Exact: $\displaystyle\int_4^9 \sqrt{x}\,dx = \left[\frac{2}{3}x^{3/2}\right]_4^9 = 18 - \frac{16}{3} = \frac{38}{3} \approx 12.6667$

Trapezoidal: $\displaystyle\int_4^9 \sqrt{x}\,dx \approx \frac{5}{16}\left[2 + 2\sqrt{\frac{37}{8}} + 2\sqrt{\frac{21}{4}} + 2\sqrt{\frac{47}{8}} + 2\sqrt{\frac{26}{4}} + 2\sqrt{\frac{57}{8}} + 2\sqrt{\frac{31}{4}} + 2\sqrt{\frac{67}{8}} + 3\right]$

≈ 12.6640

Simpson's: $\displaystyle\int_4^9 \sqrt{x}\,dx \approx \frac{5}{24}\left[2 + 4\sqrt{\frac{37}{8}} + \sqrt{21} + 4\sqrt{\frac{47}{8}} + \sqrt{26} + 4\sqrt{\frac{57}{8}} + \sqrt{31} + 4\sqrt{\frac{67}{8}} + 3\right] \approx 12.6667$

9. Exact: $\displaystyle\int_1^2 \frac{1}{(x+1)^2}\,dx = \left[-\frac{1}{x+1}\right]_1^2 = -\frac{1}{3} + \frac{1}{2} = \frac{1}{6} \approx 0.1667$

Trapezoidal: $\displaystyle\int_1^2 \frac{1}{(x+1)^2}\,dx \approx \frac{1}{8}\left[\frac{1}{4} + 2\left(\frac{1}{[(5/4)+1]^2}\right) + 2\left(\frac{1}{[(3/2)+1]^2}\right) + 2\left(\frac{1}{[(7/4)+1]^2}\right) + \frac{1}{9}\right]$

$$= \frac{1}{8}\left(\frac{1}{4} + \frac{32}{81} + \frac{8}{25} + \frac{32}{121} + \frac{1}{9}\right) \approx 0.1676$$

Simpson's: $\displaystyle\int_1^2 \frac{1}{(x+1)^2}\,dx \approx \frac{1}{12}\left[\frac{1}{4} + 4\left(\frac{1}{[(5/4)+1]^2}\right) + 2\left(\frac{1}{[(3/2)+1]^2}\right) + 4\left(\frac{1}{[(7/4)+1]^2}\right) + \frac{1}{9}\right]$

$$= \frac{1}{12}\left(\frac{1}{4} + \frac{64}{81} + \frac{8}{25} + \frac{64}{121} + \frac{1}{9}\right) \approx 0.1667$$

11. Trapezoidal: $\displaystyle\int_0^2 \sqrt{1+x^3}\,dx \approx \frac{1}{4}[1 + 2\sqrt{1+(1/8)} + 2\sqrt{2} + 2\sqrt{1+(27/8)} + 3] \approx 3.283$

Simpson's: $\displaystyle\int_0^2 \sqrt{1+x^3}\,dx \approx \frac{1}{6}[1 + 4\sqrt{1+(1/8)} + 2\sqrt{2} + 4\sqrt{1+(27/8)} + 3] \approx 3.240$

Graphing utility: 3.241

13. Trapezoidal Rule $(n = 4)$

$$\int_0^1 \sqrt{x}\sqrt{1-x}\,dx \approx \frac{1}{2(4)}\left[0 + 2\sqrt{\frac{1}{4}}\sqrt{\frac{3}{4}} + 2\sqrt{\frac{2}{4}}\sqrt{\frac{2}{4}} + 2\sqrt{\frac{3}{4}}\sqrt{\frac{1}{4}} + 0\right]$$

$$= \frac{1}{8}\left[\frac{2\sqrt{3}}{4} + \frac{2(2)}{4} + \frac{2\sqrt{3}}{4}\right] = \frac{1}{8}\left(1 + \sqrt{3}\right) \approx 0.342$$

Simpson's Rule $(n = 4)$

$$\int_0^1 \sqrt{x}\sqrt{1-x}\,dx \approx \frac{1}{3(4)}\left[0 + 4\sqrt{\frac{1}{4}}\sqrt{\frac{3}{4}} + 2\sqrt{\frac{2}{4}}\sqrt{\frac{2}{4}} + 4\sqrt{\frac{3}{4}}\sqrt{\frac{1}{4}} + 0\right]$$

$$= \frac{1}{2}\left[\frac{4\sqrt{3}}{4} + \frac{2(2)}{4} + \frac{4\sqrt{3}}{4}\right] = \frac{1}{12}\left(2\sqrt{3} + 1\right) \approx 0.372$$

Using the numerical integration capabilities of a graphing utility yields

$$\int_0^1 \sqrt{x}\sqrt{1-x}\,dx \approx 0.393.$$

15. Trapezoidal Rule with $n = 4$

$$\int_0^{\sqrt{\pi/2}} \cos x^2\,dx \approx \frac{\sqrt{\pi/2}}{2(4)}\left[\cos(0) + 2\cos\left(\frac{\sqrt{\pi/2}}{4}\right)^2 + 2\cos\left(\frac{2\sqrt{\pi/2}}{4}\right)^2 + 2\cos\left(\frac{3\sqrt{\pi/2}}{4}\right)^2 + \cos\left(\frac{4\sqrt{\pi/2}}{4}\right)^2\right]$$

$$\approx 0.957$$

Simpson's Rule with $n = 4$

$$\int_0^{\sqrt{\pi/2}} \cos x^2\,dx \approx \frac{\sqrt{\pi/2}}{3(4)}\left[\cos(0) + 4\cos\left(\frac{\sqrt{\pi/2}}{4}\right)^2 + 2\cos\left(\frac{2\sqrt{\pi/2}}{4}\right)^2 + 4\cos\left(\frac{3\sqrt{\pi/2}}{4}\right)^2 + \cos\left(\frac{4\sqrt{\pi/2}}{4}\right)^2\right]$$

$$\approx 0.978$$

Using the numerical integration capabilities of a graphing utility yields

$$\int_0^{\sqrt{\pi/2}} \cos x^2\,dx \approx 0.977.$$

17. Trapezoidal: $\displaystyle\int_{1}^{1.1} \sin x^2 \, dx \approx \frac{1}{80}[\sin(1) + 2\sin(1.025)^2 + 2\sin(1.05)^2 + 2\sin(1.075)^2 + \sin(1.1)^2] \approx 0.089$

Simpson's: $\displaystyle\int_{1}^{1.1} \sin x^2 \, dx \approx \frac{1}{120}[\sin(1) + 4\sin(1.025)^2 + 2\sin(1.05)^2 + 4\sin(1.075)^2 + \sin(1.1)^2] \approx 0.089$

Graphing utility: 0.089

19. $\displaystyle\int_{0}^{2} x \ln(x + 1) \, dx$

Trapezoidal: 1.684

Simpson's: 1.649

Graphing utility: 1.648

21. Trapezoidal: $\displaystyle\int_{0}^{\pi/4} x \tan x \, dx \approx \frac{\pi}{32}\left[0 + 2\left(\frac{\pi}{16}\right)\tan\left(\frac{\pi}{16}\right) + 2\left(\frac{2\pi}{16}\right)\tan\left(\frac{2\pi}{16}\right) + 2\left(\frac{3\pi}{16}\right)\tan\left(\frac{3\pi}{16}\right) + \frac{\pi}{4}\right] \approx 0.194$

Simpson's: $\displaystyle\int_{0}^{\pi/4} x \tan x \, dx \approx \frac{\pi}{48}\left[0 + 4\left(\frac{\pi}{16}\right)\tan\left(\frac{\pi}{16}\right) + 2\left(\frac{2\pi}{16}\right)\tan\left(\frac{2\pi}{16}\right) + 4\left(\frac{3\pi}{16}\right)\tan\left(\frac{3\pi}{16}\right) + \frac{\pi}{4}\right] \approx 0.186$

Graphing utility: 0.186

23. Trapezoidal Rule with $n = 4$

$$\int_{0}^{4} \sqrt{x}e^x \, dx \approx \frac{4}{2(4)}\left[0 + 2\sqrt{1}e^1 + 2\sqrt{2}e^2 + 2\sqrt{3}e^3 + \sqrt{4}e^4\right] \approx 102.555$$

Simpson's Rule with $n = 4$

$$\int_{0}^{4} \sqrt{x}e^x \, dx \approx \frac{4}{3(4)}\left[0 + 4\sqrt{1}e^1 + 2\sqrt{2}e^2 + 4\sqrt{3}e^3 + \sqrt{4}e^4\right] \approx 93.375$$

Using the numerical integration capabilities of a graphing utility yields

$$\int_{0}^{4} \sqrt{x}e^x \, dx \approx 92.744.$$

25. $f(x) = x^3$

$f'(x) = 3x^2$

$f''(x) = 6x$

$f'''(x) = 6$

$f^{(4)}(x) = 0$

(a) Trapezoidal: Error $\leq \dfrac{(2 - 0)^3}{12(4^2)}(12) = 0.5$ since $f''(x)$ is maximum in $[0, 2]$ when $x = 2$.

(b) Simpson's: Error $\leq \dfrac{(2 - 0)^5}{180(4^4)}(0) = 0$ since $f^{(4)}(x) = 0$.

27. $f''(x) = \dfrac{2}{x^3}$ in $[1, 3]$.

(a) $|f''(x)|$ is maximum when $x = 1$ and $|f''(1)| = 2$.

Trapezoidal: Error $\leq \dfrac{2^3}{12n^2}(2) < 0.00001$, $n^2 > 133{,}333.33$, $n > 365.15$; let $n = 366$.

$f^{(4)}(x) = \dfrac{24}{x^5}$ in $[1, 3]$

(b) $|f^{(4)}(x)|$ is maximum when $x = 1$ and when $|f^{(4)}(1)| = 24$.

Simpson's: Error $\leq \dfrac{2^5}{180n^4}(24) < 0.00001$, $n^4 > 426{,}666.67$, $n > 25.56$; let $n = 26$.

29. $f(x) = \sqrt{1 + x}$

(a) $f''(x) = -\dfrac{1}{4(1 + x)^{3/2}}$ in $[0, 2]$.

$|f''(x)|$ is maximum when $x = 0$ and $|f''(0)| = \frac{1}{4}$.

Trapezoidal: Error $\leq \dfrac{8}{12n^2}\left(\dfrac{1}{4}\right) < 0.00001$, $n^2 > 16{,}666.67$, $n > 129.10$; let $n = 130$.

(b) $f^{(4)}(x) = \dfrac{-15}{16(1 + x)^{7/2}}$ in $[0, 2]$.

$|f^{(4)}(x)|$ is maximum when $x = 0$ and $|f^{(4)}(0)| = \frac{15}{16}$.

Simpson's: Error $\leq \dfrac{32}{180n^4}\left(\dfrac{15}{16}\right) < 0.00001$, $n^4 > 16{,}666.67$, $n > 11.36$; let $n = 12$.

31. (a) Begin by letting $f(x) = \tan x^2$ and finding the second derivative of f using the symbolic differentiation utility. (*Note:* The simplification of the derivatives will differ depending on which differentiation utility is used.)

$$f'(x) = 2x \sec^2 x^2$$

$$f''(x) = \dfrac{2(\cos x^2 + 4x^2 \sin x^2)}{\cos^3 x^2}$$

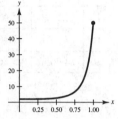

The graph of the second derivative (produced by the differentiation utility) is shown in the figure. The maximum value of $|f''(x)|$ on the interval $[0, 1]$ is $|f''(1)| \approx 50$. Thus, by Theorem 4.19, we can write

$$E \leq \dfrac{(b - a)^3}{12n^2}|f''(1)| \leq \dfrac{50}{12n^2}.$$

To obtain an error E that is less than 0.00001, we must choose n so that $50/(12n^2) \leq 0.00001$. Thus,

$$50(100{,}000) \leq 12n^2 \implies 645.5 \approx \sqrt{\dfrac{50(100{,}000)}{12}} \leq n.$$

Therefore, choose $n = 646$.

(b) Begin by letting $f(x) = \tan x^2$ and finding the fourth derivative of f using the symbolic differentiation utility. The first and second derivative are given in part (a).

$$f'''(x) = -\dfrac{8x(4x^2 \cos^2 x^2 - 3 \sin x^2 \cos x^2 - 6x^2)}{\cos^4 x^2}$$

$$f^{(4)}(x) = -\dfrac{8}{\cos^5 x^2}[24x^2 \cos^3 x^2 + (16x^4 - 3) \sin x^2 \cos^2 x^2 - 36x^2 \cos x^2 - 48x^4 \sin x^2]$$

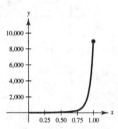

The graph of the fourth derivative (produced by the differentiation utility) is shown in the figure. The maximum value of $|f^{(4)}(x)|$ on the interval $[0, 1]$ is $|f^{(4)}(1)| \approx 9185$. Thus, by Theorem 4.19, we can write

$$E \leq \dfrac{(b - a)^5}{180n^4}|f^{(4)}(1)| \leq \dfrac{9185}{180n^4}.$$

To obtain an error E that is less than 0.00001, we must choose n so that $9185/(180n^4) \leq 0.00001$. Thus,

$$9185(100{,}000) \leq 180n^4 \implies 47.5 \approx \sqrt[4]{\dfrac{9185(100{,}000)}{180}} \leq n.$$

Therefore, choose $n = 48$.

33. Let $f(x) = Ax^3 + Bx^2 + Cx + D$. Then $f^{(4)}(x) = 0$.

Simpson's: Error $\leq \dfrac{(b-a)^5}{180n^4}(0) = 0$

Therefore, Simpson's Rule is exact when approximating the integral of a cubic polynomial.

Example: $\displaystyle\int_0^1 x^3\, dx = \dfrac{1}{6}\left[0 + 4\left(\dfrac{1}{2}\right)^3 + 1\right] = \dfrac{1}{4}$

This is the exact value of the integral.

35. $f(x) = \sqrt{2 + 3x^2}$ on $[0, 4]$.

n	$L(n)$	$M(n)$	$R(n)$	$T(n)$	$S(n)$
4	12.7771	15.3965	18.4340	15.6055	15.4845
8	14.0868	15.4480	16.9152	15.5010	15.4662
10	14.3569	15.4544	16.6197	15.4883	15.4658
12	14.5386	15.4578	16.4242	15.4814	15.4657
16	14.7674	15.4613	16.1816	15.4745	15.4657
20	14.9056	15.4628	16.0370	15.4713	15.4657

37. $f(x) = \sin\sqrt{x}$ on $[0, 4]$.

n	$L(n)$	$M(n)$	$R(n)$	$T(n)$	$S(n)$
4	2.8163	3.5456	3.7256	3.2709	3.3996
8	3.1809	3.5053	3.6356	3.4083	3.4541
10	3.2478	3.4990	3.6115	3.4296	3.4624
12	3.2909	3.4952	3.5940	3.4425	3.4674
16	3.3431	3.4910	3.5704	3.4568	3.4730
20	3.3734	3.4888	3.5552	3.4643	3.4759

39. $f(x) = 6e^{-x^2/2}$ on $[0, 2]$.

n	$L(n)$	$M(n)$	$R(n)$	$T(n)$	$S(n)$
4	8.4410	7.1945	5.8470	7.1440	7.1770
8	7.8178	7.1820	6.5208	7.1693	7.1777
10	7.6911	7.1804	6.6535	7.1723	7.1777
12	7.6063	7.1796	6.7416	7.1740	7.1777
16	7.4999	7.1788	6.8514	7.1756	7.1777
20	7.4358	7.1784	6.9170	7.1764	7.1777

41. $A = \displaystyle\int_0^{\pi/2} \sqrt{x} \cos x \, dx$

Simpson's Rule: $n = 14$

$$\int_0^{\pi/2} \sqrt{x} \cos x \, dx \approx \frac{\pi}{84}\left[\sqrt{0} \cos 0 + 4\sqrt{\frac{\pi}{28}} \cos \frac{\pi}{28} + 2\sqrt{\frac{\pi}{14}} \cos \frac{\pi}{14} + 4\sqrt{\frac{3\pi}{28}} \cos \frac{3\pi}{28} + \cdots + \sqrt{\frac{\pi}{2}} \cos \frac{\pi}{2} \right]$$

$$\approx 0.701$$

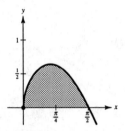

43. Simpson's Rule with $n = 12$:

$$\int_0^5 100x\sqrt{125 - x^3} \, dx \approx \frac{5}{3(12)}\Big[0 + 400\sqrt{125 - (5/12)^3} + 200\sqrt{125 - (10/12)^3}$$
$$+ 400\sqrt{125 - (15/12)^3} + 200\sqrt{125 - (20/12)^3}$$
$$+ 400\sqrt{125 - (25/12)^3} + 200\sqrt{125 - (30/12)^3}$$
$$+ 400\sqrt{125 - (35/12)^3} + 200\sqrt{125 - (40/12)^3}$$
$$+ 400\sqrt{125 - (45/12)^3} + 200\sqrt{125 - (50/12)^3}$$
$$+ 400\sqrt{125 - (55/12)^3} + 0\Big] \approx 10{,}233.58 \text{ ft-lb}$$

45. (a) Trapezoidal: Area $\approx \dfrac{160}{2(8)}[0 + 2(50) + 2(54) + 2(82) + 2(82) + 2(73) + 2(75) + 2(80) + 0] = 9920$ sq ft

(b) Simpson's: Area $\approx \dfrac{160}{3(8)}[0 + 4(50) + 2(54) + 4(82) + 2(82) + 4(73) + 2(75) + 4(80) + 0] = 10{,}413\frac{1}{3}$ sq ft

47. Area $\approx \dfrac{1000}{2(10)}[125 + 2(125) + 2(120) + 2(112) + 2(90) + 2(90) + 2(95) + 2(88) + 2(75) + 2(35)] = 89{,}250$ sq m

49. $\displaystyle\int_0^t \sin\sqrt{x} \, dx = 2, \, n = 10$

By trial and error, we obtain $t \approx 2.477$.

Section 4.7   The Natural Logarithm and Integration

1. $u = x + 1, \, du = dx$

$$\int \frac{1}{x+1} \, dx = \ln|x + 1| + C$$

3. $u = 3 - 2x, \, du = -2 \, dx$

$$\int \frac{1}{3 - 2x} \, dx = -\frac{1}{2}\int \frac{1}{3 - 2x}(-2) \, dx$$

$$= -\frac{1}{2}\ln|3 - 2x| + C$$

5. Letting $u = x^2 + 1$, you have $du = 2x\ dx$. By multiplying and dividing the integral by 2 yields

$$\int \frac{x}{x^2 + 1}\ dx = \frac{1}{2}\int \frac{2x}{x^2 + 1}\ dx$$

$$= \frac{1}{2}\int \frac{1}{u}\ du$$

$$= \frac{1}{2}\ln u + C$$

$$= \frac{1}{2}\ln(x^2 + 1) + C = \ln \sqrt{x^2 + 1} + C.$$

[Note that the absolute value signs around $(x^2 + 1)$ are unnecessary since $x^2 + 1 > 0$ for all x.]

7. $\int \frac{x^2 - 4}{x}\ dx = \int \left(\frac{x^2}{x} - \frac{4}{x}\right) dx$

$$= \int \left(x - \frac{4}{x}\right) dx = \frac{x^2}{2} - 4\ln|x| + C$$

9. $u = x^3 + 3x^2 + 9x,\ du = 3(x^2 + 2x + 3)\ dx$

$$\int \frac{x^2 + 2x + 3}{x^3 + 3x^2 + 9x}\ dx = \frac{1}{3}\int \frac{3(x^2 + 2x + 3)}{x^3 + 3x^2 + 9x}\ dx = \frac{1}{3}\ln|x^3 + 3x^2 + 9x| + C$$

11. $\int \frac{x^2 + x + 1}{x + 1}\ dx = \int \left(x + \frac{1}{x + 1}\right) dx = \frac{x^2}{2} + \ln|x + 1| + C$

13. Since the degree of the numerator of the integrand is greater than the degree of the denominator, begin by dividing.

$$x^2 + 1\overline{\smash{\big)}\ x^3 - 2x^2\qquad - 2}$$

with quotient $x - 2 + \dfrac{-x}{x^2 + 1}$

$$\begin{array}{r} x^3 \qquad\quad + x \\ \hline -2x^2 - x - 2 \\ -2x^2 \qquad - 2 \\ \hline -x \end{array}$$

$$\int \frac{x^3 - 2x^2 - 2}{x^2 + 1}\ dx = \int \left(x - 2 - \frac{x}{x^2 + 1}\right) dx$$

$$= \int (x - 2)\ dx - \frac{1}{2}\int \frac{1}{x^2 + 1}(2x)\ dx$$

$$= \frac{1}{2}x^2 - 2x - \frac{1}{2}\ln(x^2 + 1) + C$$

15. $u = \ln x,\ du = \dfrac{1}{x}\ dx$

$$\int \frac{(\ln x)^2}{x}\ dx = \frac{1}{3}(\ln x)^3 + C$$

17. $\int \frac{1}{\sqrt{x + 1}}\ dx = \int (x + 1)^{-1/2}(1)\ dx$

$$= \int u^{-1/2}\ du$$

$$= \frac{u^{1/2}}{1/2}$$

$$= 2(x + 1)^{1/2} + C = 2\sqrt{x + 1} + C$$

19. If $u = \sqrt{x} - 3$, then $x = (u + 3)^2$ and $dx = 2(u + 3)\, du$. Therefore,

$$\int \frac{\sqrt{x}}{\sqrt{x} - 3}\, dx = \int \frac{u + 3}{u} [2(u + 3)]\, du$$

$$= 2\int \frac{u^2 + 6u + 9}{u}\, du$$

$$= 2\int \left(u + 6 + \frac{9}{u} \right) du$$

$$= 2\left(\frac{u^2}{2} + 6u + 9 \ln |u| \right) + C_1$$

$$= (\sqrt{x} - 3)^2 + 12(\sqrt{x} - 3) + 18 \ln \left| \sqrt{x} - 3 \right| + C_1$$

$$= x + 6\sqrt{x} + 18 \ln \left| \sqrt{x} - 3 \right| + C.$$

21. $\displaystyle \int \frac{2x}{(x - 1)^2}\, dx = \int \frac{2x - 2 + 2}{(x - 1)^2}\, dx$

$$= \int \frac{2(x - 1)}{(x - 1)^2}\, dx + 2\int \frac{1}{(x - 1)^2}\, dx$$

$$= 2\int \frac{1}{x - 1}\, dx + 2\int (x - 1)^{-2}\, dx$$

$$= 2\int \frac{1}{u}\, du + 2\int u^{-2}\, du$$

$$= 2 \ln|u| + 2\frac{u^{-1}}{-1} + C$$

$$= 2 \ln|x - 1| - \frac{2}{x - 1} + C$$

23. $\displaystyle \int \frac{\cos \theta}{\sin \theta}\, d\theta = \ln|\sin \theta| + C$

$$(u = \sin \theta,\, du = \cos \theta\, d\theta)$$

25. $\displaystyle \int \csc 2x\, dx = \frac{1}{2}\int (\csc 2x)(2)\, dx$

$$= -\frac{1}{2} \ln|\csc 2x + \cot 2x| + C$$

27. $\displaystyle \int \frac{\cos t}{1 + \sin t}\, dt = \ln|1 + \sin t| + C$

29. Letting $u = \sec x - 1$, we have $du = \sec x \tan x\, dx$. Therefore,

$$\int \frac{\sec x \tan x}{\sec x - 1}\, dx = \int \frac{1}{u}\, du$$

$$= \ln|u| + C$$

$$= \ln|\sec x - 1| + C.$$

31. $\displaystyle y = \int \frac{3}{2 - x}\, dx$

$$= -3\int \frac{1}{x - 2}\, dx$$

$$= -3 \ln|x - 2| + C$$

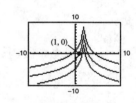

$(1, 0)$: $0 = -3 \ln|1 - 2| + C \Rightarrow C = 0$

$$y = -3 \ln|x - 2|$$

33. $\displaystyle \frac{ds}{d\theta} = \tan 2\theta$

$$s = \int \tan 2\theta\, d\theta = -\frac{1}{2}\int \overbrace{\frac{1}{\cos 2\theta}}^{1/u} \overbrace{(-2 \sin 2\theta)}^{du}\, d\theta = -\frac{1}{2} \ln|\cos 2\theta| + C$$

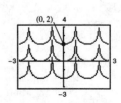

The graphs of the solution for $C = -2$, $C = 0$, and $C = 2$ are given in the figure. The solution passes through the point $(0, 2)$ when $C = 2$.

35. $\dfrac{dy}{dx} = \dfrac{1}{x+2}$, $(0, 1)$

(a)

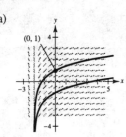

(b) $y = \displaystyle\int \dfrac{1}{x+2}\, dx = \ln|x+2| + C$

$y(0) = 1 \Rightarrow 1 = \ln 2 + C \Rightarrow C = 1 - \ln 2$

Hence, $y = \ln|x+2| + 1 - \ln 2 = \ln\left|\dfrac{x+2}{2}\right| + 1$.

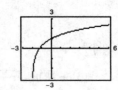

37. $\displaystyle\int_0^4 \dfrac{5}{3x+1}\, dx = \left[\dfrac{5}{3} \ln|3x+1|\right]_0^4$

$= \dfrac{5}{3} \ln 13 \approx 4.275$

39. Letting $u = 1 + \ln x$, we have $du = (1/x)\, dx$. When $x = 1$, $u = 1$ and when $x = e$, $u = 2$. Therefore,

$\displaystyle\int_1^e \dfrac{(1 + \ln x)^2}{x}\, dx = \int_1^e (1 + \ln x)^2 \left(\dfrac{1}{x}\right) dx$

$= \displaystyle\int_1^2 u^2\, du = \left[\dfrac{u^3}{3}\right]_1^2 = \dfrac{7}{3}.$

41. $\displaystyle\int_0^2 \dfrac{x^2 - 2}{x+1}\, dx = \int_0^2 \left(x - 1 - \dfrac{1}{x+1}\right) dx$

$= \left[\dfrac{1}{2}x^2 - x - \ln|x+1|\right]_0^2 = -\ln 3$

43. $\displaystyle\int_1^2 \dfrac{1 - \cos\theta}{\theta - \sin\theta}\, d\theta = \Big[\ln|\theta - \sin\theta|\Big]_1^2$

$= \ln\left|\dfrac{2 - \sin 2}{1 - \sin 1}\right| \approx 1.929$

45. $\displaystyle\int \dfrac{1}{1 + \sqrt{x}}\, dx = 2\big(1 + \sqrt{x}\big) - 2\ln\big(1 + \sqrt{x}\big) + C_1$

$= 2\big[\sqrt{x} - \ln\big(1 + \sqrt{x}\big)\big] + C$ where $C = C_1 + 2$.

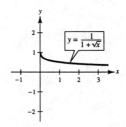

47. $\displaystyle\int \cos(1 - x)\, dx = -\sin(1 - x) + C$

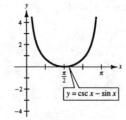

49. $\displaystyle\int_{\pi/4}^{\pi/2} (\csc x - \sin x)\, dx = \Big[-\ln|\csc x + \cot x| + \cos x\Big]_{\pi/4}^{\pi/2}$

$= \ln\big(\sqrt{2} + 1\big) - \dfrac{\sqrt{2}}{2} \approx 0.174$

51. $-\ln|\cos x| + C = \ln|(\cos x)^{-1}| + C$

$$= \ln\left|\frac{1}{\cos x}\right| + C = \ln|\sec x| + C$$

53. $\ln|\sec x + \tan x| + C = \ln\left|\frac{(\sec x + \tan x)(\sec x - \tan x)}{(\sec x - \tan x)}\right| + C = \ln\left|\frac{\sec^2 x - \tan^2 x}{\sec x - \tan x}\right| + C$

$$= \ln\left|\frac{1}{\sec x - \tan x}\right| + C = -\ln|\sec x - \tan x| + C$$

Note: In Exercises 55 and 57, you can use the Second Fundamental Theorem of Calculus or integrate the function.

55. $F(x) = \int_1^x \frac{1}{t}\,dt$

$F'(x) = \frac{1}{x}$

57. $F(x) = \int_x^{3x} \frac{1}{t}\,dt = \int_1^{3x} \frac{1}{t}\,dt - \int_1^x \frac{1}{t}\,dt$

$F'(x) = \frac{3}{3x} - \frac{1}{x} = 0$

59.

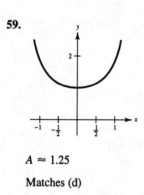

$A \approx 1.25$

Matches (d)

61. Area $= \int_1^4 \frac{x^2 + 4}{x}\,dx = \int_1^4 \left(x + \frac{4}{x}\right)dx$

$$= \left[\frac{1}{2}x^2 + 4\ln x\right]_1^4$$

$$= 8 + 4\ln 4 - \frac{1}{2}$$

$$= \frac{1}{2}(15 + 16\ln 2)$$

$$\approx 13.045 \text{ square units}$$

63. $\int_0^2 2\sec\frac{\pi x}{6}\,dx = \frac{12}{\pi}\int_0^2 \sec\left(\frac{\pi x}{6}\right)\frac{\pi}{6}\,dx$

$$= \left[\frac{12}{\pi}\ln\left|\sec\frac{\pi x}{6} + \tan\frac{\pi x}{6}\right|\right]_0^2$$

$$= \frac{12}{\pi}\ln\left|\sec\frac{\pi}{3} + \tan\frac{\pi}{3}\right| - \frac{12}{\pi}\ln|1 + 0|$$

$$= \frac{12}{\pi}\ln\left(2 + \sqrt{3}\right) \approx 5.03041$$

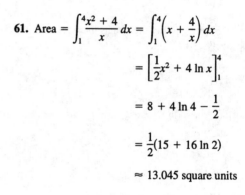

65. $P(t) = \int \frac{3000}{1 + 0.25t}\,dt = (3000)(4)\int \frac{0.25}{1 + 0.25t}\,dt = 12{,}000\ln|1 + 0.25t| + C$

$P(0) = 12{,}000\ln|1 + 0.25(0)| + C = 1000$

$\quad C = 1000$

$P(t) = 12{,}000\ln|1 + 0.25t| + 1000 = 1000[12\ln|1 + 0.25t| + 1]$

$P(3) = 1000[12(\ln 1.75) + 1] \approx 7715$

67. The average price is

$$\frac{1}{50 - 40}\int_{40}^{50} \frac{90{,}000}{400 + 3x}\,dx = \frac{90{,}000}{10}\left(\frac{1}{3}\right)\int \frac{1}{400 + 3x}(3)\,dx = 3000\left[\ln|400 + 3x|\right]_{40}^{50} \approx \$168.27.$$

69. (a) $2x^2 - y^2 = 8$

$$y^2 = 2x^2 - 8$$

$$y_1 = \sqrt{2x^2 - 8}$$

$$y_2 = -\sqrt{2x^2 - 8}$$

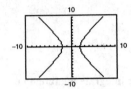

(b) $y^2 = e^{-\int (1/x)dx} = e^{-\ln x + C} = e^{\ln(1/x)}(e^C) = \dfrac{1}{x}k$

Let $k = 4$ and graph $y^2 = \dfrac{4}{x}$. $\left(\begin{array}{l} y_1 = 2/\sqrt{x} \\ y_2 = -2/\sqrt{x} \end{array}\right)$

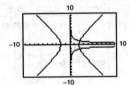

(c) In part (a), $2x^2 - y^2 = 8$

$$4x - 2yy' = 0$$

$$y' = \frac{2x}{y}.$$

In part (b), $y^2 = \dfrac{4}{x} = 4x^{-1}$

$$2yy' = \frac{-4}{x^2}$$

$$y' = \frac{-2}{yx^2} = \frac{-2y}{y^2 x^2} = \frac{-2y}{4x} = \frac{-y}{2x}.$$

Using a graphing utility the graphs intersect at $(2.214, 1.344)$. The slopes are 3.295 and $-0.304 = (-1)/3.295$, respectively.

71. False

$$\frac{1}{2}(\ln x) = \ln(x^{1/2}) \ne (\ln x)^{1/2}$$

73. True

$$\int \frac{1}{x} dx = \ln|x| + C_1$$

$$= \ln|x| + \ln|C| = \ln|Cx|, \ C \ne 0$$

75. $\dfrac{d}{dx}[\ln|x| + C] = \dfrac{1}{x}$

$$\frac{d}{dx}[\ln|u| + C] = \frac{1}{u}u'$$

Section 4.8   Inverse Trigonometric Functions and Integration

1. If $a = 1$ and $u = 3x$, then $du = 3\,dx$. Thus,

$$\int_0^{1/6} \frac{1}{\sqrt{1 - 9x^2}}\,dx = \frac{1}{3}\int_0^{1/6}\left(\frac{1}{\sqrt{1 - (3x)^2}}\right)(3)\,dx$$

$$= \frac{1}{3}\Big[\arcsin(3x)\Big]_0^{1/6}$$

$$= \frac{1}{3}\Big[\arcsin\Big(\frac{1}{2}\Big) - \arcsin 0\Big]$$

$$= \frac{1}{3}\Big(\frac{\pi}{6}\Big) = \frac{\pi}{18}.$$

3. Let $u = 2x$, $du = 2\,dx$.

$$\int_0^{\sqrt{3}/2} \frac{1}{1 + 4x^2}\,dx = \frac{1}{2}\int_0^{\sqrt{3}/2} \frac{2}{1 + (2x)^2}\,dx$$

$$= \Big[\frac{1}{2}\arctan(2x)\Big]_0^{\sqrt{3}/2} = \frac{\pi}{6}$$

5. $\displaystyle\int \frac{1}{x\sqrt{4x^2 - 1}}\,dx = \int \frac{2}{2x\sqrt{(2x)^2 - 1}}\,dx = \operatorname{arcsec}|2x| + C$

7. Since the degree of the numerator is greater than the degree of the denominator, we divide to obtain

$$\frac{x^3}{x^2 + 1} = x - \frac{x}{x^2 + 1}.$$

Therefore,

$$\int \frac{x^3}{x^2 + 1} \, dx = \int \left(x - \frac{x}{x^2 + 1} \right) dx$$

$$= \int x \, dx - \frac{1}{2} \int \frac{2x}{x^2 + 1} \, dx$$

$$= \frac{x^2}{2} - \frac{1}{2} \ln(x^2 + 1) + C$$

$$= \frac{1}{2} x^2 - \frac{1}{2} \ln(x^2 + 1) + C.$$

9. $\displaystyle\int \frac{1}{\sqrt{1 - (x + 1)^2}} \, dx = \arcsin(x + 1) + C$

11. Let $u = t^2$, $du = 2t \, dt$.

$$\int \frac{t}{\sqrt{1 - t^4}} \, dt = \frac{1}{2} \int \frac{1}{\sqrt{1 - (t^2)^2}} (2t) \, dt = \frac{1}{2} \arcsin(t^2) + C$$

13. If $u = \arcsin x$, then $du = \dfrac{1}{\sqrt{1 - x^2}} \, dx$. Thus,

$$\int_0^{1/\sqrt{2}} \frac{\arcsin x}{\sqrt{1 - x^2}} \, dx = \int_0^{1/\sqrt{2}} (\arcsin x)^1 \frac{1}{\sqrt{1 - x^2}} \, dx$$

$$= \left[\frac{(\arcsin x)^2}{2} \right]_0^{1/\sqrt{2}}$$

$$= \frac{1}{2} \left\{ \left[\arcsin \left(\frac{1}{\sqrt{2}} \right) \right]^2 - [\arcsin(0)]^2 \right\}$$

$$= \frac{1}{2} \left[\left(\frac{\pi}{4} \right)^2 - (0)^2 \right] = \frac{\pi^2}{32} \approx 0.308.$$

15. Let $u = 1 - x^2$, $du = -2x \, dx$.

$$\int_{-1/2}^0 \frac{x}{\sqrt{1 - x^2}} \, dx = -\frac{1}{2} \int_{-1/2}^0 (1 - x^2)^{-1/2} (-2x) \, dx$$

$$= \left[-\sqrt{1 - x^2} \right]_{-1/2}^0 = \frac{\sqrt{3} - 2}{2}$$

$$\approx -0.134$$

17. If $a = 2$ and $u = e^{2x}$, then $du = 2e^{2x} \, dx$. Thus

$$\int \frac{e^{2x}}{4 + e^{4x}} \, dx = \frac{1}{2} \int \frac{1}{2^2 + (e^{2x})^2} (2e^{2x}) \, dx$$

$$= \frac{1}{2} \int \frac{du}{a^2 + u^2}$$

$$= \frac{1}{2a} \arctan \frac{u}{a} + C = \frac{1}{4} \arctan \frac{e^{2x}}{2} + C.$$

19. Let $u = \cos x$, $du = -\sin x \, dx$.

$$\int_{\pi/2}^\pi \frac{\sin x}{1 + \cos^2 x} \, dx = -\int_{\pi/2}^\pi \frac{-\sin x}{1 + \cos^2 x} \, dx$$

$$= \left[-\arctan(\cos x) \right]_{\pi/2}^\pi = \frac{\pi}{4}$$

21. $\displaystyle\int_0^2 \frac{1}{x^2 - 2x + 2} \, dx = \int_0^2 \frac{1}{1 + (x - 1)^2} \, dx = \left[\arctan(x - 1) \right]_0^2 = \frac{\pi}{2}$

23. $\int \dfrac{2x}{x^2 + 6x + 13} \, dx = \int \dfrac{(2x + 6) - 6}{x^2 + 6x + 13} \, dx$

$= \int \dfrac{2x + 6}{x^2 + 6x + 13} \, dx - \int \dfrac{6}{x^2 + 6x + 13} \, dx$

$= \int \dfrac{2x + 6}{x^2 + 6x + 13} \, dx - \int \dfrac{6}{(x^2 + 6x + 9) + 4} \, dx$

$= \int \dfrac{2x + 6}{x^2 + 6x + 13} \, dx - 6 \int \dfrac{1}{(x + 3)^2 + 2^2} \, dx$

$= \ln(x^2 + 6x + 13) - 3 \arctan\left(\dfrac{x + 3}{2}\right) + C$

25. $\int \dfrac{1}{\sqrt{-x^2 - 4x}} \, dx = \int \dfrac{1}{\sqrt{-(x^2 + 4x)}} \, dx$

$= \int \dfrac{1}{\sqrt{4 - (x^2 + 4x + 4)}} \, dx$

$= \int \dfrac{1}{\sqrt{2^2 - (x + 2)^2}} \, dx$

$= \arcsin\left(\dfrac{x + 2}{2}\right) + C$

27. Let $u = -x^2 - 4x$, $du = (-2x - 4) \, dx$.

$\int \dfrac{x + 2}{\sqrt{-x^2 - 4x}} \, dx = -\dfrac{1}{2}\int (-x^2 - 4x)^{-1/2}(-2x - 4) \, dx$

$= -\sqrt{-x^2 - 4x} + C$

29. $\displaystyle\int_2^3 \dfrac{2x - 3}{\sqrt{4x - x^2}} \, dx = \int_2^3 \dfrac{(2x - 4) + 1}{\sqrt{4x - x^2}} \, dx$

$= \displaystyle\int_2^3 \dfrac{2x - 4}{\sqrt{4x - x^2}} \, dx + \int_2^3 \dfrac{1}{\sqrt{4x - x^2}} \, dx$

$= -\displaystyle\int_2^3 (4x - x^2)^{-1/2}(4 - 2x) \, dx + \int_2^3 \dfrac{1}{\sqrt{4 - (x^2 - 4x + 4)}} \, dx$

$= -\displaystyle\int_2^3 (4x - x^2)^{-1/2}(4 - 2x) \, dx + \int_2^3 \dfrac{1}{\sqrt{2^2 - (x - 2)^2}} \, dx$

$= \left[-\dfrac{(4x - x^2)^{1/2}}{1/2} + \arcsin\left(\dfrac{x - 2}{2}\right) \right]_2^3$

$= -2\sqrt{3} + \dfrac{\pi}{6} - (-4 + 0) = 4 - 2\sqrt{3} + \dfrac{\pi}{6} \approx 1.059$

31. Let $u = x^2 + 1$, $du = 2x \, dx$.

$\int \dfrac{x}{x^4 + 2x^2 + 2} \, dx = \dfrac{1}{2}\int \dfrac{2x}{(x^2 + 1)^2 + 1} \, dx$

$= \dfrac{1}{2} \arctan(x^2 + 1) + C$

33. (a) $\int \dfrac{1}{\sqrt{1 - x^2}} \, dx = \arcsin x + C$, $u = x$

(b) $\int \dfrac{x}{\sqrt{1 - x^2}} \, dx = -\sqrt{1 - x^2} + C$, $u = 1 - x^2$

(c) $\int \dfrac{1}{x\sqrt{1 - x^2}} \, dx$ cannot be evaluated using the basic integration rules.

35. (a) $\int \sqrt{x-1}\,dx = \frac{2}{3}(x-1)^{3/2} + C, \, u = x - 1$

(b) Let $u = \sqrt{x-1}$. Then $x = u^2 + 1$ and $dx = 2u\,du$.

$$\int x\sqrt{x-1}\,dx = \int (u^2+1)(u)(2u)\,du = 2\int (u^4 + u^2)\,du = 2\left(\frac{u^5}{5} + \frac{u^3}{3}\right) + C$$

$$= \frac{2}{15}u^3(3u^2 + 5) + C = \frac{2}{15}(x-1)^{3/2}[3(x-1) + 5] + C = \frac{2}{15}(x-1)^{3/2}(3x+2) + C$$

(c) Let $u = \sqrt{x-1}$. Then $x = u^2 + 1$ and $dx = 2u\,du$.

$$\int \frac{x}{\sqrt{x-1}}\,dx = \int \frac{u^2+1}{u}(2u)\,du = 2\int (u^2+1)\,du = 2\left(\frac{u^3}{3} + u\right) + C = \frac{2}{3}u(u^2+3) + C = \frac{2}{3}\sqrt{x-1}(x+2) + C$$

Note: In (b) and (c), substitution was necessary *before* the basic integration rules could be used.

37. If $u = \sqrt{e^t - 3}$, then $e^t = u^2 + 3$, $t = \ln(u^2 + 3)$, and $dt = 2u/(u^2 + 3)\,du$. Therefore,

$$\int \sqrt{e^t - 3}\,dt = \int \frac{2u^2}{u^2 + 3}\,du.$$

Since the numerator and denominator are of equal degree, divide to obtain

$$2\int \frac{u^2}{u^2+3}\,du = 2\int \left[1 - \frac{3}{u^2+3}\right]du$$

$$= 2\left[\int du - 3\int \frac{1}{(\sqrt{3})^2 + u^2}\,du\right]$$

$$= 2\left[u - 3\left(\frac{1}{\sqrt{3}}\right)\arctan\left(\frac{u}{\sqrt{3}}\right)\right] + C$$

$$= 2\sqrt{e^t - 3} - 2\sqrt{3}\arctan\left(\frac{\sqrt{e^t - 3}}{\sqrt{3}}\right) + C.$$

39. (a)

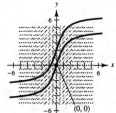

(b) $\frac{dy}{dx} = \frac{3}{1 + x^2}, \, (0, 0)$

$$y = 3\int \frac{dx}{1 + x^2} = 3\arctan x + C$$

$(0, 0): 0 = 3\arctan(0) + C \implies C = 0$

$y = 3\arctan x$

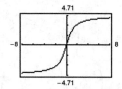

41. From the figure, we can see that the area is

$$A = \int_1^3 \frac{1}{x^2 - 2x + 5}\,dx$$

$$= \int_1^3 \frac{1}{(x^2 - 2x + 1) + 5 - 1}\,dx$$

$$= \int_1^3 \frac{1}{(x-1)^2 + 2^2}\,dx$$

$$= \frac{1}{2}\left[\arctan\frac{x-1}{2}\right]_1^3$$

$$= \frac{1}{2}[\arctan 1 - \arctan 0] = \frac{\pi}{8}.$$

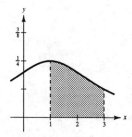

43. Area $\approx (1)(1) = 1$

Matches (c)

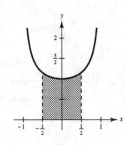

45. (a) $\displaystyle\int_0^1 \frac{4}{1+x^2}\, dx = \left[4\arctan x\right]_0^1 = 4\arctan 1 - 4\arctan 0 = 4\left(\frac{\pi}{4}\right) - 4(0) = \pi$

(b) Let $n = 6$.

$$4\int_0^1 \frac{4}{1+x^2}\, dx \approx 4\left(\frac{1}{36}\right)\left[1 + \frac{4}{1+(1/36)} + \frac{2}{1+(1/9)} + \frac{4}{1+(1/4)} + \frac{2}{1+(4/9)} + \frac{4}{1+(25/36)} + \frac{1}{2}\right] \approx 3.1415918$$

(c) 3.1415927

47. $\displaystyle\int \frac{1}{\sqrt{6x - x^2}}\, dx$

(a) $6x - x^2 = 9 - (x^2 - 6x + 9) = 9 - (x-3)^2$

$$\int \frac{1}{\sqrt{6x - x^2}}\, dx = \int \frac{dx}{\sqrt{9 - (x-3)^2}} = \arcsin\left(\frac{x-3}{3}\right) + C$$

(b) $u = \sqrt{x},\ u^2 = x,\ 2u\, du = dx$

$$\int \frac{1}{\sqrt{6u^2 - u^4}}(2u\, du) = \int \frac{2}{\sqrt{6 - u^2}}\, du = 2\arcsin\left(\frac{u}{\sqrt{6}}\right) + C = 2\arcsin\left(\frac{\sqrt{x}}{\sqrt{6}}\right) + C$$

(c)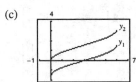

The antiderivatives differ by a constant, $\pi/2$.

Domain: $[0, 6]$

49. (a) $v(t) = -32t + 500$

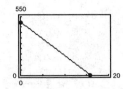

(b) $\displaystyle s(t) = \int v(t)\, dt = \int (-32t + 500)\, dt$

$\qquad = -16t^2 + 500t + C$

$s(0) = -16(0) + 500(0) + C = 0 \implies C = 0$

$s(t) = -16t^2 + 500t$

When the object reaches its maximum height, $v(t) = 0$.

$\qquad v(t) = -32t + 500 = 0$

$\qquad\quad -32t = -500$

$\qquad\qquad\quad t = 15.625$

$\qquad s(15.625) = -16(15.625)^2 + 500(15.625)$

$\qquad\qquad\quad = 3906.25$ ft (Maximum height)

(c) $\displaystyle\int \frac{1}{32 + kv^2}\, dv = -\int dt$

$\dfrac{1}{\sqrt{32k}}\arctan\left(\sqrt{\dfrac{k}{32}}\,v\right) = -t + C_1$

$\arctan\left(\sqrt{\dfrac{k}{32}}\,v\right) = -\sqrt{32k}\,t + C$

$\sqrt{\dfrac{k}{32}}\,v = \tan\left(C - \sqrt{32k}\,t\right)$

$v = \sqrt{\dfrac{32}{k}}\tan\left(C - \sqrt{32k}\,t\right)$

When $t = 0$, $v = 500$, $C = \arctan\left(500\sqrt{k/32}\right)$, and we have

$$v(t) = \sqrt{\frac{32}{k}}\tan\left[\arctan\left(500\sqrt{\frac{k}{32}}\right) - \sqrt{32k}\,t\right].$$

—CONTINUED—

49. —CONTINUED—

(d) When $k = 0.001$, $v(t) = \sqrt{32,000}\, \tan\!\left[\arctan\!\left(500\sqrt{0.00003125}\right) - \sqrt{0.032}\, t\right]$.

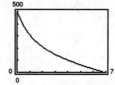

$v(t) = 0$ when $t_0 \approx 6.86$ sec.

(e) $h = \displaystyle\int_0^{6.86} \sqrt{32,000}\, \tan\!\left[\arctan\!\left(500\sqrt{0.00003125}\right) - \sqrt{0.032}\, t\right] dt$

Simpson's Rule: $n = 10$; $h \approx 1088$ feet

(f) Air resistance lowers the maximum height.

51. Let $f(x) = \arctan x - \dfrac{x}{1 + x^2}$

$$f'(x) = \frac{1}{1 + x^2} - \frac{1 - x^2}{(1 + x^2)^2} = \frac{2x^2}{(1 + x^2)} > 0 \text{ for } x > 0.$$

Since $f(0) = 0$ and f is increasing for $x > 0$, $\arctan x - \dfrac{x}{1 + x^2} > 0$ for $x > 0$. Thus,

$$\arctan x > \frac{x}{1 + x^2}.$$

Let $g(x) = x - \arctan x$

$$g'(x) = 1 - \frac{1}{1 + x^2} = \frac{x^2}{1 + x^2} > 0 \text{ for } x > 0.$$

Since $g(0) = 0$ and g is increasing for $x > 0$, $x - \arctan x > 0$ for $x > 0$. Thus, $x > \arctan x$. Therefore,

$$\frac{x}{1 + x^2} < \arctan x < x.$$

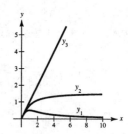

Section 4.9   Hyperbolic Functions

1. (a) $\sinh 3 = \dfrac{e^3 - e^{-3}}{2} \approx 10.018$

(b) $\tanh(-2) = \dfrac{\sinh(-2)}{\cosh(-2)} = \dfrac{e^{-2} - e^2}{e^{-2} + e^2} \approx -0.964$

3. (a) $\operatorname{csch}(\ln 2) = \dfrac{1}{\sinh(\ln 2)} = \dfrac{2}{e^{\ln 2} - e^{-\ln 2}} = \dfrac{2}{2 - (1/2)} = \dfrac{4}{3}$

(b) $\coth(\ln 5) = \dfrac{\cosh(\ln 5)}{\sinh(\ln 5)} = \dfrac{e^{\ln 5} + e^{-\ln 5}}{e^{\ln 5} - e^{-\ln 5}} = \dfrac{5 + (1/5)}{5 - (1/5)} = \dfrac{13}{12}$

5. (a) $\cosh^{-1}(2) = \ln\!\left(2 + \sqrt{3}\right) \approx 1.317$

(b) $\operatorname{sech}^{-1}\!\left(\dfrac{2}{3}\right) = \ln\!\left(\dfrac{1 + \sqrt{1 - (4/9)}}{2/3}\right) \approx 0.962$

7. $\tanh^2 x + \operatorname{sech}^2 x = \left(\dfrac{e^x - e^{-x}}{e^x + e^{-x}}\right)^2 + \left(\dfrac{2}{e^x + e^{-x}}\right)^2 = \dfrac{e^{2x} - 2 + e^{-2x} + 4}{(e^x + e^{-x})^2} = \dfrac{e^{2x} + 2 + e^{-2x}}{e^{2x} + 2 + e^{-2x}} = 1$

9. $\sinh x \cosh y + \cosh x \sinh y = \left(\dfrac{e^x - e^{-x}}{2}\right)\left(\dfrac{e^y + e^{-y}}{2}\right) + \left(\dfrac{e^x + e^{-x}}{2}\right)\left(\dfrac{e^y - e^{-y}}{2}\right)$

$$= \frac{1}{4}\left[e^{x+y} - e^{-x+y} + e^{x-y} - e^{-(x+y)} + e^{x+y} + e^{-x+y} - e^{x-y} - e^{-(x+y)}\right]$$

$$= \frac{1}{4}\left[2(e^{x+y} - e^{-(x+y)})\right] = \frac{e^{(x+y)} - e^{-(x+y)}}{2} = \sinh(x + y)$$

11. $3 \sinh x + 4 \sinh^3 x = \sinh x (3 + 4 \sinh^2 x) = \left(\dfrac{e^x - e^{-x}}{2}\right)\left[3 + 4\left(\dfrac{e^x - e^{-x}}{2}\right)^2\right]$

$$= \left(\frac{e^x - e^{-x}}{2}\right)[3 + e^{2x} - 2 + e^{-2x}] = \frac{1}{2}(e^x - e^{-x})(e^{2x} + e^{-2x} + 1)$$

$$= \frac{1}{2}[e^{3x} + e^{-x} + e^x - e^x - e^{-3x} - e^{-x}] = \frac{e^{3x} - e^{-3x}}{2} = \sinh(3x)$$

13.
$$\sinh x = \frac{3}{2}$$

$$\cosh^2 x - \left(\frac{3}{2}\right)^2 = 1 \implies \cosh^2 x = \frac{13}{4} \implies \cosh x = \frac{\sqrt{13}}{2}$$

$$\tanh x = \frac{3/2}{\sqrt{13}/2} = \frac{3\sqrt{13}}{13}$$

$$\operatorname{csch} x = \frac{1}{3/2} = \frac{2}{3}$$

$$\operatorname{sech} x = \frac{1}{\sqrt{13}/2} = \frac{2\sqrt{13}}{13}$$

$$\coth x = \frac{1}{3/\sqrt{13}} = \frac{\sqrt{13}}{3}$$

15. $y = \sinh(1 - x^2)$

$$y' = -2x \cosh(1 - x^2)$$

17. $f(x) = \ln(\sinh x)$

$$f'(x) = \frac{1}{\sinh}(\cosh x) = \coth x$$

19. $y = \ln\left(\tanh \dfrac{x}{2}\right)$

$$y' = \frac{1}{\tanh(x/2)}\left[\frac{1}{2}\operatorname{sech}^2\left(\frac{x}{2}\right)\right]$$

$$= \frac{1}{2}\left[\frac{\cosh(x/2)}{\sinh(x/2)}\right]\left[\frac{1}{\cosh^2(x/2)}\right]$$

$$= \frac{1}{2\sinh(x/2)\cosh(x/2)} = \frac{1}{\sinh x} = \operatorname{csch} x$$

21. $h(x) = \dfrac{1}{4}\sinh(2x) - \dfrac{x}{2}$

$$h'(x) = \frac{1}{2}\cosh(2x) - \frac{1}{2} = \frac{\cosh(2x) - 1}{2} = \sinh^2 x$$

23. $f(t) = \arctan(\sinh t)$

$$f'(t) = \frac{1}{1 + \sinh^2 t}(\cosh t) = \frac{\cosh t}{\cosh^2 t} = \operatorname{sech} t$$

25. Using logarithmic differentiation yields

$$y = x^{\cosh x}$$

$$\ln y = \ln(x^{\cosh x}) = (\cosh x)(\ln x)$$

$$\frac{y'}{y} = (\cosh x)\left(\frac{1}{x}\right) + (\ln x)(\sinh x)$$

$$y' = y\left[\frac{\cosh x}{x} + (\ln x)(\sinh x)\right] = \frac{y}{x}[\cosh x + x(\sinh x)\ln x].$$

27. $y = (\cosh x - \sinh x)^2$

$y' = 2(\cosh x - \sinh x)(\sinh x - \cosh x)$

$\quad = -2(\cosh x - \sinh x)^2 = -2e^{-2x}$

29. $f(x) = \sin x \sinh x - \cos x \cosh x, \; -4 \le x \le 4$

$f'(x) = \sin x \cosh x + \cos x \sinh x - \cos x \sinh x + \sin x \cosh x$

$\quad = 2 \sin x \cosh x = 0$ when $x = 0, \pm \pi$.

Relative maxima: $(\pm \pi, \cosh \pi)$

Relative minimum: $(0, -1)$

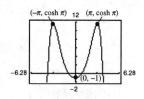

31. $g(x) = x \operatorname{sech} x = \dfrac{x}{\cosh x}$

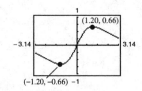

Relative maximum: $(1.20, 0.66)$

Relative minimum: $(-1.20, -0.66)$

33. $y = a \sinh x$

$y' = a \cosh x$

$y'' = a \sinh x$

$y''' = a \cosh x$

Therefore, $y''' - y' = 0$.

35. $f(x) = \tanh x \qquad\qquad f(1) \approx 0.76$

$f'(x) = \operatorname{sech}^2 x \qquad\qquad f'(1) \approx 0.42$

$f''(x) = -2 \operatorname{sech}^2 x \tanh x \quad f''(1) \approx 0.64$

$\quad P_1(x) = f(a) + f'(a)(x - a)$

$\qquad\quad = f(1) + f'(1)(x - 1)$

$\qquad\quad = 0.76 + 0.42(x - 1)$

$\quad P_2(x) = f(a) + f'(a)(x - a) + \tfrac{1}{2} f''(a)(x - a)^2$

$\qquad\quad = f(1) + f'(1)(x - 1) + \tfrac{1}{2} f''(1)(x - 1)^2$

$\qquad\quad = 0.76 + 0.42(x - 1) - 0.32(x - 1)^2$

The graphs of f, P_1, and P_2 are shown in the figure.

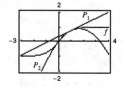

37. Let $u = 1 - 2x, \, du = -2 \, dx$.

$$\int \sinh(1 - 2x) \, dx = -\frac{1}{2} \int \sinh(1 - 2x)(-2) \, dx$$

$$= -\frac{1}{2} \cosh(1 - 2x) + C$$

39. If $u = \cosh(x - 1)$, then $du = \sinh(x - 1) \, dx$.

$$\int \cosh^2(x - 1) \sinh(x - 1) \, dx = \int u^2 \, du$$

$$= \frac{1}{3} u^3 + C$$

$$= \frac{1}{3} \cosh^3(x - 1) + C.$$

41. Let $u = \sinh x, \, du = \cosh x \, dx$.

$$\int \frac{\cosh x}{\sinh x} \, dx = \ln|\sinh x| + C$$

43. Let $u = \dfrac{x^2}{2}, \, du = x \, dx$.

$$\int x \operatorname{csch}^2 \frac{x^2}{2} \, dx = \int \left(\operatorname{csch}^2 \frac{x^2}{2} \right) x \, dx = -\coth \frac{x^2}{2} + C$$

45. If $u = \dfrac{1}{x}$, then $du = -\dfrac{1}{x^2}\,dx$ and

$$\int \frac{\operatorname{csch}(1/x)\coth(1/x)}{x^2}\,dx = -\int \operatorname{csch}\frac{1}{x}\coth\frac{1}{x}\left(-\frac{1}{x^2}\right)dx$$

$$= -\int \operatorname{csch} u\,\coth u\,du$$

$$= \operatorname{csch} u + C = \operatorname{csch}\frac{1}{x} + C.$$

47. $\displaystyle\int_0^4 \frac{1}{25-x^2}\,dx = \left[\frac{1}{10}\ln\left|\frac{5+x}{5-x}\right|\right]_0^4 = \frac{1}{10}\ln 9 = \frac{1}{5}\ln 3$

49. Let $u = 2x$, $du = 2\,dx$.

$$\int_0^{\sqrt{2}/4} \frac{1}{\sqrt{1-(2x)^2}}(2)\,dx = \Big[\arcsin(2x)\Big]_0^{\sqrt{2}/4} = \frac{\pi}{4}$$

51. Let $u = x^2$, $du = 2x\,dx$.

$$\int \frac{x}{x^4+1}\,dx = \frac{1}{2}\int \frac{2x}{(x^2)^2+1}\,dx = \frac{1}{2}\arctan(x^2) + C$$

53. $y = \cosh^{-1}(3x)$

$$y' = \frac{3}{\sqrt{9x^2-1}}$$

55. $y = \sinh^{-1}(\tan x)$

$$y' = \frac{1}{\sqrt{\tan^2 x+1}}(\sec^2 x) = |\sec x|$$

57. $y = \coth^{-1}(\sin 2x)$

$$y' = \frac{1}{1-\sin^2 2x}(2\cos 2x) = 2\sec 2x$$

59. $y = 2x\sinh^{-1}(2x) - \sqrt{1+4x^2}$

$$y' = 2x\left[\frac{1}{\sqrt{1+(2x)^2}}\right](2) + 2\sinh^{-1}(2x) - \frac{1}{2}(1+4x^2)^{-1/2}(8x)$$

$$= \frac{4x}{\sqrt{1+4x}} + 2\sinh^{-1}(2x) - \frac{4}{\sqrt{1+4x^2}} = 2\sinh^{-1}(2x)$$

61. Note that the domain of this function restricts x to the interval $(0, a)$ where $0 < a$.

$$y = a\operatorname{sech}^{-1}\left(\frac{x}{a}\right) - \sqrt{a^2-x^2}$$

$$\frac{dy}{dx} = a\left[\frac{-1}{|x/a|\sqrt{1-(x/a)^2}}\right]\left(\frac{1}{a}\right) - \frac{1}{2}(a^2-x^2)^{-1/2}(-2x)$$

$$= \frac{-1}{|x/a|\sqrt{(a^2-x^2)/a^2}} + \frac{x}{\sqrt{a^2-x^2}}$$

$$= \frac{-a^2}{x\sqrt{a^2-x^2}} + \frac{x}{\sqrt{a^2-x^2}}$$

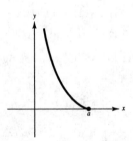

(Note that the absolute value signs can be deleted since $0 < x$.)

$$\frac{dy}{dx} = \frac{-a^2+x^2}{x\sqrt{a^2-x^2}} = \frac{-(a^2-x^2)}{x\sqrt{a^2-x^2}} = \frac{-\sqrt{a^2-x^2}}{x}$$

63. If $u = e^x$, then $du = e^x \, dx$ and we have

$$\int \frac{1}{\sqrt{1 + e^{2x}}} \, dx = \int \frac{e^x}{e^x \sqrt{1 + (e^x)^2}} \, dx$$

$$= \int \frac{du}{u\sqrt{1 + u^2}}$$

$$= -\ln\left(\frac{1 + \sqrt{1 + e^{2x}}}{e^x}\right) + C$$

$$= -\operatorname{csch}^{-1}(e^x) + C.$$

65. If $u = \sqrt{x}$, then $du = 1/(2\sqrt{x}) \, dx$ and we have

$$\int \frac{1}{\sqrt{x}\sqrt{1 + x}} \, dx = 2 \int \frac{1}{\sqrt{1 + (\sqrt{x})^2}} \left(\frac{1}{2\sqrt{x}}\right) dx$$

$$= 2 \int \frac{du}{\sqrt{1 + u^2}}$$

$$= 2 \sinh^{-1} \sqrt{x} + C$$

$$= 2 \ln\left(\sqrt{x} + \sqrt{1 + x}\right) + C.$$

67. $\displaystyle \int \frac{-1}{4x - x^2} \, dx = \int \frac{1}{(x - 2)^2 - 4} \, dx = \frac{1}{4} \ln\left|\frac{(x - 2) - 2}{(x - 2) + 2}\right| = \frac{1}{4} \ln\left|\frac{x - 4}{x}\right| + C$

69. $\displaystyle \int \frac{1}{1 - 4x - 2x^2} \, dx = \int \frac{1}{3 - 2(x + 1)^2} \, dx = \frac{-1}{\sqrt{2}} \int \frac{\sqrt{2}}{[\sqrt{2}(x + 1)]^2 - (\sqrt{3})^2} \, dx$

$$= \frac{-1}{2\sqrt{6}} \ln\left|\frac{\sqrt{2}(x + 1) - \sqrt{3}}{\sqrt{2}(x + 1) + \sqrt{3}}\right| + C = \frac{1}{2\sqrt{6}} \ln\left|\frac{\sqrt{2}(x + 1) + \sqrt{3}}{\sqrt{2}(x + 1) - \sqrt{3}}\right| + C$$

71. Let $u = 4x - 1$, $du = 4 \, dx$.

$$y = \int \frac{1}{\sqrt{80 + 8x - 16x^2}} \, dx = \frac{1}{4} \int \frac{4}{\sqrt{81 - (4x - 1)^2}} \, dx = \frac{1}{4} \arcsin\left(\frac{4x - 1}{9}\right) + C$$

73. $\displaystyle y = \int \frac{x^3 - 21x}{5 + 4x - x^2} \, dx = \int \left(-x - 4 + \frac{20}{5 + 4x - x^2}\right) dx = \int (-x - 4) \, dx + 20 \int \frac{1}{3^2 - (x - 2)^2} \, dx$

$$= -\frac{x^2}{2} - 4x + \frac{20}{6} \ln\left|\frac{(x - 2) + 3}{(x - 2) - 3}\right| + C = -\frac{x^2}{2} - 4x + \frac{10}{3} \ln\left|\frac{x + 1}{x - 5}\right| + C = \frac{-x^2}{2} - 4x - \frac{10}{3} \ln\left|\frac{x - 5}{x + 1}\right| + C$$

75. $\displaystyle A = 2 \int_0^4 \operatorname{sech} \frac{x}{2} \, dx = 2 \int_0^4 \frac{2}{e^{x/2} + e^{-x/2}} \, dx = 4 \int_0^4 \frac{e^{x/2}}{(e^{x/2})^2 + 1} \, dx = \left[8 \arctan(e^{x/2})\right]_0^4 = 8 \arctan(e^2) - 2\pi \approx 5.207$

77. The graph of the region is shown in the figure.

$$A = \int_0^2 \frac{5x}{\sqrt{x^4 + 1}} \, dx = \frac{5}{2} \int_0^2 \frac{1}{\sqrt{(x^2)^2 + 1}} (2x) \, dx$$

$$= \frac{5}{2} \left[\ln\left(x^2 + \sqrt{x^4 + 1}\right)\right]_0^2$$

$$= \frac{5}{2} \ln\left(4 + \sqrt{17}\right) \approx 5.237$$

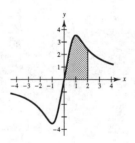

79. $\displaystyle \int \frac{3k}{16} \, dt = \int \frac{1}{x^2 - 12x + 32} \, dx$

$$\frac{3kt}{16} = \int \frac{1}{(x - 6)^2 - 4} \, dx = \frac{1}{2(2)} \ln\left|\frac{(x - 6) - 2}{(x - 6) + 2}\right| + C = \frac{1}{4} \ln\left|\frac{x - 8}{x - 4}\right| + C$$

When $x = 0$: $t = 0$

$$C = -\frac{1}{4} \ln(2)$$

—CONTINUED—

79. **—CONTINUED—**

When $x = 1$: $t = 10$

$$\frac{30k}{16} = \frac{1}{4} \ln\left|\frac{-7}{-3}\right| - \frac{1}{4} \ln(2) = \frac{1}{4} \ln\left(\frac{7}{6}\right)$$

$$k = \frac{2}{15} \ln\left(\frac{7}{6}\right)$$

When $t = 20$: $\left(\frac{3}{16}\right)\left(\frac{2}{15}\right) \ln\left(\frac{7}{6}\right)(20) = \frac{1}{4} \ln \frac{x - 8}{2x - 8}$

$$\ln\left(\frac{7}{6}\right)^2 = \ln \frac{x - 8}{2x - 8}$$

$$\frac{49}{36} = \frac{x - 8}{2x - 8}$$

$$62x = 104$$

$$x = \frac{104}{62} = \frac{52}{31} \approx 1.677 \text{ kg}$$

81. As k increases, the time required for the object to reach the ground increases.

83. $y = \cosh x = \dfrac{e^x + e^{-x}}{2}$

$$y' = \frac{e^x - e^{-x}}{2} = \sinh x$$

85. If $y = \cosh^{-1} x$, then $\cosh y = x$. Differentiating implicitly with respect to x yields the following.

$$\cosh y = x$$

$$(\sinh y) \frac{dy}{dx} = 1$$

$$\frac{dy}{dx} = \frac{1}{\sinh y} = \frac{1}{\sqrt{\cosh^2 y - 1}} = \frac{1}{\sqrt{x^2 - 1}}$$

87. $y = \operatorname{sech} x = \dfrac{2}{e^x + e^{-x}}$

$$y' = -2(e^x + e^{-x})^{-2}(e^x - e^{-x}) = \left(\frac{-2}{e^x + e^{-x}}\right)\left(\frac{e^x - e^{-x}}{e^x + e^{-x}}\right) = -\operatorname{sech} x \tanh x$$

Review Exercises for Chapter 4

1.

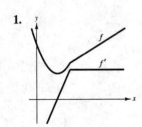

3. $\displaystyle\int (2x^2 + x - 1)\, dx = \frac{2}{3}x^3 + \frac{1}{2}x^2 - x + C$

5. $\displaystyle\int \frac{x^3 + 1}{x^2}\, dx = \int \left(\frac{x^3}{x^2} + \frac{1}{x^2}\right) dx$

$$= \int (x + x^{-2})\, dx = \frac{1}{2}x^2 + \frac{x^{-1}}{-1} + C = \frac{1}{2}x^2 - \frac{1}{x} + C$$

7. $\int (4x - 3 \sin x)\, dx = 2x^2 + 3 \cos x + C$

9. $f'(x) = -2x,\ (-1, 1)$

$$f(x) = \int -2x\, dx = -x^2 + C$$

When $x = -1$:

$$y = -1 + C = 1$$

$$C = 2$$

$$y = 2 - x^2$$

11. Let the position function of the plane be given by $s(t)$ where s is measured in feet and t is time in seconds. If $t = 0$ is the time the plane starts its take off roll, then $s(0) = 0$, $s(30) = 3600$, $s'(0) = 0$, and $s''(t) = a$ where a is constant.

$$s'(t) = \int a\, dt = at + C_1$$

$$s'(0) = 0 + C_1 = 0 \implies C_1 = 0$$

$$s(t) = \int at\, dt = \frac{a}{2}t^2 + C_2$$

$$s(0) = 0 + C_2 = 0 \implies C_2 = 0 \implies s(t) = \frac{a}{2}t^2$$

$$s(30) = \frac{a}{2}(30)^2 = 3600 \text{ or } a = \frac{3600(2)}{30^2} = 8 \text{ ft/sec}^2$$

Therefore,

$$s(t) = 4t^2,\, s'(t) = v(t) = 8t \quad \text{and}$$

$$v(30) = 8(30) = 240 \text{ ft/sec}.$$

13. $a(t) = -32$

$$v(t) = -32t + 96$$

$$s(t) = -16t^2 + 96t$$

(a) $v(t) = -32t + 96 = 0$ when $t = 3$ sec.

(b) $s(3) = -144 + 288 = 144$ ft

(c) $v(t) = -32t + 96 = \dfrac{96}{2}$ when $t = \dfrac{3}{2}$ sec.

(d) $s\left(\dfrac{3}{2}\right) = -16\left(\dfrac{9}{4}\right) + 96\left(\dfrac{3}{2}\right) = 108$ ft

15. (a) $\displaystyle\sum_{i=1}^{10} (2i - 1)$ (b) $\displaystyle\sum_{i=1}^{n} i^3$ (c) $\displaystyle\sum_{i=1}^{10} (4i + 2)$

17. (a) $S = m\left(\dfrac{b}{4}\right)\left(\dfrac{b}{4}\right) + m\left(\dfrac{2b}{4}\right)\left(\dfrac{b}{4}\right) + m\left(\dfrac{3b}{4}\right)\left(\dfrac{b}{4}\right) + m\left(\dfrac{4b}{4}\right)\left(\dfrac{b}{4}\right) = \dfrac{mb^2}{16}(1 + 2 + 3 + 4) = \dfrac{5mb^2}{8}$

$s = m(0)\left(\dfrac{b}{4}\right) + m\left(\dfrac{b}{4}\right)\left(\dfrac{b}{4}\right) + m\left(\dfrac{2b}{4}\right)\left(\dfrac{b}{4}\right) + m\left(\dfrac{3b}{4}\right)\left(\dfrac{b}{4}\right) = \dfrac{mb^2}{16}(1 + 2 + 3) = \dfrac{3mb^2}{8}$

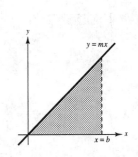

(b) $S(n) = \displaystyle\sum_{i=1}^{n} f\left(\dfrac{bi}{n}\right)\left(\dfrac{b}{n}\right) = \sum_{i=1}^{n} \left(\dfrac{mbi}{n}\right)\left(\dfrac{b}{n}\right) = m\left(\dfrac{b}{n}\right)^2 \sum_{i=1}^{n} i = \dfrac{mb^2}{n^2}\left(\dfrac{n(n+1)}{2}\right) = \dfrac{mb^2(n+1)}{2n}$

$s(n) = \displaystyle\sum_{i=0}^{n-1} f\left(\dfrac{bi}{n}\right)\left(\dfrac{b}{n}\right) = \sum_{i=0}^{n-1} m\left(\dfrac{bi}{n}\right)\left(\dfrac{b}{n}\right) = m\left(\dfrac{b}{n}\right)^2 \sum_{i=0}^{n-1} i = \dfrac{mb^2}{n^2}\left(\dfrac{(n-1)n}{2}\right) = \dfrac{mb^2(n-1)}{2n}$

(c) Area $= \displaystyle\lim_{n\to\infty} \dfrac{mb^2(n+1)}{2n} = \lim_{n\to\infty} \dfrac{mb^2(n-1)}{2n} = \dfrac{1}{2}mb^2 = \dfrac{1}{2}(b)(mb) = \dfrac{1}{2}(\text{base})(\text{height})$

(d) $\displaystyle\int_0^b mx\, dx = \left[\dfrac{1}{2}mx^2\right]_0^b = \dfrac{1}{2}mb^2$

19. (a) $\int_2^6 [f(x) + g(x)]\, dx = \int_2^6 f(x)\, dx + \int_2^6 g(x)\, dx$

$$= 10 + 3 = 13$$

(b) $\int_2^6 [f(x) - g(x)]\, dx = \int_2^6 f(x)\, dx - \int_2^6 g(x)\, dx$

$$= 10 - 3 = 7$$

(c) $\int_2^6 [2f(x) - 3g(x)]\, dx = 2\int_2^6 f(x)\, dx - 3\int_2^6 g(x)\, dx$

$$= 2(10) - 3(3) = 11$$

(d) $\int_2^6 5f(x)\, dx = 5\int_2^6 f(x)\, dx = 5(10) = 50$

21. $\int (x^2 + 1)^3\, dx = \int (x^6 + 3x^4 + 3x^2 + 1)\, dx$

$$= \frac{x^7}{7} + \frac{3}{5}x^5 + x^3 + x + C$$

23. To find $\int x^2 / \sqrt{x^3 + 3}\, dx$, let $u = x^3 + 3$. Then $du = 3x^2\, dx$.

$$\int \frac{x^2}{\sqrt{x^3 + 3}}\, dx = \frac{1}{3}\int (x^3 + 3)^{-1/2}(3x^2)\, dx$$

$$= \frac{1}{3}\int u^{-1/2}\, du$$

$$= \frac{2}{3}u^{1/2} + C$$

$$= \frac{2}{3}(x^3 + 3)^{1/2} + C$$

$$= \frac{2}{3}\sqrt{x^3 + 3} + C$$

25. $u = 1 - 3x^2,\ du = -6x\, dx$

$$\int x(1 - 3x^2)^4\, dx = -\frac{1}{6}\int (1 - 3x^2)^4(-6x\, dx)$$

$$= -\frac{1}{30}(1 - 3x^2)^5 + C$$

$$= \frac{1}{30}(3x^2 - 1)^5 + C$$

27. $\int \sin^3 x \cos x\, dx = \frac{1}{4}\sin^4 x + C$

29. $\int \frac{\sin \theta}{\sqrt{1 - \cos \theta}}\, d\theta = \int (1 - \cos \theta)^{-1/2} \sin \theta\, d\theta$

$$= 2(1 - \cos \theta)^{1/2} + C$$

$$= 2\sqrt{1 - \cos \theta} + C$$

31. Let $u = -3x^2,\ du = -6x\, dx$.

$$\int xe^{-3x^2}\, dx = -\frac{1}{6}\int e^{-3x^2}(-6x)\, dx = -\frac{1}{6}e^{-3x^2} + C$$

33. $\int \frac{e^{4x} - e^{2x} + 1}{e^x}\, dx = \int (e^{3x} - e^x + e^{-x})\, dx$

$$= \frac{e^{3x}}{3} - e^x - e^{-x} + C$$

$$= \frac{e^{4x} - 3e^{2x} - 3}{3e^x} + C$$

35. To find $\int \tan^n x \sec^2 x\, dx$, let

$$u = \tan x \text{ and } du = \sec^2 x\, dx.$$

$$\int \tan^n x \sec^2 x\, dx = \int u^n\, du$$

$$= \frac{u^{n+1}}{n + 1} + C$$

$$= \frac{\tan^{n+1}}{n + 1} + C,\ n \neq -1$$

37. $\int (1 + \sec \pi x)^2 \sec \pi x \tan \pi x \, dx = \dfrac{1}{\pi} \int (1 + \sec \pi x)^2 (\pi \sec \pi x \tan \pi x) \, dx = \dfrac{1}{3\pi}(1 + \sec \pi x)^3 + C$

39. Let $u = e^x - 1$, $du = e^x \, dx$.

$$\int \frac{e^x}{e^x - 1} \, dx = \ln|e^x - 1| + C$$

41. If we let $u = e^{2x}$, then $du = 2e^{2x} \, dx$. Thus,

$$\int \frac{1}{e^{2x} + e^{-2x}} \, dx = \int \left(\frac{1}{e^{2x} + e^{-2x}} \right)\left(\frac{e^{2x}}{e^{2x}} \right) dx$$

$$= \int \frac{e^{2x}}{e^{4x} + 1} \, dx$$

$$= \frac{1}{2} \int \left[\frac{1}{1 + (e^{2x})^2} \right](2e^{2x}) \, dx$$

$$= \frac{1}{2} \int \frac{du}{1 + u^2} = \frac{1}{2} \arctan(e^{2x}) + C.$$

43. $\int 10(4^{-0.2x}) \, dx = 10\left(\dfrac{-1}{0.2} \right) \int 4^{-0.2x}(0.2) \, dx$

$$= \frac{-50}{\ln 4}(4^{-0.2x}) + C = \frac{-25}{\ln 2}(4^{-0.2x}) + C$$

45. Let $u = x^2$, $du = 2x \, dx$.

$$\int \frac{x}{\sqrt{1 - x^4}} \, dx = \frac{1}{2} \int \frac{1}{\sqrt{1 - (x^2)^2}}(2x) \, dx = \frac{1}{2} \arcsin x^2 + C$$

47. Let $u = 16 + x^2$, $du = 2x \, dx$.

$$\int \frac{x}{16 + x^2} \, dx = \frac{1}{2} \int \frac{1}{16 + x^2}(2x) \, dx = \frac{1}{2} \ln(16 + x^2) + C$$

49. Let $u = \arctan\left(\dfrac{x}{2} \right)$, $du = \dfrac{2}{4 + x^2} \, dx$.

$$\int \frac{\arctan(x/2)}{4 + x^2} \, dx = \frac{1}{2} \int \left(\arctan \frac{x}{2} \right)\left(\frac{2}{4 + x^2} \right) dx$$

$$= \frac{1}{4}\left(\arctan \frac{x}{2} \right)^2 + C$$

51. If $u = x^2$, then $du = 2x \, dx$.

$$\int \frac{x}{\sqrt{x^4 + 1}} \, dx = \frac{1}{2} \int \frac{1}{\sqrt{(x^2)^2 - 1}}(2x) \, dx$$

$$= \frac{1}{2} \ln\left(x^2 + \sqrt{x^4 + 1}\right) + C$$

53. $\dfrac{dy}{dx} = \dfrac{x^2 + 3}{x}$

$$y = \int \frac{x^2 + 3}{x} \, dx$$

$$= \int \left(x + \frac{3}{x} \right) dx = \frac{1}{2}x^2 + 3 \ln|x| + C$$

55. $\displaystyle\int_0^4 (2 + x) \, dx = \left[2x + \dfrac{x^2}{2} \right]_0^4 = 8 + \dfrac{16}{2} = 16$

57. $\displaystyle\int_{-1}^1 (4t^3 - 2t) \, dt = \left[t^4 - t^2 \right]_{-1}^1 = 0$

59. If we let $u = 1 + x$, then $du = dx$. Also, when $x = 0$, $u = 1$, and when $x = 3$, $u = 4$. Therefore,

$$\int_0^3 \frac{1}{\sqrt{1 + x}} \, dx = \int_1^4 u^{-1/2} \, du$$

$$= \left[2u^{1/2} \right]_1^4 = 2(2 - 1) = 2$$

61. $\displaystyle\int_4^9 x\sqrt{x} \, dx = \int_4^9 x^{3/2} \, dx = \left[\dfrac{2}{5}x^{5/2} \right]_4^9 = \dfrac{2}{5}\left[(\sqrt{9})^5 - (\sqrt{4})^5 \right] = \dfrac{2}{5}(243 - 32) = \dfrac{422}{5}$

63. If we let $u = \sqrt{1 - y}$. Then

$y = 1 - u^2$ and $dy = -2u\,du$.

Furthermore, when $y = 0$, $u = 1$ and when $y = 1$, $u = 0$.

$$2\pi\int_0^1 (y + 1)\sqrt{1 - y}\,dy = 2\pi\int_1^0 (2 - u^2)(u)(-2u)\,du$$

$$= -4\pi\int_1^0 (2u^2 - u^4)\,du$$

$$= -4\pi\left[\frac{2}{3}u^3 - \frac{1}{5}u^5\right]_1^0$$

$$= \frac{28\pi}{15}$$

65. $\displaystyle\int_0^\pi \cos\left(\frac{x}{2}\right) dx = 2\int_0^\pi \cos\left(\frac{x}{2}\right)\frac{1}{2}\,dx = \left[2\sin\left(\frac{x}{2}\right)\right]_0^\pi = 2$

67. $\displaystyle\int_0^4 \left(\frac{3}{2}\right)^x dx = \left[\frac{1}{\ln(3/2)}\left(\frac{3}{2}\right)^x\right]_0^4 = \frac{1}{\ln(3/2)}\left[\left(\frac{3}{2}\right)^4 - 1\right] = \frac{65}{16\ln(3/2)}$

69. $\displaystyle\int_1^3 \frac{3}{x^2 - 4x + 5}\,dx = 3\int_1^3 \frac{1}{(x^2 - 4x + 4) + 1}\,dx$

$$= 3\int_1^3 \frac{1}{(x - 2)^2 + 1}\,dx$$

$$= 3\Big[\arctan(x - 2)\Big]_1^3$$

$$= 3[\arctan 1 - \arctan(-1)]$$

$$= 3\left[\frac{\pi}{4} - \left(-\frac{\pi}{4}\right)\right]$$

$$= \frac{3\pi}{2}$$

71. $\displaystyle\int_1^3 (2x - 1)\,dx = \left[x^2 - x\right]_1^3 = 6$

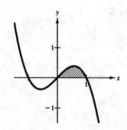

73. $\displaystyle\int_3^4 (x^2 - 9)\,dx = \left[\frac{x^3}{3} - 9x\right]_3^4$

$$= \left(\frac{64}{3} - 36\right) - (9 - 27)$$

$$= \frac{64}{3} - \frac{54}{3} = \frac{10}{3}$$

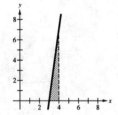

75. $\displaystyle\int_0^1 (x - x^3)\,dx = \left[\frac{x^2}{2} - \frac{x^4}{4}\right]_0^1$

$$= \frac{1}{2} - \frac{1}{4} = \frac{1}{4}$$

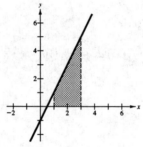

77. The graph of the region is shown in the figure.

$$A = \int_0^8 \frac{4}{\sqrt{x+1}} \, dx = 4\int_0^8 (x+1)^{-1/2} \, dx$$

$$= \left[8\sqrt{x+1} \right]_0^8$$

$$= 8\sqrt{9} - 8(1) = 16$$

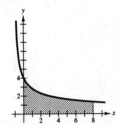

79. $\displaystyle\int_0^{\pi/3} \sec^2 x \, dx = \left[\tan x \right]_0^{\pi/3} = \sqrt{3}$

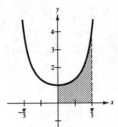

81. Area $= \displaystyle\int_0^4 xe^{-x^2} \, dx = \left[-\frac{1}{2}e^{-x^2} \right]_0^4 = -\frac{1}{2}(e^{-16} - 1) \approx 0.500$

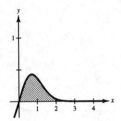

83. The average value is given by

$$\frac{1}{10-5}\int_5^{10} \frac{1}{\sqrt{x-1}} \, dx = \frac{1}{5}\int_5^{10} (x-1)^{-1/2}(1) \, dx$$

$$= \left[\frac{2}{5}(x-1)^{1/2} \right]_5^{10} = \frac{2}{5}.$$

To find the value of x where the function assumes its mean value on $[5, 10]$, solve

$$\frac{1}{\sqrt{x-1}} = \frac{2}{5}$$

$$\sqrt{x-1} = \frac{5}{2}$$

$$x - 1 = \frac{25}{4}$$

$$x = \frac{29}{4}.$$

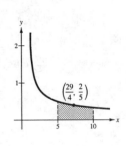

85. $\displaystyle\frac{1}{4-0}\int_0^4 x \, dx = \left[\frac{x^2}{8} \right]_0^4 = 2$

$$x = 2$$

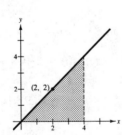

87. Trapezoidal Rule: $n = 4$

$$\int_1^2 \frac{1}{1+x^3} \, dx \approx \frac{2-1}{2(4)}\left(\frac{1}{1+1^3} + \frac{2}{1+(1.25)^3} + \frac{2}{1+(1.5)^3} + \frac{2}{1+(1.75)^3} + \frac{1}{1+2^3} \right) \approx 0.257$$

Simpson's Rule: $n = 4$

$$\int_1^2 \frac{1}{1+x^3} \, dx \approx \frac{2-1}{3(4)}\left(\frac{1}{1+1^3} + \frac{4}{1+(1.25)^3} + \frac{2}{1+(1.5)^3} + \frac{4}{1+(1.75)^3} + \frac{1}{1+2^3} \right) \approx 0.254$$

Using the numerical integration capabilities of a graphing utility, we have

$$\int_1^2 \frac{1}{1+x^3} \, dx \approx 0.254.$$

89. (a) $C = 0.1 \int_8^{20} \left[12 \sin \frac{\pi(t-8)}{12} \right] dt = \left[-\frac{14.4}{\pi} \cos \frac{\pi(t-8)}{12} \right]_8^{20} = \frac{-14.4}{\pi}(-1-1) \approx \$9.17$

(b) $C = 0.1 \int_{10}^{18} \left[12 \sin \frac{\pi(t-8)}{12} - 6 \right] dt = \left[-\frac{14.4}{\pi} \cos \frac{\pi(t-8)}{12} - 0.6t \right]_{10}^{18}$

$$= \left[\frac{-14.4}{\pi}\left(\frac{-\sqrt{3}}{2} \right) - 10.8 \right] - \left[\frac{-14.4}{\pi}\left(\frac{\sqrt{3}}{2} \right) - 6 \right] \approx \$3.14$$

Savings $\approx 9.17 - 3.14 = \$6.03$.

91. Since $p = 1.20 + 0.04t$, the annual cost is given by

$$C = \frac{15,000}{M} \int_t^{t+1} (1.20 + 0.04s)\, ds = \frac{15,000}{M} \left[1.20s + 0.02s^2 \right]_t^{t+1}.$$

(a) For the year 2005, $t = 10$.

$$C = \frac{15,000}{M} \left[1.20s + 0.02s^2 \right]_{10}^{11} = \frac{24,300}{M}$$

(b) For the year 2005, $t = 15$.

$$C = \frac{15,000}{M} \left[1.20s + 0.02s^2 \right]_{15}^{16} = \frac{27,300}{M}$$

93. $u = 1 - x,\, x = 1 - u,\, dx = -du$

When $x = a,\, u = 1 - a$. When $x = b,\, u = 1 - b$.

$$P_{a,b} = \int_a^b \frac{1155}{32} x^3 (1-x)^{3/2}\, dx = \frac{1155}{32} \int_{1-a}^{1-b} -(1-u)^3 u^{3/2}\, du$$

$$= \frac{1155}{32} \int_{1-a}^{1-b} (u^{9/2} - 3u^{7/2} + 3u^{5/2} - u^{3/2})\, du = \frac{1155}{32} \left[\frac{2}{11}u^{11/2} - \frac{2}{3}u^{9/2} + \frac{6}{7}u^{7/2} - \frac{2}{5}u^{5/2} \right]_{1-a}^{1-b}$$

$$= \frac{1155}{32} \left[\frac{2u^{5/2}}{1155}(105u^3 - 385u^2 + 495u - 231) \right]_{1-a}^{1-b} = \left[\frac{u^{5/2}}{16}(105u^3 - 385u^2 + 495u - 231) \right]_{1-a}^{1-b}$$

(a) $P_{0,\,0.25} = \left[\frac{u^{5/2}}{16}(105u^3 - 385u^2 + 495u - 231) \right]_1^{0.75} \approx 0.025 = 2.5\%$

(b) $P_{0.5,\,1} = \left[\frac{u^{5/2}}{16}(105u^3 - 385u^2 + 495u - 231) \right]_{0.5}^0 \approx 0.736 = 73.6\%$

95. $\dfrac{dv}{dt} = kv - 9.8$

(a) $\displaystyle \int \frac{dv}{kv - 9.8} = \int dt$

$\dfrac{1}{k} \ln|kv - 9.8| = t + C_1$

$\ln|kv - 9.8| = kt + C_2$

$kv - 9.8 = e^{kt + C_2} = C_3 e^{kt}$

$v = \dfrac{1}{k}\left[9.8 + C_3 e^{kt} \right]$

At $t = 0,\, v_0 = \dfrac{1}{k}(9.8 + C_3) \Rightarrow C_3 = kv_0 - 9.8$

$v = \dfrac{1}{k}[9.8 + (kv_0 - 9.8)e^{kt}]$

Note that $k < 0$ since the object is moving downward.

(b) $\displaystyle \lim_{t \to \infty} v(t) = \frac{9.8}{k}$

(c) $s(t) = \displaystyle \int \frac{1}{k}[9.8 + (kv_0 - 9.8)e^{kt}]\, dt$

$= \dfrac{1}{k}\left[9.8t + \dfrac{1}{k}(kv_0 - 9.8)e^{kt} \right] + C$

$= \dfrac{9.8t}{k} + \dfrac{1}{k^2}(kv_0 - 9.8)e^{kt} + C$

$s(0) = \dfrac{1}{k^2}(kv_0 - 9.8) + C \Rightarrow C = s_0 - \dfrac{1}{k^2}(kv_0 - 9.8)$

$s(t) = \dfrac{9.8t}{k} + \dfrac{1}{k^2}(kv_0 - 9.8)e^{kt} + s_0 - \dfrac{1}{k^2}(kv_0 - 9.8)$

$= \dfrac{9.8t}{k} + \dfrac{1}{k^2}(kv_0 - 9.8)(e^{kt} - 1) + s_0$

97. (a) $\int_0^4 f(t)\, dt \approx 5.67$

$\int_0^4 g(t)\, dt \approx 5.67$

$\int_0^4 h(t)\, dt \approx 5.67$

(b)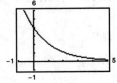

(c) The functions appear to be equal: $f(t) = g(t) = h(t)$

Analytically,

$$f(t) = 4\left(\frac{3}{8}\right)^{2t/3} = 4\left[\left(\frac{3}{8}\right)^{2/3}\right]^t = 4\left(\frac{9^{1/3}}{4}\right)^t = g(t)$$

$$h(t) = 4e^{-0.653886t} = 4\left[e^{-0.653886}\right]^t = 4(0.52002)^t$$

$$g(t) = 4\left(\frac{9^{1/3}}{4}\right)^t = 4(0.52002)^t$$

No. The definite integrals over a given interval may be equal when the functions are not equal.

99. False

$$\int -\frac{1}{x^2}\, dx = \frac{1}{x} + C \text{ or } \frac{d}{dx}\left[-\frac{1}{x^2}\right] \neq \frac{1}{x}.$$

101. True

$$\frac{1}{2\pi - 0}\int_0^{2\pi} \sin x\, dx = \left[-\frac{1}{2\pi}\cos x\right]_0^{2\pi} = 0$$

CHAPTER 5
Logarithmic, Exponential, and Other Transcendental Functions

CHAPTER 5
Logarithmic, Exponential, and Other Transcendental Functions

Section 5.1   Differential Equations: Growth and Decay
Solutions to Odd-Numbered Exercises

1. $y' = \dfrac{5x}{y}$

$yy' = 5x$

$\displaystyle\int yy'\,dx = \int 5x\,dx$

$\displaystyle\int y\,dy = \int 5x\,dx$

$\dfrac{1}{2}y^2 = \dfrac{5}{2}x^2 + C_1$

$y^2 - 5x^2 = C$

3. $y' = \sqrt{xy}$

$\dfrac{1}{y}y'\,dx = \sqrt{x}\,dx$

$\displaystyle\int \dfrac{1}{y}y'\,dx = \int \sqrt{x}\,dx$

$\displaystyle\int \dfrac{1}{y}\,dy = \int x^{1/2}\,dx$

$\ln y = \dfrac{2}{3}x^{3/2} + C_1$

$y = e^{2x^{3/2}/3 + C_1}$

$y = e^{C_1}e^{2x^{3/2}/3} = Ce^{2x^{3/2}/3}$

5. $(1 + x^2)y' - 2xy = 0$

$y' = \dfrac{2xy}{1 + x^2}$

$\dfrac{y'}{y} = \dfrac{2x}{1 + x^2}$

$\displaystyle\int \dfrac{y'}{y}\,dx = \int \dfrac{2x}{1 + x^2}\,dx$

$\displaystyle\int \dfrac{dy}{y} = \int \dfrac{2x}{1 + x^2}\,dx$

$\ln y = \ln(1 + x^2) + C_1$

$\ln y = \ln(1 + x^2) + \ln C$

$\ln y = \ln C(1 + x^2)$

$y = C(1 + x^2)$

7. (a)

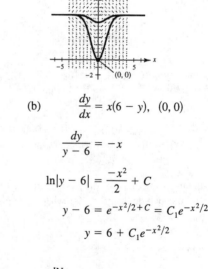

(b) $\dfrac{dy}{dx} = x(6 - y),\quad (0, 0)$

$\dfrac{dy}{y - 6} = -x$

$\ln|y - 6| = \dfrac{-x^2}{2} + C$

$y - 6 = e^{-x^2/2 + C} = C_1 e^{-x^2/2}$

$y = 6 + C_1 e^{-x^2/2}$

9. $\dfrac{dQ}{dt} = \dfrac{k}{t^2}$

$\displaystyle\int \dfrac{dQ}{dt}\,dt = \int \dfrac{k}{t^2}\,dt$

$\displaystyle\int dQ = -\dfrac{k}{t} + C$

$Q = -\dfrac{k}{t} + C$

11. $\dfrac{dN}{ds} = k(250 - s)$

$\displaystyle\int \dfrac{dN}{ds}\,ds = \int k(250 - s)\,ds$

$\displaystyle\int dN = -\dfrac{k}{2}(250 - s)^2 + C$

$N = -\dfrac{k}{2}(250 - s)^2 + C$

13. $\dfrac{dy}{dt} = \dfrac{1}{2}t$

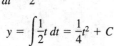

$y = \displaystyle\int \dfrac{1}{2}t\, dt = \dfrac{1}{4}t^2 + C$

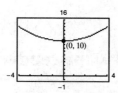

Since the solution passes through the point (0, 10), we have

$$10 = \dfrac{1}{4}(0^2) + C \implies C = 10.$$

Therefore, $f(t) = (1/4)t^2 + 10$ and its graph is shown in the figure.

15. $\dfrac{dy}{dt} = -\dfrac{1}{2}y,\ \ (0, 10)$

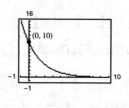

$\displaystyle\int \dfrac{dy}{y} = \int -\dfrac{1}{2}\, dt$

$\ln y = -\dfrac{1}{2}t + C_1$

$y = e^{-(t/2)+C_1} = e^{C_1}e^{-t/2} = Ce^{-t/2}$

$10 = Ce^0 \implies C = 10$

$y = 10e^{-t/2}$

17. $y = Ce^{kt},\ \left(0, \dfrac{1}{2}\right),\ (5, 5)$

$C = \dfrac{1}{2}$

$y = \dfrac{1}{2}e^{kt}$

$5 = \dfrac{1}{2}e^{5k}$

$k = \dfrac{\ln 10}{5} \approx 0.4605$

$y = \dfrac{1}{2}e^{0.4605t}$

19. $\quad y = Ce^{kt},\ (1, 1),\ (5, 5)$

$1 = Ce^{k}$

$5 = Ce^{5k}$

$5Ce^{k} = Ce^{5k}$

$5e^{k} = e^{5k}$

$5 = e^{4k}$

$k = \dfrac{\ln 5}{4} \approx 0.4024$

$y = Ce^{0.4024t}$

$1 = Ce^{0.4024}$

$C \approx 0.6687$

$y = 0.6687e^{0.4024t}$

21. Since the initial quantity is 10 grams, $y = 10e^{[\ln(1/2)/1620]t}$. When $t = 1000$, $y = 10e^{[\ln(1/2)/1620](1000)} \approx 6.52$ grams. When $t = 10,000$, $y = 10e^{[\ln(1/2)/1620](10,000)} \approx 0.14$ gram.

23. Since $y = Ce^{[\ln(1/2)/5730]t}$, we have $2.0 = Ce^{[\ln(1/2)/5730](10,000)} \implies C \approx 6.70$ which implies that the initial quantity is 6.70 grams. When $t = 1000$, we have $y = 6.70e^{[\ln(1/2)/5730](1000)} \approx 5.94$ grams.

25. Let y represent the mass (in grams) of the isotope after t years. Since the rate of decay is proportional to y, apply the Law of Exponential Decay to conclude that $y = y_0e^{kt}$ where y_0 is the initial amount. Since the half life of Pu^{239} is 24,360 years, we have

$$y_0e^{24,360k} = \dfrac{1}{2}y_0$$

$$e^{24,360k} = \dfrac{1}{2}$$

$$24,360k = \ln\dfrac{1}{2}$$

$$k = \dfrac{-\ln 2}{24,360}.$$

—**CONTINUED**—

25. —CONTINUED—

Therefore, $y = y_0 e^{(-\ln 2/24,360)t}$. Since $y = 2.1$ when $t = 1000$, we have

$$y_0 e^{(-\ln 2/24,360)1000} = 2.1$$

$$y_0 = 2.1 e^{1000 \ln 2/24,360} \approx 2.16 \text{ grams.}$$

After 10,000 years the amount of the isotope remaining will be $y = 2.16 e^{(-\ln 2/24,360)10,000} \approx 1.6$ grams.

27. Since $\dfrac{dy}{dx} = ky$, $y = Ce^{kt}$ or $y = y_0 e^{kt}$.

$$\frac{1}{2} y_0 = y_0 e^{1620k}$$

$$k = \frac{-\ln 2}{1620}$$

$$y = y_0 e^{-(\ln 2)t/1620}$$

When $t = 100$, $y = y_0 e^{-(\ln 2)/16.2} \approx y_0(0.9581)$.
Therefore, 95.81% of the present amount still exists.

29. Since $A = 1000 e^{0.06t}$, the time to double is given by $2000 = 1000 e^{0.06t}$ and we have

$$2 = e^{0.06t}$$

$$\ln 2 = 0.06t$$

$$t = \frac{\ln 2}{0.06} \approx 11.55 \text{ years.}$$

Amount after 10 years: $A = 1000 e^{(0.06)(10)} \approx \$1822.12$

31. Since the interest is compounded continuously, use the formula $A = Pe^{rt}$. To determine the rate, use the fact that the investment doubles in $7\frac{3}{4}$ years.

$$2(750) = 750 e^{r(7.75)}$$

$$2 = e^{7.75r}$$

$$\ln 2 = \ln e^{7.75r} = 7.75r$$

$$r = \frac{\ln 2}{7.75} \approx 0.0894 = 8.94\%$$

The amount after 10 years is given by

$$A = 750 e^{(0.0894)10} \approx \$1833.67.$$

33. Since $A = 500 e^{rt}$ and $A = 1292.85$ when $t = 10$, we have the following.

$$1292.85 = 500 e^{10r}$$

$$r = \frac{\ln(1292.85/500)}{10} \approx 0.0950 = 9.50\%$$

The time to double is given by

$$1000 = 500 e^{0.0950t}$$

$$t = \frac{\ln 2}{0.095} \approx 7.30 \text{ years.}$$

35. $500,000 = P\left(1 + \dfrac{0.075}{12}\right)^{(12)(20)}$

$$P = 500,000\left(1 + \frac{0.075}{12}\right)^{-240} \approx \$112,087.09$$

37. (a) $2000 = 1000(1 + 0.07)^t$

$$2 = 1.07^t$$

$$\ln 2 = t \ln 1.07$$

$$t = \frac{\ln 2}{\ln 1.07} \approx 10.24 \text{ years}$$

(b) $2000 = 1000\left(1 + \dfrac{0.07}{12}\right)^{12t}$

$$2 = \left(1 + \frac{0.007}{12}\right)^{12t}$$

$$\ln 2 = 12t \ln\left(1 + \frac{0.07}{12}\right)$$

$$t = \frac{\ln 2}{12 \ln(1 + (0.07/12))} \approx 9.93 \text{ years}$$

(c) $2000 = 1000\left(1 + \dfrac{0.07}{365}\right)^{365t}$

$$2 = \left(1 + \frac{0.07}{365}\right)^{365t}$$

$$\ln 2 = 365t \ln\left(1 + \frac{0.07}{365}\right)$$

$$t = \frac{\ln 2}{365 \ln(1 + (0.07/365))} \approx 9.90 \text{ years}$$

(d) $2000 = 1000 e^{(0.07)t}$

$$2 = e^{0.07t}$$

$$\ln 2 = 0.07t$$

$$t = \frac{\ln 2}{0.07} \approx 9.90 \text{ years}$$

39. Since the population of the city is 4.22 million and 6.49 million in the years 1990 and 2000, respectively, and $t = 0$ corresponds to the year 1990, the model $y = Ce^{kt}$ has solution points $(0, 4.22)$ and $(10, 6.49)$.

$$y = Ce^{kt}$$

$$4.22 = Ce^{k(0)} = C$$

$$y = 4.22e^{kt}$$

$$6.49 = 4.22e^{k(10)}$$

$$e^{10k} = \frac{6.49}{4.22}$$

$$\ln e^{10k} = \ln\left(\frac{6.49}{4.22}\right)$$

$$10k = \ln\left(\frac{6.49}{4.22}\right) \Rightarrow k = \frac{1}{10}\ln\left(\frac{6.49}{4.22}\right) \approx 0.0430$$

Therefore, the model is $y \approx 4.22e^{0.0430t}$. When $t = 10$,

$$y \approx 4.22e^{0.430} \approx 9.97 \text{ million.}$$

41. Let $t = 0$ represent 1990.

$$y = Ce^{kt}, \quad (0, 3.0), (10, 2.74)$$

$$C = 3.0$$

$$2.74 = 3.0e^{10k}$$

$$k = \frac{\ln(2.74/3.0)}{10} \approx -0.0091$$

$$y \approx 3.0e^{-0.0091t}$$

When $t = 20$ (for 2010), $y \approx 2.51$ million.

43. (a) k; the larger the value of k, the greater the rate of growth of the population.

(b) k; if $k > 0$, there is growth. If $k < 0$, decrease.

45.
$$P = Ce^{kx}, \quad (0, 760), (1000, 672.71)$$

$$C = 760$$

$$672.71 = 760e^{1000x}$$

$$x = \frac{\ln(672.71/760)}{1000} \approx -0.000122$$

$$P \approx 760e^{-0.000122x}$$

When $x = 3000$, $P \approx 527.06$ mm Hg.

47. (a) Since $N(20) = 19$, it follows that

$$19 = 30(1 - e^{20k})$$

$$30e^{20k} = 11$$

$$e^{20k} = \frac{11}{30}$$

$$k = \frac{\ln(11/30)}{20} \approx -0.0502.$$

Therefore, $N(t) = 30(1 - e^{-0.0502t})$.

(b) To determine the time when the worker will be producing 25 units per day solve the equation

$$25 = 30(1 - e^{-0.0502t})$$

$$e^{-0.0502t} = \frac{1}{6}$$

$$t = \frac{-\ln 6}{-0.0502} \approx 36 \text{ days.}$$

49. $S = Ce^{k/t}$

(a)
$$S = 5 \text{ when } t = 1$$

$$5 = Ce^{k}$$

$$\lim_{t \to \infty} Ce^{k/t} = C = 30$$

$$5 = 30e^{k}$$

$$k = \ln\tfrac{1}{6} \approx -1.7918$$

$$S \approx 30e^{-1.7918/t}$$

(b) When $t = 5$, $S \approx 20.9646$ which is 20,965 units.

(c)

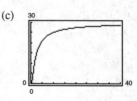

51. $A(t) = V(t)e^{-0.10t} = 100{,}000e^{0.8\sqrt{t}}\,e^{-0.10t} = 100{,}000e^{0.8\sqrt{t}-0.10t}$

$\dfrac{dA}{dt} = 100{,}000\left(\dfrac{0.4}{\sqrt{t}} - 0.10\right)e^{0.8\sqrt{t}-0.10t} = 0$ when 16.

The timber should be harvested in the year 2014, (1998 + 16). *Note:* You could also use a graphing utility to graph $A(t)$ and find the maximum of $A(t)$. Use the viewing rectangle $0 \le x \le 30$ and $0 \le y \le 600{,}000$.

53. $\beta(I) = 10\log_{10}\dfrac{I}{I_0}, I_0 = 10^{-16}$

(a) $\beta(10^{-14}) = 10\log_{10}\dfrac{10^{-14}}{10^{-16}} = 20$ decibels

(b) $\beta(10^{-9}) = 10\log_{10}\dfrac{10^{-9}}{10^{-16}} = 70$ decibels

(c) $\beta(10^{-6.5}) = 10\log_{10}\dfrac{10^{-6.5}}{10^{-16}} = 95$ decibels

(d) $\beta(10^{-4}) = 10\log_{10}\dfrac{10^{-4}}{10^{-16}} = 120$ decibels

55. $R = \dfrac{\ln I - 0}{\ln 10}, I = e^{R\ln 10} = 10^R$

(a) $8.3 = \dfrac{\ln I - 0}{\ln 10}$

$I = 10^{8.3} \approx 199{,}526{,}231.5$

(b) $2R = \dfrac{\ln I - 0}{\ln 10}$

$I = e^{2R\ln 10} = e^{2R\ln 10} = (e^{R\ln 10})^2 = (10^R)^2$

Increases by a factor of $e^{2R\ln 10}$ or 10^R.

(c) $\dfrac{dR}{dI} = \dfrac{1}{I\ln 10}$

57. Let y be the temperature reading of the thermometer at time t. From Newton's Law of Cooling, we know that the rate of change of y is proportional to the difference between y and $20°$. This can be written as

$$\frac{dy}{dt} = k(y - 20)$$

$$\left(\frac{1}{y-20}\right)\frac{dy}{dt} = k$$

$$\int\frac{1}{y-20}\,dy = \int k\,dt$$

$$\ln|y - 20| = kt + C$$

Using $y = 72$ when $t = 0$ yields $C = \ln 52$, which implies that

$$kt = \ln|y - 20| - \ln 52.$$

Since $y = 48$ when $t = 1$, we know that

$$k = \ln 28 - \ln 52 = \ln\frac{28}{52} = \ln\frac{7}{13}.$$

Therefore,

$$\ln|y - 20| = \ln\frac{7}{13}t + \ln 52$$

$$y - 20 = e^{[\ln(7/13)]t + \ln 52}$$

$$y = e^{\ln 52}e^{[\ln(7/13)]t} + 20 = 52e^{[\ln(7/13)]t} + 20.$$

After 5 minutes the reading on the thermometer is

$$y = 52e^{5\ln(7/13)} + 20 \approx 22.35°.$$

59. (a) $u = 985.93 - \left(985.93 - \dfrac{(120,000)(0.095)}{12}\right)\left(1 + \dfrac{0.095}{12}\right)^{12t}$

$v = \left(985.93 - \dfrac{(120,000)(0.095)}{12}\right)\left(1 + \dfrac{0.095}{12}\right)^{12t}$

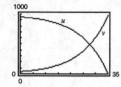

(b) The larger part goes for interest. The curves intersect when $t \approx 27.7$ years.

(c) The slopes are negatives of each other. Analytically,

$$u = 985.93 - v \quad \Rightarrow \quad \frac{du}{dt} = -\frac{dv}{dt}$$

$$u'(15) = -v'(15) = -14.06.$$

(d) $t = 12.7$ years

Again, the larger part goes for interest.

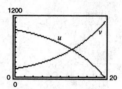

Section 5.2   Differential Equations: Separation of Variables

1. Differential equation: $y' = 4y$

Solution: $y = Ce^{4x}$

Check: $y' = 4Ce^{4x} = 4y$

3. Differential equation: $y'' + y = 0$

Solution: $y = C_1 \cos x + C_2 \sin x$

Check: $y' = -C_1 \sin x + C_2 \cos x$

$y'' = -C_1 \cos x - C_2 \sin x$

$y'' + y = -C_1 \cos x - C_2 \sin x + C_1 \cos x + C_2 \sin x = 0$

5. $y = -\cos x \ln|\sec x + \tan x|$

$y' = (-\cos x)\dfrac{1}{\sec x + \tan x}(\sec x \cdot \tan x + \sec^2 x) + \sin x \ln|\sec x + \tan x|$

$\quad = \dfrac{(-\cos x)}{\sec x + \tan x}(\sec x)(\tan x + \sec x) + \sin x \ln|\sec x + \tan x|$

$\quad = -1 + \sin x \ln|\sec x + \tan x|$

$y'' = (\sin x)\dfrac{1}{\sec x + \tan x}(\sec x \cdot \tan x + \sec^2 x) + \cos x \ln|\sec x + \tan x|$

$\quad = (\sin x)(\sec x) + \cos x \ln|\sec x + \tan x|$

Substituting, $y'' + y = (\sin x)(\sec x) + \cos x \ln|\sec x + \tan x| - \cos x \ln|\sec x + \tan x| = \tan x.$

In Exercises 7 and 9, the differential equation is $y^{(4)} - 16y = 0$.

7. $y = 3 \cos x$

$y^{(4)} = 3 \cos x$

$y^{(4)} - 16y = -45 \cos x \neq 0,$ No.

9. Since $y = e^{-2x}$, we have

$y' = -2e^{-2x}$

$y'' = 4e^{-2x}$

$y''' = -8e^{-2x}$

$y^{(4)} = 16e^{-2x}.$

Therefore, $y^{(4)} - 16y = 16e^{-2x} - 16(e^{-2x}) = 0$ and the function is a solution to the differential equation.

11. $y = C_1 e^{2x} + C_2 e^{-2x} + C_3 \sin 2x + C_4 \cos 2x$

$y^{(4)} = 16C_1 e^{2x} + 16C_2 e^{-2x} + 16C_3 \sin 2x + 16C_4 \cos 2x$

$y^{(4)} - 16y = 0$,   Yes.

In 13–17, the differential equation is $xy' - 2y = x^3 e^x$.

13. $y = x^2$, $y' = 2x$

$xy' - 2y = x(2x) - 2(x^2) = 0 \neq x^3 e^x$,   No.

15. $y = x^2(2 + e^x)$, $y' = x^2(e^x) + 2x(2 + e^x)$

$xy' - 2y = x[x^2 e^x + 2xe^x + 4x] - 2[x^2 e^x + 2x^2] = x^3 e^x$

Yes

17. $y = \ln x, y' = \dfrac{1}{x}$

$xy' - 2y = x\left(\dfrac{1}{x}\right) - 2\ln x \neq x^3 e^x$,   No.

19. Since $y = Ce^{kx}$ is a solution to the differential equation, begin by substituting the derivative of the solution into the differential equation.

$y = Ce^{kx}$

$\dfrac{dy}{dx} = Ce^{kx}(k) = k(Ce^{ky}) = ky = 0.07y$

Therefore, $k = 0.07$.

21. $y = Ce^{-x/2}$ passes through $(0, 3)$.

$3 = Ce^0 = C \Rightarrow C = 3$

Particular solution: $y = 3e^{-x/2}$

23. $y^2 = Cx^3$ passes through $(4, 4)$

$16 = C(64) \implies C = \frac{1}{4}$

Particular solution: $y^2 = \frac{1}{4}x^3$ or $4y^2 = x^3$

25. Differential equation: $4yy' - x = 0$

General solution: $4y^2 - x^2 = C$

Particular solutions: $C = 0$, Two interesecting lines
$\qquad\qquad\qquad\quad C = \pm 1$, $C = \pm 4$, Hyperbolas

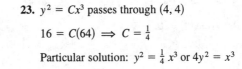

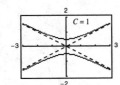 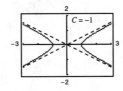 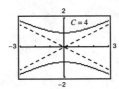 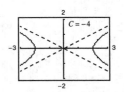

27. Differential equation: $y' + 2y = 0$

General solution: $y = Ce^{-2x}$

$y' + 2y = C(-2)e^{-2x} + 2(Ce^{-2x}) = 0$

Initial condition: $y(0) = 3, 3 = Ce^0 = C$

Particular solution: $y = 3e^{-2x}$

29. Since $y = C_1 \sin 3x + C_2 \cos 3x$, we have

$$y' = 3C_1 \cos 3x - 3C_2 \sin 3x$$

$$y'' = -9C_1 \sin 3x - 9C_2 \cos 3x.$$

Therefore,

$$y'' + 9y = -9C_1 \sin 3x - 9C_2 \cos 3x + 9(C_1 \sin 3x + C_2 \cos 3x) = 0$$

and the function is a solution to the differential equation. Furthermore, since $y = 2$ and $y' = 1$ when $x = \pi/6$, we have

$$2 = C_1 \sin 3\left(\frac{\pi}{6}\right) + C_2 \cos 3\left(\frac{\pi}{6}\right) \implies 2 = C_1(1) + C_2(0)$$

$$1 = 3C_1 \cos 3\left(\frac{\pi}{6}\right) - 3C_2 \sin 3\left(\frac{\pi}{6}\right) \implies 1 = 3C_1(0) - 3C_2(1).$$

Therefore, $C_1 = 2$, $C_2 = -1/3$, and the particular solution is

$$y = 2 \sin 3x - \frac{1}{3} \cos 3x.$$

31. Differential equation: $x^2 y'' - 3xy' + 3y = 0$

General solution: $y = C_1 x + C_2 x^3$

$y' = C_1 + 3C_2 x^2$, $y'' = 6C_2 x$

$x^2 y'' - 3xy' + 3y = x^2(6C_2 x) - 3x(C_1 + 3C_2 x^2) + 3(C_1 x + C_2 x^3) = 0$

Initial conditions: $y(2) = 0$, $y'(2) = 4$

$$0 = 2C_1 + 8C_2$$

$$y' = C_1 + 3C_2 x^2$$

$$4 = C_1 + 12C_2$$

$$\left.\begin{array}{l} C_1 + 4C_2 = 0 \\ C_1 + 12C_2 = 4 \end{array}\right\} \quad C_2 = \tfrac{1}{2}, \ C_1 = -2$$

Particular solution: $y = -2x + \frac{1}{2}x^3$

33. $\dfrac{dy}{dx} = 3x^2$

$$y = \int 3x^2 \, dx = x^3 + C$$

35. $\dfrac{dy}{dx} = \dfrac{x-2}{x}$

$$y = \int \frac{x-2}{x} \, dx$$

$$= \int \left(1 - \frac{2}{x}\right) dx$$

$$= x - 2\ln|x| + C = x - \ln x^2 + C$$

37. $\dfrac{dy}{dx} = \sin 2x$

$$y = \int \sin 2x \, dx = -\frac{1}{2}\cos 2x + C$$

$(u = 2x, \ du = 2dx)$

39. $\dfrac{dy}{dx} = x\sqrt{x-3}$

Let $u = \sqrt{x-3}$, then $x = u^2 + 3$ and $dx = 2u \, du$.

$$y = \int x\sqrt{x-3} \, dx = \int (u^2 + 3)(u)(2u)du$$

$$= 2\int (u^4 + 3u^2) \, du$$

$$= 2\left(\frac{u^5}{5} + u^3\right) + C = \frac{2}{5}(x-3)^{5/2} + 2(x-3)^{3/2} + C$$

41. $\dfrac{dy}{dx} = \dfrac{x}{\sqrt{1-x^4}}$

$$y = \int \frac{x}{\sqrt{1-x^4}}\, dx$$

$$= \frac{1}{2} \int \frac{2x}{\sqrt{1-(x^2)^2}}\, dx$$

$$= \frac{1}{2} \arcsin x^2 + C$$

43. $\dfrac{dy}{dx} = \dfrac{1}{2}(2^x) + 3x$

$$y = \int \left[\frac{1}{2}(2^x) + 3x \right] dx$$

$$= \frac{1}{2} \frac{2^x}{\ln 2} + \frac{3x^2}{2} + C$$

$$= \frac{2^x}{\ln 4} + \frac{3}{2}x^2 + C$$

45. $\dfrac{dy}{dx} = \dfrac{x}{y}$

$$\int y\, dy = \int x\, dx$$

$$\frac{y^2}{2} = \frac{x^2}{2} + C_1$$

$$y^2 - x^2 = C$$

47. $\dfrac{dr}{ds} = 0.05r$

$$\int \frac{dr}{r} = \int 0.05\, ds$$

$$\ln|r| = 0.05s + C_1$$

$$r = e^{0.05s + C_1} = Ce^{0.05s}$$

49. Begin by separating the variables as follows.

$$(2+x)y' = 3y$$

$$(2+x)\frac{dy}{dx} = 3y$$

$$\frac{1}{y}\, dy = \frac{3}{2+x}\, dx$$

By integration we obtain

$$\int \frac{1}{y}\, dy = 3 \int \frac{1}{2+x}\, dx$$

$$\ln|y| = 3\ln|2+x| + \ln C$$

$$\ln y = \ln|C(2+x)^3|$$

$$y = C(2+x)^3.$$

51. $yy' = \sin x$

$$\int y\, dy = \int \sin x\, dx$$

$$\frac{y^2}{2} = -\cos x + C_1$$

$$y^2 = -2\cos x + C$$

53. $y \ln x - xy' = 0$

$$\int \frac{dy}{y} = \int \frac{\ln x}{x}\, dx \quad \left(u = \ln x,\ du = \frac{dx}{x} \right)$$

$$\ln y = \frac{1}{2}(\ln x)^2 + C_1$$

$$y = e^{(1/2)(\ln x)^2 + C_1} = Ce^{(\ln x)^2/2}$$

55. $\sqrt{1-x^2}\,\dfrac{dy}{dx} = \sqrt{1-y^2}$

$$\int \frac{1}{\sqrt{1-y^2}}\, dy = \int \frac{1}{\sqrt{1-x^2}}\, dx$$

$\arcsin y = \arcsin x + C$ or $\arcsin x - \arcsin y = C_1$

Taking the sine of both sides:

$$\sin[\arcsin x - \arcsin y] = \sin C_1 = C_2$$

$$x[\cos(\arcsin y)] - y[\cos(\arcsin x)] = C_2$$

$$x\sqrt{1-y^2} - y\sqrt{1-x^2} = C_2$$

57. $yy' - e^x = 0$

$$\int y \, dy = \int e^x \, dx$$

$$\frac{y^2}{2} = e^x + C_1$$

$$y^2 = 2e^x + C$$

Initial condition: $y(0) = 4$, $16 = 2 + C$, $C = 14$

Particular solution: $y^2 = 2e^x + 14$

59. Begin by separating the variables to obtain

$$y(x + 1) + y' = 0$$

$$\frac{dy}{dx} = -y(x + 1)$$

$$\frac{dy}{y} = -(x + 1) \, dx.$$

Integration yields

$$\int \frac{dy}{y} = -\int (x + 1) \, dx$$

$$\ln|y| = -\frac{(x + 1)^2}{2} + C_1$$

$$y = e^{C_1 - (x+1)^2/2} = Ce^{-(x+1)^2/2}.$$

Since $y = 1$ when $x = -2$, it follows that

$$1 = Ce^{-(-2+1)^2/2} = Ce^{-1/2} \quad \text{or} \quad C = e^{1/2}.$$

Therefore, the particular solution is

$$y = e^{1/2}e^{-(x^2+2x)/2} = e^{[-(x+1)^2/2 + 1/2]} = e^{-(x^2+2x)/2}.$$

61. $y(1 + x^2)\dfrac{dy}{dx} = x(1 + y^2)$

$$\frac{y}{1 + y^2} \, dy = \frac{x}{1 + x^2} \, dx$$

$$\frac{1}{2}\ln(1 + y^2) = \frac{1}{2}\ln(1 + x^2) + C_1$$

$$\ln(1 + y^2) = \ln(1 + x^2) + \ln C = \ln[C(1 + x^2)]$$

$$1 + y^2 = C(1 + x^2)$$

$$y(0) = \sqrt{3}: \ 1 + 3 = C \implies C = 4$$

$$1 + y^2 = 4(1 + x^2)$$

$$y^2 = 3 + 4x^2$$

63. $\dfrac{du}{dv} = uv \sin v^2$

$$\int \frac{du}{u} = \int v \sin v^2 \, dv$$

$$\ln u = -\frac{1}{2}\cos v^2 + C_1$$

$$u = Ce^{-(\cos v^2)/2}$$

Initial condition: $u(0) = 1$, $C = \dfrac{1}{e^{-1/2}} = e^{1/2}$

Particular solution: $u = e^{(1 - \cos v^2)/2}$

65. $dP - kP \, dt = 0$

$$\int \frac{dP}{P} = k \int dt$$

$$\ln P = kt + C_1$$

$$P = Ce^{kt}$$

Initial condition: $P(0) = P_0$, $P_0 = Ce^0 = C$

Particular solution: $P = P_0 e^{kt}$

67. $\dfrac{dy}{dx} = -\dfrac{9x}{16y}$

$$16y \, dy = -9x \, dx$$

$$\int 16y \, dy = \int (-9x) \, dx$$

$$8y^2 = -\frac{9}{2}x^2 + C$$

$$\frac{9}{2}x^2 + 8y^2 = C$$

Since $(1, 1)$ is a solution point, we have

$$\frac{9}{2}(1^2) + 8(1)^2 = \frac{25}{2} = C.$$

The required equation is

$$\frac{9}{2}x^2 + 8y^2 = \frac{25}{2} \quad \text{or} \quad 9x^2 + 16y^2 = 25.$$

69. $\dfrac{dy}{dx} = \dfrac{1 + y^2}{e^{0.5x}}; \quad (0, 0)$

$\displaystyle\int \dfrac{1}{1 + y^2}\, dy = \int e^{-0.5x}\, dx$

$\arctan y = -2e^{-0.5x} + C$

$\arctan(0) = -2e^0 + C \Rightarrow C = 2$

$y = \tan[2 - 2e^{-0.5x}]$

71. $m = \dfrac{dy}{dx} = \dfrac{0 - y}{(x + 2) - x} = -\dfrac{y}{2}$

$\displaystyle\int \dfrac{dy}{y} = \int -\dfrac{1}{2}\, dx$

$\ln y = -\dfrac{1}{2}x + C_1$

$y = Ce^{-x/2}$

73. $f(x, y) = x^3 - 4xy^2 + y^3$

$f(tx, ty) = t^3 x^3 - 4t\,xt^2\,y^2 + t^3\,y^3$

$\qquad = t^3(x^3 - 4xy^2 + y^3)$

Homogeneous of degree 3

75. $f(x, y) = 2 \ln xy$

$f(tx, ty) = 2 \ln tx\,ty$

$\qquad = 2 \ln t^2 xy = 2(\ln t^2 + \ln xy)$

Not homogeneous

77. $f(x, y) = 2 \ln \dfrac{x}{y}$

$f(tx, ty) = 2 \ln \dfrac{tx}{ty} = 2 \ln \dfrac{x}{y} = t^0 f(x, y)$

Therefore, f is homogeneous of degree 0.

79. $y' = \dfrac{x + y}{2x}, \; y = vx$

$v + x\dfrac{dv}{dx} = \dfrac{x + vx}{2x}$

$x\dfrac{dv}{dx} = \dfrac{1 + v}{2} - v$

$2\displaystyle\int \dfrac{dv}{1 - v} = \int \dfrac{dx}{x}$

$-\ln(1 - v)^2 = \ln|x| + \ln C = \ln|Cx|$

$\dfrac{1}{(1 - v^2)} = |Cx|$

$\dfrac{1}{[1 - (y/x)]^2} = |Cx|$

$\dfrac{x^2}{(x - y)^2} = |Cx| = C|x|$

$|x| = C(x - y)^2$

81. $y' = \dfrac{x - y}{x + y}, \; y = vx$

$v + x\dfrac{dv}{dx} = \dfrac{x - xv}{x + xv}$

$v\, dx + x\, dv = \dfrac{1 - v}{1 + v}\, dx$

$\displaystyle\int \dfrac{v + 1}{v^2 + 2v - 1}\, dv = -\int \dfrac{dx}{x}$

$\dfrac{1}{2}\ln|v^2 + 2v - 1| = -\ln|x| + \ln C_1 = \ln\left|\dfrac{C_1}{x}\right|$

$|v^2 + 2v - 1| = \dfrac{C}{x^2}$

$\left|\dfrac{y^2}{x^2} + 2\dfrac{y}{x} - 1\right| = \dfrac{C}{x^2}$

$|y^2 + 2xy - x^2| = C$

83. Letting $y = vx$, yields

$$y' = \frac{xy}{x^2 - y^2}$$

$$v + x\frac{dv}{dx} = \frac{x(vx)}{x^2 - v^2x^2} = \frac{v}{1 - v^2}$$

$$x\frac{dv}{dx} = \frac{v}{1 - v^2} - v = \frac{v^3}{1 - v^2}$$

$$x\,dv = \frac{v^3}{1 - v^2}\,dx.$$

Separating variables, we obtain

$$\frac{1 - v^2}{v^3}\,dv = \frac{dx}{x}$$

$$\int\left(v^{-3} - \frac{1}{v}\right)dv = \int\frac{dx}{x}$$

$$\frac{v^{-2}}{-2} - \ln|v| = \ln|x| + \ln|C_1|$$

$$\frac{1}{-2x^2} = \ln|v| + \ln|x| + \ln|C_1| = \ln|C_1\,vx|$$

$$\frac{x^2}{-2y^2} = \ln|C_1\,y|$$

$$e^{-x^2/2y^2} = C_1 y \implies y = Ce^{-x^2/2y^2}.$$

87. Letting $y = vx$, yields

$$\left[x\sec\left(\frac{vx}{x}\right) + vx\right]dx - x(v\,dx + x\,dv) = 0$$

$$x\sec v\,dx + vx\,dx - vx\,dx - x^2\,dx = 0$$

$$x\sec v\,dx = x^2\,dv$$

$$\frac{x}{x^2}\,dx = \frac{dv}{\sec v}.$$

Integration yields

$$\int\frac{dx}{x} = \int\cos v\,dv$$

$$\ln|x| = \sin v + C_1 = \sin\frac{y}{x} + C_1.$$

Since $y = 0$ when $x = 1$, we have

$$0 = \sin(0) + C_1 = C_1$$

and it follows that

$$\ln|x| = \sin\frac{y}{x} \implies x = e^{\sin(y/x)}.$$

85.

$$x\,dy - (2xe^{-y/x} + y)\,dx = 0, \, y = vx$$

$$x(v\,dx + x\,dv) - (2xe^{-v} + vx)\,dx = 0$$

$$\int e^v\,dv = \int\frac{2}{x}\,dx$$

$$e^v = \ln C_1 x^2$$

$$e^{y/x} = \ln C_1 + \ln x^2$$

$$e^{y/x} = C + \ln x^2$$

Initial condition: $y(1) = 0, 1 = C$

Particular solution: $e^{y/x} = 1 + \ln x^2$

89. $\dfrac{dy}{dx} = x$

(a)

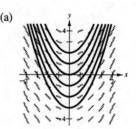

(b) $y = \displaystyle\int x\,dx = \frac{1}{2}x^2 + C$

91. $\dfrac{dy}{dx} = 4 - y$

(a)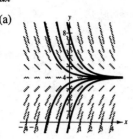

(b) $\displaystyle\int \dfrac{dy}{4-y} = \int dx$

$\ln|4-y| = -x + C_1$

$4 - y = e^{-x+C_1}$

$y = 4 + Ce^{-x}$

93. $\dfrac{dy}{dx} = k(y-4)$

The direction field satisfies $(dy/dx) = 0$ along $y = 4$; but not along $y = 0$. Matches (a).

95. $\dfrac{dy}{dx} = ky(y-4)$

The direction field satisfies $(dy/dx) = 0$ along $y = 0$ and $y = 4$. Matches (c).

97. (a) The differential equation is

$$\dfrac{dS}{dt} = kS(L - S).$$

To verify that

$$S = \dfrac{L}{1 + Ce^{-kt}}$$

is a solution, find and simplify both sides of the differential equation to show they are equal.

$$S = \dfrac{L}{1 + Ce^{-kt}} = L(1 + Ce^{-kt})^{-1}$$

$$\dfrac{dS}{dt} = -L(1 + Ce^{-kt})^{-2}(Ce^{-kt})(-k) = \dfrac{kCLe^{-kt}}{(1 + Ce^{-kt})^2}$$

$$kS(L-S) = k\left(\dfrac{L}{1 + Ce^{-kt}}\right)\left(L - \dfrac{L}{1 + Ce^{-kt}}\right) = kL\left[\dfrac{1}{1 + Ce^{-kt}} - \dfrac{1}{(1 + Ce^{-kt})^2}\right] = \dfrac{kCLe^{-kt}}{(1 + Ce^{-kt})^2}$$

Therefore, $dS/dt = kS(L - S)$. Since $L = 100$, it follows that

$$S = \dfrac{100}{1 + Ce^{-kt}}.$$

Since $S = 10$ when $t = 0$, we have

$$10 = \dfrac{100}{1 + Ce^{-k(0)}} = \dfrac{100}{1 + C}.$$

Hence, $C = 9$. Substituting $C = 9$ and $S = 20$ when $t = 1$ yields

$$20 = \dfrac{100}{1 + 9e^{-k}}$$

$$20 + 180e^{-k} = 100$$

$$180e^{-k} = 80$$

$$e^{-k} = \dfrac{80}{180} \implies k = -\ln\dfrac{4}{9} \approx 0.8109.$$

Therefore, the model is

$$S = \dfrac{100}{1 + 9e^{-0.8109t}}.$$

—CONTINUED—

97. —CONTINUED—

(b) $\dfrac{dS}{dt} = kS(L - S)\left(\ln\dfrac{4}{9}\right)S(100 - S)$

$\dfrac{d^2S}{dt^2} = \ln\left(\dfrac{4}{9}\right)\left[S\left(\dfrac{dS}{dt}\right) + (100 - S)\dfrac{dS}{dt}\right]$

$\qquad = \ln\left(\dfrac{4}{9}\right)(100 - 2S)\dfrac{dS}{dt}$

The second derivative is zero when $S = 50$ or $dS/dt = 0$. Choosing $S = 50$, we have

$$50 = \dfrac{100}{1 + 9e^{-0.8109t}}$$

$$1 + 9e^{-0.8109t} = 2$$

$$e^{-0.8109t} = \dfrac{1}{9}$$

$$t = \dfrac{-\ln 9}{-0.8109} \approx 2.7 \text{ months.}$$

(c)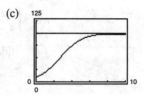

(d)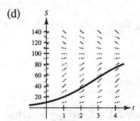

(e) Sales will decrease toward the line $S = L$.

99. $\dfrac{dy}{dt} = ky,\ y = Ce^{kt}$

Initial conditions: $\quad y(0) = y_0$

$\qquad\qquad\qquad y(1620) = \dfrac{y_0}{2}$

$\qquad\qquad\qquad C = y_0$

$\qquad\qquad\qquad \dfrac{y_0}{2} = y_0 e^{1620k}$

$\qquad\qquad\qquad k = \dfrac{\ln(1/2)}{1620}$

Particular solution: $y = y_0 e^{-t(\ln 2)/1620}$

When $t = 25$, $y \approx 0.989 y_0$, $y = 98.9\%$ of y_0.

101. $\displaystyle\int \dfrac{3k}{16}\,dt = \int \dfrac{1}{x^2 - 12x + 32}\,dx$

$\qquad \dfrac{3kt}{16} = \displaystyle\int \dfrac{1}{(x - 6)^2 - 4}\,dx$

$\qquad\qquad = \dfrac{1}{2(2)}\ln\left|\dfrac{(x - 6) - 2}{(x - 6) + 2}\right| + C$

$\qquad\qquad = \dfrac{1}{4}\ln\left|\dfrac{x - 8}{x - 4}\right| + C$

When $x = 0$: $t = 0$

$\qquad\qquad C = -\dfrac{1}{4}\ln(2)$

When $x = 1$: $t = 10$

$\qquad \dfrac{30k}{16} = \dfrac{1}{4}\ln\left|\dfrac{-7}{-3}\right| - \dfrac{1}{4}\ln(2) = \dfrac{1}{4}\ln\left(\dfrac{7}{6}\right)$

$\qquad\qquad k = \dfrac{2}{15}\ln\left(\dfrac{7}{6}\right)$

When $t = 20$: $\left(\dfrac{3}{16}\right)\left(\dfrac{2}{15}\right)\ln\left(\dfrac{7}{6}\right)(20) = \dfrac{1}{4}\ln\dfrac{x - 8}{2x - 8}$

$\qquad\qquad\qquad \ln\left(\dfrac{7}{6}\right)^2 = \ln\dfrac{x - 8}{2x - 8}$

$\qquad\qquad\qquad \dfrac{49}{36} = \dfrac{x - 8}{2x - 8}$

$\qquad\qquad\qquad 62x = 104$

$\qquad\qquad\qquad x = \dfrac{104}{62}$

$\qquad\qquad\qquad = \dfrac{52}{31} \approx 1.677 \text{ kg}$

103. (a)
$$\frac{dv}{dt} = k(W - v)$$

$$\int \frac{dv}{W - v} = \int k\, dt$$

$$-\ln(W - v) = kt + C_1$$

$$v = W - Ce^{-kt}$$

Initial conditions:

$W = 20,\ v = 0$ when $t = 0$, and

$v = 5$ when $t = 1$.

$C = 20,\ k = -\ln(3/4)$

Particular solution:

$$v = 20(1 - e^{\ln(3/4)t}) \approx 20(1 - e^{-0.2877t})$$

(b) 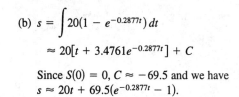 $s = \int 20(1 - e^{-0.2877t})\, dt$

$$\approx 20[t + 3.4761e^{-0.2877t}] + C$$

Since $S(0) = 0,\ C \approx -69.5$ and we have
$s \approx 20t + 69.5(e^{-0.2877t} - 1)$.

105. Given family (circles): $\quad x^2 + y^2 = C$

$$2x + 2yy' = 0$$

$$y' = -\frac{x}{y}$$

Orthogonal trajectory (lines): $\quad y' = \dfrac{y}{x}$

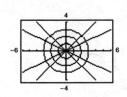

$$\int \frac{dy}{y} = \int \frac{dx}{x}$$

$$\ln y = \ln x + \ln K$$

$$y = Kx$$

107. Given family (parabolas): $\quad x^2 = Cy$

$$2x = Cy'$$

$$y' = \frac{2x}{C} = \frac{2x}{x^2/y} = \frac{2y}{x}$$

Orthogonal trajectory (ellipses): $\quad y' = -\dfrac{x}{2y}$

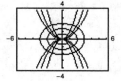

$$2\int y\, dy = -\int x\, dx$$

$$y^2 = -\frac{x^2}{2} + K_1$$

$$x^2 + 2y^2 = K$$

109. First, solve for C in the given equation and obtain

$$C = \frac{y^2}{x^3}.$$

Then, differentiating $y^2 = Cx^3$ implicitly with respect to x and substituting the expression for C given above, we have

$$2yy' = 3Cx^2 = 3\left(\frac{y^2}{x^3}\right)x^2 = \frac{3y^2}{x}.$$

Therefore,

$$\frac{dy}{dx} = \frac{3y}{2x}. \quad \text{Slope of given family}$$

Since dy/dx represents the slope of the given family of curves at (x, y), it follows that the orthogonal family has the negative reciprocal slope, and we write

$$\frac{dy}{dx} = -\frac{2x}{3y}. \quad \text{Slope of orthogonal family}$$

Now, find the orthogonal family by separating variables and integrating to obtain

$$3\int y\, dy = -2\int x\, dx$$

$$\frac{3}{2}y^2 = -x^2 + K$$

$$2x^2 + 3y^2 = K.$$

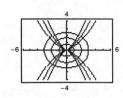

111. (a) Begin by separating variables as follows.

$$y' = 0.5xy$$

$$\frac{2}{y}\frac{dy}{dx} = x$$

$$\frac{1}{y}\,dy = \frac{1}{2}x\,dx$$

Integration yields

$$\int \frac{1}{y}\,dy = \frac{1}{2}\int x\,dx$$

$$\ln|y| = \frac{1}{4}x^2 + C_1$$

$$y = Ce^{x^2/4}.$$

Since $(0, 3)$ is a solution point, we have $3 = Ce^0$ and $C = 3$. Therefore, the particular solution is $y = 3e^{x^2/4}$ and $y(1) = 3e^{1/4} \approx 3.8521$.

(b) Using Euler's Method with $f(x, y) = 0.5xy$, $x_0 = 0$, $y_0 = 3$, and $\Delta x = 0.25$, we have the following iterations.

$$y_1 = y_0 + f(x_0, y_0)\Delta x = 3 + 0.5(0)(3)(0.25) = 3$$

$$y_2 = y_1 + f(x_1, y_1)\Delta x = 3 + 0.5(0.25)(3)(0.25) \approx 3.0938$$

$$y_3 = y_2 + f(x_2, y_2)\Delta x = 3.0938 + 0.5(0.5)(3.0938)(0.25) \approx 3.2872$$

$$y_4 = y_3 + f(x_3, y_3)\Delta x = 3.2872 + 0.5(0.75)(3.2872)(0.25) \approx 3.5954$$

Therefore, $y(1) \approx 3.5954$. Using Euler's Method with $f(x, y) = 0.5xy$, $x_0 = 0$, $y_0 = 3$, and $\Delta x = 0.1$, we have the following iterations.

$$y_1 = y_0 + f(x_0, y_0)\Delta x = 3 + 0.5(0)(3)(0.1) = 3$$

$$y_2 = y_1 + f(x_1, y_1)\Delta x = 3 + 0.5(0.1)(3)(0.1) = 3.015$$

$$y_3 = y_2 + f(x_2, y_2)\Delta x = 3.015 + 0.5(0.2)(3.015)(0.1) \approx 3.0452$$

$$y_4 = y_3 + f(x_3, y_3)\Delta x = 3.0452 + 0.5(0.3)(3.0452)(0.1) \approx 3.0909$$

$$y_5 = y_4 + f(x_4, y_4)\Delta x = 3.0909 + 0.5(0.4)(3.0909)(0.1) \approx 3.1527$$

$$y_6 = y_5 + f(x_5, y_5)\Delta x = 3.1527 + 0.5(0.5)(3.1527)(0.1) \approx 3.2315$$

$$y_7 = y_6 + f(x_6, y_6)\Delta x = 3.2315 + 0.5(0.6)(3.2315)(0.1) \approx 3.3284$$

$$y_8 = y_7 + f(x_7, y_7)\Delta x = 3.3284 + 0.5(0.7)(3.3284)(0.1) \approx 3.4449$$

$$y_9 = y_8 + f(x_8, y_8)\Delta x = 3.4449 + 0.5(0.8)(3.4449)(0.1) \approx 3.5827$$

$$y_{10} = y_9 + f(x_9, y_9)\Delta x = 3.5827 + 0.5(0.9)(3.5827)(0.1) \approx 3.7439$$

Therefore, $y(1) \approx 3.7439$. The approximation becomes more accurate as Δx is decreased.

113. $y' = x + 0.4y^2$, $y(0) = 1$, $\Delta x = 0.1$,

$y(1.5) \approx y_{15} \approx 4.7400$

115. $y' = (x + 1)e^{-y^2/100}$, $y(0) = 4$, $\Delta x = 0.2$,

$y(2) \approx y_{10} \approx 6.8492$

117. False. Consider Example 2. $y = x^3$ is a solution to $xy' - 3y = 0$, but $y = x^3 + 1$ is not a solution.

119. False

$$f(tx, ty) = t^2x^2 + t^2\,xy + 2 \neq t^2 f(x, y)$$

Section 5.3   First-Order Linear Differential Equations

1. False

$y' + xy = x^2$ is first-order linear.

3. (a),(c)

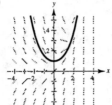

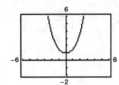

(b) $\dfrac{dy}{dx} = e^x - y$

$\dfrac{dy}{dx} + y = e^x$ Integrating factor: $e^{\int dx} = e^x$

$e^x y' + e^x y = e^{2x}$

$(ye^x) = \displaystyle\int e^{2x}\, dx$

$ye^x = \dfrac{1}{2}e^{2x} + C$

$y(0) = 1 \Rightarrow 1 = \dfrac{1}{2} + C \Rightarrow C = \dfrac{1}{2}$

$ye^x = \dfrac{1}{2}e^{2x} + \dfrac{1}{2}$

$y = \dfrac{1}{2}e^x + \dfrac{1}{2}e^{-x} = \dfrac{1}{2}(e^x + e^{-x})$

5. $\dfrac{dy}{dx} + \left(\dfrac{1}{x}\right)y = 3x + 4$

The differential equation is a first-order linear equation in standard form. Thus,

$\displaystyle\int P(x)\, dx = \int \dfrac{1}{x}\, dx = \ln|x|$

and the integrating factor is

$e^{\int P(x)\, dx} = e^{\ln|x|} = x.$

Multiplying both members of the standard form of the differential equation by the integrating factor yields:

$x\dfrac{dy}{dx} + y = 3x^2 + 4x$

$\dfrac{d}{dx}[xy] = 3x^2 + 4x$

$xy = \displaystyle\int (3x^2 + 4x)\, dx$

$xy = x^3 + 2x^2 + C \Longrightarrow y = x^2 + 2x + \dfrac{C}{x}$

7. $y' - y = 10$

Integrating factor: $e^{\int -1\, dx} = e^{-x}$

$e^{-x}y' - e^{-x}y = 10e^{-x}$

$ye^{-x} = \displaystyle\int 10e^{-x}\, dx = -10e^{-x} + C$

$y = -10 + Ce^x$

9. $(y + 1)\cos x\, dx = dy$

$y' = (y + 1)\cos x = y\cos x + \cos x$

$y' - (\cos x)y = \cos x$

Integrating factor: $e^{\int -\cos x\, dx} = e^{-\sin x}$

$y'e^{-\sin x} - (\cos x)e^{-\sin x}y = (\cos x)e^{-\sin x}$

$ye^{-\sin x} = \displaystyle\int (\cos x)e^{-\sin x}\, dx$

$= -e^{-\sin x} + C$

$y = -1 + Ce^{\sin x}$

11. $(x - 1)y' + y = x^2 - 1$.

In standard form the equation is

$$y' + \left(\frac{1}{x - 1}\right)y = x + 1.$$

Thus,

$$\int P(x)\, dx = \int \frac{1}{x - 1}\, dx = \ln|x - 1|$$

and the integrating factor is $e^{\int P(x)\, dx} = e^{\ln|x - 1|} = x - 1$. Therefore, multiplying both members of the standard form of the differential equation yields

$$y'(x - 1) + y = (x + 1)(x - 1)$$

$$\frac{d}{dx}[y(x - 1)] = (x + 1)(x - 1)$$

$$y(x - 1) = \int (x - 1)(x + 1)\, dx$$

$$= \int (x^2 - 1)\, dx = \frac{x^3}{3} - x + C_1$$

$$y = \frac{x^3 - 3x + C}{3(x - 1)}.$$

13. $y' \cos^2 x + y - 1 = 0$

$$y' + (\sec^2 x)y = \sec^2 x$$

Integrating factor: $e^{\int \sec^2 x\, dx} = e^{\tan x}$

$$ye^{\tan x} = \int \sec^2 x e^{\tan x}\, dx = e^{\tan x} + C$$

$$y = 1 + Ce^{-\tan x}$$

Initial condition: $y(0) = 5, C = 4$

Particular solution: $y = 1 + 4e^{-\tan x}$

15. $y' + y \tan x = \sec x + \cos x$

The integrating factor is given by $e^{\int P\, dx} = e^{\int \tan x\, dx} = e^{\ln|\sec x|} = \sec x$. Therefore, multiplying both members of the differential equation in standard form yields

$$y'(\sec x) + (\sec x \tan x)y = \sec x(\sec x + \cos x)$$

$$\frac{d}{dx}[y \sec x] = \sec^2 x + 1$$

$$y \sec x = \int (\sec^2 x + 1)\, dx = \tan x + x + C$$

$$y = \cos x(\tan x + x + C) = \sin x + x \cos x + C \cos x.$$

Since $y = 1$ when $x = 0$, you have

$$1 = \sin 0 + 0 \cos 0 + C \cos 0$$

$$1 = C.$$

Therefore, the particular solution is $y = \sin x + (x + 1) \cos x$.

17. $y' + \left(\frac{1}{x}\right)y = 0$

Integrating factor: $e^{\int (1/x)\, dx} = e^{\ln|x|} = x$

Separation of variables:

$$\frac{dy}{dx} = -\frac{y}{x}$$

$$\int \frac{1}{y}\, dy = \int -\frac{1}{x}\, dx$$

$$\ln y = -\ln x + \ln C$$

$$\ln xy = \ln C$$

$$xy = C$$

Initial condition: $y(2) = 2, C = 4$

Particular solution: $xy = 4$

19. $y' + 3x^2 y = x^2 y^3$

$$n = 3, Q = x^2, P = 3x^2$$

$$y^{-2}e^{\int (-2)3x^2\, dx} = \int (-2)x^2 e^{\int (-2)3x^2\, dx}\, dx$$

$$y^{-2}e^{-2x^3} = -\int 2x^2 e^{-2x^3}\, dx$$

$$y^{-2}e^{-2x^3} = \frac{1}{3}e^{-2x^3} + C$$

$$y^{-2} = \frac{1}{3} + Ce^{2x^3}$$

$$\frac{1}{y^2} = Ce^{2x^3} + \frac{1}{3}$$

21. $y' + \left(\dfrac{1}{x}\right)y = xy^2.$

For the given Bernoulli equation we have $n = 2$, and $1 - n = -1$. If $z = y^{1-n} = y^{-1}$, then $z' = y^{-2}y'$. Multiplying both members of the differential equation by $-y^{-2}$ produces

$$y' + \left(\frac{1}{x}\right)y = xy^2$$

$$-y^{-2}y' - \left(\frac{1}{x}\right)y^{-1} = -x$$

$$z' - \left(\frac{1}{x}\right)z = -x.$$

This equation is linear in z. Using $P(x) = -1/x$ produces

$$-\int \frac{1}{x}\,dx = -\ln|x| \quad\Rightarrow\quad e^{-\ln|x|} = \frac{1}{x}$$

as the integrating factor. Multiplying the linear equation by this factor produces

$$z'\left(\frac{1}{x}\right) - \left(\frac{1}{x^2}\right)z = -1$$

$$\frac{d}{dx}\left[\frac{z}{x}\right] = -1$$

$$\frac{z}{x} = \int (-1)\,dx = -x + C$$

$$z = -x^2 + Cx$$

$$\frac{1}{y} = -x^2 + Cx$$

$$y = \frac{1}{Cx - x^2}.$$

23. $y' - y = e^x\sqrt[3]{y}, \quad n = \dfrac{1}{3}, \quad Q = e^x, \quad P = -1$

$$e^{\int -(2/3)\,dx} = e^{-(2/3)x}$$

$$y^{2/3}e^{-(2/3)x} = \int \frac{2}{3}e^x e^{-(2/3)x}\,dx = \int \frac{2}{3}e^{(1/3)x}\,dx$$

$$y^{2/3}e^{-(2/3)x} = 2e^{(1/3)x} + C$$

$$y^{2/3} = 2e^x + Ce^{2x/3}$$

25. (a)

(c)

(b) $\dfrac{dy}{dx} - \dfrac{1}{x}y = x^2$

Integrating factor: $e^{\int -1/x\,dx} = e^{-\ln x} = \dfrac{1}{x}$

$$\frac{1}{x}y' - \frac{1}{x^2}y = x$$

$$\left(\frac{1}{x}y\right) = \int x\,dx = \frac{x^2}{2} + C$$

$$y = \frac{x^3}{2} + Cx$$

$(-2, 4)$: $4 = \dfrac{-8}{2} - 2C \Rightarrow C = -4 \Rightarrow y = \dfrac{x^3}{2} - 4x = \dfrac{1}{2}x(x^2 - 8)$

$(2, 8)$: $8 = \dfrac{8}{2} + 2C \Rightarrow C = 2 \Rightarrow y = \dfrac{x^3}{2} + 2x = \dfrac{1}{2}x(x^2 + 4)$

27. $\dfrac{dy}{dx} + (\cot x)y = 2$

(a) The graph of the direction field is shown in the figure.

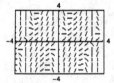

(c) The graphs of the particular solutions are shown in the figure.

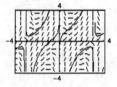

(b) The integrating factor is $e^{\int P\,dx} = e^{\int \cot x\,dx} = e^{\ln|\sin x|} = \sin x$. Multiplying both sides of the differential equation by the integrating factor yields

$$\sin x\,\frac{dy}{dx} + \sin x(\cot x)y = 2\sin x$$

$$\sin x\,\frac{dy}{dx} + y\cos x = 2\sin x$$

$$\frac{d}{dx}[y\sin x] = 2\sin x$$

$$y\sin x = 2\int \sin x\,dx$$

$$= -2\cos x + C.$$

We now find the particular solution passing through the point $(1, 1)$.

$$\sin 1 = -2\cos 1 + C \Longrightarrow C = \sin 1 + 2\cos 1$$

Therefore,

$$y\sin x = -2\cos x + \sin 1 + 2\cos 1$$

$$y = -2\cot x + (\sin 1 + 2\cos 1)\csc x.$$

We now find the particular solution passing through the point $(3, -1)$.

$$-\sin 3 = -2\cos 3 + C \Longrightarrow C = 2\cos 3 - \sin 3$$

Therefore, $y\sin x = -2\cos x + 2\cos 3 - \sin 3$

$$y = -2\cot x + (2\cos 3 - \sin 3)\csc x.$$

29. $L\dfrac{dI}{dt} + RI = E_0,\ I' + \dfrac{R}{L}I = \dfrac{E_0}{L}$

Integrating factor: $e^{\int (R/L)\,dt} = e^{Rt/L}$

$$I\,e^{Rt/L} = \int \frac{E_0}{L}e^{Rt/L}\,dt = \frac{E_0}{R}e^{Rt/L} + C$$

$$I = \frac{E_0}{R} + Ce^{-Rt/L}$$

31. $\qquad\qquad \dfrac{dP}{dt} = kP + N,\ N\text{ constant}$

$$\frac{dP}{kP + N} = dt$$

$$\int \frac{1}{kP + N}\,dP = \int dt$$

$$\frac{1}{k}\ln(kP + N) = t + C_1$$

$$\ln(kP + N) = kt + C_2$$

$$kP + N = e^{kt + C_2}$$

$$P = \frac{C_3 e^{kt} - N}{k}$$

$$P = Ce^{kt} - \frac{N}{k}$$

When $t = 0$: $P = P_0$

$$P_0 = C - \frac{N}{k} \Longrightarrow C = P_0 + \frac{N}{k}$$

$$P = \left(P_0 + \frac{N}{k}\right)e^{kt} - \frac{N}{k}$$

33. (a) $A = \frac{P}{r}(e^{rt} - 1)$

$A = \frac{100,000}{0.06}(e^{0.06(5)} - 1) \approx 583,098.01$

(b) $A = \frac{250,000}{0.05}(e^{0.05(10)} - 1) \approx 3,243,606.35$

35. (a) Let $Q(t)$ be the amount of glucose in the bloodstream at any time. The rate of change of Q is given by

$$\frac{dQ}{dt} = \text{(rate administered)} - \text{(rate removed)}$$

$$\frac{dQ}{dt} = q - kQ$$

$$\frac{dQ}{dt} + kQ = q$$

where t is time in minutes and k is a constant of proportionality.

(c) $\lim_{t \to \infty} Q(t) = \lim_{t \to \infty} \left[\frac{q}{k} + \left(Q_0 - \frac{q}{k} \right) e^{-kt} \right] = \frac{q}{k}$

(b) To solve this linear equation begin by finding the integrating factor $e^{\int P(t)\, dt} = e^{\int k\, dt} = e^{kt}$. Therefore, the general solution has the form

$$Qe^{kt} = \int qe^{kt}\, dt = \frac{q}{k}e^{kt} + C$$

$$Q(t) = \frac{q}{k} + Ce^{-kt}.$$

Since $Q(0) = Q_0$, we have

$$Q_0 = \frac{q}{k} + C$$

$$Q_0 - \frac{q}{k} = C$$

$$Q(t) = \frac{q}{k} + \left(Q_0 - \frac{q}{k} \right) e^{-kt}.$$

37. Let Q be the number of pounds of concentrate in the solution at any time t. Since the number of gallons of solution in the tank at any time t is $v_0 + (r_1 - r_2)t$ and since the tank loses r_2 gallons of solution per minute, it must lose concentrate at the rate

$$\left[\frac{Q}{v_0 + (r_1 - r_2)t} \right] r_2.$$

The solution gains concentrate at the rate $r_1 q_1$. Therefore, the net rate of change is

$$\frac{dQ}{dt} = q_1 r_1 - \left[\frac{Q}{v_0 + (r_1 - r_2)t} \right] r_2 \quad \text{or} \quad \frac{dQ}{dt} + \frac{r_2 Q}{v_0 + (r_1 - r_2)t} = q_1 r_1.$$

39. (a) Using Exercise 37, we have $r_1 = 10$, $r_2 = 10$, $q_1 = 0$, and $v_0 = 200$. Thus,

$$\frac{dQ}{dt} + \frac{10Q}{200 + (0)t} = 0$$

$$\frac{dQ}{dt} = \frac{-10Q}{200} = -\frac{Q}{20}.$$

Separating variables, we have

$$\frac{dQ}{Q} = -\frac{dt}{20}$$

$$\ln|Q| = -\frac{t}{20} + C_1$$

$$Q(t) = e^{C_1 - (t/20)} = Ce^{-t/20}.$$

Since $Q(0) = 25$, we have

$$Q(t) = 25e^{-t/20}.$$

(b) When $Q = 15$, we have

$$15 = 25e^{-t/20}$$

$$\frac{3}{5} = e^{-t/20}$$

$$\ln 3 - \ln 5 = -\frac{t}{20}$$

$$t = 20(\ln 5 - \ln 3) \approx 10.2 \text{ min.}$$

(c) $\lim_{t \to \infty} Q(t) = \lim_{t \to \infty} Ce^{-t/20} = 0$

41. (a) The volume of the solution in the tank is given by $v_0 + (r_1 - r_2)t$. Therefore, $100 + (5 - 3)t = 200$ or $t = 50$ minutes.

(b) $Q' + \dfrac{r_2 Q}{v_0 + (r_1 - r_2)t} = q_1 r_1$

$Q(0) = q_0, q_0 = 0, q_1 = 0.5, v_0 = 100, r_1 = 5, r_2 = 3, Q' + \dfrac{3}{100 + 2t}Q = 2.5$

Integrating factor: $e^{\int [3/(100 + 2t)]\, dt} = (50 + t)^{3/2}$

$Q(50 + t)^{3/2} = \displaystyle\int 2.5(50 + t)^{3/2}\, dt = (50 + t)^{5/2} + C$

$Q = (50 + t) + C(50 + t)^{-3/2}$

Initial condition: $Q(0) = 0, 0 = 50 + C(50^{-3/2}), C = -50^{5/2}$

Particular solution: $\quad Q = (50 + t) - 50^{-5/2}(50 + t)^{-3/2}$

$Q(50) = 100 - 50^{5/2}(100)^{-3/2} = 100 - \dfrac{25}{\sqrt{2}} \approx 82.32 \text{ lbs}$

43. $y' - 2x = 0$

$\displaystyle\int dy = \int 2x\, dx$

$y = x^2 + C$

Matches c.

45. $y' - 2xy = 0$

$\displaystyle\int \dfrac{dy}{y} = \int 2x\, dx$

$\ln y = x^2 + C_1$

$y = Ce^{x^2}$

Matches a.

47. $\dfrac{dy}{dx} = \dfrac{e^{2x+y}}{e^{x-y}}$

Separating variables yields

$e^{2x+y}\, dx = e^{x-y}\, dy$

$e^{2x} e^y\, dx = e^x e^{-y}\, dy$

$e^x\, dx = e^{-2y}\, dy$

$\displaystyle\int e^x\, dx = \int e^{-2y}\, dy$

$e^x = -\dfrac{1}{2}e^{-2y} + C_1$

$2e^x + e^{-2y} = C.$

49. $(y \cos x - \cos x)\, dx + dy = 0$

Separation of variables:

$\displaystyle\int \cos x\, dx = \int \dfrac{-1}{y - 1}\, dy$

$\sin x = -\ln(y - 1) + \ln C$

$\ln(y - 1) = -\sin x + \ln C$

$y = Ce^{-\sin x} + 1$

51. $(3y^2 + 4xy)\, dx + (2xy + x^2)\, dy = 0$

Homogeneous: $y = vx, dy = v\, dx + x\, dv$

$(3v^2x^2 + 4vx^2)\, dx + (2vx^2 + x^2)(v\, dx + x\, dv) = 0$

$\displaystyle\int \dfrac{5}{x}\, dx + \int \left(\dfrac{2v + 1}{v^2 + v}\right) dv = 0$

$\ln x^5 + \ln|v^2 + v| = \ln C$

$x^5(v^2 + v) = C$

$x^3y^2 + x^4y = C$

53. $(2y - e^x)\, dx + x\, dy = 0$

Linear: $y' + \left(\dfrac{2}{x}\right)y = \dfrac{1}{x}e^x$

Integrating factor: $e^{\int (2/x)\, dx} = e^{\ln x^2} = x^2$

$yx^2 = \displaystyle\int x^2 \dfrac{1}{x}e^x\, dx = e^x(x - 1) + C$

$y = \dfrac{e^x}{x^2}(x - 1) + \dfrac{C}{x^2}$

55. $(x^2y^4 - 1)\,dx + x^3y^3\,dy = 0$

Rewriting the differential equation we have

$$x^3y^3\frac{dy}{dx} + x^2y^4 = 1$$

$$\frac{dy}{dx} + \left(\frac{1}{x}\right)y = x^{-3}y^{-3}.$$

For this Bernoulli equation, $n = -3$ and use the substitution $z = y^{1-n} = y^4$ and $z' = 4y^3y'$. Multiplying the equation in standard form by $4y^3$ produces

$$4y^3y' + 4\left(\frac{1}{x}\right)y^4 = \frac{4}{x^3}$$

$$z' + \left(\frac{4}{x}\right)z = \frac{4}{x^3}.$$

This equation in linear in z. Using $P(x) = 4/x$ produces

$$\int P(x)\,dx = \int \frac{4}{x}\,dx = 4\ln|x| = \ln x^4$$

which implies that $e^{\ln x^4} = x^4$ is an integrating factor. Multiplying the linear equation by this factor produces

$$x^4z' + 4x^3z = 4x$$

$$\frac{d}{dx}[x^4z] = 4x$$

$$x^4z = \int 4x\,dx = 2x^2 + C$$

$$x^4y^4 = 2x^2 + C$$

$$x^4y^4 - 2x^2 = C.$$

57. $3(y - 4x^2)\,dx = -x\,dy$

$$x\frac{dy}{dx} = -3y + 12x^2$$

$$y' + \frac{3}{x}y = 12x$$

Integrating factor: $e^{\int(3/x)\,dx} = e^{3\ln x} = x^3$

$$y'x^3 + \frac{3}{x}x^3y = 12x(x^3) = 12x^4$$

$$yx^3 = \int 12x^4\,dx = \frac{12}{5}x^5 + C$$

$$y = \frac{12}{5}x^2 + \frac{C}{x^3}$$

Review Exercises for Chapter 5

1. $y = Ce^{-2x}$

$y' = -2Ce^{-2x} = -2y$

3. $y = C(\sec x + \tan x)$

$y' = C(\sec x \cdot \tan x + \sec^2 x)$

$= C(\tan x + \sec x)\sec x$

$= y \cdot \sec x$

$$= \frac{2}{x^2 + C}; \ \left(1, \frac{1}{2}\right)$$

$$\frac{1}{2} = \frac{2}{1 + C} \Longrightarrow C = 3 \Longrightarrow y = \frac{2}{x^2 + 3}$$

7. (a)

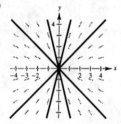

(b) $$\frac{dy}{dx} = \frac{y}{x}$$

$$\int \frac{dy}{y} = \int \frac{dx}{x}$$

$$\ln y = \ln x + \ln C$$

$$y = Cx$$

9. Begin by separating variables.

$$\frac{dy}{dx} = 4x(1 + y^2)$$

$$\frac{1}{1 + y^2} \, dy = 4x \, dx$$

Integration yields the following.

$$\int \frac{1}{1 + y^2} \, dy = \int 4x \, dx$$

$$\arctan y = 2x^2 + C$$

$$y = \tan(2x^2 + C)$$

11. $y' - 2xy = 0$

$$\frac{dy}{dx} = 2xy$$

$$\int \frac{1}{y} \, dy = \int 2x \, dx$$

$$\ln|y| = x^2 + C_1$$

$$e^{x^2 + C_1} = y$$

$$y = Ce^{x^2}$$

13. $\dfrac{dy}{dx} - \dfrac{y}{x} = 2 + \sqrt{x}$

Integrating factor: $e^{-\int (1/x) \, dx} = e^{-\ln|x|} = \dfrac{1}{x}$

$$y\left(\frac{1}{x}\right) = \int \frac{1}{x}(2 + \sqrt{x}) \, dx = \ln x^2 + 2\sqrt{x} + C$$

$$y = x \ln x^2 + 2x^{3/2} + Cx$$

15. $y' - \dfrac{2y}{x} = \dfrac{1}{x}y'$

$$(x - 1)\frac{dy}{dx} = 2y$$

$$\int \frac{1}{y} \, dy = \int \frac{2}{x - 1} \, dx$$

$$\ln|y| = \ln(x - 1)^2 + \ln C$$

$$y = C(x - 1)^2$$

17. $\dfrac{dy}{dx} - \dfrac{y}{x} = \dfrac{x}{y}$

The given equation

$$\frac{dy}{dx} - \left(\frac{1}{x}\right)y = xy^{-1}$$

is a Bernoulli equation with $n = -1$, and $1 - n = 2$. Let $z = y^{1-n} = y^2$, then $z' = 2yy'$. Multiplying the original differential equation by $2y$ produces

$$2yy' - 2\left(\frac{1}{x}\right)y^2 = 2x$$

$$z' - \left(\frac{2}{x}\right)z = 2x.$$

—CONTINUED—

17. —CONTINUED—

This equation is linear in z. Using $P(x) = -2/x$ yields

$$\int P(x)\, dx = \int \frac{-2}{x}\, dx = -2 \ln x = \ln x^{-2}$$

which implies that $e^{\ln x^{-2}} = x^{-2}$ is an integrating factor. Multiplying the linear equation by this factor produces

$$\left(\frac{1}{x^2}\right) z' - \left(\frac{2}{x^3}\right) z = \frac{2}{x}$$

$$\frac{d}{dx}\left[\frac{1}{x^2}\, (z)\right] = \frac{2}{x}$$

$$z\left(\frac{1}{x^2}\right) = \int \frac{2}{x}\, dx = 2 \ln|x| + C$$

$$y^2 = 2x^2 \ln|x| + Cx^2 = x^2 \ln x^2 + Cx^2.$$

19.
$$\frac{dy}{dx} = \frac{x^2 + y^2}{2xy} \quad \text{(homogeneous differential equation)}$$

$$(x^2 + y^2)\, dx - 2xy\, dy = 0$$

Let $y = vx$, $dy = x\, dv + v\, dx$.

$$(x^2 + v^2 x^2)\, dx - 2x(vx)(x\, dv + v\, dx) = 0$$

$$(x^2 + v^2 x^2 - 2x^2 v^2)\, dx - 2x^3 v\, dv = 0$$

$$(x^2 - x^2 v^2)\, dx = 2x^3 v\, dv$$

$$(1 - v^2)\, dx = 2x\, dv$$

$$\int \frac{dx}{x} = \int \frac{2v}{1 - v^2}\, dv$$

$$\ln|x| = -\ln|1 - v^2| + C_1 = -\ln|1 - v^2| + \ln C$$

$$x = \frac{C}{1 - v^2} = \frac{C}{1 - (y/x)^2} = \frac{Cx^2}{x^2 - y^2}$$

$$1 = \frac{Cx}{x^2 - y^2} \quad \text{or} \quad C_1 = \frac{x}{x^2 - y^2}$$

21. $3x^2 y^2\, dx + (2x^3 y + x^3 y^4)\, dy = 0$

$$3x^2 y^2\, dx + x^3(2y + y^4)\, dy = 0$$

$$\int \frac{3}{x}\, dx + \int \left(\frac{2}{y} + y^2\right) dy = 0$$

$$\ln x^3 + \ln y^2 + \frac{1}{3} y^3 = C_1$$

$$3 \ln x^3 y^2 + y^3 = C$$

23. $(1 + x^2)\, dy = (1 + y^2)\, dx$

Since the variables are separable, we have

$$\frac{dy}{1 + y^2} = \frac{dx}{1 + x^2}$$

$$\int \frac{dy}{1 + y^2} = \int \frac{dx}{1 + x^2}$$

$$\arctan y = \arctan x + C_1.$$

Now taking the tangent of this equation and using the identity for $\tan(A - B)$, yields

$$\tan(\arctan y - \arctan x) = \tan C_1$$

$$\frac{\tan \arctan y - \tan \arctan x}{1 + \tan(\arctan y)\tan(\arctan x)} = C$$

$$\frac{y - x}{1 + xy} = C$$

as the general solution.

25. $y' - \left(\dfrac{a}{x}\right)y = bx^3$

Integrating factor: $e^{-\int (a/x)\,dx} = e^{-a \ln x} = x^{-a}$

$$yx^{-a} = \int bx^3(x^{-a})\,dx = \frac{b}{4-a}x^{4-a} + C$$

$$y = \frac{bx^4}{4-a} + Cx^a$$

27. $y' - 2y = e^x$

Integrating factor: $e^{\int -2\,dx} = e^{-2x}$

$$ye^{-2x} = \int e^{-2x}e^x\,dx + C = -e^{-x} + C$$

$$y = Ce^{2x} - e^x$$

Initial condition: $y(0) = 4$

$$4 = C - 1 \implies C = 5$$

Particular solution: $y = 5e^{2x} - e^x$

29.
$$x\,dy = (x + y + 2)\,dx$$
$$x\,dy = y\,dx + (x + 2)\,dx$$
$$dy = \left(\frac{1}{x}\right)y\,dx + \frac{x+2}{x}\,dx$$
$$\frac{dy}{dx} - \left(\frac{1}{x}\right)y = \left(1 + \frac{2}{x}\right)$$

The integrating factor is

$$e^{\int P\,dx} = e^{\int (-1/x)\,dx} = e^{-\ln x} = e^{\ln(1/x)} = \frac{1}{x}.$$

Multiplying both sides of the differential equation by $1/x$ yields

$$\left(\frac{1}{x}\right)\frac{dy}{dx} - \left(\frac{1}{x^2}\right)y = \left(\frac{1}{x} + \frac{2}{x^2}\right)$$

$$\frac{d}{dx}\left[y\left(\frac{1}{x}\right)\right] = \left(\frac{1}{x} + \frac{2}{x^2}\right)$$

$$y\left(\frac{1}{x}\right) = \int\left(\frac{1}{x} + \frac{2}{x^2}\right)dx$$

$$y\left(\frac{1}{x}\right) = \ln|x| - \frac{2}{x} + C$$

$$y = x\ln|x| - 2 + Cx.$$

Since $y = 10$ when $x = 1$, we have $10 = 1 \ln 1 - 2 + C \implies C = 12$. Therefore, the particular solution is $y = x\ln|x| - 2 + 12x$.

31.
$$\ln(1 + y)\,dx + \left(\frac{1}{1+y}\right)dy = 0$$

$$\int dx + \int \frac{1}{(1+y)\ln(1+y)}\,dy = C_1$$

$$x + \ln|\ln(1+y)| = C_1$$

$$\ln|\ln(1+y)| = C_1 - x$$

$$\ln|1 + y| = e^{C_1 - x} = Ce^{-x}$$

Initial condition: $y(0) = 2$

$$\ln 3 = C$$

Particular solution: $\ln|1 + y| = (\ln 3)e^{-x}$

33.
$$(x - C)^2 + y^2 = C^2$$
$$x^2 - 2Cx + C^2 + y^2 = C^2$$
$$\frac{x^2 + y^2}{x} = 2C$$
$$\frac{x(2x + 2yy') - (x^2 + y^2)}{x^2} = 0$$
$$2x^2 + 2xyy' - x^2 - y^2 = 0$$
$$y' = \frac{y^2 - x^2}{2xy}$$

The negative reciprocal of y' is the slope of the orthogonal trajectories.

$$\frac{dy}{dx} = \frac{2xy}{x^2 - y^2}$$

$$2xy\,dx + (y^2 - x^2)dy = 0$$

Homogeneous

$x = vy, \quad dx = v\,dy + y\,dv$

$$2vy^2(v\,dy + y\,dv) + (y^2 - v^2y^2)dy = 0$$

$$\int \frac{2v}{1 + v^2}\,dv + \int \frac{1}{y}\,dy = 0$$

$$\ln(1 + v^2) + \ln|y| = \ln K_1$$

$$y^2 + x^2 = K_1 y$$

Circles: $x^2 + (y - K)^2 = K^2$

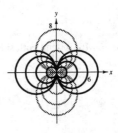

35. $y' = x^2 - y^2, \quad y(0) = 1, \quad \Delta x = 0.05,$

$y(0.8) \approx y_{16} \approx 0.6724$

37. (a) Since the rate of change of the number of miles s of road cleared per hour is inversely proportional to the depth of the snow d, the differential equation is

$$\frac{ds}{dd} = \frac{k}{d}.$$

This is a separable differential equation. Therefore,

$$\frac{ds}{dd} = \frac{k}{d}$$

$$ds = k\frac{1}{d}\,dd$$

$$\int ds = k\int \frac{1}{d}\,dd$$

$$s = k\ln d + C.$$

(b) To find the particular solution use the fact that $s = 25$ when $d = 2$ and $s = 12$ when $d = 10$ to obtain the following system of equations:

$$25 = k\ln 2 + C$$

$$12 = k\ln 10 + C$$

Subtracting the second equation from the first yields

$$13 = k(\ln 2 - \ln 10) = k\ln \frac{1}{5} = -k\ln 5.$$

Thus, $k = -13/\ln 5$. Substituting this expression for k into the first equation of the system produces

$$25 = -\frac{13}{\ln 5}\ln 2 + C \implies C = 25 + \frac{13}{\ln 5}\ln 2.$$

Substituting the results for k and C into the general solution of the differential equation yields the particular solution

$$s = -\frac{13}{\ln 5}\ln d + 25 + \frac{13}{\ln 5}\ln 2$$

$$= 25 - \frac{13}{\ln 5}(\ln d - \ln 2)$$

$$= 25 - \frac{13\ln(d/2)}{\ln 5}, \quad 2 \le d \le 15.$$

39. (a)
$$\frac{dy}{ds} = -0.012y, \quad s > 50$$

$$\frac{-1}{0.012} \int \frac{dy}{y} = \int ds$$

$$\frac{-1}{0.012} \ln y = s + C_1$$

$$y = Ce^{-0.012s}$$

When $s = 50$,

$$y = 28 = Ce^{-0.012(50)} \Rightarrow C = 28e^{0.6}$$

$$y = 28e^{0.6 - 0.012s}, \quad s > 50.$$

(b)

Speed (s)	50	55	60	65	70
Miles per gal (y)	28	26.4	24.8	23.4	22.0

41. $\dfrac{dA}{dt} = rA - P$

$$\frac{dA}{dt} - rA = -P$$

The integrating factor is $e^{\int -r\,dt} = e^{-rt}$. Multiplying both sides of the differential equation by the integrating factor yields

$$e^{-rt}\frac{dA}{dt} - rAe^{-rt} = Pe^{-rt}$$

$$\frac{d}{dt}[Ae^{-rt}] = -Pe^{-rt}$$

$$Ae^{-rt} = \int -Pe^{-rt}\,dt$$

$$Ae^{-rt} = \frac{P}{r}e^{-rt} + C$$

$$A = \frac{P}{r} + Ce^{rt}.$$

If $A = A_0$ when $t = 0$, then

$$A_0 = \frac{P}{r} + C \Rightarrow C = A_0 - \frac{P}{r}$$

and the particular solution is

$$A = \frac{P}{r} + \left(A_0 - \frac{P}{r}\right)e^{rt}.$$

43. $A = \dfrac{200{,}000}{0.14} + \left(1{,}000{,}000 - \dfrac{200{,}000}{0.14}\right)e^{0.14t}$

$$0 = 200{,}000\left[\frac{50}{7} + \left(5 - \frac{50}{7}\right)e^{0.14t}\right]$$

$$e^{0.14t} = \frac{10}{3}$$

$$t = \frac{\ln(10/3)}{0.14} \approx 8.6 \text{ years}$$

CHAPTER 6
Applications of Integration

CHAPTER 6
Applications of Integration

Section 6.1   Area of a Region Between Two Curves

Solutions to Odd-Numbered Exercises

1. $A = \int_0^6 [0 - (x^2 - 6x)] \, dx = -\int_0^6 (x^2 - 6x) \, dx$

3. $A = \int_0^3 [(-x^2 + 2x + 3) - (x^2 - 4x + 3)] \, dx$

$\qquad = \int_0^3 (-2x^2 + 6x) \, dx$

5. $A = 2\int_{-1}^0 3(x^3 - x) \, dx = 6\int_{-1}^0 (x^3 - x) \, dx$

$\qquad$ or $-6\int_0^1 (x^3 - x) \, dx$

7. $\int_0^4 \left[(x + 1) - \dfrac{x}{2} \right] dx$

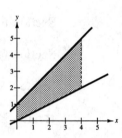

9. $\int_0^6 \left[4(2^{-x/3}) - \dfrac{x}{6} \right] dx$

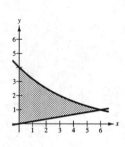

11. $f(x) = x + 1$

$\qquad g(x) = (x - 1)^2$

$\qquad A \approx 4$

$\qquad$ Matches (d)

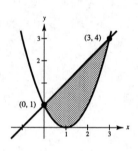

13. The points of intersection are given by:

$\qquad x^2 - 4x = 0$

$\qquad x(x - 4) = 0$ when $x = 0, 4$

$\qquad A = \int_0^4 [g(x) - f(x)] \, dx$

$\qquad = -\int_0^4 (x^2 - 4x) \, dx$

$\qquad = -\left[\dfrac{x^3}{3} - 2x^2 \right]_0^4$

$\qquad = \dfrac{32}{3}$

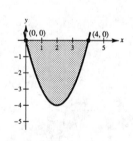

15. The points of intersection f and g are found by solving

$$f(x) = g(x)$$

$$x^2 + 2x + 1 = 3x + 3$$

$$x^2 - x - 2 = 0$$

$$(x - 2)(x + 1) = 0 \implies x = -1, 2.$$

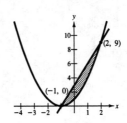

Since $x^2 + 2x + 1 \le 3x + 3$ for $-1 \le x \le 2$, we have

$$\text{Area} = \int_{-1}^{2} [(3x + 3) - (x^2 + 2x + 1)]\, dx$$

$$= \int_{-1}^{2} (-x^2 + x + 2)\, dx$$

$$= \left[\frac{-x^3}{3} + \frac{x^2}{2} + 2x \right]_{-1}^{2}$$

$$= \left(\frac{-8}{3} + 2 + 4 \right) - \left(\frac{1}{3} + \frac{1}{2} - 2 \right)$$

$$= \frac{-16 + 12 + 24 - 2 - 3 + 12}{6} = \frac{27}{6} = \frac{9}{2}.$$

17. The points of intersection are given by:

$$x = 2 - x \quad \text{and} \quad x = 0 \quad \text{and} \quad 2 - x = 0$$

$$x = 1 \qquad\qquad x = 0 \qquad\qquad x = 2$$

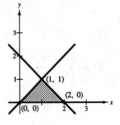

$$A = \int_{0}^{1} [(2 - y) - (y)]\, dy = \left[2y - y^2 \right]_{0}^{1} = 1$$

Note that if we integrate with respect to x, we need two integrals. Also, note that the region is a triangle.

19. The points of intersection are given by:

$$\sqrt{3x} + 1 = x + 1$$

$$\sqrt{3x} = x \quad \text{when} \quad x = 0, 3$$

$$A = \int_{0}^{3} [f(x) - g(x)]\, dx$$

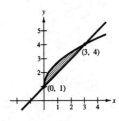

$$= \int_{0}^{3} \left[(\sqrt{3x} + 1) - (x + 1) \right] dx$$

$$= \int_{0}^{3} [(3x)^{1/2} - x]\, dx$$

$$= \left[\frac{2}{9} (3x)^{3/2} - \frac{x^2}{2} \right]_{0}^{3} = \frac{3}{2}$$

21. The points of intersection are given by:

$$y^2 = y + 2$$

$$(y - 2)(y + 1) = 0 \quad \text{when} \quad y = -1, 2$$

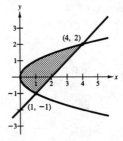

$$A = \int_{-1}^{2} [g(y) - f(y)]\, dy$$

$$= \int_{-1}^{2} [(y + 2) - y^2]\, dy$$

$$= \left[2y + \frac{y^2}{2} - \frac{y^3}{3} \right]_{-1}^{2} = \frac{9}{2}$$

23. Using horizontal representative rectangles, we have

$$\text{Area} = \int_{-1}^{2} (y^2 + 1)\, dy = \left[\frac{y^3}{3} + y \right]_{-1}^{2}$$

$$= \left(\frac{8}{3} + 2 \right) - \left(\frac{-1}{3} - 1 \right)$$

$$= \frac{8 + 6 + 1 + 3}{3} = 6.$$

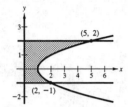

25. $y = \dfrac{4}{x} \implies x = \dfrac{4}{y}$

$$A = \int_{1}^{4} \left[\frac{4}{y} - 0 \right] dy$$

$$= \left[4 \ln|y| \right]_{1}^{4}$$

$$= 4 \ln 4$$

$$= 8 \ln 2 \approx 5.545$$

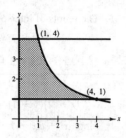

27. The points of intersection are given by:

$$x^3 - 3x^2 + 3x = x^2$$

$$x(x - 1)(x - 3) = 0 \quad \text{when} \quad x = 0, 1, 3$$

$$A = \int_{0}^{1} \left[f(x) - g(x) \right] dx + \int_{1}^{3} \left[g(x) - f(x) \right] dx$$

$$= \int_{0}^{1} \left[(x^3 - 3x^2 + 3x) - x^2 \right] dx + \int_{1}^{3} \left[x^2 - (x^3 - 3x^2 + 3x) \right] dx$$

$$= \int_{0}^{1} (x^3 - 4x^2 + 3x)\, dx + \int_{1}^{3} (-x^3 + 4x^2 - 3x)\, dx$$

$$= \left[\frac{x^4}{4} - \frac{4}{3}x^3 + \frac{3}{2}x^2 \right]_{0}^{1} + \left[\frac{-x^4}{4} + \frac{4}{3}x^3 - \frac{3}{2}x^2 \right]_{1}^{3} = \frac{37}{12}$$

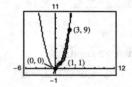

Numerical approximation: $0.417 + 2.667 \approx 3.083$

29. The points of intersection are given by:

$$x^2 - 4x + 3 = 3 + 4x - x^2$$

$$2x(x - 4) = 0 \quad \text{when} \quad x = 0, 4$$

$$A = \int_{0}^{4} \left[(3 + 4x - x^2) - (x^2 - 4x + 3) \right] dx$$

$$= \int_{0}^{4} (-2x^2 + 8x)\, dx$$

$$= \left[-\frac{2x^3}{3} + 4x^2 \right]_{0}^{4} = \frac{64}{3}$$

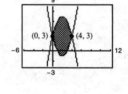

Numerical approximation: 21.333

31. $f(x) = x^4 - 4x^2, \quad g(x) = x^2 - 4$

The points of intersection are given by:

$$x^4 - 4x^2 = x^2 - 4$$

$$x^4 - 5x^2 + 4 = 0$$

$$(x^2 - 4)(x^2 - 1) = 0 \quad \text{when} \quad x = \pm 2, \pm 1$$

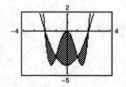

—CONTINUED—

31. —CONTINUED—

By symmetry,

$$A = 2\int_0^1 [(x^4 - 4x^2) - (x^2 - 4)]\, dx + 2\int_1^2 [(x^2 - 4) - (x^4 - 4x^2)]\, dx$$

$$= 2\int_0^1 (x^4 - 5x^2 + 4)\, dx + 2\int_1^2 (-x^4 + 5x^2 - 4)\, dx$$

$$= 2\left[\frac{x^5}{5} - \frac{5x^3}{3} + 4x\right]_0^1 + 2\left[-\frac{x^5}{5} + \frac{5x^3}{3} - 4x\right]_1^2$$

$$= 2\left[\frac{1}{5} - \frac{5}{3} + 4\right] + 2\left[\left(-\frac{32}{5} + \frac{40}{3} - 8\right) - \left(-\frac{1}{5} + \frac{5}{3} - 4\right)\right] = 8.$$

Numerical approximation: $5.067 + 2.933 = 8.0$

33. The graph of the region is shown in the figure. To find the points of intersection, solve the equation $f(x) = g(x)$.

$$\frac{1}{1 + x^2} = \frac{x^2}{2}$$

$$x^4 + x^2 - 2 = 0$$

$$(x^2 + 2)(x^2 - 1) = 0$$

$$(x^2 + 2)(x + 1)(x - 1) = 0 \implies x = \pm 1$$

Therefore, the points of intersection are $\left(-1, \frac{1}{2}\right)$ and $\left(1, \frac{1}{2}\right)$. Using the integration capabilities of a graphing utility and symmetry, we have

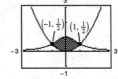

$$\text{Area} = \int_{-1}^{1} [f(x) - g(x)]\, dx$$

$$= 2\int_0^1 \left(\frac{1}{1 + x^2} - \frac{x^2}{2}\right) dx = \frac{\pi}{2} - \frac{1}{3} \approx 1.237.$$

35. $\sqrt{1 + x^3} \le \frac{1}{2}x + 2$ on $[0, 2]$

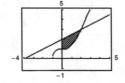

Numerical approximation: 1.759

$$A = \int_0^2 \left[\frac{1}{2}x + 2 - \sqrt{1 + x^3}\right] dx \approx 1.759$$

37. Since f and g are symmetric to the origin, the area of the region bounded by their graphs for $-\pi/3 \le x \le \pi/3$ is twice the area of the region bounded by their graphs for $0 \le x \le \pi/3$. Since $\tan x \le 2\sin x$ for $0 \le x \le \pi/3$, we have

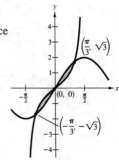

$$\text{Area} = 2\int_0^{\pi/3} (2\sin x - \tan x)\, dx$$

$$= 2\left[-2\cos x + \ln|\cos x|\right]_0^{\pi/3}$$

$$= 2\left[-2\left(\frac{1}{2}\right) + \ln\left(\frac{1}{2}\right) - (-2)\right]$$

$$= 2(1 - \ln 2) \approx 0.614.$$

39. $A = \displaystyle\int_0^1 \left[xe^{-x^2} - 0 \right] dx$

$= \left[-\dfrac{1}{2}e^{-x^2} \right]_0^1$

$= \dfrac{1}{2}\left(1 - \dfrac{1}{e} \right) \approx 0.316$

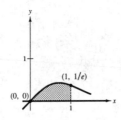

41. $A = \displaystyle\int_0^\pi \left[(2 \sin x + \sin 2x) - 0 \right] dx$

$= \left[-2 \cos x - \dfrac{1}{2}\cos 2x \right]_0^\pi = 4.0$

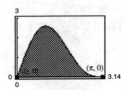

43. The graph of the region is shown in the figure. Using the integration capabilities of a graphing utility, we have

$\text{Area} = \displaystyle\int_1^3 \left(\dfrac{1}{x^2}e^{1/x} - 0 \right) dx = \int_1^3 \dfrac{1}{x^2}e^{1/x}\, dx \approx 1.323.$

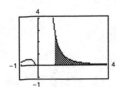

45. (a) $y = \sqrt{\dfrac{x^3}{4 - x}}, \quad y = 0, \quad x = 3$

(b) $A = \displaystyle\int_0^3 \sqrt{\dfrac{x^3}{4 - x}}\, dx,$

No, it cannot be evaluated by hand.

(c) 4.7721

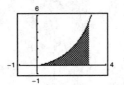

47. From the figure, observe that the triangular region is bounded by $y = (c/b)x$, $y = [c/(b - a)](x - a)$, and $y = 0$. Therefore, the area is given by

$\text{Area} = \displaystyle\int_0^b \dfrac{c}{b}x\, dx + \int_b^a \left(\dfrac{c}{b - a} \right)(x - a)\, dx$

$= \dfrac{c}{b}\left[\dfrac{x^2}{2} \right]_0^b + \left(\dfrac{c}{b - a} \right)\left[\dfrac{x^2}{2} - ax \right]_b^a$

$= \dfrac{1}{2}bc + \left(\dfrac{c}{b - a} \right)\left[\left(\dfrac{a^2}{2} - a^2 \right) - \left(\dfrac{b^2}{2} - ab \right) \right]$

$= \dfrac{1}{2}bc + \dfrac{1}{2}(a - b)c = \dfrac{1}{2}ac.$

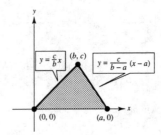

49. Since $f(x) = x^3$, $f'(x) = 3x^2$, and $f'(1) = 3$ (slope of the tangent line), the equation of the tangent line to the graph of f is given by

$y - 1 = 3(x - 1)$

$y = 3x - 2.$

The x-coordinates of the points of intersection of the tangent line and the function are the solutions to the equation

$x^3 = 3x - 2$

$x^3 - 3x + 2 = 0$

$(x - 1)(x^2 + x - 2) = 0$

$(x - 1)^2(x + 2) = 0 \implies x = -2, 1.$

Therefore, the points of intersection are given by $(1, 1)$ and $(-2, -8)$. (See the figure.)

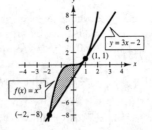

$\text{Area} = \displaystyle\int_{-2}^1 \left[x^3 - (3x - 2) \right] dx = \int_{-2}^1 (x^3 - 3x + 2)\, dx = \left[\dfrac{1}{4}x^4 - \dfrac{3}{2}x^2 + 2x \right]_{-2}^1 = \left(\dfrac{1}{4} - \dfrac{3}{2} + 2 \right) - (4 - 6 - 4) = \dfrac{27}{4}$

51. $x^4 - 2x^2 + 1 \le 1 - x^2$ on $[-1, 1]$

$$A = \int_{-1}^{1} [(1 - x^2) - (x^4 - 2x^2 + 1)] \, dx$$

$$= \int_{-1}^{1} (x^2 - x^4) \, dx$$

$$= \left[\frac{x^3}{3} - \frac{x^5}{5} \right]_{-1}^{1} = \frac{4}{15}$$

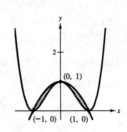

You can use a single integral because $x^4 - 2x^2 + 1 \le 1 - x^2$ on $[-1, 1]$.

53.

$$A = \int_{-3}^{3} (9 - x^2) \, dx = 36$$

$$\int_{-\sqrt{9-b}}^{\sqrt{9-b}} [(9 - x^2) - b] \, dx = 18$$

$$\int_{0}^{\sqrt{9-b}} [(9 - b) - x^2] \, dx = 9$$

$$\left[(9 - b)x - \frac{x^3}{3} \right]_{0}^{\sqrt{9-b}} = 9$$

$$\frac{2}{3}(9 - b)^{3/2} = 9$$

$$(9 - b)^{3/2} = \frac{27}{2}$$

$$9 - b = \frac{9}{\sqrt[3]{4}}$$

$$b = 9 - \frac{9}{\sqrt[3]{4}} \approx 3.330$$

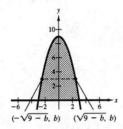

55. $\displaystyle \lim_{\|\Delta\| \to 0} \sum_{i=1}^{n} (x_i - x_i^2) \, \Delta x$

where $x_i = \dfrac{i}{n}$ and $\Delta x = \dfrac{1}{n}$ is the same as

$$\int_{0}^{1} (x - x^2) \, dx = \left[\frac{x^2}{2} - \frac{x^3}{3} \right]_{0}^{1} = \frac{1}{6}.$$

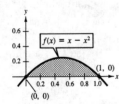

57. The reduction in revenue is approximated by the area between the two models over the interval $0 \le t \le 5$.

$$\int_{0}^{5} [(7.21 + 0.58t) - (7.21 + 0.45t)] \, dt = \int_{0}^{5} 0.13t \, dt$$

$$= \left[\frac{0.13t^2}{2} \right]_{0}^{5}$$

$$= \$1.625 \text{ billion}$$

59. $f(t) = \begin{cases} 27.77 - 0.36t & 5 \le t \le 10 \\ 21.00 + 0.27t & 10 \le t \le 14 \end{cases}$

(a)

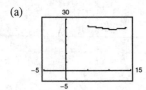

(b) $\displaystyle\int_{10}^{14} [(21.00 + 0.27t) - (27.77 - 0.36t)] \, dt = \int_{10}^{14} [-6.77 + 0.63t] \, dt$

$$= \left[-6.77t + 0.315t^2 \right]_{10}^{14} = 3.16 \text{ billion pounds}$$

61. 5%: $P_1 = 893,000 \, e^{(0.05)t}$

$3\frac{1}{2}$%: $P_2 = 893,000 \, e^{(0.035)t}$

Difference in profits over 5 years:

$$\int_0^5 [893,000e^{0.05t} - 893,000e^{0.035t}] \, dt = 893,000 \left[\frac{e^{0.05t}}{0.05} - \frac{e^{0.035t}}{0.035} \right]_0^5$$

$$\approx 893,000[(25.6805 - 34.0356) - (20 - 28.5714)]$$

$$\approx 893,000(0.2163) \approx \$193,156$$

Note: Using a graphing utility you obtain $193,183.

63. The total area is 8 times the area of the shaded region to the right. A point (x, y) is on the upper boundary of the region if

$$\sqrt{x^2 + y^2} = 2 - y$$

$$x^2 + y^2 = 4 - 4y + y^2$$

$$x^2 = 4 - 4y$$

$$4y = 4 - x^2$$

$$y = 1 - \frac{x^2}{4}.$$

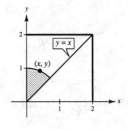

We now determine where this curve intersects the line $y = x$.

$$x = 1 - \frac{x^2}{4}$$

$$x^2 + 4x - 4 = 0$$

$$x = \frac{-4 \pm \sqrt{16 + 16}}{2} = -2 \pm 2\sqrt{2} \implies x = -2 + 2\sqrt{2}$$

Total area $= 8 \displaystyle\int_0^{-2+2\sqrt{2}} \left(1 - \frac{x^2}{4} - x \right) dx$

$$= 8 \left[x - \frac{x^3}{12} - \frac{x^2}{2} \right]_0^{-2+2\sqrt{2}} \approx 8(0.4379) = 3.503$$

65. (a) $A = 2 \left[\displaystyle\int_0^5 \left(1 - \frac{1}{3} \sqrt{5 - x} \right) dx + \int_5^{5.5} (1 - 0) \, dx \right]$

$$= 2 \left(\left[x + \frac{2}{9} (5 - x)^{3/2} \right]_0^5 + \left[x \right]_5^{5.5} \right) = 2 \left(5 - \frac{10\sqrt{5}}{9} + 5.5 - 5 \right) \approx 6.031 \text{ m}^2$$

(b) $V = 2A \approx 2(6.031) \approx 12.062 \text{ m}^3$

(c) $5000 \, V \approx 5000(12.062) = 60,310$ pounds

67. Solving the equations simultaneously yields the point of equilibrium to be (80, 10). Therefore,

$$\text{Consumer Surplus} = \int_0^{80} [(50 - 0.5x) - 10]\, dx$$

$$= \left[40x - 0.25x^2 \right]_0^{80} = 1600$$

$$\text{Producer Surplus} = \int_0^{80} (10 - 0.125x)\, dx$$

$$= \left[10x - 0.0625x^2 \right]_0^{80} = 400.$$

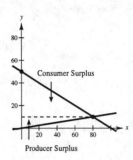

69. True

Section 6.2   Volume: The Disc Method

1. $V = \pi \int_0^1 (-x + 1)^2\, dx = \pi \int_0^1 (x^2 - 2x + 1)\, dx = \pi \left[\dfrac{x^3}{3} - x^2 + x \right]_0^1 = \dfrac{\pi}{3}$

3. $V = \pi \int_1^4 (\sqrt{x})^2\, dx = \pi \int_1^4 x\, dx = \pi \left[\dfrac{x^2}{2} \right]_1^4 = \dfrac{15\pi}{2}$

5. From the figure we have

$R(x) = x^2$ Outer radius

$r(x) = x^3.$ Inner radius

Now, integrating between 0 and 1, we have

$$V = \pi \int_a^b ([R(x)]^2 - [r(x)]^2)\, dx$$

$$= \pi \int_0^1 (x^4 - x^6)\, dx$$

$$= \pi \left[\dfrac{x^5}{5} - \dfrac{x^7}{7} \right]_0^1 = \pi \left(\dfrac{1}{5} - \dfrac{1}{7} \right) = \dfrac{2\pi}{35}.$$

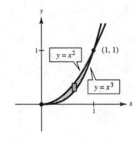

7. $y = x^2 \implies x = \sqrt{y}$

$$V = \pi \int_0^4 (\sqrt{y})^2\, dy = \pi \int_0^4 y\, dy = \pi \left[\dfrac{y^2}{2} \right]_0^4 = 8\pi$$

9. $y = x^{2/3} \implies x = y^{3/2}$

$$V = \pi \int_0^1 (y^{3/2})^2\, dy = \pi \int_0^1 y^3\, dy = \pi \left[\dfrac{y^4}{4} \right]_0^1 = \dfrac{\pi}{4}$$

11. (a) From the figure, we have

$R(x) = y = \sqrt{x}.$

$$V = \pi \int_a^b ([R(x)]^2 - [r(x)]^2)\, dx$$

$$= \pi \int_0^4 (\sqrt{x})^2\, dx$$

$$= \pi \int_0^4 x\, dx = \pi \left[\dfrac{x^2}{2} \right]_0^4 = \dfrac{16\pi}{2} = 8\pi$$

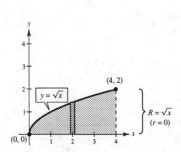

—CONTINUED—

11. **—CONTINUED—**

(b) From the figure we have

$R(y) = 4$ Outer radius

$r(y) = y^2.$ Inner radius

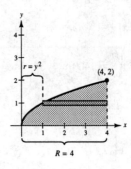

$V = \pi \int_a^b \left([R(y)]^2 - [r(y)]^2 \right) dy$

$= \pi \int_0^2 \left[4^2 - (y^2)^2 \right] dy$

$= \pi \int_0^2 (16 - y^4) \, dy$

$= \left[16y - \dfrac{y^5}{5} \right]_0^2$

$= \pi \left[32 - \dfrac{32}{5} \right] = \dfrac{128\pi}{5}$

(c) From the figure, we have

$R(y) = 4 - y^2.$

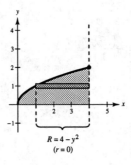

$V = \pi \int_a^b \left([R(y)]^2 - [r(y)]^2 \right) dy$

$= \pi \int_0^2 (4 - y^2)^2 \, dy$

$= \pi \int_0^2 (16 - 8y^2 + y^4) \, dy$

$= \pi \left[16y - \dfrac{8y^3}{3} + \dfrac{y^5}{5} \right]_0^2$

$= \pi \left[32 - \dfrac{64}{3} + \dfrac{32}{5} \right] = \dfrac{256\pi}{15}$

(d) From the figure, we have

$R(y) = 6 - y^2$ Outer radius

$r(y) = 2.$ Inner radius

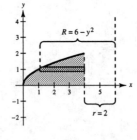

$V = \pi \int_a^b \left([R(y)]^2 - [r(y)]^2 \right) dy$

$= \pi \int_0^2 \left[(6 - y^2)^2 - 2^2 \right] dy$

$= \pi \int_0^2 (32 - 12y^2 + y^4) \, dy$

$= \pi \left[32y - 4y^3 + \dfrac{y^5}{5} \right]_0^2$

$= \pi \left[64 - 32 + \dfrac{32}{5} \right] = \dfrac{192\pi}{5}$

13. The points of intersection of the graphs of the two functions are $(0, 0)$ and $(2, 4)$.

(a) From the figure, we have

$$R(x) = 4x - x^2 \quad \text{Outer radius}$$

$$r(x) = x^2. \quad \text{Inner radius}$$

$$V = \pi \int_a^b ([R(x)]^2 - [r(x)]^2)\, dx$$

$$= \pi \int_0^2 [(4x - x^2)^2 - (x^2)^2]\, dx$$

$$= \pi \int_0^2 (16x^2 - 8x^3)\, dx$$

$$= \pi \left[\frac{16}{3}x^3 - 2x^4 \right]_0^2$$

$$= 8\pi \left[\frac{16}{3} - 4 \right]$$

$$= \frac{32\pi}{3}$$

(b) From the figure, we have

$$R(y) = 6 - (4x - x^2) \quad \text{Outer radius}$$

$$r(y) = 6 - x^2. \quad \text{Inner radius}$$

$$V = \pi \int_a^b ([R(x)]^2 - [r(x)]^2)\, dx$$

$$= \pi \int_0^2 [(6 - x^2)^2 - (6 - 4x + x^2)^2]\, dx$$

$$= 8\pi \int_0^2 (x^3 - 5x^2 + 6x)\, dx$$

$$= 8\pi \left[\frac{x^4}{4} - \frac{5}{3}x^3 + 3x^2 \right]_0^2$$

$$= 32\pi \left(1 - \frac{10}{3} + 3 \right)$$

$$= \frac{64\pi}{3}$$

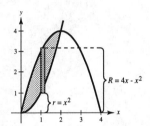

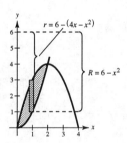

15. $R(x) = 4 - x, \ r(x) = 1$

$$V = \pi \int_0^3 [(4 - x)^2 - (1)^2]\, dx$$

$$= \pi \int_0^3 (x^2 - 8x + 15)\, dx$$

$$= \pi \left[\frac{x^3}{3} - 4x^2 + 15x \right]_0^3$$

$$= 18\pi$$

17. $R(x) = 4, \ r(x) = 4 - \dfrac{1}{x}$

$$V = \pi \int_1^4 \left[(4)^2 - \left(4 - \frac{1}{x} \right)^2 \right] dx$$

$$= \pi \int_1^4 \left(\frac{8}{x} - \frac{1}{x^2} \right) dx$$

$$= \pi \left[8 \ln|x| + \frac{1}{x} \right]_1^4$$

$$= \pi \left(8 \ln 4 - \frac{3}{4} \right)$$

$$\approx 32.49$$

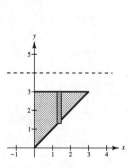

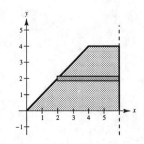

19. $R(y) = 6 - y, \ r(y) = 0$

$$V = \pi \int_0^4 (6 - y)^2\, dy$$

$$= \pi \int_0^4 (y^2 - 12y + 36)\, dy$$

$$= \pi \left[\frac{y^3}{3} - 6y^2 + 36y \right]_0^4 = \frac{208\pi}{3}$$

21. From the figure, we have

$$R(y) = 6 - y^2 \qquad \text{Outer radius}$$

$$r(y) = 2. \qquad \text{Inner radius}$$

$$V = \pi \int_{-2}^{2} [(6 - y^2)^2 - (2)^2]\, dy$$

$$= 2\pi \int_{0}^{2} (y^4 - 12y^2 + 32)\, dy = 2\pi \left[\frac{y^5}{5} - 4y^3 + 32y \right]_{0}^{2} = \frac{384\pi}{5}$$

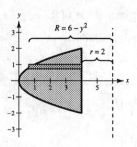

23. $R(x) = \dfrac{1}{\sqrt{x + 1}},\ r(x) = 0$

$$V = \pi \int_{0}^{3} \left(\frac{1}{\sqrt{x + 1}} \right)^2 dx$$

$$= \pi \int_{0}^{3} \frac{1}{x + 1}\, dx$$

$$= \left[\pi \ln|x + 1| \right]_{0}^{3}$$

$$= \pi \ln 4$$

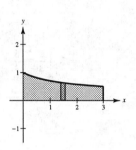

25. $R(x) = \dfrac{1}{x},\ r(x) = 0$

$$V = \pi \int_{1}^{4} \left(\frac{1}{x} \right)^2 dx$$

$$= \pi \left[-\frac{1}{x} \right]_{1}^{4}$$

$$= \frac{3\pi}{4}$$

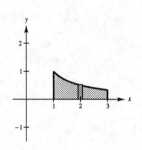

27. $V = \pi \displaystyle\int_{0}^{1} (e^{-x})^2\, dx$

$$= \pi \int_{0}^{1} e^{-2x}\, dx = \left[-\frac{\pi}{2} e^{-2x} \right]_{0}^{1} = \frac{\pi}{2}\left(1 - \frac{1}{e^2} \right) \approx 1.358$$

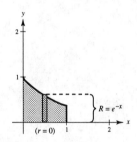

29. $y = 6 - 3x \implies x = \dfrac{1}{3}(6 - y)$

$$V = \pi \int_{0}^{6} \left[\frac{1}{3}(6 - y) \right]^2 dy$$

$$= \frac{\pi}{9} \int_{0}^{6} [36 - 12y + y^2]\, dy$$

$$= \frac{\pi}{9} \left[36y - 6y^2 + \frac{y^3}{3} \right]_{0}^{6}$$

$$= \frac{\pi}{9} \left[216 - 216 + \frac{216}{3} \right]$$

$$= 8\pi$$

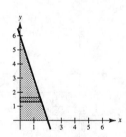

31. $V = \pi \displaystyle\int_{0}^{\pi} [\sin x]^2\, dx \approx 4.9348$

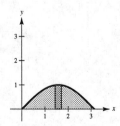

33. $V = \pi \displaystyle\int_{0}^{2} [e^{-x^2}]^2\, dx \approx 1.9686$

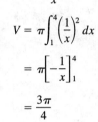

35. From the figure we have $R(x) = e^{x/2} + e^{-x/2}$ and $r(x) = 0$. Using a graphing utility to approximate the definite integral yields

$$V = \pi \int_{-1}^{2} (e^{x/2} + e^{-x/2})\, dx \approx 49.02.$$

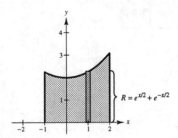

37. $A \approx 3$

Matches (a)

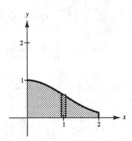

39. (a) $R(x) = 4x - x^2$, $r(x) = 0$

$$V = \pi \int_{0}^{4} (4x - x^2)^2\, dx$$

$$= \pi \int_{0}^{4} (16x^2 - 8x^3 + x^4)\, dx$$

$$= \pi \left[\frac{16}{3}x^3 - 2x^4 + \frac{x^5}{5} \right]_{0}^{4}$$

$$= \frac{512\pi}{15}$$

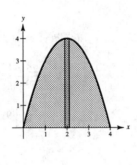

(b) Completing the square, we have

$$4x - x^2 = 4 - (x^2 - 4x + 4)$$

$$= 4 - (x - 2)^2.$$

Thus, $y = 4 - x^2$ has the same volume as in part (a) since the solid has been translated only horizontally.

41. $R(x) = \dfrac{1}{2}x$, $r(x) = 0$

$$V = \pi \int_{0}^{6} \frac{1}{4}x^2\, dx$$

$$= \left[\frac{\pi}{12}x^3 \right]_{0}^{6} = 18\pi$$

Note: $V = \dfrac{1}{3}\pi r^2 h$

$$= \frac{1}{3}\pi(3^2)6$$

$$= 18\pi$$

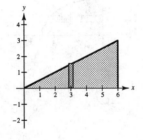

43. Let $y = \sqrt{r^2 - x^2}$ and let the region bounded by $y = \sqrt{r^2 - x^2}$ and $y = 0$ be revolved about the x-axis. The resulting solid of revolution is a sphere with volume

$$V = \pi \int_{-r}^{r} \left(\sqrt{r^2 - x^2} \right)^2 dx$$

$$= \pi \int_{-r}^{r} (r^2 - x^2)\, dx$$

$$= \pi \left[r^2 x - \frac{x^3}{3} \right]_{-r}^{r}$$

$$= \pi \left[\left(r^3 - \frac{r^3}{3} \right) - \left(-r^3 + \frac{r^3}{3} \right) \right] = \frac{4\pi r^3}{3}.$$

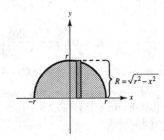

45. $x = r - \dfrac{r}{H}y = r\left(1 - \dfrac{y}{H}\right)$, $R(y) = r\left(1 - \dfrac{y}{H}\right)$, $r(y) = 0$

$$V = \pi \int_0^h \left[r\left(1 - \dfrac{y}{H}\right)\right]^2 dy = \pi r^2 \int_0^h \left(1 - \dfrac{2}{H}y + \dfrac{1}{H^2}y^2\right) dy$$

$$= \pi r^2 \left[y - \dfrac{1}{H}y^2 + \dfrac{1}{3H^2}y^3\right]_0^h$$

$$= \pi r^2 \left(h - \dfrac{h^2}{H} + \dfrac{h^3}{3H^2}\right)$$

$$= \pi r^2 h\left(1 - \dfrac{h}{H} + \dfrac{h^2}{3H^2}\right)$$

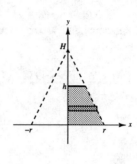

47. $V = \pi \int_0^2 \left(\dfrac{1}{8}x^2 \sqrt{2-x}\right)^2 dx = \dfrac{\pi}{64} \int_0^2 x^4(2-x)\, dx = \dfrac{\pi}{64}\left[\dfrac{2x^5}{5} - \dfrac{x^6}{6}\right]_0^2 = \dfrac{\pi}{30}$

49. (a) $R(x) = \dfrac{3}{5}\sqrt{25 - x^2}$, $r(x) = 0$

$$V = \dfrac{9\pi}{25} \int_{-5}^5 (25 - x^2)\, dx$$

$$= \dfrac{18\pi}{25} \int_0^5 (25 - x^2)\, dx$$

$$= \dfrac{18\pi}{25}\left[25x - \dfrac{x^3}{3}\right]_0^5 = 60\pi$$

(b) $R(y) = \dfrac{5}{3}\sqrt{9 - y^2}$, $r(y) = 0$, $x \geq 0$

$$V = \dfrac{25\pi}{9} \int_0^3 (9 - y^2)\, dy$$

$$= \dfrac{25\pi}{9}\left[9y - \dfrac{y^3}{3}\right]_0^3 = 50\pi$$

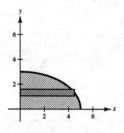

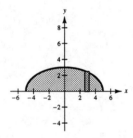

51. The total volume of the sphere is

$$V = \dfrac{4}{3}\pi r^3 = \dfrac{4\pi(50)^3}{3} = \dfrac{500{,}000\pi}{3}\ \text{ft}^3.$$

The volume of the portion filled with water (see figure) is

$$\dfrac{1}{4}V = \dfrac{125{,}000\pi}{3} = \pi \int_{-50}^{y_0} \left(\sqrt{2500 - y^2}\right)^2 dy$$

$$= \pi \int_{-50}^{y_0} (2500 - y^2)\, dy = \pi\left[2500y - \dfrac{y^3}{3}\right]_{-50}^{y_0}$$

$$= \pi\left[\left(2500y_0 - \dfrac{y_0^3}{3}\right) - \left(-125{,}000 + \dfrac{125{,}000}{3}\right)\right] = \pi\left[2500y_0 - \dfrac{y_0^3}{3} + \dfrac{250{,}000}{3}\right].$$

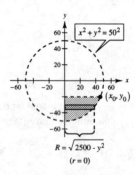

Simplifying yields the equation $y_0^3 - 7500y_0 - 125{,}000 = 0$.

Using the root-finding capabilities of a graphing utility yields the approximate root $y_0 = -17.36$. When the tank is one-fourth full the approximate depth of the water is $[-17.36 - (-50)] = 32.64$ feet. By symmetry, the tank is three-fourth full when the depth of the water is 67.36 feet.

53. (a) $\pi \displaystyle\int_0^h r^2\, dx$ (ii)

is the volume of a right circular cylinder with radius r and height h.

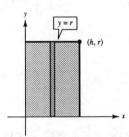

(b) $\pi \displaystyle\int_{-b}^b \left(a\sqrt{1 - \dfrac{x^2}{b^2}} \right)^2 dx$ (iv)

is the volume of an ellipsoid with axes $2a$ and $2b$.

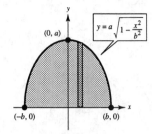

(c) $\pi \displaystyle\int_{-r}^r \left(\sqrt{r^2 - x^2} \right)^2 dx$ (iii)

is the volume of a sphere with radius r.

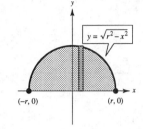

(d) $\pi \displaystyle\int_0^h \left(\dfrac{rx}{h} \right)^2 dx$ (i)

is the volume of a right circular cone with the radius of the base as r and height h.

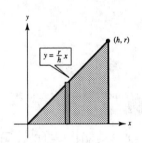

(e) $\pi \displaystyle\int_{-r}^r \left[\left(R + \sqrt{r^2 - x^2} \right)^2 - \left(R - \sqrt{r^2 - x^2} \right)^2 \right] dx$ (v)

is the volume of a torus with the radius of its circular cross section as r and the distance from the axis of the torus to the center of its cross section as R.

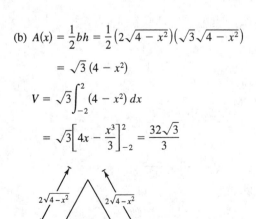

55.

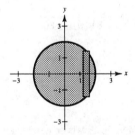

Base of cross section $= 2\sqrt{4 - x^2}$

(a) $A(x) = b^2 = \left(2\sqrt{4 - x^2} \right)^2$

$$V = \int_{-2}^2 4(4 - x^2)\, dx$$

$$= 4\left[4x - \frac{x^3}{3} \right]_{-2}^2 = \frac{128}{3}$$

(b) $A(x) = \dfrac{1}{2}bh = \dfrac{1}{2}\left(2\sqrt{4 - x^2} \right)\left(\sqrt{3}\sqrt{4 - x^2} \right)$

$$= \sqrt{3}\,(4 - x^2)$$

$$V = \sqrt{3} \int_{-2}^2 (4 - x^2)\, dx$$

$$= \sqrt{3}\left[4x - \frac{x^3}{3} \right]_{-2}^2 = \frac{32\sqrt{3}}{3}$$

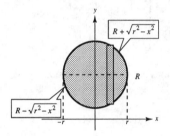

—CONTINUED—

55. —CONTINUED—

(c) $A(x) = \frac{1}{2}\pi r^2 = \frac{\pi}{2}\left(\sqrt{4-x^2}\right)^2 = \frac{\pi}{2}(4-x^2)$

$V = \frac{\pi}{2}\int_{-2}^{2}(4-x^2)\,dx = \frac{\pi}{2}\left[4x - \frac{x^3}{3}\right]_{-2}^{2} = \frac{16\pi}{3}$

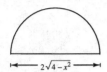

(d) $A(x) = \frac{1}{2}bh = \frac{1}{2}\left(2\sqrt{4-x^2}\right)\left(\sqrt{4-x^2}\right) = 4-x^2$

$V = \int_{-2}^{2}(4-x^2)\,dx = \left[4x - \frac{x^3}{3}\right]_{-2}^{2} = \frac{32}{3}$

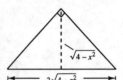

57. The base of the solid is shown in the figure. Since the cross sections are taken perpendicular to the *y*-axis, the base of each cross section is given by $(1-x) = \left(1 - \sqrt[3]{y}\right)$.

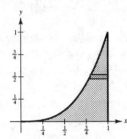

(a) The cross sections are squares whose sides are given by $s = \left(1 - \sqrt[3]{y}\right)$. Thus, $A(y) = s^2 = \left(1 - \sqrt[3]{y}\right)^2$ and

$V = \int_{0}^{1}\left(1 - \sqrt[3]{y}\right)^2 dy = \int_{0}^{1}\left(1 - 2y^{1/3} + y^{2/3}\right) dy$

$= \left[y - \frac{2y^{4/3}}{4/3} + \frac{y^{5/3}}{5/3}\right]_{0}^{1} = 1 - \frac{3}{2} + \frac{3}{5} = \frac{1}{10}.$

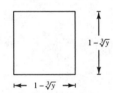

(b) The cross sections are semicircles whose radii are given by $r = \left(\frac{1}{2}\right)\left(1 - \sqrt[3]{y}\right)$. Thus,

$A(y) = \left(\frac{1}{2}\right)\pi\left[\left(\frac{1}{2}\right)\left(1 - \sqrt[3]{y}\right)\right]^2 = \frac{\pi}{8}\left(1 - \sqrt[3]{y}\right)^2$

and

$V = \frac{\pi}{8}\int_{0}^{1}\left(1 - \sqrt[3]{y}\right)^2 dy = \frac{\pi}{8}\left(\frac{1}{10}\right) = \frac{\pi}{80}.$ From part (a)

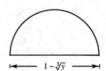

(c) The cross sections are equilateral triangles whose sides are given by $1 - \sqrt[3]{y}$. Thus,

$A(y) = \frac{1}{2}bh = \frac{1}{2}\left(1 - \sqrt[3]{y}\right)\left[\frac{\sqrt{3}}{2}\left(1 - \sqrt[3]{y}\right)\right]$

$= \frac{\sqrt{3}}{4}\left(1 - \sqrt[3]{y}\right)^2$

and

$V = \frac{\sqrt{3}}{4}\int_{0}^{1}\left(1 - \sqrt[3]{y}\right)^2 dy$

$= \frac{\sqrt{3}}{4}\left(\frac{1}{10}\right) = \frac{\sqrt{3}}{40}.$ From part (a)

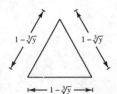

(d) The cross sections are semiellipses whose heights are twice the lengths of their bases. Thus $a = 2b$, where $b = 1 - \sqrt[3]{y}$. Thus,

$A(y) = \left(\frac{1}{2}\right)\pi(a)\left(\frac{b}{2}\right) = \frac{\pi}{2}b^2 = \frac{\pi}{2}\left(1 - \sqrt[3]{y}\right)^2$

and

$V = \frac{\pi}{2}\int_{0}^{1}\left(1 - \sqrt[3]{y}\right)^2 dy = \frac{\pi}{2}\left(\frac{1}{10}\right) = \frac{\pi}{20}.$ From part (a)

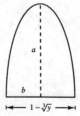

59. Assume that the oil just hits the top of the cylinder, which means that the volume of oil is one-half of the volume of the cylinder. Then we have

$$\sin 20° = \frac{d \sin 70°}{h}$$

$$h = \frac{d \sin 70°}{\sin 20°}$$

$$\text{Volume} = \frac{1}{2}(\pi r^2 h)$$

$$= \frac{\pi}{2}\left(\frac{d}{2}\right)^2\left(\frac{d \sin 70°}{\sin 20°}\right)$$

$$= \frac{\pi d^3 \sin 70°}{8 \sin 20°} = \pi d^3 \cot 20°.$$

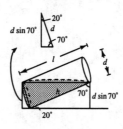

61. (a) Since $\theta = 45°$, the cross sections are isosceles right triangles for which the base and height are equal. Thus,

$$A(x) = \frac{1}{2}bh$$

$$= \frac{1}{2}\left(\sqrt{r^2 - x^2}\right)\left(\sqrt{r^2 - x^2}\right) = \frac{1}{2}(r^2 - x^2)$$

and

$$V = \frac{1}{2}\int_{-r}^{r}(r^2 - x^2)\,dx$$

$$= \frac{1}{2}\left[r^2 x - \frac{x^3}{3}\right]_{-r}^{r}$$

$$= \frac{1}{2}\left[\left(r^3 - \frac{r^3}{3}\right) - \left(-r^3 + \frac{r^3}{3}\right)\right] = \frac{2r^3}{3}\text{ in}^3.$$

(b) For the arbitrary angle θ, $(0 < \theta < 90°)$, the cross sections are right triangles with base $\sqrt{r^2 - x^2}$ and height $\sqrt{r^2 - x^2}\tan\theta$. Thus,

$$A(x) = \frac{1}{2}bh$$

$$= \frac{1}{2}\left(\sqrt{r^2 - x^2}\right)\left(\sqrt{r^2 - x^2}\right)\tan\theta$$

$$= \frac{1}{2}(r^2 - x^2)\tan\theta.$$

Since the integration is with respect to x, we can use the result of part (a) and determine that the volume is

$$V = \frac{2r^3}{3}(\tan\theta).$$

As θ increases, the volume of the wedge increases.

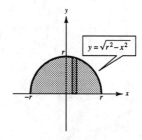

63. $\dfrac{4}{3}\pi(25 - r^2)^{3/2} = \dfrac{1}{2}\left(\dfrac{4}{3}\right)\pi(125)$

$$(25 - r^2)^{3/2} = \frac{125}{2}$$

$$25 - r^2 = \left(\frac{125}{2}\right)^{2/3}$$

$$25 - \frac{25}{(2^{2/3})} = r^2$$

$$25(1 - 2^{-2/3}) = r^2$$

$$r = 5\sqrt{1 - 2^{-2/3}} \approx 3.0415$$

Section 6.3   Volume: The Shell Method

1. $p(x) = x$

$h(x) = x$

$V = 2\pi \int_0^2 x(x)\, dx = \left[\dfrac{2\pi x^3}{3} \right]_0^2 = \dfrac{16\pi}{3}$

3. $p(x) = x$

$h(x) = \sqrt{x}$

$V = 2\pi \int_0^4 x\sqrt{x}\, dx$

$= 2\pi \int_0^4 x^{3/2}\, dx = \left[\dfrac{4\pi}{5} x^{5/2} \right]_0^4 = \dfrac{128\pi}{5}$

5. $p(x) = x$

$h(x) = x^2$

$V = 2\pi \int_0^2 x^3\, dx$

$= \left[\dfrac{\pi}{2} x^4 \right]_0^2 = 8\pi$

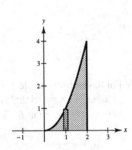

7. The distance from the center of the rectangle to the axis of revolution is $p(x) = x$, and the height of the rectangle is $h(x) = (4x - x^2) - (x^2)$.

$V = 2\pi \int_a^b p(x)h(x)\, dx$

$= 2\pi \int_0^2 x[(4x - x^2) - (x^2)]\, dx$

$= 2\pi \int_0^2 x(4x - 2x^2)\, dx$

$= 4\pi \int_0^2 (2x^2 - x^3)\, dx$

$= 4\pi \left[\dfrac{2x^3}{3} - \dfrac{x^4}{4} \right]_0^2 = 4\pi \left[\dfrac{16}{3} - 4 \right] = \dfrac{16\pi}{3}$

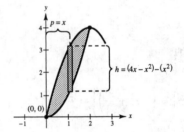

9. $p(x) = x$

$h(x) = 4 - (4x - x^2) = x^2 - 4x + 4$

$V = 2\pi \int_0^2 (x^3 - 4x^2 + 4x)\, dx$

$= 2\pi \left[\dfrac{x^4}{4} - \dfrac{4}{3} x^3 + 2x^2 \right]_0^2 = \dfrac{8\pi}{3}$

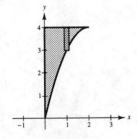

11. $p(x) = x$

$h(x) = \dfrac{1}{\sqrt{2\pi}} e^{-x^2/2}$

$V = 2\pi \int_0^1 x \left(\dfrac{1}{\sqrt{2\pi}} e^{-x^2/2} \right) dx$

$= \sqrt{2\pi} \int_0^1 e^{-x^2/2} x\, dx$

$= \left[-\sqrt{2\pi}\, e^{-x^2/2} \right]_0^1 = \sqrt{2\pi} \left(1 - \dfrac{1}{\sqrt{e}} \right) \approx 0.986$

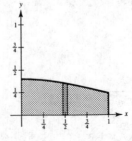

13. The distance from the center of the rectangle to the axis
of revolution is $p(y) = y$, and the height of the rectangle
is $h(y) = 2 - y$.

$$V = 2\pi \int_a^b p(y)h(y)\,dy$$

$$= 2\pi \int_0^2 y(2 - y)\,dy$$

$$= 2\pi \int_0^2 (2y - y)^2\,dy$$

$$= 2\pi \left[y^2 - \frac{y^3}{3} \right]_0^2 = 2\pi \left[4 - \frac{8}{3} \right] = \frac{8\pi}{3}$$

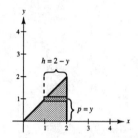

15. $p(y) = y$ and $h(y) = 1$ if $0 \le y < \frac{1}{2}$.

$p(y) = y$ and $h(y) = \dfrac{1}{y} - 1$ if $\dfrac{1}{2} \le y \le 1$.

$$V = 2\pi \int_0^{1/2} y\,dy + 2\pi \int_{1/2}^1 (1 - y)\,dy$$

$$= 2\pi \left[\frac{y^2}{2} \right]_0^{1/2} + 2\pi \left[y - \frac{y^2}{2} \right]_{1/2}^1 = \frac{\pi}{4} + \frac{\pi}{4} = \frac{\pi}{2}$$

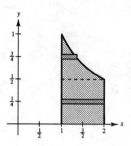

17. The distance from the center of the rectangle to the axis of revolution is $p(x) = 4 - x$, and the height of the rectangle is
$h(x) = (4x - x^2) - (x^2)$.

$$V = 2\pi \int_a^b p(x)h(x)\,dx$$

$$= 2\pi \int_0^2 (4 - x)[(4x - x^2) - (x^2)]\,dx$$

$$= 2\pi \int_0^2 (4 - x)(4x - 2x^2)\,dx$$

$$= 4\pi \int_0^2 (8x - 6x^2 + x^3)\,dx$$

$$= 4\pi \left[4x^2 - 2x^3 + \frac{x^4}{4} \right]_0^2$$

$$= 4\pi[16 - 16 + 4] = 16\pi$$

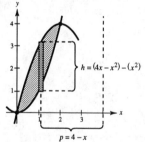

19. $p(x) = 5 - x$

$h(x) = 4x - x^2$

$$V = 2\pi \int_0^4 (5 - x)(4x - x^2)\,dx$$

$$= 2\pi \int_0^4 (x^3 - 9x^2 + 20x)\,dx$$

$$= 2\pi \left[\frac{x^4}{4} - 3x^3 + 10x^2 \right]_0^4 = 64\pi$$

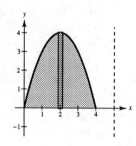

21. (a) Disc Method

$$V = \pi \int_a^b ([R(x)]^2 - [r(x)]^2)\, dx$$

$$= \pi \int_0^2 [(x^3)^2 - (0)^2]\, dx$$

$$= \pi \int_0^2 x^6\, dx$$

$$= \pi \left[\frac{x^7}{7}\right]_0^2 = \frac{128\pi}{7}$$

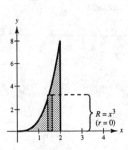

$R = x^3$
$(r = 0)$

(b) Shell Method

$$V = 2\pi \int_a^b p(x)h(x)\, dx$$

$$= 2\pi \int_0^2 x(x^3)\, dx$$

$$= 2\pi \int_0^2 x^4\, dx$$

$$= 2\pi \left[\frac{x^5}{5}\right]_0^2 = \frac{64\pi}{5}$$

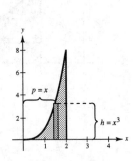

$p = x$

$h = x^3$

(c) Shell Method

$$V = 2\pi \int_a^b p(x)h(x)\, dx$$

$$= 2\pi \int_0^2 (4 - x)x^3\, dx$$

$$= 2\pi \int_0^2 (4x^3 - x^4)\, dx$$

$$= 2\pi \left[x^4 - \frac{x^5}{5}\right]_0^2 = \frac{96\pi}{5}$$

$h = x^3$

$p = 4 - x$

23. (a) Shell

$$p(y) = y$$

$$h(y) = (a^{1/2} - y^{1/2})^2$$

$$V = 2\pi \int_0^a y(a - 2a^{1/2}y^{1/2} + y)\, dy$$

$$= 2\pi \int_0^a (ay - 2a^{1/2}y^{3/2} + y^2)\, dy$$

$$= 2\pi \left[\frac{a}{2}y^2 - \frac{4a^{1/2}}{5}y^{5/2} + \frac{y^3}{3}\right]_0^a$$

$$= 2\pi \left[\frac{a^3}{2} - \frac{4a^3}{5} + \frac{a^3}{3}\right] = \frac{\pi a^3}{15}$$

(c) Shell

$$p(x) = a - x$$

$$h(x) = (a^{1/2} - x^{1/2})^2$$

$$V = 2\pi \int_0^a (a - x)(a^{1/2} - x^{1/2})^2\, dx$$

$$= 2\pi \int_0^a (a^2 - 2a^{3/2}x^{1/2} + 2a^{1/2}x^{3/2} - x^2)\, dx$$

$$= 2\pi \left[a^2x - \frac{4}{3}a^{3/2}x^{3/2} + \frac{4}{5}a^{1/2}x^{5/2} - \frac{1}{3}x^3\right]_0^a = \frac{4\pi a^3}{15}$$

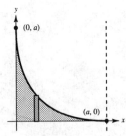

$(0, a)$

$(a, 0)$

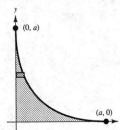

$(0, a)$

$(a, 0)$

(b) Same as part a by symmetry

25. (a) The graph of the region is shown in the figure.

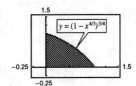

(b) Solving for y in the equation $x^{4/3} + y^{4/3} = 1$ yields $y = \pm(1 - x^{4/3})^{3/4}$. Since the required region is in the first quadrant, $h(x) = (1 - x^{4/3})^{3/4}$. Also, $p(x) = x$. Using a graphing utility to approximate the definite integral yields

$$V = 2\pi \int_a^b p(x)h(x)\, dx$$

$$= 2\pi \int_0^1 x(1 - x^{4/3})^{3/4}\, dx \approx 1.506.$$

27. (a)

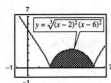

(b) $V = 2\pi \displaystyle\int_2^6 x\sqrt[3]{(x - 2)^2(x - 6)^2}\, dx \approx 187.249$

29. (a)

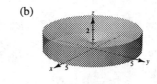

(b)

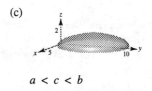

(c)

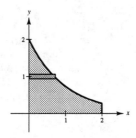

$a < c < b$

31. $y = 2e^{-x},\ y = 0,\ x = 0,\ x = 2$

Volume ≈ 7.5

Matches (d)

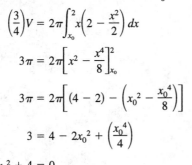

33. The total volume of the solid is given by

$$V = 2\pi \int_0^2 x\left(2 - \frac{x^2}{2}\right) dx = 2\pi \int_0^2 \left(2x - \frac{x^3}{2}\right) dx = 2\pi\left[x^2 - \frac{x^4}{8}\right]_0^2 = 2\pi(4 - 2) = 4\pi.$$

If a hole drilled in the center with a radius of x_0 removes $\frac{1}{4}$ of this volume, we have

$$\left(\frac{3}{4}\right)V = 2\pi \int_{x_0}^2 x\left(2 - \frac{x^2}{2}\right) dx$$

$$3\pi = 2\pi\left[x^2 - \frac{x^4}{8}\right]_{x_0}^2$$

$$3\pi = 2\pi\left[(4 - 2) - \left(x_0^2 - \frac{x_0^4}{8}\right)\right]$$

$$3 = 4 - 2x_0^2 + \left(\frac{x_0^4}{4}\right)$$

$$x_0^4 - 8x_0^2 + 4 = 0$$

$$x_0^2 = \frac{8 \pm \sqrt{64 - 16}}{2}$$

$$x_0 = \sqrt{4 - 2\sqrt{3}}.$$

(Since $0 < x_0 < 2$, you are not interested in $x_0 = \sqrt{4 + 2\sqrt{3}} \approx 2.7$.) Finally, since radius $= x_0 = \sqrt{4 - 2\sqrt{3}} = 0.732$ we have diameter $= 2x_0 = 2\sqrt{4 - 2\sqrt{3}} \approx 1.464$.

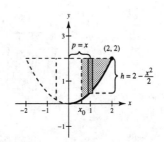

35. $x = \sqrt{r^2 - \left(\dfrac{h}{2}\right)^2} = \dfrac{\sqrt{4r^2 - h^2}}{2}$

$V = 4\pi \displaystyle\int_{\sqrt{4r^2-h^2}/2}^{r} x\sqrt{r^2 - x^2}\, dx = \left[-2\pi\left(\dfrac{2}{3}\right)(r^2 - x^2)^{3/2}\right]_{\sqrt{4r^2-h^2}/2}^{r}$

$= 0 + \dfrac{4\pi}{3}\left[r^2 - \dfrac{4r^2 - h^2}{4}\right]^{3/2} = \dfrac{4\pi}{3}\left(\dfrac{h^2}{4}\right)^{3/2} = \dfrac{4\pi}{3}\cdot\dfrac{h^3}{8} = \dfrac{\pi h^3}{6}$ (independent of r!)

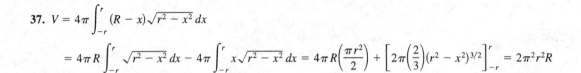

37. $V = 4\pi \displaystyle\int_{-r}^{r} (R - x)\sqrt{r^2 - x^2}\, dx$

$= 4\pi R \displaystyle\int_{-r}^{r} \sqrt{r^2 - x^2}\, dx - 4\pi \displaystyle\int_{-r}^{r} x\sqrt{r^2 - x^2}\, dx = 4\pi R\left(\dfrac{\pi r^2}{2}\right) + \left[2\pi\left(\dfrac{2}{3}\right)(r^2 - x^2)^{3/2}\right]_{-r}^{r} = 2\pi^2 r^2 R$

39. $\pi \displaystyle\int_{1}^{5} (x - 1)\, dx = \pi \displaystyle\int_{1}^{5} \left(\sqrt{x - 1}\right)^2 dx$

This integral represents the volume of the solid generated by revolving the region bounded by $y = \sqrt{x - 1}$, $y = 0$, and $x = 5$ about the x-axis by using the Disc Method.

$2\pi \displaystyle\int_{0}^{2} y[5 - (y^2 + 1)]\, dy$

represents this same volume by using the Shell Method.

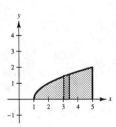

Disc Method

41. (a) $2\pi \displaystyle\int_{0}^{r} hx\left(1 - \dfrac{x}{r}\right) dx$ (ii)

is the volume of a right circular cone with the radius of the base as r and height h.

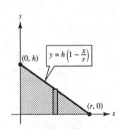

(b) $2\pi \displaystyle\int_{-r}^{r} (R - x)\left(2\sqrt{r^2 - x^2}\right) dx$ (v)

is the volume of a torus with the radius of its circular cross section as r and the distance from the axis of the torus to the center of its cross section as R.

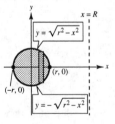

(c) $2\pi \displaystyle\int_{0}^{r} 2x\sqrt{r^2 - x^2}\, dx$ (iii) is

the volume of a sphere with radius r.

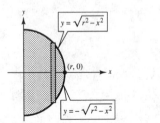

(d) $2\pi \displaystyle\int_{0}^{r} hx\, dx$ (i) is the volume of a

right circular cylinder with a radius of r and a height of h.

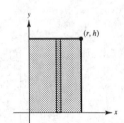

(e) $2\pi \displaystyle\int_{0}^{b} 2ax\sqrt{1 - (x^2/b^2)}\, dx$ (iv)

is the volume of an ellipsoid with axes $2a$ and $2b$.

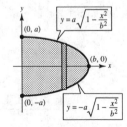

43. (a) The distance from the center of the rectangle to the axis of revolution is $p(x) = x$ and the height $h(x)$ is the depth of the water. Therefore,

$$V = 2\pi \int_0^{200} xh(x)\, dx$$

$$\approx \frac{2\pi(200)}{3(8)}[0 + 4(25)(19) + 2(50)(19) + 4(75)(17) + 2(100)(15) + 4(125)(14)$$

$$+ 2(150)(10) + 4(175)(6) + 0]$$

$$\approx 1{,}366{,}593 \text{ cubic feet.}$$

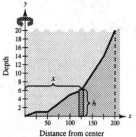

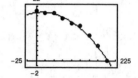

Distance from center

(b) Using the regression capabilities of a graphing utility yields the following quadratic model for the data.

$$h(x) = -0.000561x^2 + 0.0189x + 19.39$$

A plot of the data and a graph of the model are given in the figure.

(c) Using the model of part (b) and the integration capabilities of a graphing utility, we obtain the following approximation of the volume of the pond.

$$V \approx 2\pi \int_0^{200} x(-0.000561x^2 + 0.0189x + 19.39)\, dx$$

$$\approx 1{,}343{,}345 \text{ cubic feet}$$

(d) Since there are approximately 7.48 gallons per cubic foot of water, the approximate volume of the pond, in gallons, is

$$1{,}343{,}345(7.48) \approx 10{,}048{,}221 \text{ gallons.}$$

Section 6.4   Arc Length and Surfaces of Revolution

1. $(0, 0)$, $(5, 12)$

(a) $d = \sqrt{(5 - 0)^2 + (12 - 0)^2} = 13$

(b) $y = \dfrac{12}{5}x$

$y' = \dfrac{12}{5}$

$s = \displaystyle\int_0^5 \sqrt{1 + \left(\frac{12}{5}\right)^2}\, dx = \left[\frac{13}{5}x\right]_0^5 = 13$

3. $y = \dfrac{2}{3}x^{3/2} + 1$

$y' = x^{1/2}$, $[0, 1]$

$s = \displaystyle\int_0^1 \sqrt{1 + x}\, dx$

$= \left[\dfrac{2}{3}(1 + x)^{3/2}\right]_0^1$

$= \dfrac{2}{3}(\sqrt{8} - 1) \approx 1.219$

5. $y = \dfrac{3}{2}x^{2/3}$

$y' = \dfrac{1}{x^{1/3}}$, $[1, 8]$

$s = \displaystyle\int_1^8 \sqrt{1 + \left(\frac{1}{x^{1/3}}\right)^2}\, dx$

$= \displaystyle\int_1^8 \sqrt{\frac{x^{2/3} + 1}{x^{2/3}}}\, dx = \frac{3}{2}\int_1^8 \sqrt{x^{2/3} + 1}\left(\frac{2}{3x^{1/3}}\right) dx = \frac{3}{2}\left[\frac{2}{3}(x^{2/3} + 1)^{3/2}\right]_1^8 = 5\sqrt{5} - 2\sqrt{2} \approx 8.352$

7. $y = \dfrac{x^4}{8} + \dfrac{1}{4x^2}$

$y' = \dfrac{x^3}{2} - \dfrac{1}{2x^3}$

$s = \displaystyle\int_1^2 \sqrt{1 + (y')^2}\, dx = \int_1^2 \sqrt{1 + \left(\dfrac{x^3}{2} - \dfrac{1}{2x^3}\right)^2}\, dx$

$= \displaystyle\int_1^2 \sqrt{1 + \dfrac{x^6}{4} - \dfrac{1}{2} + \dfrac{1}{4x^6}}\, dx$

$= \displaystyle\int_1^2 \sqrt{\dfrac{x^6}{4} + \dfrac{1}{2} + \dfrac{1}{4x^6}}\, dx$

$= \displaystyle\int_1^2 \sqrt{\left(\dfrac{x^3}{2} + \dfrac{1}{2x^3}\right)^2}\, dx$

(Note that $0 < (x^3/2) + 2/(2x^3)$ for $1 \le x \le 2$.)

$s = \displaystyle\int_1^2 \left(\dfrac{x^3}{2} + \dfrac{1}{2x^3}\right) dx = \left[\dfrac{x^4}{8} - \dfrac{1}{4x^2}\right]_1^2$

$= \left(\dfrac{16}{8} - \dfrac{1}{16}\right) - \left(\dfrac{1}{8} - \dfrac{1}{4}\right) = \dfrac{32 - 1 - 2 + 4}{16} = \dfrac{33}{16}$

9. (a) $y = 4 - x^2, 0 \le x \le 2$

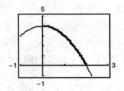

(b) $y' = -2x$

$1 + (y')^2 = 1 + 4x^2$

$L = \displaystyle\int_0^2 \sqrt{1 + 4x^2}\, dx$

(c) $L \approx 4.647$

11. (a) $y = \dfrac{1}{x}, 1 \le x \le 3$

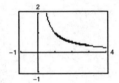

(b) $y' = -\dfrac{1}{x^2}$

$1 + (y')^2 = 1 + \dfrac{1}{x^4}$

$L = \displaystyle\int_1^3 \sqrt{1 + \dfrac{1}{x^4}}\, dx$

(c) $L \approx 2.147$

13. (a) $y = \sin x, 0 \le x \le \pi$

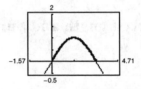

(b) $y' = \cos x$

$1 + (y')^2 = 1 + \cos^2 x$

$L = \displaystyle\int_0^\pi \sqrt{1 + \cos^2 x}\, dx$

(c) $L \approx 3.820$

15. (a) $x = e^{-y}, 0 \le y \le 2$

$y = -\ln x$

$1 \ge x \ge e^{-2} \approx 0.135$

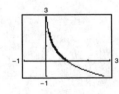

(b) $y' = -\dfrac{1}{x}$

$1 + (y')^2 = 1 + \dfrac{1}{x^2}$

$L = \displaystyle\int_{e^{-2}}^1 \sqrt{1 + \dfrac{1}{x^2}}\, dx$

(c) $L \approx 2.221$

Alternatively, you can do all the computations with respect to y.

(a) $x = e^{-y}\ \ 0 \le y \le 2$

(b) $\dfrac{dx}{dy} = -e^{-y}$

$1 + \left(\dfrac{dx}{dy}\right)^2 = 1 + e^{-2y}$

$L = \displaystyle\int_0^2 \sqrt{1 + e^{-2y}}\, dy$

(c) $L \approx 2.221$

17. (a) The required graph of $y = 2 \arctan x$ is shown in the figure.

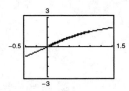

   (b) $y = 2 \arctan x$

$$y' = \frac{2}{1 + x^2}$$

$$s = \int_0^1 \sqrt{1 + (y')^2} \, dx$$

$$= \int_0^1 \sqrt{1 + \left(\frac{2}{1 + x^2}\right)^2} \, dx$$

   (c) Using the integration capabilities of a graphing utility, $s \approx 1.871$.

19. $\int_0^2 \sqrt{1 + \left[\frac{d}{dx}\left(\frac{5}{x^2 + 1}\right)\right]^2} \, dx$

$s \approx 5$

Matches (b)

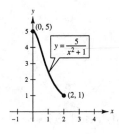

21. $y = x^3$, $[0, 4]$

   (a) $d = \sqrt{(4 - 0)^2 + (64 - 0)^2} \approx 64.125$

   (b) $d = \sqrt{(1 - 0)^2 + (1 - 0)^2} + \sqrt{(2 - 1)^2 + (8 - 1)^2} + \sqrt{(3 - 2)^2 + (27 - 8)^2} + \sqrt{(4 - 3)^2 + (64 - 27)^2}$

$$\approx 64.525$$

   (c) $s = \int_0^4 \sqrt{1 + (3x^2)^2} \, dx = \int_0^4 \sqrt{1 + 9x^4} \, dx \approx 64.666$

   (d) 64.672

23. (a)

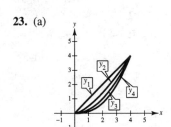

   (b) y_1, y_2, y_3, y_4

   (c) $y_1' = 1$, $L_1 = \int_0^4 \sqrt{2} \, dx \approx 5.657$

$$y_2' = \frac{3}{4} x^{1/2}, \quad L_2 = \int_0^4 \sqrt{1 + \frac{9x}{16}} \, dx \approx 5.759$$

$$y_3' = \frac{1}{2} x, \quad L_3 = \int_0^4 \sqrt{1 + \frac{x^2}{4}} \, dx \approx 5.916$$

$$y_4' = \frac{5}{16} x^{3/2}, \quad L_4 = \int_0^4 \sqrt{1 + \frac{25}{256} x^3} \, dx \approx 6.063$$

25. The y-intercept of $y = \frac{1}{3}(x^{3/2} - 3x^{1/2} + 2)$ is $\left(0, \frac{2}{3}\right)$. Therefore, the fleeing object traveled from $(0, 0)$ to $\left(0, \frac{2}{3}\right)$, a distance of $\frac{2}{3}$.

$$y = \frac{1}{3}(x^{3/2} - 3x^{1/2} + 2)$$

$$y' = \frac{1}{3}\left[\frac{3}{2}x^{1/2} - \frac{3}{2}x^{-1/2}\right] = \frac{1}{2}\left(\sqrt{x} - \frac{1}{\sqrt{x}}\right) = \frac{x - 1}{2\sqrt{x}}$$

$$1 + (y')^2 = 1 + \left(\frac{x - 1}{2\sqrt{x}}\right)^2 = \frac{4x + (x^2 - 2x + 1)}{4x} = \frac{x^2 + 2x + 1}{4x} = \frac{(x + 1)^2}{4x}$$

—CONTINUED—

25. —CONTINUED—

Therefore, the distance traveled by the pursuer is given by

$$s = \int_0^1 \sqrt{1 + (y')^2}\,dx$$

$$= \frac{1}{2}\int_0^1 \frac{x+1}{\sqrt{x}}\,dx$$

$$= \frac{1}{2}\int_0^1 (x^{1/2} + x^{-1/2})\,dx$$

$$= \frac{1}{2}\left[\frac{2}{3}x^{3/2} + 2x^{1/2}\right]_0^1 = \frac{4}{3}.$$

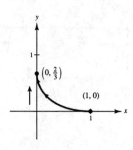

$(0, \frac{2}{3})$

$(1, 0)$

Thus the pursuer traveled a distance of $\frac{4}{3}$, twice the distance of the fleeing object.

27. $y = 20\cosh\dfrac{x}{20},\ -20 \le x \le 20$

$$y' = \sinh\frac{x}{20}$$

$$1 + (y')^2 = 1 + \sinh^2\frac{x}{20} = \cosh^2\frac{x}{20}$$

$$L = \int_{-20}^{20} \cosh\frac{x}{20}\,dx$$

$$= 2\int_0^{20} \cosh\frac{x}{20}\,dx = 2(20)\sinh\frac{x}{20}\Big]_0^{20}$$

$$= 40\sinh(1) \approx 47.008\ \text{m}.$$

29. $y = \sqrt{9 - x^2}$

$$y' = \frac{-x}{\sqrt{9 - x^2}}$$

$$1 + (y')^2 = \frac{9}{9 - x^2}$$

$$s = \int_0^2 \sqrt{\frac{9}{9 - x^2}}\,dx$$

$$= \int_0^2 \frac{3}{\sqrt{9 - x^2}}\,dx$$

$$= \left[3\arcsin\frac{x}{3}\right]_0^2$$

$$= 3\left(\arcsin\frac{2}{3} - \arcsin 0\right)$$

$$= 3\arcsin\frac{2}{3} \approx 2.1892$$

31. $y = \dfrac{x^3}{3}$

$$y' = x^2,\ [0, 3]$$

$$S = 2\pi\int_0^3 \frac{x^3}{3}\sqrt{1 + x^4}\,dx$$

$$= \frac{\pi}{6}\int_0^3 (1 + x^4)^{1/2}(4x^3)\,dx$$

$$= \left[\frac{\pi}{9}(1 + x^4)^{3/2}\right]_0^3$$

$$= \frac{\pi}{9}\left(82\sqrt{82} - 1\right) \approx 258.85$$

33. $y = \dfrac{x^3}{6} + \dfrac{1}{2x}$

$$y' = \frac{1}{2}x^2 - \frac{1}{2x^2} = \frac{x^4 - 1}{2x^2}$$

$$1 + (y')^2 = 1 + \left(\frac{x^4 - 1}{2x^2}\right)^2$$

$$= \frac{4x^4 + (x^8 - 2x^4 + 1)}{4x^2}$$

$$= \frac{x^8 + 2x^4 + 1}{4x^4} = \left(\frac{x^4 + 1}{2x^2}\right)^2$$

$$S = 2\pi\int_1^2 y\sqrt{1 + (y')^2}\,dx$$

$$= 2\pi\int_1^2 \left(\frac{x^3}{6} + \frac{1}{2x}\right)\left(\frac{x^4 + 1}{2x^2}\right)dx$$

$$= 2\pi\int_1^2 \left(\frac{x^5}{12} + \frac{x}{3} + \frac{1}{4x^3}\right)dx$$

$$= 2\pi\left[\frac{x^6}{72} + \frac{x^2}{6} - \frac{1}{8x^2}\right]_1^2 = \frac{47\pi}{16}$$

35. $y = \sqrt[3]{x} + 2$

$$y' = \frac{1}{3}x^{-2/3}$$

$$S = 2\pi \int_1^8 x\sqrt{1 + (y')^2}\, dx$$

$$= 2\pi \int_1^8 x\sqrt{1 + \left(\frac{1}{3x^{2/3}}\right)^2}\, dx$$

$$= 2\pi \int_1^8 x\sqrt{\frac{9x^{4/3} + 1}{9x^{4/3}}}\, dx$$

$$= 2\pi \int_1^8 \frac{x}{3x^{2/3}}\sqrt{9x^{4/3} + 1}\, dx$$

$$= \frac{2\pi}{3}\left(\frac{1}{12}\right)\int_1^8 (9x^{4/3} + 1)^{1/2}(12x^{1/3})\, dx$$

$$= \frac{\pi}{18}\left[\frac{(9x^{4/3} + 1)^{3/2}}{3/2}\right]_1^8$$

$$= \frac{\pi}{27}\left[145\sqrt{145} - 10\sqrt{10}\right] \approx 199.48$$

39. The distance between the y-axis and the graph of the line $y = hx/r$ is

$$r(y) = g(y) = \frac{ry}{h}$$

and since $g'(y) = r/h$, the surface area is given by

$$S = 2\pi \int_0^h r(y)\sqrt{1 + [g'(y)]^2}\, dy$$

$$= 2\pi \int_0^h \left(\frac{ry}{h}\right)\sqrt{1 + \left(\frac{r}{h}\right)^2}\, dy$$

$$= \frac{2\pi r\sqrt{r^2 + h^2}}{h^2}\int_0^h y\, dy$$

$$= \frac{2\pi r\sqrt{r^2 + h^2}}{h^2}\left[\frac{1}{2}y^2\right]_0^h = \pi r\sqrt{r^2 + h^2}.$$

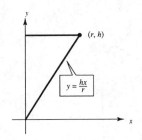

37. $y = \sin x$

$$y' = \cos x,\ [0, \pi]$$

$$S = 2\pi \int_0^\pi \sin x\sqrt{1 + \cos^2 x}\, dx$$

$$\approx 14.4236$$

41. $y = \sqrt{9 - x^2}$

$$y' = \frac{-x}{\sqrt{9 - x^2}}$$

$$S = 2\pi \int_0^2 x\sqrt{1 + \left(\frac{-x}{\sqrt{9 - x^2}}\right)^2}\, dx$$

$$= 2\pi \int_0^2 x\sqrt{\frac{9}{9 - x^2}}\, dx$$

$$= 2\pi \int_0^2 3x(9 - x^2)^{-1/2}\, dx$$

$$= -3\pi \int_0^2 (9 - x^2)^{-1/2}(-2x)\, dx$$

$$= -3\pi\left[\frac{(9 - x^2)^{1/2}}{1/2}\right]_0^2$$

$$= -6\pi\left(\sqrt{5} - 3\right) = 6\pi\left(3 - \sqrt{5}\right) \approx 14.40$$

43. $y = \dfrac{1}{3}x^{1/2} - x^{3/2}$

$y' = \dfrac{1}{6}x^{-1/2} - \dfrac{3}{2}x^{1/2} = \dfrac{1}{6}(x^{-1/2} - 9x^{1/2})$

$1 + (y')^2 = 1 + \dfrac{1}{36}(x^{-1} - 18 + 81x) = \dfrac{1}{36}(x^{-1/2} + 9x^{1/2})^2$

$S = 2\pi \displaystyle\int_0^{1/3} \left(\dfrac{1}{3}x^{1/2} - x^{3/2}\right)\sqrt{\dfrac{1}{36}(x^{-1/2} + 9^{1/2})^2}\, dx = \dfrac{2\pi}{6}\displaystyle\int_0^{1/3}\left(\dfrac{1}{3}x^{1/2} - x^{3/2}\right)(x^{-1/2} + 9x^{1/2})\, dx$

$\quad = \dfrac{\pi}{3}\displaystyle\int_0^{1/3}\left(\dfrac{1}{3} + 2x - 9x^2\right)dx = \dfrac{\pi}{3}\left[\dfrac{1}{3}x + x^2 - 3x^3\right]_0^{1/3} = \dfrac{\pi}{27}\text{ ft}^2 \approx 0.1164\text{ ft}^2 \approx 16.8\text{ in}^2$

Amount of glass needed: $V = \dfrac{\pi}{27}\left(\dfrac{0.015}{12}\right) \approx 0.00015\text{ ft}^3 \approx 0.25\text{ in}^3$

45. Individual project, see Exercise 44.

47. (a) $\dfrac{ds}{dx} = \sqrt{1 + [f'(x)]^2}$ (Second Fundamental Theorem of Calculus)

(b) $ds = \sqrt{1 + [f'(x)]^2}\, dx$

$(ds)^2 = \left[1 + [f'(x)]^2\right](dx)^2 = \left[1 + \left(\dfrac{dy}{dx}\right)^2\right](dx)^2 = (dx)^2 + (dy)^2$

(c) $s(x) = \displaystyle\int_1^x \sqrt{1 + \left(\dfrac{3}{2}t^{1/2}\right)^2}\, dt = \displaystyle\int_1^x \sqrt{1 + \dfrac{9}{4}t}\, dt = \left[\dfrac{4}{9}\left(\dfrac{2}{3}\right)\left(1 + \dfrac{9}{4}t\right)^{3/2}\right]_1^x$

$\quad = \dfrac{8}{27}\left[\left(1 + \dfrac{9}{4}x\right)^{3/2} - \left(\dfrac{13}{4}\right)^{3/2}\right] = \dfrac{8}{27}\left[\dfrac{(4 + 9x)^{3/2}}{8} - \dfrac{13\sqrt{13}}{8}\right] = \dfrac{1}{27}\left[(4 + 9x)^{3/2} - 13\sqrt{13}\right]$

$s(2) = \dfrac{1}{27}\left[22\sqrt{22} - 13\sqrt{13}\right] = \dfrac{22}{27}\sqrt{22} - \dfrac{13}{27}\sqrt{13} \approx 2.086$

49. (a) Area of circle with radius L: $A = \pi L^2$

Area of sector with central angle θ (in radians)

$S = \dfrac{\theta}{2\pi}A = \dfrac{\theta}{2\pi}(\pi L^2) = \dfrac{1}{2}L^2\theta$

(b) Let s be the arc length of the sector, which is the circumference of the base of the cone. Here, $s = L\theta = 2\pi r$, and you have

$S = \dfrac{1}{2}L^2\theta = \dfrac{1}{2}L^2\left(\dfrac{s}{L}\right) = \dfrac{1}{2}Ls = \dfrac{1}{2}L(2\pi r) = \pi rL.$

(c) The lateral surface area of the frustum is the difference of the large cone and the small one.

$S = \pi r_2(L + L_1) - \pi r_1 L_1$

$\quad = \pi r_2 L + \pi L_1(r_2 - r_1)$

By similar triangles, $\dfrac{L + L_1}{r_2} = \dfrac{L_1}{r_1} \implies Lr_1 = L_1(r_2 - r_1).$

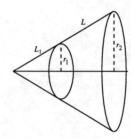

Hence,

$S = \pi r_2 L + \pi L_1(r_2 - r_1) = \pi r_2 L + \pi Lr_1$

$\quad = \pi L(r_1 + r_2).$

Section 6.5 Work

1. $W = Fd = (100)(10) = 1000$ ft · lb

3. $W = Fd = (112)(4) = 448$ joules (newton-meters)

5. Since the work equals the area under the force function, you have $(c) < (d) < (a) < (b)$.

7. $F(x) = kx$

$5 = k(4)$

$k = \dfrac{5}{4}$

$W = \displaystyle\int_0^7 \frac{5}{4} x \, dx = \left[\frac{5}{8} x^2 \right]_0^7$

$= \dfrac{245}{8}$ in · lb $= 30.625$ in · lb ≈ 2.55 ft · lb

9. Let $F(x)$ be the force required to stretch a spring x units. By Hooke's Law, $F(x) = kx$. Since a force of 250 newtons stretches the spring 30 centimeters, it follows that

$$250 = k(30) \quad \text{or} \quad k = \frac{25}{3}.$$

Therefore, the work done by stretching the spring from 20 centimeters to 50 centimeters is

$W = \displaystyle\int_{20}^{50} \underbrace{F(x)}_{\text{(force)}} \; \underbrace{dx}_{\text{(distance)}}$

$= \displaystyle\int_{20}^{50} \frac{25}{3} x \, dx$

$= \left[\dfrac{25}{6} x^2 \right]_{20}^{50}$

$= \dfrac{25}{6}(2500 - 400)$

$= 8750$ newton · centimeters $= 87.5$ newton · meters.

11. $F(x) = kx$

$15 = 6k$

$k = \dfrac{5}{2}$

$W = \displaystyle\int_0^{12} \frac{5}{2} x \, dx = \left[\frac{5}{4} x^2 \right]_0^{12}$

$= 180$ in · lb $= 15$ ft · lb

13. $W = 18 = \displaystyle\int_0^{1/3} kx \, dx = \left. \frac{kx^2}{2} \right]_0^{1/3} = \frac{k}{18} \implies k = 324$

$W = \displaystyle\int_{1/3}^{7/12} 324x \, dx = \left. 162x^2 \right]_{1/3}^{7/12} = 37.125$ ft · lbs

$\left[\textit{Note:} \ 4 \text{ inches} = \frac{1}{3} \text{ foot} \right]$

15. Assume that the earth has a radius of 4000 miles.

$F(x) = \dfrac{k}{x^2}$

$4 = \dfrac{k}{(4000)^2}$

$k = 64,000,000$

$F(x) = \dfrac{64,000,000}{x^2}$

(a) $W = \displaystyle\int_{4000}^{4200} \frac{64,000,000}{x^2} \, dx = \left[-\frac{64,000,000}{x} \right]_{4000}^{4200} \approx -15,238.095 + 16,000$

$= 761.905$ mi · ton $\approx 8.05 \times 10^9$ ft · lb

(b) $W = \displaystyle\int_{4000}^{4400} \frac{64,000,000}{x^2} \, dx = \left[-\frac{64,000,000}{x} \right]_{4000}^{4400} \approx -14,545.455 + 16,000$

$= 1454.545$ mi · ton $\approx 1.54 \times 10^{10}$ ft · lb

17. Because the weight of a body varies inversely as the square of its distance from the center of the earth, the force $F(x)$ exerted by gravity is

$$F(x) = \frac{C}{x^2}.$$

Because the satellite weighs 10 tons on the surface of the earth and the radius of the earth is approximately 4000 miles, you have

$$10 = \frac{C}{(4000)^2} \implies C = 160,000,000.$$

(a) $W = \displaystyle\int_{4000}^{15,000} \frac{160,000,000}{x^2}\,dx$

$= \left[-\dfrac{160,000,000}{x} \right]_{4000}^{15,000}$

$= 2.93 \times 10^4 \text{ mi} \cdot \text{tons} \approx 3.10 \times 10^{11} \text{ ft} \cdot \text{lb}$

(b) $W = \displaystyle\int_{4000}^{26,000} \frac{160,000,000}{x^2}\,dx$

$= \left[-\dfrac{160,000,000}{x} \right]_{4000}^{26,000}$

$= 3.38 \times 10^4 \text{ mi} \cdot \text{tons} \approx 3.57 \times 10^{11} \text{ ft} \cdot \text{lb}$

19. Weight of each layer: $62.4(20)\,\Delta y$

Distance: $4 - y$

(a) $W = \displaystyle\int_{2}^{4} 62.4(20)(4-y)\,dy = \left[4992y - 624y^2 \right]_{2}^{4} = 2496 \text{ ft} \cdot \text{lb}$

(b) $W = \displaystyle\int_{0}^{4} 62.4(20)(4-y)\,dy = \left[4992y - 624y^2 \right]_{0}^{4} = 9984 \text{ ft} \cdot \text{lb}$

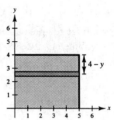

21. Volume of disc of water: $\pi(2)^2\,\Delta y = 4\pi\,\Delta y$

Weight of disc of water: $(9800)(4\pi\,\Delta y)$

Distance the disc of water is moved: $5 - y$

$$W = \int_{0}^{4} (5-y)(39,200\pi)\,dy = 39,200\pi \int_{0}^{4}(5-y)\,dy = 39,200\pi\left[5y - \frac{y^2}{2} \right]_{0}^{4} = 39,200\pi[12] = 470,400\pi \text{ N} \cdot \text{m}$$

23. A disc of water at height y must be lifted $(6-y)$ feet to the top of the tank and has volume of $\pi x^2\Delta y$. To find x in terms of y, solve the equation

$$\frac{6-0}{4-0} = \frac{y-0}{x-0}$$

$$x = \frac{2y}{3}.$$

Thus, the work done in moving the water over the top of the tank is

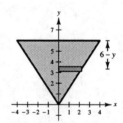

$$W = \int_{0}^{6} \underbrace{(6-y)}_{\text{(distance)}} \underbrace{\left[62.4\pi\left(\frac{2y}{3}\right)^2 dy \right]}_{\text{(force: weight of water)}}$$

$$= \frac{4}{9}(62.4)\pi \int_{0}^{6}(6y^2 - y^3)\,dy$$

$$= \frac{83.2}{3}\pi\left[2y^3 - \frac{y^4}{4} \right]_{0}^{6}$$

$$= \frac{83.2}{3}\pi(432 - 324) = 2995.2\pi \text{ ft} \cdot \text{lb}.$$

25. To fill the tank with water through a hole in the bottom, all the water is not moved to a height of 6 ft. Some of the water must be moved 6 ft, some 5 ft, some 4 ft, and so on. In general, the "disc" of water that must be moved y feet has a volume of

$$\pi x^2 \Delta y = \pi\left(\sqrt{36 - y^2}\right)^2 \Delta y = \pi(36 - y^2)\Delta y \text{ cubic feet.}$$

The weight of the disc of water is

$$62.4(\pi)(36 - y^2)\Delta y \text{ pounds.}$$

Thus, the work done in filling the tank from the bottom is

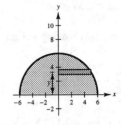

$$W = \int_0^6 \underbrace{(y)}_{\text{(distance)}} \underbrace{\left[62.4\pi(36 - y^2)\,dy\right]}_{\text{(force: weight of water)}}$$

$$= 62.4\pi \int_0^6 (36y - y^3)\,dy$$

$$= 62.4\pi\left[18y^2 - \frac{y^4}{4}\right]_0^6$$

$$= 62.4\pi(648 - 324) = 20{,}217.6\pi \text{ ft} \cdot \text{lb.}$$

27. A layer of gasoline at height y (see figure) is lifted $\left(\frac{13}{2} - y\right)$ feet and has a volume $V = lwh = 4(2x)\Delta y$. To find x in terms of y, solve for x in the equation of the circle representing a cross-section of the tank and obtain

$$x^2 + y^2 = \frac{9}{4}$$

$$x^2 = \frac{9}{4} - y^2$$

$$x = \sqrt{\frac{9}{4} - y^2}.$$

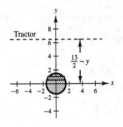

Thus the work done is

$$W = \int_{-1.5}^{1.5} \underbrace{\left(\frac{13}{2} - y\right)}_{\text{(distance)}} \underbrace{\left[42(4)\left(2\sqrt{\frac{9}{4} - y^2}\right)dy\right]}_{\text{(force: weight of water)}}$$

$$= 336\left[\frac{13}{2}\int_{-1.5}^{1.5}\sqrt{\frac{9}{4} - y^2}\,dy - \int_{-1.5}^{1.5} y\sqrt{\frac{9}{4} - y^2}\,dy\right].$$

The first integral represents the area of a semicircle of radius $\frac{3}{2}$ and the second integral is zero since the integrand is odd and the limits of integration are symmetric to the origin. Therefore,

$$W = 336\left(\frac{13}{2}\right)\left(\frac{1}{2}\right)(\pi)\left(\frac{3}{2}\right)^2 = 2457\pi \text{ ft} \cdot \text{lb.}$$

29. Weight of section of chain: $3\,\Delta y$

Distance: $15 - y$

$$W = 3\int_0^{15} (15 - y)\,dy$$

$$= \left[-\frac{3}{2}(15 - y)^2\right]_0^{15}$$

$$= 337.5 \text{ ft} \cdot \text{lb}$$

31. The lower 5 feet of chain are raised 10 feet with a constant force.

$$W_1 = 3(5)(10) = 150 \text{ ft} \cdot \text{lb}$$

The top 10 feet of chain are raised with a variable force.

Weight per section: $3\,\Delta y$

Distance: $10 - y$

$$W_2 = 3\int_0^{10} (10 - y)\,dy$$

$$= \left[-\frac{3}{2}(10 - y)^2\right]_0^{10} = 150 \text{ ft} \cdot \text{lb}$$

$$W = W_1 + W_2 = 300 \text{ ft} \cdot \text{lb}$$

33. A small piece of chain of length Δy at height y must be moved so that it is y feet from the top. Therefore, the distance moved (as seen in the figure) is $15 - 2y$. (For example, the chain at an initial height of 7.5 is moved 0 ft.) The weight of a piece of chain of length Δy is

$$\frac{3 \text{ pounds}}{\text{foot}} \Delta y \text{ feet} = 3\Delta y \text{ pounds}.$$

Finally, since you are only moving a chain that has an initial height between 0 and 7.5 ft, we have

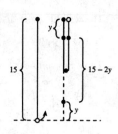

$$W = \int_0^{7.5} \underbrace{(15 - 2y)}_{\text{(distance)}} \underbrace{(3 \, dy)}_{\text{(force)}}$$

$$= 3\left[15y - y^2 \right]_0^{7.5} = 3(112.5 - 56.25) = 168.75 \text{ ft} \cdot \text{lb}.$$

35. Work to pull up the ball: $W_1 = 500(15) = 7500$ ft $\cdot$ lb

Work to wind up the top 15 feet of cable: force is variable

Weight per section: $1 \Delta y$

Distance: $15 - x$

$$W_2 = \int_0^{15} (15 - x) \, dx = \left[-\frac{1}{2}(15 - x)^2 \right]_0^{15}$$

$$= 112.5 \text{ ft} \cdot \text{lb}$$

Work to lift the lower 25 feet of cable with a constant force:

$$W_3 = (1)(25)(15) = 375 \text{ ft} \cdot \text{lb}$$

$$W = W_1 + W_2 + W_3 = 7500 + 112.5 + 375$$

$$= 7987.5 \text{ ft} \cdot \text{lb}$$

37.
$$p = \frac{k}{V}$$

$$1000 = \frac{k}{2}$$

$$k = 2000$$

$$W = \int_2^3 \frac{2000}{V} \, dV = \left[2000 \ln |V| \right]_2^3$$

$$= 2000 \ln\left(\frac{3}{2}\right) \approx 810.93 \text{ ft} \cdot \text{lb}$$

39. Let $(x, 4)$ be a point on the line segment from $(-2, 4)$ to $(1, 4)$. The distance between the point $(x, 4)$ and $(2, 4)$ is $2 - x$. Since the two electrons repel each other with a force that varies inversely as the square of the distance between them, it follows that

$$F(x) = \frac{k}{(2 - x)^2}.$$

$$W = \int_{-2}^1 \frac{k}{(2 - x)^2} \, dx$$

$$= \left[\frac{k}{2 - x} \right]_{-2}^1 = k\left(1 - \frac{1}{4}\right) = \frac{3k}{4} \text{ units of work}$$

41. $W = \int_0^5 1000[1.8 - \ln(x + 1)] \, dx \approx 3249.44$

43. $W = \int_0^5 100x\sqrt{125 - x^3} \, dx \approx 10{,}330.3$ ft $\cdot$ lb

Section 6.6 Moments, Centers of Mass, and Centroids

1. $\bar{x} = \dfrac{6(-5) + 3(1) + 5(3)}{6 + 3 + 5} = -\dfrac{6}{7}$

3. $\bar{x} = \dfrac{1(7) + 1(8) + 1(12) + 1(15) + 1(18)}{1 + 1 + 1 + 1 + 1} = 12$

5. (a) $\bar{x} = \dfrac{(7 + 5) + (8 + 5) + (12 + 5) + (15 + 5) + (18 + 5)}{5} = 17 = 12 + 5$

(b) $\bar{x} = \dfrac{12(-3 - 3) + 1(-2 - 3) + 6(-1 - 3) + 3(0 - 3) + 11(4 - 3)}{12 + 1 + 6 + 3 + 11} = -3 = 0 - 3$

7. The moment produced by each child is the mass of the child times the child's distance from the fulcrum. From the figure we have

left moment $= \frac{50}{32}x$ and right moment $= \frac{75}{32}(10 - x)$.

To balance the seesaw the moments must be equal.

$$\frac{50}{72}x = \frac{75}{32}(10 - x)$$

$$2x = 3(10 - x)$$

$$5x = 30 \implies x = 6 \text{ feet}$$

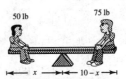

9. $\bar{x} = \dfrac{5(2) + 1(-3) + 3(1)}{5 + 1 + 3} = \dfrac{10}{9}$

$\bar{y} = \dfrac{5(2) + 1(1) + 3(-4)}{5 + 1 + 3} = -\dfrac{1}{9}$

$(\bar{x}, \bar{y}) = \left(\dfrac{10}{9}, -\dfrac{1}{9}\right)$

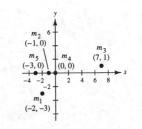

11. $\bar{x} = \dfrac{m_1x_1 + m_2x_2 + m_3x_3 + m_4x_4 + m_5x_5}{m_1 + m_2 + m_3 + m_4 + m_5} = \dfrac{3(-2) + 4(-1) + 2(7) + 1(0) + 6(-3)}{3 + 4 + 2 + 1 + 6} = -\dfrac{7}{8}$

$\bar{y} = \dfrac{m_1y_1 + m_2y_2 + m_3y_3 + m_4y_4 + m_5y_5}{m_1 + m_2 + m_3 + m_4 + m_5} = \dfrac{3(-3) + 4(0) + 2(1) + 1(0) + 6(0)}{3 + 4 + 2 + 1 + 6} = -\dfrac{7}{16}$

Therefore, $(\bar{x}, \bar{y}) = \left(-\dfrac{7}{8}, -\dfrac{7}{16}\right).$

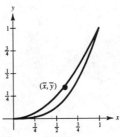

13. $m = \rho \displaystyle\int_0^4 \sqrt{x}\, dx = \left[\dfrac{2\rho}{3}x^{3/2}\right]_0^4 = \dfrac{16\rho}{3}$

$M_x = \rho \displaystyle\int_0^4 \dfrac{\sqrt{x}}{2}(\sqrt{x})\, dx = \left[\rho\dfrac{x^2}{4}\right]_0^4 = 4\rho$

$\bar{y} = \dfrac{M_x}{m} = 4\rho\left(\dfrac{3}{16\rho}\right) = \dfrac{3}{4}$

$M_y = \rho \displaystyle\int_0^4 x\sqrt{x}\, dx = \left[\rho\dfrac{2}{5}x^{5/2}\right]_0^4 = \dfrac{64\rho}{5}$

$\bar{x} = \dfrac{M_y}{m} = \dfrac{64\rho}{5}\left(\dfrac{3}{16\rho}\right) = \dfrac{12}{5}$

$(\bar{x}, \bar{y}) = \left(\dfrac{12}{5}, \dfrac{3}{4}\right)$

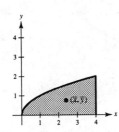

15. $m = \rho \displaystyle\int_0^1 (x^2 - x^3)\, dx = \rho\left[\dfrac{x^3}{3} - \dfrac{x^4}{4}\right]_0^1 = \dfrac{\rho}{12}$

$M_x = \rho \displaystyle\int_0^1 \dfrac{(x^2 + x^3)}{2}(x^2 - x^3)\, dx$

$= \dfrac{\rho}{2} \displaystyle\int_0^1 (x^4 - x^6)\, dx = \dfrac{\rho}{2}\left[\dfrac{x^5}{5} - \dfrac{x^7}{7}\right]_0^1 = \dfrac{\rho}{35}$

$\bar{y} = \dfrac{M_x}{m} = \dfrac{\rho}{35}\left(\dfrac{12}{\rho}\right) = \dfrac{12}{35}$

$M_y = \rho \displaystyle\int_0^1 x(x^2 - x^3)\, dx$

$= \rho \displaystyle\int_0^1 (x^3 - x^4)\, dx = \rho\left[\dfrac{x^4}{4} - \dfrac{x^5}{5}\right]_0^1 = \dfrac{\rho}{20}$

$\bar{x} = \dfrac{M_y}{m} = \dfrac{\rho}{20}\left(\dfrac{12}{\rho}\right) = \dfrac{3}{5}$

$(\bar{x}, \bar{y}) = \left(\dfrac{3}{5}, \dfrac{12}{35}\right)$

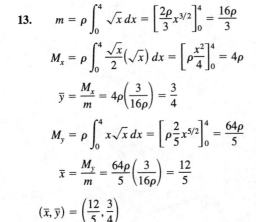

17. $m = \rho \int_0^3 [(-x^2 + 4x + 2) - (x + 2)]\, dx = -\rho\left[\dfrac{x^3}{3} + \dfrac{3x^2}{2}\right]_0^3 = \dfrac{9\rho}{2}$

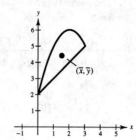

$M_x = \rho \int_0^3 \left[\dfrac{(-x^2 + 4x + 2) + (x + 2)}{2}\right][(-x^2 + 4x + 2) - (x + 2)]\, dx$

$= \dfrac{\rho}{2}\int_0^3 (-x^2 + 5x + 4)(-x^2 + 3x)\, dx = \dfrac{\rho}{2}\int_0^3 (x^4 - 8x^3 + 11x^2 + 12x)\, dx$

$= \dfrac{\rho}{2}\left[\dfrac{x^5}{5} - 2x^4 + \dfrac{11x^3}{3} + 6x^2\right]_0^3 = \dfrac{99\rho}{5}$

$\bar{y} = \dfrac{M_x}{m} = \dfrac{99\rho}{5}\left(\dfrac{2}{9\rho}\right) = \dfrac{22}{5}$

$M_y = \rho \int_0^3 x[(-x^2 + 4x - 2) - (x + 2)]\, dx = \rho \int_0^3 (-x^3 + 3x^2)\, dx = \rho\left[-\dfrac{x^4}{4} + x^3\right]_0^3 = \dfrac{27\rho}{4}$

$\bar{x} = \dfrac{M_y}{m} = \dfrac{27\rho}{4}\left(\dfrac{2}{9\rho}\right) = \dfrac{3}{2}$

$(\bar{x}, \bar{y}) = \left(\dfrac{3}{2}, \dfrac{22}{5}\right)$

19. $m = \rho \int_0^8 x^{2/3}\, dx = \rho\left[\dfrac{3}{5}x^{5/3}\right]_0^8 = \dfrac{96\rho}{5}$

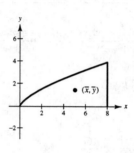

$M_x = \rho \int_0^8 \dfrac{x^{2/3}}{2}(x^{2/3})\, dx = \dfrac{\rho}{2}\left[\dfrac{3}{7}x^{7/3}\right]_0^8 = \dfrac{192\rho}{7}$

$\bar{y} = \dfrac{M_x}{m} = \dfrac{192\rho}{7}\left(\dfrac{5}{96\rho}\right) = \dfrac{10}{7}$

$M_y = \rho \int_0^8 x(x^{2/3})\, dx = \rho\left[\dfrac{3}{8}x^{8/3}\right]_0^8 = 96\rho$

$\bar{x} = \dfrac{M_y}{m} = 96\rho\left(\dfrac{5}{96\rho}\right) = 5$

$(\bar{x}, \bar{y}) = \left(5, \dfrac{10}{7}\right)$

21. Since the region is symmetric with respect to the x-axis, we know that

$M_x = 0$ and $\bar{y} = \dfrac{M_x}{m} = 0$.

To find $\bar{x}$, observe that x is a function of y, and use the formula

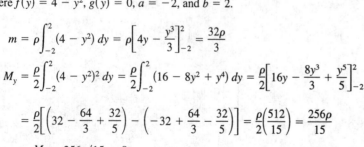

$\bar{x} = \dfrac{\displaystyle\int_a^b \left[\dfrac{f(y) + g(y)}{2}\right][f(y) - g(y)]\, dy}{m} = \dfrac{M_y}{m}$

where $f(y) = 4 - y^2$, $g(y) = 0$, $a = -2$, and $b = 2$.

$m = \rho\int_{-2}^2 (4 - y^2)\, dy = \rho\left[4y - \dfrac{y^3}{3}\right]_{-2}^2 = \dfrac{32\rho}{3}$

$M_y = \dfrac{\rho}{2}\int_{-2}^2 (4 - y^2)^2\, dy = \dfrac{\rho}{2}\int_{-2}^2 (16 - 8y^2 + y^4)\, dy = \dfrac{\rho}{2}\left[16y - \dfrac{8y^3}{3} + \dfrac{y^5}{5}\right]_{-2}^2$

$= \dfrac{\rho}{2}\left[\left(32 - \dfrac{64}{3} + \dfrac{32}{5}\right) - \left(-32 + \dfrac{64}{3} - \dfrac{32}{5}\right)\right] = \dfrac{\rho}{2}\left(\dfrac{512}{15}\right) = \dfrac{256\rho}{15}$

$\bar{x} = \dfrac{M_y}{m} = \dfrac{256\rho/15}{32\rho/3} = \dfrac{8}{5}$

Therefore, $(\bar{x}, \bar{y}) = (8/5, 0)$.

23.
$$m = \rho \int_0^3 [(2y - y^2) - (-y)] \, dy = \rho \left[\frac{3y^2}{2} - \frac{y^3}{3} \right]_0^3 = \frac{9\rho}{2}$$

$$M_y = \rho \int_0^3 \frac{[(2y - y^2) + (-y)]}{2} [(2y - y^2) - (-y)] \, dy = \frac{\rho}{2} \int_0^3 (y - y^2)(3y - y^2) \, dy$$

$$= \frac{\rho}{2} \int_0^3 (y^4 - 4y^3 + 3y^2) \, dy = \frac{\rho}{2} \left[\frac{y^5}{5} - y^4 + y^3 \right]_0^3 = -\frac{27\rho}{10}$$

$$\bar{x} = \frac{M_y}{m} = -\frac{27\rho}{10} \left(\frac{2}{9\rho} \right) = -\frac{3}{5}$$

$$M_x = \rho \int_0^3 y[(2y - y^2) - (-y)] \, dy = \rho \int_0^3 (3y^2 - y^3) \, dy = \rho \left[y^3 - \frac{y^4}{4} \right]_0^3 = \frac{27\rho}{4}$$

$$\bar{y} = \frac{M_x}{m} = \frac{27\rho}{4} \left(\frac{2}{9\rho} \right) = \frac{3}{2}$$

$$(\bar{x}, \bar{y}) = \left(-\frac{3}{5}, \frac{3}{2} \right)$$

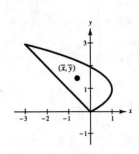

25. The two graphs intersect at the points $(0, 0)$ and $(1, 1)$. The area is given by

$$A = \int_0^1 [f(x) - g(x)] \, dx = \int_0^1 (x - x^2) \, dx = \left[\frac{1}{2}x^2 - \frac{1}{3}x^3 \right]_0^1 = \frac{1}{6}.$$

$$M_x = \int_0^1 \left[\frac{f(x) + g(x)}{2} \right] [f(x) - g(x)] \, dx = \int_0^1 \left(\frac{x + x^2}{2} \right)(x - x^2) \, dx = \frac{1}{15}$$

$$M_y = \int_0^1 x[f(x) - g(x)] \, dx = \int_0^1 x(x - x^2) \, dx = \frac{1}{12}$$

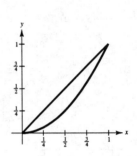

27.
$$A = \int_0^3 (2x + 4) \, dx = \left[x^2 + 4x \right]_0^3 = 9 + 12 = 21$$

$$M_x = \frac{1}{2} \int_0^3 (2x + 4)^2 \, dx = \int_0^3 (2x^2 + 8x + 8) \, dx = \left[\frac{2x^3}{3} + 4x^2 + 8x \right]_0^3 = 18 + 36 + 24 = 78$$

$$M_y = \int_0^3 (2x^2 + 4x) \, dx = \left[\frac{2x^3}{3} + 2x^2 \right]_0^3 = 18 + 18 = 36$$

29.
$$m = \rho \int_0^5 10x\sqrt{125 - x^3} \, dx \approx 1033.0\rho$$

$$M_x = \rho \int_0^5 \left(\frac{10x\sqrt{125 - x^3}}{2} \right)(10x\sqrt{125 - x^3}) \, dx = 50\rho \int_0^5 x^2(125 - x^3) \, dx = \frac{3,124,375\rho}{24} \approx 130,208\rho$$

$$M_y = \rho \int_0^5 10x^2\sqrt{125 - x^3} \, dx = -\frac{10\rho}{3} \int_0^5 \sqrt{125 - x^3}(-3x^2) \, dx = \frac{12,500\sqrt{5}\rho}{9} \approx 3105.6\rho$$

$$\bar{x} = \frac{M_y}{m} \approx 3.0$$

$$\bar{y} = \frac{M_x}{m} \approx 126.0$$

Therefore, the centroid is $(3.0, 126.0)$.

31. $m = \rho \int_{-20}^{20} 5\sqrt[3]{400 - x^2}\, dx \approx 1239.76\rho$

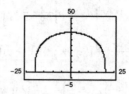

$M_x = \rho \int_{-20}^{20} \frac{5\sqrt[3]{400 - x^2}}{2}\left(5\sqrt[3]{400 - x^2}\right) dx$

$= \frac{25\rho}{2} \int_{-20}^{20} (400 - x^2)^{2/3}\, dx \approx 20064.27$

$\bar{y} = \frac{M_x}{m} \approx 16.18$

$\bar{x} = 0$ by symmetry. Therefore, the centroid is $(0, 16.2)$.

33. The equation of the line containing $(-a, 0)$ and (b, c) is $y = \left(\dfrac{c}{b + a}\right)(x + a)$.

The equation of the line containing $(a, 0)$ and (b, c) is $y = \left(\dfrac{c}{b - a}\right)(x - a)$.

Since the area of the triangle is $A = \left(\dfrac{1}{2}\right)(2a)(c) = ac$, we have

$$\bar{x} = \frac{\displaystyle\int_{-a}^{b} x\left(\frac{c}{b + a}\right)(x + a)\, dx + \int_{b}^{a} x\left(\frac{c}{b - a}\right)(x - a)\, dx}{ac}$$

$$= \frac{1}{ac}\left[\frac{c}{b + a}\int_{-a}^{b}(x^2 + ax)\, dx + \frac{c}{b - a}\int_{a}^{b}(x^2 - ax)\, dx\right]$$

$$= \frac{1}{ac}\left(\frac{c}{b + a}\left[\frac{x^3}{3} + \frac{ax^2}{2}\right]_{-a}^{b} + \frac{c}{b - a}\left[\frac{x^3}{3} - \frac{ax^2}{2}\right]_{b}^{a}\right)$$

$$= \frac{1}{ac}\left[\frac{c}{b + a}\left(\frac{b^3}{3} + \frac{ab^2}{2} + \frac{a^3}{3} - \frac{a^3}{2}\right) + \frac{c}{b - a}\left(\frac{a^3}{3} - \frac{a^3}{2} - \frac{b^3}{3} + \frac{ab^2}{2}\right)\right]$$

$$= \frac{2b^3 + 3ab^2 - a^3}{6a(b + a)} + \frac{-2b^3 + 3ab^2 - a^3}{6a(b - a)}$$

$$= \frac{(2b^2 + ab - a^2)(a + b)}{6a(b + a)} + \frac{(-2b^2 + ab + a^2)(b - a)}{6a(b - a)}$$

$$= \frac{2ab}{6a} = \frac{b}{3}$$

$$\bar{y} = \frac{\dfrac{1}{2}\displaystyle\int_{-a}^{b}\left[\frac{c}{b + a}(x + a)\right]^2 dx + \frac{1}{2}\int_{b}^{a}\left[\frac{c}{b - a}(x - a)\right]^2 dx}{ac}$$

$$= \frac{1}{2ac}\left\{\frac{c^2}{(b + a)^2}\left[\frac{(x + a)^3}{3}\right]_{-a}^{b} + \frac{c^2}{(b - a)^2}\left[\frac{(x - a)^3}{3}\right]_{b}^{a}\right\}$$

$$= \frac{1}{2ac}\left\{\frac{c^2}{(b + a)^2}\left[\frac{(b + a)^3}{3}\right] - \frac{c^2}{(b - a)^2}\left[\frac{(b - a)^3}{3}\right]\right\}$$

$$= \frac{1}{2ac}\left[\frac{c^2(b + a)}{3} - \frac{c^2(b - a)}{3}\right] = \frac{c}{3}.$$

From Exercise 66, Section P.2, we know that the point $(b/3, c/3)$ is the intersection of the medians of the triangle.

35. $A = \dfrac{c}{2}(a + b)$

$$\dfrac{1}{A} = \dfrac{2}{c(a + b)}$$

$$\bar{x} = \dfrac{2}{c(a + b)}\int_0^c x\left(\dfrac{b - a}{c}x + a\right) dx = \dfrac{2}{c(a + b)}\int_0^c \left(\dfrac{b - a}{c}x^2 + ax\right) dx = \dfrac{2}{c(a + b)}\left[\dfrac{b - a}{c}\dfrac{x^3}{3} + \dfrac{ax^2}{2}\right]_0^c$$

$$= \dfrac{2}{c(a + b)}\left[\dfrac{(b - a)c^2}{3} + \dfrac{ac^2}{2}\right] = \dfrac{2}{c(a + b)}\left[\dfrac{2bc^2 - 2ac^2 + 3ac^2}{6}\right] = \dfrac{c(2b + a)}{3(a + b)} = \dfrac{(a + 2b)c}{3(a + b)}$$

$$\bar{y} = \dfrac{2}{c(a + b)}\dfrac{1}{2}\int_0^c \left(\dfrac{b - a}{c}x + a\right)^2 dx = \dfrac{1}{c(a + b)}\int_0^c \left[\left(\dfrac{b - a}{c}\right)^2 x^2 + \dfrac{2a(b - a)}{c}x + a^2\right] dx$$

$$= \dfrac{1}{c(a + b)}\left[\left(\dfrac{b - a}{c}\right)^2\dfrac{x^3}{3} + \dfrac{2a(b - a)}{c}\dfrac{x^2}{2} + a^2 x\right]_0^c = \dfrac{1}{c(a + b)}\left[\dfrac{(b - a)^2 c}{3} + ac(b - a) + a^2 c\right]$$

$$= \dfrac{1}{3c(a + b)}[(b^2 - 2ab + a^2)c + 3ac(b - a) + 3a^2 c]$$

$$= \dfrac{1}{3(a + b)}[b^2 - 2ab + a^2 + 3ab - 3a^2 + 3a^2] = \dfrac{a^2 + ab + b^2}{3(a + b)}$$

Thus,

$$(\bar{x}, \bar{y}) = \left(\dfrac{(a + 2b)c}{3(a + b)}, \dfrac{a^2 + ab + b^2}{3(a + b)}\right).$$

The one line passes through $(0, a/2)$ and $(c, b/2)$. It's equation is

$$y = \dfrac{b - a}{2c}x + \dfrac{a}{2}.$$

The other line passes through $(0, -b)$ and $(c, a + b)$. It's equation is

$$y = \dfrac{a + 2b}{c}x - b.$$

$(\bar{x}, \bar{y})$ is the point of intersection of these two lines.

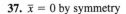

37. $\bar{x} = 0$ by symmetry

$$A = \dfrac{1}{2}\pi ab$$

$$\dfrac{1}{A} = \dfrac{2}{\pi ab}$$

$$\bar{y} = \dfrac{2}{\pi ab}\dfrac{1}{2}\int_{-a}^a \left(\dfrac{b}{a}\sqrt{a^2 - x^2}\right)^2 dx$$

$$= \dfrac{1}{\pi ab}\left(\dfrac{b^2}{a^2}\right)\left[a^2 x - \dfrac{x^3}{3}\right]_{-a}^a = \dfrac{b}{\pi a^3}\left[\dfrac{4a^3}{3}\right] = \dfrac{4b}{3\pi}$$

$$(\bar{x}, \bar{y}) = \left(0, \dfrac{4b}{3\pi}\right)$$

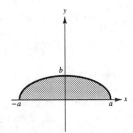

39. (a)

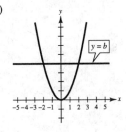

(b) $\bar{x} = 0$ by symmetry

(c) $M_y = \displaystyle\int_{-\sqrt{b}}^{\sqrt{b}} x(b - x^2) dx = 0$ because $bx - x^3$ is odd.

(d) $\bar{y} > \dfrac{b}{2}$ since there is more area above $y = \dfrac{b}{2}$ than below.

—CONTINUED—

39. **—CONTINUED—**

(e) $M_x = \int_{-\sqrt{b}}^{\sqrt{b}} \frac{(b + x^2)(b - x^2)}{2} \, dx = \int_{-\sqrt{b}}^{\sqrt{b}} \frac{b^2 - x^4}{2} \, dx = \frac{1}{2}\left[b^2 x - \frac{x^5}{5} \right]_{-\sqrt{b}}^{\sqrt{b}} = b^2\sqrt{b} - \frac{b^2\sqrt{b}}{5} = \frac{4b^2\sqrt{b}}{5}$

$A = \int_{-\sqrt{b}}^{\sqrt{b}} (b - x^2) \, dx = \left[bx - \frac{x^3}{3} \right]_{-\sqrt{b}}^{\sqrt{b}} = \left(b\sqrt{b} - \frac{b\sqrt{b}}{3} \right)2 = 4\frac{b\sqrt{b}}{3}$

$\bar{y} = \frac{M_x}{A} = \frac{4b^2\sqrt{b}/5}{4b\sqrt{b}/3} = \frac{3}{5}b.$

41. (a) From the symmetry of the glass it follows that $\bar{x} = 0$. To approximate the mass of the glass, use its symmetry with respect to the y-axis and Simpson's Rule with $n = 4$ to obtain

$m = 2\rho\int_0^{40} y \, dx$

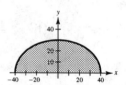

$\approx 2\rho\left[\frac{40 - 0}{3(4)} \right][30 + 4(29) + 2(26) + 4(20) + 0] \approx 1853.33\rho.$

To approximate M_x, use the symmetry of the glass and Simpson's Rule with $n = 4$ to obtain

$M_x = 2\rho\int_0^{40}\left(\frac{y}{2} \right)y \, dx = \rho\int_0^{40} y^2 \, dx \approx \rho\left[\frac{40 - 0}{3(4)} \right][30^2 + 4(29^2) + 2(26^2) + 4(20^2) + 0^2] \approx 24{,}053.33\rho.$

Therefore, $\bar{y} = \frac{M_x}{m} \approx \frac{24{,}053.33\rho}{1853.33\rho} \approx 12.98.$

(b) Using the regression capabilities to find a fourth-degree polynomial for the data yields

$y = (-1.02 \times 10^{-5})x^4 - 0.0019x^2 + 29.28.$

(c) Use the integration capabilities of a graphing utility to approximate the following integrals where y is the model in part (b).

$m = 2\rho\int_0^{40} y \, dx \approx 1843.54\rho$

$M_x = 2\rho\int_0^{40}\left(\frac{y}{2} \right)y \, dx = \rho\int_0^{40} y^2 \, dx \approx 23{,}697.68\rho$

Therefore. $\bar{y} = \frac{M_x}{m} \approx \frac{23{,}697.68\rho}{1843.54\rho} \approx 12.85.$

43. Although a coordinate system may be introduced in many different ways, the one shown in the figure is a natural choice. Since both the circle and square have a uniform density, their masses are proportional to their areas, π and 4, respectively. (For simplicity, assume the density to be 1 unit of mass per 1 unit of area.) Again, because of the uniform density, both the circle and the square have their centers of mass at their geometrical centers, $(3, 0)$ and $(1, 0)$, respectively. Therefore, we can find the center of mass of the plate by considering a mass of π centered at $(3, 0)$ and a mass of 4 centered at $(1, 0)$. Thus,

$\bar{x} = \frac{\pi(3) + 4(1)}{\pi + 4} = \frac{3\pi + 4}{\pi + 4}$

and $\bar{y} = \frac{\pi(0) + 4(0)}{\pi + 4} = 0.$

45. Centroids of the given regions: $\left(0, \frac{3}{2} \right)$, $(0, 5)$, and $\left(0, \frac{15}{2} \right)$

Area: $A = 15 + 12 + 7 = 34$

$\bar{x} = \frac{15(0) + 12(0) + 7(0)}{34} = 0$

$\bar{y} = \frac{15(3/2) + 12(5) + 7(15/2)}{34} = \frac{135}{34}$

$(\bar{x}, \bar{y}) = \left(0, \frac{135}{34} \right)$

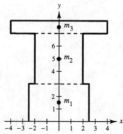

47. Centroids of the given regions: $(1, 0)$ and $(3, 0)$

Mass: $4 + 2\pi$

$$\bar{x} = \frac{4(1) + 2\pi(3)}{4 + 2\pi} = \frac{2 + 3\pi}{2 + \pi}$$

$$\bar{y} = 0$$

$$(\bar{x}, \bar{y}) = \left(\frac{2 + 3\pi}{2 + \pi}, 0\right) \approx (2.22, 0)$$

49. $V = 2\pi rA = 2\pi(5)(16\pi) = 160\pi^2 \approx 1579.14$

51. $A = \dfrac{1}{2}(4)(4) = 8$

$$\bar{y} = \left(\frac{1}{8}\right)\frac{1}{2}\int_0^4 (4 + x)(4 - x)\,dx = \frac{1}{16}\left[16x - \frac{x^3}{3}\right]_0^4 = \frac{8}{3}$$

$$r = \bar{y} = \frac{8}{3}$$

$$V = 2\pi rA = 2\pi\left(\frac{8}{3}\right)(8) = \frac{128\pi}{3} \approx 134.04$$

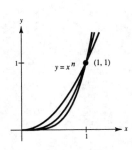

53. The surface area of the sphere is $S = 4\pi r^2$. The arc length of C is $s = \pi r$. The distance traveled by the centroid is

$$d = \frac{S}{s} = \frac{4\pi r^2}{\pi r} = 4r.$$

This distance is also the circumference of the circle of radius y, $d = 2\pi y$. Thus, $2\pi y = 4r$ and we have $y = 2r/\pi$. Therefore, the centroid of the semicircle $y = \sqrt{r^2 - x^2}$ is $(0, 2r/\pi)$.

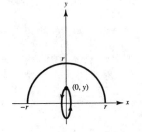

55. $A = \displaystyle\int_0^1 x^n\,dx = \left[\frac{x^{n+1}}{n+1}\right]_0^1 = \frac{1}{n+1}$

$$m = \rho A = \frac{\rho}{n+1}$$

$$M_x = \frac{\rho}{2}\int_0^1 (x^n)^2\,dx = \left[\frac{\rho}{2} \cdot \frac{x^{2n+1}}{2n+1}\right]_0^1 = \frac{\rho}{2(2n+1)}$$

$$M_y = \rho\int_0^1 x(x^n)\,dx = \left[\rho \cdot \frac{x^{n+2}}{n+2}\right]_0^1 = \frac{\rho}{n+2}$$

$$\bar{x} = \frac{M_y}{m} = \frac{n+1}{n+2}$$

$$\bar{y} = \frac{M_x}{m} = \frac{n+1}{2(2n+1)} = \frac{n+1}{4n+2}$$

Centroid: $\left(\dfrac{n+1}{n+2}, \dfrac{n+1}{4n+2}\right)$

As $n \to \infty$, $(\bar{x}, \bar{y}) \to \left(1, \frac{1}{4}\right)$. The graph approaches the x-axis and the line $x = 1$ as $n \to \infty$.

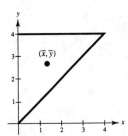

Section 6.7   Fluid Pressure and Fluid Force

1. $F = PA = [62.4(5)](3) = 936 \text{ lb}$

3. $F = 62.4(h + 2)(6) - (62.4)(h)(6)$

$\qquad = 62.4(2)(6) = 748.8 \text{ lb}$

5. $h(y) = 3 - y$

$L(y) = 4$

$F = 62.4 \displaystyle\int_0^3 (3 - y)(4) \, dy$

$\quad = 249.6 \displaystyle\int_0^3 (3 - y) \, dy$

$\quad = 249.6 \left[3y - \dfrac{y^2}{2} \right]_0^3 = 1123.2 \text{ lb}$

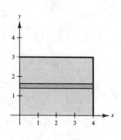

7. The force against a representative rectangle of length $2x$ is

$\Delta F = (\text{density})(\text{depth})(\text{area}) = (62.4)(3 - y)(2x \, \Delta y)$

$\qquad = (62.4)(3 - y)(2)\left(\dfrac{1}{3}y + 1\right) \Delta y.$

Since y ranges from 0 to 3, the total force is

$F = \displaystyle\int_0^3 (62.4)(3 - y)(2)\left(\dfrac{1}{3}y + 1\right) dy = 124.8 \int_0^3 \left(3 - \dfrac{1}{3}y^2\right) dy$

$\quad = 124.8 \left[3y - \dfrac{1}{9}y^3 \right]_0^3 = 748.8 \text{ lb.}$

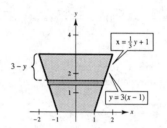

9. $h(y) = 4 - y$

$L(y) = 2\sqrt{y}$

$F = 2(62.4) \displaystyle\int_0^4 (4 - y)\sqrt{y} \, dy$

$\quad = 124.8 \displaystyle\int_0^4 (4y^{1/2} - y^{3/2}) \, dy$

$\quad = 124.8 \left[\dfrac{8y^{3/2}}{3} - \dfrac{2y^{5/2}}{5} \right]_0^4 = 1064.96 \text{ lb}$

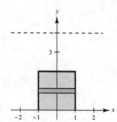

11. $h(y) = 4 - y$

$L(y) = 2$

$F = 9800 \displaystyle\int_0^2 2(4 - y) \, dy$

$\quad = 9800 \left[8y - y^2 \right]_0^2 = 117,600 \text{ N}$

13. The force against a representative rectangle of length x is

$$\Delta F = (\text{density})(\text{depth})(\text{area})$$

$$= (9800)(12 - y)\left(-\frac{2}{3}y + 6\right)\Delta y$$

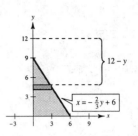

Since y ranges from 0 to 9, the total force is

$$F = \int_0^9 9800(12 - y)\left(-\frac{2}{3}y + 6\right)dy = 9800\int_0^9\left(\frac{2}{3}y^2 - 14y + 72\right)dy$$

$$= 9800\left[\frac{2}{9}y^3 - 7y^2 + 72y\right]_0^9 = 2{,}381{,}400 \text{ N.}$$

15. $h(y) = 2 - y$

$L(y) = 10$

$$F = 140.7\int_0^2 (2 - y)(10)\, dy$$

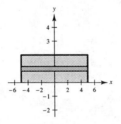

$$= 1407\int_0^2 (2 - y)\, dy$$

$$= 1407\left[2y - \frac{y^2}{2}\right]_0^2 = 2814 \text{ lb}$$

17. $h(y) = 4 - y$

$L(y) = 6$

$$F = 140.7\int_0^4 (4 - y)(6)\, dy$$

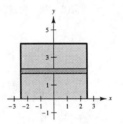

$$= 844.2\int_0^4 (4 - y)\, dy$$

$$= 844.2\left[4y - \frac{y^2}{2}\right]_0^4 = 6753.6 \text{ lb}$$

19. The force against a representative rectangle of length $2x$ is

$$\Delta F = (\text{density})(\text{depth})(\text{area}) = (42)(-y)(2x\,\Delta y)$$

$$= (42)(-y)(2)\left(\frac{1}{2}\right)(9 - 4y^2)^{1/2}\,\Delta y = -42y(9 - 4y^2)^{1/2}\,\Delta y.$$

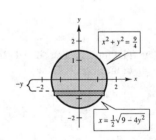

Since y ranges from $-\frac{3}{2}$ to 0, the total force is

$$F = \int_{-3/2}^0 (-42)y(9 - 4y^2)^{1/2}\, dy = \frac{42}{8}\int_{-3/2}^0 (9 - 4y^2)^{1/2}(-8y)\, dy$$

$$= \frac{21}{4}\left(\frac{2}{3}\right)\left[(9 - 4y^2)^{3/2}\right]_{-3/2}^0 = 94.5 \text{ lb.}$$

21. $h(y) = k - y$

$L(y) = 2\sqrt{r^2 - y^2}$

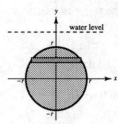

water level

$$F = w \int_{-r}^{r} (k - y)\sqrt{r^2 - y^2}\,(2)\,dy$$

$$= w\left[2k \int_{-r}^{r} \sqrt{r^2 - y^2}\,dy + \int_{-r}^{r} \sqrt{r^2 - y^2}\,(-2y)\,dy\right]$$

The second integral is zero since its integrand is odd and the limits of integration are symmetric to the origin. The first integral is the area of a semicircle with radius r.

$$F = w\left[(2k)\frac{\pi r^2}{2} + 0\right] = wk\pi r^2$$

23. From Exercise 22:

$$F = 64(15)(1)(1) = 960 \text{ lb}$$

25. $h(y) = 4 - y$

$$F = 62.4 \int_{0}^{4} (4 - y)L(y)\,dy$$

Using Simpson's Rule with $n = 8$ we have:

$$F \approx 62.4\left(\frac{4 - 0}{3(8)}\right)[0 + 4(3.5)(3) + 2(3)(5) + 4(2.5)(8) + 2(2)(9) + 4(1.5)(10) + 2(1)(10.25) + 4(0.5)(10.5) + 0]$$

$$= 3010.8 \text{ lb}$$

27. $h(y) = 12 - y$

$L(y) = 2(4^{2/3} - y^{2/3})^{3/2}$

$$F = 62.4 \int_{0}^{4} 2(12 - y)(4^{2/3} - y^{2/3})^{3/2}\,dy$$

$$\approx 6448.73 \text{ lb}$$

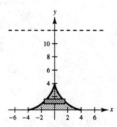

29. (a) If the fluid force is one half of 1123.2 lb, and the height of the water is b, then

$$h(y) = b - y$$

$$L(y) = 4$$

$$F = 62.4 \int_{0}^{b} (b - y)(4)\,dy = \frac{1}{2}(1123.2)$$

$$\int_{0}^{b} (b - y)\,dy = 2.25$$

$$\left[by - \frac{y^2}{2}\right]_{0}^{b} = 2.25$$

$$b^2 - \frac{b^2}{2} = 2.25$$

$$b^2 = 4.5 \implies b \approx 2.12 \text{ ft.}$$

(b) The pressure increases with increasing depth.

Review Exercises for Chapter 6

1. $A = \int_1^5 \frac{1}{x^2} dx = \left[-\frac{1}{x} \right]_1^5 = \frac{4}{5}$

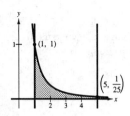

3. The graph of the region is shown in the figure. The area is given by

$$\text{Area} = \int_{-1}^{1} \frac{1}{x^2 + 1} dx$$

$$= 2 \int_0^1 \frac{1}{x^2 + 1} dx = 2 \left[\arctan \right]_0^1$$

$$= 2 \arctan 1 = \frac{\pi}{2}.$$

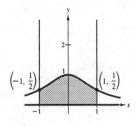

5. $A = 2 \int_0^1 (x - x^3) \, dx$

$$= 2 \left[\frac{1}{2} x^2 - \frac{1}{4} x^4 \right]_0^1$$

$$= \frac{1}{2}$$

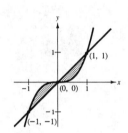

7. $A = \int_0^2 (e^2 - e^x) \, dx$

$$= \left[x e^2 - e^x \right]_0^2$$

$$= e^2 + 1$$

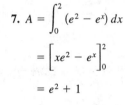

9. $A = \int_{\pi/4}^{5\pi/4} (\sin x - \cos x) \, dx$

$$= \left[-\cos x - \sin x \right]_{\pi/4}^{5\pi/4}$$

$$= \left(\frac{1}{\sqrt{2}} + \frac{1}{\sqrt{2}} \right) - \left(-\frac{1}{\sqrt{2}} - \frac{1}{\sqrt{2}} \right)$$

$$= \frac{4}{\sqrt{2}} = 2\sqrt{2}$$

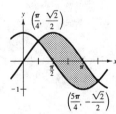

11. $A = \int_0^8 \left[(3 + 8x - x^2) - (x^2 - 8x + 3) \right] dx$

$$= \int_0^8 (16x - 2x^2) \, dx$$

$$= \left[8x^2 - \frac{2}{3} x^3 \right]_0^8 = \frac{512}{3} \approx 170.667$$

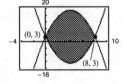

13. Solving the equation $\sqrt{x} + \sqrt{y} = 1$ for y yields $y = \left(1 - \sqrt{x} \right)^2$ for $0 \le x \le 1$. The graph of the region is shown in the figure. Using the integration capabilities of a graphing utility yields the following area.

$$\text{Area} = \int_0^1 \left(1 - \sqrt{x} \right)^2 dx = \frac{1}{6}$$

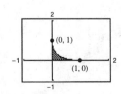

15. To find the y-intercepts of the graph, solve the equation

$$y^2 - 2y = 0$$

$$y(y - 2) = 0 \implies y = 0, 2.$$

The graph of the equation is a parabola opening to the right as shown in the figure. To find the area of the region by using vertical representative rectangles, begin by solving the equation for y.

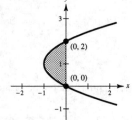

$$x = y^2 - 2y \implies 0 = y^2 - 2y - x$$

Using the Quadratic Formula with $a = 1$, $b = -2$, and $c = -x$, we have

$$y = \frac{-(-2) \pm \sqrt{(-2)^2 - 4(1)(-x)}}{2(1)}$$

$$= \frac{1}{2}\left[2 \pm \sqrt{4 + 4x}\right] = 1 \pm \sqrt{1 + x}.$$

Therefore, the top half and bottom halves of the parabola are given by $f(x) = 1 + \sqrt{1 + x}$ and $g(x) = 1 - \sqrt{1 + x}$, respectively. Thus, the area of the region is given by

$$A = \int_{-1}^{0} \left[(1 + \sqrt{1 + x}) - (1 - \sqrt{1 + x})\right] dx = \int_{-1}^{0} \left(2\sqrt{1 + x}\right) dx.$$

Using horizontal representative rectangles and the fact that $y^2 - 2y \leq 0$ for $0 \leq y \leq 2$, we have

$$A = \int_{0}^{2} [0 - (y^2 - 2y)] \, dy = \int_{0}^{2} (-y^2 + 2y) \, dy = \left[\frac{-y^3}{3} + y^2\right]_{0}^{2} = -\frac{8}{3} + 4 = \frac{4}{3}.$$

17. $A = \int_{0}^{2} \left[1 - \left(1 - \frac{x}{2}\right)\right] dx + \int_{2}^{3} [1 - (x - 2)] \, dx$

$$= \int_{0}^{2} \frac{x}{2} \, dx + \int_{2}^{3} (3 - x) \, dx$$

$$y = 1 - \frac{x}{2} \implies x = 2 - 2y$$

$$y = x - 2 \implies x = y + 2, y = 1$$

$$A = \int_{0}^{1} [(y + 2) - (2 - 2y)] \, dy$$

$$= \int_{0}^{1} 3y \, dy = \left[\frac{3}{2}y^2\right]_{0}^{1} = \frac{3}{2}$$

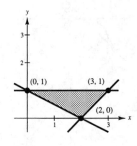

19. Job 1 is better. The salary for Job 1 is greater than the salary for Job 2 for all the years except the first and 10th years.

21. (a) Disc

$$V = \pi \int_{0}^{4} x^2 \, dx = \left[\frac{\pi x^3}{3}\right]_{0}^{4} = \frac{64\pi}{3}$$

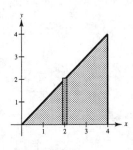

(b) Shell

$$V = 2\pi \int_{0}^{4} x^2 \, dx = \left[\frac{2\pi}{3}x^3\right]_{0}^{4} = \frac{128\pi}{3}$$

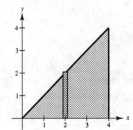

—CONTINUED—

21. —CONTINUED—

(c) Shell

$$V = 2\pi \int_0^4 (4 - x)x\, dx$$

$$= 2\pi \int_0^4 (4x - x^2)\, dx$$

$$= 2\pi \left[2x^2 - \frac{x^3}{3} \right]_0^4 = \frac{64\pi}{3}$$

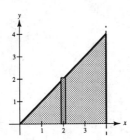

(d) Shell

$$V = 2\pi \int_0^4 (6 - x)x\, dx$$

$$= 2\pi \int_0^4 (6x - x^2)\, dx$$

$$= 2\pi \left[3x^2 - \frac{1}{3}x^3 \right]_0^4 = \frac{160\pi}{3}$$

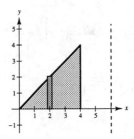

23. (a) Revolving the first quadrant portion of the ellipse about the y-axis will generate one-half the solid. Solving the equation for y yields.

$$y = \frac{3}{4}\sqrt{16 - x^2}.$$

Therefore, using the symmetry and the Shell Method we have

$$V = 2\pi \int_{-4}^4 x f(x)\, dx$$

$$= 4\pi \int_0^4 x \left(\frac{3}{4} \right) \sqrt{16 - x^2}\, dx$$

$$= 3\pi \int_0^4 x\sqrt{16 - x^2}\, dx$$

$$= -\frac{3\pi}{2} \int (16 - x^2)^{1/2}(-2x)\, dx$$

$$= -\frac{3\pi}{2} \left(\frac{2}{3} \right) \left[(16 - x^2)^{3/2} \right]_0^4$$

$$= -\pi[0 - 16^{3/2}] = 64\pi.$$

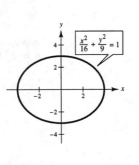

(b) Revolving the first quadrant portion of the ellipse about the x-axis will generate one-half the solid. Solving the equation for y^2 yields.

$$y^2 = \frac{9}{16}(16 - x^2).$$

Therefore, using the symmetry and the Disc Method we have

$$V = \pi \int_{-4}^4 [f(x)]^2\, dx$$

$$= 2\pi \int_0^4 \frac{9}{16}(16 - x^2)\, dx$$

$$= \frac{9\pi}{8} \left[16x - \frac{1}{3}x^3 \right]_0^4$$

$$= \frac{9\pi}{8} \left[64 - \frac{64}{3} \right] = 48\pi.$$

25. Shell

$$V = 2\pi \int_0^1 \frac{x}{x^4 + 1}\, dx$$

$$= \pi \int_0^1 \frac{(2x)}{(x^2)^2 + 1}\, dx$$

$$= \left[\pi \arctan(x^2) \right]_0^1$$

$$= \pi \left[\frac{\pi}{4} - 0 \right] = \frac{\pi^2}{4}$$

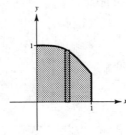

27. Shell

$$u = \sqrt{x - 2}$$

$$x = u^2 + 2$$

$$dx = 2u\, du$$

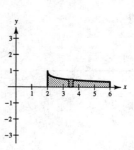

$$V = 2\pi \int_2^6 \frac{x}{1 + \sqrt{x - 2}}\, dx = 4\pi \int_0^2 \frac{(u^2 + 2)u}{1 + u}\, du$$

$$= 4\pi \int_0^2 \frac{u^3 + 2u}{1 + u}\, du = 4\pi \int_0^2 \left(u^2 - u + 3 - \frac{3}{1 + u} \right) du$$

$$= 4\pi \left[\frac{1}{3}u^3 - \frac{1}{2}u^2 + 3u - 3\ln(1 + u) \right]_0^2 = \frac{4\pi}{3}(20 - 9\ln 3) \approx 42.359$$

29. Since $y \le 0, A = -\int_{-1}^0 x\sqrt{x + 1}\, dx.$

$$u = x + 1$$

$$x = u - 1$$

$$dx = du$$

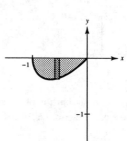

$$A = -\int_0^1 (u - 1)\sqrt{u}\, du = -\int_0^1 (u^{3/2} - u^{1/2})\, du$$

$$= -\left[\frac{2}{5}u^{5/2} - \frac{2}{3}u^{3/2} \right]_0^1 = \frac{4}{15}$$

31. From Exercise 23(a) we have: $V = 64\pi \text{ ft}^3$

$$\frac{1}{4}V = 16\pi$$

Disc: $\pi \int_{-3}^{y_0} \frac{16}{9}(9 - y^2)\, dy = 16\pi$

$$\frac{1}{9}\int_{-3}^{y_0} (9 - y^2)\, dy = 1$$

$$\left[9y - \frac{1}{3}y^3 \right]_{-3}^{y_0} = 9$$

$$\left(9y_0 - \frac{1}{3}y_0^3 \right) - (-27 + 9) = 9$$

$$y_0^3 - 27y_0 - 27 = 0$$

By Newton's Method, $y_0 \approx -1.042$ and the depth of the gasoline is $3 - 1.042 = 1.958$ ft.

33. Since $f(x) = \frac{4}{5}x^{5/4}$ and $f'(x) = x^{1/4}$, we have

$$s = \int_0^4 \sqrt{1 + [f'(x)]^2}\, dx = \int_0^4 \sqrt{1 + \sqrt{x}}\, dx.$$

Let $u = \sqrt{1 + \sqrt{x}}$. Then $u^2 = 1 + \sqrt{x}, x = (u^2 - 1)^2$, and $dx = 2(u^2 - 1)(2u)\, du$. If $x = 0$, then $u = 1$, and if $x = 4$, then $u = \sqrt{3}$. Thus,

$$s = \int_0^4 \sqrt{1 + \sqrt{x}}\, dx$$

$$= \int_1^{\sqrt{3}} u(2)(u^2 - 1)(2u)\, du$$

$$= 4\int_0^{\sqrt{3}} (u^4 - u^2)\, du$$

$$= 4\left[\frac{u^5}{5} - \frac{u^3}{3} \right]_1^{\sqrt{3}} = \frac{8}{15}(6\sqrt{3} + 1) \approx 6.076.$$

35. $y = 300 \cosh\left(\frac{x}{2000} \right) - 280, -2000 \le x \le 2000$

$$y' = \frac{3}{20} \sinh\left(\frac{x}{2000} \right)$$

$$s = \int_{-2000}^{2000} \sqrt{1 + \left[\frac{3}{20} \sinh\left(\frac{x}{2000} \right) \right]^2}\, dx = \frac{1}{20}\int_{-2000}^{2000} \sqrt{400 + 9\sinh^2\left(\frac{x}{2000} \right)}\, dx$$

$$\approx 4018.2 \text{ ft (by Simpson's Rule or graphing utility)}$$

37. $y = \dfrac{3}{4}x$

$$y' = \dfrac{3}{4}$$

$$1 + (y')^2 = \dfrac{25}{16}$$

$$S = 2\pi \int_0^4 \left(\dfrac{3}{4}x\right)\sqrt{\dfrac{25}{16}}\,dx = \left[\left(\dfrac{15\pi}{8}\right)\dfrac{x^2}{2}\right]_0^4 = 15\pi$$

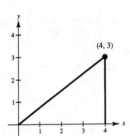

39. $F = kx$

$$4 = k(1)$$

$$F = 4x$$

$$W = \int_0^5 4x\,dx = \Big[2x^2\Big]_0^5$$

$$= 50 \text{ in} \cdot \text{lb} \approx 4.167 \text{ ft} \cdot \text{lb}$$

41. A disk of water at height y must be lifted $(175 - y)$ feet and has a volume of $\pi\left(\dfrac{1}{3}\right)^2 \Delta y$. Thus, the work done in lifting the water to the top of the well is

$$W = \int_0^{150} \underbrace{(175 - y)}_{\text{(distance)}} \underbrace{\left[62.4\pi\left(\dfrac{1}{3}\right)^2 dy\right]}_{\text{(force: weight of water)}}$$

$$= \dfrac{62.4\pi}{9}\int_0^{150} (175 - y)\,dy$$

$$= \dfrac{62.4\pi}{9}\left[175y - \dfrac{1}{2}y^2\right]_0^{150}$$

$$= 104{,}000\pi \text{ ft} \cdot \text{lb} \approx 163.4 \text{ ft} \cdot \text{ton.}$$

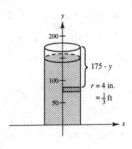

43. Weight of section of chain: $5\,\Delta x$

Distance moved: $10 - x$

$$W = 5\int_0^{10} (10 - x)\,dx$$

$$= \left[-\dfrac{5}{2}(10 - x)^2\right]_0^{10} = 250 \text{ ft} \cdot \text{lb}$$

45. $W = \displaystyle\int_a^b F(x)\,dx$

$$80 = \int_0^4 ax^2\,dx = \dfrac{ax^3}{3}\Big]_0^4 = \dfrac{64}{3}a$$

$$a = \dfrac{3(80)}{64} = \dfrac{15}{4} = 3.75$$

47. Solving the equation $\sqrt{x} + \sqrt{y} = \sqrt{a}$ for y yields $y = \left(\sqrt{a} - \sqrt{x}\right)^2$.

$$A = \int_0^a \left(\sqrt{a} - \sqrt{x}\right)^2 dx = \int_0^a \left(a - 2\sqrt{a}\,x^{1/2} + x\right) dx = \left[ax - \dfrac{4}{3}\sqrt{a}\,x^{3/2} + \dfrac{1}{2}x^2\right]_0^a = \dfrac{a^2}{6}$$

$$\bar{x} = \dfrac{1}{(a^2/6)}\int_0^a x\left(\sqrt{a} - \sqrt{x}\right)^2 dx$$

$$= \dfrac{6}{a^2}\int_0^a \left(ax - 2\sqrt{a}\,x^{3/2} + x^2\right) dx$$

$$= \dfrac{6}{a^2}\left[\dfrac{ax^2}{2} - \dfrac{4}{5}\sqrt{a}\,x^{5/2} + \dfrac{1}{3}x^3\right]_0^a = \dfrac{1}{5}a$$

By symmetry, we have $\bar{y} = \dfrac{a}{5}$. Therefore, $(\bar{x}, \bar{y}) = \left(\dfrac{a}{5}, \dfrac{a}{5}\right)$.

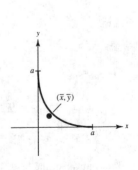

49. By symmetry, $x = 0$.

$$A = 2 \int_0^1 (a^2 - x^2)\, dx = 2\left[a^2 x - \frac{x^3}{3} \right]_0^a = \frac{4a^3}{3}$$

$$\frac{1}{A} = \frac{3}{4a^3}$$

$$\bar{y} = \left(\frac{3}{4a^3} \right) \frac{1}{2} \int_{-a}^a (a^2 - x^2)^2\, dx$$

$$= \frac{6}{8a^3} \int_0^a (a^4 - 2a^2 x^2 + x^4)\, dx$$

$$= \frac{6}{8a^3} \left[a^4 x - \frac{2a^2}{3} x^3 + \frac{1}{5} x^5 \right]_0^a$$

$$= \frac{6}{8a^3} \left(a^5 - \frac{2}{3} a^5 + \frac{1}{5} a^5 \right) = \frac{2a^2}{5}$$

$$(\bar{x}, \bar{y}) = \left(0, \frac{2a^2}{5} \right)$$

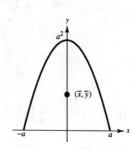

51. Since the region is symmetrical to the x-axis, $\bar{y} = 0$. The mass of the region is the sum of the mass of the trapezoid and the mass of the semicircle.

$$m = \left(\frac{2 + 4}{2} \right) 6\rho + \left(\frac{1}{2} \right) (\pi)(2)^2 \rho = 18\rho + 2\pi\rho = 2\rho(9 + \pi)$$

The moment of the region about the y-axis is the sum of the moment of the trapezoid about the y-axis and the moment of the semicircle about the y-axis.

$$M_y = 2\rho \int_0^6 x\left(\frac{1}{6} x + 1 \right) dx + 2\rho \int_6^8 x\sqrt{4 - (x - 6)^2}\, dx$$

Evaluating the first integral, we have

$$2\rho \int_0^6 x\left(\frac{1}{6} x + 1 \right) dx = 2\rho \int_0^6 \left(\frac{1}{6} x^2 + x \right) dx$$

$$= 2\rho \left[\frac{1}{18} x^3 + \frac{1}{2} x^2 \right]_0^6 = 2\rho(12 + 18) = 60\rho.$$

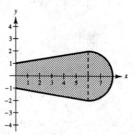

To evaluate the second integral, let $u = x - 6$. Then $x = u + 6$, $dx = du$, $u = 0$ when $x = 6$, and $u = 2$ when $x = 8$.

$$2\rho \int_6^8 x\sqrt{4 - (x - 6)^2}\, dx = 2\rho \int_0^2 (u + 6)\sqrt{4 - u^2}\, du$$

$$= 2\rho \int_0^2 u\sqrt{4 - u^2}\, du + 12\rho \int_0^2 \sqrt{4 - u^2}\, du$$

Note that the second integral is the area of one-fourth of a circle of radius 2.

$$= 2\rho \left[\left(-\frac{1}{2} \right)\left(\frac{2}{3} \right)(4 - u^2)^{3/2} \right]_0^2 + 12\rho \left[\frac{\pi(2)^2}{4} \right]$$

$$= \frac{16\rho}{3} + 12\pi\rho = \frac{4\rho(4 + 9\pi)}{3}$$

Therefore, $M_y = 60\rho + \dfrac{4\rho(4 + 9p)}{3}$, and

$$\bar{x} = \frac{M_y}{m} = \frac{60\rho + \dfrac{4\rho(4 + 9\pi)}{3}}{2\rho(9 + \pi)} = \frac{2(9\pi + 49)}{3(\pi + 9)}.$$

The centroid of the blade is $\left(\dfrac{2(9\pi + 49)}{3(\pi + 9)}, 0 \right)$.

53. Wall at shallow end:

$$F = 62.4 \int_0^5 y(20) \, dy = \left[(1248) \frac{y^2}{2} \right]_0^5 = 15{,}600 \text{ lb}$$

Wall at deep end:

$$F = 62.4 \int_0^{10} y(20) \, dy = \left[(624)y^2 \right]_0^{10} = 62{,}400 \text{ lb}$$

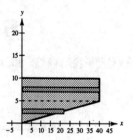

Side wall:

$$F_1 = 62.4 \int_0^5 y(40) \, dy = \left[(1248)y^2 \right]_0^5 = 31{,}200 \text{ lb}$$

$$F_2 = 62.4 \int_0^5 (10 - y)8y \, dy = 62.4 \int_0^5 (80y - 8y^2) \, dy$$

$$F = F_1 + F_2 = 72{,}800 \text{ lb}$$

55. $F = 62.4(16\pi)5 = 4992\pi \text{ lb}$

C H A P T E R   7
Integration Techniques, L'Hôpital's Rule, and Improper Integrals

CHAPTER 7
Integration Techniques, L'Hôpital's Rule, and Improper Integrals

Section 7.1   Basic Integration Formulas

Solutions to Odd-Numbered Exercises

1. (a) $\dfrac{d}{dx}\left[2\sqrt{x^2+1}+C\right]=2\left(\dfrac{1}{2}\right)(x^2+1)^{-1/2}(2x)=\dfrac{2x}{\sqrt{x^2+1}}$

    (b) $\dfrac{d}{dx}\left[\sqrt{x^2+1}+C\right]=\dfrac{1}{2}(x^2+1)^{-1/2}(2x)=\dfrac{x}{\sqrt{x^2+1}}$

    (c) $\dfrac{d}{dx}\left[\dfrac{1}{2}\sqrt{x^2+1}+C\right]=\dfrac{1}{2}\left(\dfrac{1}{2}\right)(x^2+1)^{-1/2}(2x)=\dfrac{x}{2\sqrt{x^2+1}}$

    (d) $\dfrac{d}{dx}[\ln(x^2+1)+C]=\dfrac{2x}{x^2+1}$

$\displaystyle\int\dfrac{x}{\sqrt{x^2+1}}\,dx$ matches (b).

3. (a) $\dfrac{d}{dx}\left[\ln\sqrt{x^2+1}+C\right]=\dfrac{1}{2}\left(\dfrac{2x}{x^2+1}\right)=\dfrac{x}{x^2+1}$

    (b) $\dfrac{d}{dx}\left[\dfrac{2x}{(x^2+1)^2}+C\right]=\dfrac{(x^2+1)^2(2)-(2x)(2)(x^2+1)(2x)}{(x^2+1)^4}=\dfrac{2(1-3x^2)}{(x^2+1)^3}$

    (c) $\dfrac{d}{dx}[\arctan x+C]=\dfrac{1}{1+x^2}$

    (d) $\dfrac{d}{dx}[\ln(x^2+1)+C]=\dfrac{2x}{x^2+1}$

$\displaystyle\int\dfrac{1}{x^2+1}\,dx$ matches (c).

5. If we let $u=3x-2$, then $du=3\,dx$ and

$$\int(3x-2)^4\,dx=\dfrac{1}{3}\int(3x-2)^4(3)\,dx=\dfrac{1}{3}\int u^4\,du.$$

7. $\displaystyle\int\dfrac{1}{\sqrt{x}\left(1-2\sqrt{x}\right)}\,dx$

$u=1-2\sqrt{x},\ du=-\dfrac{1}{\sqrt{x}}\,dx$

Use $\displaystyle\int\dfrac{du}{u}$.

9. $\displaystyle\int\dfrac{3}{\sqrt{1-t^2}}\,dt$

$u=t,\ du=dt,\ a=1$

Use $\displaystyle\int\dfrac{du}{\sqrt{a^2-u^2}}$

11. If we let $u=t^2$, then $du=2t\,dt$ and

$$\int t\sin t^2\,dt=\dfrac{1}{2}\int\sin(t^2)(2t)\,dt=\dfrac{1}{2}\int\sin u\,du.$$

13. $\displaystyle\int \cos x e^{\sin x}\, dx$

$u = \sin x,\, du = \cos x\, dx$

Use $\displaystyle\int e^u\, du.$

15. Let $u = -2x + 5,\, du = -2\, dx.$

$$\int (-2x + 5)^{3/2}\, dx = -\frac{1}{2}\int (-2x + 5)^{3/2}(-2)\, dx$$

$$= -\frac{1}{5}(-2x + 5)^{5/2} + C$$

17. $\displaystyle\int \left[v + \frac{1}{(3v - 1)^3} \right] dv = \int v\, dv + \frac{1}{3}\int (3v - 1)^{-3}(3)dv \;=\; \frac{1}{2}v^2 - \frac{1}{6(3v - 1)^2} + C$

19. If we let $u = -t^3 + 9t + 1$, then

$$du = (-3t^2 + 9)\, dt = -3(t^2 - 3)\, dt.$$

Thus,

$$\int \frac{t^2 - 3}{-t^3 + 9t + 1}\, dt = -\frac{1}{3}\int \frac{1}{-t^3 + 9t + 1}[-3(t^2 - 3)]\, dt$$

$$= -\frac{1}{3}\int \frac{1}{u}\, du = -\frac{1}{3}\ln|-t^3 + 9t + 1| + C.$$

21. $\displaystyle\int \frac{x^2}{x - 1}\, dx = \int (x + 1)\, dx + \int \frac{1}{x - 1}\, dx$

$$= \frac{1}{2}x^2 + x + \ln|x - 1| + C$$

23. Let $u = 1 + e^x,\, du = e^x\, dx.$

$$\int \frac{e^x}{1 + e^x}\, dx = \ln(1 + e^x) + C$$

25. $\displaystyle\int (1 + 2x^2)^2\, dx = \int (4x^4 + 4x^2 + 1)dx = \frac{4}{5}x^5 + \frac{4}{3}x^3 + x + C = \frac{x}{15}(12x^4 + 20x^2 + 15) + C$

27. If we let $u = 2\pi x^2$, then $du = 4\pi x\, dx$ and

$$\int x \cos 2\pi x^2\, dx = \frac{1}{4\pi}\int (\cos 2\pi x^2)(4\pi x)\, dx$$

$$= \frac{1}{4\pi}\int \cos u\, du$$

$$= \frac{1}{4\pi}\sin 2\pi x^2 + C.$$

29. Let $u = \pi x,\, du = \pi\, dx.$

$$\int \csc(\pi x) \cot(\pi x)\, dx = \frac{1}{\pi}\int \csc(\pi x) \cot(\pi x)\pi\, dx$$

$$= -\frac{1}{\pi}\csc(\pi x) + C$$

31. Let $u = 5x,\, du = 5\, dx.$

$$\int e^{5x}\, dx = \frac{1}{5}\int e^{5x}(5)\, dx = \frac{1}{5}e^{5x} + C$$

33. Let $u = 1 + e^x,\, du = e^x\, dx.$

$$\int \frac{2}{e^{-x} + 1}\, dx = 2\int \left(\frac{1}{e^{-x} + 1} \right)\left(\frac{e^x}{e^x} \right) dx$$

$$= 2\int \frac{e^x}{1 + e^x}\, dx = 2\ln(1 + e^x) + C$$

35. $\displaystyle\int \frac{1 + \sin x}{\cos x}\, dx = \int (\sec x + \tan x)\, dx$

$$= \ln|\sec x + \tan x| + \ln|\sec x| + C$$

$$= \ln|\sec x(\sec x + \tan x)| + C$$

37. $\displaystyle\int \frac{2t - 1}{t^2 + 4}\, dt = \int \frac{2t}{t^2 + 4}\, dt - \int \frac{1}{t^2 + 2^2}\, dt$

$$= \ln(t^2 + 4) - \frac{1}{2}\arctan\frac{t}{2} + C$$

39. If we let $u = 2t - 1$, then $du = 2\,dt$. Thus,

$$\int \frac{-1}{\sqrt{1 - (2t - 1)^2}}\,dt = \frac{-1}{2}\int \frac{2}{\sqrt{1 - (2t - 1)^2}}\,dt$$

$$= \frac{-1}{2}\int \frac{1}{\sqrt{a^2 - u^2}}\,du$$

$$= -\frac{1}{2}\arcsin(2t - 1) + C.$$

41. Let $u = \cos\left(\dfrac{2}{t}\right)$, $du = \dfrac{2\sin(2/t)}{t^2}\,dt$.

$$\int \frac{\tan(2/t)}{t^2}\,dt = \frac{1}{2}\int \frac{1}{\cos(2/t)}\left[\frac{2\sin(2/t)}{t^2}\right]dt$$

$$= \frac{1}{2}\ln\left|\cos\left(\frac{2}{t}\right)\right| + C$$

43. By completing the square we have

$$\int \frac{3}{\sqrt{6x - x^2}}\,dx = 3\int \frac{1}{\sqrt{9 - (9 - 6x + x^2)}}\,dx$$

$$= 3\int \frac{1}{\sqrt{9 - (x - 3)^2}}\,dx$$

$$= 3\arcsin\left(\frac{x - 3}{3}\right) + C.$$

45. $\displaystyle\int \frac{4}{4x^2 + 4x + 65}\,dx = \int \frac{1}{[x + (1/2)]^2 + 16}\,dx$

$$= \frac{1}{4}\arctan\left[\frac{x + (1/2)}{4}\right] + C$$

$$= \frac{1}{4}\arctan\left(\frac{2x + 1}{8}\right) + C$$

47. $\dfrac{ds}{dt} = \dfrac{t}{\sqrt{1 - t^4}}$, $\left(0, -\dfrac{1}{2}\right)$

(a)

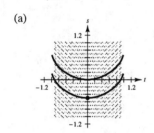

(b) $u = t^2$, $du = 2t\,dt$

$$\int \frac{t}{\sqrt{1 - t^4}}\,dt = \frac{1}{2}\int \frac{2t}{\sqrt{1 - (t^2)^2}}\,dt = \frac{1}{2}\arcsin t^2 + C$$

$$\left(0, -\frac{1}{2}\right): \quad -\frac{1}{2} = \frac{1}{2}\arcsin 0 + C \implies C = -\frac{1}{2}$$

$$s = \frac{1}{2}\arcsin t^2 - \frac{1}{2}$$

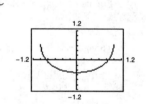

49. $\displaystyle y = \int (1 + e^x)^2\,dx = \int (e^{2x} + 2e^x + 1)\,dx$

$$= \frac{1}{2}e^{2x} + 2e^x + x + C$$

51. $(4 + \tan^2 x)y' = \sec^2 x$

$$y' = \frac{\sec^2 x}{4 + \tan^2 x}$$

$$\int y'\,dx = \int \frac{\sec^2 x}{4 + \tan^2 x}\,dx$$

If we let $u = \tan x$, then $du = \sec^2 x\,dx$ and

$$y = \int \frac{\sec^2 x}{4 + \tan^2 x}\,dx$$

$$= \int \frac{1}{a^2 + u^2}\,du$$

$$= \frac{1}{2}\arctan\left(\frac{\tan x}{2}\right) + C.$$

53. Let $u = 2x$, $du = 2\,dx$.

$$\int_0^{\pi/4} \cos 2x\,dx = \frac{1}{2}\int_0^{\pi/4} \cos 2x(2)\,dx$$

$$= \left[\frac{1}{2}\sin 2x\right]_0^{\pi/4} = \frac{1}{2}$$

55. Let $u = -x^2$, $du = -2x\,dx$.

$$\int_0^1 xe^{-x^2}\,dx = -\frac{1}{2}\int_0^1 e^{-x^2}(-2x)\,dx = \left[-\frac{1}{2}e^{-x^2}\right]_0^1$$

$$= \frac{1}{2}(1 - e^{-1}) \approx 0.316$$

57. Let $u = x^2 + 9$, $du = 2x\, dx$.

$$\int_0^4 \frac{2x}{\sqrt{x^2 + 9}}\, dx = \int_0^4 (x^2 + 9)^{-1/2}(2x)\, dx$$

$$= \left[2\sqrt{x^2 + 9} \right]_0^4 = 4$$

59. Let $a = 2$ and $u = 3x$. Then $du = 3\, dx$ and

$$\int_0^{2/\sqrt{3}} \frac{1}{4 + 9x^2}\, dx = \frac{1}{3}\int_0^{2/\sqrt{3}} \frac{1}{2^2 + (3x)^2}(3)\, dx$$

$$= \frac{1}{6}\left[\arctan\left(\frac{3x}{2}\right) \right]_0^{2/\sqrt{3}}$$

$$= \frac{1}{6}\arctan\frac{3}{\sqrt{3}} = \frac{\pi}{18}.$$

61. $\displaystyle\int \frac{1}{x^2 + 4x + 13}\, dx = \frac{1}{3}\arctan\left(\frac{x + 2}{3}\right) + C$

The antiderivatives are vertical translations of each other.

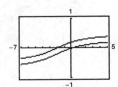

63. $\displaystyle\int \frac{1}{1 + \sin\theta}\, d\theta = \tan\theta - \sec\theta + C\left(\text{or } \frac{-2}{1 + \tan(\theta/2)}\right)$

The antiderivatives are vertical translations of each other.

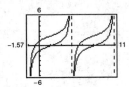

65. $\sin x + \cos x = a\sin(x + b)$

$\sin x + \cos x = a\sin x\cos b + a\cos x\sin b$

$\sin x + \cos x = (a\cos b)\sin x + (a\sin b)\cos x$

Equate coefficients of like terms to obtain the following.

$\quad 1 = a\cos b \quad$ and $\quad 1 = a\sin b$

Thus, $a = 1/\cos b$. Now, substitute for a in $1 = a\sin b$.

$$1 = \left(\frac{1}{\cos b}\right)\sin b$$

$$1 = \tan b \implies b = \frac{\pi}{4}$$

Since $b = \dfrac{\pi}{4}$, $a = \dfrac{1}{\cos(\pi/4)} = \sqrt{2}$. Thus, $\sin x + \cos x = \sqrt{2}\sin\left(x + \dfrac{\pi}{4}\right)$.

$$\int \frac{dx}{\sin x + \cos x} = \int \frac{dx}{\sqrt{2}\sin(x + (\pi/4))} = \frac{1}{\sqrt{2}}\int \csc\left(x + \frac{\pi}{4}\right) dx = -\frac{1}{\sqrt{2}}\ln\left|\csc\left(x + \frac{\pi}{4}\right) + \cot\left(x + \frac{\pi}{4}\right)\right| + C$$

67. $\displaystyle\int_0^2 \frac{4x}{x^2 + 1}\, dx \approx 3$

Matches (a).

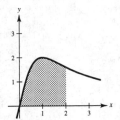

69. The graph $y^2 = x^2(1 - x^2)$ is shown in the figure. The first quadrant portion of the curve is given by $y = x\sqrt{1 - x^2}$ where $0 \le x \le 1$. By symmetry we have

$$\text{Area} = 4\int_0^1 x\sqrt{1 - x^2}\,dx$$

$$= -2\int_0^1 \underbrace{(1 - x^2)^{1/2}}_{u^{1/2}}\underbrace{(-2x)\,dx}_{du} = -2\left[\frac{2}{3}(1 - x^2)^{3/2}\right]_0^1 = \frac{4}{3}.$$

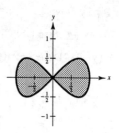

71. $\displaystyle\int_0^{1/a} (x - ax^2)\,dx = \left[\frac{1}{2}x^2 - \frac{a}{3}x^3\right]_0^{1/a}$

$$= \frac{1}{6a^2}$$

Let $\dfrac{1}{6a^2} = \dfrac{2}{3},\ 12a^2 = 3,\ a = \dfrac{1}{2}.$

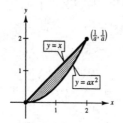

73. (a) By using the Shell Method we have

$$V = 2\pi\int_a^b p(x)h(x)\,dx$$

$$= 2\pi\int_0^b xe^{-x^2}\,dx$$

$$= -\pi\int_0^b e^{-x^2}(-2x\,dx) \quad (\text{Let } u = -x^2,\ du = -2x\,dx)$$

$$= \left[-\pi e^{-x^2}\right]_0^b = \pi(1 - e^{-b^2}).$$

When $b = 1$, $V = \pi(1 - e^{-1}) \approx 1.986.$

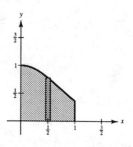

(b) Setting the expression for the volume equal to $4/3$ and solving for b yields

$$\pi(1 - e^{-b^2}) = \frac{4}{3}$$

$$3\pi - 3\pi e^{-b^2} = 4$$

$$e^{-b^2} = \frac{3\pi - 4}{3\pi}$$

$$-b^2 = \ln\left(\frac{3\pi - 4}{3\pi}\right),$$

$$b = \sqrt{\ln\left(\frac{3\pi - 4}{3\pi}\right)^{-1}} = \sqrt{\ln\left(\frac{3\pi}{3\pi - 4}\right)} \approx 0.743.$$

75. $\displaystyle A = \int_0^4 \frac{5}{\sqrt{25 - x^2}}\,dx = \left[5\arcsin\frac{x}{5}\right]_0^4 = 5\arcsin\frac{4}{5}$

$$\bar{x} = \frac{1}{A}\int_0^4 x\left(\frac{5}{\sqrt{25 - x^2}}\right)dx = \frac{1}{5\arcsin(4/5)}\left(-\frac{5}{2}\right)\int_0^4 (25 - x^2)^{-1/2}(-2x)\,dx$$

$$= \frac{1}{5\arcsin(4/5)}(-5)\left[(25 - x^2)^{1/2}\right]_0^4$$

$$= -\frac{1}{\arcsin(4/5)}[3 - 5] = \frac{2}{\arcsin(4/5)} \approx 2.157$$

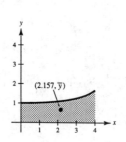

77.
$$y = \tan(\pi x)$$
$$y' = \pi \sec^2(\pi x)$$
$$1 + (y')^2 = 1 + \pi^2 \sec^4(\pi x)$$
$$s = \int_0^{1/4} \sqrt{1 + \pi^2 \sec^4(\pi x)}\, dx$$
$$\approx 1.0320$$

79. True. If $u = x^4 - 1$, then $du = 4x^3\, dx$.
$$\int \frac{x^3}{x^4 - 1}\, dx = \frac{1}{4} \int \frac{4x^3\, dx}{x^4 - 1} = \frac{1}{4} \int \frac{du}{u}$$

Section 7.2   Integration by Parts

1. (a) $\dfrac{d}{dx}[\sin x - x \cos x] = \cos x - (-x \sin x + \cos x) = x \sin x$. Matches (ii)

(b) $\dfrac{d}{dx}[x^2 \sin x + 2x \cos x - 2 \sin x] = x^2 \cos x + 2x \sin x - 2x \sin x + 2 \cos x - 2 \cos x = x^2 \cos x$. Matches (iv)

(c) $\dfrac{d}{dx}[x^2 e^x - 2x e^x + 2e^x] = x^2 e^x + 2x e^x - 2x e^x - 2e^x + 2e^x = x^2 e^x$. Matches (iii)

(d) $\dfrac{d}{dx}[-x + x \ln x] = -1 + x\left(\dfrac{1}{x}\right) + \ln x = \ln x$. Matches (i)

3. $\displaystyle\int x e^{2x}\, dx$

$u = x,\ dv = e^{2x}\, dx$

5. $\displaystyle\int (\ln x)^2\, dx$

$u = (\ln x)^2,\ dv = dx$

7. $\displaystyle\int x \sec^2 x\, dx$

$u = x,\ dv = \sec^2 x\, dx$

9. Letting $u = x$ and $dv = e^{-2x}\, dx$, we have
$$dv = e^{-2x}\, dx \implies v = \int e^{-2x}\, dx = -\frac{1}{2} e^{-2x}$$
$$u = x \qquad \implies du = dx.$$
Therefore, we have
$$\int u\, dv = uv - \int v\, du$$
$$\int x e^{-2x}\, dx = x\left(-\frac{1}{2} e^{-2x}\right) - \int -\frac{1}{2} e^{-2x}\, dx$$
$$= -\frac{x}{2} e^{-2x} - \frac{1}{4} e^{-2x} + C$$
$$= -\frac{1}{4 e^{2x}}(2x + 1) + C.$$

11. Use integration by parts three times.

(1) $dv = e^x\, dx \implies v = \displaystyle\int e^x\, dx = e^x$

$u = x^3 \qquad \implies du = 3x^2\, dx$

(2) $dv = e^x\, dx \implies v = \displaystyle\int e^x\, dx = e^x$

$u = x^2 \qquad \implies du = 2x\, dx$

(3) $dv = e^x\, dx \implies v = \displaystyle\int e^x\, dx = e^x$

$u = x \qquad \implies du = dx$

$$\int x^3 e^x\, dx = x^3 e^x - 3 \int x^2 e^x\, dx$$
$$= x^3 e^x - 3x^2 e^x + 6 \int x e^x\, dx$$
$$= x^3 e^x - 3x^2 e^x + 6x e^x - 6e^x + C$$
$$= e^x(x^3 - 3x^2 + 6x - 6) + C$$

13. $\displaystyle\int x^2 e^{x^3}\, dx = \frac{1}{3} \int e^{x^3}(3x^2)\, dx = \frac{1}{3} e^{x^3} + C$

15. Letting $u = \ln(t + 1)$ and $dv = t\, dt$, we have

$$dv = t\, dt \quad \Rightarrow \quad v = \int t\, dt = \frac{t^2}{2}$$

$$u = \ln(t + 1) \Rightarrow du = \frac{1}{t + 1}\, dt.$$

Therefore, we have

$$\int u\, dv = uv - \int v\, du$$

$$\int t \ln(t + 1)\, dt = \frac{t^2}{2} \ln(t + 1) - \frac{1}{2}\int \frac{t^2}{t + 1}\, dt$$

$$= \frac{t^2}{2} \ln(t + 1) - \frac{1}{2}\int\left(t - 1 + \frac{1}{t + 1}\right) dt$$

$$= \frac{t^2}{2} \ln(t + 1) - \frac{1}{2}\left[\frac{t^2}{2} - t + \ln(t + 1)\right] + C$$

$$= \frac{1}{4}[2(t^2 - 1) \ln|t + 1| - t^2 + 2t] + C.$$

17. Let $u = \ln x$, $du = \frac{1}{x}\, dx$.

$$\int \frac{(\ln x)^2}{x}\, dx = \int (\ln x)^2 \left(\frac{1}{x}\right) dx = \frac{(\ln x)^3}{3} + C$$

19. $dv = \dfrac{1}{(2x + 1)^2}\, dx \Rightarrow v = \displaystyle\int (2x + 1)^{-2}\, dx = -\frac{1}{2(2x + 1)}$

$u = xe^{2x} \qquad\qquad \Rightarrow du = (2xe^{2x} + e^{2x})\, dx = e^{2x}(2x + 1)\, dx$

$$\int \frac{xe^{2x}}{(2x + 1)^2}\, dx = -\frac{xe^{2x}}{2(2x + 1)} + \int \frac{e^{2x}}{2}\, dx = \frac{-xe^{2x}}{2(2x + 1)} + \frac{e^{2x}}{4} + C = \frac{e^{2x}}{4(2x + 1)} + C$$

21. Use integration by parts twice.

(1) $dv = e^x\, dx \Rightarrow v = \displaystyle\int e^x\, dx = e^x$ \qquad\qquad (2) $dv = e^x\, dx \Rightarrow v = \displaystyle\int e^x\, dx = e^x$

$\quad u = x^2 \quad \Rightarrow du = 2x\, dx$ \qquad\qquad\qquad\qquad\qquad $u = x \quad \Rightarrow du = dx$

$$\int (x^2 - 1)e^x\, dx = \int x^2 e^x\, dx - \int e^x\, dx = x^2 e^x - 2\int xe^x\, dx - e^x$$

$$= x^2 e^x - 2\left[xe^x - \int e^x\, dx\right] - e^x = x^2 e^x - 2xe^x + e^x + C = (x - 1)^2 e^x + C$$

23. Letting $u = x$ and $dv = \sqrt{x - 1}\, dx$, we have

$$dv = \sqrt{x - 1}\, dx \Rightarrow v = \int \sqrt{x - 1}\, dx = \frac{2}{3}(x - 1)^{3/2}$$

$$u = x \qquad\qquad \Rightarrow du = dx.$$

Therefore,

$$\int u\, dv = uv - \int v\, du$$

$$\int x\sqrt{x - 1}\, dx = \frac{2}{3}x(x - 1)^{3/2} - \int \frac{2}{3}(x - 1)^{3/2}\, dx = \frac{2}{3}x(x - 1)^{3/2} - \frac{4}{15}(x - 1)^{5/2} + C$$

$$= \frac{2}{15}(x - 1)^{3/2}[5x - 2(x - 1)] + C = \frac{2}{15}(x - 1)^{3/2}(3x + 2) + C.$$

25. $dv = \cos x \, dx \implies v = \int \cos x \, dx = \sin x$

$u = x \qquad \implies du = dx$

$\int x \cos x \, dx = x \sin x - \int \sin x \, dx = x \sin x + \cos x + C$

27. Letting $u = \arctan x$ and $dv = dx$, we have

$dv = dx \qquad \implies v = \int dx = x$

$u = \arctan x \implies du = \dfrac{1}{1 + x^2} \, dx.$

Therefore, we have

$\int \arctan x \, dx = x \arctan x - \int \dfrac{x}{1 + x^2} \, dx$

$= x \arctan x - \dfrac{1}{2} \ln(1 + x^2) + C.$

29. Letting $u = e^{2x}$ and $dv = \sin dx$, we have

$dv = \sin x \, dx \implies v = \int \sin x \, dx = -\cos x$

$u = e^{2x} \qquad \implies du = 2e^{2x} \, dx.$

$\int e^{2x} \sin x \, dx = -e^{2x} \cos x + \int \cos x (2e^{2x}) \, dx.$

Using integration by parts again, we have

$dv = \cos x \, dx \implies v = \int \cos x \, dx = \sin x$

$u = 2e^{2x} \qquad \implies du = 4e^{2x} \, dx.$

$\int e^{2x} \sin x \, dx = -e^{2x} \cos x + 2e^{2x} \sin x - \int 4e^{2x} \sin x \, dx$

Adding the integral in the right hand member of the equation to both members of the equation yields

$5 \int e^{2x} \sin x \, dx = -e^{2x} \cos x + 2e^{2x} \sin x + C_1.$

Finally, dividing both members of the equation by 5 yields

$\int e^{2x} \sin x \, dx = \dfrac{e^{2x}}{5}(2 \sin x - \cos x) + C.$

31. $y' = xe^{x^2}$

$y = \int xe^{x^2} \, dx = \dfrac{1}{2}e^{x^2} + C$

33. Use integration by parts twice.

(1) $dv = \dfrac{1}{\sqrt{2 + 3t}} \, dt \implies v = \int (2 + 3t)^{-1/2} \, dt = \dfrac{2}{3}\sqrt{2 + 3t}$

$u = t^2 \qquad \qquad \implies du = 2t \, dt$

(2) $dv = \sqrt{2 + 3t} \, dt \implies v = \int (2 + 3t)^{1/2} \, dt = \dfrac{2}{9}(2 + 3t)^{3/2}$

$u = t \qquad \qquad \implies du = dt$

$y = \int \dfrac{t^2}{\sqrt{2 + 3t}} \, dt = \dfrac{2t^2\sqrt{2 + 3t}}{3} - \dfrac{4}{3}\int t\sqrt{2 + 3t} \, dt = \dfrac{2t^2\sqrt{2 + 3t}}{3} - \dfrac{4}{3}\left[\dfrac{2t}{9}(2 + 3t)^{3/2} - \dfrac{2}{9}\int (2 + 3t)^{3/2} \, dt\right]$

$= \dfrac{2t^2\sqrt{2 + 3t}}{3} - \dfrac{8t}{27}(2 + 3t)^{3/2} + \dfrac{16}{405}(2 + 3t)^{5/2} + C = \dfrac{2\sqrt{2 + 3t}}{405}(27t^2 - 24t + 32) + C$

35. $(\cos y)y' = 2x$

$$\int \cos y \, dy = \int 2x \, dx$$

$$\sin y = x^2 + C$$

37. (a)

(b) $\dfrac{dy}{dx} = x\sqrt{y} \cos x, \, (0, 4)$

$$\int \frac{dy}{\sqrt{y}} = \int x \cos x \, dx$$

$$\int y^{-1/2} \, dy = \int x \cos x \, dx \qquad (u = x, du = dx, dv = \cos x \, dx, v = \sin x)$$

$$2y^{1/2} = x \sin x - \int \sin x \, dx = x \sin x + \cos x + C$$

$$(0, 4){:} \ 2(4)^{1/2} = 0 + 1 + C \implies C = 3$$

$$2\sqrt{y} = x \sin x + \cos x + 3$$

39. $dv = \sin 2x \, dx \implies v = \displaystyle\int \sin 2x \, dx = -\frac{1}{2} \cos 2x$

$u = x \qquad \implies du = dx$

$$\int x \sin 2x \, dx = \frac{-1}{2} x \cos 2x + \frac{1}{2} \int \cos 2x \, dx = \frac{-1}{2} x \cos 2x + \frac{1}{4} \sin 2x + C = \frac{1}{4}(\sin 2x - 2x \cos 2x) + C$$

Thus, $\displaystyle\int_0^{\pi} x \sin 2x \, dx = \left[\frac{1}{4}(\sin 2x - 2x \cos 2x) \right]_0^{\pi} = -\frac{\pi}{2}.$

41. Use integration by parts twice.

(1) $dv = e^x \, dx \implies v = \displaystyle\int e^x \, dx = e^x$ $\qquad\qquad$ (2) $dv = e^x \, dx \implies v = \displaystyle\int e^x \, dx = e^x$

$\quad\ u = \sin x \implies du = \cos x \, dx$ $\qquad\qquad\qquad\qquad u = \cos x \implies du = -\sin x \, dx$

$$\int e^x \sin x \, dx = e^x \sin x - \int e^x \cos x \, dx = e^x \sin x - e^x \cos x - \int e^x \sin x \, dx$$

$$2 \int e^x \sin x \, dx = e^x(\sin x - \cos x)$$

$$\int e^x \sin x \, dx = \frac{e^x}{2}(\sin x - \cos x) + C$$

Thus, $\displaystyle\int_0^1 e^x \sin x \, dx = \left[\frac{e^x}{2}(\sin x - \cos x) \right]_0^1 = \frac{e}{2}(\sin 1 - \cos 1) + \frac{1}{2} = \frac{e(\sin 1 - \cos 1) + 1}{2} \approx 0.909.$

43. $dv = \cos dx \implies v = \displaystyle\int \cos dx = \sin x$

$\quad\ u = x \qquad \implies du = dx$

$$\int x \cos x \, dx = x \sin x - \int \sin x \, dx$$

$$= x \sin x + \cos x + C$$

Finally,

$$\int_0^{\pi/2} x \cos x \, dx = \left[x \sin x + \cos x \right]_0^{\pi/2} = \frac{\pi}{2} - 1.$$

45. Begin by letting $u = x^2$ and $dv = v' \, dx = e^{2x} \, dx$. We next create a table consisting of three columns as follows.

Alternate Signs	u and its Derivatives	v' and its Antiderivatives
+	x^2	e^{2x}
−	$2x$	$\frac{1}{2}e^{2x}$
+	2	$\frac{1}{4}e^{2x}$
−	0	$\frac{1}{8}e^{2x}$

Finally, the solution is given by multiplying the signed products of the diagonal entries of the table to obtain

$$\int x^2 e^{2x} \, dx = \frac{1}{2}x^2 e^{2x} - 2x\left(\frac{1}{4}\right)e^{2x} + 2\left(\frac{1}{8}\right)e^{2x} + C$$

$$= \frac{e^{2x}}{4}(2x^2 - 2x + 1) + C.$$

47. $\displaystyle\int x^3 \sin x \, dx = x^3(-\cos x) - 3x^2(-\sin x) + 6x \cos x - 6 \sin x + C$

$$= -x^3 \cos x + 3x^2 \sin x + 6x \cos x - 6 \sin x + C$$

$$= (3x^2 - 6) \sin x - (x^3 - 6x) \cos x + C$$

Alternate signs	u and its derivatives	v' and its antiderivatives
+	x^3	$\sin x$
−	$3x^2$	$-\cos x$
+	$6x$	$-\sin x$
−	6	$\cos x$
+	0	$\sin x$

49. $\displaystyle\int x \sec^2 x \, dx = x \tan x + \ln|\cos x| + C$

Alternate signs	u and its derivatives	v' and its antiderivatives
+	x	$\sec^2 x$
−	1	$\tan x$
+	0	$-\ln|\cos x|$

51. $\displaystyle\int t^3 e^{-4t} \, dt = -\frac{e^{-4t}}{128}(32t^3 + 24t^2 + 12t + 3) + C$

53. $\displaystyle\int_0^{\pi/2} e^{-2x} \sin 3x \, dx = \left[\frac{e^{-2x}(-2 \sin 3x - 3 \cos 3x)}{13}\right]_0^{\pi/2}$

$$= \frac{1}{13}(2e^{-\pi} + 3) \approx 0.2374$$

55. (a) $dv = \sqrt{2x - 3} \, dx \implies v = \int (2x - 3)^{1/2} \, dx = \frac{1}{3}(2x - 3)^{3/2}$

$u = 2x \qquad\qquad \implies du = 2 \, dx$

$$\int 2x\sqrt{2x - 3} \, dx = \frac{2}{3}x(2x - 3)^{3/2} - \frac{2}{3}\int (2x - 3)^{3/2} \, dx$$

$$= \frac{2}{3}x(2x - 3)^{3/2} - \frac{2}{15}(2x - 3)^{5/2} + C$$

$$= \frac{2}{15}(2x - 3)^{3/2}(3x + 3) + C = \frac{2}{5}(2x - 3)^{3/2}(x + 1) + C$$

—CONTINUED—

55. **—CONTINUED—**

(b) $u = \sqrt{2x - 3} \implies x = \frac{1}{2}(u^2 + 3)$ and $dx = u\, du$

$$\int 2x\sqrt{2x - 3}\, dx = \int 2\left(\frac{1}{2}\right)(u^2 + 3)(u)(u)\, du$$

$$= \int (u^4 + 3u^2)\, du$$

$$= \frac{1}{5}u^5 + u^3 + C$$

$$= \frac{1}{5}u^3(u^2 + 5) + C$$

$$= \frac{1}{5}(2x - 3)^{3/2}[(2x - 3) + 5] + C$$

$$= \frac{2}{5}(2x - 3)^{3/2}(x + 1) + C$$

57. (a) $dv = \dfrac{x}{\sqrt{4 + x^2}}\, dx \implies v = \int (4 + x^2)^{-1/2}x\, dx = \sqrt{4 + x^2}$

$u = x^2 \implies du = 2x\, dx$

$$\int \frac{x^3}{\sqrt{4 + x^2}}\, dx = x^2\sqrt{4 + x^2} - 2\int x\sqrt{4 + x^2}\, dx$$

$$= x^2\sqrt{4 + x^2} - \frac{2}{3}(4 + x^2)^{3/2} + C = \frac{1}{3}\sqrt{4 + x^2}\,(x^2 - 8) + C$$

(b) $u = 4 + x^2 \implies x^2 = u - 4$ and $2x\, dx = du \implies x\, dx = \dfrac{1}{2}du$

$$\int \frac{x^3}{\sqrt{4 + x^2}}\, dx = \int \frac{x^2}{\sqrt{4 + x^2}}\, x\, dx = \int \frac{u - 4}{\sqrt{u}}\frac{1}{2}\, du$$

$$= \frac{1}{2}\int (u^{1/2} - 4u^{-1/2})\, du = \frac{1}{2}\left(\frac{2}{3}u^{3/2} - 8u^{1/2}\right) + C$$

$$= \frac{1}{3}u^{1/2}(u - 12) + C = \frac{1}{3}\sqrt{4 + x^2}\,[(4 + x^2) - 12] + C = \frac{1}{3}\sqrt{4 + x^2}\,(x^2 - 8) + C$$

59. $n = 0$: $\displaystyle\int \ln x\, dx = x(\ln x - 1) + C$

$n = 1$: $\displaystyle\int x \ln x\, dx = \frac{x^2}{4}(2 \ln x - 1) + C$

$n = 2$: $\displaystyle\int x^2 \ln x\, dx = \frac{x^3}{9}(3 \ln x - 1) + C$

$n = 3$: $\displaystyle\int x^3 \ln x\, dx = \frac{x^4}{16}(4 \ln x - 1) + C$

$n = 4$: $\displaystyle\int x^4 \ln x\, dx = \frac{x^5}{25}(5 \ln x - 1) + C$

In general,

$$\int x^n \ln x\, dx = \frac{x^{n+1}}{(n + 1)^2}[(n + 1)\ln x - 1] + C.$$

(See Exercise 63)

61. $dv = \sin x\, dx \implies v = -\cos x$

$u = x^n \qquad \implies du = nx^{n-1}\, dx$

$$\int x^n \sin x\, dx = -x^n \cos x + n\int x^{n-1} \cos x\, dx$$

63. $dv = x^n \, dx \implies \qquad v = \int x^n \, dx = \dfrac{x^{n+1}}{n+1}$

$\qquad u = \ln x \implies du = \dfrac{1}{x} dx$

$\displaystyle \int x^n \ln x \, dx = \dfrac{x^{n+1}}{n+1} \ln x - \int \dfrac{x^{n+1}}{n+1}\left(\dfrac{1}{x}\right) dx$

$\qquad = \dfrac{x^{n+1}}{n+1} \ln x - \dfrac{1}{n+1}\int x^n \, dx$

$\qquad = \dfrac{x^{n+1}}{n+1} \ln x - \dfrac{x^{n+1}}{(n+1)^2} + C$

$\qquad = \dfrac{x^{n+1}}{(n+1)^2}[-1 + (n+1)\ln x] + C$

65. Use integration by parts twice.

(1) $dv = e^{ax} \, dx \implies v = \dfrac{1}{a}e^{ax}$

$\quad u = \sin bx \implies du = b \cos bx \, dx$

(2) $dv = e^{ax} \, dx \implies v = \dfrac{1}{a}e^{ax}$

$\quad u = \cos bx \implies du = -b \sin bx \, dx$

$\displaystyle \int e^{ax} \sin bx \, dx = \dfrac{e^{ax} \sin bx}{a} - \dfrac{b}{a}\int e^{ax} \cos bx \, dx$

$\qquad = \dfrac{e^{ax} \sin bx}{a} - \dfrac{b}{a}\left[\dfrac{e^{ax} \cos bx}{a} + \dfrac{b}{a}\int e^{ax} \sin bx \, dx\right] = \dfrac{e^{ax} \sin bx}{a} - \dfrac{b^2}{a^2}\int e^{ax} \sin bx \, dx$

Therefore, $\left(1 + \dfrac{b^2}{a^2}\right)\displaystyle\int e^{ax} \sin bx \, dx = \dfrac{e^{ax}(a \sin bx - b \cos bx)}{a^2}$

$\displaystyle \int e^{ax} \sin bx \, dx = \dfrac{e^{ax}(a \sin bx - b \cos bx)}{a^2 + b^2} + C.$

67. $n = 3$ (Use formula in Exercise 63.)

$\displaystyle \int x^3 \ln x \, dx = \dfrac{x^4}{16}[4 \ln x - 1] + C$

69. $a = 2, b = 3$ (Use formula in Exercise 66.)

$\displaystyle \int e^{2x} \cos 3x \, dx = \dfrac{e^{2x}(2 \cos 3x + 3 \sin 3x)}{13} + C$

71. $dv = e^{-x} \, dx \implies v = -e^{-x}$

$\qquad u = x \qquad \implies du = dx$

$A = \displaystyle\int_0^4 xe^{-x} \, dx = \left[-xe^{-x}\right]_0^4 + \int_0^4 e^{-x} \, dx = \dfrac{-4}{e^4} - \left[e^{-x}\right]_0^4$

$\qquad = 1 - \dfrac{5}{e^4} \approx 0.908$

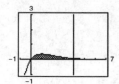

73. $A = \displaystyle\int_0^1 e^{-x} \sin(\pi x) \, dx$

$\qquad = \left[\dfrac{e^{-x}(-\sin \pi x - \pi \cos \pi x)}{1 + \pi^2}\right]_0^1$

$\qquad = \dfrac{1}{1 + \pi^2}\left(\dfrac{\pi}{e} + \pi\right) = \dfrac{\pi}{1 + \pi^2}\left(\dfrac{1}{e} + 1\right)$

$\qquad \approx 0.395$ (See Exercise 65.)

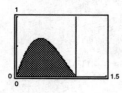

75. (a) From the figure we have

$$A = \int_1^e \ln x \, dx.$$

$$dv = dx \quad \Longrightarrow \quad v = x$$

$$u = \ln x \quad \Longrightarrow \quad du = \frac{1}{x} \, dx.$$

Therefore,

$$A = \int_1^e \ln x \, dx = \left[x \ln x \right]_1^e - \int_1^e dx$$

$$= \left[x \ln x - x \right]_1^e = 1.$$

(b) Using the Disc Method we have

$$V = \pi \int_1^e (\ln x)^2 \, dx.$$

Let,

$$dv = dx \quad \Longrightarrow \quad v = x$$

$$u = (\ln x)^2 \quad \Longrightarrow \quad du = \frac{2 \ln x}{x} \, dx.$$

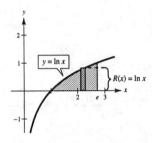

Therefore,

$$\int (\ln x)^2 \, dx = x(\ln x)^2 - 2 \int \ln x \, dx$$

$$= x(\ln x)^2 - 2x(\ln x - 1). \quad \text{From part (a)}$$

Finally,

$$V = \pi \int_1^e (\ln x)^2 \, dx$$

$$= \pi \left[x(\ln x)^2 - 2x(\ln x - 1) \right]_1^e = \pi(e - 2) \approx 2.257.$$

(c) Using the Shell Method we have

$$V = 2\pi \int_1^e x \ln x \, dx.$$

Let,

$$dv = x \, dx \quad \Longrightarrow \quad v = \frac{x^2}{2}$$

$$u = \ln x \quad \Longrightarrow \quad du = \frac{1}{x} \, dx.$$

Therefore,

$$\int x \ln x \, dx = \frac{x^2}{2} \ln x - \frac{1}{2} \int x \, dx = \frac{x^2}{2} \ln x - \frac{x^2}{4}.$$

Finally,

$$V = 2\pi \int_1^e x \ln x \, dx$$

$$= 2\pi \left[\frac{x^2}{4} (2 \ln x - 1) \right]_1^e = \frac{\pi}{2} (e^2 + 1) \approx 13.177.$$

—CONTINUED—

75. —CONTINUED—

(d) $\bar{x} = \dfrac{1}{A} \displaystyle\int_1^e x \ln x \, dx$

$= \left[\dfrac{x^2}{4}(2 \ln x - 1) \right]_1^e \qquad$ From part (c)

$= \dfrac{1}{4}(e^2 + 1) \approx 2.097$

$\bar{y} = \dfrac{1}{2A} \displaystyle\int_1^e (\ln x)^2 \, dx$

$= \dfrac{1}{2}\left[x(\ln x)^2 - 2x(\ln x - 1) \right]_1^e \qquad$ From part (b)

$= \dfrac{e - 2}{2} \approx 0.359$

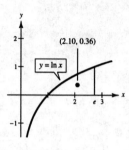

77. Average value $= \dfrac{1}{\pi} \displaystyle\int_0^\pi e^{-4t}(\cos 2t + 5 \sin 2t) \, dt$

$= \dfrac{1}{\pi}\left[e^{-4t}\left(\dfrac{-4 \cos 2t + 2 \sin 2t}{20} \right) + 5e^{-4t}\left(\dfrac{-4 \sin 2t - 2 \cos 2t}{20} \right) \right]_0^\pi \ $ (From Exercises 65 and 66)

$= \dfrac{7}{10\pi}(1 - e^{-4t}) \approx 0.223$

79. $c(t) = 100,000 + 4000t, \ r = 5\%, \ t_1 = 10$

$P = \displaystyle\int_0^{10} (100,000 + 4000t)e^{-0.05t} \, dt = 4000 \int_0^{10} (25 + t)e^{-0.05t} \, dt$

Let $u = 25 + t, \ dv = e^{-0.05t} dt, \ du = dt, \ v = -\dfrac{100}{5}e^{-0.05t}$

$P = 4000\left\{ \left[(25 + t)\left(-\dfrac{100}{5}e^{-0.05t} \right) \right]_0^{10} + \dfrac{100}{5}\int_0^{10} e^{-0.05t} \, dt \right\}$

$= 4000\left\{ \left[(25 + t)\left(-\dfrac{100}{5}e^{-0.05t} \right) \right]_0^{10} - \left[\dfrac{10,000}{25}e^{-0.05t} \right]_0^{10} \right\} \approx \$931,265$

81. $\displaystyle\int_{-\pi}^{\pi} x \sin nx \, dx = \left[-\dfrac{x}{n}\cos nx + \dfrac{1}{n^2}\sin nx \right]_{-\pi}^{\pi}$

$= -\dfrac{\pi}{n}\cos \pi n - \dfrac{\pi}{n}\cos(-\pi n)$

$= -\dfrac{2\pi}{n}\cos \pi n = \begin{cases} -(2\pi/n), & \text{if } n \text{ is even} \\ (2\pi/n), & \text{if } n \text{ is odd} \end{cases}$

83. Let $u = x, \ dv = \sin\left(\dfrac{n\pi}{2}x \right) dx, \ du = dx, \ v = -\dfrac{2}{n\pi}\cos\left(\dfrac{n\pi}{2}x \right).$

$I_1 = \displaystyle\int_0^1 x \sin\left(\dfrac{n\pi}{2}x \right) dx = \left[\dfrac{-2x}{n\pi}\cos\left(\dfrac{n\pi}{2}x \right) \right]_0^1 + \dfrac{2}{n\pi}\int_0^1 \cos\left(\dfrac{n\pi}{2}x \right) dx$

$= -\dfrac{2}{n\pi}\cos\left(\dfrac{n\pi}{2} \right) + \left[\left(\dfrac{2}{n\pi} \right)^2 \sin\left(\dfrac{n\pi}{2}x \right) \right]_0^1$

$= -\dfrac{2}{n\pi}\cos\left(\dfrac{n\pi}{2} \right) + \left(\dfrac{2}{n\pi} \right)^2 \sin\left(\dfrac{n\pi}{2} \right)$

—CONTINUED—

83. —CONTINUED—

Let $u = (-x + 2)$, $dv = \sin\left(\frac{n\pi}{2}x\right) dx$, $du = -dx$, $v = -\frac{2}{n\pi}\cos\left(\frac{n\pi}{2}x\right)$.

$$I_2 = \int_1^2 (-x + 2) \sin\left(\frac{n\pi}{2}x\right) dx = \left[\frac{-2(-x + 2)}{n\pi}\cos\left(\frac{n\pi}{2}x\right)\right]_1^2 - \frac{2}{n\pi}\int_1^2 \cos\left(\frac{n\pi}{2}x\right) dx$$

$$= \frac{2}{n\pi}\cos\left(\frac{n\pi}{2}\right) - \left[\left(\frac{2}{n\pi}\right)^2 \sin\left(\frac{n\pi}{2}x\right)\right]_1^2$$

$$= \frac{2}{n\pi}\cos\left(\frac{n\pi}{2}\right) + \left(\frac{2}{n\pi}\right)^2 \sin\left(\frac{n\pi}{2}\right)$$

$$h(I_1 + I_2) = b_n = h\left[\left(\frac{2}{n\pi}\right)^2 \sin\left(\frac{n\pi}{2}\right) + \left(\frac{2}{n\pi}\right)^2 \sin\left(\frac{n\pi}{2}\right)\right] = \frac{8h}{(n\pi)^2}\sin\left(\frac{n\pi}{2}\right)$$

(Note that $b_n = 0$ when n is even.)

85. Shell Method:

$$V = 2\pi\int_a^b x f(x)\, dx$$

$$dv = x\, dx \implies v = \frac{x^2}{2}$$

$$u = f(x) \implies du = f'(x)\, dx$$

$$V = 2\pi\left[\frac{x^2}{2}f(x) - \int \frac{x^2}{2}f'(x)\, dx\right]_a^b$$

$$= \pi\left[(b^2 f(b) - a^2 f(a)) - \int_a^b x^2 f'(x)\, dx\right]$$

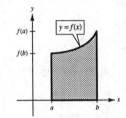

Disc Method:

$$V = \pi\int_0^{f(a)} (b^2 - a^2)\, dy + \pi\int_{f(a)}^{f(b)} [b^2 - [f^{-1}(y)]^2]\, dy$$

$$= \pi(b^2 - a^2) f(a) + \pi b^2(f(b) - f(a)) - \pi\int_{f(a)}^{f(b)} [f^{-1}(y)]^2\, dy$$

$$= \pi\left[(b^2 f(b) - a^2 f(a)) - \int_{f(a)}^{f(b)} [f^{-1}(y)]^2\, dy\right]$$

Since $x = f^{-1}(y)$, we have $f(x) = y$ and $f'(x)dx = dy$. When $y = f(a)$, $x = a$. When $y = f(b)$, $x = b$. Thus,

$$\int_{f(a)}^{f(b)} [f^{-1}(y)]^2\, dy = \int_a^b x^2 f'(x)\, dx$$

and the volumes are the same.

87. $f'(x) = \cos\sqrt{x}$, $f(0) = 2$

(a) It cannot be solved by integration.

(b) You obtain the points

n	x_n	y_n
0	0	0
1	0.05	2.05
2	0.10	2.098755
3	0.15	2.146276
$\vdots$	$\vdots$	$\vdots$
80	4.0	2.8403565

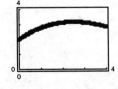

Section 7.3   Trigonometric Integrals

1. $f(x) = \sin^4 x + \cos^4 x$

(a) $\sin^4 x + \cos^4 x = \left(\dfrac{1 - \cos 2x}{2}\right)^2 + \left(\dfrac{1 + \cos 2x}{2}\right)^2$

$$= \frac{1}{4}[1 - 2\cos 2x + \cos^2 2x + 1 + 2\cos 2x + \cos^2 2x]$$

$$= \frac{1}{4}\left[2 + 2\,\frac{1 + \cos 4x}{2}\right]$$

$$= \frac{1}{4}[3 + \cos 4x]$$

(b) $\sin^4 x + \cos^4 x = (\sin^2 x)^2 + \cos^4 x$

$$= (1 - \cos^2 x)^2 + \cos^4 x$$

$$= 1 - 2\cos^2 x + 2\cos^4 x$$

(c) $\sin^4 x + \cos^4 x = \sin^4 x + 2\sin^2 x \cos^2 x + \cos^4 x - 2\sin^2 x \cos^2 x$

$$= (\sin^2 x + \cos^2 x)^2 - 2\sin^2 x \cos^2 x$$

$$= 1 - 2\sin^2 x \cos^2 x$$

(d) $1 - 2\sin^2 x \cos^2 x = 1 - (2\sin x \cos x)(\sin x \cos x)$

$$= 1 - (\sin 2x)\left(\frac{1}{2}\sin 2x\right)$$

$$= 1 - \frac{1}{2}\sin^2(2x)$$

(e) Four ways. There is often more than one way to rewrite a trigonometric expression.

3. Let $u = \cos x,\ du = -\sin x\,dx$.

$$\int \cos^3 x \sin x\,dx = -\int \cos^3 x(-\sin x)\,dx$$

$$= -\frac{1}{4}\cos^4 x + C$$

5. Let $u = \sin 2x,\ du = 2\cos 2x\,dx$.

$$\int \sin^5 2x \cos 2x\,dx = \frac{1}{2}\int \sin^5 2x(2\cos 2x)\,dx$$

$$= \frac{1}{12}\sin^6 2x + C$$

7. $\displaystyle\int \sin^5 x \cos^2 x\,dx = \int \sin x(\sin^2 x)^2 \cos^2 x\,dx$

$$= \int \sin x(1 - \cos^2 x)^2 \cos^2 x\,dx$$

$$= -\int (\cos^2 x - 2\cos^4 x + \cos^6 x)(-\sin x)\,dx$$

$$= -\frac{1}{3}\cos^3 x + \frac{2}{5}\cos^5 x - \frac{1}{7}\cos^7 x + C$$

9. $\displaystyle\int \cos^2 3x\,dx = \int \frac{1 + \cos 6x}{2}\,dx$

$$= \frac{1}{2}\left(x + \frac{1}{6}\sin 6x\right) + C$$

$$= \frac{1}{12}(6x + \sin 6x) + C$$

11. Use Integration By Part by letting $u = x$ and $dv = \sin^2 x\, dx$. Then $du = dx$ and

$$v = \int \sin^2 x\, dx$$

$$= \int \frac{1 - \cos 2x}{2}\, dx$$

$$= \frac{1}{2}\left(x - \frac{1}{2}\sin 2x\right) = \frac{1}{4}(2x - \sin 2x).$$

Therefore,

$$\int u\, dv = uv - \int v\, du$$

$$\int x \sin 2x\, dx = \frac{1}{4}x(2x - \sin 2x) - \frac{1}{4}\int(2x - \sin 2x)\, dx$$

$$= \frac{1}{4}(2x - \sin 2x) - \frac{1}{4}\left(x^2 + \frac{1}{2}\cos 2x\right) + C$$

$$= \frac{1}{8}(2x^2 - 2x \sin 2x - \cos 2x) + C.$$

13. Let $u = \sin x$, $du = \cos x\, dx$.

$$\int_0^{\pi/2} \cos^3 x\, dx = \int_0^{\pi/2}(1 - \sin^2 x)\cos x\, dx = \left[\sin x - \frac{1}{3}\sin^3 x\right]_0^{\pi/2} = \frac{2}{3}$$

15. Let $u = \sin x$, $du = \cos x\, dx$.

$$\int_0^{\pi/2} \cos^7 x\, dx = \int_0^{\pi/2}(1 - \sin^2 x)^3 \cos x\, dx = \int_0^{\pi/2}(1 - 3\sin^2 x + 3\sin^4 x - \sin^6 x)\cos x\, dx$$

$$= \left[\sin x - \sin^3 x + \frac{3}{5}\sin^5 x - \frac{1}{7}\sin^7 x\right]_0^{\pi/2} = \frac{16}{35}$$

17. $\displaystyle \int \sec(3x)\, dx = \frac{1}{3}\ln|\sec 3x + \tan 3x| + C$

19. $\displaystyle \int \sec^4 5x\, dx = \int(1 + \tan^2 5x)\sec^2 5x\, dx$

$$= \frac{1}{5}\left(\tan 5x + \frac{\tan^3 5x}{3}\right) + C$$

$$= \frac{\tan 5x}{15}(3 + \tan^2 5x) + C$$

21. $dv = \sec^2 \pi x\, dx \implies v = \frac{1}{\pi}\tan \pi x$

$u = \sec \pi x \implies du = \pi \sec \pi x \tan \pi x\, dx$

$$\int \sec^3 \pi x\, dx = \frac{1}{\pi}\sec \pi x \tan \pi x - \int \sec \pi x \tan^2 \pi x\, dx = \frac{1}{\pi}\sec \pi x \tan \pi x - \int \sec \pi x(\sec^2 \pi x - 1)\, dx$$

$$2\int \sec^3 \pi x\, dx = \frac{1}{\pi}(\sec \pi x \tan \pi x + \ln|\sec \pi x + \tan \pi x|) + C_1$$

$$\int \sec^3 \pi x\, dx = \frac{1}{2\pi}(\sec \pi x \tan \pi x + \ln|\sec \pi x + \tan \pi x|) + C$$

23. $\int \tan^5 \frac{x}{4} dx = \int \tan^2 \frac{x}{4} \tan^3 \frac{x}{4} dx$

$= \int \left(\sec^2 \frac{x}{4} - 1\right) \tan^3 \frac{x}{4} dx$

$= \int \tan^3 \frac{x}{4} \sec^2 \frac{x}{4} dx - \int \tan^3 \frac{x}{4} dx$

$= \tan^4 \frac{x}{4} - \int \tan^2 \frac{x}{4} \tan \frac{x}{4} dx$

$= \tan^4 \frac{x}{4} - \int \left(\sec^2 \frac{x}{4} - 1\right) \tan \frac{x}{4} dx$

$= \tan^4 \frac{x}{4} - \int \tan \frac{x}{4} \sec^2 \frac{x}{4} dx + \int \tan \frac{x}{4} dx$

$= \tan^4 \frac{x}{4} - 2 \tan^2 \frac{x}{4} - 4 \ln\left|\cos \frac{x}{4}\right| + C$

27. $\int \tan^2 x \sec^2 x \, dx = \frac{\tan^3 x}{3} + C$

29. $\int \sec^6 4x \tan 4x \, dx = \int (\sec^2 4x)(\sec^2 4x)^2 \tan 4x \, dx$

$= \frac{1}{4} \int \tan 4x (\tan^2 4x + 1)^2 (4 \sec^2 4x) \, dx$

$= \frac{1}{4} \int (\tan^5 4x + 2 \tan^3 4x + \tan 4x)(4 \sec^2 4x) \, dx$

$= \frac{1}{4}\left[\frac{\tan^6 4x}{6} + \frac{\tan^4 4x}{2} + \frac{\tan^2 4x}{2}\right] + C$

$= \frac{1}{24}(\tan^2 4x)(\tan^4 4x + 3 \tan^2 4x + 3) + C$

or

$\int \sec^6 4x \tan 4x \, dx = \frac{1}{4} \int \sec^5 4x (4 \sec 4x \tan 4x) \, dx$

$= \frac{1}{24} \sec^6 4x + C_1$

(See Exercise 71 for a comparison of the two methods.)

31. Let $u = \sec x$, $du = \sec x \tan x \, dx$.

$\int \sec^3 x \tan x \, dx = \int \sec^2 x (\sec x \tan x) \, dx$

$= \frac{1}{3} \sec^3 x + C$

25. $u = \tan x$, $du = \sec^2 x \, dx$

$\int \sec^2 x \tan x \, dx = \frac{1}{2} \tan^2 x + C$

33. $\dfrac{dr}{d\theta} = \sin^4 \pi\theta$

$\displaystyle\int \dfrac{dr}{d\theta}\, d\theta = \sin^4 \pi\theta\, d\theta$

$\displaystyle r = \int (\sin^2 \pi\theta)^2\, d\theta$

$\displaystyle = \int \left(\dfrac{1 - \cos 2\pi\theta}{2}\right)^2 d\theta$

$\displaystyle = \dfrac{1}{4}\int (1 - 2\cos 2\pi\theta + \cos^2 2\pi\theta)\, d\theta$

$\displaystyle = \dfrac{1}{4}\int \left(1 - 2\cos 2\pi\theta + \dfrac{1 + \cos 4\pi\theta}{2}\right) d\theta$

$\displaystyle = \dfrac{1}{8}\int (3 - 4\cos 2\pi\theta + \cos 4\pi\theta)\, d\theta$

$\displaystyle = \dfrac{1}{8}\left(3\theta - \dfrac{2}{\pi}\sin 2\pi\theta + \dfrac{1}{4\pi}\sin 4\pi\theta\right) + C$

$\displaystyle = \dfrac{1}{32\pi}(12\pi\theta - 8\sin 2\pi\theta + \sin 4\pi\theta) + C$

35. $\displaystyle y = \int \tan^3 3x \sec 3x\, dx$

$\displaystyle = \int (\sec^2 3x - 1)\sec 3x \tan 3x\, dx$

$\displaystyle = \dfrac{1}{3}\int \sec^2 3x(3\sec 3x \tan 3x)\, dx - \dfrac{1}{3}\int 3\sec 3x \tan 3x\, dx$

$\displaystyle = \dfrac{1}{9}\sec^3 3x - \dfrac{1}{3}\sec 3x + C$

37. (a)

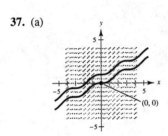

(0, 0)

(b) $\dfrac{dy}{dx} = \sin^2 x,\ (0, 0)$

$\displaystyle y = \int \sin^2 x\, dx = \int \dfrac{1 - \cos 2x}{2}\, dx$

$\displaystyle = \dfrac{1}{2}x - \dfrac{\sin 2x}{4} + C$

$(0, 0):\ 0 = C,\ y = \dfrac{1}{2}x - \dfrac{\sin 2x}{4}$

39. Using the trigonometric identity

$$\sin u \cos v = \dfrac{1}{2}[\sin(u + v) + \sin(u - v)],$$

we have

$\displaystyle \int \sin 3x \cos 2x\, dx = \int \dfrac{1}{2}(\sin 5x + \sin x)\, dx$

$\displaystyle = \dfrac{1}{2}\left(\dfrac{1}{5}\right)\int \sin 5x(5)\, dx + \dfrac{1}{2}\int \sin x\, dx$

$\displaystyle = -\dfrac{1}{10}\cos 5x - \dfrac{1}{2}\cos x + C$

$\displaystyle = -\dfrac{1}{10}(\cos 5x + 5\cos x) + C.$

41. $\displaystyle \int \sin \theta \sin 3\theta\, d\theta = \dfrac{1}{2}\int (\cos 2\theta - \cos 4\theta)\, d\theta$

$\displaystyle = \dfrac{1}{2}\left(\dfrac{1}{2}\sin 2\theta - \dfrac{1}{4}\sin 4\theta\right) + C$

$\displaystyle = \dfrac{1}{8}(2\sin 2\theta - \sin 4\theta) + C$

43. $\displaystyle \int \cot^3 2x\, dx = \int (\csc^2 2x - 1)\cot 2x\, dx$

$\displaystyle = -\dfrac{1}{2}\int \cot 2x(-2\csc^2 2x)\, dx - \dfrac{1}{2}\int \dfrac{2\cos 2x}{\sin 2x}\, dx$

$\displaystyle = -\dfrac{1}{4}\cot^2 2x - \dfrac{1}{2}\ln|\sin 2x| + C$

$\displaystyle = \dfrac{1}{4}(\ln|\csc^2 2x| - \cot^2 2x) + C$

45. Let $u = \cot \theta,\ du = -\csc^2 \theta\, d\theta$.

$\displaystyle \int \csc^4 \theta\, d\theta = \int \csc^2 \theta(1 + \cot^2 \theta)\, d\theta$

$\displaystyle = \int \csc^2 \theta\, d\theta + \int \csc^2 \theta \cot^2 \theta\, d\theta$

$\displaystyle = -\cot \theta - \dfrac{1}{3}\cot^3 \theta + C$

47. $\displaystyle\int \frac{\cot^2 t}{\csc t}\,dt = \int \frac{\csc^2 t - 1}{\csc t}\,dt$

$\displaystyle = \int (\csc t - \sin t)\,dt$

$\displaystyle = \ln|\csc t - \cot t| + \cos t + C$

49. $\displaystyle\int \frac{1}{\sec x \tan x}\,dx = \int \frac{\cos^2 x}{\sin x}\,dx = \int \frac{1 - \sin^2 x}{\sin x}\,dx$

$\displaystyle = \int (\csc x - \sin x)\,dx$

$\displaystyle = \ln|\csc x - \cot x| + \cos x + C$

51. $\displaystyle\int (\tan^4 t - \sec^4 t)\,dt = \int (\tan^2 t + \sec^2 t)(\tan^2 t - \sec^2 t)\,dt \qquad (\tan^2 t - \sec^2 t = -1)$

$\displaystyle = -\int (\tan^2 t + \sec^2 t)\,dt = -\int (2\sec^2 t - 1)\,dt = -2\tan t + t + C$

53. $\displaystyle\int_{-\pi}^{\pi} \sin^2 x\,dx = 2\int_0^{\pi} \frac{1 - \cos 2x}{2}\,dx$

$\displaystyle = \left[x - \frac{1}{2}\sin 2x \right]_0^{\pi} = \pi$

55. $\displaystyle\int_0^{\pi/4} \tan^3 x\,dx = \int_0^{\pi/4} (\sec^2 x - 1)(\tan x)\,dx$

$\displaystyle = \int_0^{\pi/4} \tan x \sec^2 x\,dx - \int_0^{\pi/4} \tan x\,dx$

$\displaystyle = \left[\frac{1}{2}\tan^2 x + \ln|\cos x| \right]_0^{\pi/4} = \frac{1}{2}(1 - \ln 2)$

57. Let $u = 1 + \sin t,\ du = \cos t\,dt$.

$\displaystyle\int_0^{\pi/2} \frac{\cos t}{1 + \sin t}\,dt = \left[\ln|1 + \sin t| \right]_0^{\pi/2} = \ln 2$

59. Let $u = \sin x,\ du = \cos x\,dx$.

$\displaystyle\int_{-\pi/2}^{\pi/2} \cos^3 x\,dx = 2\int_0^{\pi/2} (1 - \sin^2 x)\cos x\,dx$

$\displaystyle = 2\left[\sin x - \frac{1}{3}\sin^3 x \right]_0^{\pi/2} = \frac{4}{3}$

61. $\displaystyle\int \cos^4 \frac{x}{2}\,dx = \frac{1}{16}[6x + 8\sin x + \sin 2x] + C$

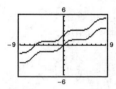

63. $\displaystyle\int \sec^5 \pi x\,dx = \frac{1}{4\pi}\left\{ \sec^3 \pi x \tan \pi x + \frac{3}{2}[\sec \pi x \tan \pi x + \ln|\sec \pi x + \tan \pi x|] \right\} + C$

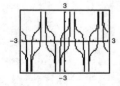

65. Using a symbolic integration utility to perform the integration yields

$\displaystyle\int \sec^5 \pi x \tan \pi x\,dx = \frac{1}{5\pi}\sec^5 \pi x + C.$

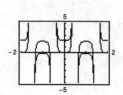

The graphs of the antiderivative for $C = 1$ and $C = -2$ are shown in the figure.

67. $\displaystyle\int_0^{\pi/4} \sin 2\theta \sin 3\theta\, d\theta = \frac{1}{2}\left[\sin\theta - \frac{1}{5}\sin 5\theta\right]_0^{\pi/4} = \frac{3\sqrt{2}}{10}$

69. $\displaystyle\int_0^{\pi/2} \sin^4 x\, dx = \frac{1}{4}\left[\frac{3x}{2} - \sin 2x + \frac{1}{8}\sin 4x\right]_0^{\pi/2} = \frac{3\pi}{16}$

71. (a) Method 1: Since there is an odd power of the tangent, write

$$\int \sec^4 3x \tan^3 3x\, dx = \int \sec^3 3x \tan^2 3x(\sec 3x \tan 3x)\, dx$$

$$= \int \sec^3 3x(\sec^2 3x - 1)\sec 3x \tan 3x\, dx$$

$$= \frac{1}{3}\int (\sec^5 3x - \sec^3 3x)(3\sec 3x \tan 3x\, dx)$$

$$= \frac{1}{3}\left(\frac{1}{6}\sec^6 3x - \frac{1}{4}\sec^4 3x\right) + C.$$

Method 2: Since the power of the secant is even, write

$$\int \sec^4 3x \tan^3 3x\, dx = \int \sec^2 3x \tan^3 3x(\sec^2 3x)\, dx$$

$$= \int (1 + \tan^2 3x)\tan^3 3x(\sec^2 3x)\, dx$$

$$= \frac{1}{3}\int (\tan^3 3x + \tan^5 3x)(3\sec^2 3x)\, dx$$

$$= \frac{1}{3}\left(\frac{\tan^4 3x}{4} + \frac{\tan^6 3x}{6}\right) + C.$$

(b) The graphs of Method 1 and Method 2 with $C = 0$ are shown in the figure.

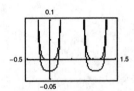

(c) Comparing the results of the two methods, we have

$$\frac{1}{3}\left[\frac{1}{4}\tan^4 3x + \frac{1}{6}\tan^6 3x\right] + C = \frac{1}{3}\left[\frac{1}{4}(\sec^2 3x - 1)^2 + \frac{1}{6}(\sec^2 3x - 1)^3\right] + C$$

$$= \frac{1}{3}\left[\frac{1}{4}(\sec^4 3x - 2\sec^2 3x + 1) + \frac{1}{6}(\sec^6 3x - 3\sec^4 3x + 3\sec^2 3x - 1)\right] + C$$

$$= \frac{1}{3}\left[\frac{1}{6}\sec^6 3x - \frac{1}{4}\sec^4 3x + \frac{1}{4} - \frac{1}{6}\right] + C.$$

Therefore, the results differ only by the constant $\dfrac{1}{3}\left(\dfrac{1}{4} - \dfrac{1}{6}\right)$.

73. $A = \displaystyle\int_0^1 \sin^2(\pi x)\, dx$

$$= \int_0^1 \frac{1 - \cos(2\pi x)}{2}\, dx$$

$$= \left[\frac{x}{2} - \frac{1}{4\pi}\sin(2\pi x)\right]_0^1 = \frac{1}{2}$$

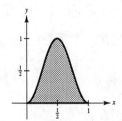

75. (a) $V = \pi \int_0^\pi R^2 \, dx = \pi \int_0^\pi \sin^2 x \, dx$

$$= \pi \int_0^\pi \frac{1 - \cos 2x}{2} \, dx$$

$$= \frac{\pi}{2} \int_0^\pi (1 - \cos 2x) \, dx$$

$$= \frac{\pi}{2} \left[x - \frac{1}{2} \sin 2x \right]_0^\pi = \frac{\pi}{2} \left[\pi - \frac{1}{2}(0) - 0 \right] = \frac{\pi^2}{2}$$

(b) By symmetry $\bar{x} = \frac{\pi}{2}$.

The area of the region is given by

$$A = \int_0^\pi \sin x \, dx = \left[-\cos x \right]_0^\pi = 2.$$

Therefore,

$$\bar{y} = \frac{1}{2A} \int_0^\pi \sin^2 x \, dx$$

$$= \frac{1}{8} \int_0^\pi (1 - \cos 2x) \, dx = \left[\frac{1}{8} \left(x - \frac{1}{2} \sin 2x \right) \right]_0^\pi = \frac{\pi}{8}.$$

Thus,

$$(\bar{x}, \bar{y}) = \left(\frac{\pi}{2}, \frac{\pi}{8} \right).$$

77. $dv = \sin x \, dx \implies v = -\cos x$

$u = \sin^{n-1} x \implies du = (n-1) \sin^{n-2} x \cos x \, dx$

$$\int \sin^n x \, dx = -\sin^{n-1} x \cos x + (n-1) \int \sin^{n-2} x \cos^2 x \, dx$$

$$= -\sin^{n-1} x \cos x + (n-1) \int \sin^{n-2} x (1 - \sin^2 x) \, dx$$

$$= -\sin^{n-1} x \cos x + (n-1) \int \sin^{n-2} x \, dx - (n-1) \int \sin^n x \, dx$$

Therefore, $n \int \sin^n x \, dx = -\sin^{n-1} x \cos x + (n-1) \int \sin^{n-2} x \, dx$

$$\int \sin^n x \, dx = \frac{-\sin^{n-1} x \cos x}{n} + \frac{n-1}{n} \int \sin^{n-2} x \, dx.$$

79. Let $dv = \cos^m x \sin x \, dx$ and $u = \sin^{n-1} x$. Then $v = (-\cos^{m+1} x)/(m+1)$ and $du = (n-1) \sin^{n-2} x (\cos x) \, dx$. Therefore,

$$\int \cos^m x \sin^n x \, dx = -\frac{\sin^{n-1} x \cos^{m+1} x}{m+1} + \frac{n-1}{m+1} \int \sin^{n-2} x \cos^{m+2} x \, dx$$

$$= -\frac{\sin^{n-1} x \cos^{m+1} x}{m+1} + \frac{n-1}{m+1} \int \sin^{n-2} x \cos^m x (1 - \sin^2 x) \, dx$$

$$= -\frac{\sin^{n-1} x \cos^{m+1} x}{m+1} + \frac{n-1}{m+1} \int \sin^{n-2} x \cos^m x \, dx - \frac{n-1}{m+1} \int \sin^n x \cos^m x \, dx.$$

Now observe that the last integral is a multiple of the original. Adding yields

$$\frac{m+n}{m+1} \int \cos^m x \sin^n x \, dx = -\frac{\sin^{n-1} x \cos^{m+1} x}{m+1} + \frac{n-1}{m+1} \int \cos^m x \sin^{n-2} x \, dx$$

$$\int \cos^m x \sin^n x \, dx = -\frac{\cos^{m+1} x \sin^{n-1} x}{m+n} + \frac{n-1}{m+n} \int \cos^m x \sin^{n-2} x \, dx.$$

81. $\displaystyle\int \sin^5 x \, dx = -\frac{\sin^4 x \cos x}{5} + \frac{4}{5}\int \sin^3 x \, dx$

$\displaystyle = -\frac{\sin^4 x \cos x}{5} + \frac{4}{5}\left[-\frac{\sin^2 x \cos x}{3} + \frac{2}{3}\int \sin x \, dx \right]$

$\displaystyle = -\frac{1}{5}\sin^4 x \cos x - \frac{4}{15}\sin^2 x \cos x - \frac{8}{15}\cos x + C$

$\displaystyle = -\frac{\cos x}{15}[3 \sin^4 x + 4 \sin^2 x + 8] + C$

83. $\displaystyle\int \sec^4\!\left(\frac{2\pi x}{5}\right) dx = \frac{5}{2\pi}\int \sec^4\!\left(\frac{2\pi x}{5}\right)\frac{2\pi}{5}\, dx$

$\displaystyle = \frac{5}{2\pi}\left[\frac{1}{3}\sec^2\!\left(\frac{2\pi x}{5}\right)\tan\!\left(\frac{2\pi x}{5}\right) + \frac{2}{3}\int \sec^2\!\left(\frac{2\pi x}{5}\right)\frac{2\pi}{5}\, dx \right]$

$\displaystyle = \frac{5}{6\pi}\left[\sec^2\!\left(\frac{2\pi x}{5}\right)\tan\!\left(\frac{2\pi x}{5}\right) + 2\tan\!\left(\frac{2\pi x}{5}\right) \right] + C$

$\displaystyle = \frac{5}{6\pi}\tan\!\left(\frac{2\pi x}{5}\right)\left[\sec^2\!\left(\frac{2\pi x}{5}\right) + 2 \right] + C$

85. (a) n is odd and $n \geq 3$.

$\displaystyle\int_0^{\pi/2} \cos^n x \, dx = \left[\frac{\cos^{n-1} x \sin x}{n} \right]_0^{\pi/2} + \frac{n-1}{n}\int_0^{\pi/2} \cos^{n-2} x \, dx$

$\displaystyle = \frac{n-1}{n}\left[\left[\frac{\cos^{n-3} x \sin x}{n-2} \right]_0^{\pi/2} + \frac{n-3}{n-2}\int_0^{\pi/2} \cos^{n-4} x \, dx \right]$

$\displaystyle = \frac{n-1}{n}\cdot\frac{n-3}{n-2}\left[\left[\frac{\cos^{n-5} x \sin x}{n-4} \right]_0^{\pi/2} + \frac{n-5}{n-4}\int_0^{\pi/2} \cos^{n-6} x \, dx \right]$

$\displaystyle = \frac{n-1}{n}\cdot\frac{n-3}{n-2}\cdot\frac{n-5}{n-4}\int_0^{\pi/2} \cos^{n-6} x \, dx$

$\displaystyle = \frac{n-1}{n}\cdot\frac{n-3}{n-2}\cdot\frac{n-5}{n-4}\cdots\int_0^{\pi/2} \cos x \, dx$

$\displaystyle = \left[\frac{n-1}{n}\cdot\frac{n-3}{n-2}\cdot\frac{n-5}{n-4}\cdots (\sin x) \right]_0^{\pi/2}$

$\displaystyle = \frac{n-1}{n}\cdot\frac{n-3}{n-2}\cdot\frac{n-5}{n-4}\cdots 1 \qquad \text{(Reverse the order)}$

$\displaystyle = (1)\left(\frac{2}{3}\right)\left(\frac{4}{5}\right)\left(\frac{6}{7}\right)\cdots\left(\frac{n-1}{n}\right)$

$\displaystyle = \left(\frac{2}{3}\right)\left(\frac{4}{5}\right)\left(\frac{6}{7}\right)\cdots\left(\frac{n-1}{n}\right)$

—**CONTINUED**—

85. —CONTINUED—

(b) n is even and $n \geq 2$.

$$\int_0^{\pi/2} \cos^n x \, dx = \frac{n-1}{n} \cdot \frac{n-3}{n-2} \cdot \frac{n-5}{n-4} \cdots \int_0^{\pi/2} \cos^2 x \, dx \quad \text{(From part (a).)}$$

$$= \left[\frac{n-1}{n} \cdot \frac{n-3}{n-2} \cdot \frac{n-5}{n-4} \cdots \left(\frac{x}{2} + \frac{1}{4} \sin 2x \right) \right]_0^{\pi/2}$$

$$= \frac{n-1}{n} \cdot \frac{n-3}{n-2} \cdot \frac{n-5}{n-4} \cdots \frac{\pi}{4} \quad \text{(Reverse the order)}$$

$$= \left(\frac{\pi}{2} \cdot \frac{1}{2} \right) \left(\frac{3}{4} \right) \left(\frac{5}{6} \right) \cdots \left(\frac{n-1}{n} \right)$$

$$= \left(\frac{1}{2} \right) \left(\frac{3}{4} \right) \left(\frac{5}{6} \right) \cdots \left(\frac{n-1}{n} \right) \left(\frac{\pi}{2} \right)$$

87. (a) $f(t) = a_0 + a_1 \cos \dfrac{\pi t}{6} + b_1 \sin \dfrac{\pi t}{6}$ where:

$$a_0 = \frac{1}{12} \int_0^{12} f(t) \, dt$$

$$a_1 = \frac{1}{6} \int_0^{12} f(t) \cos \frac{\pi t}{6} \, dt$$

$$b_1 = \frac{1}{6} \int_0^{12} f(t) \sin \frac{\pi t}{6} \, dt$$

$$a_0 \approx \frac{12-0}{3(12)^2} [30.9 + 4(32.2) + 2(41.1) + 4(53.7) + 2(64.6) + 4(74.0) + 2(78.2) + 4(77.0) + 2(71.0) +$$

$$4(60.1) + 2(47.1) + 4(35.7) + 30.9] \approx 55.46$$

$$a_1 \approx \frac{12-0}{6(3)(12)} \left[30.9 \cos 0 + 4 \left(32.2 \cos \frac{\pi}{6} \right) + 2 \left(41.1 \cos \frac{\pi}{3} \right) + 4 \left(53.7 \cos \frac{\pi}{2} \right) + 2 \left(64.6 \cos \frac{2\pi}{3} \right) + \right.$$

$$4 \left(74.0 \cos \frac{5\pi}{6} \right) + 2(78.2 \cos \pi) + 4 \left(77.0 \cos \frac{7\pi}{6} \right) + 2 \left(71.0 \cos \frac{4\pi}{3} \right) +$$

$$\left. 4 \left(60.1 \cos \frac{3\pi}{2} \right) + 2 \left(47.1 \cos \frac{5\pi}{3} \right) + 4 \left(35.7 \cos \frac{11\pi}{6} \right) + 30.9 \cos 2\pi \right] \approx -23.88$$

$$b_1 \approx \frac{12-0}{6(3)(12)} \left[30.9 \sin 0 + 4 \left(32.2 \sin \frac{\pi}{6} \right) + 2 \left(41.1 \sin \frac{\pi}{3} \right) + 4 \left(53.7 \sin \frac{\pi}{2} \right) + 2 \left(64.6 \sin \frac{2\pi}{3} \right) + \right.$$

$$4 \left(74.0 \sin \frac{5\pi}{6} \right) + 2(78.2 \sin \pi) + 4 \left(77.0 \sin \frac{7\pi}{6} \right) + 2 \left(71.0 \sin \frac{4\pi}{3} \right) +$$

$$\left. 4 \left(60.1 \sin \frac{3\pi}{2} \right) + 2 \left(47.1 \sin \frac{5\pi}{3} \right) + 4 \left(35.7 \sin \frac{11\pi}{6} \right) + 30.9 \sin 2\pi \right] \approx -3.34$$

$$H(t) \approx 55.46 - 23.88 \cos \frac{\pi t}{6} - 3.34 \sin \frac{\pi t}{6}$$

—CONTINUED—

87. —CONTINUED—

(b) $a_0 \approx \dfrac{12 - 0}{3(12)^2}[18.0 + 4(17.7) + 2(25.8) + 4(36.1) + 2(45.4) + 4(55.2) + 2(59.9) + 4(59.4) + 2(53.1) +$

$$4(43.2) + 2(34.3) + 4(24.2) + 18.0] \approx 39.34$$

$a_1 \approx \dfrac{12 - 0}{6(3)(12)}\left[18.0 \cos 0 + 4\left(17.7 \cos \dfrac{\pi}{6}\right) + 2\left(25.8 \cos \dfrac{\pi}{3}\right) + 4\left(36.1 \cos \dfrac{\pi}{2}\right) + 2\left(45.4 \cos \dfrac{2\pi}{3}\right) +\right.$

$$4\left(55.2 \cos \dfrac{5\pi}{6}\right) + 2(59.9 \cos \pi) + 4\left(59.4 \cos \dfrac{7\pi}{6}\right) + 2\left(53.1 \cos \dfrac{4\pi}{3}\right) +$$

$$\left. 4\left(43.2 \cos \dfrac{3\pi}{2}\right) + 2\left(34.3 \cos \dfrac{5\pi}{3}\right) + 4\left(24.2 \cos \dfrac{11\pi}{6}\right) + 18 \cos 2\pi\right] \approx -20.78$$

$b_1 \approx \dfrac{12 - 0}{6(3)(12)}\left[18.0 \sin 0 + 4\left(17.7 \sin \dfrac{\pi}{6}\right) + 2\left(25.8 \sin \dfrac{\pi}{3}\right) + 4\left(36.1 \sin \dfrac{\pi}{2}\right) + 2\left(45.4 \sin \dfrac{2\pi}{3}\right) +\right.$

$$4\left(55.2 \sin \dfrac{5\pi}{6}\right) + 2(59.9 \sin \pi) + 4\left(59.4 \sin \dfrac{7\pi}{6}\right) + 2\left(53.1 \sin \dfrac{4\pi}{3}\right) +$$

$$\left. 4\left(43.2 \sin \dfrac{3\pi}{2}\right) + 2\left(34.3 \sin \dfrac{5\pi}{3}\right) + 4\left(24.2 \sin \dfrac{11\pi}{6}\right) + 18 \sin 2\pi\right] \approx -4.33$$

$$L(t) \approx 39.34 - 20.78 \cos \dfrac{\pi t}{6} - 4.33 \sin \dfrac{\pi t}{6}$$

(c) The difference between the maximum and minimum temperatures is greatest in the summer.

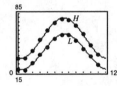

Section 7.4   Trigonometric Substitution

1. $\dfrac{d}{dx}\left[4 \ln\left|\dfrac{\sqrt{x^2 + 16} - 4}{x}\right| + \sqrt{x^2 + 16} + C\right] = \dfrac{d}{dx}\left[4 \ln\left|\sqrt{x^2 + 16} - 4\right| - 4 \ln|x| + \sqrt{x^2 + 16} + C\right]$

$$= 4\left[\dfrac{x/\sqrt{x^2 + 16}}{\sqrt{x^2 + 16} - 4}\right] - \dfrac{4}{x} + \dfrac{x}{\sqrt{x^2 + 16}}$$

$$= \dfrac{4x}{\sqrt{x^2 + 16}\left(\sqrt{x^2 + 16} - 4\right)} - \dfrac{4}{x} + \dfrac{x}{\sqrt{x^2 + 16}}$$

$$= \dfrac{4x^2 - 4\sqrt{x^2 + 16}\left(\sqrt{x^2 + 16} - 4\right) + x^2\left(\sqrt{x^2 + 16} - 4\right)}{x\sqrt{x^2 + 16}\left(\sqrt{x^2 + 16} - 4\right)}$$

$$= \dfrac{4x^2 - 4(x^2 + 16) + 16\sqrt{x^2 + 16} + x^2\sqrt{x^2 + 16} - 4x^2}{x\sqrt{x^2 + 16}\left(\sqrt{x^2 + 16} - 4\right)}$$

$$= \dfrac{\sqrt{x^2 + 16}(x^2 + 16) - 4(x^2 + 16)}{x\sqrt{x^2 + 16}\left(\sqrt{x^2 + 16} - 4\right)}$$

$$= \dfrac{(x^2 + 16)\left(\sqrt{x^2 + 16} - 4\right)}{x\sqrt{x^2 + 16}\left(\sqrt{x^2 + 16} - 4\right)} = \dfrac{\sqrt{x^2 + 16}}{x}$$

Indefinite integral: $\displaystyle\int \dfrac{\sqrt{x^2 + 16}}{x}\,dx$ Matches (b)

3. $\dfrac{d}{dx}\left[8\arcsin\dfrac{x}{4} - \dfrac{x\sqrt{16-x^2}}{2} + C\right] = 8\dfrac{1/4}{\sqrt{1-(x/4)^2}} - \dfrac{x(1/2)(16-x^2)^{-1/2}(-2x) + \sqrt{16-x^2}}{2}$

$$= \dfrac{8}{\sqrt{16-x^2}} + \dfrac{x^2}{2\sqrt{16-x^2}} - \dfrac{\sqrt{16-x^2}}{2}$$

$$= \dfrac{16}{2\sqrt{16-x^2}} + \dfrac{x^2}{2\sqrt{16-x^2}} - \dfrac{(16-x^2)}{2\sqrt{16-x^2}} = \dfrac{x^2}{\sqrt{16-x^2}}$$

Matches (a)

5. Let $x = 5\sin\theta$, $dx = 5\cos\theta\,d\theta$, $\sqrt{25-x^2} = 5\cos\theta$.

$$\int \dfrac{1}{(25-x^2)^{3/2}}\,dx = \int \dfrac{5\cos\theta}{(5\cos\theta)^3}\,d\theta = \dfrac{1}{25}\int \sec^2\theta\,d\theta$$

$$= \dfrac{1}{25}\tan\theta + C$$

$$= \dfrac{x}{25\sqrt{25-x^2}} + C$$

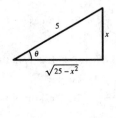

7. Let $x = 5\sin\theta$. Then $\sqrt{25-x^2} = 5\cos\theta$ and $dx = 5\cos\theta\,d\theta$. Thus,

$$\int \dfrac{\sqrt{25-x^2}}{x}\,dx = \int \dfrac{5\cos\theta}{5\sin\theta}5\cos\theta\,d\theta$$

$$= 5\int \dfrac{\cos^2\theta}{\sin\theta}\,d\theta$$

$$= 5\int \dfrac{1-\sin^2\theta}{\sin\theta}\,d\theta$$

$$= 5\int (\csc\theta - \sin\theta)\,d\theta$$

$$= 5(\ln|\csc\theta - \cot\theta| + \cos\theta) + C$$

$$= 5\left(\ln\left|\dfrac{5}{x} - \dfrac{\sqrt{25-x^2}}{x}\right| + \dfrac{\sqrt{25-x^2}}{5}\right) + C$$

$$= 5\ln\left|\dfrac{5 - \sqrt{25-x^2}}{x}\right| + \sqrt{25-x^2} + C.$$

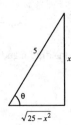

9. Let $x = 2\sec\theta$, $dx = 2\sec\theta\tan\theta\,d\theta$, $\sqrt{x^2-4} = 2\tan\theta$.

$$\int \dfrac{1}{\sqrt{x^2-4}}\,dx = \int \dfrac{2\sec\theta\tan\theta\,d\theta}{2\tan\theta}$$

$$= \int \sec\theta\,d\theta = \ln|\sec\theta + \tan\theta| + C_1$$

$$= \ln\left|\dfrac{x}{2} + \dfrac{\sqrt{x^2-4}}{2}\right| + C_1$$

$$= \ln\left|x + \sqrt{x^2-4}\right| - \ln 2 + C_1$$

$$= \ln\left|x + \sqrt{x^2-4}\right| + C$$

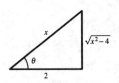

11. Let $x = 2 \sec \theta$. Then $\sqrt{x^2 - 4} = 2 \tan \theta$ and $dx = 2 \sec \theta \tan \theta \, d\theta$. Thus,

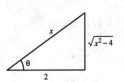

$$\int x^3 \sqrt{x^2 - 4} \, dx = \int (2 \sec \theta)^3 (2 \tan \theta)(2 \sec \theta \tan \theta) \, d\theta$$

$$= 32 \int \sec^4 \theta \tan^2 \theta \, d\theta$$

$$= 32 \int \sec^2 \theta \tan^2 \theta \sec^2 \theta \, d\theta$$

$$= 32 \int (\tan^2 \theta + 1) \tan^2 \theta \sec^2 \theta \, d\theta$$

$$= 32 \int (\tan^4 \theta + \tan^2 \theta) \sec^2 \theta \, d\theta$$

$$= 32 \left[\frac{1}{5} \tan^5 \theta + \frac{1}{3} \tan^3 \theta \right] + C$$

$$= 32 \left[\frac{1}{5} \left(\frac{\sqrt{x^2 - 4}}{2} \right)^5 + \frac{1}{3} \left(\frac{\sqrt{x^2 - 4}}{2} \right)^3 \right] + C$$

$$= \frac{1}{15}(x^2 - 4)^{3/2}(3x^2 + 8) + C.$$

13. Let $x = \tan \theta$, $dx = \sec^2 \theta \, d\theta$, $\sqrt{1 + x^2} = \sec \theta$.

$$\int x \sqrt{1 + x^2} \, dx = \int \tan \theta (\sec \theta) \sec^2 \theta \, d\theta = \frac{\sec^3 \theta}{3} + C = \frac{1}{3}(1 + x^2)^{3/2} + C$$

Note: This integral could have been evaluated with the Power Rule.

15. Let $x = \tan \theta$. Then $1 + x^2 = \sec^2 \theta$ and $dx = \sec^2 \theta \, d\theta$. Thus,

$$\int \frac{1}{(1 + x^2)^2} \, dx = \int \frac{1}{\sec^4 \theta}(\sec^2 \theta) \, d\theta = \int \cos^2 \theta \, d\theta$$

$$= \frac{1}{2} \int (1 + \cos 2\theta) \, d\theta$$

$$= \frac{1}{2} \left(\theta + \frac{1}{2} \sin 2\theta \right) + C$$

$$= \frac{1}{2}(\theta + \sin \theta \cos \theta) + C$$

$$= \frac{1}{2} \left(\arctan x + \frac{x}{\sqrt{1 + x^2}} \cdot \frac{1}{\sqrt{1 + x^2}} \right) + C$$

$$= \frac{1}{2} \left(\arctan x + \frac{x}{1 + x^2} \right) + C.$$

17. Let $u = 3x$, $a = 2$, and $du = 3 \, dx$.

$$\int \sqrt{4 + 9x^2} \, dx = \frac{1}{3} \int \sqrt{(2)^2 + (3x)^2} \, 3 \, dx$$

$$= \frac{1}{3} \left(\frac{1}{2} \right) \left(3x \sqrt{4 + 9x^2} + 4 \ln \left| 3x + \sqrt{4 + 9x^2} \right| \right) + C$$

$$= \frac{1}{2} x \sqrt{4 + 9x^2} + \frac{2}{3} \ln \left| 3x + \sqrt{4 + 9x^2} \right| + C$$

19. $\int \dfrac{x}{\sqrt{x^2 + 9}}\, dx = \dfrac{1}{2}\int (x^2 + 9)^{-1/2}(2x)\, dx$

$$= \sqrt{x^2 + 9} + C$$

(Power Rule)

21. Let $x = 2 \sin \theta,\ dx = 2 \cos \theta\, d\theta,\ \sqrt{4 - x^2} = 2 \cos \theta$.

$$\int_0^2 \sqrt{16 - 4x^2}\, dx = 2\int_0^2 \sqrt{4 - x^2}\, dx$$

$$= 2\int_0^{\pi/2} 2\cos\theta(2\cos\theta\, d\theta)$$

$$= 8\int_0^{\pi/2} \cos^2\theta\, d\theta$$

$$= 4\int_0^{\pi/2} (1 + \cos 2\theta)\, d\theta$$

$$= 4\left[\theta + \frac{1}{2}\sin 2\theta\right]_0^{\pi/2} = 2\pi$$

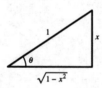

23. Let $x = 3 \sec \theta,\ dx = 3 \sec \theta \tan \theta\, d\theta,\ \sqrt{x^2 - 9} = 3 \tan \theta$.

$$\int \frac{1}{\sqrt{x^2 - 9}}\, dx = \int \frac{3 \sec \theta \tan \theta\, d\theta}{3 \tan \theta}$$

$$= \int \sec \theta\, d\theta$$

$$= \ln|\sec \theta + \tan \theta| + C_1$$

$$= \ln\left|\frac{x}{3} + \frac{\sqrt{x^2 - 9}}{3}\right| + C_1$$

$$= \ln\left|x + \sqrt{x^2 - 9}\right| + C$$

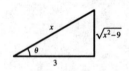

25. Let $x = \sin \theta,\ dx = \cos \theta\, d\theta,\ \sqrt{1 - x^2} = \cos \theta$.

$$\int \frac{\sqrt{1 - x^2}}{x^4}\, dx = \int \frac{\cos\theta(\cos\theta\, d\theta)}{\sin^4\theta}$$

$$= \int \cot^2\theta \csc^2\theta\, d\theta$$

$$= -\frac{1}{3}\cot^3\theta + C$$

$$= \frac{-(1 - x^2)^{3/2}}{3x^3} + C$$

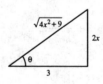

27. Let $2x = 3 \tan \theta$. Then $x = \frac{3}{2}\tan\theta,\ \sqrt{4x^2 + 9} = 3\sec\theta$, and $dx = \frac{3}{2}\sec^2\theta\, d\theta$.

$$\int \frac{1}{x\sqrt{4x^2 + 9}}\, dx = \int \frac{(3/2)\sec^2\theta\, d\theta}{(3/2)\tan\theta(3\sec\theta)} = \frac{1}{3}\int \csc\theta\, d\theta$$

$$= \frac{1}{3}\ln|\csc\theta - \cot\theta| + C$$

$$= \frac{1}{3}\ln\left|\frac{\sqrt{4x^2 + 9} - 3}{2x}\right| + C$$

$$= -\frac{1}{3}\ln\left|\frac{2x}{\sqrt{4x^2 + 9} - 3}\right| + C$$

$$= -\frac{1}{3}\left|\ln\left(\frac{2x}{\sqrt{4x^2 + 9} - 3}\right)\left(\frac{\sqrt{4x^2 + 9} + 3}{\sqrt{4x^2 + 9} + 3}\right)\right| + C$$

$$= -\frac{1}{3}\ln\left|\frac{3 + \sqrt{4x^2 + 9}}{2x}\right| + C$$

29. Same substitutions as in Exercise 28

$$\int \frac{x}{(x^2 + 3)^{3/2}}\, dx = \int \frac{\sqrt{3}\tan\theta\left(\sqrt{3}\sec^2\theta\, d\theta\right)}{3\sqrt{3}\sec^3\theta} = \frac{\sqrt{3}}{3}\int \sin\theta\, d\theta = -\frac{\sqrt{3}}{3}\cos\theta + C = \frac{-1}{\sqrt{x^2 + 3}} + C$$

Note: This integral could have been evaluated with the Power Rule: $u = x^2 + 3$, $du = 2x\, dx$

31. Let $u = 1 + e^{2x}$, $du = 2e^{2x}\, dx$.

$$\int e^{2x}\sqrt{1 + e^{2x}}\, dx = \frac{1}{2}\int (1 + e^{2x})^{1/2}(2e^{2x})dx = \frac{1}{3}(1 + e^{2x})^{3/2} + C$$

33. Let $e^x = \sin\theta$, $e^x\, dx = \cos\theta\, d\theta$, $\sqrt{1 - e^{2x}} = \cos\theta$.

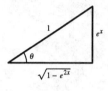

$$\int$$

$$= \frac{1}{2}\left[\theta + \frac{\sin 2\theta}{2}\right]$$

$$= \frac{1}{2}(\theta + \sin\theta\cos\theta) + C = \frac{1}{2}\left(\arcsin e^x + e^x\sqrt{1 - e^{2x}}\right) + C$$

35. $\displaystyle\int \frac{1}{4 + 4x^2 + x^4}\, dx = \int \frac{1}{(2 + x^2)^2}\, dx$

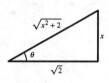

Let $x = \sqrt{2}\tan\theta$. Then $2 + x^2 = 2\sec^2\theta$ and $dx = \sqrt{2}\sec^2\theta\, d\theta$. Thus,

$$\int \frac{1}{(2 + x^2)^2}\, dx = \int \frac{\sqrt{2}\sec^2\theta\, d\theta}{(2\sec^2\theta)^2} = \frac{\sqrt{2}}{4}\int \cos^2\theta\, d\theta$$

$$= \frac{\sqrt{2}}{4}\int \frac{1 + \cos 2\theta}{2}\, d\theta = \frac{\sqrt{2}}{8}\left(\theta + \frac{1}{2}\sin 2\theta\right) + C$$

$$= \frac{\sqrt{2}}{8}(\theta + \sin\theta\cos\theta) + C$$

$$= \frac{\sqrt{2}}{8}\left[\arctan\frac{x}{\sqrt{2}} + \left(\frac{x}{\sqrt{x^2 + 2}}\right)\left(\frac{\sqrt{2}}{\sqrt{x^2 + 2}}\right)\right] + C$$

$$= \frac{1}{4}\left[\frac{x}{x^2 + 2} + \frac{1}{\sqrt{2}}\arctan\frac{x}{\sqrt{2}}\right] + C.$$

37. Let

$$dv = dx \quad\Longrightarrow\quad v = x$$

$$u = \operatorname{arcsec} x \Longrightarrow du = \frac{1}{x\sqrt{4x^2 - 1}}\, dx.$$

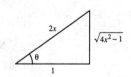

Therefore,

$$\int \operatorname{arcsec} 2x\, dx = uv - \int v\, du = x\operatorname{arcsec} 2x - \int x\left(\frac{1}{x\sqrt{4x^2 - 1}}\right)dx$$

$$= x\operatorname{arcsec} 2x - \frac{1}{2}\int \frac{2}{\sqrt{(2x)^2 - 1^2}}\, dx \quad (\text{Let } 2x = \sec\theta)$$

$$= x\operatorname{arcsec} 2x - \int \frac{(1/2)\sec\theta\tan\theta\, d\theta}{\tan\theta}$$

$$= x\operatorname{arcsec} 2x - \frac{1}{2}\int \sec\theta\, d\theta$$

$$= x\operatorname{arcsec} 2x - \frac{1}{2}\ln|\sec\theta + \tan\theta| + C$$

$$= x\operatorname{arcsec} 2x - \frac{1}{2}\ln|2x + \sqrt{4x^2 - 1}| + C.$$

39. $\displaystyle\int \frac{1}{\sqrt{4x - x^2}}\, dx = \int \frac{1}{\sqrt{4 - (x - 2)^2}}\, dx = \arcsin\left(\frac{x - 2}{2}\right) + C$

41. Let $x + 2 = 2\tan\theta$, $dx = 2\sec^2\theta\, d\theta$, $\sqrt{(x+2)^2 + 4} = 2\sec\theta$.

$$\int \frac{x}{\sqrt{x^2 + 4x + 8}}\, dx = \int \frac{x}{\sqrt{(x+2)^2 + 4}}\, dx = \int \frac{(2\tan\theta - 2)(2\sec^2\theta)\, d\theta}{2\sec\theta}$$

$$= 2\int (\tan\theta - 1)(\sec\theta)\, d\theta$$

$$= 2[\sec\theta - \ln|\sec\theta + \tan\theta|] + C_1$$

$$= 2\left[\frac{\sqrt{(x+2)^2 + 4}}{2} - \ln\left|\frac{\sqrt{(x+2)^2 + 4}}{2} + \frac{x+2}{2}\right|\right] + C_1$$

$$= \sqrt{x^2 + 4x + 8} - 2\left[\ln\left|\sqrt{x^2 + 4x + 8} + (x + 2)\right| - \ln 2\right] + C_1$$

$$= \sqrt{x^2 + 4x + 8} - 2\ln\left|\sqrt{x^2 + 4x + 8} + (x + 2)\right| + C$$

43. If we let $t = \sin\theta$, then $dt = \cos\theta\, d\theta$ and $1 - t^2 = \cos^2\theta$.

$$\int \frac{t^2}{(1 - t^2)^{3/2}}\, dt = \int \frac{\sin^2\theta\cos\theta}{\cos^3\theta}\, d\theta$$

$$= \int \tan^2\theta\, d\theta = \int (\sec^2\theta - 1)\, d\theta$$

$$= \tan\theta - \theta = \frac{t}{\sqrt{1 - t^2}} - \arcsin t + C \quad \text{(See figure)}$$

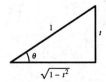

(a) Using the antiderivative from above, it follows that

$$\int_0^{\sqrt{3}/2} \frac{t^2}{(1 - t^2)^{3/2}}\, dt = \left[\frac{t}{\sqrt{1 - t^2}} - \arcsin t\right]_0^{\sqrt{3}/2} = \frac{\sqrt{3}/2}{\sqrt{1/4}} - \arcsin\frac{\sqrt{3}}{2} = \sqrt{3} - \frac{\pi}{3} \approx 0.685.$$

(b) Using the substitution from above, we have $\theta = 0$ when $t = 0$ and $\theta = \pi/3$ when $t = \sqrt{3}/2$.

$$\int_0^{\sqrt{3}/2} \frac{t^2}{(1 - t^2)^{3/2}}\, dt = \int_0^{\pi/3} \frac{\sin^2\theta\cos\theta}{\cos^3\theta}\, d\theta = \left[\tan\theta - \theta\right]_0^{\pi/3} = \sqrt{3} - \frac{\pi}{3} \approx 0.685$$

45. (a) Let $x = 3\tan\theta$, $dx = 3\sec^2\theta\, d\theta$, $\sqrt{x^2 + 9} = 3\sec\theta$.

$$\int \frac{x^3}{\sqrt{x^2 + 9}}\, dx = \int \frac{(27\tan^3\theta)(3\sec^2\theta\, d\theta)}{3\sec\theta}$$

$$= 27\int (\sec^2\theta - 1)\sec\theta\tan\theta\, d\theta$$

$$= 27\left[\frac{1}{3}\sec^3\theta - \sec\theta\right] + C = 9[\sec^3\theta - 3\sec\theta] + C$$

$$= 9\left[\left(\frac{\sqrt{x^2 + 9}}{3}\right)^3 - 3\left(\frac{\sqrt{x^2 + 9}}{3}\right)\right] + C = \frac{1}{3}(x^2 + 9)^{3/2} - 9\sqrt{x^2 + 9} + C$$

Thus, $\displaystyle\int_0^3 \frac{x^3}{\sqrt{x^2 + 9}}\, dx = \left[\frac{1}{3}(x^2 + 9)^{3/2} - 9\sqrt{x^2 + 9}\right]_0^3$

$$= \left(\frac{1}{3}(54\sqrt{2}) - 27\sqrt{2}\right) - (9 - 27)$$

$$= 18 - 9\sqrt{2} = 9(2 - \sqrt{2}) \approx 5.272.$$

(b) When $x = 0$, $\theta = 0$. When $x = 3$, $\theta = \pi/4$. Thus,

$$\int_0^3 \frac{x^3}{\sqrt{x^2 + 9}}\, dx = 9\left[\sec^3\theta - 3\sec\theta\right]_0^{\pi/4} = 9(2\sqrt{2} - 3\sqrt{2}) - 9(1 - 3) = 9(2 - \sqrt{2}) \approx 5.272.$$

47. $\displaystyle\int \frac{x^2}{\sqrt{x^2 + 10x + 9}}\,dx = \frac{1}{2}\sqrt{x^2 + 10x + 9}\,(x - 15) + 33\ln\left|(x + 5) + \sqrt{x^2 + 10x + 9}\right| + C$

49. $\displaystyle\int \frac{x^2}{\sqrt{x^2 - 1}}\,dx = \frac{1}{2}\left(x\sqrt{x^2 - 1} + \ln\left|x + \sqrt{x^2 - 1}\right|\right) + C$

51. $A = 4\displaystyle\int_0^a \frac{b}{a}\sqrt{a^2 - x^2}\,dx$

$\qquad = \dfrac{4b}{a}\displaystyle\int_0^a \sqrt{a^2 - x^2}\,dx$

$\qquad = \left[\dfrac{4b}{a}\left(\dfrac{1}{2}\right)\left(a^2\arcsin\dfrac{x}{a} + x\sqrt{a^2 - x^2}\right)\right]_0^a$

$\qquad = \dfrac{2b}{a}\left(a^2\left(\dfrac{\pi}{2}\right)\right)$

$\qquad = \pi ab$

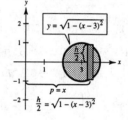

Note: See Theorem 7.2 for $\int\sqrt{a^2 - x^2}\,dx$.

53. Shell Method

$$V = 2\pi\int_2^4 x\left[2\sqrt{1 - (x - 3)^2}\right]dx = 4\pi\int_2^4 x\sqrt{1 - (x - 3)^2}\,dx$$

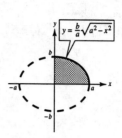

Let $x - 3 = \sin\theta$. Then $\sqrt{1 - (x - 3)^2} = \cos\theta$ and $dx = \cos\theta\,d\theta$. Also, when $x = 2$, $\sin\theta = -1$ and $\theta = -\pi/2$. When $x = 4$, $\sin\theta = 1$ and $\theta = \pi/2$. Therefore,

$$V = 4\pi\int_{-\pi/2}^{\pi/2}(3 + \sin\theta)(\cos\theta)(\cos\theta)\,d\theta$$

$$= 4\pi\left[\int_{-\pi/2}^{\pi/2} 3\cos^2\theta\,d\theta + \int_{-\pi/2}^{\pi/2}\cos^2\theta\sin\theta\,d\theta\right]$$

$$= 4\pi\left[\int_{-\pi/2}^{\pi/2}\frac{3}{2}(1 + \cos 2\theta)\,d\theta + \int_{-\pi/2}^{\pi/2}\cos^2\theta\sin\theta\,d\theta\right]$$

$$= 4\pi\left[\frac{3}{2}\left(\theta + \frac{1}{2}\sin 2\theta\right) - \frac{1}{3}\cos^3\theta\right]_{-\pi/2}^{\pi/2} = 6\pi^2.$$

55. $y = \ln x,\ y' = \dfrac{1}{x},\ 1 + (y')^2 = 1 + \dfrac{1}{x^2} = \dfrac{x^2 + 1}{x^2}$

Let $x = \tan\theta,\ dx = \sec^2\theta\,d\theta,\ \sqrt{x^2 + 1} = \sec\theta$.

$$s = \int_1^5 \sqrt{\frac{x^2 + 1}{x^2}}\,dx = \int_1^5 \frac{\sqrt{x^2 + 1}}{x}\,dx$$

$$= \int_a^b \frac{\sec\theta}{\tan\theta}\sec^2\theta\,d\theta = \int_a^b \frac{\sec\theta}{\tan\theta}(1 + \tan^2\theta)\,d\theta$$

$$= \int_a^b (\csc\theta + \sec\theta\tan\theta)\,d\theta$$

$$= \left[-\ln|\csc\theta + \cot\theta| + \sec\theta\right]_a^b$$

$$= \left[-\ln\left|\frac{\sqrt{x^2 + 1}}{x} + \frac{1}{x}\right| + \sqrt{x^2 + 1}\right]_1^5$$

$$= \left[-\ln\left(\frac{\sqrt{26} + 1}{5}\right) + \sqrt{26}\right] - \left[-\ln(\sqrt{2} + 1) + \sqrt{2}\right]$$

$$= \ln\left[\frac{5(\sqrt{2} + 1)}{\sqrt{26} + 1}\right] + \sqrt{26} - \sqrt{2} \approx 4.367 \text{ or } \ln\left[\frac{\sqrt{26} - 1}{5(\sqrt{2} - 1)}\right] + \sqrt{26} - \sqrt{2}$$

57. Length of one arch of sine curve: $y = \sin x$, $y' = \cos x$

$$L_1 = \int_0^\pi \sqrt{1 + \cos^2 x} \, dx$$

Length of one arch of cosine curve: $y = \cos x$, $y' = -\sin x$

$$L_2 = \int_{-\pi/2}^{\pi/2} \sqrt{1 + \sin^2 x} \, dx$$

$$= \int_{-\pi/2}^{\pi/2} \sqrt{1 + \cos^2\left(x - \frac{\pi}{2}\right)} \, dx \qquad u = x - \frac{\pi}{2}, du = dx$$

$$= \int_{-\pi}^0 \sqrt{1 + \cos^2 u} \, du$$

$$= \int_0^\pi \sqrt{1 + \cos^2 u} \, du = L_1$$

59. (a)

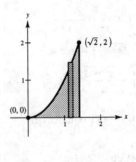

(b) $y = 0$ for $x = 200$ (range)

(c) $y = x - 0.005x^2$, $y' = 1 - 0.01x$, $1 + (y')^2 = 1 + (1 - 0.01x)^2$

Let $u = 1 - 0.01x$, $du = -0.01 \, dx$, $a = 1$. (See Theorem 7.2.)

$$s = \int_0^{200} \sqrt{1 + (1 - 0.01x)^2} \, dx = -100 \int_0^{200} \sqrt{(1 - 0.01x)^2 + 1} \, (-0.01) \, dx$$

$$= -50 \left[(1 - 0.01x)\sqrt{(1 - 0.01x)^2 + 1} + \ln\left|(1 - 0.01x) + \sqrt{(1 - 0.01x)^2 + 1}\right| \right.$$

$$= -50\left[\left(-\sqrt{2} + \ln\left|-1 + \sqrt{2}\right|\right) - \left(\sqrt{2} + \ln\left|1 + \sqrt{2}\right|\right)\right]$$

$$= 100\sqrt{2} + 50\ln\left(\frac{\sqrt{2} + 1}{\sqrt{2} - 1}\right) \approx 229.559$$

61. $S = 2\pi \int_a^b y\sqrt{1 + (y')^2} \, dx = 2\pi \int_0^{\sqrt{2}} x^2 \sqrt{1 + 4x^2} \, dx$

Using trigonometric substitution, let $2x = \tan \theta$. Then
$\sqrt{1 + 4x^2} = \sec \theta$, $x^2 = \frac{1}{4} \tan^2 \theta$, and $dx = \frac{1}{2} \sec^2 \theta \, d\theta$.
Therefore,

$$\int x^2 \sqrt{1 + 4x^2} \, dx = \int \frac{\tan^2 \theta}{4} (\sec \theta)\left(\frac{1}{2} \sec^2 \theta\right) d\theta$$

$$= \frac{1}{8} \int \sec^3 \theta \tan^2 \theta \, d\theta$$

$$= \frac{1}{8} \int \sec^3 \theta \, (\sec^2 \theta - 1) \, d\theta$$

$$= \frac{1}{8}\left[\int \sec^5 \theta \, d\theta - \int \sec^3 \theta \, d\theta\right].$$

Now using Integration By Parts to evaluate $\int \sec^5 \theta \, d\theta$, let

$$dv = \sec^2 \theta \, d\theta \implies v = \tan \theta$$

—CONTINUED—

61. —CONTINUED—

Thus,

$$\int \sec^5 \theta \, d\theta = \sec^3 \theta \tan \theta - 3 \int \sec^3 \theta \tan^2 \theta \, d\theta$$

$$= \sec^3 \theta \tan \theta - 3 \int \sec^3 \theta (\sec^2 \theta - 1) \, d\theta$$

$$= \sec^3 \theta \tan \theta - 3 \int \sec^5 \theta \, d\theta + 3 \int \sec^3 \theta \, d\theta$$

$$4 \int \sec^5 \theta \, d\theta = \sec^3 \theta \tan \theta + 3 \int \sec^3 \theta \, d\theta$$

$$\int \sec^5 \theta \, d\theta = \frac{1}{4} \left(\sec^3 \tan \theta + 3 \int \sec^3 \theta \, d\theta \right).$$

Hence,

$$\int x^2 \sqrt{1 + 4x^2} \, dx = \frac{1}{8} \left[\frac{1}{4} \sec^3 \theta \tan \theta + \frac{3}{4} \int \sec^3 \theta \, d\theta - \int \sec^3 \theta \, d\theta \right]$$

$$= \frac{1}{32} \left(\sec^3 \theta \tan \theta - \int \sec^3 \theta \, d\theta \right).$$

Using the formula for $\int \sec^3 \theta \, d\theta$ from Section 7.2, we have

$$\int x^2 \sqrt{1 + 4x^2} \, dx = \frac{1}{32} \left[\sec^2 \theta \tan \theta - \frac{1}{2} (\sec \theta \tan \theta + \ln|\sec \theta + \tan \theta|) \right] + C.$$

Finally, when $x = 0$, $\theta = 0$, and when $x = \sqrt{2}$, $\theta = \arctan 2\sqrt{2}$. Therefore,

$$S = 2\pi \int_0^{\sqrt{2}} x^2 \sqrt{1 + 4x^2} \, dx$$

$$= \frac{\pi}{16} \left[\sec^3 \theta \tan \theta - \frac{1}{2} (\sec \theta \tan \theta + \ln|\sec \theta + \tan \theta|) \right]_0^{\arctan 2\sqrt{2}}$$

$$= \frac{\pi}{16} \left[51\sqrt{2} - \frac{1}{2} \ln\left(2\sqrt{2} + 3\right) \right]$$

$$= \frac{\pi}{32} \left[102\sqrt{2} - \ln\left(2\sqrt{2} + 3\right) \right] \approx 13.989.$$

63. First find where the curves intersect.

$$y^2 = 16 - (x - 4)^2 = \frac{1}{16} x^4$$

$$16^2 - 16(x - 4)^2 = x^4$$

$$16^2 - 16x^2 + 128x - 16^2 = x^4$$

$$x^4 + 16x^2 - 128x = 0$$

$$x(x - 4)(x^2 + 4x + 32) \implies x = 0, 4$$

$$A = \int_0^4 \frac{1}{4} x^2 \, dx + \frac{1}{4} \pi (4)^2 = \frac{1}{12} x^3 \Big]_0^4 + 4\pi = \frac{16}{3} + 4\pi$$

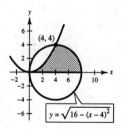

—CONTINUED—

63. —CONTINUED—

$$M_y = \int_0^4 x\left[\frac{1}{4}x^2\right] dx + \int_4^8 x\sqrt{16 - (x-4)^2}\, dx$$

$$= \frac{x^4}{16}\bigg]_0^4 + \int_4^8 (x-4)\sqrt{16 - (x-4)^2}\, dx + \int_4^8 4\sqrt{16 - (x-4)^2}\, dx$$

$$= 16 + \left[\frac{-1}{3}(16 - (x-4)^2)^{3/2}\right]_4^8 + 2\left[16\arcsin\frac{x-4}{4} + (x-4)\sqrt{16 - (x-4)^2}\right]_4^8$$

$$= 16 + \frac{1}{3}16^{3/2} + 2\left[16\left(\frac{\pi}{2}\right)\right] = 16 + \frac{64}{3} + 16\pi = \frac{112}{3} + 16\pi$$

$$M_x = \int_0^4 \frac{1}{2}\left(\frac{1}{4}x^2\right)^2 dx + \int_4^8 \frac{1}{2}(16 - (x-4)^2)\, dx$$

$$= \left[\frac{1}{32}\cdot\frac{x^5}{5}\right]_0^4 + \left[8x - \frac{(x-4)^3}{6}\right]_4^8$$

$$= \frac{32}{5} + \left(64 - \frac{64}{6}\right) - 32 = \frac{416}{15}$$

$$\bar{x} = \frac{M_y}{A} = \frac{112/3 + 16\pi}{16/3 + 4\pi} = \frac{112 + 48\pi}{16 + 12\pi} = \frac{28 + 12\pi}{4 + 3\pi} \approx 4.89$$

$$\bar{y} = \frac{M_x}{A} = \frac{416/15}{(16/3) + 4\pi} = \frac{104}{5(4 + 3\pi)} \approx 1.55$$

$$(\bar{x}, \bar{y}) \approx (4.89, 1.55)$$

65. (a) Area of representative rectangle: $2\sqrt{1 - y^2}\,\Delta y$

Pressure: $2(62.4)(3 - y)\sqrt{1 - y^2}\,\Delta y$

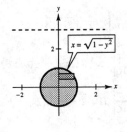

$$F = 124.8\int_{-1}^{1} (3 - y)\sqrt{1 - y^2}\, dy$$

$$= 124.8\left[3 + \int_{-1}^{1}\sqrt{1 - y^2}\, dy - \int_{-1}^{1} y\sqrt{1 - y^2}\, dy\right]$$

$$= 124.8\left[\frac{3}{2}\left(\arcsin y + y\sqrt{1 - y^2}\right) + \frac{1}{2}\left(\frac{2}{3}\right)(1 - y^2)^{3/2}\right]_{-1}^{1}$$

$$= (62.4)3[\arcsin 1 - \arcsin(-1)] = 187.2\pi \text{ lb}$$

(b) $F = 124.8\displaystyle\int_{-1}^{1} (d - y)\sqrt{1 - y^2}\, dy = 124.8d\int_{-1}^{1}\sqrt{1 - y^2}\, dy - 124.8\int_{-1}^{1} y\sqrt{1 - y^2}\, dy$

$$= 124.8\left(\frac{d}{2}\right)\left[\arcsin y + y\sqrt{1 - y^2}\right]_{-1}^{1} - 124.8(0) = 62.4\pi d \text{ lb}$$

67. (a) Using the figure and the formula for the slope of a line we have

$$m = \frac{dy}{dx} = \frac{y - \left(y + \sqrt{144 - x^2}\right)}{x - 0} = -\frac{\sqrt{144 - x^2}}{x}.$$

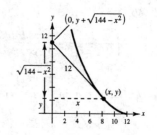

(b) If $x = 12 \sin \theta$ in the following integral, then $dx = 12 \cos \theta \, d\theta$ and $\sqrt{144 - x^2} = 12 \cos \theta$.

$$y = -\int \frac{\sqrt{144 - x^2}}{x} \, dx$$

$$= -\int \frac{12 \cos \theta}{12 \sin \theta} 12 \cos \theta \, d\theta = -12 \int \frac{1 - \sin^2 \theta}{\sin \theta} \, d\theta$$

$$= -12 \int (\csc \theta - \sin \theta) \, d\theta = -12 \ln|\csc \theta - \cot \theta| - 12 \cos \theta + C$$

$$= -12 \ln \left| \frac{12}{x} - \frac{\sqrt{144 - x^2}}{x} \right| - 12 \left(\frac{\sqrt{144 - x^2}}{12} \right) + C$$

$$= -12 \ln \left| \frac{12 - \sqrt{144 - x^2}}{x} \right| - \sqrt{144 - x^2} + C$$

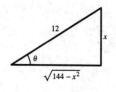

When $x = 12$, $y = 0 \implies C = 0$. Thus,

$$y = -12 \ln \left(\frac{12 - \sqrt{144 - x^2}}{x} \right) - \sqrt{144 - x^2}.$$

Note: $\dfrac{12 - \sqrt{144 - x^2}}{x} > 0$ for $0 < x \le 12$.

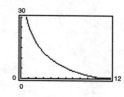

(c) Vertical asymptote: $x = 0$

(d) When the person has reached the point $(0, 12)$, we have

$$y + \sqrt{144 - x^2} = 12 \implies y = 12 - \sqrt{144 - x^2}.$$

Thus,

$$12 - \sqrt{144 - x^2} = -12 \ln \left(\frac{12 - \sqrt{144 - x^2}}{x} \right) = \sqrt{144 - x^2}$$

$$-1 = \ln \left(\frac{12 - \sqrt{144 - x^2}}{x} \right)$$

$$xe^{-1} = 12 - \sqrt{144 - x^2}$$

$$(xe^{-1} - 12)^2 = \left(-\sqrt{144 - x^2}\right)^2$$

$$x^2 e^{-2} - 24xe^{-1} + 144 = 144 - x^2$$

$$x^2(e^{-2} + 1) - 24xe^{-1} = 0$$

$$x[x(e^{-2} + 1) - 24e^{-1}] = 0$$

$$x = 0 \text{ or } x = \frac{24e^{-1}}{e^{-2} + 1} \approx 7.77665.$$

Therefore,

$$s = \int_{7.77665}^{12} \sqrt{1 + \left(-\frac{\sqrt{144 - x^2}}{x}\right)^2} \, dx = \int_{7.77665}^{12} \sqrt{\frac{x^2 + (144 - x^2)}{x^2}} \, dx$$

$$= \int_{7.77665}^{12} \frac{12}{x} \, dx = \left[12 \ln|x| \right]_{7.77665}^{12} = 12(\ln 12 - \ln 7.77665) \approx 5.2 \text{ feet.}$$

69. True

$$\int \frac{dx}{\sqrt{1-x^2}} = \int \frac{\cos\theta\, d\theta}{\cos\theta} = \int d\theta$$

71. False

$$\int_0^{\sqrt{3}} \frac{dx}{(\sqrt{1+x^2})^3} = \int_0^{\pi/3} \frac{\sec^2\theta\, d\theta}{\sec^3\theta} = \int_0^{\pi/3} \cos\theta\, d\theta$$

73. Let $u = a\sin\theta$, $du = a\cos\theta\, d\theta$, $\sqrt{a^2 - u^2} = a\cos\theta$.

$$\int \sqrt{a^2 - u^2}\, du = \int a^2 \cos^2\theta\, d\theta = a^2 \int \frac{1 + \cos 2\theta}{2}\, d\theta$$

$$= \frac{a^2}{2}\left(\theta + \frac{1}{2}\sin 2\theta\right) + C = \frac{a^2}{2}(\theta + \sin\theta\cos\theta) + C$$

$$= \frac{a^2}{2}\left[\arcsin\frac{u}{a} + \left(\frac{u}{a}\right)\left(\frac{\sqrt{a^2 + u^2}}{a}\right)\right] + C = \frac{1}{2}\left[a^2 \arcsin\frac{u}{a} + u\sqrt{a^2 - u^2}\right] + C$$

Let $u = a\sec\theta$, $du = a\sec\theta\tan\theta\, d\theta$, $\sqrt{u^2 - a^2} = a\tan\theta$.

$$\int \sqrt{u^2 - a^2}\, du = \int a\tan\theta(a\sec\theta\tan\theta)\, d\theta = a^2 \int \tan^2\theta\sec\theta\, d\theta$$

$$= a^2 \int (\sec^2\theta - 1)\sec\theta\, d\theta = a^2 \int (\sec^3\theta - \sec\theta)\, d\theta$$

$$= a^2\left[\frac{1}{2}\sec\theta\tan\theta + \frac{1}{2}\int \sec\theta\, d\theta\right] - a^2\int \sec\theta\, d\theta = a^2\left[\frac{1}{2}\sec\theta\tan\theta - \frac{1}{2}\ln|\sec\theta + \tan\theta|\right]$$

$$= \frac{a^2}{2}\left[\frac{u}{a}\cdot\frac{\sqrt{u^2 - a^2}}{a} - \ln\left|\frac{u}{a} + \frac{\sqrt{u^2 - a^2}}{a}\right|\right] + C_1 = \frac{1}{2}\left[u\sqrt{u^2 - a^2} - a^2\ln|u + \sqrt{u^2 - a^2}|\right] + C$$

Let $u = a\tan\theta$, $du = a\sec^2\theta\, d\theta$, $\sqrt{u^2 + a^2} = a\sec\theta\, d\theta$.

$$\int \sqrt{u^2 + a^2}\, du = \int (a\sec\theta)(a\sec^2\theta)\, d\theta$$

$$= a^2 \int \sec^3\theta\, d\theta = a^2\left[\frac{1}{2}\sec\theta\tan\theta + \frac{1}{2}\ln|\sec\theta + \tan\theta|\right] + C_1$$

$$= \frac{a^2}{2}\left[\frac{\sqrt{u^2 + a^2}}{a}\cdot\frac{u}{a} + \ln\left|\frac{\sqrt{u^2 + a^2}}{a} + \frac{u}{a}\right|\right] + C_1 = \frac{1}{2}\left[u\sqrt{u^2 + a^2} + a^2\ln|u + \sqrt{u^2 + a^2}|\right] + C$$

Section 7.5   Partial Fractions

1. $\dfrac{5}{x^2 - 10x} = \dfrac{5}{x(x - 10)} = \dfrac{A}{x} + \dfrac{B}{x - 10}$

3. $\dfrac{2x - 3}{x^3 + 10x} = \dfrac{2x - 3}{x(x^2 + 10)} = \dfrac{A}{x} + \dfrac{Bx + C}{x^2 + 10}$

5. $\dfrac{16x}{x^3 - 10x^2} = \dfrac{16x}{x^2(x - 10)} = \dfrac{A}{x} + \dfrac{B}{x^2} + \dfrac{C}{x - 10}$

7. $\dfrac{1}{x^2 - 1} = \dfrac{1}{(x + 1)(x - 1)} = \dfrac{A}{x + 1} + \dfrac{B}{x - 1}$

$1 = A(x - 1) + B(x + 1)$

When $x = -1$, $1 = -2A$, $A = -\frac{1}{2}$.

When $x = 1$, $1 = 2B$, $B = \frac{1}{2}$.

$$\int \frac{1}{x^2 - 1}\, dx = -\frac{1}{2}\int \frac{1}{x + 1}\, dx + \frac{1}{2}\int \frac{1}{x - 1}\, dx$$

$$= -\frac{1}{2}\ln|x + 1| + \frac{1}{2}\ln|x - 1| + C$$

$$= \frac{1}{2}\ln\left|\frac{x - 1}{x + 1}\right| + C$$

9. $\dfrac{3}{x^2 + x - 2} = \dfrac{3}{(x - 1)(x + 2)} = \dfrac{A}{x - 1} + \dfrac{B}{x + 2}$

$3 = (x + 2) + B(x - 1)$

When $x = 1$, $3 = 3A$, $A = 1$.

When $x = -2$, $3 = -3B$, $B = -1$.

$$\int \frac{3}{x^2 + x - 2}\, dx = \int \frac{1}{x - 1}\, dx - \int \frac{1}{x + 2}\, dx$$

$$= \ln|x - 1| - \ln|x + 2| + C$$

$$= \ln\left|\frac{x - 1}{x + 2}\right| + C$$

11. $\dfrac{5 - x}{2x^2 + x - 1} = \dfrac{5 - x}{(2x - 1)(x + 1)} = \dfrac{A}{2x - 1} + \dfrac{B}{x + 1}$

$$5 - x = A(x + 1) + B(2x - 1)$$

When $x = \frac{1}{2}, \frac{9}{2} = \frac{3}{2}A, A = 3$. When $x = -1, 6 = -3B, B = -2$.

$$\int \dfrac{5 - x}{2x^2 + x - 1}\, dx = 3\int \dfrac{1}{2x - 1}\, dx - 2\int \dfrac{1}{x + 1}\, dx$$

$$= \dfrac{3}{2}\ln|2x - 1| - 2\ln|x + 1| + C$$

13. $\dfrac{x^2 + 12x + 12}{x^3 - 4x} = \dfrac{x^2 + 12x + 12}{x(x - 2)(x + 2)} = \dfrac{A}{x} + \dfrac{B}{x - 2} + \dfrac{C}{x + 2}$

Multiplying by $(x)(x - 2)(x + 2)$, yields

$$x^2 + 12x + 12 = A(x - 2)(x + 2) + B(x)(x + 2) + C(x)(x - 2).$$

If $x = 0$, then $12 = A(-2)(2)$ or $A = -3$.

If $x = 2$, then $4 + 24 + 12 = B(2)(4)$ or $B = 5$.

If $x = -2$, then $4 - 24 + 12 = C(-2)(-4)$ or $C = -1$.

Thus,

$$\int \dfrac{x^2 + 12x + 12}{x^3 - 4x}\, dx = \int \left(\dfrac{-3}{x} + \dfrac{5}{x - 2} + \dfrac{-1}{x + 2} \right) dx$$

$$= -3\ln|x| + 5\ln|x - 2| - \ln|x + 2| + C$$

$$= \ln\left| \dfrac{(x - 2)^5}{x^3(x + 2)} \right| + C.$$

15. $\dfrac{2x^3 - 4x^2 - 15x + 5}{x^2 - 2x - 8} = 2x + \dfrac{x + 5}{(x - 4)(x + 2)} = 2x + \dfrac{A}{x - 4} + \dfrac{B}{x + 2}$

$$x + 5 = A(x + 2) + B(x - 4)$$

When $x = 4, 9 = 6A, A = \frac{3}{2}$. When $x = -2, 3 = -6B, B = -\frac{1}{2}$.

$$\int \dfrac{2x^3 - 4x^2 - 15x + 5}{x^2 - 2x - 8}\, dx = \int \left[2x + \dfrac{3/2}{x - 4} - \dfrac{1/2}{x + 2} \right] dx$$

$$= x^2 + \dfrac{3}{2}\ln|x - 4| - \dfrac{1}{2}\ln|x + 2| + C$$

17. $\dfrac{4x^2 + 2x - 1}{x^2(x + 1)} = \dfrac{A}{x} + \dfrac{B}{x^2} + \dfrac{C}{x + 1}$

$$4x^2 + 2x - 1 = Ax(x + 1) + B(x + 1) + Cx^2$$

When $x = 0, B = -1$. When $x = -1, C = 1$.
When $x = 1, A = 3$.

$$\int \dfrac{4x^2 + 2x - 1}{x^3 + x^2}\, dx = \int \left[\dfrac{3}{x} - \dfrac{1}{x^2} + \dfrac{1}{x + 1} \right] dx$$

$$= 3\ln|x| + \dfrac{1}{x} + \ln|x + 1| + C$$

$$= \dfrac{1}{x} + \ln|x^4 + x^3| + C$$

19. $\dfrac{x^2 - 1}{x(x^2 + 1)} = \dfrac{A}{x} + \dfrac{Bx + C}{x^2 + 1}$

$$x^2 - 1 = A(x^2 + 1) + (Bx + C)x$$

When $x = 0, A = -1$. When $x = 1, 0 = -2 + B + C$.
When $x = -1, 0 = -2 + B + C$. Solving these
equations we have $A = -1, B = 2, C = 0$.

$$\int \dfrac{x^2 - 1}{x^3 + x}\, dx = -\int \dfrac{1}{x}\, dx + \int \dfrac{2x}{x^2 + 1}\, dx$$

$$= \ln|x^2 + 1| - \ln|x| + C$$

$$= \ln\left| \dfrac{x^2 + 1}{x} \right| + C$$

21. $\dfrac{x^2}{x^4 - 2x^2 - 8} = \dfrac{A}{x - 2} + \dfrac{B}{x + 2} + \dfrac{Cx + D}{x^2 + 2}$

$$x^2 = A(x + 2)(x^2 + 2) + B(x - 2)(x^2 + 2) + (Cx + D)(x + 2)(x - 2)$$

When $x = 2, 4 = 24A$. When $x = -2, 4 = -24B$. When $x = 0, 0 = 4A - 4B - 4D$, and when $x = 1$, $1 = 9A - 3B - 3C - 3D$. Solving these equations we have $A = \frac{1}{6}, B = -\frac{1}{6}, C = 0, D = \frac{1}{3}$.

$$\int \frac{x^2}{x^4 - 2x^2 - 8}\,dx = \frac{1}{6}\left[\int \frac{1}{x - 2}\,dx - \int \frac{1}{x + 2}\,dx + 2\int \frac{1}{x^2 + 2}\,dx\right] = \frac{1}{6}\left[\ln\left|\frac{x - 2}{x + 2}\right| + \sqrt{2}\arctan\frac{x}{\sqrt{2}}\right] + C$$

23. $\dfrac{x}{(2x - 1)(2x + 1)(4x^2 + 1)} = \dfrac{A}{2x - 1} + \dfrac{B}{2x + 1} + \dfrac{Cx + D}{4x^2 + 1}$

$$x = A(2x + 1)(4x^2 + 1) + B(2x - 1)(4x^2 + 1) + (Cx + D)(2x - 1)(2x + 1)$$

When $x = \frac{1}{2}, \frac{1}{2} = 4A$. When $x = -\frac{1}{2}, -\frac{1}{2} = -4B$. When $x = 0, 0 = A - B - D$, and when $x = 1$, $1 = 15A + 5B + 3C + 3D$. Solving these equations we have $A = \frac{1}{8}, B = \frac{1}{8}, C = -\frac{1}{2}, D = 0$.

$$\int \frac{x}{16x^4 - 1}\,dx = \frac{1}{8}\left[\int \frac{1}{2x - 1}\,dx + \int \frac{1}{2x + 1}\,dx - 4\int \frac{x}{4x^2 + 1}\,dx\right]$$

$$= \frac{1}{16}\ln\left|\frac{4x^2 - 1}{4x^2 + 1}\right| + C$$

25. Since $x^3 - x^2 + x + 3 = (x + 1)(x^2 - 2x + 3)$, we have

$$\frac{x^2 + 5}{x^3 - x^2 + x + 3} = \frac{A}{x + 1} + \frac{Bx + C}{x^2 - 2x + 3}.$$

Multiplying by $(x + 1)(x^2 - 2x + 3)$ yields

$$x^2 + 5 = A(x^2 - 2x + 3) + (Bx + C)(x + 1).$$

If $x = -1$, then $1 + 5 = A(1 + 2 + 3)$ or $A = 1$.

Therefore,

$$x^2 + 5 = x^2 - 2x + 3 + Bx^2 + Bx + Cx + C$$

$$2x + 2 = Bx^2 + (B + C)x + C.$$

Equating coefficients, yields $B = 0, B + C = 2$, and $C = 2$. Finally,

$$\int \frac{x^2}{x^3 - x^2 + x + 3}\,dx = \int\left(\frac{1}{x + 1} + \frac{2}{x^2 - 2x + 3}\right)dx$$

$$= \int \frac{1}{x + 1}\,dx + 2\int \frac{1}{(x - 1)^2 + 2}\,dx$$

$$= \ln|x + 1| + 2\left(\frac{1}{\sqrt{2}}\right)\arctan\left(\frac{x - 1}{\sqrt{2}}\right) + C$$

$$= \ln|x + 1| + \sqrt{2}\arctan\left(\frac{x - 1}{\sqrt{2}}\right) + C.$$

27. $\dfrac{3}{(2x + 1)(x + 2)} = \dfrac{A}{2x + 1} + \dfrac{B}{x + 2}$

$$3 = A(x + 2) + B(2x + 1)$$

When $x = -\frac{1}{2}, A = 2$. When $x = -2, B = -1$.

$$\int_0^1 \frac{3}{2x^2 + 5x + 2}\,dx = \int_0^1 \frac{2}{2x + 1}\,dx - \int_0^1 \frac{1}{x + 2}\,dx$$

$$= \left[\ln|2x - 1| - \ln|x + 2|\right]_0^1 = \ln 2$$

29. $\dfrac{x + 1}{x(x^2 + 1)} = \dfrac{A}{x} + \dfrac{Bx + C}{x^2 + 1}$

Multiplying by $(x)(x^2 + 1)$ yields

$$x + 1 = A(x^2 + 1) + (Bx + C)x = Ax^2 + A + Bx^2 + Cx$$

$$= (A + B)x^2 + Cx + A.$$

By equating coefficients, you have $A + B = 0$, $C = 1$, and $A = 1$. Thus, $B = -1$, and we obtain

$$\int_1^2 \frac{x + 1}{x(x^2 + 1)}\, dx = \int_1^2 \left(\frac{1}{x} + \frac{-x + 1}{x^2 + 1} \right) dx$$

$$= \int_1^2 \frac{1}{x}\, dx - \frac{1}{2} \int_1^2 \frac{2x}{x^2 + 1}\, dx + \int_1^2 \frac{1}{x^2 + 1}\, dx$$

$$= \left[\ln|x| - \frac{1}{2} \ln|x^2 + 1| + \arctan x \right]_1^2$$

$$= \ln 2 - \frac{1}{2} \ln 5 + \arctan 2 - \ln 1 + \frac{1}{2} \ln 2 - \arctan 1$$

$$= \frac{3}{2} \ln 2 - \frac{1}{2} \ln 5 + \arctan 2 - \frac{\pi}{4}$$

$$= \frac{1}{2} \ln \frac{8}{5} + \arctan 2 - \frac{\pi}{4} \approx 0.557.$$

31. $\displaystyle \int \frac{3x\, dx}{x^2 - 6x + 9} = 3 \ln|x - 3| - \frac{9}{x - 3} + C$

$(4, 0)$: $3 \ln|4 - 3| - \dfrac{9}{4 - 3} + C = 0 \Rightarrow C = 9$

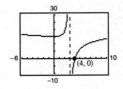

33. Using a symbolic integration utility to perform the integration yields

$$\int \frac{x^2 + x + 2}{(x^2 + 2)^2}\, dx = \frac{\sqrt{2}}{2} \arctan \frac{x}{\sqrt{2}} - \frac{1}{2(x^2 + 2)} + C.$$

Substitute the solution point $(0, 1)$ into the antiderivative and solve for the constant of integration.

$$y = \frac{\sqrt{2}}{2} \arctan \frac{x}{\sqrt{2}} - \frac{1}{2(x^2 + 2)} + C$$

$$1 = \frac{\sqrt{2}}{2} \arctan \frac{0}{\sqrt{2}} - \frac{1}{2(0^2 + 2)} + C$$

$$1 = -\frac{1}{4} + C \Rightarrow C = \frac{5}{4}$$

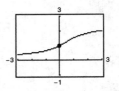

The graph of the function

$$y = \frac{\sqrt{2}}{2} \arctan \frac{x}{\sqrt{2}} - \frac{1}{2(x^2 + 2)} + \frac{5}{4}$$

is shown in the figure.

35. $\displaystyle \int \frac{2x^2 - 2x + 3}{x^3 - x^2 - x - 2}\, dx = \ln|x - 2| + \frac{1}{2} \ln|x^2 + x + 1| - \sqrt{3} \arctan \left(\frac{2x + 1}{\sqrt{3}} \right) + C$

$(3, 10)$: $0 + \dfrac{1}{2} \ln 13 - \sqrt{3} \arctan \dfrac{7}{\sqrt{3}} + C = 10 \Rightarrow C = 10 - \dfrac{1}{2} \ln 13 + \sqrt{3} \arctan \dfrac{7}{\sqrt{3}}$

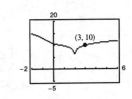

37. $\int \dfrac{x^2 - x + 2}{x^3 - x^2 + x - 1}\, dx = -\arctan x + \ln|x - 1| + C$

$(2, 6)$: $-\arctan 2 + 0 + C = 6 \Longrightarrow C = 6 + \arctan 2$

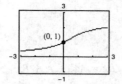

39. Let $u = \cos x \quad du = -\sin x\, dx$.

$$\frac{1}{u(u - 1)} = \frac{A}{u} + \frac{B}{u - 1}$$

$$1 = A(u - 1) + Bu$$

When $u = 0$, $A = -1$. When $u = 1$, $B = 1$, $u = \cos x$, $du = -\sin x\, dx$.

$$\int \frac{\sin x}{\cos x(\cos x - 1)}\, dx = -\int \frac{1}{u(u - 1)}\, du$$

$$= \int \frac{1}{u}\, du - \int \frac{1}{u - 1}\, du$$

$$= \ln|u| - \ln|u - 1| + C$$

$$= \ln\left|\frac{u}{u - 1}\right| + C$$

$$= \ln\left|\frac{\cos x}{\cos x - 1}\right| + C$$

41. $\int \dfrac{3\cos x}{\sin^2 x + \sin x - 2}\, dx = 3 \int \dfrac{1}{u^2 + u - 2}\, du$

$$= \ln\left|\frac{u - 1}{u + 2}\right| + C$$

$$= \ln\left|\frac{-1 + \sin x}{2 + \sin x}\right| + C$$

(From Exercise 9 with $u = \sin x$, $du = \cos x\, dx$)

43. If $u = e^x$, then $du = e^x\, dx$, and

$$\int \frac{e^x}{(e^x - 1)(e^x + 4)}\, dx = \int \frac{du}{(u - 1)(u + 4)}.$$

Using partial fractions yields

$$\frac{1}{(u - 1)(u + 4)} = \frac{A}{u - 1} + \frac{B}{u + 4}.$$

Multiplying by $(u - 1)(u + 4)$ yields

$$1 = A(u + 4) + B(u - 1).$$

If $u = 1$, then $1 = A(5)$ or $A = \dfrac{1}{5}$.

If $u = -4$, then $1 = B(-5)$ or $B = -\dfrac{1}{5}$.

Therefore,

$$\int \frac{du}{(u - 1)(u + 4)} = \frac{1}{5} \int \left(\frac{1}{u - 1} - \frac{1}{u + 4}\right) du$$

$$= \frac{1}{5}(\ln|u - 1| - \ln|u + 4|) + C$$

$$= \frac{1}{5} \ln\left|\frac{u - 1}{u + 4}\right| + C$$

$$= \frac{1}{5} \ln\left|\frac{e^x - 1}{e^x + 4}\right| + C.$$

45. $\dfrac{1}{x(a + bx)} = \dfrac{A}{x} + \dfrac{B}{a + bx}$

$$1 = A(a + bx) + Bx$$

When $x = 0$, $1 = aA \Longrightarrow A = 1/a$.
When $x = -a/b$, $1 = -(a/b)B \Longrightarrow B = -b/a$.

$$\int \frac{1}{x(a + bx)}\, dx = \frac{1}{a} \int \left(\frac{1}{x} - \frac{b}{a + bx}\right) dx$$

$$= \frac{1}{a}(\ln|x| - \ln|a + bx|) + C$$

$$= \frac{1}{a} \ln\left|\frac{x}{a + bx}\right| + C$$

47. $\dfrac{x}{(a + bx)^2} = \dfrac{A}{a + bx} + \dfrac{B}{(a + bx)^2}$

$$x = A(a + bx) + B$$

When $x = -a/b$, $B = -a/b$.
When $x = 0$, $0 = aA + B \Rightarrow A = 1/b$.

$$\int \frac{x}{(a + bx)^2}\,dx = \int \left(\frac{1/b}{a + bx} + \frac{-a/b}{(a + bx)^2}\right) dx$$

$$= \frac{1}{b}\int \frac{1}{a + bx}\,dx - \frac{a}{b}\int \frac{1}{(a + bx)^2}\,dx$$

$$= \frac{1}{b^2}\ln|a + bx| + \frac{a}{b^2}\left(\frac{1}{a + bx}\right) + C$$

$$= \frac{1}{b^2}\left(\frac{a}{a + bx} + \ln|a + bx|\right) + C$$

49. $A = \displaystyle\int_1^3 \frac{10}{x(x^2 + 1)}\,dx \approx 3$

Matches (c)

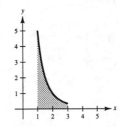

51. (a) $V = \pi\displaystyle\int_0^3 \left(\frac{2x}{x^2 + 1}\right)^2 dx = 4\pi\int_0^3 \frac{x^2}{(x^2 + 1)^2}\,dx$

$$= 4\pi\int_0^3 \left(\frac{1}{x^2 + 1} - \frac{1}{(x^2 + 1)^2}\right) dx \qquad \text{(partial fractions)}$$

$$= 4\pi\left[\arctan x - \frac{1}{2}\left(\arctan x + \frac{x}{x^2 + 1}\right)\right]_0^3 \qquad \text{(trigonometric substitution)}$$

$$= 2\pi\left[\arctan x - \frac{x}{x^2 + 1}\right]_0^3 = 2\pi\left[\arctan 3 - \frac{3}{10}\right] \approx 5.963$$

(b) $A = \displaystyle\int_0^3 \frac{2x}{x^2 + 1}\,dx = \left[\ln(x^2 + 1)\right]_0^3 = \ln 10$

$$\bar{x} = \frac{1}{A}\int_0^3 \frac{2x^2}{x^2 + 1}\,dx = \frac{1}{\ln 10}\int_0^3 \left(2 - \frac{2}{x^2 + 1}\right) dx$$

$$= \frac{1}{\ln 10}\left[2x - 2\arctan x\right]_0^3 = \frac{2}{\ln 10}[3 - \arctan 3] \approx 1.521$$

$$\bar{y} = \frac{1}{A}\left(\frac{1}{2}\right)\int_0^3 \left(\frac{2x}{x^2 + 1}\right)^2 dx = \frac{2}{\ln 10}\int_0^3 \frac{x^2}{(x^2 + 1)^2}\,dx$$

$$= \frac{2}{\ln 10}\int_0^3 \left(\frac{1}{x^2 + 1} - \frac{1}{(x^2 + 1)^2}\right) dx \qquad \text{(partial fractions)}$$

$$= \frac{2}{\ln 10}\left[\arctan x - \frac{1}{2}\left(\arctan x + \frac{x}{x^2 + 1}\right)\right]_0^3 \qquad \text{(trigonometric substitution)}$$

$$= \frac{2}{\ln 10}\left[\frac{1}{2}\arctan x - \frac{x}{2(x^2 + 1)}\right]_0^3 = \frac{1}{\ln 10}\left[\arctan x - \frac{x}{x^2 + 1}\right]_0^3 = \frac{1}{\ln 10}\left[\arctan 3 - \frac{3}{10}\right] \approx 0.412$$

$(\bar{x}, \bar{y}) \approx (1.521, 0.412)$

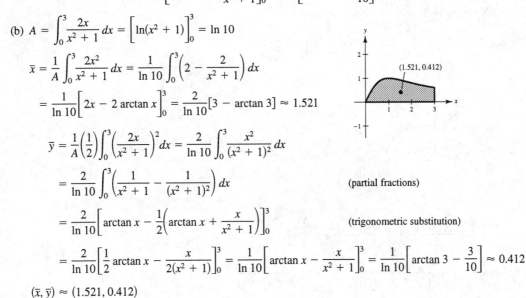

53. $\dfrac{1}{(x + 1)(n - x)} = \dfrac{A}{x + 1} + \dfrac{B}{n - x}$

Multiplying by $(x + 1)(n - x)$ yields

$$1 = A(n - x) + B(x + 1).$$

If $x = -1$, then $1 = A(n + 1)$ or $A = \dfrac{1}{n + 1}$.

If $x = n$, then $1 = B(n + 1)$ or $B = \dfrac{1}{n + 1}$.

—CONTINUED—

53. —CONTINUED—

Therefore,

$$\int \frac{1}{(x+1)(n-x)}\,dx = \int k\,dt$$

$$\frac{1}{n+1}\int\left(\frac{1}{x+1} + \frac{1}{n-x}\right)dx = \int k\,dt$$

$$\frac{1}{n+1}[\ln(x+1) - \ln(n-x) = kt + C$$

$$\left(\frac{1}{n+1}\right)\ln\left(\frac{x+1}{n-x}\right) = kt + C.$$

When $t = 0$, $x = 0$. Thus,

$$\left(\frac{1}{n+1}\right)\ln\left(\frac{1}{n}\right) = C.$$

Therefore,

$$\ln\left(\frac{x+1}{n-x}\right) = k(n+1)t + \ln\left(\frac{1}{n}\right)$$

$$\frac{x+1}{n-x} = \frac{1}{n}e^{k(n+1)t}$$

$$x = \frac{n[e^{(n+1)kt} - 1]}{e^{(n+1)kt} + n}.$$

55. $\dfrac{x}{1+x^4} = \dfrac{Ax+B}{x^2+\sqrt{2}\,x+1} + \dfrac{Cx+D}{x^2-\sqrt{2}\,x+1}$

$$x = (Ax+B)\left(x^2 - \sqrt{2}\,x + 1\right) + (Cx+D)\left(x^2 + \sqrt{2}\,x + 1\right)$$

$$= (A+C)x^3 + \left(B+D-\sqrt{2}\,A+\sqrt{2}\,C\right)x^2 + \left(A+C-\sqrt{2}\,B+\sqrt{2}\,D\right)x + (B+D)$$

$0 = A + C \implies C = -A$

$\left.\begin{array}{l} 0 = B + D - \sqrt{2}\,A + \sqrt{2}\,C \\[2mm] 1 = A + C - \sqrt{2}\,B + \sqrt{2}\,D \end{array}\right\}$ $\begin{array}{l} -2\sqrt{2}\,A = 0 \implies A = 0 \text{ and } C = 0 \\[2mm] -2\sqrt{2}\,B = 1 \implies B = -\dfrac{\sqrt{2}}{4} \text{ and } D = \dfrac{\sqrt{2}}{4} \end{array}$

$0 = B + D \implies D = -B$

Thus,

$$\int_0^1 \frac{x}{1+x^4}\,dx = \int_0^1\left[\frac{-\sqrt{2}/4}{x^2+\sqrt{2}\,x+1} + \frac{\sqrt{2}/4}{x^2-\sqrt{2}\,x+1}\right]dx$$

$$= \frac{\sqrt{2}}{4}\int_0^1\left[\frac{-1}{\left[x+\left(\sqrt{2}/2\right)\right]^2+(1/2)} + \frac{1}{\left[x-\left(\sqrt{2}/2\right)\right]^2+(1/2)}\right]dx$$

$$= \frac{\sqrt{2}}{4}\cdot\frac{1}{1/\sqrt{2}}\left[-\arctan\left(\frac{x+\left(\sqrt{2}/2\right)}{1/\sqrt{2}}\right) + \arctan\left(\frac{x-\left(\sqrt{2}/2\right)}{1/\sqrt{2}}\right)\right]_0^1$$

$$= \frac{1}{2}\left[-\arctan\left(\sqrt{2}\,x+1\right) + \arctan\left(\sqrt{2}\,x-1\right)\right]_0^1$$

$$= \frac{1}{2}\left[\left(-\arctan\left(\sqrt{2}+1\right) + \arctan\left(\sqrt{2}-1\right)\right) - \left(-\arctan 1 + \arctan(-1)\right)\right]$$

$$= \frac{1}{2}\left[\arctan\left(\sqrt{2}-1\right) - \arctan\left(\sqrt{2}+1\right) + \frac{\pi}{4} + \frac{\pi}{4}\right].$$

Since $\arctan x - \arctan y = \arctan[(x-y)/(1+xy)]$, we have:

$$\int_0^1 \frac{x}{1+x^4}\,dx = \frac{1}{2}\left[\arctan\left(\frac{\left(\sqrt{2}-1\right)-\left(\sqrt{2}+1\right)}{1+\left(\sqrt{2}-1\right)\left(\sqrt{2}+1\right)}\right) + \frac{\pi}{2}\right] = \frac{1}{2}\left[\arctan\left(\frac{-2}{2}\right) + \frac{\pi}{2}\right] = \frac{1}{2}\left[-\frac{\pi}{4} + \frac{\pi}{2}\right] = \frac{\pi}{8}$$

57. $\dfrac{x^3 - 3x^2 + 1}{x^4 - 13x^2 + 12x} = \dfrac{P_1}{x} + \dfrac{P_2}{x - 1} + \dfrac{P_3}{x + 4} + \dfrac{P_4}{x - 3} \Rightarrow c_1 = 0,\ c_2 = 1,\ c_3 = -4,\ c_4 = 3$

$N(x) = x^3 - 3x^2 + 1$

$D'(x) = 4x^3 - 26x + 12$

$P_1 = \dfrac{N(0)}{D'(0)} = \dfrac{1}{12}$

$P_2 = \dfrac{N(1)}{D'(1)} = \dfrac{-1}{-10} = \dfrac{1}{10}$

$P_3 = \dfrac{N(-4)}{D'(-4)} = \dfrac{-111}{-140} = \dfrac{111}{140}$

$P_4 = \dfrac{N(3)}{D'(3)} = \dfrac{1}{42}$

Thus, $\dfrac{x^3 - 3x^2 + 1}{x^4 - 13x^2 + 12x} = \dfrac{1/12}{x} + \dfrac{1/10}{x - 1} + \dfrac{111/140}{x + 4} + \dfrac{1/42}{x - 3}.$

Section 7.6   Integration by Tables and Other Integration Techniques

1. By Formula 6: $\displaystyle\int \dfrac{x^2}{1 + x}\, dx = -\dfrac{x}{2}(2 - x) + \ln|1 + x| + C$

3. Consider the form

$$\int \sqrt{u^2 \pm a^2}\, du = \dfrac{1}{2}\left(u\sqrt{u^2 \pm a^2} \pm a^2 \ln|u + \sqrt{u^2 \pm a^2}|\right) + C$$

with $a = 1$, $u = e^x$ and $du = e^x\, dx$. Then,

$$\int e^x \sqrt{1 + e^{2x}}\, dx = \int \sqrt{1^2 + (e^x)^2}\, e^x\, dx$$

$$= \dfrac{1}{2}\left[e^x \sqrt{e^{2x} + 1} + \ln\left(e^x + \sqrt{e^{2x} + 1}\right)\right] + C.$$

5. By Formula 44: $\displaystyle\int \dfrac{1}{x^2\sqrt{1 - x^2}}\, dx = -\dfrac{\sqrt{1 - x^2}}{x} + C$

7. By Formulas 50 and 48: $\displaystyle\int \sin^4(2x)\, dx = \dfrac{1}{2}\int \sin^4(2x)(2)\, dx$

$$= \dfrac{1}{2}\left[\dfrac{-\sin^3(2x)\cos(2x)}{4} + \dfrac{3}{4}\int \sin^2(2x)(2)\, dx\right]$$

$$= \dfrac{1}{2}\left[\dfrac{-\sin^3(2x)\cos(2x)}{4} + \dfrac{3}{8}(2x - \sin 2x \cos 2x)\right] + C$$

$$= \dfrac{1}{16}(6x - 3\sin 2x \cos 2x - 2\sin^3 2x \cos 2x) + C$$

9. Consider the form

$$\int \frac{1}{1 \pm \cos u}\, du = -\cot u \pm \csc u + C$$

with $u = \sqrt{x}$ and $du = 1/(2\sqrt{x})\, dx$. Then,

$$\int \frac{1}{\sqrt{x}(1 - \cos\sqrt{x})}\, dx = 2 \int \frac{1/(2\sqrt{x})}{1 - \cos\sqrt{x}}\, dx$$

$$= 2\left(-\cot\sqrt{x} - \csc\sqrt{x}\right) + C$$

$$= -2\left(\cot\sqrt{x} + \csc\sqrt{x}\right) + C.$$

11. Consider the form

$$\int \frac{1}{1 + e^u}\, du = u - \ln(1 + e^u) + C$$

with $u = 2x$ and $du = 2\, dx$. Then,

$$\int \frac{1}{1 + e^{2x}}\, dx = \frac{1}{2} \int \frac{2}{1 + e^{2x}}\, dx$$

$$= \frac{1}{2}[2x - \ln(1 + e^{2x})] + C$$

$$= x - \frac{1}{2}\ln(1 + e^{2x}) + C.$$

13. By Formula 89:

$$\int x^3 \ln x\, dx = \frac{x^4}{16}(4\ln|x| - 1) + C$$

15. (a) By Formulas 83 and 82: $\displaystyle\int x^2 e^x\, dx = x^2 e^x - 2\int xe^x\, dx$

$$= x^2 e^x - 2[(x - 1)e^x + C_1]$$

$$= x^2 e^x - 2xe^x + 2e^x + C$$

(b) Integration by parts: $u = x^2$, $du = 2x\, dx$, $dv = e^x\, dx$, $v = e^x$

$$\int x^2 e^x\, dx = x^2 e^x - \int 2xe^x\, dx$$

Parts again: $u = 2x$, $du = 2\, dx$, $dv = e^x\, dx$, $v = e^x$

$$\int x^2 e^x\, dx = x^2 e^x - \left[2xe^x - \int 2e^x\, dx\right] = x^2 e^x - 2xe^x + 2e^x + C$$

17. (a) Consider the form

$$\int \frac{1}{u^2(a + bu)}\, du = -\frac{1}{a}\left(\frac{1}{u} + \frac{b}{a}\ln\left|\frac{u}{a + bu}\right|\right) + C$$

with $a = 1$, $b = 1$, $u = x$ and $du = dx$. Then,

$$\int \frac{1}{x^2(x + 1)}\, dx = -\left(\frac{1}{x} + \ln\left|\frac{x}{1 + x}\right|\right) + C$$

$$= \ln\left|\frac{x + 1}{x}\right| - \frac{1}{x} + C.$$

(b) $\displaystyle\frac{1}{x^2(x + 1)} = \frac{A}{x} + \frac{B}{x^2} + \frac{C}{x + 1}$

Multiplying by $x^2(x + 1)$ yields

$$1 = Ax(x + 1) + B(x + 1) + Cx^2.$$

If $x = 0$, then $1 = B$.

If $x = -1$, then $1 = C$.

If $x = 1$, $B = 1$, and $C = 1$, then $1 = 2A + 2 + 1$ or $A = -1$.

Thus,

$$\int \frac{1}{x^2(x + 1)}\, dx = \int\left(\frac{-1}{x} + \frac{1}{x^2} + \frac{1}{x + 1}\right) dx$$

$$= -\ln|x| - \frac{1}{x} + \ln|x + 1| + C$$

$$= \ln\left|\frac{x + 1}{x}\right| - \frac{1}{x} + C.$$

19. By Formula 81: $\displaystyle\int xe^{x^2} = \frac{1}{2}e^{x^2} + C$

21. By Formula 79: $\displaystyle\int x\,\text{arcsec}(x^2 + 1)\,dx = \frac{1}{2}\int \text{arcsec}(x^2 + 1)(2x)\,dx$

$$= \frac{1}{2}\Big[(x^2 + 1)\,\text{arcsec}(x^2 + 1) - \ln\big((x^2 + 1) + \sqrt{x^4 + 2x^2}\big)\Big] + C$$

$u = x^2 + 1,\, du = 2x\,dx$

23. By Formula 89:

$$\int x^2 \ln x\,dx = \frac{x^3}{9}\big(-1 + 3\ln|x|\big) + C$$

25. Consider the form

$$\int \frac{1}{u^2\sqrt{u^2 \pm a^2}}\,du = \mp\frac{\sqrt{u^2 \pm a^2}}{a^2 u} + C$$

where $u = x$ and $a = 2$. Then,

$$\int \frac{1}{x^2\sqrt{x^2 - 4}}\,dx = \int \frac{1}{u^2\sqrt{u^2 - a^2}}\,du$$

$$= \frac{\sqrt{u^2 - a^2}}{a^2 u} + C = \frac{\sqrt{x^2 - 4}}{4x} + C.$$

27. Consider the form

$$\int \frac{u}{(a + bu)^2}\,du = \frac{1}{b^2}\Big(\frac{a}{a + bu} + \ln|a + bu|\Big) + C$$

where $a = 1$, $b = -3$, $u = x$, and $du = dx$. Then,

$$\int \frac{2x}{(1 - 3x)^2}\,dx = 2\int \frac{x}{(1 - 3x)^2}\,dx$$

$$= \frac{2}{9}\Big[\frac{1}{1 - 3x} + \ln|1 - 3x|\Big] + C.$$

29. By Formula 76:

$$\int e^x \arccos e^x\,dx = e^x \arccos e^x - \sqrt{1 - e^{2x}} + C$$

$u = e^x,\, du = e^x\,dx$

31. By Formula 73:

$$\int \frac{x}{1 - \sec x^2}\,dx = \frac{1}{2}\int \frac{2x}{1 - \sec x^2}\,dx$$

$$= \frac{1}{2}(x^2 + \cot x^2 + \csc x^2) + C$$

33. By Formula 23:

$$\int \frac{\cos x}{1 + \sin^2 x}\,dx = \arctan(\sin x) + C$$

$u = \sin x,\, du = \cos x\,dx$

35. By Formula 14:

$$\int \frac{\cos\theta}{3 + 2\sin\theta + \sin^2\theta}\,d\theta = \frac{\sqrt{2}}{2}\arctan\Big(\frac{1 + \sin\theta}{\sqrt{2}}\Big) + C$$

$u = \sin\theta,\, du = \cos\theta\,d\theta$

37. By Formula 35:

$$\int \frac{1}{x^2\sqrt{2 + 9x^2}}\,dx = 3\int \frac{3}{(3x)^2\sqrt{(\sqrt{2})^2 + (3x)^2}}\,dx$$

$$= -\frac{3\sqrt{2 + 9x^2}}{6x} + C$$

$$= -\frac{\sqrt{2 + 9x^2}}{2x} + C$$

39. By Formulas 55 and 54: $\displaystyle\int t^4 \cos t\,dt = t^4 \sin t - 4\int t^3 \sin t\,dt$

$$= t^4 \sin t - 4\Big[-t^3 \cos t + 3\int t^2 \cos t\,dt\Big]$$

$$= t^4 \sin t + 4t^3 \cos t - 12\Big[t^2 \sin t - 2\int t \sin t\,dt\Big]$$

$$= t^4 \sin t + 4t^3 \cos t - 12t^2 \sin t + 24(-t \cos t + \sin t) + C$$

$$= (t^4 - 12t^2 + 24)\sin t + (4t^3 - 24t)\cos t + C$$

41. Consider the form

$$\int \frac{u}{a + bu} \, du = \frac{1}{b^2}(bu - a \ln|a + bu|) + C$$

where $u = \ln x$, $a = 3$, $b = 2$, and $du = (1/x) \, dx$. Then,

$$\int \frac{\ln x}{x(3 + 2 \ln x)} \, dx = \int \frac{\ln x}{3 + 2 \ln x}\left(\frac{1}{x}\right) dx$$

$$= \frac{1}{4}[2 \ln|x| - 3 \ln|3 + 2 \ln|x||] + C.$$

43. By Formulas 1, 25, and 33: $\displaystyle\int \frac{x}{(x^2 - 6x + 10)^2} \, dx = \frac{1}{2}\int \frac{2x - 6 + 6}{(x^2 - 6x + 10)^2} \, dx$

$$= \frac{1}{2}\int (x^2 - 6x + 10)^{-2}(2x - 6) \, dx + 3 \int \frac{1}{[(x - 3)^2 + 1]^2} \, dx$$

$$= -\frac{1}{2(x^2 - 6x + 10)} + \frac{3}{2}\left[\frac{x - 3}{x^2 - 6x + 10} + \arctan(x - 3)\right] + C$$

$$= \frac{3x - 10}{2(x^2 - 6x + 10)} + \frac{3}{2}\arctan(x - 3) + C$$

45. By Formula 31:

$$\int \frac{x}{\sqrt{x^4 - 6x^2 + 5}} \, dx = \frac{1}{2}\int \frac{2x}{\sqrt{(x^2 - 3)^2 - 4}} \, dx = \frac{1}{2}\ln|x^2 - 3 + \sqrt{x^4 - 6x^2 + 5}| + C$$

$$u = x^2 - 3, \, du = 2x \, dx$$

47. Consider the form

$$\int \frac{u}{\sqrt{a + bu}} \, du = \frac{-2(2u - bu)}{3b^2}\sqrt{a + bu} + C$$

where $u = x^2$, $a = 4$, $b = -1$, $du = 2x \, dx$, and $\sqrt{a + bu} = \sqrt{4 - x^2}$. Then,

$$\int \frac{x^3}{\sqrt{4 - x^2}} \, dx = \frac{1}{2}\int \frac{x^2}{\sqrt{4 - x^2}}(2x) \, dx$$

$$= \frac{1}{2}\left[\frac{(-2)(8 + x^2)}{3}\right]\sqrt{4 - x^2} + C$$

$$= -\left(\frac{x^2 + 8}{3}\right)\sqrt{4 - x^2} + C.$$

49. By Formula 8:

$$\int \frac{e^{3x}}{(1 + e^x)^3} \, dx = \int \frac{(e^x)^2}{(1 + e^x)^3}(e^x) \, dx$$

$$= \frac{2}{1 + e^x} - \frac{1}{2(1 + e^x)^2} + \ln|1 + e^x| + C$$

$$u = e^x, \, du = e^x \, dx$$

51. Since the numerator and denominator are of the same degree, begin by dividing

$$\frac{u^2}{(a + bu)^2} = \frac{1}{b^2} - \frac{(2a/b)u + (a^2/b^2)}{(a + bu)^2}.$$

Now use partial fractions to obtain

$$\frac{(2a/b)u + (a^2/b^2)}{(a + bu)^2} = \frac{A}{a + bu} + \frac{B}{(a + bu)^2}.$$

Multiplying by $(a + bu)^2$ yields

$$\left(\frac{2a}{b}\right)u + \frac{a^2}{b^2} = A(a + bu) + B = bAu + (aA + B).$$

—CONTINUED—

51. —CONTINUED—

Equating the coefficients of like terms, we have

$$bA = \frac{2a}{b} \quad \text{and} \quad A = \frac{2a}{b^2}$$

$$aA + B = \frac{a^2}{b^2} \quad \text{and} \quad B = \frac{a^2}{b^2} - a\left(\frac{2a}{b^2}\right) = -\frac{a^2}{b^2}.$$

Therefore,

$$\int \frac{u^2}{(a + bu)^2}\, du = \frac{1}{b^2}\int du - \frac{2a}{b^2}\left(\frac{1}{b}\right)\int \frac{b}{a + bu}\, du + \frac{a^2}{b^2}\left(\frac{1}{b}\right)\int \frac{b}{(a + bu)^2}\, du$$

$$= \left(\frac{1}{b^2}\right)u - \frac{2a}{b^3}(\ln|a + bu|) - \frac{a^2}{b^3}\left(\frac{1}{a + bu}\right) + C$$

$$= \frac{1}{b^3}\left[bu - \frac{a^2}{a + bu} - 2a\ln|a + bu|\right] + C.$$

53. When we have $u^2 + a^2$:

$$u = a\tan\theta$$

$$du = a\sec^2\theta\, d\theta$$

$$u^2 + a^2 = a^2\sec^2\theta$$

$$\int \frac{1}{(u^2 + a^2)^{3/2}}\, du = \int \frac{a\sec^2\theta\, d\theta}{a^3\sec^3\theta}$$

$$= \frac{1}{a^2}\int \cos\theta\, d\theta$$

$$= \frac{1}{a^2}\sin\theta + C$$

$$= \frac{u}{a^2\sqrt{u^2 + a^2}} + C$$

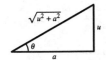

When we have $u^2 - a^2$:

$$u = a\sec\theta$$

$$du = a\sec\theta\tan\theta\, d\theta$$

$$u^2 - a^2 = a^2\tan^2\theta$$

$$\int \frac{1}{(u^2 - a^2)^{3/2}}\, du = \int \frac{a\sec\theta\tan\theta\, d\theta}{a^3\tan^3\theta}$$

$$= \frac{1}{a^2}\int \frac{\cos\theta}{\sin^2\theta}\, d\theta$$

$$= -\frac{1}{a^2}\csc\theta + C$$

$$= \frac{-u}{a^2\sqrt{u^2 - a^2}} + C$$

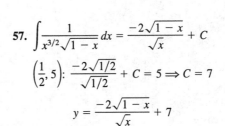

55. $\displaystyle\int (\arctan u)\, du = u\arctan u - \frac{1}{2}\int \frac{2u}{1 + u^2}\, du$

$$= u\arctan u - \frac{1}{2}\ln(1 + u^2) + C$$

$$= u\arctan u - \ln\sqrt{1 + u^2} + C$$

$$w = \arctan u,\ dv = du,\ dw = \frac{du}{1 + u^2},\ v = u$$

57. $\displaystyle\int \frac{1}{x^{3/2}\sqrt{1 - x}}\, dx = \frac{-2\sqrt{1 - x}}{\sqrt{x}} + C$

$$\left(\frac{1}{2}, 5\right): \frac{-2\sqrt{1/2}}{\sqrt{1/2}} + C = 5 \Rightarrow C = 7$$

$$y = \frac{-2\sqrt{1 - x}}{\sqrt{x}} + 7$$

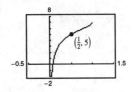

59. Using a symbolic integration utility to perform the integration yields

$$\int \frac{\sqrt{2 - 2x - x^2}}{x + 1} \, dx = \sqrt{2 - 2x - x^2} - \sqrt{3} \ln\left|\frac{\sqrt{3} + \sqrt{2 - 2x - x^2}}{x + 1}\right| + C.$$

Substitute the solution point $\left(0, \sqrt{2}\right)$ into the antiderivative and solve for the constant of integration.

$$y = \sqrt{2 - 2x - x^2} - \sqrt{3} \ln\left|\frac{\sqrt{3} + \sqrt{2 - 2x - x^2}}{x + 1}\right| + C$$

$$\sqrt{2} = \sqrt{2} - \sqrt{3} \ln\left(\sqrt{3} + \sqrt{2}\right) + C \Rightarrow C = \sqrt{3} \ln\left(\sqrt{3} + \sqrt{2}\right)$$

The graph of the function

$$y = \sqrt{2 - 2x - x^2} - \sqrt{3} \ln\left|\frac{\sqrt{3} + \sqrt{2 - 2x - x^2}}{x + 1}\right| + \sqrt{3} \ln\left(\sqrt{3} + \sqrt{2}\right)$$

is shown in the figure.

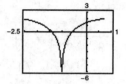

61. $\int \frac{1}{\sin \theta \tan \theta} \, d\theta = -\csc \theta + C$

$\left(\frac{\pi}{4}, 2\right): \ -\frac{2}{\sqrt{2}} + C = 2 \Rightarrow C = 2 + \sqrt{2}$

$y = -\csc \theta + 2 + \sqrt{2}$

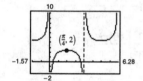

63. $\int \frac{1}{2 - 3 \sin \theta} \, d\theta = \int \left[\frac{\frac{2 \, du}{1 + u^2}}{2 - 3\left(\frac{2u}{1 + u^2}\right)}\right]$

$= \int 2 \frac{2}{(1 + u^2) - 6u} \, du$

$= \int \frac{1}{u^2 - 3u + 1} \, du$

$= \int \frac{1}{\left(u - \frac{3}{2}\right)^2 - \frac{5}{4}} \, du$

$= \frac{1}{\sqrt{5}} \ln\left|\frac{\left(u - \frac{3}{2}\right) - \frac{\sqrt{5}}{2}}{\left(u - \frac{3}{2}\right) + \frac{\sqrt{5}}{2}}\right| + C$

$= \frac{1}{\sqrt{5}} \ln\left|\frac{2u - 3 - \sqrt{5}}{2u - 3 + \sqrt{5}}\right| + C$

$= \frac{1}{\sqrt{5}} \ln\left|\frac{2 \tan\left(\frac{\theta}{2}\right) - 3 - \sqrt{5}}{2 \tan\left(\frac{\theta}{2}\right) - 3 + \sqrt{5}}\right| + C$

$$u = \tan\frac{\theta}{2}$$

65. Let $u = \frac{\sin \theta}{1 + \cos \theta}$. Then,

$\cos \theta = \frac{1 - u^2}{1 + u^2}$, $\sin \theta = \frac{2u}{1 + u^2}$, and $d\theta = \frac{2 \, du}{1 + u^2}$.

Furthermore, when $\theta = \pi/2, u = 1$, and when $\theta = 0, u = 0$.

$$\int_0^{\pi/2} \frac{1}{1 + \sin \theta + \cos \theta} \, d\theta = \int_0^1 \frac{[2/(1 + u^2)] \, du}{1 + (2u)/(1 + u^2) + (1 - u^2)/(1 + u^2)}$$

$$= \int_0^1 \frac{1}{u + 1} \, du = \left[\ln|u + 1|\right]_0^1 = \ln 2$$

67. $\displaystyle\int \frac{\sin\theta}{3 - 2\cos\theta}\, d\theta = \frac{1}{2}\int \frac{2\sin\theta}{3 - 2\cos\theta}\, d\theta$

$\qquad\qquad\qquad = \frac{1}{2}\ln|u| + C$

$\qquad\qquad\qquad = \frac{1}{2}\ln(3 - 2\cos\theta) + C$

$u = 3 - 2\cos\theta,\; du = 2\sin\theta\, d\theta$

69. $\displaystyle\int \frac{\cos\sqrt{\theta}}{\sqrt{\theta}}\, d\theta = 2\int \cos\sqrt{\theta}\left(\frac{1}{2\sqrt{\theta}}\right) d\theta$

$\qquad\qquad\qquad = 2\sin\sqrt{\theta} + C$

$u = \sqrt{\theta},\; du = \frac{1}{2\sqrt{\theta}}\, d\theta$

71. $\displaystyle A = \int_0^8 \frac{x}{\sqrt{x+1}}\, dx$

$\qquad = \left[\frac{-2(2-x)}{3}\sqrt{x+1}\right]_0^8$

$\qquad = 12 - \left(-\frac{4}{3}\right)$

$\qquad = \frac{40}{3} \approx 13.333 \text{ square units}$

73. $\displaystyle W = \int_0^5 2000xe^{-x}\, dx$

$\qquad = -2000\int_0^5 -xe^{-x}\, dx$

$\qquad = 2000\int_0^5 (-x)e^{-x}(-1)\, dx$

$\qquad = 2000\left[(-x)e^{-x} - e^{-x}\right]_0^5$

$\qquad = 2000\left(-\frac{6}{e^5} + 1\right)$

$\qquad \approx 1919.145 \text{ ft} \cdot \text{lbs}$

75. (a) $\displaystyle V = 20(2)\int_0^3 \frac{2}{\sqrt{1+y^2}}\, dy$

$\qquad = \left[80\ln\left|y + \sqrt{1+y^2}\right|\right]_0^3$

$\qquad = 80\ln\left(3 + \sqrt{10}\right)$

$\qquad \approx 145.5 \text{ cubic feet}$

$W = 148\left(80\ln\left(3 + \sqrt{10}\right)\right)$

$\quad = 11{,}840\ln\left(3 + \sqrt{10}\right)$

$\quad \approx 21{,}530.4 \text{ lb}$

(b) By symmetry, $\bar{x} = 0$.

$\qquad M = \rho(2)\int_0^3 \frac{2}{\sqrt{1+y^2}}\, dy = \left[4\rho\ln\left|y + \sqrt{1+y^2}\right|\right]_0^3 = 4\rho\ln\left(3 + \sqrt{10}\right)$

$\qquad M_x = 2\rho\int_0^3 \frac{2y}{\sqrt{1+y^2}}\, dy = \left[4\rho\sqrt{1+y^2}\right]_0^3 = 4\rho\left(\sqrt{10} - 1\right)$

$\qquad \bar{y} = \frac{M_x}{M} = \frac{4\rho\left(\sqrt{10} - 1\right)}{4\rho\ln\left(3 + \sqrt{10}\right)} \approx 1.19$

Centroid: $\left(\bar{x}, \bar{y}\right) \approx (0, 1.19)$

77. (a) $\displaystyle\int_0^4 \frac{k}{2 + 3x}\, dx = 10$

$\qquad k = \frac{10}{\displaystyle\int_0^4 \frac{1}{2 + 3x}\, dx} \approx \frac{10}{0.6486}$

$\qquad = 15.417 \;\left(= \frac{30}{\ln 7}\right)$

(b) $\displaystyle\int_0^4 \frac{15.417}{2 + 3x}\, dx$

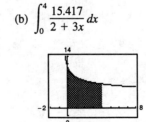

Section 7.7   Indeterminate Forms and L'Hôpital's Rule

1. $\lim\limits_{x \to 0} \dfrac{\sin 5x}{\sin 2x} \approx 2.5 \left(\text{exact: } \dfrac{5}{2} \right)$

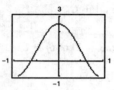

x	-0.1	-0.01	-0.001	0.001	0.01	0.1
$f(x)$	2.4132	2.4991	2.500	2.500	2.4991	2.4132

3. $\lim\limits_{x \to \infty} x^5 e^{-x/100} \approx 0$

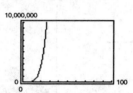

x	1	10	10^2	10^3	10^4	10^5
$f(x)$	0.9901	90,484	3.7×10^9	4.5×10^{10}	0	0

5. (a) Using the Cancellation Technique from Chapter 1 yields

$$\lim_{x \to 3} \frac{2(x - 3)}{x^2 - 9} = \lim_{x \to 3} \frac{2(x - 3)}{(x + 3)(x - 3)} = \lim_{x \to 3} \frac{2}{x + 3} = \frac{1}{3}.$$

(b) Using L'Hôpital's Rule yields

$$\lim_{x \to 3} \frac{2(x - 3)}{x^2 - 9} = \lim_{x \to 3} \frac{(d/dx)[2(x - 3)]}{(d/dx)[x^2 - 9]} = \lim_{x \to 3} \frac{2}{2x} = \frac{1}{3}.$$

7. (a) $\lim\limits_{x \to 3} \dfrac{\sqrt{x + 1} - 2}{x - 3} = \lim\limits_{x \to 3} \dfrac{\sqrt{x + 1} - 2}{x - 3} \cdot \dfrac{\sqrt{x + 1} + 2}{\sqrt{x + 1} + 2} = \lim\limits_{x \to 3} \dfrac{(x + 1) - 4}{(x - 3)\left[\sqrt{x + 1} + 2\right]} = \lim\limits_{x \to 3} \dfrac{1}{\sqrt{x + 1} + 2} = \dfrac{1}{4}$

(b) $\lim\limits_{x \to 3} \dfrac{\sqrt{x + 1} - 2}{x - 3} = \lim\limits_{x \to 3} \dfrac{(d/dx)\left[\sqrt{x + 1} - 2\right]}{(d/dx)[x - 3]} = \lim\limits_{x \to 3} \dfrac{1/(2\sqrt{x + 1})}{1} = \dfrac{1}{4}$

9. (a) $\lim\limits_{x \to \infty} \dfrac{5x^2 - 3x + 1}{3x^2 - 5} = \lim\limits_{x \to \infty} \dfrac{5 - (3/x) + (1/x^2)}{3 - (5/x^2)} = \dfrac{5}{3}$

(b) $\lim\limits_{x \to \infty} \dfrac{5x^2 - 3x + 1}{3x^2 - 5} = \lim\limits_{x \to \infty} \dfrac{(d/dx)[5x^2 - 3x + 1]}{(d/dx)[3x^2 - 5]} = \lim\limits_{x \to \infty} \dfrac{10x - 3}{6x} = \lim\limits_{x \to \infty} \dfrac{(d/dx)[10x - 3]}{(d/dx)[6x]} = \lim\limits_{x \to \infty} \dfrac{10}{6} = \dfrac{5}{3}$

11. $\lim\limits_{x \to 2} \dfrac{x^2 - x - 2}{x - 2} = \lim\limits_{x \to 2} \dfrac{2x - 1}{1} = 3$

13. Since a direct substitution of $x = 0$ yields the indeterminate form $0/0$, apply L'Hôpital's Rule to obtain

$$\lim_{x \to 0} \frac{\sqrt{4 - x^2} - 2}{x} = \lim_{x \to 0} \frac{(1/2)(4 - x^2)^{-1/2}(-2x)}{1}$$

$$= \lim_{x \to 0} \frac{-x}{\sqrt{4 - x^2}} = \frac{0}{2} = 0.$$

15. $\lim\limits_{x \to 0} \dfrac{e^x - (1 - x)}{x} = \lim\limits_{x \to 0} \dfrac{e^x + 1}{1} = 2$

17. Case 1: $n = 1$ (Apply L'Hôpital's Rule once.)

$$\lim_{x \to 0^+} \frac{e^x - (1 + x)}{x} = \lim_{x \to 0^+} \frac{e^x - 1}{1} = 0$$

Case 2: $n = 2$ (Apply L'Hôpital's Rule twice.)

$$\lim_{x \to 0^+} \frac{e^x - (1 + x)}{x^2} = \lim_{x \to 0^+} \frac{e^x - 1}{2x} = \lim_{x \to 0^+} \frac{e^x}{2} = \frac{1}{2}$$

Case 3: $n \geq 3$ (Apply L'Hôpital's Rule twice.)

$$\lim_{x \to 0^+} \frac{e^x - (1 + x)}{x^n} = \lim_{x \to 0^+} \frac{e^x - 1}{nx^{n-1}}$$

$$= \lim_{x \to 0^+} \frac{e^x}{n(n-1)x^{n-2}} = \infty$$

19. $\lim\limits_{x \to 0} \dfrac{\sin 2x}{\sin 3x} = \lim\limits_{x \to 0} \dfrac{2 \cos 2x}{3 \cos 3x} = \dfrac{2}{3}$

21. $\lim\limits_{x \to 0} \dfrac{\arcsin x}{x} = \lim\limits_{x \to 0} \dfrac{1/\sqrt{1 - x^2}}{1} = 1$

23. $\lim\limits_{x \to \infty} \dfrac{3x^2 - 2x + 1}{2x^2 + 3} = \lim\limits_{x \to \infty} \dfrac{6x - 2}{4x} = \lim\limits_{x \to \infty} \dfrac{6}{4} = \dfrac{3}{2}$

25. $\lim\limits_{x \to \infty} \dfrac{x^2 + 2x + 3}{x - 1} = \lim\limits_{x \to \infty} \dfrac{2x + 2}{1} = \infty$

27. $\lim\limits_{x \to \infty} \dfrac{x}{\sqrt{x^2 + 1}} = \lim\limits_{x \to \infty} \dfrac{1}{\sqrt{1 + (1/x^2)}} = 1$

Note: L'Hôpital's Rule does not work on this limit. See Exercise 67.

29. Since direct substitution leads to the indeterminate form ∞/∞, use L'Hôpital's Rule.

$$\lim_{x \to \infty} \frac{\ln x}{x} = \lim_{x \to \infty} \frac{1/x}{1} = \lim_{x \to \infty} \frac{1}{x} = 0$$

31. (a) $\lim\limits_{x \to 0^+} (-x \ln x) = (-0)(-\infty) = (0)(\infty)$

(b) $\lim\limits_{x \to 0^+} (-x \ln x) = \lim\limits_{x \to 0^+} \dfrac{\ln x}{-1/x}$

$$= \lim_{x \to 0^+} \frac{1/x}{1/x^2}$$

$$= \lim_{x \to 0^+} x = 0$$

(c)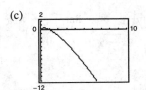

33. (a) Since direct substitution yields the indeterminate form $\infty \cdot 0$, use L'Hôpital's Rule.

(b) $\lim\limits_{x \to \infty} x \sin \dfrac{1}{x} = \lim\limits_{x \to \infty} \dfrac{\sin(1/x)}{1/x}$

$$= \lim_{x \to \infty} \frac{(-1/x^2) \cos(1/x)}{-1/x^2}$$

$$= \lim_{x \to \infty} \cos \frac{1}{x} = 1$$

(c)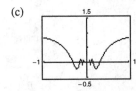

35. (a) 0^∞ is not an indeterminate form.

(b) $\lim\limits_{x \to 0^+} x^{1/x} = 0^\infty = 0$

(c)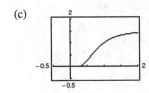

37. (a) Direct substitution yields the indeterminate form ∞^0.

(b) Begin by taking the natural logarithm of both members of the equation

$$y = \lim_{x \to \infty} x^{1/x}.$$

We obtain

$$\ln y = \ln\left[\lim_{x \to \infty} x^{1/x}\right]$$

$$= \lim_{x \to \infty}\left[\frac{1}{x}\ln x\right] = \lim_{x \to \infty}\frac{\ln x}{x} = \lim_{x \to \infty}\frac{1/x}{1} = 0.$$

Finally, as $\ln y \to 0$, we know that $y \to 1$ and conclude that $\lim_{x \to \infty} x^{1/x} = 1$.

(c)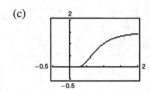

39. (a) $\lim_{x \to 0^+} (1 + x)^{1/x} = 1^{\infty}$

(b) Let $y = \lim_{x \to 0^+} (1 + x)^{1/x}$.

$$\ln y = \lim_{x \to 0^+}\frac{\ln(1 + x)}{x}$$

$$= \lim_{x \to 0^+}\left(\frac{1/(1 + x)}{1}\right) = 1$$

Thus, $\ln y = 1 \implies y = e^1 = e$.
Therefore, $\lim_{x \to 0^+} (1 + x)^{1/x} = e$.

(c)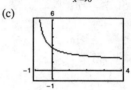

41. (a) $\lim_{x \to 2^+}\left(\dfrac{8}{x^2 - 4} - \dfrac{x}{x - 2}\right) = \infty - \infty$

(b) $\lim_{x \to 2^+}\left(\dfrac{8}{x^2 - 4} - \dfrac{x}{x - 2}\right) = \lim_{x \to 2^+}\dfrac{8 - x(x + 2)}{x^2 - 4}$

$$= \lim_{x \to 2^+}\frac{(2 - x)(4 + x)}{(x + 2)(x - 2)}$$

$$= \lim_{x \to 2^+}\frac{-(x + 4)}{x + 2} = \frac{-3}{2}$$

(c)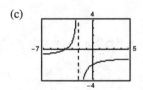

43. (a) $\lim_{x \to 1^+}\left(\dfrac{3}{\ln x} - \dfrac{2}{x - 1}\right) = \infty - \infty$

(b) $\lim_{x \to 1^+}\left(\dfrac{3}{\ln x} - \dfrac{2}{x - 1}\right) = \lim_{x \to 1^+}\dfrac{3x - 3 - 2\ln x}{(x - 1)\ln x}$

$$= \lim_{x \to 1^+}\frac{3 - (2/x)}{[(x - 1)/x] + \ln x} = \infty$$

(c)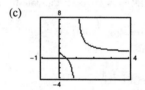

45. (a) The graph of the function is shown in the figure.

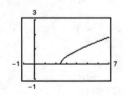

(b) Since direct substitution leads to the indeterminate form $0/0$, use L'Hôpital's Rule.

$$\lim_{x \to 3}\frac{x - 3}{\ln(2x - 5)} = \lim_{x \to 3}\frac{1}{\dfrac{2}{2x - 5}} = \lim_{x \to 3}\frac{2x - 5}{2} = \frac{1}{2}$$

47. (a)

(b) $\lim_{x \to \infty}\left(\sqrt{x^2 + 5x + 2} - x\right) = \lim_{x \to \infty}\left(\sqrt{x^2 + 5x + 2} - x\right)\dfrac{\left(\sqrt{x^2 + 5x + 2} + x\right)}{\left(\sqrt{x^2 + 5x + 2} + x\right)}$

$$= \lim_{x \to \infty}\frac{(x^2 + 5x + 2) - x^2}{\sqrt{x^2 + 5x + 2} + x}$$

$$= \lim_{x \to \infty}\frac{5x + 2}{\sqrt{x^2 + 5x + 2} + x}$$

$$= \lim_{x \to \infty}\frac{5 + (2/x)}{\sqrt{1 + (5/x) + (2/x^2)} + 1} = \frac{5}{2}$$

49. (a) Let $f(x) = x^2 - 25$ and $g(x) = x - 5$.

    (b) Let $f(x) = (x - 5)^2$ and $g(x) = x^2 - 25$.

    (c) Let $f(x) = x^2 - 25$ and $g(x) = (x - 5)^3$.

51. $\displaystyle\lim_{x \to \infty} \frac{x^2}{e^{5x}} = \lim_{x \to \infty} \frac{2x}{5e^{5x}} = \lim_{x \to \infty} \frac{2}{25e^{5x}} = 0$

53. $\displaystyle\lim_{x \to \infty} \frac{(\ln x)^3}{x} = \lim_{x \to \infty} \frac{3(\ln x)^2(1/x)}{1}$

$\displaystyle\qquad = \lim_{x \to \infty} \frac{3(\ln x)^2}{x}$

$\displaystyle\qquad = \lim_{x \to \infty} \frac{6(\ln x)(1/x)}{1}$

$\displaystyle\qquad = \lim_{x \to \infty} \frac{6(\ln x)}{x} = \lim_{x \to \infty} \frac{6}{x} = 0$

55. $\displaystyle\lim_{x \to \infty} \frac{(\ln x)^n}{x^m} = \lim_{x \to \infty} \left[\frac{n(\ln x)^{n-1}(1/x)}{mx^{m-1}} \right] = \lim_{x \to \infty} \left[\frac{n(\ln x)^{n-1}}{mx^m} \right]$

If $n - 1 \leq 0$, this limit is zero. If $n - 1 > 0$, repeat L'Hôpital's Rule to obtain

$$\lim_{x \to \infty} \left[\frac{n(n-1)(\ln x)^{n-2}}{m^2 x^m} \right].$$

Again, if $n - 2 \leq 0$, this limit is zero. If $n - 2 > 0$, repeated applications of L'Hôpital's Rule will eventually yield a form where the numerator approaches a finite number and the denominator approaches infinity. Thus, in every case the limit is 0.

57.

x	10	10^2	10^4	10^6	10^8	10^{10}
$\dfrac{(\ln x)^4}{x}$	2.811	4.498	0.720	0.036	0.001	0.000

59. $y = x^{1/x},\ x > 0$

Horizontal asymptote: $y = 1$ (See Exercise 37)

$\ln y = \dfrac{1}{x} \ln x$

$\dfrac{1}{y} \dfrac{dy}{dx} = \dfrac{1}{x}\left(\dfrac{1}{x}\right) + (\ln x)\left(-\dfrac{1}{x^2}\right)$

$\dfrac{dy}{dx} = x^{1/x}\left(\dfrac{1}{x^2}\right)(1 - \ln x) = x^{(1/x)-2}(1 - \ln x) = 0$

Critical number: $x = e$

    Intervals: $(0, e)$ (e, ∞)

Sign of dy/dx: $+$ $-$

    $y = f(x)$: Increasing   Decreasing

Relative maximum: $(e, e^{1/e})$

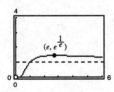

61. $y = 2xe^{-x}$

$\displaystyle\lim_{x \to \infty} \frac{2x}{e^x} = \lim_{x \to \infty} \frac{2}{e^x} = 0$

Horizontal asymptote: $y = 0$

$\dfrac{dy}{dx} = 2x(-e^{-x}) + 2e^{-x}$

$\qquad = 2e^{-x}(1 - x) = 0$

Critical number: $x = 1$

    Intervals: $(-\infty, 1)$ $(1, \infty)$

Sign of dy/dx: $+$ $-$

    $y = f(x)$: Increasing Decreasing

Relative maximum: $\left(1, \dfrac{2}{e}\right)$

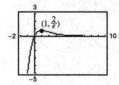

63. $\displaystyle\lim_{x \to 0} \frac{e^{2x} - 1}{e^x} = \frac{0}{1} = 0$

Limit is not of the form $0/0$ or ∞/∞. L'Hôpital's Rule does not apply.

65. $\displaystyle\lim_{x \to \infty} x \cos \frac{1}{x} = \infty(1) = \infty$

Limit is not of the form $0/0$ or ∞/∞. L'Hôpital's Rule does not apply.

67. (a) $\lim\limits_{x\to\infty}\dfrac{x}{\sqrt{x^2+1}} = \lim\limits_{x\to\infty}\dfrac{x/x}{\sqrt{x^2+1}/x}$

$$= \lim\limits_{x\to\infty}\dfrac{1}{\sqrt{x^2+1}/\sqrt{x^2}}$$

$$= \lim\limits_{x\to\infty}\dfrac{1}{\sqrt{1+(1/x^2)}}$$

$$= \dfrac{1}{\sqrt{1+0}} = 1$$

(b) $\lim\limits_{x\to\infty}\dfrac{x}{\sqrt{x^2+1}} = \lim\limits_{x\to\infty}\dfrac{1}{x/\sqrt{x^2+1}}$

$$= \lim\limits_{x\to\infty}\dfrac{\sqrt{x^2+1}}{x} = \lim\limits_{x\to\infty}\dfrac{x/\sqrt{x^2+1}}{1}$$

$$= \lim\limits_{x\to\infty}\dfrac{x}{\sqrt{x^2+1}}$$

Applying L'Hôpital's rule twice results in the original limit, so L'Hôpital's rule fails.

(c)

69. $\lim\limits_{k\to0}\dfrac{32}{k}\left(1 - e^{-kt} + \dfrac{v_0ke^{-kt}}{32}\right) = \lim\limits_{k\to0}\dfrac{32(1 - e^{-kt})}{k} + \lim\limits_{k\to0}\left[\dfrac{32}{k}\cdot\dfrac{v_0ke^{-kt}}{32}\right]$

$$= \lim\limits_{k\to0}\dfrac{32te^{-kt}}{1} + v_0 = 32t + v_0$$

(Apply L'Hôpital's Rule to the first limit in the right-hand member of the equation.)

71. Area of triangle: $\dfrac{1}{2}(2x)(1 - \cos x) = x - x\cos x$

Shaded area: Area of rectangle − Area under curve

$$2x(1 - \cos x) - 2\int_0^x(1 - \cos t)\,dt = 2x(1 - \cos x) - 2\Big[t - \sin t\Big]_0^x$$

$$= 2x(1 - \cos x) - 2(x - \sin x) = 2\sin x - 2x\cos x$$

Ratio: $\lim\limits_{x\to0}\dfrac{x - x\cos x}{2\sin x - 2x\cos x} = \lim\limits_{x\to0}\dfrac{1 + x\sin x - \cos x}{2\cos x + 2x\sin x - 2\cos x}$

$$= \lim\limits_{x\to0}\dfrac{1 + x\sin x - \cos x}{2x\sin x}$$

$$= \lim\limits_{x\to0}\dfrac{x\cos x + \sin x + \sin x}{2x\cos x + 2\sin x}$$

$$= \lim\limits_{x\to0}\dfrac{x\cos x + 2\sin x}{2x\cos x + 2\sin x}\cdot\dfrac{1/\cos x}{1/\cos x}$$

$$= \lim\limits_{x\to0}\dfrac{x + 2\tan x}{2x + 2\tan x}$$

$$= \lim\limits_{x\to0}\dfrac{1 + 2\sec^2 x}{2 + 2\sec^2 x} = \dfrac{3}{4}$$

73. $f(x) = x^3$, $g(x) = x^2 + 1$, $[0, 1]$

$$\dfrac{f(b) - f(a)}{g(b) - g(a)} = \dfrac{f'(c)}{g'(c)}$$

$$\dfrac{f(1) - f(0)}{g(1) - g(0)} = \dfrac{3c^2}{2c}$$

$$\dfrac{1}{1} = \dfrac{3c}{2}$$

$$c = \dfrac{2}{3}$$

75. $\dfrac{f'(c)}{g'(c)} = \dfrac{f(b) - f(a)}{g(b) - g(a)}$

$$\dfrac{\cos c}{-\sin c} = \dfrac{\sin(\pi/2) - \sin 0}{\cos(\pi/2) - \cos 0}$$

$$-\cot c = -1 \implies c = \dfrac{\pi}{4}$$

77. False. L'Hôpital's Rule does not apply since

$$\lim_{x \to 0} (x^2 + x + 1) \neq 0.$$

$$\lim_{x \to 0} \frac{x^2 + x + 1}{x} = \lim_{x \to 0} \left(x + 1 + \frac{1}{x} \right) = 1 + \infty = \infty$$

79. True

81. (a) $\sin \theta = BD$

$\cos \theta = DO \implies AD = 1 - \cos \theta$

Area $\triangle ABD = \frac{1}{2}bh = \frac{1}{2}(1 - \cos \theta) \sin \theta = \frac{1}{2} \sin \theta - \frac{1}{2} \sin \theta \cos \theta$

(b) Area of sector: $\frac{1}{2}\theta$

Shaded area: $\frac{1}{2}\theta - $ Area $\triangle OBD = \frac{1}{2}\theta - \frac{1}{2}(\cos \theta)(\sin \theta) = \frac{1}{2}\theta - \frac{1}{2} \sin \theta \cos \theta$

(c) $R = \dfrac{(1/2) \sin \theta - (1/2) \sin \theta \cos \theta}{(1/2)\theta - (1/2) \sin \theta \cos \theta} = \dfrac{\sin \theta - \sin \theta \cos \theta}{\theta - \sin \theta \cos \theta}$

(d) $\lim_{\theta \to 0} R = \lim_{\theta \to 0} \dfrac{\sin \theta - (1/2) \sin 2\theta}{\theta - (1/2) \sin 2\theta}$

$= \lim_{\theta \to 0} \dfrac{\cos \theta - \cos 2\theta}{1 - \cos 2\theta} = \lim_{\theta \to 0} \dfrac{-\sin \theta + 2 \sin 2\theta}{2 \sin 2\theta} = \lim_{\theta \to 0} \dfrac{-\cos \theta + 4 \cos 2\theta}{4 \cos 2\theta} = \dfrac{3}{4}$

83. $\lim_{x \to a} f(x)^{g(x)}$

$y = f(x)^{g(x)}$

$\ln y = g(x) \ln f(x)$

$\lim_{x \to a} g(x) \ln f(x) = (\infty)(-\infty) = -\infty$

As $x \to a$, $\ln y \implies -\infty$, and hence $y = 0$. Thus,

$\lim_{x \to a} f(x)^{g(x)} = 0.$

85. $f'(a)(b - a) - \displaystyle\int_a^b f''(t)(t - b)\, dt = f'(a)(b - a) - \left\{ \left[f'(t)(t - b) \right]_a^b - \int_a^b f'(t)\, dt \right\}$

$$= f'(a)(b - a) + f'(a)(a - b) + \left[f(t) \right]_a^b = f(b) - f(a)$$

$dv = f''(t)dt \implies v = f'(t)$

$u = t - b \implies du = dt$

Section 7.8   Improper Integrals

1. Infinite discontinuity at $x = 0$.

$$\int_0^4 \frac{1}{\sqrt{x}}\, dx = \lim_{b \to 0^+} \int_b^4 \frac{1}{\sqrt{x}}\, dx$$

$$= \lim_{b \to 0^+} \left[2\sqrt{x} \right]_b^4$$

$$= \lim_{b \to 0^+} \left(4 - 2\sqrt{b} \right) = 4$$

Converges

3. $\displaystyle\int_0^2 \frac{1}{(x-1)^2}\,dx = \lim_{b\to 1^-}\int_0^b (x-1)^{-2}\,dx + \lim_{c\to 1^+}\int_c^2 (x-1)^{-2}\,dx$

$\displaystyle\qquad = \lim_{b\to 1^-}\left[\frac{-1}{x-1}\right]_0^b + \lim_{c\to 1^+}\left[\frac{-1}{x-1}\right]_c^2$

$\displaystyle\qquad = \lim_{b\to 1^-}\left[\frac{-1}{b-1} - 1\right] + \lim_{c\to 1^+}\left[-1 - \frac{-1}{c-1}\right] = \infty$

Therefore, the improper integral diverges.

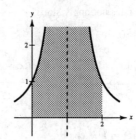

5. Infinite limit of integration.

$\displaystyle\int_0^\infty e^{-x}\,dx = \lim_{b\to\infty}\int_0^b e^{-x}\,dx$

$\displaystyle\qquad = \lim_{b\to\infty}\left[-e^{-x}\right]_0^b = 0 + 1 = 1$

Converges

7. $\displaystyle\int_{-1}^1 \frac{1}{x^2}\,dx \neq -2$

because the integrand is not defined at $x = 0$.
Diverges

9. $\displaystyle\int_{-\infty}^0 xe^{-2x}\,dx = \lim_{b\to-\infty}\int_b^0 xe^{-2x}\,dx = \lim_{b\to-\infty}\frac{1}{4}\left[(-2x-1)e^{-2x}\right]_b^0 = \lim_{b\to-\infty}\frac{1}{4}\left[-1 + (2b+1)e^{-2b}\right] = -\infty$ (Integration by parts)

Diverges

11. $\displaystyle\int_0^\infty x^2 e^{-x}\,dx = \lim_{b\to\infty}\int_0^b x^2 e^{-x}\,dx = \lim_{b\to\infty}\left[-e^{-x}(x^2 + 2x + 2)\right]_0^b = \lim_{b\to\infty}\left(-\frac{b^2 + 2b + 2}{e^b} + 2\right) = 2$

Since $\displaystyle\lim_{b\to\infty}\left(-\frac{b^2 + 2b + 2}{e^b}\right) = 0$ by L'Hôpital's Rule.

13. $\displaystyle\int_1^\infty \frac{1}{x^2}\,dx = \lim_{b\to\infty}\int_1^b \frac{1}{x^2}\,dx = \lim_{b\to\infty}\left[-\frac{1}{x}\right]_1^b = 1$

15. Since

$\displaystyle\int e^{-x}\cos x\,dx = \frac{1}{2}e^{-x}(-\cos x + \sin x) + C,$

we have

$\displaystyle\int_0^\infty e^{-x}\cos x\,dx = \lim_{b\to\infty}\int_0^b e^{-x}\cos x\,dx$

$\displaystyle\qquad = \lim_{b\to\infty}\frac{1}{2}\left[\frac{(-\cos x + \sin x)}{e^x}\right]_0^b$

$\displaystyle\qquad = \lim_{b\to\infty}\frac{1}{2}\left[\frac{-\cos b + \sin b}{e^b} - (-1)\right]$

$\displaystyle\qquad = \frac{1}{2}[0 - (-1)] = \frac{1}{2}.$

17. $\displaystyle\int_{-\infty}^\infty \frac{1}{1+x^2}\,dx = \int_{-\infty}^0 \frac{1}{1+x^2}\,dx + \int_0^\infty \frac{1}{1+x^2}\,dx$

$\displaystyle\qquad = \lim_{b\to-\infty}\int_b^0 \frac{1}{1+x^2}\,dx + \lim_{c\to\infty}\int_0^c \frac{1}{1+x^2}\,dx$

$\displaystyle\qquad = \lim_{b\to-\infty}\left[\arctan x\right]_b^0 + \lim_{c\to\infty}\left[\arctan x\right]_0^c$

$\displaystyle\qquad = \frac{\pi}{2} + \frac{\pi}{2} = \pi$

19. $\displaystyle\int_0^\infty \frac{1}{e^x + e^{-x}}\,dx = \lim_{b\to\infty}\int_0^b \frac{e^x}{1 + e^{2x}}\,dx$

$\displaystyle\qquad = \lim_{b\to\infty}\left[\arctan(e^x)\right]_0^b$

$\displaystyle\qquad = \frac{\pi}{2} - \frac{\pi}{4} = \frac{\pi}{4}$

21. $\displaystyle\int_0^\infty \cos \pi x\,dx = \lim_{b\to\infty}\left[\frac{1}{\pi}\sin \pi x\right]_0^b$

Diverges since $\sin \pi x$ does not approach a limit as $x \to \infty$.

23. $\int_0^1 \frac{1}{x^2}\, dx = \lim_{b\to 0^+} \left[\frac{-1}{x}\right]_b^1 = -1 + \infty$

Diverges

25. $\int_0^8 \frac{1}{\sqrt[3]{8-x}}\, dx = \lim_{b\to 8^-} \int_0^b \frac{1}{\sqrt[3]{8-x}}\, dx$

$= \lim_{b\to 8^-} \left[-\frac{(8-x)^{2/3}}{2/3}\right]_0^b$

$= \lim_{b\to 8^-} \left[\frac{3}{2}(8-b)^{2/3} + \frac{3}{2}(8-0)^{2/3}\right]$

$= -\frac{3}{2}(0) + \frac{3}{2}(4) = 6$

27. $\int_0^1 x \ln x\, dx = \lim_{b\to 0^+}\left[\frac{x^2}{2}\ln|x| - \frac{x^2}{4}\right]_b^1 = \lim_{b\to 0^+}\left[\frac{-1}{4} - \frac{b^2 \ln b}{2} + \frac{b^2}{4}\right] = \frac{-1}{4}$ since $\lim_{b\to 0^+}(b^2 \ln b) = 0$ by L'Hopital's Rule.

29. $\int_0^{\pi/2} \tan\theta\, d\theta = \lim_{b\to(\pi/2)^-}\left[\ln|\sec\theta|\right]_0^b = \infty,$

Diverges

31. $\int_2^4 \frac{1}{\sqrt{x^2-4}}\, dx = \lim_{a\to 2^+}\int_a^4 \frac{1}{\sqrt{x^2-4}}\, dx$

$= \lim_{a\to 2^+}\left[\ln|x + \sqrt{x^2-4}|\right]_a^4$

$= \lim_{a\to 2^+}\left[\ln(4 + \sqrt{12}) - \ln|a + \sqrt{a^2-4}|\right]$

$= \ln(4 + \sqrt{12}) - \ln(2 + 0)$

$= \ln\left(\frac{4 + 2\sqrt{3}}{2}\right) = \ln(2 + \sqrt{3})$

33. $\int_0^2 \frac{1}{\sqrt[3]{x-1}}\, dx = \int_0^1 \frac{1}{\sqrt[3]{x-1}}\, dx + \int_1^2 \frac{1}{\sqrt[3]{x-1}}\, dx$

$= \lim_{b\to 1^-}\left[\frac{3}{2}(x-1)^{2/3}\right]_0^b + \lim_{c\to 1^+}\left[\frac{3}{2}(x-1)^{2/3}\right]_c^2 = \frac{-3}{2} + \frac{3}{2} = 0$

35. If $p = 1$, $\int_1^\infty \frac{1}{x}\, dx = \lim_{b\to\infty}\int_1^b \frac{1}{x}\, dx = \lim_{b\to\infty} \ln x\Big]_1^b.$

Diverges. For $p \ne 1$,

$\int_1^\infty \frac{1}{x^p}\, dx = \lim_{b\to\infty}\left[\frac{x^{1-p}}{1-p}\right]_1^b = \lim_{b\to\infty}\left[\frac{b^{1-p}}{1-p} - \frac{1}{1-p}\right].$

This converges to $\frac{1}{p-1}$ if $1 - p < 0$ or $p > 1$.

37. When $n = 1$, the integral converges, since

$\int_0^\infty xe^{-x}\, dx = \lim_{b\to\infty}\int_0^b xe^{-x}\, dx$

$= \lim_{b\to\infty}\left[-e^{-x}(x+1)\right]_0^b$ (Integration by parts)

$= \lim_{b\to\infty}\left[-e^{-b}(b+1) + 1\right]$

$= 0 + 1 = 1.$ (L'Hôpital's Rule)

—CONTINUED—

37. —CONTINUED—

Now assume that the integral converges for $n = k$ and verify that it converges for $n = k + 1$.

$$\int_0^\infty x^{k+1} e^{-x} \, dx = \lim_{b \to \infty} \int_0^b x^{k+1} e^{-x} \, dx$$

$$= \lim_{b \to \infty} \left[-x^{k+1} e^{-x} - \frac{k+1}{-1} \int_0^b x^k e^{-x} \, dx \right]_0^\infty \qquad \text{(Integration by parts)}$$

$$= 0 + (k+1) \int_0^\infty x^k e^{-x} \, dx \qquad \text{(L'Hôpital's Rule)}$$

$$= (k+1) \int_0^\infty x^k e^{-x} \, dx$$

Therefore, we have shown the integral for $n = k + 1$ converges if the integral for $n = k$ converges. Combining this with the results for $n = 1$, it follows by mathematical induction that the integral converges for any positive integer n.

39. $\displaystyle\int_0^1 \frac{1}{x^3} \, dx$ diverges.

(See Exercise 36, $p = 3 \not< 1$.)

41. $\displaystyle\int_1^\infty \frac{1}{x^3} \, dx = \frac{1}{3-1} = \frac{1}{2}$ converges.

(See Exercise 35, $p = 3$.)

43. Since $\dfrac{1}{x^2 + 5} \le \dfrac{1}{x^2}$ on $[1, \infty)$ and $\displaystyle\int_1^\infty \frac{1}{x^2} \, dx$ converges by Exercise 35, $\displaystyle\int_1^\infty \frac{1}{x^2 + 5} \, dx$ converges.

45. Since $\dfrac{1}{\sqrt[3]{x(x-1)}} \ge \dfrac{1}{\sqrt[3]{x^2}}$ on $[2, \infty)$ and $\displaystyle\int_2^\infty \frac{1}{\sqrt[3]{x^2}} \, dx$ diverges by Exercise 35, $\displaystyle\int_2^\infty \frac{1}{\sqrt[3]{x(x-1)}} \, dx$ diverges.

47. On $[1, \infty)$ we have

$$x \le x^2$$

$$e^x \le e^{x^2}$$

$$\frac{1}{e^x} \ge \frac{1}{e^{x^2}}$$

$$e^{-x} \ge e^{-x^2}.$$

Therefore, by Exercise 38 we have

$$\int_0^\infty e^{-x^2} \, dx = \int_0^1 e^{-x^2} \, dx + \int_1^\infty e^{-x^2} \, dx$$

$$\le \int_0^1 e^{-x^2} \, dx + \int_1^\infty e^{-x} \, dx$$

$$= \int_0^1 e^{-x^2} \, dx + \left[-e^{-x} \right]_1^\infty$$

$$= \int_0^1 e^{-x^2} \, dx + e^{-1}.$$

Therefore, the integral converges.

49. $f(t) = 1$

$$F(s) = \int_0^\infty e^{-st} \, dx = \lim_{b \to \infty} \left[-\frac{1}{s} e^{-st} \right]_0^b = \frac{1}{s}, \, s > 0$$

51. $f(t) = t^2$

$$F(s) = \int_0^\infty t^2 e^{-st} \, dx = \lim_{b \to \infty} \left[\frac{1}{s^3} (-s^2 t^2 - 2st - 2) e^{-st} \right]_0^b$$

$$= \frac{2}{s^3}, \, s > 0$$

53. To evaluate $\int e^{-st} \cos at \, dt$ use Integration By Parts.

$$dv = \cos at \, dt \implies v = \int \cos at \, dt = \frac{1}{a} \sin at$$

$$u = e^{-st} \qquad \implies du = -se^{-st} \, dt$$

$$\int e^{-st} \cos at \, dt = \frac{1}{a} e^{-st} \sin at + \frac{s}{a} \int e^{-st} \sin at \, dt$$

Use Integration By Parts again.

$$dv = \sin at \, dt \implies v = \int \sin at \, dt = -\frac{1}{a} \cos at$$

$$u = e^{-st} \qquad \implies du = -se^{-st} \, dt$$

$$\int e^{-st} \cos at \, dt = \frac{1}{a} e^{-st} \sin at + \frac{s}{a} \left(-\frac{1}{a} e^{-st} \cos at - \frac{s}{a} \int e^{-st} \cos at \, dt \right)$$

Solving for the integral in the equation yields

$$\int e^{-st} \cos at \, dt = \frac{e^{-st}}{s^2 + a^2} (a \sin at - s \cos at) + C.$$

Therefore,

$$\int_0^\infty e^{-st} \cos at \, dt = \lim_{b \to \infty} \left[\frac{e^{-st}}{s^2 + a^2} (a \sin at - s \cos at) \right]_0^b$$

$$= 0 + \frac{s}{s^2 + a^2} = \frac{s}{s^2 + a^2}, \, s > 0.$$

55. $f(t) = \cosh at$

$$F(s) = \int_0^\infty e^{-st} \cosh at \, dt = \int_0^\infty e^{-st} \left(\frac{e^{at} + e^{-at}}{2} \right) dt = \frac{1}{2} \int_0^\infty \left[e^{t(-s+a)} + e^{t(-s-a)} \right] dt$$

$$= \lim_{b \to \infty} \frac{1}{2} \left[\frac{1}{(-s+a)} e^{t(-s+a)} + \frac{1}{(-s-a)} e^{t(-s-a)} \right]_0^b = 0 - \frac{1}{2} \left[\frac{1}{(-s+a)} + \frac{1}{(-s-a)} \right]$$

$$= \frac{-1}{2} \left[\frac{1}{(-s+a)} + \frac{1}{(-s-a)} \right] = \frac{s}{s^2 - a^2}, \, s > |a|$$

57. (a) $A = \int_0^\infty e^{-x} \, dx$

$$= \lim_{b \to \infty} \left[-e^{-x} \right]_0^b$$

$$= 0 - (-1) = 1$$

(b) **Disc:**

$$V = \pi \int_0^\infty (e^{-x})^2 \, dx$$

$$= \lim_{b \to \infty} \pi \left[-\frac{1}{2} e^{-2x} \right]_0^b = \frac{\pi}{2}$$

(c) **Shell:**

$$V = 2\pi \int_0^\infty x e^{-x} \, dx$$

$$= \lim_{b \to \infty} \left\{ 2\pi \left[-e^{-x}(x+1) \right]_0^b \right\}$$

$$= 2\pi$$

59. By symmetry the perimeter of this figure is four times the length of the arc in the first quadrant. Thus,

$$s = 4 \int_0^1 \sqrt{1 + (y')^2} \, dx.$$

By implicit differentiation we have

$$x^{2/3} + y^{2/3} = 1$$

$$\frac{2}{3} x^{-1/3} + \frac{2}{3} y^{-1/3} y' = 0$$

$$y' = -\frac{y^{1/3}}{x^{1/3}}.$$

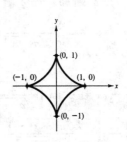

—CONTINUED—

59. —CONTINUED—

Therefore,

$$s = 4\int_0^1 \sqrt{1 + \left(-\frac{y^{1/3}}{x^{1/3}}\right)^2}\, dx = 4\int_0^1 \sqrt{\frac{x^{2/3} + y^{2/3}}{x^{2/3}}}\, dx$$

$$= 4\lim_{b\to 0^+}\int_b^1 \sqrt{\frac{1}{x^{2/3}}}\, dx = 4\lim_{b\to 0^+}\int_b^1 x^{-1/3}\, dx$$

$$= 4\lim_{b\to 0^+}\left[\frac{x^{2/3}}{2/3}\right]_b^1 = 4\left(\frac{3}{2}\right) = 6.$$

61. $\Gamma(n) = \displaystyle\int_0^\infty x^{n-1}e^{-x}\, dx$

(a) $\Gamma(1) = \displaystyle\int_0^\infty e^{-x}\, dx = \lim_{b\to\infty}\left[-e^{-x}\right]_0^b = 1$

$\Gamma(2) = \displaystyle\int_0^\infty xe^{-x}\, dx = \lim_{b\to\infty}\left[-e^{-x}(x+1)\right]_0^b = 1$

$\Gamma(3) = \displaystyle\int_0^\infty x^2 e^{-x}\, dx = \lim_{b\to\infty}\left[-x^2 e^{-x} - 2xe^{-x} - 2e^{-x}\right]_0^b = 2$

(b) $\Gamma(n+1) = \displaystyle\int_0^\infty x^n e^{-x}\, dx = \lim_{b\to\infty}\left[-x^n e^{-x}\right]_0^b + \lim_{b\to\infty} n\int_0^b x^{n-1}e^{-x}\, dx = 0 + n\Gamma(n)$ $\quad (u = x^n,\ dv = e^{-x}\, dx)$

(c) $\Gamma(n) = (n-1)!$

63. (a) $\displaystyle\int_{-\infty}^\infty \frac{1}{7}e^{-t/7}\, dt = \int_0^\infty \frac{1}{7}e^{-t/7}\, dt = \lim_{b\to\infty}\left[-e^{-t/7}\right]_0^b = 1$

(b) $\displaystyle\int_0^4 \frac{1}{7}e^{-t/7}\, dt = \left[-e^{-t/7}\right]_0^4 = -e^{-4/7} + 1 \approx 0.4353 = 43.53\%$

(c) $\displaystyle\int_0^\infty t\left[\frac{1}{7}e^{-t/7}\right] dt = \lim_{b\to\infty}\left[-te^{-t/7} - 7e^{-t/7}\right]_0^b = 0 + 7 = 7$

65. (a) $C = 650{,}000 + \displaystyle\int_0^5 25{,}000e^{-0.06t}\, dt$

$= 650{,}000 - \left[\dfrac{25{,}000}{0.06}e^{-0.06t}\right]_0^5 \approx \$757{,}992.41$

(b) $C = 650{,}000 + \displaystyle\int_0^{10} 25{,}000e^{-0.06t}\, dt$

$= 650{,}000 - \left[\dfrac{25{,}000}{0.06}e^{-0.06t}\right]_0^{10} \approx \$837{,}995.15$

(c) $C = 650{,}000 + \displaystyle\int_0^\infty 25{,}000e^{-0.06t}\, dt$

$= 650{,}000 - \lim_{b\to\infty}\left[\dfrac{25{,}000}{0.06}e^{-0.06t}\right]_0^b \approx \$1{,}066{,}666.67$

67. Let $x = a\tan\theta$, $dx = a\sec^2\theta\, d\theta$, $\sqrt{a^2 + x^2} = a\sec\theta$.

$$\int \frac{1}{(a^2 + x^2)^{3/2}}\, dx = \int \frac{a\sec^2\theta\, d\theta}{a^3\sec^3\theta} = \frac{1}{a^2}\int \cos\theta\, d\theta$$

$$= \frac{1}{a^2}\sin\theta = \frac{1}{a^2}\frac{x}{\sqrt{a^2 + x^2}}$$

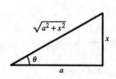

Hence,

$$P = k\int_1^\infty \frac{1}{(a^2 + x^2)^{3/2}}\, dx = \frac{k}{a^2}\lim_{b\to\infty}\left[\frac{x}{\sqrt{a^2 + x^2}}\right]_1^b$$

$$= \frac{k}{a^2}\left[1 - \frac{1}{\sqrt{a^2 + x^2}}\right] = \frac{k\sqrt{a^2 + x^2} - 1}{a^2\sqrt{a^2 + x^2}}$$

69. For $n = 1$,

$$I_1 = \int_0^\infty \frac{x}{(x^2 + 1)^4}\, dx = \lim_{b \to \infty} \frac{1}{2} \int_0^b (x^2 + 1)^{-4} (2x\, dx) = \lim_{b \to \infty} \left[-\frac{1}{6} \frac{1}{(x^2 + 1)^3} \right]_0^b = \frac{1}{6}.$$

For $n > 1$,

$$I_n = \int_0^\infty \frac{x^{2n-1}}{(x^2 + 1)^{n+3}}\, dx = \lim_{b \to \infty} \left[\frac{-x^{2n-2}}{2(n+2)(x^2 + 1)^n} + 2 \right]_0^b + \frac{n-1}{n+2} \int_0^\infty \frac{x^{2n-3}}{(x^2 + 1)^{n+2}}\, dx = 0 + \frac{n-1}{n+2}(I_{n-1})$$

$$u = x^{2n-2},\ du = (2n-2)x^{2n-3}\, dx,\ dv = \frac{x}{(x^2 + 1)^{n+3}}\, dx,\ v = \frac{-1}{2(n+2)(x^2 + 1)^{n+2}}$$

(a) $\displaystyle \int_0^\infty \frac{x}{(x^2 + 1)^4}\, dx = \lim_{b \to \infty} \left[-\frac{1}{6(x^2 + 1)^3} \right]_0^b = \frac{1}{6}$

(b) $\displaystyle \int_0^\infty \frac{x^3}{(x^2 + 1)^5}\, dx = \frac{1}{4} \int_0^\infty \frac{x}{(x^2 + 1)^4}\, dx = \frac{1}{4}\left(\frac{1}{6}\right) = \frac{1}{24}$

(c) $\displaystyle \int_0^\infty \frac{x^5}{(x^2 + 1)^6} = \frac{2}{5} \int_0^\infty \frac{x^3}{(x^2 + 1)^5}\, dx = \frac{2}{5}\left(\frac{1}{24}\right) = \frac{1}{60}$

71. False. $f(x) = 1/(x + 1)$ is continuous on $[0, \infty)$, $\displaystyle\lim_{x \to \infty} 1/(x + 1) = 0$, but

$$\int_0^\infty \frac{1}{x + 1}\, dx = \lim_{b \to \infty} \left[\ln|x + 1| \right]_0^b = \infty.$$

Diverges

73. True

Review Exercises for Chapter 7

1. $\displaystyle \int e^{2x} \sin 3x\, dx = -\frac{1}{3}e^{2x} \cos 3x + \frac{2}{3} \int e^{2x} \cos 3x\, dx$

$$= -\frac{1}{3}e^{2x} \cos 3x + \frac{2}{3}\left(\frac{1}{3}e^{2x} \sin 3x - \frac{2}{3} \int e^{2x} \sin 3x\, dx\right)$$

$$\frac{13}{9} \int e^{2x} \sin 3x\, dx = -\frac{1}{3}e^{2x} \cos 3x + \frac{2}{9}e^{2x} \sin 3x$$

$$\int e^{2x} \sin 3x\, dx = \frac{e^{2x}}{13}(2 \sin 3x - 3 \cos 3x) + C$$

(1) $dv = \sin 3x\, dx \implies v = -\frac{1}{3} \cos 3x$

$\quad u = e^{2x} \quad\quad \implies du = 2e^{2x}\, dx$

(2) $dv = \cos 3x\, dx \implies v = \frac{1}{3} \sin 3x$

$\quad u = e^{2x} \quad\quad \implies du = 2e^{2x}\, dx$

3. $\displaystyle \int \cos^3(\pi x - 1)\, dx = \int [1 - \sin^2(\pi x - 1)] \cos(\pi x - 1)\, dx$

$$= \frac{1}{\pi}\left[\sin(\pi x - 1) - \frac{1}{3} \sin^3(\pi x - 1) \right] + C$$

$$= \frac{1}{3\pi} \sin(\pi x - 1)[3 - \sin^2(\pi x - 1)] + C$$

$$= \frac{1}{3\pi} \sin(\pi x - 1)[3 - (1 - \cos^2(\pi x - 1))] + C$$

$$= \frac{1}{3\pi} \sin(\pi x - 1)[2 + \cos^2(\pi x - 1)] + C$$

5. $\displaystyle\int \sec^4 \frac{x}{2}\, dx = \int \sec^2 \frac{x}{2} \sec^2 \frac{x}{2}\, dx$

$$= \int \left[\tan^2 \frac{x}{2} + 1 \right] \sec^2 \frac{x}{2}\, dx$$

$$= 2\int \tan^2 \frac{x}{2} \sec^2 \frac{x}{2}\left(\frac{1}{2}\right) dx + 2\int \sec^2 \frac{x}{2}\left(\frac{1}{2}\right) dx$$

$$= \frac{2}{3} \tan^3 \frac{x}{2} + 2 \tan \frac{x}{2} + C$$

$$= \frac{2}{3}\left[\tan^3 \frac{x}{2} + 3 \tan \frac{x}{2} \right] + C$$

7. $\displaystyle\int \frac{-12}{x^2\sqrt{4 - x^2}}\, dx = \int \frac{-24 \cos \theta\, d\theta}{(4 \sin^2 \theta)(2 \cos \theta)}$

$$= -3\int \csc^2 \theta\, d\theta$$

$$= 3 \cot \theta + C$$

$$= \frac{3\sqrt{4 - x^2}}{x} + C$$

$x = 2 \sin \theta,\, dx = 2 \cos \theta\, d\theta,\, \sqrt{4 - x^2} = 2 \cos \theta$

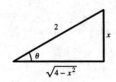

9. Since $x^3 - x^2 + x - 1 = (x - 1)(x^2 + 1)$, we have

$$\frac{x^2 + 2x}{(x - 1)(x^2 + 1)} = \frac{A}{x - 1} + \frac{Bx + C}{x^2 + 1}.$$

Multiplying by $(x - 1)(x^2 + 1)$ yields

$$x^2 + 2x = A(x^2 + 1) + (Bx + C)(x - 1).$$

If $x = 1$, then $1 + 2 = A(2) + (B + C)(0)$ or $A = \dfrac{3}{2}$.

Furthermore,

$$x^2 + 2x = Ax^2 + A + Bx^2 - Bx + Cx - C$$

$$= (A + B)x^2 + (C - B)x + (A - C).$$

Now by equating the coefficients, we have

$$1 = A + B = \frac{3}{2} + B \qquad \text{or} \qquad B = -\frac{1}{2}$$

$$2 = C - B = C + \frac{1}{2} \qquad \text{or} \qquad C = \frac{3}{2}.$$

Therefore,

$$\int \frac{x^2 + 2x}{(x - 1)(x^2 + 1)}\, dx = \int \left[\frac{3/2}{x - 1} + \frac{(-x/2) + (3/2)}{x^2 + 1} \right] dx$$

$$= \frac{3}{2}\int \frac{1}{x - 1}\, dx - \frac{1}{2}\int \frac{x}{x^2 + 1}\, dx + \frac{3}{2}\int \frac{1}{x^2 + 1}\, dx$$

$$= \frac{3}{2} \ln|x - 1| - \frac{1}{4} \ln(x^2 + 1) + \frac{3}{2} \arctan x + C$$

$$= \frac{1}{4}[6 \ln|x - 1| - \ln(x^2 + 1) + 6 \arctan x] + C.$$

11. $\dfrac{x^2}{x^2 + 2x - 15} = 1 + \dfrac{15 - 2x}{x^2 + 2x - 15}$

$\dfrac{15 - 2x}{(x - 3)(x + 5)} = \dfrac{A}{x - 3} + \dfrac{B}{x + 5}$

$15 - 2x = A(x + 5) + B(x - 3)$

Let $x = 3$: $9 = 8A \implies A = \dfrac{9}{8}$

Let $x = -5$: $25 = -8B \implies B = -\dfrac{25}{8}$

$\displaystyle\int \dfrac{x^2}{x^2 + 2x - 15}\, dx = \int dx + \dfrac{9}{8}\int \dfrac{1}{x - 3}\, dx - \dfrac{25}{8}\int \dfrac{1}{x + 5}\, dx$

$\qquad = x + \dfrac{9}{8}\ln|x - 3| - \dfrac{25}{8}\ln|x + 5| + C$

13. $\displaystyle\int \dfrac{1}{1 - \sin\theta}\, d\theta = \int \dfrac{1}{1 - \sin\theta}\left(\dfrac{1 + \sin\theta}{1 + \sin\theta}\right) d\theta$

$\qquad = \displaystyle\int \dfrac{1 + \sin\theta}{1 - \sin^2\theta}\, d\theta = \int \dfrac{1 + \sin\theta}{\cos^2\theta}\, d\theta$

$\qquad = \displaystyle\int \left(\dfrac{1}{\cos^2\theta} + \dfrac{\sin\theta}{\cos\theta\cos\theta}\right) d\theta$

$\qquad = \displaystyle\int (\sec^2\theta + \sec\theta\tan\theta)\, d\theta$

$\qquad = \tan\theta + \sec\theta + C$

15. Using Integration By Parts, let

$dv = \dfrac{1}{x^2}\, dx \implies v = -\dfrac{1}{x}$

$u = \ln(2x) \implies du = \dfrac{1}{x}\, dx.$

$\displaystyle\int \dfrac{\ln(2x)}{x^2}\, dx = -\dfrac{\ln(2x)}{x} - \int \dfrac{1}{x}\left(-\dfrac{1}{x}\right) dx$

$\qquad = -\dfrac{\ln(2x)}{x} + \displaystyle\int x^{-2}\, dx$

$\qquad = -\dfrac{\ln(2x)}{x} - \dfrac{1}{x} + C$

$\qquad = -\dfrac{1}{x}(1 + \ln 2x) + C$

17. $\displaystyle\int \sqrt{4 - x^2}\, dx = \int (2\cos\theta)(2\cos\theta)\, d\theta$

$\qquad = 2\displaystyle\int (1 + \cos 2\theta)\, d\theta$

$\qquad = 2\left(\theta + \dfrac{1}{2}\sin 2\theta\right) + C$

$\qquad = 2(\theta + \sin\theta\cos\theta) + C$

$\qquad = 2\left[\arcsin\left(\dfrac{x}{2}\right) + \dfrac{x}{2}\left(\dfrac{\sqrt{4 - x^2}}{2}\right)\right] + C$

$\qquad = \dfrac{1}{2}\left[4\arcsin\left(\dfrac{x}{2}\right) + x\sqrt{4 - x^2}\right] + C$

$x = 2\sin\theta,\ dx = 2\cos\theta\, d\theta,\ \sqrt{4 - x^2} = 2\cos\theta$

19. $\dfrac{3x^3 + 4x}{(x^2 + 1)^2} = \dfrac{Ax + B}{x^2 + 1} + \dfrac{Cx + D}{(x^2 + 1)^2}$

$3x^3 + 4x = (Ax + B)(x^2 + 1) + Cx + D$

$\qquad = Ax^3 + Bx^2 + (A + C)x + (B + D)$

$A = 3, B = 0, A + C = 4 \implies C = 1,$

$B + D = 0 \implies D = 0$

$\displaystyle\int \dfrac{3x^3 + 4x}{(x^2 + 1)^2}\, dx = 3\int \dfrac{x}{x^2 + 1}\, dx + \int \dfrac{x}{(x^2 + 1)^2}\, dx$

$\qquad = \dfrac{3}{2}\ln(x^2 + 1) - \dfrac{1}{2(x^2 + 1)} + C$

21. $\int \dfrac{16}{\sqrt{16 - x^2}}\, dx = 16 \arcsin\left(\dfrac{x}{4}\right) + C$

23. $\int \dfrac{x}{x^2 + 4x + 8}\, dx = \dfrac{1}{2} \int \dfrac{2x + 4 - 4}{x^2 + 4x + 8}\, dx$

$$= \dfrac{1}{2} \int \dfrac{2x + 4}{x^2 + 4x + 8}\, dx - 2 \int \dfrac{1}{(x + 2)^2 + 4}\, dx = \dfrac{1}{2} \ln|x^2 + 4x + 8| - \arctan\left(\dfrac{x + 2}{2}\right) + C$$

25. To evaluate $\int \theta \sin\theta \cos\theta\, d\theta$ use Integration By Parts.

$$dv = \sin\theta \cos\theta\, d\theta \implies v = \int \sin\theta \cos\theta\, d\theta = \dfrac{1}{2} \sin^2\theta$$

$$u = \theta \qquad\qquad \implies du = d\theta$$

$$\int \theta \sin\theta \cos\theta\, du = \dfrac{1}{2}\theta \sin^2\theta - \dfrac{1}{2} \int \sin^2\theta\, d\theta$$

$$= \dfrac{1}{2}\theta \sin^2\theta - \dfrac{1}{4} \int (1 - \cos 2\theta)\, d\theta$$

$$= \dfrac{1}{2}\theta \sin^2\theta - \dfrac{1}{4}\left(\theta - \dfrac{1}{2}\sin 2\theta\right) + C$$

$$= \dfrac{1}{2}\theta \sin^2\theta - \dfrac{1}{4}\theta + \dfrac{1}{8}\sin 2\theta + C$$

$$= \dfrac{1}{8}(4\theta \sin^2\theta + \sin 2\theta - 2\theta) + C$$

$$= \dfrac{1}{8}\left[4\theta\left(\dfrac{1 - \cos 2\theta}{2}\right) - \sin 2\theta - 2\theta\right] + C$$

$$= \dfrac{1}{8}(\sin 2\theta - 2\theta \cos 2\theta) + C$$

A second method of evaluating the integral is to use the double angle identity on the integrand and integrate by parts.

$$dv = \sin 2\theta\, d\theta \implies v = \int \sin 2\theta\, d\theta = -\dfrac{1}{2}\cos\theta$$

$$u = \theta \qquad \implies du = d\theta$$

$$\int \theta \sin\theta \cos\theta\, d\theta = \dfrac{1}{2} \int \theta \sin 2\theta\, d\theta$$

$$= -\dfrac{1}{4}\theta \cos 2\theta + \dfrac{1}{4} \int \cos 2\theta\, d\theta$$

$$= -\dfrac{1}{4}\theta \cos 2\theta + \dfrac{1}{8}\sin 2\theta = \dfrac{1}{8}(\sin 2\theta - 2\theta \cos 2\theta) + C$$

27. $\int (\sin\theta + \cos\theta)^2\, d\theta = \int (\sin^2\theta + 2\sin\theta \cos\theta + \cos^2\theta)\, d\theta$

$$= \int (1 + \sin 2\theta)\, d\theta = \theta - \dfrac{1}{2}\cos 2\theta + C = \dfrac{1}{2}(2\theta - \cos 2\theta) + C$$

29. $\displaystyle\int \sqrt{1 + \cos x}\, dx = \int \frac{\sin x}{\sqrt{1 - \cos x}}\, dx$

$$= \int (1 - \cos x)^{-1/2}(\sin x)\, dx$$

$$= 2\sqrt{1 - \cos x} + C$$

$u = 1 - \cos x,\ du = \sin x\, dx$

31. $\displaystyle\int \cos x \ln(\sin x)\, dx = \sin x \ln(\sin x) - \int \cos x\, dx$

$$= \sin x \ln(\sin x) - \sin x + C$$

$dv = \cos x\, dx \implies v = \sin x$

$u = \ln(\sin x) \implies du = \dfrac{\cos x}{\sin x}\, dx$

33. $\displaystyle\int x \arcsin 2x\, dx = \frac{x^2}{2} \arcsin 2x - \int \frac{x^2}{\sqrt{1 - 4x^2}}\, dx$

$$= \frac{x^2}{2} \arcsin 2x - \frac{1}{8} \int \frac{2(2x)^2}{\sqrt{1 - (2x)^2}}\, dx$$

$$= \frac{x^2}{2} \arcsin 2x - \frac{1}{8}\left(\frac{1}{2}\right)\left[-(2x)\sqrt{1 - 4x^2} + \arcsin 2x\right] + C \quad \text{(by Formula 43 of Integration Tables)}$$

$$= \frac{1}{16}\left[(8x^2 - 1)\arcsin 2x + 2x\sqrt{1 - 4x^2}\right] + C$$

$dv = x\, dx \implies v = \dfrac{x^2}{2}$

$u = \arcsin 2x \implies du = \dfrac{2}{\sqrt{1 - 4x^2}}\, dx$

35. Let $u = x^{1/4}$. Then $u^4 = x$, $u^2 = x^{1/2}$, $dx = 4u^3\, du$, and

$$\int \frac{x^{1/4}}{1 + x^{1/2}}\, dx = \int \frac{u}{1 + u^2}(4u^3\, du) = 4 \int \frac{u^4}{1 + u^2}\, du$$

$$= 4 \int \left(u^2 - 1 + \frac{1}{1 + u^2}\right) du$$

$$= 4\left(\frac{u^3}{3} - u + \arctan u\right) + C$$

$$= \frac{4}{3}(x^{3/4} - 3x^{1/4} + 3 \arctan x^{1/4}) + C.$$

37. $\displaystyle\int \frac{x^4}{(x - 1)^3}\, dx = \frac{1}{2}x^2 + 3x - \frac{1}{2(x - 1)^2} - \frac{4}{x - 1} + 6 \ln|x - 1| + C$

$(2, 4)$: $4 = 2 + 6 - \dfrac{1}{2} - 4 + C \implies C = \dfrac{1}{2}$

$y = 6 \ln|x - 1| + \dfrac{1}{2}x^2 + 3x + \dfrac{1}{2} - \dfrac{1}{2(x - 1)^2} - \dfrac{4}{x - 1}$

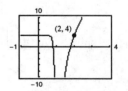

39. $\displaystyle\int \frac{6x^2 - 3x + 14}{x^3 - 2x^2 + 4x - 8}\, dx = 4 \ln|x - 2| + \ln(x^2 + 4) + \frac{1}{2} \arctan\left(\frac{1}{2}x\right) + C$

$(3, 2)$: $\ln 13 + \dfrac{1}{2} \arctan \dfrac{3}{2} + C = 2 \implies C = 2 - \ln 13 - \dfrac{1}{2} \arctan\left(\dfrac{3}{2}\right)$

$y = \dfrac{1}{2} \arctan \dfrac{x}{2} + \ln(x^2 + 4) + 4 \ln|x - 2| - \dfrac{1}{2} \arctan \dfrac{3}{2} - \ln 13 + 2$

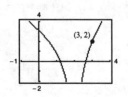

41. $\displaystyle\int \frac{d\theta}{2 - 3\sin\theta} = \frac{\sqrt{5}}{5}\ln\left|\frac{\cos\theta - \sqrt{5}(\sin\theta - 1)}{\cos\theta + \sqrt{5}(\sin\theta - 1)}\right| + C$

$(1, 1)$: $\displaystyle\frac{\sqrt{5}}{5}\ln\left|\frac{\cos(1) - \sqrt{5}(\sin(1) - 1)}{\cos(1) + \sqrt{5}(\sin(1) - 1)}\right| + C = 1 \implies C \approx 0.297$

$\displaystyle\frac{\sqrt{5}}{5}\ln\left|\frac{\cos\theta - \sqrt{5}(\sin\theta - 1)}{\cos\theta + \sqrt{5}(\sin\theta - 1)}\right| + 0.297$

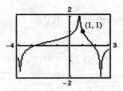

43. Using a symbolic integration utility to perform the integration yields

$$\int \frac{1}{1 + \sin\theta + \cos\theta}\, d\theta = \ln\left|\frac{1 + \sin\theta + \cos\theta}{1 + \cos\theta}\right| + C.$$

Substitute the solution point $(0, 0)$ into the antiderivative and solve for the constant of integration.

$$y = \ln\left|\frac{1 + \sin\theta + \cos\theta}{1 + \cos\theta}\right| + C$$

$$0 = \ln\left|\frac{1 + \sin 0 + \cos 0}{1 + \cos 0}\right| + C = \ln 1 + C = C$$

The graph of the function

$$y = \ln\left|\frac{1 + \sin\theta + \cos\theta}{1 + \cos\theta}\right|$$

45. $\displaystyle\int \frac{\sin\theta}{3 - 2\cos\theta}\, d\theta = \frac{1}{2}\ln|3 - 2\cos\theta| + C$

$(0, 0)$: $\displaystyle\frac{1}{2}\ln 1 + C = 0 \implies C = 0$

$$y = \frac{1}{2}\ln(3 - 2\cos\theta)$$

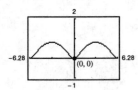

47. $y = \displaystyle\int \frac{9}{x^2 - 9}\, dx = \frac{3}{2}\ln\left|\frac{x - 3}{x + 3}\right| + C$ (by Formula 24 of Integration Tables)

49. $y = \displaystyle\int \ln(x^2 + x)\, dx = x\ln|x^2 + x| - \int \frac{2x^2 + x}{x^2 + x}\, dx = x\ln|x^2 + x| - \int \frac{2x + 1}{x + 1}\, dx$

$\displaystyle\qquad\qquad = x\ln|x^2 + x| - \int 2\, dx + \int \frac{1}{x + 1}\, dx$

$\displaystyle\qquad\qquad = x\ln|x^2 + x| - 2x + \ln|x + 1| + C$

$dv = dx \qquad \implies \quad v = x$

$u = \ln(x^2 + x) \implies du = \dfrac{2x + 1}{x^2 + x}\, dx$

51. (a) $\displaystyle \int \frac{1}{x^2\sqrt{4+x^2}}\,dx = \frac{1}{4}\int \frac{\cos\theta}{\sin^2\theta}\,d\theta$

$$= \frac{-1}{4\sin\theta} + C$$

$$= -\frac{1}{4}\csc\theta + C$$

$$= \frac{-\sqrt{4+x^2}}{4x} + C$$

$x = 2\tan\theta,\ dx = 2\sec^2\theta\,d\theta,\ \sqrt{4+x^2} = 2\sec\theta$

(b) $\displaystyle \int \frac{1}{x^2\sqrt{4+x^2}}\,dx = -\frac{1}{4}\int \frac{u}{\sqrt{1+u^2}}\,du$

$$= -\frac{1}{4}\sqrt{1+u^2} + C$$

$$= -\frac{1}{4}\sqrt{1+\frac{4}{x^2}}$$

$$= \frac{-\sqrt{4+x^2}}{4x} + C$$

$$x = \frac{2}{u},\ dx = -\frac{2du}{u^2}$$

53. (a) Let $x = 2\tan\theta$. Then $\sqrt{4+x^2} = 2\sec\theta$ and $dx = 2\sec^2\theta\,d\theta$. Thus,

$$\int \frac{x^3}{\sqrt{4+x^2}}\,dx = \int \frac{(2\tan\theta)^3}{2\sec\theta}(2\sec^2\theta\,d\theta)$$

$$= 8\int \tan^3\theta\sec\theta\,d\theta$$

$$= 8\int (\sec^2\theta - 1)\tan\theta\sec\theta\,d\theta$$

$$= 8\left(\frac{1}{3}\sec^3\theta - \sec\theta\right) + C$$

$$= \frac{8}{3}\sec\theta(\sec^2\theta - 3) + C$$

$$= \frac{\sqrt{4+x^2}}{3}(x^2 - 8) + C.$$

(b) Let $u^2 = 4 + x^2$. Then, $2u\,du = 2x\,dx$ and we have

$$\int \frac{x^3}{\sqrt{4+x^3}}\,dx = \int \frac{x^2(x\,dx)}{\sqrt{4+x^2}}$$

$$= \int \frac{(u^2 - 4)(u\,du)}{u}$$

$$= \int (u^2 - 4)\,du$$

$$= \frac{1}{3}u^3 - 4u + C$$

$$= \frac{u}{3}(u^2 - 12) + C$$

$$= \frac{\sqrt{4+x^2}}{3}(x^2 - 8) + C.$$

(c) Let

$$dv = \frac{x}{\sqrt{4+x^2}}\,dx \implies v = \int \frac{x}{\sqrt{4+x^2}}\,dx = \sqrt{4+x^2}$$

$$u = x^2 \qquad \implies du = 2x\,dx.$$

$$\int u\,dv = uv - \int v\,du$$

$$\int \frac{x^3}{\sqrt{4+x^2}}\,dx = x^2\sqrt{4+x^2} - \int 2x\sqrt{4+x^2}\,dx$$

$$= x^2\sqrt{4+x^2} - \frac{2}{3}(4+x^2)^{3/2} + C$$

$$= \frac{\sqrt{4+x^2}}{3}(x^2 - 8) + C$$

55. $\displaystyle\int_2^{\sqrt5} x(x^2 - 4)^{3/2}\, dx = \left[\frac{1}{5}(x^2 - 4)^{5/2}\right]_2^{\sqrt5} = \frac{1}{5}$

57. $\displaystyle\int_1^4 \frac{\ln x}{x}\, dx = \left[\frac{1}{2}(\ln x)^2\right]_1^4 = \frac{1}{2}(\ln 4)^2 = 2(\ln 2)^2 \approx 0.961$

59. $\displaystyle\int_0^\pi x \sin x\, dx = \left[-x \cos x + \sin x\right]_0^\pi = \pi$

61. $A = \displaystyle\int_0^4 x\sqrt{4 - x}\, dx = \int_2^0 (4 - u^2)u(-2u)\, du$

$= \displaystyle\int_2^0 2(u^4 - 4u^2)\, du$

$= \left[2\left(\dfrac{u^5}{5} - \dfrac{4u^3}{3}\right)\right]_2^0 = \dfrac{128}{15}$

$u = \sqrt{4 - x},\ x = 4 - u^2,\ dx = -2u\, du$

63. The graph of the region is shown in the figure. Since the region is symmetric to the y-axis, $\bar{x} = 0$. The area of the region is $A = \pi/2$.

$M_x = \dfrac{1}{2}\displaystyle\int_{-1}^1 \left(\sqrt{1 - x^2}\right)^2 dx$

$= \displaystyle\int_0^1 (1 - x^2)\, dx = \left[x - \dfrac{1}{3}x^3\right]_0^1 = \dfrac{2}{3}$

$\bar{y} = \dfrac{M_x}{A} = \dfrac{2/3}{\pi/2} = \dfrac{4}{3\pi}$

$(\bar{x}, \bar{y}) = \left(0, \dfrac{4}{3\pi}\right)$

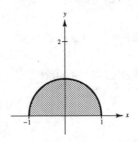

65. (a) $\displaystyle\int_0^1 e^x\, dx = \left[e^x\right]_0^1 = e - 1 \approx 1.72$

(b) $\displaystyle\int_0^1 xe^x\, dx = \left[e^x(x - 1)\right]_0^1 = 1.00$

(c) $\displaystyle\int_0^1 xe^{x^2}\, dx = \left[\dfrac{1}{2}e^{x^2}\right]_0^1 = \dfrac{1}{2}(e - 1) \approx 0.86$

(d) Simpson's Rule $(n = 8)$

$\displaystyle\int_0^1 e^{x^2}\, dx = \dfrac{1}{24}\left[1 + 4e^{(1/8)^2} + 2e^{(1/4)^2} + 4e^{(3/8)^2} + 2e^{(1/2)^2} + 4e^{(5/8)^2} + 2e^{(3/4)^2} + 4e^{(7/8)^2} + e\right] \approx 1.46$

67. $s = \displaystyle\int_0^\pi \sqrt{1 + \cos^2 x}\, dx \approx 3.82$

69. $\displaystyle\lim_{x \to 1}\left[\dfrac{(\ln x)^2}{x - 1}\right] = \lim_{x \to 1}\left[\dfrac{2(1/x)\ln x}{1}\right] = 0$

71. $\displaystyle\lim_{x \to \infty} \dfrac{e^{2x}}{x^2} = \lim_{x \to \infty} \dfrac{2e^{2x}}{2x} = \lim_{x \to \infty} \dfrac{4e^{2x}}{2} = \infty$

73. Begin by taking the natural logarithm of both members of the equation

$$y = \lim_{x \to \infty} (\ln x)^{2/x}.$$

Then we obtain

$$\ln y = \ln\left[\lim_{x \to \infty} (\ln x)^{2/x}\right]$$

$$= \lim_{x \to \infty} \left[\frac{2}{x} \ln(\ln x)\right]$$

$$= 2 \lim_{x \to \infty} \frac{(1/\ln x)(1/x)}{1} = 0.$$

Finally, as $\ln y \to 0$, we know that $y \to 1$ and conclude that

$$\lim_{x \to \infty} (\ln x)^{2/x} = 1.$$

75. $\displaystyle \lim_{n \to \infty} 1000\left(1 + \frac{0.09}{n}\right)^n = 1000 \lim_{n \to \infty} \left(1 + \frac{0.09}{n}\right)^n$

Let $\displaystyle y = \lim_{n \to \infty} \left(1 + \frac{0.09}{n}\right)^n$.

$$\ln y = \lim_{n \to \infty} n \ln\left(1 + \frac{0.09}{n}\right) = \lim_{n \to \infty} \frac{\ln\left(1 + \dfrac{0.09}{n}\right)}{\dfrac{1}{n}} = \lim_{n \to \infty} \left(\frac{\dfrac{-0.09/n^2}{1 + (0.09/n)}}{-\dfrac{1}{n^2}}\right) = \lim_{n \to \infty} \frac{0.09}{1 + \left(\dfrac{0.09}{n}\right)} = 0.09$$

Thus, $\ln y = 0.09 \implies y = e^{0.09}$ and $\displaystyle \lim_{n \to \infty} 1000\left(1 + \frac{0.09}{n}\right)^n = 1000e^{0.09} \approx 1094.17$.

77. $\displaystyle \int_0^{16} \frac{1}{\sqrt[4]{x}}\, dx = \lim_{b \to 0^+} \left[\frac{4}{3} x^{3/4}\right]_b^{16} = \frac{32}{3}$

Converges

79. $\displaystyle \int_1^{\infty} x^2 \ln x\, dx = \lim_{b \to \infty} \left[\frac{x^3}{9}(-1 + 3 \ln x)\right]_1^b = \infty$

Diverges

81. $\displaystyle \int_0^{t_0} 500{,}000 e^{-0.05t}\, dt = \left[\frac{500{,}000}{-0.05} e^{-0.05t}\right]_0^{t_0} = \frac{-500{,}000}{0.05}(e^{-0.05t_0} - 1) = 10{,}000{,}000(1 - e^{-0.05t_0})$

(a) $t_0 = 20$: $6,321,205.59

(b) $t_0 \to \infty$: $10,000,000

83. (a) $\displaystyle P(13 \le x < \infty) = \frac{1}{0.95\sqrt{2\pi}} \int_{13}^{\infty} e^{-(x-12.9)^2/2(0.95)^2}\, dx \approx 0.4581$

(b) $\displaystyle P(15 \le x < 20) = \frac{1}{0.95\sqrt{2\pi}} \int_{15}^{\infty} e^{-(x-12.9)^2/2(0.95)^2}\, dx \approx 0.0135$

85. $dv = dx \implies v = x$

$$u = (\ln x)^n \implies du = n(\ln x)^{n-1}\frac{1}{x}dx$$

$$\int (\ln x)^n\, dx = x(\ln x)^n - n\int (\ln x)^{n-1}\, dx$$

87. False

$$u = \ln x^2 = 2 \ln x \implies du = \frac{2}{x}dx$$

$$\int \frac{\ln x^2}{x}\, dx = \frac{1}{2}\int (\ln x^2)\frac{2}{x}\, dx = \frac{1}{2}\int u\, du$$

89. False

$$\int_{-1}^{1} \sqrt{x^2 - x^3} \, dx = \int_{-1}^{1} \sqrt{x^2(1 - x)} \, dx$$

$$= \int_{-1}^{1} |x| \sqrt{1 - x} \, dx$$

91. $\displaystyle\int_{x}^{1} \frac{1}{1 + t^2} \, dt = \left[\arctan t \right]_{x}^{1} = \frac{\pi}{4} - \arctan x$

$$\int_{1}^{1/x} \frac{1}{1 + t^2} \, dt = \left[\arctan t \right]_{1}^{1/x} = \arctan \frac{1}{x} - \frac{\pi}{4}$$

Since $\arctan x + \arctan \dfrac{1}{x} = \dfrac{\pi}{2}, x > 0$, we have:

$$\arctan \frac{1}{x} = \frac{\pi}{4} + \frac{\pi}{4} - \arctan x$$

$$\arctan \frac{1}{x} - \frac{\pi}{4} = \frac{\pi}{4} - \arctan x$$

Therefore, $\displaystyle\int_{1}^{1/x} \frac{1}{1 + t^2} \, dt = \int_{x}^{1} \frac{1}{1 + t^2} \, dt.$

CHAPTER 8
Infinite Series

CHAPTER 8
Infinite Series

Section 8.1   Sequences

Solutions to Odd-Numbered Exercises

1. $a_n = 2^n$

$a_1 = 2^1 = 2$

$a_2 = 2^2 = 4$

$a_3 = 2^3 = 8$

$a_4 = 2^4 = 16$

$a_5 = 2^5 = 32$

3. $a_n = \left(-\dfrac{1}{2}\right)^n$

$a_1 = \left(-\dfrac{1}{2}\right)^1 = -\dfrac{1}{2}$

$a_2 = \left(-\dfrac{1}{2}\right)^2 = \dfrac{1}{4}$

$a_3 = \left(-\dfrac{1}{2}\right)^3 = -\dfrac{1}{8}$

$a_4 = \left(-\dfrac{1}{2}\right)^4 = \dfrac{1}{16}$

$a_5 = \left(-\dfrac{1}{2}\right)^5 = -\dfrac{1}{32}$

5. $a_n = \dfrac{(-1)^{n(n+1)/2}}{n^2}$

$a_1 = \dfrac{(-1)^1}{1^2} = -1$

$a_2 = \dfrac{(-1)^3}{2^2} = -\dfrac{1}{4}$

$a_3 = \dfrac{(-1)^6}{3^2} = \dfrac{1}{9}$

$a_4 = \dfrac{(-1)^{10}}{4^2} = \dfrac{1}{16}$

$a_5 = \dfrac{(-1)^{15}}{5^2} = -\dfrac{1}{25}$

7. $a_n = \dfrac{3^n}{n!}$

$a_1 = \dfrac{3}{1!} = 3$

$a_2 = \dfrac{3^2}{2!} = \dfrac{9}{2}$

$a_3 = \dfrac{3^3}{3!} = \dfrac{27}{6}$

$a_4 = \dfrac{3^4}{4!} = \dfrac{81}{24}$

$a_5 = \dfrac{3^5}{5!} = \dfrac{243}{120}$

9. Since $a_1 = 3$, and $a_{k+1} = 2(a_k - 1)$, we have

$a_1 = 3$

$a_2 = 2(a_1 - 1) = 2(3 - 1) = 4$

$a_3 = 2(a_2 - 1) = 2(4 - 1) = 6$

$a_4 = 2(a_3 - 1) = 2(6 - 1) = 10$

$a_5 = 2(a_4 - 1) = 2(10 - 1) = 18.$

11. $a_1 = 32,\ a_{k+1} = \dfrac{1}{2}a_k$

$a_2 = \dfrac{1}{2}a_1 = \dfrac{1}{2}(32) = 16$

$a_3 = \dfrac{1}{2}a_2 = \dfrac{1}{2}(16) = 8$

$a_4 = \dfrac{1}{2}a_3 = \dfrac{1}{2}(8) = 4$

$a_5 = \dfrac{1}{2}a_4 = \dfrac{1}{2}(4) = 2$

13. Because $a_1 = 8/(1 + 1) = 4$ and $a_2 = 8/(2 + 1) = \frac{8}{3}$, the sequence matches graph (d).

15. This sequence decreases and $a_1 = 4$, $a_2 = 4(0.5) = 2$.
Matches (c).

17. 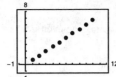   **19.** 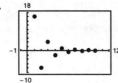   **21.**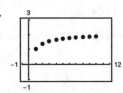

23. The difference between two consecutive terms in the sequence 2, 5, 8, 11, . . . is 3. Therefore, the sequence can be defined recursively as $a_1 = 2$ and $a_{k+1} = a_k + 3$. The next two terms of the sequence are 14 and 17.

25. $a_n = \dfrac{3}{(-2)^{n-1}}$

$a_n = \dfrac{3}{(-2)^4} = \dfrac{3}{16}$

$a_6 = \dfrac{3}{(-2)^5} = -\dfrac{3}{32}$

27. $\dfrac{10!}{8!} = \dfrac{8!(9)(10)}{8!}$

$= (9)(10) = 90$

29. $\dfrac{(n+1)!}{n!} = \dfrac{n!(n+1)}{n!}$

$= n+1$

31. $\dfrac{(2n-1)!}{(2n+1)!} = \dfrac{(2n-1)(2n-2)\cdots 3 \cdot 2 \cdot 1}{(2n+1)(2n)(2n-1)(2n-2)\cdots 3 \cdot 2 \cdot 1} = \dfrac{1}{(2n+1)(2n)}$

33. $a_n = 3n - 2$

35. $-1, 2, 7, 14, 23, \ldots$

Compare the terms of the sequence $-1, 2, 7, 14, 23, \ldots$ with the sequence of squares

$$1^2, 2^2, 3^2, 4^2, 5^2, \ldots = 1, 4, 9, 16, 25, \ldots.$$

Observe that each term of the given sequence is two less than the sequence of squares. Thus, we write the nth term of the given sequence as $a_n = n^2 - 2$.

37. $a_n = \dfrac{n+1}{n+2}$

39. $2, -1, \dfrac{1}{2}, \dfrac{-1}{4}, \dfrac{1}{8}, \ldots$

First observe that the denominators are powers of 2, where for $n = 4$ the denominator is 2^2. This implies that the nth term has a denominator 2^{n-2}. Note further that the signs alternate starting with a positive sign, and thus the nth term is

$$a_n = (-1)^{n-1}\left(\dfrac{1}{2^{n-2}}\right) = \dfrac{(-1)^{n-1}}{2^{n-2}}.$$

41. $a_n = 1 + \dfrac{1}{n} = \dfrac{n+1}{n}$

43. $a_n = \dfrac{n}{(n+1)(n+2)}$

45. $1, -\dfrac{1}{1 \cdot 3}, \dfrac{1}{1 \cdot 3 \cdot 5}, -\dfrac{1}{1 \cdot 3 \cdot 5 \cdot 7}, \ldots$

The denominator of the nth term is the product of the first n positive odd integers. Note further that the signs alternate starting with a positive sign, and thus the nth term is

$$a_n = \dfrac{(-1)^{n-1}}{1 \cdot 3 \cdot 5 \cdots (2n-1)}.$$

—CONTINUED—

45. —CONTINUED—

A second form of the nth term is obtained when we multiply the numerator and denominator by the n missing even integers. Then,

$$
\begin{aligned}
a_n &= \frac{(-1)^{n-1}}{1 \cdot 3 \cdot 5 \cdots (2n-1)} \\
&= \frac{(-1)^{n-1} 2 \cdot 4 \cdot 6 \cdot 8 \cdots (2n)}{1 \cdot 2 \cdot 3 \cdot 4 \cdot 5 \cdots (2n-1)(2n)} \\
&= \frac{(-1)^{n-1} 2^n (1 \cdot 2 \cdot 3 \cdot 4 \cdots n)}{1 \cdot 2 \cdot 3 \cdot 4 \cdot 5 \cdots (2n-1)(2n)} \\
&= \frac{(-1)^{n-1} 2^n n!}{(2n)!}.
\end{aligned}
$$

47.

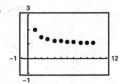

The graph seems to indicate that the sequence converges to 1. Analytically,

$$
\lim_{n \to \infty} a_n = \lim_{n \to \infty} \frac{n+1}{n} = \lim_{x \to \infty} \frac{x+1}{x} = \lim_{x \to \infty} 1 = 1.
$$

49.

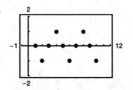

The graph seems to indicate that the sequence diverges. Analytically, the sequence is

$$
\{a_n\} = \{0, -1, 0, 1, 0, -1, \ldots\}.
$$

Hence, $\lim\limits_{n \to \infty} a_n$ does not exist.

51. $a_n = (-1)^n \left(\dfrac{n}{n+1} \right)$

Since

$$
\lim_{n \to \infty} a_n = \lim_{n \to \infty} (-1)^n \left(\frac{n}{n+1} \right) = \pm 1,
$$

the limit does not exist and the sequence $\{a_n\}$ diverges.

53. $\lim\limits_{n \to \infty} \dfrac{3n^2 - n + 4}{2n^2 + 1} = \dfrac{3}{2}$, converges

55. $\lim\limits_{n \to \infty} \dfrac{1 + (-1)^n}{n} = 0$ converges

57. $\lim\limits_{n \to \infty} \left(\dfrac{3}{4} \right)^n = 0$, converges

59. $a_n = \dfrac{(n+1)!}{n!}$

Since

$$
\begin{aligned}
\lim_{n \to \infty} a_n &= \lim_{n \to \infty} \frac{(n+1)!}{n!} \\
&= \lim_{n \to \infty} \frac{(n+1)(n)(n-1) \cdots 3 \cdot 2 \cdot 1}{n(n-1) \cdots 3 \cdot 2 \cdot 1} \\
&= \lim_{n \to \infty} (n+1) = \infty,
\end{aligned}
$$

the sequence $\{a_n\}$ diverges.

61.

$$
\begin{aligned}
\lim_{n \to \infty} \left(\frac{n-1}{n} - \frac{n}{n-1} \right) &= \lim_{n \to \infty} \frac{(n-1)^2 - n^2}{n(n-1)} \\
&= \lim_{n \to \infty} \frac{1 - 2n}{n^2 - n} = 0, \quad \text{converges}
\end{aligned}
$$

63. $\lim\limits_{n\to\infty} \dfrac{n^p}{e^n} = 0$, converges

$(p > 0, n \ge 2)$

65. $a_n = \left(1 + \dfrac{k}{n}\right)^n$

$$\lim_{n\to\infty} a_n = \lim_{n\to\infty}\left(1 + \frac{k}{n}\right)^n = \lim_{n\to\infty}\left[\left(1 + \frac{k}{n}\right)^{n/k}\right]^k$$

Now let $u = k/n$. Then as n approaches infinity, u approaches zero, and

$$\lim_{n\to\infty} a_n = \lim_{u\to 0}\left[(1 + u)^{1/u}\right]^k = e^k.$$

Therefore the sequence converges to e^k.

67. $a_n = 4 - \dfrac{1}{n} < 4 - \dfrac{1}{n+1} = a_{n+1}$,

monotonic; $|a_n| < 4$ bounded.

69. $a_n = \dfrac{\cos n}{n}$

$a_1 = 0.5403$

$a_2 = -0.2081$

$a_3 = -0.3230$

$a_4 = -0.1634$

Not monotonic; $|a_n| \le 1$, bounded

71. $a_n = (-1)^n\left(\dfrac{1}{n}\right)$

Writing out the first few terms of the sequence we have

$$a_1 = -1, a_2 = \frac{1}{2}, a_3 = -\frac{1}{3}, a_4 = \frac{1}{4}, \cdots.$$

Because of the alternating signs, observe that the terms are neither nondecreasing nor nonincreasing. Therefore, the sequence is *not* monotonic. The sequence is bounded since $-1 \le a_n \le 1$ for all n.

73. $a_n = \left(\dfrac{2}{3}\right)^n > \left(\dfrac{2}{3}\right)^{n+1} = a_{n+1}$

Monotonic; $|a_n| \le \dfrac{2}{3}$, bounded

75. $a_n = \sin\left(\dfrac{n\pi}{6}\right)$

$a_1 = 0.500$

$a_2 = 0.8660$

$a_3 = 1.000$

$a_4 = 0.8660$

Not monotonic; $|a_n| \le 1$, bounded

77. (a) $a_n = 5 + \dfrac{1}{n}$

$\left|5 + \dfrac{1}{n}\right| \le 6 \implies \{a_n\}$ bounded

$a_n = 5 + \dfrac{1}{n} > 5 + \dfrac{1}{n+1}$

$= a_{n+1} \implies \{a_n\}$ monotonic

Therefore, $\{a_n\}$ converges.

(b)

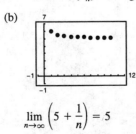

$$\lim_{n\to\infty}\left(5 + \frac{1}{n}\right) = 5$$

79. (a) $a_n = \dfrac{1}{3}\left(1 - \dfrac{1}{3^n}\right)$

$\left|\dfrac{1}{3}\left(1 - \dfrac{1}{3^n}\right)\right| < \dfrac{1}{3} \implies \{a_n\}$ bounded

$a_n = \dfrac{1}{3}\left(1 - \dfrac{1}{3^n}\right) < \dfrac{1}{3}\left(1 - \dfrac{1}{3^{n+1}}\right)$

$= a_{n+1} \implies \{a_n\}$ monotonic

Therefore, $\{a_n\}$ converges.

(b)

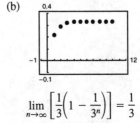

$$\lim_{n\to\infty}\left[\frac{1}{3}\left(1 - \frac{1}{3^n}\right)\right] = \frac{1}{3}$$

81. (a) $a_n = 10 - \dfrac{1}{n}$

(b) Not possible; a bounded monotonic sequence must converge—see Theorem 8.5.

(c) $a_n = \dfrac{3n}{4n + 1}$

(d) Not possible; an unbounded sequence does not converge.

85. (a) If we let A_n be the amount budgeted after n years, we have

$A_1 = 2.5 - 0.2(2.5) = 0.8(2.5)$ billion

$A_2 = A_1 - 0.2A_1 = 0.8A_1 = 0.8^2(2.5)$ billion

$A_3 = A_2 - 0.2A_2 = 0.8A_2 = 0.8^2(2.5)$ billion

$\vdots$

$A_n = 2.5(0.8)^n$ billion.

87. (a) $a_n = 59.69n + 697.32$

(b) For the year 2000, $n = 10$ and $a_{10} \approx \$1294$

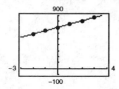

91. $a_n = \dfrac{10^n}{n!}$

(a) $a_9 = a_{10} = \dfrac{10^9}{9!}$

$= \dfrac{1,000,000,000}{362,880}$

$= \dfrac{1,562,500}{567}$

(b) Decreasing

(c) Factorials increase more rapidly than exponentials.

83. $A_n = P\left[1 + \dfrac{r}{12}\right]^n$

(a) $\lim\limits_{n \to \infty} A_n = \infty$, divergent. The amount will grow arbitrarily large over time.

(b) $A_n = 9000\left[1 + \dfrac{0.115}{12}\right]^n$

$A_1 = \$9086.25$	$A_6 = \$9530.06$
$A_2 = \$9173.33$	$A_7 = \$9621.39$
$A_3 = \$9261.24$	$A_8 = \$9713.59$
$A_4 = \$9349.99$	$A_9 = \$9806.68$
$A_5 = \$9439.60$	$A_{10} = \$9900.66$

(b) $A_1 = 2.5(0.8) = \$2$ billion

$A_2 = 2.5(0.8)^2 = \$1.6$ billion

$A_3 = 2.5(0.8)^3 = \$1.28$ billion

$A_4 = 2.5(0.8)^4 = \$1.024$ billion

(c) $\lim\limits_{n \to \infty} 2.5(0.8)^n = 0$ and therefore the sequence converges.

89. $S_6 = 130 + 70 + 40 = 240$

$S_7 = 240 + 130 + 70 = 440$

$S_8 = 440 + 240 + 130 = 810$

$S_9 = 810 + 440 + 240 = 1490$

$S_{10} = 1490 + 810 + 440 = 2740$

93. $\{a_n\} = \left\{\sqrt[n]{n}\right\} = \{n^{1/n}\}$

$a_1 = 1^{1/1} = 1$

$a_2 = \sqrt{2} \approx 1.4142$

$a_3 = \sqrt[3]{3} \approx 1.4422$

$a_4 = \sqrt[4]{4} \approx 1.4142$

$a_5 = \sqrt[5]{5} \approx 1.3797$

$a_6 = \sqrt[6]{6} \approx 1.3480$

Let $y = \lim\limits_{n \to \infty} n^{1/n}$.

$\ln y = \lim\limits_{n \to \infty} \left(\dfrac{1}{n}\ln n\right) = \lim\limits_{n \to \infty} \dfrac{\ln n}{n} = \lim\limits_{n \to \infty} \dfrac{1/n}{1} = 0$

Since $\ln y = 0$, we have $y = e^0 = 1$. Therefore,

$\lim\limits_{n \to \infty} \sqrt[n]{n} = 1$.

95. $a_{n+2} = a_n + a_{n+1}$

(a)

$a_1 = 1$	$a_7 = 8 + 5 = 13$
$a_2 = 1$	$a_8 = 13 + 8 = 21$
$a_3 = 1 + 1 = 2$	$a_9 = 21 + 13 = 34$
$a_4 = 2 + 1 = 3$	$a_{10} = 34 + 21 = 55$
$a_5 = 3 + 2 = 5$	$a_{11} = 55 + 34 = 89$
$a_6 = 5 + 3 = 8$	$a_{12} = 89 + 55 = 144$

(c) $1 + \dfrac{1}{b_{n-1}} = 1 + \dfrac{1}{\dfrac{a_n}{a_{n-1}}}$

$$= 1 + \frac{a_{n-1}}{a_n}$$

$$= \frac{a_n + a_{n-1}}{a_n} = \frac{a_{n+1}}{a_n} = b_n$$

(b) $b_n = \dfrac{a_{n+1}}{a_n}, n \geq 1$

$b_1 = \dfrac{1}{1} = 1$	$b_6 = \dfrac{13}{8}$
$b_2 = \dfrac{2}{1} = 2$	$b_7 = \dfrac{21}{13}$
$b_3 = \dfrac{3}{2}$	$b_8 = \dfrac{34}{21}$
$b_4 = \dfrac{5}{3}$	$b_9 = \dfrac{55}{34}$
$b_5 = \dfrac{8}{5}$	$b_{10} = \dfrac{89}{55}$

(d) If $\lim\limits_{n \to \infty} b_n = \rho$, then $\lim\limits_{n \to \infty} \left(1 + \dfrac{1}{b_{n-1}}\right) = \rho$.

Since $\lim\limits_{n \to \infty} b_n = \lim\limits_{n \to \infty} b_{n-1}$ we have $1 + (1/\rho) = \rho$.

$$\rho + 1 = \rho^2$$
$$0 = \rho^2 - \rho - 1$$
$$\rho = \frac{1 \pm \sqrt{1 + 4}}{2} = \frac{1 \pm \sqrt{5}}{2}$$

Since a_n, and thus b_n, is positive,

$$\rho = \left(1 + \sqrt{5}\right)/2 \approx 1.6180.$$

97. True

99. True

101. $a_1 = \sqrt{2} \approx 1.4142$

$a_2 = \sqrt{2 + \sqrt{2}} \approx 1.8478$

$a_3 = \sqrt{2 + \sqrt{2 + \sqrt{2}}} \approx 1.9616$

$a_4 = \sqrt{2 + \sqrt{2 + \sqrt{2 + \sqrt{2}}}} \approx 1.9904$

$a_5 = \sqrt{2 + \sqrt{2 + \sqrt{2 + \sqrt{2 + \sqrt{2}}}}} \approx 1.9976$

$\{a_n\}$ is increasing and bounded by 2, and hence converges to L. Letting $\lim\limits_{n \to \infty} a_n = L$ implies that $\sqrt{2 + L} = L \Rightarrow L = 2$. Hence, $\lim\limits_{n \to \infty} a_n = 2$.

Section 8.2   Series and Convergence

1. $S_1 = 1$

$S_2 = 1 + \frac{1}{4} = 1.2500$

$S_3 = 1 + \frac{1}{4} + \frac{1}{9} \approx 1.3611$

$S_4 = 1 + \frac{1}{4} + \frac{1}{9} + \frac{1}{16} \approx 1.4236$

$S_5 = 1 + \frac{1}{4} + \frac{1}{9} + \frac{1}{16} + \frac{1}{25} \approx 1.4636$

3. $3 - \dfrac{9}{2} + \dfrac{27}{4} - \dfrac{81}{8} + \dfrac{243}{16} - \cdots$

$S_1 = 3$

$S_2 = 3 - \dfrac{9}{2} = -\dfrac{3}{2} = -1.5$

$S_3 = 3 - \dfrac{9}{2} + \dfrac{27}{4} = \dfrac{21}{4} = 5.25$

$S_4 = 3 - \dfrac{9}{2} + \dfrac{27}{4} - \dfrac{81}{8} = -\dfrac{39}{8} = -4.875$

$S_5 = 3 - \dfrac{9}{2} + \dfrac{27}{4} - \dfrac{81}{8} + \dfrac{243}{16} = \dfrac{165}{16} = 10.3125$

5. $S_1 = 3$

$S_2 = 3 + \frac{3}{2} = 4.5$

$S_3 = 3 + \frac{3}{2} + \frac{3}{4} = 5.250$

$S_4 = 3 + \frac{3}{2} + \frac{3}{4} + \frac{3}{8} = 5.625$

$S_5 = 3 + \frac{3}{2} + \frac{3}{4} + \frac{3}{8} + \frac{3}{16} = 5.8125$

7. $\displaystyle\sum_{n=1}^{\infty} \frac{n}{n+1}$

$\displaystyle\lim_{n\to\infty} \frac{n}{n+1} = 1 \neq 0$

Diverges by Theorem 8.9

9. $\displaystyle\sum_{n=1}^{\infty} \frac{n^2}{n^2+1}$

$\displaystyle\lim_{n\to\infty} \frac{n^2}{n^2+1} = 1 \neq 0$

Diverges by Theorem 8.9

11. $\displaystyle\sum_{n=0}^{\infty} 3\left(\frac{3}{2}\right)^n = 3 + \frac{9}{2} + \frac{27}{4} + \frac{81}{8} + \cdots$

The series is geometric with common ratio $r = \frac{3}{2}$. Since $|r| \geq 1$, the series diverges.

13. $\displaystyle\sum_{n=0}^{\infty} 1000(1.055)^n$ Geometric series

$r = 1.055 > 1$

Diverges by Theorem 8.6

15. $\displaystyle\sum_{n=0}^{\infty} \frac{2^n+1}{2^{n+1}}$

$\displaystyle\lim_{n\to\infty} a_n = \lim_{n\to\infty} \frac{2^n-1}{2^{n+1}} = \lim_{n\to\infty} \frac{1-(1/2^n)}{2} = \frac{1}{2} \neq 0$

Therefore, the series diverges by the nth-Term Test for Divergence.

17. $\displaystyle\sum_{n=0}^{\infty} 2\left(\frac{3}{4}\right)^n = 2 + \frac{3}{2} + \frac{9}{8} + \frac{27}{32} + \frac{81}{128} + \cdots$

The series is geometric with $a = 2$ and $r = \frac{3}{4}$. Since $|r| < 1$, the series converges.

19. $\displaystyle\sum_{n=0}^{\infty} (0.9)^n$

Geometric series with $r = 0.9 < 1$.

Converges by Theorem 8.6

21. $\displaystyle\sum_{n=1}^{\infty} \frac{1}{n(n+1)}$

Using partial fractions, we can write

$$a_n = \frac{1}{n(n+1)} = \frac{1}{n} - \frac{1}{n+1}.$$

Therefore,

$$\sum_{n=1}^{\infty} \frac{1}{n(n+1)} = \sum_{n=1}^{\infty} \left(\frac{1}{n} - \frac{1}{n+1}\right)$$

$$= \left(1 - \frac{1}{2}\right) + \left(\frac{1}{2} - \frac{1}{3}\right) + \left(\frac{1}{3} - \frac{1}{4}\right) + \cdots$$

where each term after the first term of 1 cancels. Thus, the series converges to 1.

23. $\displaystyle\sum_{n=0}^{\infty} \frac{9}{4}\left(\frac{1}{4}\right)^n = \frac{9}{4}\left[1 + \frac{1}{4} + \frac{1}{16} + \cdots\right]$

$S_0 = \frac{9}{4}, S_1 = \frac{9}{4} \cdot \frac{5}{4} = \frac{45}{16}, S_2 = \frac{9}{4} \cdot \frac{21}{16} \approx 2.95, \ldots$

Matches graph (c).

Analytically, the series is geometric:

$$\sum_{n=0}^{\infty} \left(\frac{9}{4}\right)\left(\frac{1}{4}\right)^n = \frac{9/4}{1 - 1/4} = \frac{9/4}{3/4} = 3$$

25. $\displaystyle\sum_{n=0}^{\infty} \frac{15}{4}\left(-\frac{1}{4}\right)^n = \frac{15}{4}\left[1 - \frac{1}{4} + \frac{1}{16} - \cdots\right]$

$S_0 = \frac{15}{4}, S_1 = \frac{45}{16}, S_2 \approx 3.05, \ldots$

Matches graph (a).

Analytically, the series is geometric:

$$\sum_{n=0}^{\infty} \frac{15}{4}\left(-\frac{1}{4}\right)^n = \frac{15/4}{1 - (-1/4)} = \frac{15/4}{5/4} = 3$$

27. (a) $\displaystyle\sum_{n=1}^{\infty} 2(0.9)^{n-1} = \sum_{n=0}^{\infty} 2(0.9)^n = \frac{2}{1-0.9} = 20$

(b)

n	5	10	20	50	100
S_n	8.1902	13.0264	17.5685	19.8969	19.9995

(c) The graph is shown if the figure.

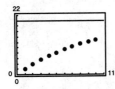

(d) The terms of the series decrease in magnitude slowly, and the sequence of partial sums approaches the sum of the series relatively slowly.

29. (a) $\displaystyle\sum_{n=1}^{\infty} 10(0.25)^{n-1} = \frac{10}{1-0.25} = \frac{40}{3} \approx 13.3333$

(b)

n	5	10	20	50	100
S_n	13.3203	13.3333	13.3333	13.3333	13.3333

(c)

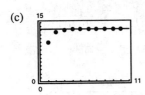

(d) The terms of the series decrease in magnitude rapidly. Thus, the sequence of partial sums approaches the sum rapidly.

31. $\displaystyle\sum_{n=0}^{\infty} \left(\frac{1}{2}\right)^n = \frac{1}{1-(1/2)} = 2$

33. $\displaystyle\sum_{n=0}^{\infty} \left(-\frac{1}{2}\right)^n = \frac{1}{1-(-1/2)} = \frac{2}{3}$

35. The series

$$1 + 0.1 + 0.01 + 0.001 + \cdots = \sum_{n=0}^{\infty} (0.1)^n$$

is geometric with $a = 1$ and $r = 0.1$. Therefore, the sum is

$$S = \frac{a}{1-r} = \frac{1}{1-0.1} = \frac{10}{9}.$$

37. $\displaystyle\sum_{n=0}^{\infty} 3\left(-\frac{1}{3}\right)^n = \frac{3}{1-(-1/3)} = \frac{9}{4}$

39. $\displaystyle\sum_{n=2}^{\infty} \frac{1}{n^2-1} = \sum_{n=2}^{\infty} \left(\frac{1/2}{n-1} - \frac{1/2}{n+1}\right) = \frac{1}{2}\sum_{n=2}^{\infty} \left(\frac{1}{n-1} - \frac{1}{n+1}\right)$

$$= \frac{1}{2}\left[\left(1 - \frac{1}{3}\right) + \left(\frac{1}{2} - \frac{1}{4}\right) + \left(\frac{1}{3} - \frac{1}{5}\right) + \left(\frac{1}{4} - \frac{1}{6}\right) + \cdots\right]$$

$$= \frac{1}{2}\left(1 + \frac{1}{2}\right) = \frac{3}{4}$$

41. $\displaystyle\sum_{n=1}^{\infty} \frac{4}{n(n+2)}$

Using partial fractions, we have

$$\frac{4}{n(n+2)} = \frac{A}{n} + \frac{B}{n+2}.$$

Multiplying by $n(n+2)$, yields

$$4 = A(n+2) + Bn.$$

If $n = 0$, then $4 = 2A$ or $A = 2$. If $n = -2$, then $4 = -2B$ or $B = -2$. Thus,

$$\sum_{n=1}^{\infty} \frac{4}{n(n+2)} = \sum_{n=1}^{\infty} \left[\frac{2}{n} - \frac{2}{n+2} \right]$$

$$= \left[2 - \frac{2}{3} \right] + \left[\frac{2}{2} - \frac{2}{4} \right] + \left[\frac{2}{3} - \frac{2}{5} \right] + \left[\frac{2}{4} - \frac{2}{6} \right] + \left[\frac{2}{5} - \frac{2}{7} \right] + \cdots = 2 + 1 = 3.$$

43. $\displaystyle\sum_{n=0}^{\infty} \left(\frac{1}{2^n} - \frac{1}{3^n} \right) = \sum_{n=0}^{\infty} \left(\frac{1}{2} \right)^n - \sum_{n=0}^{\infty} \left(\frac{1}{3} \right)^n = \frac{1}{1 - (1/2)} - \frac{1}{1 - (1/3)} = 2 - \frac{3}{2} = \frac{1}{2}$

45. $\displaystyle 0.\overline{4} = \sum_{n=0}^{\infty} \frac{4}{10} \left(\frac{1}{10} \right)^n$

Geometric series with $a = \frac{4}{10}$ and $r = \frac{1}{10}$

$$S = \frac{a}{1-r} = \frac{4/10}{1 - (1/10)} = \frac{4}{9}$$

47. $0.07\overline{575} = 0.075 + 0.00075 + 0.0000075 + \cdots$

$$= 0.075(1 + 0.01 + 0.0001 + \cdots)$$

$$= \sum_{n=0}^{\infty} \frac{75}{1000} \left(\frac{1}{100} \right)^n = \sum_{n=0}^{\infty} \frac{3}{40} \left(\frac{1}{100} \right)^n$$

This is a geometric series with $a = \frac{3}{40}$ and $r = \frac{1}{100}$. Therefore,

$$0.07\overline{575} = \frac{a}{1-r} = \frac{3/40}{1 - (1/100)} = \frac{5}{66}.$$

49. $\displaystyle\sum_{n=1}^{\infty} \frac{n+10}{10n+1}$

$$\lim_{n \to \infty} \frac{n+10}{10n+1} = \frac{1}{10} \neq 0$$

Diverges by Theorem 8.9

51. $\displaystyle\sum_{n=1}^{\infty} \left(\frac{1}{n} - \frac{1}{n+2} \right) = \left(1 - \frac{1}{3} \right) + \left(\frac{1}{2} - \frac{1}{4} \right) + \left(\frac{1}{3} - \frac{1}{5} \right) + \left(\frac{1}{4} - \frac{1}{6} \right) + \cdots = 1 + \frac{1}{2} = \frac{3}{2}$, converges

53. $\displaystyle\sum_{n=1}^{\infty} \frac{3n-1}{2n+1}$

Since

$$\lim_{n \to \infty} a_n = \lim_{n \to \infty} \frac{3n-1}{2n+1} = \frac{3}{2} \neq 0,$$

the series diverges by the nth-Term Test for Divergence.

55. $\displaystyle\sum_{n=0}^{\infty} \frac{4}{2^n} = 4 \sum_{n=0}^{\infty} \left(\frac{1}{2} \right)^n$

Geometric series with $r = \frac{1}{2}$

Converges by Theorem 8.6

57. $\displaystyle\sum_{n=0}^{\infty} (1.075)^n$

Geometric series with $r = 1.075$

Diverges by Theorem 8.6

59. $\displaystyle\sum_{n=2}^{\infty} \frac{n}{\ln n}$

$$\lim_{n \to \infty} \frac{n}{\ln n} = \lim_{n \to \infty} \frac{1}{1/n} = \infty$$

(by L'Hôpital's Rule) Diverges by Theorem 8.9

61. (a) The ratios of consecutive terms are x. Therefore, the series is geometric with common ratio x.

(b) Since the first term is $a = 1$ and the common ratio is $r = x$, the series will converge if $|x| < 1$.

$$1 + x + x^2 + x^3 + \cdots = \sum_{n=0}^{\infty} x^n$$

$$= \frac{a}{1 - r} = \frac{1}{1 - x}$$

$$f(x) = \frac{1}{1 - x}, \quad |x| < 1$$

(c) The graph is given in the figure.

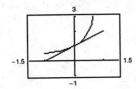

63. $f(x) = 3\left[\dfrac{1 - 0.5^x}{1 - 0.5}\right]$

Horizontal asymptote: $y = 6$

$$\sum_{n=0}^{\infty} 3\left(\frac{1}{2}\right)^n$$

$$S = \frac{3}{1 - (1/2)} = 6$$

The horizontal asymptote is the sum of the series. $f(n)$ is the nth partial sum.

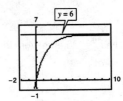

65. $\dfrac{1}{n(n + 1)} < 0.001$

$$10{,}000 < n^2 + n$$

$$0 < n^2 + n - 10{,}000$$

$$n = \frac{-1 \pm \sqrt{1^2 - 4(1)(-10{,}000)}}{2}$$

Choosing the positive value for n we have $n \approx 99.5012$. The first *term* that is less than 0.001 is $n = 100$.

$$\left(\frac{1}{8}\right)^n < 0.001$$

$$10{,}000 < 8^n$$

This inequality is true when $n = 5$. This series converges at a faster rate.

67. $\displaystyle\sum_{i=0}^{n-1} 8000(0.9)^i = \frac{8000[1 - (0.9)^{(n-1)+1}]}{1 - 0.9}$

$$= 80{,}000(1 - 0.9^n), \quad n > 0$$

69. $D_1 = 16$

$$D_2 = \underbrace{0.81(16)}_{\text{up}} + \underbrace{0.81(16)}_{\text{down}} = 32(0.81)$$

$$D_3 = 16(0.81)^2 + 16(0.81)^2 = 32(0.81)^2$$

$$\vdots$$

$$D = 16 + 32(0.81) + 32(0.81)^2 + \ldots$$

$$= -16 + \sum_{n=0}^{\infty} 32(0.81)^n = -16 + \frac{32}{1 - 0.81}$$

$$= 152.42 \text{ ft}$$

71. $P(n) = \dfrac{1}{2}\left(\dfrac{1}{2}\right)^n$

$$P(2) = \frac{1}{2}\left(\frac{1}{2}\right)^2 = \frac{1}{8}$$

The series

$$\sum_{n=0}^{\infty} \frac{1}{2}\left(\frac{1}{2}\right)^n$$

is geometric with $a = \frac{1}{2}$ and $r = \frac{1}{2}$. Therefore, it converges and

$$\sum_{n=0}^{\infty} \frac{1}{2}\left(\frac{1}{2}\right)^n = \frac{1/2}{1 - (1/2)} = 1.$$

73. (a) $64 + 32 + 16 + 8 + 4 + 2 = 126$ in.^{2}

(b) $\displaystyle\sum_{n=0}^{\infty} 64\left(\frac{1}{2}\right)^n = \frac{64}{1 - (1/2)} = 128$ in.^{2}

Note: This is one-half of the area of the original square!

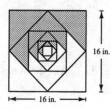

16 in.

16 in.

75. Since the wage keeps doubling every day, the sequence of wages is geometric with $a = 0.01$ and $r = 2$. Therefore, the total wage W after n days is

$$\sum_{n=0}^{n-1} 0.01(2)^n = \frac{0.01(1 - 2^n)}{1 - 2} = 0.01(2^n - 1).$$

(a) When $n = 29$, $W = \$5,368,709.11$.

(b) When $n = 30$, $W = \$10,737,418.23$.

(c) When $n = 31$, $W = \$21,474,836.47$.

77. (a) Use $P = \$50$, $r = 0.03$, and $t = 20$ in the formula

$$A = P\left(\frac{12}{r}\right)\left[\left(1 + \frac{r}{12}\right)^{12t} - 1\right]$$

to obtain

$$A = 50\left(\frac{12}{0.03}\right)\left[\left(1 + \frac{0.03}{12}\right)^{12 \cdot 20} - 1\right]$$

$$= \$16,415.10.$$

(b) Use $P = \$50$, $r = 0.03$, and $t = 20$ in the formula

$$A = \frac{P(e^{rt} - 1)}{e^{r/12} - 1}$$

to obtain

$$A = \frac{50(e^{0.03 \cdot 20} - 1)}{e^{0.03/12} - 1} = \$16,421.83.$$

79. $P = 100$, $r = 0.04$, $t = 40$

(a) $A = 100\left(\dfrac{12}{0.04}\right)\left[\left(1 + \dfrac{0.04}{12}\right)^{12(40)} - 1\right] \approx \$118,196.13$

(b) $A = \dfrac{100(e^{0.04(40)} - 1)}{e^{0.04/12} - 1} \approx \$118,393.43$

81. $x = 0.749999\ldots = 0.74 + \displaystyle\sum_{n=0}^{\infty} 0.009(0.1)^n$

$$= 0.74 + \frac{0.009}{1 - 0.1}$$

$$= 0.74 + 0.01 = 0.75$$

83. By letting $S_0 = 0$, we have $a_n = \displaystyle\sum_{k=1}^{n} a_k - \sum_{k=1}^{n-1} a_k = S_n - S_{n-1}$. Thus,

$$\sum_{n=1}^{\infty} a_n = \sum_{n=1}^{\infty} (S_n - S_{n-1}) = \sum_{n=1}^{\infty} (S_n - S_{n-1} + c - c) = \sum_{n=1}^{\infty} [(c - S_{n-1}) - (c - S_n)].$$

85. $\displaystyle\sum_{n=0}^{39} 30{,}000(1.05)^n = \frac{30{,}000(1 - 1.05^{40})}{1 - 1.05} \approx \$3{,}623{,}993.23$

87. Let $\displaystyle\sum a_n = \sum_{n=0}^{\infty} 1$ and $\displaystyle\sum b_n = \sum_{n=0}^{\infty} (-1)$.

Both are divergent series.

$$\sum (a_n + b_n) = \sum_{n=0}^{\infty} [1 + (-1)] = \sum_{n=0}^{\infty} [1 - 1] = 0$$

89. False. $\displaystyle\lim_{n \to \infty} \frac{1}{n} = 0$, but $\displaystyle\sum_{n=1}^{\infty} \frac{1}{n}$ diverges.

91. False

$$\sum_{n=1}^{\infty} ar^n = \left(\frac{a}{1 - r}\right) - a$$

The formula requires that the geometric series begins with $n = 0$.

93. Let H represent the half-life of the drug. If a patient receives n equal doses of P units each of this drug, administered at equal time interval of length t, the total amount of the drug in the patient's system at the time the last dose is administered is given by

$$T_n = P + Pe^{kt} + Pe^{2kt} + \cdots + Pe^{(n-1)kt}$$

where $k = -(\ln 2)/H$. One time interval *after* the last dose is administered is given by

$$T_{n+1} = Pe^{kt} + Pe^{2kt} + Pe^{3kt} + \cdots + Pe^{nkt}.$$

Two time intervals *after* the last dose is administered is given by

$$T_{n+1} = Pe^{2kt} + Pe^{3kt} + Pe^{4kt} + \cdots + Pe^{(n+1)kt}$$

and so on. Since $k < 0$, $T_n \to 0$ as $n \to \infty$.

Section 8.3   The Integral Test and *p*-Series

1. $\displaystyle\sum_{n=1}^{\infty} \frac{1}{n+1}$

Let $f(x) = \dfrac{1}{x+1}$.

f is positive, continuous and decreasing for $x \geq 1$.

$$\int_1^{\infty} \frac{1}{x+1}\, dx = \Big[\ln(x+1)\Big]_1^{\infty} = \infty$$

Diverges by Theorem 8.10

3. $\displaystyle\sum_{n=1}^{\infty} e^{-n}$

Let $f(x) = e^{-x}$.

f is positive, continuous, and decreasing for $x \geq 1$.

$$\int_1^{\infty} e^{-x}\, dx = \Big[-e^{-x}\Big]_1^{\infty} = \frac{1}{e}$$

Converges by Theorem 8.10

5. $\displaystyle\sum_{n=1}^{\infty} \frac{1}{n^2+1}$

Let $f(x) = \dfrac{1}{x^2+1}$.

f is positive, continuous, and decreasing for $x \geq 1$.

$$\int_1^{\infty} \frac{1}{x^2+1}\, dx = \Big[\arctan x\Big]_1^{\infty} = \frac{\pi}{4}$$

Converges by Theorem 8.10

7. $\dfrac{\ln 2}{2} + \dfrac{\ln 3}{3} + \dfrac{\ln 4}{4} + \dfrac{\ln 5}{5} + \cdots$

First observe that the nth term of the series is $a_n = \dfrac{\ln n}{n}$.

Since $f(x) = \dfrac{\ln x}{x}$ is positive, continuous, and decreasing for $x \geq 2$, we use the Integral Test.

$$\int_2^{\infty} \frac{\ln x}{x}\, dx = \int_2^{\infty} (\ln x)\frac{1}{x}\, dx = \left[\frac{(\ln x)^2}{2}\right]_2^{\infty} = \infty$$

Therefore, the series diverges by the Integral Test.

9. $\displaystyle\sum_{n=1}^{\infty} \frac{n^{k-1}}{n^k+c}$

Let $f(x) = \dfrac{x^{k-1}}{x^k+c}$.

f is positive, continuous, and decreasing for $x > \sqrt[k]{c(k-1)}$ since

$$f'(x) = \frac{x^{k-2}[c(k-1)-x^k]}{(x^k+c)^2} < 0$$

for $x > \sqrt[k]{c(k-1)}$.

$$\int_1^{\infty} \frac{x^{k-1}}{x^k+c}\, dx = \left[\frac{1}{k}\ln(x^k+c)\right]_1^{\infty} = \infty$$

Diverges by Theorem 8.10

11. $\displaystyle\sum_{n=1}^{\infty} \frac{1}{n^3}$

Let $f(x) = \dfrac{1}{x^3}$.

f is positive, continuous, and decreasing for $x \geq 1$.

$$\int_1^{\infty} \frac{1}{x^3}\, dx = \left[-\frac{1}{2x^2}\right]_1^{\infty} = \frac{1}{2}$$

Converges by Theorem 8.10

13. $\displaystyle\sum_{n=2}^{\infty} \frac{1}{n(\ln n)^p}$

$$f(x) = \frac{1}{x(\ln x)^p}$$

The conditions of the Integral Test are satisfied if we let $f(x) = \dfrac{1}{x(\ln x)^p}$.

If $u = \ln x$ then $du = (1/x)\, dx$. Thus,

$$\int_2^{\infty} \frac{1}{x(\ln x)^p}\, dx = \lim_{b \to \infty} \int_2^b (\ln x)^{-p} \frac{1}{x}\, dx$$

$$= \lim_{b \to \infty} \left[\frac{(\ln x)^{-p+1}}{-p+1} \right]_2^b$$

$$= \lim_{b \to \infty} \left[\left(\frac{1}{1-p} \right) \frac{1}{(\ln b)^{p-1}} - \left(\frac{1}{1-p} \right) \frac{1}{(\ln 2)^{p-1}} \right]$$

$$= 0 + \frac{1}{(p-1)(\ln 2)^{p-1}} \quad \text{for } p - 1 > 0.$$

Therefore, the given series converges if $p > 1$.

15. $\displaystyle\sum_{n=1}^{\infty} \frac{1}{\sqrt[5]{n}} = \sum_{n=1}^{\infty} \frac{1}{n^{1/5}}$

Divergent p-series with $p = \frac{1}{5} < 1$

17. $\displaystyle\sum_{n=1}^{\infty} \frac{1}{n^{1/2}}$

Divergent p-series with $p = \frac{1}{2} < 1$

19. Since

$$1 + \frac{1}{2\sqrt{2}} + \frac{1}{3\sqrt{3}} + \frac{1}{4\sqrt{4}} + \frac{1}{5\sqrt{5}} + \cdots = \sum_{n=1}^{\infty} \frac{1}{n\sqrt{n}} = \sum_{n=1}^{\infty} \frac{1}{n^{3/2}},$$

we have a p-series with $p = \frac{3}{2}$. Since $p > 1$, the series converges.

21. $\displaystyle\sum_{n=1}^{\infty} \frac{1}{n^{1.04}}$

Convergent p-series with $p = 1.04 > 1$

23. $\displaystyle\sum_{n=1}^{\infty} \frac{2}{\sqrt[4]{n^3}} = \frac{2}{1} + \frac{2}{2^{3/4}} + \frac{2}{3^{3/4}} + \cdots$

$S_1 = 2$

$S_2 \approx 3.189$

$S_3 \approx 4.067$

Matches (a)

Diverges—p-series with $p = \frac{3}{4} < 1$

25. $\displaystyle\sum_{n=1}^{\infty} \frac{2}{n\sqrt{n}} = 2 + 2/2^{3/2} + 2/3^{3/2} + \cdots$

$S_1 = 2$

$S_2 \approx 2.707$

$S_3 \approx 3.092$

Matches (b)

Converges—p-series with $p = \frac{3}{2} > 1$

27. No. Theorem 8.9 says that if the series converges, then the terms a_n tend to zero. Some of the series in Exercises 23-26 converge because the terms tend to 0 very rapidly.

29. $\displaystyle\sum_{n=1}^{N} \frac{1}{n} = 1 + \frac{1}{2} + \frac{1}{3} + \frac{1}{4} + \cdots + \frac{1}{N} > M$

(a)

M	2	4	6	8
N	4	31	227	1674

(b) No. Since the terms are decreasing (approaching zero), more and more terms are required to increase the partial sum by 2.

31. Since f is positive, continuous, and decreasing for $x \geq 1$ and $a_n = f(n)$, we have,

$$R_N = S - S_N = \sum_{n=1}^{\infty} a_n - \sum_{n=1}^{N} a_n = \sum_{n=N+1}^{\infty} a_n > 0.$$

Also, $R_N = S - S_N = \displaystyle\sum_{n=N+1}^{\infty} a_n \leq a_{N+1} + \int_{N+1}^{\infty} f(x)\, dx \leq \int_{N}^{\infty} f(x)\, dx.$ Thus,

$$0 \leq R_N \leq \int_{N}^{\infty} f(x)\, dx.$$

33. $\displaystyle\sum_{n=1}^{\infty} \frac{1}{n^4}$

$$S_6 = 1 + \frac{1}{2^4} + \frac{1}{3^4} + \frac{1}{4^4} + \frac{1}{5^4} + \frac{1}{6^4} \approx 1.0811$$

$$R_6 \leq \int_{6}^{\infty} \frac{1}{x^4}\, dx = \left[-\frac{1}{3x^3} \right]_{6}^{\infty} \approx 0.0015$$

$$1.0811 \leq \sum_{n=1}^{\infty} \frac{1}{n^4} \leq 1.0811 + 0.0015 = 1.0826$$

35. $S_{10} = \dfrac{1}{2} + \dfrac{1}{5} + \dfrac{1}{10} + \dfrac{1}{17} + \dfrac{1}{26} + \dfrac{1}{37} + \dfrac{1}{50} + \dfrac{1}{65} + \dfrac{1}{82} + \dfrac{1}{101} \approx 0.9818$

$$R_{10} = \ \leq \int_{10}^{\infty} \frac{1}{x^2 + 1}\, dx = \left[\arctan x \right]_{10}^{\infty} = \frac{\pi}{2} - \arctan 10 \approx 0.0997$$

$$0.9818 \leq \sum_{n=1}^{\infty} \frac{1}{n^5} \leq 0.9818 + 0.0997 = 1.0815$$

37. $\displaystyle\sum_{n=1}^{\infty} ne^{-n^2}$

$$S_4 = e^{-1} + 2e^{-4} + 3e^{-9} + 4e^{-16} \approx 0.4049$$

$$R_4 \leq \int_{4}^{\infty} xe^{-x^2}\, dx = \left[-\frac{1}{2}e^{-x^2} \right]_{4}^{\infty} \approx 5.6 \times 10^{-8}$$

$$0.4049 \leq \sum_{n=1}^{\infty} ne^{-n^2} \leq 0.4049 + (5.6 \times 10^{-8})$$

39. $0 < R_N < \displaystyle\int_{N}^{\infty} \frac{1}{x^4}\, dx = \left[-\frac{1}{3x^3} \right]_{N}^{\infty} = \frac{1}{3N^3} < 0.001$

$$\frac{1}{N^3} < 0.003$$

$$N^3 > 333.33$$

$$N > 6.93$$

$$N \geq 7$$

41. $R_N < \displaystyle\int_{N}^{\infty} e^{-5x}\, dx = \left[-\frac{1}{5}e^{-5x} \right]_{N}^{\infty} = \frac{e^{-5N}}{5} < 0.001$

$$\frac{1}{e^{5N}} < 0.005$$

$$e^{5N} > 200$$

$$5N > \ln 200$$

$$N > \frac{\ln 200}{5}$$

$$N > 1.0597$$

$$N \geq 2$$

43. Your friend is not correct. The series

$$\sum_{n=10,000}^{\infty} \frac{1}{n} = \frac{1}{10,000} + \frac{1}{10,001} + \cdots$$

is the harmonic series, starting with the 10,000th term, and hence diverges.

45. (a) $\displaystyle\sum_{n=2}^{\infty} \frac{1}{n^{1.1}}$. This is a convergent *p*-series with $p = 1.1 > 1$.

$\displaystyle\sum_{n=2}^{\infty} \frac{1}{n \ln n}$ is a divergent series. Use the Integral Test.

$$\int_{2}^{\infty} \frac{1}{x \ln x} \, dx = \left[\ln|\ln x| \right]_{2}^{\infty} = \infty$$

(b) $\displaystyle\sum_{n=2}^{6} \frac{1}{n^{1.1}} = \frac{1}{2^{1.1}} + \frac{1}{3^{1.1}} + \frac{1}{4^{1.1}} + \frac{1}{5^{1.1}} + \frac{1}{6^{1.1}} \approx 0.4665 + 0.2987 + 0.2176 + 0.1703 + 0.1393$

$\displaystyle\sum_{n=2}^{6} \frac{1}{n \ln n} = \frac{1}{2 \ln 2} + \frac{1}{3 \ln 3} + \frac{1}{4 \ln 4} + \frac{1}{5 \ln 5} + \frac{1}{6 \ln 6} \approx 0.7213 + 0.3034 + 0.1803 + 0.1243 + 0.0930$

The terms of the convergent series **seem** to be larger than those of the divergent series!

(c) $\dfrac{1}{n^{1.1}} < \dfrac{1}{n \ln n}$

$n \ln n < n^{1.1}$

$\ln n < n^{0.1}$

This inequality holds when $n \geq 3.5 \times 10^{15}$. Or, $n > e^{40}$. Then $\ln e^{40} = 40 < (e^{40})^{0.1} = e^{4} \approx 55$.

47. The harmonic series $\displaystyle\sum_{n=1}^{\infty} \frac{1}{n}$.

49. $\displaystyle\sum_{n=1}^{\infty} \frac{1}{2n - 1}$

Let $f(x) = \dfrac{1}{2x - 1}$.

f is positive, continuous, and decreasing for $x \geq 1$. Therefore,

$$\int_{1}^{\infty} \frac{1}{2x - 1} = \left[\ln\sqrt{2x - 1} \right]_{1}^{\infty} = \infty,$$

and the series diverges by the Integral Test.

51. $\displaystyle\sum_{n=1}^{\infty} \frac{1}{n\sqrt[4]{n}} = \sum_{n=1}^{\infty} \frac{1}{n^{5/4}}$

p-series with $p = \frac{5}{4}$

Converges by Theorem 8.11

53. $\displaystyle\sum_{n=0}^{\infty} \left(\frac{2}{3} \right)^{n}$

Geometric series with $r = \frac{2}{3}$

Converges by Theorem 8.6

55. $\displaystyle\sum_{n=1}^{\infty} \frac{n}{\sqrt{n^2 + 1}}$

$\displaystyle\lim_{n \to \infty} \frac{n}{\sqrt{n^2 + 1}} = \lim_{n \to \infty} \frac{1}{\sqrt{1 + (1/n^2)}} = 1 \neq 0$

Therefore, the series diverges by *n*th-Term Test for Divergence.

57. $\displaystyle\sum_{n=1}^{\infty} \left(1 + \frac{1}{n} \right)^{n}$

$\displaystyle\lim_{n \to \infty} \left(1 + \frac{1}{n} \right)^{n} = e \neq 0$

Fails *n*th Term Test

Diverges by Theorem 8.9

59. $\displaystyle\sum_{n=2}^{\infty} \frac{1}{n(\ln n)^3}$

Let $f(x) = \dfrac{1}{x(\ln x)^3}$.

f is positive, continuous and decreasing for $x \geq 2$.

$$\int_{2}^{\infty} \frac{1}{x(\ln x)^3} \, dx = \int_{2}^{\infty} (\ln x)^{-3} \frac{1}{x} \, dx = \left[\frac{(\ln x)^{-2}}{-2} \right]_{2}^{\infty} = \left[-\frac{1}{2(\ln x)^2} \right]_{2}^{\infty} = \frac{1}{2(\ln 2)^2}$$

Converges by Theorem 8.10. See Exercise 13.

Section 8.4   Comparisons of Series

1. (a) $\displaystyle\sum_{n=1}^{\infty} \frac{6}{n^{3/2}} = \frac{6}{1} + \frac{6}{2^{3/2}} + \cdots \quad S_1 = 6$

$\displaystyle\sum_{n=1}^{\infty} \frac{6}{n^{3/2} + 3} = \frac{6}{4} + \frac{6}{2^{3/2} + 3} + \cdots \quad S_1 = \frac{3}{2}$

$\displaystyle\sum_{n=1}^{\infty} \frac{6}{n\sqrt{n^2 + 0.5}} = \frac{6}{1\sqrt{1.5}} + \frac{6}{2\sqrt{4.5}} + \cdots \quad S_1 = \frac{6}{\sqrt{1.5}} \approx 4.9$

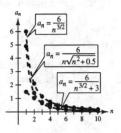

(b) The first series is a *p*-series. It converges ($p = 3/2 > 1$).

(c) The magnitude of the terms of the other two series are less than the corresponding terms at the convergent *p*-series. Hence, the other two series converge.

(d) The smaller the magnitude of the terms, the smaller the magnitude of the terms of the sequence of partial sums.

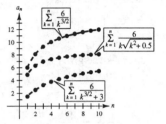

3. $\dfrac{1}{n^2 + 1} < \dfrac{1}{n^2}$

Therefore,

$$\sum_{n=1}^{\infty} \frac{1}{n^2 + 1}$$

converges by comparison with the convergent *p*-series

$$\sum_{n=1}^{\infty} \frac{1}{n^2}.$$

5. $\displaystyle\sum_{n=2}^{\infty} \frac{1}{n - 1}$

This series resembles $\displaystyle\sum_{n=2}^{\infty} \frac{1}{n}$, a divergent *p*-series.

Term-by-term comparison yields

$$a_n = \frac{1}{n} < \frac{1}{n - 1} = b_n.$$

By the Direct Comparison Test, the series diverges.

7. $\dfrac{1}{3^n + 1} < \dfrac{1}{3^n}$

Therefore,

$$\sum_{n=0}^{\infty} \frac{1}{3^n + 1}$$

converges by comparison with the convergent geometric series

$$\sum_{n=0}^{\infty} \left(\frac{1}{3}\right)^n.$$

9. For $n \geq 3$, $\dfrac{\ln n}{n + 1} > \dfrac{1}{n + 1}$.

Therefore,

$$\sum_{n=1}^{\infty} \frac{\ln n}{n + 1}$$

diverges by comparison with the divergent series

$$\sum_{n=1}^{\infty} \frac{1}{n + 1}.$$

Note: $\displaystyle\sum_{n=1}^{\infty} \frac{1}{n + 1}$ diverges by the integral test.

11. $\displaystyle\sum_{n=0}^{\infty} \frac{1}{n!}$

Compare the given series to the convergent *p*-series

$$\sum_{n=1}^{\infty} \frac{1}{n^2}.$$

If $n > 3$, then $n^2 < n!$ and $\dfrac{1}{n!} < \dfrac{1}{n^2}$.

By the Direct Comparison Test, the series converges.

13. $\dfrac{1}{e^{n^2}} \leq \dfrac{1}{e^n}$

Therefore,

$$\sum_{n=0}^{\infty} \frac{1}{e^{n^2}}$$

converges by comparison with the convergent geometric series

$$\sum_{n=0}^{\infty} \left(\frac{1}{e}\right)^n.$$

15. $\displaystyle\sum_{n=1}^{\infty} \frac{n}{n^2+1}$

The series can be compared with

$$\sum_{n=1}^{\infty} \frac{1}{n}$$

since the degree of the denominator is only one greater than the degree of the numerator. Furthermore, since

$$\lim_{n\to\infty} \frac{n/(n^2+1)}{1/n} = \lim_{n\to\infty} \frac{n^2}{n^2+1} = 1$$

and since the series

$$\sum_{n=1}^{\infty} \frac{1}{n}$$

diverges, the given series also diverges by the Limit Comparison Test.

19. $\displaystyle\lim_{n\to\infty} \frac{\dfrac{2n^2-1}{3n^5+2n+1}}{1/n^3} = \lim_{n\to\infty} \frac{2n^5-n^3}{3n^5+2n+1} = \frac{2}{3}$

Therefore,

$$\sum_{n=1}^{\infty} \frac{2n^2-1}{3n^5+2n+1}$$

converges by a limit comparison with the convergent *p*-series

$$\sum_{n=1}^{\infty} \frac{1}{n^3}.$$

23. $\displaystyle\sum_{n=1}^{\infty} \frac{1}{n\sqrt{n^2+1}}$

For "large" values of n

$$\frac{1}{n\sqrt{n^2+1}} \approx \frac{1}{n\sqrt{n^2}} = \frac{1}{n^2}.$$

By comparing the given series with the convergent *p*-series

$$\sum_{n=1}^{\infty} \frac{1}{n^2},$$

we have

$$\lim_{n\to\infty} \frac{a_n}{b_n} = \lim_{n\to\infty} \left(\frac{1}{n\sqrt{n^2+1}}\right)\left(\frac{n^2}{1}\right)$$

$$= \lim_{n\to\infty} \frac{1}{\sqrt{1+(1/n)}} = 1.$$

By the Limit Comparison Test, the given series converges.

17. $\displaystyle\lim_{n\to\infty} \frac{1/\sqrt{n^2+1}}{1/n} = \lim_{n\to\infty} \frac{n}{\sqrt{n^2+1}} = 1$

Therefore,

$$\sum_{n=0}^{\infty} \frac{1}{\sqrt{n^2+1}}$$

diverges by a limit comparison with the divergent *p*-series

$$\sum_{n=1}^{\infty} \frac{1}{n}.$$

21. $\displaystyle\lim_{n\to\infty} \frac{\dfrac{n+3}{n(n+2)}}{1/n} = \lim_{n\to\infty} \frac{n^2+3n}{n^2+2n} = 1$

Therefore,

$$\sum_{n=1}^{\infty} \frac{n+3}{n(n+2)}$$

diverges by a limit comparison with the divergent *p*-series

$$\sum_{n=1}^{\infty} \frac{1}{n}.$$

25. $\displaystyle\lim_{n\to\infty} \frac{(n^{k-1})/(n^k+1)}{1/n} = \lim_{n\to\infty} \frac{n^k}{n^k+1} = 1$

Therefore,

$$\sum_{n=1}^{\infty} \frac{n^{k-1}}{n^k+1}$$

diverges by a limit comparison with the divergent *p*-series

$$\sum_{n=1}^{\infty} \frac{1}{n}.$$

27. $\lim\limits_{n\to\infty} \dfrac{\sin(1/n)}{1/n} = \lim\limits_{n\to\infty} \dfrac{(-1/n^2)\cos(1/n)}{-1/n^2} = \lim\limits_{n\to\infty} \cos\left(\dfrac{1}{n}\right) = 1$

Therefore, $\sum\limits_{n=1}^{\infty} \sin\left(\dfrac{1}{n}\right)$ diverges by a limit comparison with the divergent p-series $\sum\limits_{n=1}^{\infty} \dfrac{1}{n}$.

29. $\sum\limits_{n=1}^{\infty} \dfrac{\sqrt{n}}{n} = \sum\limits_{n=1}^{\infty} \dfrac{1}{\sqrt{n}}$

Diverges

p-series with $p = \frac{1}{2}$

31. $\sum\limits_{n=1}^{\infty} \dfrac{1}{3^n + 2}$

Converges

Direct comparison with $\sum\limits_{n=1}^{\infty} \left(\dfrac{1}{3}\right)^n$

33. $\sum\limits_{n=1}^{\infty} \dfrac{n}{2n + 3}$

Since

$$\lim\limits_{n\to\infty} a_n = \lim\limits_{n\to\infty} \dfrac{n}{2n + 3} = \dfrac{1}{2} \neq 0,$$

the series diverges by the nth-Term Divergence Test for Divergence.

35. $\sum\limits_{n=1}^{\infty} \dfrac{n}{(n^2 + 1)^2}$

Converges; integral test

37. $\lim\limits_{n\to\infty} \dfrac{a_n}{1/n} = \lim\limits_{n\to\infty} na_n \neq 0$

Therefore,

$\sum\limits_{n=1}^{\infty} a_n$ diverges by a limit comparison with the p-series $\sum\limits_{n=1}^{\infty} \dfrac{1}{n}$.

39. $\dfrac{1}{2} + \dfrac{2}{5} + \dfrac{3}{10} + \dfrac{4}{17} + \dfrac{5}{26} + \cdots$

The nth term of the series is

$$a_n = \dfrac{n}{n^2 + 1}$$

and the series has the form

$$\sum\limits_{n=1}^{\infty} \dfrac{n}{n^2 + 1} = \sum\limits_{n=1}^{\infty} \dfrac{P(n)}{Q(n)}.$$

$P(n)$ has degree $k = 1$ and $Q(n)$ has degree $k = 2$. Hence, it follows from the Polynomial Test (Exercise 38) that the series diverges.

41. $\sum\limits_{n=1}^{\infty} \dfrac{1}{n^3 + 1}$

converges since the degree of the numerator is three less than the degree of the denominator.

43. $\lim\limits_{n\to\infty} n\left(\dfrac{n^3}{5n^4 + 3}\right) = \lim\limits_{n\to\infty} \dfrac{n^4}{5n^4 + 3} = \dfrac{1}{5} \neq 0$

Therefore, $\sum\limits_{n=1}^{\infty} \dfrac{n^3}{5n^4 + 3}$ diverges.

45. (a) $\sum_{n=1}^{\infty} \frac{1}{(2n-1)^2}$

Since the degree of the numerator is 2 less than the degree of the denominator, the series converges by the Polynomial Test given in Exercise 38.

(c) Since

$$\sum_{n=1}^{2} \frac{1}{(2n-1)^2} + \sum_{n=3}^{\infty} \frac{1}{(2n-1)^2} = \sum_{n=1}^{\infty} \frac{1}{(2n-1)^2}$$

$$= \frac{\pi^2}{8},$$

we have

$$\sum_{n=3}^{\infty} \frac{1}{(2n-1)^2} = \frac{\pi^2}{8} - \sum_{n=1}^{2} \frac{1}{(2n-1)^2}$$

$$= \frac{\pi^2}{8} - \left(1 + \frac{1}{9}\right) = 0.1226.$$

(b)

n	5	10	20	50	100
S_n	1.1839	1.2087	1.2212	1.2287	1.2312

(d) Since

$$\sum_{n=1}^{9} \frac{1}{(2n-1)^2} + \sum_{n=10}^{\infty} \frac{1}{(2n-1)^2} = \sum_{n=1}^{\infty} \frac{1}{(2n-1)^2}$$

$$= \frac{\pi^2}{8},$$

we have

$$\sum_{n=10}^{\infty} \frac{1}{(2n-1)^2} = \frac{\pi^2}{8} - \sum_{n=1}^{9} \frac{1}{(2n-1)^2}$$

$$= \frac{\pi^2}{8} - S_9 = 0.0277.$$

(Note that in parts (c) and (d) we know the series converges because only a finite number of terms have been subtracted from a known convergent series.)

47. False. Let $a_n = 1/n^3$ and $b_n = 1/n^2$. $0 < a_n \leq b_n$ and both

$$\sum_{n=1}^{\infty} \frac{1}{n^3} \text{ and } \sum_{n=1}^{\infty} \frac{1}{n^2}$$

converge.

49. True

51. Since $\sum_{n=1}^{\infty} b_n$ converges, $\lim_{n \to \infty} b_n = 0$. There exists N such that $b_n < 1$ for $n > N$. Thus,

$$a_n b_n < a_n \text{ for } n > N \text{ and } \sum_{n=1}^{\infty} a_n b_n$$

converges by comparison to the convergent series $\sum_{i=1}^{\infty} a_n$.

53. $\sum \frac{1}{n^2}$ and $\sum \frac{1}{n^3}$ both converge, and hence so does

$$\sum \left(\frac{1}{n^2}\right)\left(\frac{1}{n^3}\right) = \sum \frac{1}{n^5}$$

55. (a) Suppose Σb_n converges and Σa_n diverges. Then there exists N such that $0 < b_n < a_n$ for $n \geq N$. This means that $1 < a_n/b_n$ for $n \geq N$. Therefore, $\lim_{n \to \infty} a_n/b_n \neq 0$. Thus, Σa_n must also converge.

(b) Suppose Σb_n diverges and Σa_n converges. Then there exists N such that $0 < a_n < b_n$ for $n \geq N$. This means that $0 < a_n/b_n < 1$ for $n \geq N$. Therefore, $\lim_{n \to \infty} a_n/b_n \neq \infty$. Thus, Σa_n must also diverge.

57. Since $0 < a_n < 1$, $0 < a_n^2 < a_n < 1$. The squared terms will be below the others.

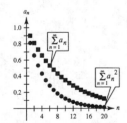

Section 8.5   Alternating Series

1. $\displaystyle\sum_{n=1}^{\infty} \frac{6}{n^2} = \frac{6}{1} + \frac{6}{4} + \frac{6}{9} + \cdots$

$S_1 = 6, S_2 = 7.5$

Matches (b)

3. $\displaystyle\sum_{n=1}^{\infty} \frac{10}{n2^n} = \frac{10}{2} + \frac{10}{8} + \cdots$

$S_1 = 5, S_2 = 6.25$

Matches (c)

5. $\displaystyle\sum_{n=1}^{\infty} \frac{(-1)^{n-1}}{2n-1} = \frac{\pi}{4} \approx 0.7854$

(a)

n	1	2	3	4	5	6	7	8	9	10
S_n	1	0.6667	0.8667	0.7238	0.8349	0.7440	0.8209	0.7543	0.8131	0.7605

(b)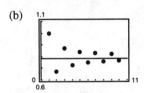

(c) The points alternate sides of the horizontal line that represents the sum of the series. The distance between successive points and the line decreases.

(d) The distance in part (c) is always less than the magnitude of the next term of the series.

7. $\displaystyle\sum_{n=1}^{\infty} \frac{(-1)^{n-1}}{n^2} = \frac{\pi^2}{12} \approx 0.8225$

(a)

n	1	2	3	4	5	6	7	8	9	10
S_n	1	0.75	0.8611	0.7986	0.8386	0.8108	0.8312	0.8156	0.8280	0.8180

(b)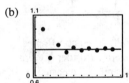

(c) The points alternate sides of the horizontal line that represents the sum of the series. The distance between successive points and the line decreases.

(d) The distance in part (c) is always less than the magnitude of the next series.

9. $\displaystyle\sum_{n=1}^{\infty} \frac{(-1)^{n+1}}{n}$

$a_{n+1} = \dfrac{1}{n+1} < \dfrac{1}{n} = a_n$

$\displaystyle\lim_{n\to\infty} \frac{1}{n} = 0$

Converges by Theorem 8.14.

11. $\displaystyle\sum_{n=1}^{\infty} \frac{(-1)^{n+1}}{2n-1}$

Observe that

$$\lim_{n\to\infty} a_n = \lim_{n\to\infty} \frac{1}{2n-1} = 0$$

and

$$a_{n+1} = \frac{1}{2(n+1)-1} = \frac{1}{2n+1} < \frac{1}{2n-1} = a_n$$

for all n. Therefore, by the Alternating Series Test, the series converges.

13. $\displaystyle\sum_{n=1}^{\infty} \frac{(-1)^n n^2}{n^2+1}$

$\displaystyle\lim_{n\to\infty} \frac{n^2}{n^2+1} = 1$

Diverges by the nth Term Test

15. $\displaystyle\sum_{n=1}^{\infty} \frac{(-1)^n}{\sqrt{n}}$

$$a_{n+1} = \frac{1}{\sqrt{n+1}} < \frac{1}{\sqrt{n}} = a_n$$

$$\lim_{n\to\infty} \frac{1}{\sqrt{n}} = 0$$

Converges by Theorem 8.14

17. $\displaystyle\sum_{n=1}^{\infty} \frac{(-1)^{n+1}(n+1)}{\ln(n+1)}$

Using L'Hôpital's Rule we have

$$\lim_{n\to\infty} a_n = \lim_{n\to\infty} \frac{n+1}{\ln(n+1)}$$

$$= \lim_{n\to\infty} \frac{1}{\dfrac{1}{(n+1)}} = \lim_{n\to\infty} (n+1) = \infty \neq 0.$$

Therefore, the series diverges by the nth-Term Test for Divergence.

19. $\displaystyle\sum_{n=1}^{\infty} \sin\left[\frac{(2n-1)\pi}{2}\right] = \sum_{n=1}^{\infty} (-1)^{n+1}$

Diverges by the nth Term Test

21. $\displaystyle\sum_{n=1}^{\infty} \frac{1}{n} \sin\left[\frac{(2n-1)\pi}{2}\right] = \sum_{n=1}^{\infty} \frac{(-1)^{n+1}}{n}$

Converges; (see Exercise 9)

23. $\displaystyle\sum_{n=0}^{\infty} \frac{(-1)^n}{n!}$

$$a_{n+1} = \frac{1}{(n+1)!} < \frac{1}{n!} = a_n$$

$$\lim_{n\to\infty} \frac{1}{n!} = 0$$

Converges by Theorem 8.14

25. $\displaystyle\sum_{n=1}^{\infty} \frac{(-1)^{n+1}\sqrt{n}}{n+2}$

$$a_{n+1} = \frac{\sqrt{n+1}}{(n+1)+2} < \frac{\sqrt{n}}{n+2} \text{ for } n \geq 2$$

$$\lim_{n\to\infty} \frac{\sqrt{n}}{n+2} = 0$$

Converges by Theorem 8.14

27. $\displaystyle\sum_{n=1}^{\infty} \frac{2(-1)^{n+1}}{e^n + e^{-n}}$

Use differentiation to establish that $a_{n+1} \leq a_n$.

$$f(x) = \frac{2}{e^x + e^{-x}}$$

$$f'(x) = \frac{-2(e^x - e^{-x})}{(e^x + e^{-x})^2}$$

Observe that $f'(x)$ is negative for $x > 0$. Hence, f is a decreasing function and it follows that $a_{n+1} \leq a_n$ for $n \geq 1$. Since

$$\lim_{n\to\infty} \frac{2}{e^n + e^{-n}} = 0,$$

the series converges by the Alternating Series Test.

29. (a) $\displaystyle\sum_{n=0}^{\infty} \frac{(-1)^n}{n!}$

The series is alternating, and since

$$\lim_{n\to\infty} \frac{1}{n!} = 0 \text{ and } \frac{1}{(n+1)!} < \frac{1}{n!}$$

the series converges. By the Alternating Series Remainder Theorem, the error R_N after N terms satisfies $|R_N| \leq a_{N+1}$. Therefore, to ensure an error less than 0.001, choose N sufficiently large so that

$$\frac{1}{(N+1)!} \leq 0.001.$$

Since $1/6! = 1/720 = 0.0013888$ and $1/7! = 1/5040 < 0.001$, let $N = 6$ and use 7 terms of the series.

(b) Using a graphing utility, we obtain

$$\sum_{n=0}^{6} \frac{(-1)^n}{n!} \approx 0.368.$$

The approximation is within 0.001 of the actual sum $1/e$.

31. $\displaystyle\sum_{n=0}^{\infty} \frac{(-1)^n}{(2n+1)!}$

   (a) By Theorem 8.15,

$$|R_N| \le a_{N+1} = \frac{1}{[2(N+1)+1]!} < 0.001.$$

   This inequality is valid when $N = 2$.

   (b) We may approximate the series by

$$\sum_{n=0}^{2} \frac{(-1)^n}{(2n+1)!} = 1 - \frac{1}{6} + \frac{1}{120} \approx 0.842.$$

   (3 terms. Note that the sum begins with $n = 0$.)

33. $\displaystyle\sum_{n=1}^{\infty} \frac{(-1)^{n+1}}{n}$

   (a) By Theorem 8.15,

$$|R_N| \le a_{N+1} = \frac{1}{N+1} < 0.001.$$

   This inequality is valid when $N = 1000$.

   (b) We may approximate the series by

$$\sum_{n=1}^{1000} \frac{(-1)^{n+1}}{n} = 1 - \frac{1}{2} + \frac{1}{3} - \frac{1}{4} + \cdots - \frac{1}{1000}$$

$$\approx 0.693.$$

   (1000 terms)

35. $\displaystyle\sum_{n=1}^{\infty} \frac{(-1)^{n+1}}{2n^3 - 1}$

By the Alternating Series Remainder Theorem, the error R_N after N terms satisfies $|R_N| \le a_{N+1}$. Therefore, to insure an error less than 0.001, choose N sufficiently large so that

$$\frac{1}{2(N+1)^3 - 1} \le 0.001$$

$$1000 \le 2(N+1)^3 - 1$$

$$\frac{1001}{2} \le (N+1)^3$$

$$7.9 \approx \sqrt[3]{\frac{1001}{2}} \le N + 1$$

$$6.9 \le N.$$

Therefore, choose $N = 7$.

37. $\displaystyle\sum_{n=1}^{\infty} \frac{(-1)^{n+1}}{(n+1)^2}$

$$\sum_{n=1}^{\infty} \frac{1}{(n+1)^2} \text{ converges by comparison to the } p\text{-series}$$

$$\sum_{n=1}^{\infty} \frac{1}{n^2}.$$

Therefore, the given series converge absolutely.

39. $\displaystyle\sum_{n=1}^{\infty} \frac{(-1)^{n+1}}{\sqrt{n}}$

In this case, the Alternating Series Test verifies that the series converges. However, the series

$$\sum_{n=1}^{\infty} \left| \frac{(-1)^{n+1}}{\sqrt{n}} \right| = \sum_{n=1}^{\infty} \frac{1}{\sqrt{n}}$$

is a divergent p-series with $p = \frac{1}{2}$. Therefore, the given series converges conditionally.

41. $\displaystyle\sum_{n=1}^{\infty} \frac{(-1)^{n+1} n^2}{(n+1)^2}$

$$\lim_{n \to \infty} \frac{n^2}{(n+1)^2} = 1 \text{ Therefore, the series diverges by the}$$

nth Term Test.

43. $\displaystyle\sum_{n=2}^{\infty} \frac{(-1)}{\ln(n)}$

The given series converges by the Alternating Series Test, but does not converge absolutely since the series

$$\sum_{n=2}^{\infty} \frac{1}{\ln n}$$

diverges by comparison to the harmonic series

$$\sum_{n=1}^{\infty} \frac{1}{n}.$$

Therefore, the series converges conditionally.

45. $\displaystyle\sum_{n=2}^{\infty} \frac{(-1)^n n}{n^3 - 1}$

The Alternating Series Test verifies that the series converges. Also, the series

$$\sum_{n=2}^{\infty} \left| \frac{(-1)^{n+1} n}{n^3 - 1} \right| = \sum_{n=2}^{\infty} \frac{n}{n^3 - 1}$$

converges by the Limit Comparison Test with the series

$$\sum_{n=2}^{\infty} \frac{1}{n^2}.$$

Therefore, the given series converges absolutely.

47. $\displaystyle\sum_{n=0}^{\infty} \frac{(-1)^n}{(2n+1)!}$

$\displaystyle\sum_{n=0}^{\infty} \frac{1}{(2n+1)!}$

is convergent by comparison to the convergent geometric series

$$\sum_{n=0}^{\infty} \left(\frac{1}{2}\right)^n$$

since

$$\frac{1}{(2n+1)!} < \frac{1}{2^n} \text{ for } n > 0.$$

Therefore, the given series converges absolutely.

51. $\displaystyle\sum_{n=1}^{\infty} \frac{\cos n\pi}{n^2} = \sum_{n=1}^{\infty} \frac{(-1)^n}{n^2}$

$\displaystyle\sum_{n=1}^{\infty} \frac{1}{n^2}$ is a convergent p-series. Therefore, the given

series converges absolutely.

53. $\displaystyle\sum_{n=1}^{\infty} \frac{(-1)^n}{n^p}$

If $p = 0$, then

$$\lim_{n\to\infty} \frac{1}{n^p} = 1$$

and the series diverges. If $p > 0$, then

$$\lim_{n\to\infty} \frac{1}{n^p} = 0 \text{ and } \frac{1}{(n+1)^p} < \frac{1}{n^p}.$$

Therefore, the series converge by the Alternating Series Test.

57. (a) $\displaystyle\sum_{n=1}^{\infty} \frac{x^n}{n}$

converges absolutely (by comparison) for

$-1 < x < 1,$

since

$$\left|\frac{x^n}{n}\right| < |x^n| \text{ and } \sum x^n$$

is a convergent geometric series for $-1 < x < 1$.

49. $\displaystyle\sum_{n=0}^{\infty} \frac{\cos n\pi}{n+1} = \sum_{n=0}^{\infty} \frac{(-1)^n}{n+1}$

The given series converges by the Alternating Series Test, but

$$\sum_{n=0}^{\infty} \frac{|\cos n\pi|}{n+1} = \sum_{n=0}^{\infty} \frac{1}{n+1}$$

diverges by a limit comparison to the divergent harmonic series,

$$\sum_{n=1}^{\infty} \frac{1}{n}.$$

$\displaystyle\lim_{n\to\infty} \frac{|\cos n\pi|/(n+1)}{1/n} = 1$, therefore the series

converges conditionally.

55. $\displaystyle\sum_{n=1}^{\infty} \frac{(-1)^{n-1}}{n}$ converges, but $\displaystyle\sum_{n=1}^{\infty} \frac{1}{n}$ diverges

(b) When $x = -1$, we have the convergent alternating series

$$\sum_{n=1}^{\infty} \frac{(-1)^n}{n}.$$

When $x = 1$, we have the divergent harmonic series $\dfrac{1}{n}$.

Therefore,

$$\sum_{n=1}^{\infty} \frac{x^n}{n}$$

converges conditionally for $x = -1$.

59. False

Let $a_n = \dfrac{(-1)^n}{n}$.

Section 8.6   The Ratio and Root Tests

1. $\dfrac{(n+1)!}{(n-2)!} = \dfrac{(n+1)(n)(n-1)(n-2)!}{(n-2)!} = (n+1)(n)(n-1)$

3. Use Mathematical Induction to verify the formula

$$1 \cdot 3 \cdot 5 \cdots (2k-1) = \frac{(2k)!}{2^k k!}.$$

The formula is valid when $k = 1$ since

$$1 = \frac{(2 \cdot 1)!}{2^1 1!}.$$

Assume that the formula is true when $k = n$ and then show that it is true when $k = n + 1$. Assuming it is true when $k = n$, we have

$$1 \cdot 3 \cdot 5 \cdots (2n-1) = \frac{(2n)!}{2^n n}.$$

When $k = n + 1$, we have

$$1 \cdot 3 \cdot 5 \cdots (2n-1)(2n+1) = [1 \cdot 3 \cdot 5 \cdots (2n-1)](2n+1)$$

$$= \frac{(2n)!}{2^n n!} \cdot (2n+1)$$

$$= \frac{(2n)!(2n+1)}{2^n n!} \cdot \frac{(2n+2)}{2(n+1)}$$

$$= \frac{(2n)!(2n+1)(2n+2)}{2^{n+1} n!(n+1)}$$

$$= \frac{(2n+2)!}{2^{n+1}(n+1)!}$$

Therefore, the formula is valid for all $n \geq 1$.

5. $\displaystyle\sum_{n=1}^{\infty} n\left(\frac{3}{4}\right)^n = 1\left(\frac{3}{4}\right) + 2\left(\frac{9}{16}\right) + \cdots$

$S_1 = \dfrac{3}{4}, S_2 \approx 1.875$

Matches (d)

7. $\displaystyle\sum_{n=1}^{\infty} \frac{(-3)^{n+1}}{n!} = 9 - \frac{3^3}{2} + \cdots$

$S_1 = 9$

Matches (a)

9. (a) Ratio Test: $\displaystyle\lim_{n\to\infty} \left|\frac{a_{n+1}}{a_n}\right| = \lim_{n\to\infty} \frac{(n+1)^2(5/8)^{n+1}}{n^2(5/8)^n} = \lim_{n\to\infty}\left(\frac{n+1}{n}\right)^2 \frac{5}{8} = \frac{5}{8} < 1.$ Converges

(b)

n	5	10	15	20	25
S_n	9.2104	16.7598	18.8016	19.1878	19.2491

(c)

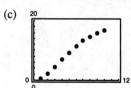

(d) The sum is approximately 19.26.

(e) The more rapidly the terms of the series approach 0, the more rapidly the sequence of the partial sums approaches the sum of the series.

11. $\displaystyle\sum_{n=0}^{\infty} \frac{n!}{3^n}$

$$\lim_{n\to\infty}\left|\frac{a_{n+1}}{a_n}\right| = \lim_{n\to\infty}\left|\frac{(n+1)!}{3^{n+1}}\cdot\frac{3^n}{n!}\right|$$

$$= \lim_{n\to\infty}\frac{n+1}{3} = \infty$$

Therefore, by the Ratio Test, the series diverges.

13. $\displaystyle\sum_{n=0}^{\infty} \frac{3^n}{n!}$

$$\lim_{n\to\infty}\left|\frac{a_{n+1}}{a_n}\right| = \lim_{n\to\infty}\left|\frac{3^{n+1}/(n+1)!}{3^n/n!}\right|$$

$$= \lim_{n\to\infty}\left|\frac{3^{n+1}}{1\cdot 2\cdot 3\cdot 4\cdots n\cdot(n+1)}\cdot\frac{1\cdot 2\cdot 3\cdot 4\cdots n}{3^n}\right|$$

$$= \lim_{n\to\infty}\frac{3}{n+1} = 0 < 1$$

Therefore, by the Ratio Test, the series converges.

15. $\displaystyle\sum_{n=1}^{\infty} \frac{n}{2^n}$

$$\lim_{n\to\infty}\left|\frac{a_{n+1}}{a_n}\right| = \lim_{n\to\infty}\left|\frac{n+1}{2^{n+1}}\cdot\frac{2^n}{n}\right|$$

$$= \lim_{n\to\infty}\frac{n+1}{2n} = \frac{1}{2}$$

Therefore, by the Ratio Test, the series converges.

17. $\displaystyle\sum_{n=1}^{\infty} \frac{2^n}{n^2}$

$$\lim_{n\to\infty}\left|\frac{a_{n+1}}{a_n}\right| = \lim_{n\to\infty}\left|\frac{2^{n+1}}{(n+1)^2}\cdot\frac{n^2}{2^n}\right|$$

$$= \lim_{n\to\infty}\frac{2n^2}{(n+1)^2} = 2$$

Therefore, by the Ratio Test, the series diverges.

19. $\displaystyle\sum_{n=0}^{\infty} \frac{(-1)^n 2^n}{n!}$

$$\lim_{n\to\infty}\left|\frac{a_{n+1}}{a_n}\right| = \lim_{n\to\infty}\left|\frac{2^{n+1}}{(n+1)!}\cdot\frac{n!}{2^n}\right|$$

$$= \lim_{n\to\infty}\frac{2}{n+1} = 0$$

Therefore, by the Ratio Test, the series converges.

21. $\displaystyle\sum_{n=1}^{\infty} \frac{n!}{n3^n}$

$$\lim_{n\to\infty}\left|\frac{a_{n+1}}{a_n}\right| = \lim_{n\to\infty}\left|\frac{(n+1)!}{(n+1)3^{n+1}}\cdot\frac{n3^n}{n!}\right|$$

$$= \lim_{n\to\infty}\frac{n}{3} = \infty$$

Therefore, by the Ratio Test, the series diverges.

23. $\displaystyle\sum_{n=0}^{\infty} \frac{4^n}{n!}$

$$\lim_{n\to\infty}\left|\frac{a_{n+1}}{a_n}\right| = \lim_{n\to\infty}\left|\frac{4^{n+1}}{(n+1)!}\cdot\frac{n!}{4^n}\right| = \lim_{n\to\infty}\frac{4}{n+1} = 0$$

Therefore, by the Ratio Test, the series converges.

25. $\displaystyle\sum_{n=0}^{\infty} \frac{3^n}{(n+1)^n}$

$$\lim_{n\to\infty}\left|\frac{a_{n+1}}{a_n}\right| = \lim_{n\to\infty}\left|\frac{3^{n+1}}{(n+2)^{n+1}}\cdot\frac{(n+1)^n}{3^n}\right| = \lim_{n\to\infty}\frac{3(n+1)^n}{(n+2)^{n+1}} = \lim_{n\to\infty}\frac{3}{n+2}\left(\frac{n+1}{n+2}\right)^n = (0)\left(\frac{1}{e}\right) = 0$$

To find $\displaystyle\lim_{n\to\infty}\left(\frac{n+1}{n+2}\right)^n$, let $y = \displaystyle\lim_{n\to\infty}\left(\frac{n+1}{n+2}\right)^n$. Then,

$$\ln y = \lim_{n\to\infty} n\ln\left(\frac{n+1}{n+2}\right) = \lim_{n\to\infty}\frac{\ln[(n+1)/(n+2)]}{1/n} = \frac{0}{0}$$

$$\ln y = \lim_{n\to\infty}\frac{[(1)/(n+1)]-[(1)/(n+2)]}{-(1/n^2)} = -1 \text{ by L'Hôpital's Rule}$$

$$y = e^{-1} = \frac{1}{e}.$$

Therefore, by the Ratio Test, the series converges.

27. $\displaystyle\sum_{n=0}^{\infty} \frac{4n}{3^n+1}$

$$\lim_{n\to\infty}\left|\frac{a_{n+1}}{a_n}\right| = \lim_{n\to\infty}\left[\frac{4^{n+1}}{3^{n+1}+1}\cdot\frac{3^n+1}{4^n}\right]$$

$$= \lim_{n\to\infty}\left[\frac{4(3^n+1)}{3^{n+1}+1}\right]$$

$$= 4\lim_{n\to\infty}\left[\frac{1+(1/3^n)}{3+(1/3^n)}\right] = \frac{4}{3} > 1$$

Therefore, by the Ratio Test, the series diverges.

29. $\displaystyle\sum_{n=0}^{\infty} \frac{(-1)^{n+1}n!}{1\cdot 3\cdot 5\cdots(2n+1)}$

$$\lim_{n\to\infty}\left|\frac{a_{n+1}}{a_n}\right| = \lim_{n\to\infty}\left[\frac{(n+1)!}{1\cdot 3\cdot 5\cdots(2n+1)(2n+3)}\cdot\frac{1\cdot 3\cdot 5\cdots(2n+1)}{n!}\right]$$

$$= \lim_{n\to\infty}\frac{(n+1)}{(2n+3)} = \frac{1}{2}$$

Therefore, by the Ratio Test, the series converges.

31. (a) $\displaystyle\sum_{n=1}^{\infty} \frac{1}{n^{3/2}}$

$$\lim_{n\to\infty}\left|\frac{a_{n+1}}{a_n}\right| = \lim_{n\to\infty}\left|\frac{1}{(n+1)^{3/2}}\cdot\frac{n^{3/2}}{1}\right| = \lim_{n\to\infty}\left(\frac{n}{n+1}\right)^{3/2} = 1$$

(b) $\displaystyle\sum_{n=1}^{\infty} \frac{1}{n^{1/2}}$

$$\lim_{n\to\infty}\left|\frac{a_{n+1}}{a_n}\right| = \lim_{n\to\infty}\left|\frac{1}{(n+1)^{1/2}}\cdot\frac{n^{1/2}}{1}\right| = \lim_{n\to\infty}\left(\frac{n}{n+1}\right)^{1/2} = 1$$

33. $\displaystyle\sum_{n=1}^{\infty} \left(\frac{n}{2n+1}\right)^n$

$$\lim_{n\to\infty}\sqrt[n]{|a_n|} = \lim_{n\to\infty}\sqrt[n]{\left(\frac{n}{2n+1}\right)^n}$$

$$= \lim_{n\to\infty}\frac{n}{2n+1} = \frac{1}{2}$$

Therefore, by the Root Test, the series converges.

35. $\displaystyle\sum_{n=2}^{\infty} \frac{(-1)^n}{(\ln n)^n}$

$$\lim_{n\to\infty}\sqrt[n]{|a_n|} = \lim_{n\to\infty}\sqrt[n]{\left|\frac{(-1)^n}{(\ln n)^n}\right|}$$

$$= \lim_{n\to\infty}\frac{1}{|\ln n|} = 0$$

Therefore, by the Root Test, the series converges.

37. $\displaystyle\sum_{n=1}^{\infty} \left(2\sqrt[n]{n} + 1\right)^n$

Using the Root Test, we have

$$\lim_{n\to\infty} \sqrt[n]{a_n} = \lim_{n\to\infty} \sqrt[n]{\left(2\sqrt[n]{n} + 1\right)^n} = \lim_{n\to\infty} \left(2\sqrt[n]{n} + 1\right).$$

Now let $y = \sqrt[n]{n} = n^{1/n}$. Then $\ln y = (1/n) \ln n$ and by L'Hôpital's Rule, we have

$$\lim_{n\to\infty} \left(\frac{\ln n}{n}\right) = \lim_{n\to\infty} \left(\frac{1/n}{1}\right) = 0.$$

Thus, $\ln y = 0$, $y = e^0 = 1$, and

$$\lim_{n\to\infty} \left(2\sqrt[n]{n} + 1\right) = 2(1) + 1 = 3.$$

The series diverges by the Root Test.

39. $\displaystyle\sum_{n=3}^{\infty} \frac{1}{(\ln n)^n}$

$$\lim_{n\to\infty} \sqrt[n]{|a_n|} = \lim_{n\to\infty} \sqrt[n]{\frac{1}{(\ln n)^n}} = \lim_{n\to\infty} \frac{1}{\ln n} = 0$$

Therefore, by the Root Test, the series converges.

41. $\displaystyle\sum_{n=1}^{\infty} \frac{(-1)^{n+1} 5}{n}$

$$a_{n+1} = \frac{5}{n+1} < \frac{5}{n} = a_n$$

$$\lim_{n\to\infty} \frac{5}{n} = 0$$

Therefore, by the Alternating Series Test, the series converges (conditional convergence).

43. $\displaystyle\sum_{n=1}^{\infty} \frac{3}{n\sqrt{n}} = 3\sum_{n=1}^{\infty} \frac{1}{n^{3/2}}$

This is a p-series with $p = \frac{3}{2}$. Therefore, the series converges.

45. $\displaystyle\sum_{n=1}^{\infty} \frac{2n}{n+1}$

$$\lim_{n\to\infty} \frac{2n}{n+1} = 2 \neq 0$$

This diverges by the nth Term Test for Divergence.

47. $\displaystyle\sum_{n=1}^{\infty} \frac{(-1)^n 3^{n-2}}{2^n} = \sum_{n=1}^{\infty} \frac{(-1)^n 3^n 3^{-2}}{2^n} = \sum_{n=1}^{\infty} \frac{1}{9}\left(-\frac{3}{2}\right)^n$

Since $|r| = \frac{3}{2} > 1$, this is a divergent geometric series.

49. $\displaystyle\sum_{n=1}^{\infty} \frac{10n + 3}{n2^n}$

Compare the given series to the convergent geometric series

$$\sum_{n=0}^{\infty} \frac{1}{2^n}.$$

Since

$$\lim_{n\to\infty} \frac{(10n+3)/(n2^n)}{1/2^n} = \lim_{n\to\infty} \frac{10n+3}{n} = 10,$$

the series converges by the Limit Comparison Test.

51. $\displaystyle\sum_{n=1}^{\infty} \frac{\cos n}{2^n}$

Since $|\cos n| \le 1$, it follows that

$$\left|\frac{\cos n}{2^n}\right| \le \frac{1}{2^n}.$$

Since the series

$$\sum_{n=0}^{\infty} \frac{1}{2^n}$$

is a convergent geometric series, the series

$$\sum_{n=1}^{\infty} \left|\frac{\cos(n)}{2^n}\right|$$

converges by the Comparison Test. Finally, by the Absolute Convergence Theorem, the series

$$\sum_{n=1}^{\infty} \frac{\cos n}{2^n}$$

also converges.

53. $\displaystyle\sum_{n=1}^{\infty} \frac{n7^n}{n!}$

$$\lim_{n\to\infty} \left|\frac{a_{n+1}}{a_n}\right| = \lim_{n\to\infty} \left|\frac{(n+1)7^{n+1}}{(n+1)!} \cdot \frac{n!}{n7^n}\right| = \lim_{n\to\infty} \frac{7}{n} = 0$$

Therefore, by the Ratio Test, the series converges.

55. $\displaystyle\sum_{n=1}^{\infty} \frac{(-1)^n 3^{n-1}}{n!}$

$$\lim_{n\to\infty} \left|\frac{a_{n+1}}{a_n}\right| = \lim_{n\to\infty} \left|\frac{3^n}{(n+1)!} \cdot \frac{n!}{3^{n-1}}\right| = \lim_{n\to\infty} \frac{3}{n+1} = 0$$

Therefore, by the Ratio Test, the series converges.

57. $\displaystyle\sum_{n=1}^{\infty} \frac{(-3)^n}{3 \cdot 5 \cdot 7 \cdots (2n+1)}$

Use the Ratio Test to test for convergence or divergence and obtain

$$\lim_{n\to\infty} \left|\frac{a_{n+1}}{a_n}\right| = \lim_{n\to\infty} \left|\frac{(-3)^{n+1}}{3 \cdot 5 \cdot 7 \cdots (2n+1)[2(n+1)+1]} \cdot \frac{3 \cdot 5 \cdot 7 \cdots (2n+1)}{(-3)^n}\right|$$

$$= \lim_{n\to\infty} \left|\frac{-3}{2(n+1)+1}\right| = 0 < 1.$$

Therefore, by the Ratio Test the series converges.

59. (a) and (c)

$$\sum_{n=1}^{\infty} \frac{n5^n}{n!} = \sum_{n=0}^{\infty} \frac{(n+1)5^{n+1}}{(n+1)!}$$

$$= 5 + \frac{(2)(5)^2}{2!} + \frac{(3)(5)^3}{3!} + \frac{(4)(5)^4}{4!} + \cdots$$

61. (a) and (b) are the same.

63. Replace n with $n+1$.

$$\sum_{n=1}^{\infty} \frac{n}{4^n} = \sum_{n=0}^{\infty} \frac{n+1}{4^{n+1}}$$

65. Since

$$\frac{3^{10}}{2^{10}\,10!} = 1.59 \times 10^{-5},$$

use 9 terms.

$$\sum_{k=1}^{9} \frac{(-3)^k}{2^k\,k!} \approx -0.7769$$

67. No. Let $a_n = \dfrac{1}{n + 10,000}$.

The series $\displaystyle\sum_{n=1}^{\infty} \frac{1}{n + 10,000}$ diverges.

69. First, let

$$\lim_{n \to \infty} \sqrt[n]{|a_n|} = r < 1$$

and choose R such that $0 \le r < R < 1$. There must exist some $N > 0$ such that $\sqrt[n]{|a_n|} < R$ for all $n > N$. Thus, for $n > N$, we $|a_n| < R^n$ and since the geometric series

$$\sum_{n=0}^{\infty} R^n$$

converges, we can apply the Comparison Test to conclude that

$$\sum_{n=1}^{\infty} |a_n|$$

converges which in turn implies that $\displaystyle\sum_{n=1}^{\infty} a_n$ converges.

Second, let

$$\lim_{n \to \infty} \sqrt[n]{|a_n|} = r > R > 1.$$

Then there must exist some $M > 0$ such that $\sqrt[n]{|a_n|} > R$ for all $n > M$. Thus, for $n > M$, we have $|a_n| > R_n > 1$ which implies that $\displaystyle\lim_{n \to \infty} a_n \ne 0$ which in turn implies that

$$\sum_{n=1}^{\infty} a_n \text{ diverges.}$$

Section 8.7   Taylor Polynomials and Approximations

1. $y = -\frac{1}{2}x^2 + 1$

Parabola

Matches (d)

3. $y = e^{-1/2}[(x + 1) + 1]$

Linear

Matches (a)

5. $f(x) = \cos x$

$P_2(x) = 1 - \frac{1}{2}x^2$

$P_4(x) = 1 - \frac{1}{2}x^2 + \frac{1}{24}x^4$

$P_6(x) = 1 - \frac{1}{2}x^2 + \frac{1}{24}x^4 - \frac{1}{720}x^6$

(a)

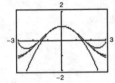

(c) In general, $f^{(n)}(0) = P_n^{(n)}(0)$ for all n.

(b)

$f'(x) = -\sin x$	$P_2'(x) = -x$
$f''(x) = -\cos x$	$P_2''(x) = -1$
$f''(0) = P_2''(0) = -1$	
$f'''(x) = \sin x$	$P_4'''(x) = x$
$f^{(4)}(x) = \cos x$	$P_4^{(4)}(x) = 1$
$f^{(4)}(0) = 1 = P_4^{(4)}(0)$	
$f^{(5)}(x) = -\sin x$	$P_6^{(5)}(x) = -x$
$f^{(6)}(x) = -\cos x$	$P^{(6)}(x) = -1$
$f^{(6)}(0) = -1 = P_6^{(6)}(0)$	

7. $f(x) = e^{-x}$ $f(0) = 1$

$f'(x) = -e^{-x}$ $f'(0) = -1$

$f''(x) = e^{-x}$ $f''(0) = 1$

$f'''(x) = -e^{-x}$ $f'''(0) = -1$

$P_3(x) = f(0) + f'(0)x + \dfrac{f''(0)}{2!}x^2 + \dfrac{f'''(0)}{3!}x^3$

$= 1 - x + \dfrac{x^2}{2} - \dfrac{x^3}{6}$

9. $f(x) = e^{2x}$ $f(0) = 1$

$f'(x) = 2e^{2x}$ $f'(0) = 2$

$f''(x) = 4e^{2x}$ $f''(0) = 4$

$f'''(x) = 8e^{2x}$ $f'''(0) = 8$

$f^{(4)}(x) = 16^{2x}$ $f^{(4)}(0) = 16$

$P_4(x) = 1 + 2x + \dfrac{4}{2!}x^2 + \dfrac{8}{3!}x^3 + \dfrac{16}{4!}x^4$

$= 1 + 2x + 2x^2 + \dfrac{4}{3}x^3 + \dfrac{2}{3}x^4$

11. $f(x) = \sin x$ $f(0) = 0$

   $f'(x) = \cos x$ $f'(0) = 1$

   $f''(x) = -\sin x$ $f''(0) = 0$

   $f'''(x) = -\cos x$ $f'''(0) = -1$

   $f^{(4)}(x) = \sin x$ $f^{(4)}(0) = 0$

   $f^{(5)}(x) = \cos x$ $f^{(5)}(0) = 1$

Therefore, the expansion yields

$$P_5(x) = f(0) + f'(0)x + \frac{f''(0)}{2!}x^2 + \frac{f'''(0)}{3!}x^3 + \frac{f^{(4)}(0)}{4!}x^4 + \frac{f^{(5)}(0)}{5!}x^5$$

$$= x - \frac{x^3}{6} + \frac{x^5}{120}.$$

13. $f(x) = xe^x$ $f(0) = 0$

   $f'(x) = xe^x + e^x$ $f'(0) = 1$

   $f''(x) = xe^x + 2e^x$ $f''(0) = 2$

   $f'''(x) = xe^x + 3e^x$ $f'''(0) = 3$

   $f^{(4)}(x) = xe^x + 4e^x$ $f^{(4)}(0) = 4$

$$P_4(x) = 0 + x + \frac{2}{2!}x^2 + \frac{3}{3!}x^3 + \frac{4}{4!}x^4$$

$$= x + x^2 + \frac{1}{2}x^3 + \frac{1}{6}x^4$$

15. $f(x) = \dfrac{1}{x + 1}$ $f(0) = 1$

   $f'(x) = \dfrac{-1}{(x + 1)^2}$ $f'(0) = -1$

   $f''(x) = \dfrac{2}{(x + 1)^3}$ $f''(0) = 2$

   $f'''(x) = \dfrac{-6}{(x + 1)^4}$ $f'''(0) = -6$

   $f^{(4)}(x) = \dfrac{24}{(x + 1)^5}$ $f^{(4)}(0) = 24$

Therefore, the expansion yields

$$P_4(x) = f(0) + f'(0)x + \frac{f''(0)}{2!}x^2 + \frac{f'''(0)}{3!}x^3 + \frac{f^{(4)}(0)}{4!}x^4$$

$$= 1 - x + x^2 - x^3 + x^4.$$

17. $f(x) = \dfrac{1}{x}$ $f(1) = 1$

   $f'(x) = -\dfrac{1}{x^2}$ $f'(1) = -1$

   $f''(x) = \dfrac{2}{x^3}$ $f''(1) = 2$

   $f'''(x) = -\dfrac{6}{x^4}$ $f'''(1) = -6$

   $f^{(4)}(x) = \dfrac{24}{x^5}$ $f^{(4)}(1) = 24$

$$P_4(x) = 1 - (x - 1) + \frac{2}{2!}(x - 1)^2 + \frac{-6}{3!}(x - 1)^3 + \frac{24}{4!}(x - 1)^4 \quad = 1 - (x - 1) + (x - 1)^2 - (x - 1)^3 + (x - 1)^4$$

19. $f(x) = \ln x$ $f(1) = 0$

$f'(x) = \dfrac{1}{x}$ $f'(1) = 1$

$f''(x) = -\dfrac{1}{x^2}$ $f''(1) = -1$

$f'''(x) = \dfrac{2}{x^3}$ $f'''(1) = 2$

$f^{(4)}(x) = -\dfrac{6}{x^4}$ $f^{(4)}(1) = -6$

Therefore, the expansion yields

$$P_4(x) = f(1) + f'(1)(x-1) + \frac{f''(1)}{2!}(x-1)^2 + \frac{f'''(1)}{3!}(x-1)^3 + \frac{f^{(4)}(1)}{4!}(x-1)^4$$

$$= (x-1) - \frac{1}{2}(x-1)^2 + \frac{1}{3}(x-1)^3 - \frac{1}{4}(x-1)^4.$$

21. $f(x) = \tan x$

$f'(x) = \sec^2 x$

$f''(x) = 2\sec^2 x \tan x$

$f'''(x) = 4\sec^2 x \tan^2 x + 2\sec^4 x$

$f^{(4)}(x) = 8\sec^2 x \tan^3 x + 16\sec^4 x \tan x$

$f^{(5)}(x) = 16\sec^2 x \tan^4 x + 88\sec^4 x \tan^2 x + 16\sec^6 x$

(a) $n = 3, c = 0$

$$P_3(x) = 0 + x + \frac{0}{2!}x^2 + \frac{2}{3!}x^3 = x + \frac{1}{3}x^3$$

(b) $n = 5, c = 0$

$$P_5(x) = 0 + x + \frac{0}{2!}x^2 + \frac{2}{3!}x^3 + \frac{0}{4!}x^4 + \frac{16}{5!}x^5 = x + \frac{1}{3}x^3 + \frac{2}{15}x^5$$

(c) $n = 3, c = \dfrac{\pi}{4}$

$$Q_3(x) = 1 + 2\left(x - \frac{\pi}{4}\right) + \frac{4}{2!}\left(x - \frac{\pi}{4}\right)^2 + \frac{16}{3!}\left(x - \frac{\pi}{4}\right)^3 = 1 + 2\left(x - \frac{\pi}{4}\right) + 2\left(x - \frac{\pi}{4}\right)^2 + \frac{8}{3}\left(x - \frac{\pi}{4}\right)^3$$

23. $f(x) = \sin x$

$P_1(x) = x$

$P_3(x) = x - \frac{1}{6}x^3$

$P_5(x) = x - \frac{1}{6}x^3 + \frac{1}{120}x^5$

$P_7(x) = x - \frac{1}{6}x^3 + \frac{1}{120}x^5 - \frac{1}{5040}x^7$

(a)

x	0.00	0.25	0.50	0.75	1.00
$\sin x$	0.0000	0.2474	0.4794	0.6816	0.8415
$P_1(x)$	0.0000	0.2500	0.5000	0.7500	1.0000
$P_3(x)$	0.0000	0.2474	0.4792	0.6797	0.8333
$P_5(x)$	0.0000	0.2474	0.4794	0.6817	0.8417
$P_7(x)$	0.0000	0.2474	0.4794	0.6816	0.8415

(b)

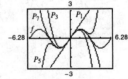

(c) As the distance increases, the accuracy decreases

25. (a) $f(x) = \arcsin x$ $f(0) = 0$

$$f'(x) = \frac{1}{\sqrt{1 - x^2}} \qquad f'(0) = 1$$

$$f''(x) = \frac{x}{(1 - x^2)^{3/2}} \qquad f''(0) = 0$$

$$f'''(x) = \frac{2x^2 + 1}{(1 - x^2)^{5/2}} \qquad f'''(0) = 1$$

$$P_3(x) = f(0) + f'(0)x + \frac{f''(0)}{2!}x^2 + \frac{f'''(0)}{3!}x^3 = x + \frac{x^3}{6}$$

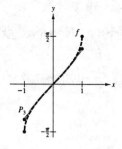

(b)

x	-0.75	-0.50	-0.25	0	0.25	0.50	0.75
$f(x)$	-0.848	-0.524	-0.253	0	0.253	0.524	0.848
$P_3(x)$	-0.820	-0.521	-0.253	0	0.253	0.521	0.820

27. $f(x) = \cos x$

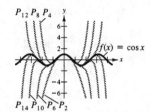

29. $f(x) = e^{-x} \approx 1 - x + \dfrac{x^2}{2} - \dfrac{x^3}{6}$

$$f\left(\frac{1}{2}\right) \approx 0.6042$$

31. From Exercise 19, we have the following 4th-degree polynomial for $f(x) = \ln x$.

$$f(x) \approx P_4(x) = (x - 1) - \frac{1}{2}(x - 1)^2 + \frac{1}{3}(x - 1)^3 - \frac{1}{4}(x - 1)^4$$

$$f(1.2) \approx P_4(1.2) = (1.2 - 1) - \frac{1}{2}(1.2 - 1)^2 + \frac{1}{3}(1.2 - 1)^3 - \frac{1}{4}(1.2 - 1)^4 \approx 0.1823$$

(The actual functional value accurate to four decimal places is also 0.1823.)

33. $f(x) = \cos x; f^{(5)}(x) = -\sin x \Longrightarrow$ Max on $[0, 0.3]$ is 1.

$$R_4(x) \le \frac{1}{5!}(0.3)^5 = 2.025 \times 10^{-5}$$

35. Using Taylor's Theorem, we have

$$\arcsin(0.4) \approx 0.4 + \frac{(0.4)^3}{2 \cdot 3} + R_3(x) = 0.4 + \frac{(0.4)^3}{2 \cdot 3} + \frac{f^{(4)}(z)}{4!}x^4$$

where $0 < z < 0.4$. Using a symbolic differentiation utility to find the $f^{(4)}(x)$ and sketch its graph, yields

$$f^{(4)}(x) = \frac{3x(2x^2 + 3)}{(1 - x^2)^{7/2}}.$$

—CONTINUED—

35. —CONTINUED—

From the graph of the fourth derivative, it follows that $f^{(4)}(x) < 7.3340$ in the interval $[0, 0.4]$. Therefore,

$$0 < R_3(0.4) = \frac{f^{(4)}(z)}{4!}(0.4)^4 < \frac{7.3340}{4!}(0.4)^4 \approx 7.82 \times 10^{-3}.$$

Since

$$\arcsin(0.4) \approx 0.4 + \frac{(0.4)^3}{2 \cdot 3} = 0.41067,$$

we have

$$0.41067 < \arcsin(0.4) = 0.41067 + R_3(0.4) < 0.41067 + (7.82 \times 10^{-3})$$

$$0.41067 < \arcsin(0.4) < 0.41849.$$

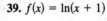

(graph with point (0.4, 7.4330))

37. $g(x) = \sin x$

$g^{(n+1)}(x) \le 1$ for all x

$$R_n(x) \le \frac{1}{(n+1)!}(0.3)^{n+1} < 0.001$$

By trial and error, $n = 3$.

39. $f(x) = \ln(x + 1)$

$$f^{(n+1)}(x) = \frac{(-1)^{n+1}n!}{(x+1)^{n+1}} \Rightarrow \text{Max on } [0, 0.5] \text{ is } n!.$$

$$R_n \le \frac{n!}{(n+1)!}(0.5)^{n+1} = \frac{(0.5)^{n+1}}{n+1} < 0.0001$$

By trial and error, $n = 9$. (See Example 9.) Using 9 terms, $\ln(1.5) \approx 0.4055$.

41. From Taylor's Theorem we have

$$e^x = 1 + x + \frac{x^2}{2!} + \frac{x^3}{3!} + R_3$$

where

$$R_3 = \frac{f^{(4)}(z)}{4!}x^4 = \frac{e^z}{4!}x^4.$$

For $z < 0$ we have

$$R_3 = \frac{e^z x^4}{4!} < \frac{x^4}{4!}$$

and we wish to find $x < 0$ such that

$$\frac{x^4}{4!} < 0.001$$

$$x^4 < 24(0.001) = 0.024$$

$$|x| < (0.024)^{1/4} \approx 0.3936.$$

Therefore, for values of x such that $-0.3936 < x\ 0$,

$$e^x \approx 1 + x + \frac{x^2}{2!} + \frac{x^3}{3!}.$$

43. (a) $f(x) = e^x$

$$P_4(x) = 1 + x + \frac{1}{2}x^2 + \frac{1}{6}x^3 + \frac{1}{24}x^4$$

$$g(x) = xe^x$$

$$Q_5(x) = x + x^2 + \frac{1}{2}x^3 + \frac{1}{6}x^4 + \frac{1}{24}x^5$$

$$Q_5(x) = x P_4(x)$$

(b) $f(x) = \sin x$

$$P_5(x) = x - \frac{x^3}{3!} + \frac{x^5}{5!}$$

$$g(x) = x \sin x$$

$$Q_6(x) = x P_5(x) = x^2 - \frac{x^4}{3!} + \frac{x^6}{5!}$$

(c) $g(x) = \frac{\sin x}{x} = \frac{1}{x}P_5(x) = 1 - \frac{x^2}{3!} + \frac{x^4}{5!}$

45. Let f be an odd function and P_n be the nth Maclaurin polynomial for f. Since f is odd, f' is even:

$$f'(-x) = \lim_{h \to 0}\frac{f(-x+h) - f(-x)}{h} = \lim_{h \to 0}\frac{-f(x-h) + f(x)}{h} = \lim_{h \to 0}\frac{f(x + (-h)) - f(x)}{-h} = f'(x).$$

Similarly, f'' is odd, f''' is even, etc. Therefore, $f, f'', f^{(4)}$, etc. are all odd functions, which implies that $f(0) = f''(0) = \ldots = 0$. Hence, in the formula

$$P_n(x) = f(0) + f'(0)x + \frac{f''(0)x^2}{2!} + \cdots \text{ all the coefficients of the even power of } x \text{ are zero.}$$

47. Let $P_n(x) = a_0 + a_1(x - c) + a_2(x - c)^2 + \cdots + a_n(x - c)^n$ where $a_i = \dfrac{f^{(i)}(c)}{i!}$.

$P_n(c) = a_0 = f(c)$

For $1 \leq k \leq n$, $P_n^{(k)}(c) = a_n k! = \left(\dfrac{f^{(k)}(c)}{k!}\right)k! = f^{(k)}(c)$.

Section 8.8   Power Series

1. $\displaystyle\sum_{n=0}^{\infty} (-1)^n \frac{x^n}{n+1}$

$L = \displaystyle\lim_{n\to\infty}\left|\frac{u_{n+1}}{u_n}\right| = \lim_{n\to\infty}\left|\frac{(-1)^{n+1}x^{n+1}}{n+2} \cdot \frac{n+1}{(-1)^n x^n}\right|$

$= \displaystyle\lim_{n\to\infty}\left|\frac{n+1}{n+2}\right||x| = |x|$

$|x| < 1 \Rightarrow R = 1$

3. $\displaystyle\sum_{n=1}^{\infty} \frac{(2x)^n}{n^2}$

$L = \displaystyle\lim_{n\to\infty}\left|\frac{u_{n+1}}{u_n}\right| = \lim_{n\to\infty}\left|\frac{(2x)^{n+1}}{(n+1)^2} \cdot \frac{n^2}{(2x)^n}\right|$

$= \displaystyle\lim_{n\to\infty}\left|\frac{2n^2 x}{(n+1)^2}\right| = 2|x|$

$2|x| < 1 \Rightarrow R = \dfrac{1}{2}$

5. $\displaystyle\sum_{n=0}^{\infty} \frac{(2x)^n}{n!}$

$L = \displaystyle\lim_{n\to\infty}\left|\frac{u_{n+1}}{u_n}\right| = \lim_{n\to\infty}\left|\frac{(2x)^{n+1}}{(n+1)!} \cdot \frac{n!}{(2x)^n}\right|$

$= \displaystyle\lim_{n\to\infty}\left|\frac{2x}{n+1}\right| = 0$

Thus, the series converges for all x. R is infinite.

$R = \infty$

7. $\displaystyle\sum_{n=0}^{\infty} \left(\frac{x}{2}\right)^n$

Since the series is geometric, it converges only if $|x/2| < 1$ or $-2 < x < 2$.

9. $\displaystyle\sum_{n=1}^{\infty} \frac{(-1)^n x^n}{n}$

Letting $u_n = (-1)^n x^n / n$ produces

$\displaystyle\lim_{n\to\infty}\left|\frac{u_{n+1}}{u_n}\right| = \lim_{n\to\infty}\left|\frac{(-1)^{n+1}x^{n+1}/(n+1)}{(-1)^2 x^n/n}\right|$

$= \displaystyle\lim_{n\to\infty}\left[\frac{x^{n+1}}{n+1} \cdot \frac{n}{x}\right]$

$= \displaystyle\lim_{n\to\infty}\left|\frac{nx}{n+1}\right| = |x|.$

By the Ratio Test, the series converges if $|x| < 1$. Hence, the radius of convergence is 1 and the interval of convergence includes $-1 < x < 1$. When $x = -1$, we have the harmonic series

$\displaystyle\sum_{n=1}^{\infty} \frac{1}{n}$

which diverges. When $x = 1$, we have the alternating series

$\displaystyle\sum_{n=1}^{\infty} \frac{(-1)^n}{n}$

which converges. Thus, the interval of convergence is $-1 < x \leq 1$.

11. $\displaystyle\sum_{n=0}^{\infty} \frac{x^n}{n!}$

$$\lim_{n\to\infty} \left|\frac{u_{n+1}}{u_n}\right| = \lim_{n\to\infty} \left|\frac{x^{n+1}}{(n+1)!} \cdot \frac{n!}{x^n}\right|$$

$$= \lim_{n\to\infty} \left|\frac{x}{n+1}\right| = 0$$

The series converges for all x. Therefore, the interval of convergence is $-\infty < x < \infty$.

13. $\displaystyle\sum_{n=0}^{\infty} (2n)!\left(\frac{x}{2}\right)^n$

Letting $u_n = (2n)!\left(\frac{x}{2}\right)^n$ produces

$$\lim_{n\to\infty} \left|\frac{u_{n+1}}{u_n}\right| = \lim_{n\to\infty} \left|\frac{(2n+2)!/(x/2)^{n+1}}{(2n)!/(x/2)^n}\right|$$

$$= \lim_{n\to\infty} \left|\frac{(2n+2)(2n+1)x}{2}\right| = \infty$$

for any real $x \neq 0$. Therefore, by the Ratio Test, the series converges only when $x = 0$.

15. $\displaystyle\sum_{n=1}^{\infty} \frac{(-1)^{n+1}x^n}{4^n}$

Since the series is geometric, it converges only if $|x/4| < 1$ or $-4 < x < 4$.

17. $\displaystyle\sum_{n=1}^{\infty} \frac{(-1)^{n+1}(x-5)^n}{n5^n}$

Letting $u_n = \dfrac{(-1)^{n+1}(x-5)^n}{n5^n}$ produces

$$\lim_{n\to\infty} \left|\frac{u_{n+1}}{u_n}\right| = \lim_{n\to\infty} \left|\frac{n5^n(x-5)}{(n+1)5^{n+1}}\right|$$

$$= \lim_{n\to\infty} \left|\frac{x-5}{5}\left(\frac{n}{n+1}\right)\right| = \left|\frac{x-5}{5}\right|.$$

By the Ratio Test, the series converges if $|(x-5)/5| < 1$, or $|x-5| < 5$. Hence, the radius of convergence is $R = 5$, and since the series is centered at $x = 5$, the series will converge in the interval $(0, 10)$. Furthermore, when $x = 0$ we have the series

$$\sum_{n=1}^{\infty} \frac{(-1)^{n+1}(-1)^n}{n} = \sum_{n=1}^{\infty} \frac{(-1)^{2n+1}}{n} = -\sum_{n=1}^{\infty} \frac{1}{n}$$

which diverges $(p = 1)$. When $x = 10$, we have the series

$$\sum_{n=1}^{\infty} \frac{(-1)^{n+1}}{n}$$

which converges by the Alternating Series Test. Hence, the interval of convergence of the given series is $0 < x \leq 10$.

19. $\displaystyle\sum_{n=0}^{\infty} \frac{(-1)^{n+1}(x-1)^{n+1}}{n+1}$

$$\lim_{n\to\infty} \left|\frac{u_{n+1}}{u_n}\right| = \lim_{n\to\infty} \left|\frac{(-1)^{n+2}(x-1)^{n+2}}{n+2} \cdot \frac{n+1}{(-1)^{n+1}(x-1)^{n+1}}\right| = \lim_{n\to\infty} \left|\frac{(n+1)(x-1)}{n+2}\right| = |x-1|$$

$R = 1$

Center: $x = 1$

Interval: $-1 < x - 1 < 1$ or $0 < x < 2$

When $x = 0$, the series $\displaystyle\sum_{n=0}^{\infty} \frac{1}{n+1}$ diverges by the integral test.

When $x = 2$, the alternating series $\displaystyle\sum_{n=0}^{\infty} \frac{(-1)^{n+1}}{n+1}$ converges.

Therefore, the interval of convergence is $0 < x \leq 2$.

21. $\sum\limits_{n=1}^{\infty} \dfrac{(x-c)^{n-1}}{c^{n-1}}$

$\lim\limits_{n\to\infty} \left| \dfrac{u_{n+1}}{u_n} \right| = \lim\limits_{n\to\infty} \left| \dfrac{(x-c)^n}{c^n} \cdot \dfrac{c^{n-1}}{(x-c)^{n-1}} \right| = \dfrac{1}{c}|x-c|$

$R = c$

Center: $x = c$

Interval: $-c < x - c < c$ or $0 < x < 2c$

When $x = 0$, the series $\sum\limits_{n=1}^{\infty} (-1)^{n-1}$ diverges.

When $x = 2c$, the series $\sum\limits_{n=1}^{\infty} 1$ diverges.

Therefore, the interval of convergence is $0 < x < 2c$.

23. $\sum\limits_{n=1}^{\infty} \dfrac{n}{n+1}(-2x)^{n-1}$

$\lim\limits_{n\to\infty} \left| \dfrac{u_{n+1}}{u_n} \right| = \lim\limits_{n\to\infty} \left| \dfrac{(n+1)(-2x)^n}{n+2} \cdot \dfrac{n+1}{n(-2x)^{n-1}} \right|$

$= \lim\limits_{n\to\infty} \left| \dfrac{(-2x)(n+1)^2}{n(n+2)} \right| = 2|x|$

$R = \dfrac{1}{2}$

Interval: $-\dfrac{1}{2} < x < \dfrac{1}{2}$

When $x = -\dfrac{1}{2}$, the series $\sum\limits_{n=1}^{\infty} \dfrac{n}{n+1}$ diverges by the nth Term Test.

When $x = \dfrac{1}{2}$, the alternating series $\sum\limits_{n=1}^{\infty} \dfrac{(-1)^{n-1}n}{n+1}$ diverges.

Therefore, the interval of convergence is $-\dfrac{1}{2} < x < \dfrac{1}{2}$.

25. $\sum\limits_{n=0}^{\infty} \dfrac{x^{2n+1}}{(2n+1)!}$

$\lim\limits_{n\to\infty} \left| \dfrac{u_{n+1}}{u_n} \right| = \lim\limits_{n\to\infty} \left| \dfrac{x^{2n+3}}{(2n+3)!} \cdot \dfrac{(2n+1)!}{x^{2n+1}} \right| = \lim\limits_{n\to\infty} \left| \dfrac{x^2}{(2n+2)(2n+3)} \right| = 0$

Therefore, the interval of convergence is $-\infty < x < \infty$.

27. $\sum\limits_{n=1}^{\infty} \dfrac{k(k+1)(k+2)\cdots(k+n-1)x^n}{n!}$ $(k \ge 1)$

Since

$\lim\limits_{n\to\infty} \left| \dfrac{u_{n+1}}{u_n} \right| = \lim\limits_{n\to\infty} \left| \dfrac{k(k+1)\cdots(k+n-1)(k+n)x^{n+1}}{(n+1)!} \cdot \dfrac{n!}{k(k+1)\cdots(k+n-1)x^n} \right|$

$= \lim\limits_{n\to\infty} \left| \dfrac{(k+n)x}{n+1} \right| = |x|,$

the radius of convergence is $R = 1$. Since the series is centered at $x = 0$, it will converge on the interval $(-1, 1)$. To test for convergence at the endpoints, note that for $k \ge 1$,

$\lim\limits_{n\to\infty} a_n = \lim\limits_{n\to\infty} \left[\left(\dfrac{k}{1}\right)\left(\dfrac{k+1}{2}\right)\left(\dfrac{k+2}{3}\right)\cdots\left(\dfrac{k+n-1}{n}\right) \right] \ne 0.$

Thus, for $x = \pm 1$ the series diverges, and the interval of convergence is $-1 < x < 1$.

29. $\sum\limits_{n=1}^{\infty} \dfrac{(-1)^{n+1}3 \cdot 7 \cdot 11 \cdots (4n-1)(x-3)^n}{4^n}$

$\lim\limits_{n\to\infty} \left| \dfrac{u_{n+1}}{u_n} \right| = \lim\limits_{n\to\infty} \left| \dfrac{(-1)^{n+2} \cdot 3 \cdot 7 \cdot 11 \cdots (4n-1)(4n+3)(x-3)^{n+1}}{4^{n+1}} \cdot \dfrac{4^n}{(-1)^{n+1} \cdot 3 \cdot 7 \cdot 11 \cdots (4n-1)(x-3)^n} \right|$

$= \lim\limits_{n\to\infty} \left| \dfrac{(4n+3)(x-3)}{4} \right| = \infty$

$R = 0$

Center: $x = 3$

Therefore, the series converges only for $x = 3$.

31. $f(x) = \sum_{n=0}^{\infty} \left(\frac{x}{2}\right)^n$

(a) The given series is geometric with $r = x/2$ and converges if

$$\left|\frac{x}{2}\right| < 1 \quad \text{or} \quad -2 < x < 2.$$

(b) $f'(x) = \sum_{n=1}^{\infty} n\left(\frac{x}{2}\right)^{n-1}\left(\frac{1}{2}\right) = \sum_{n=1}^{\infty} \left(\frac{n}{2}\right)\left(\frac{x}{2}\right)^{n-1}$

Therefore the series for $f'(x)$ diverges for $x = \pm 2$, and its interval of convergence is $-2 < x < 2$.

(c) $f''(x) = \sum_{n=2}^{\infty} \left(\frac{n}{2}\right)(n-1)\left(\frac{x}{2}\right)^{n-2}\left(\frac{1}{2}\right)$

$= \sum_{n=2}^{\infty} \frac{n(n-1)}{4}\left(\frac{x}{2}\right)^{n-2}$

Therefore, the series for $f''(x)$ diverges for $x = \pm 2$, and its interval of convergence is $-2 < x < 2$.

(d) The series for $\int f(x)\, dx$ is

$$\sum_{n=0}^{\infty} \frac{2}{n+1}\left(\frac{x}{2}\right)^{n+1}$$

and it converges (Alternating Series Test) for $x = -2$ and diverges [Limit Comparison Test with $\sum_{n=1}^{\infty}(1/n)$] for $x = 2$. Therefore, its interval of convergence is

$$-2 \le x < 2.$$

33. (a) $f(x) = \sum_{n=0}^{\infty} \frac{(-1)^{n+1}(x-1)^{n+1}}{n+1}, 0 < x \le 2$

(b) $f'(x) = \sum_{n=0}^{\infty} (-1)^{n+1}(x-1)^n, \ 0 < x < 2$

(c) $f''(x) = \sum_{n=1}^{\infty} (-1)^{n+1}n(x-1)^{n-1}, 0 < x < 2$

(d) $\int f(x)\, dx = \sum_{n=1}^{\infty} \frac{(-1)^{n+1}(x-1)^{n+2}}{(n+1)(n+2)}, 0 \le x \le 2$

35. $g(1) = \sum_{n=0}^{\infty} \left(\frac{1}{3}\right)^n = 1 + \frac{1}{3} + \frac{1}{9} + \cdots$

$S_1 = 1, S_2 = 1.33.$

Matches (c)

37. $g(3.1) = \sum_{n=0}^{\infty} \left(\frac{3.1}{3}\right)^n$ diverges.

Matches (b)

39. (a) $f(x) = \sum_{n=0}^{\infty} \frac{(-1)^n x^{2n+1}}{(2n+1)!}, -\infty < x < \infty$ (See Exercise 25)

$g(x) = \sum_{n=0}^{\infty} \frac{(-1)^n x^{2n}}{(2n)!}, -\infty < x < \infty$

(b) $f'(x) = \sum_{n=0}^{\infty} \frac{(-1)^n x^{2n}}{(2n)!} = g(x)$

(c) $g'(x) = \sum_{n=1}^{\infty} \frac{(-1)^n x^{2n-1}}{(2n-1)!} = \sum_{n=0}^{\infty} \frac{(-1)^{n+1}x^{2n+1}}{(2n+1)!} = -\sum_{n=0}^{\infty} \frac{(-1)^n x^{2n+1}}{(2n+1)!} = -f(x)$

(d) $f(x) = \sin x$ and $g(x) = \cos x$

41.
$$y = \sum_{n=0}^{\infty} \frac{x^{2n}}{2^n n!}$$

$$y' = \sum_{n=1}^{\infty} \frac{2n x^{2n-1}}{2^n n!}$$

$$y'' = \sum_{n=1}^{\infty} \frac{2n(2n-1) x^{2n-2}}{2^n n!}$$

$$y'' - xy' - y = \sum_{n=1}^{\infty} \frac{2n(2n-1) x^{2n-2}}{2^n n!} - \sum_{n=1}^{\infty} \frac{2n x^{2n}}{2^n n!} - \sum_{n=0}^{\infty} \frac{x^{2n}}{2^n n!}$$

$$= \sum_{n=1}^{\infty} \frac{2n(2n-1) x^{2n-2}}{2^n n!} - \sum_{n=0}^{\infty} \frac{(2n+1) x^{2n}}{2^n n!}$$

$$= \sum_{n=0}^{\infty} \left[\frac{(2n+2)(2n+1) x^{2n}}{2^{n+1}(n+1)!} - \frac{(2n+1) x^{2n}}{2^n n!} \cdot \frac{2(n+1)}{2(n+1)} \right]$$

$$= \sum_{n=0}^{\infty} \frac{2(n+1) x^{2n} [(2n+1) - (2n+1)]}{2^{n+1}(n+1)!}$$

$$= 0$$

43. $J_0(x) = \displaystyle\sum_{k=0}^{\infty} \frac{(-1)^k x^{2k}}{2^{2k} (k!)^2}$

(a) $\displaystyle\lim_{k \to \infty} \left| \frac{u_{k+1}}{u_k} \right| = \lim_{k \to \infty} \left| \frac{(-1)^{k+1} x^{2k+2}}{2^{2k+2} [(k+1)!]^2} \cdot \frac{2^{2k} (k!)^2}{(-1)^k x^{2k}} \right| = \lim_{k \to \infty} \left| \frac{(-1) x^2}{2^2 (k+1)^2} \right| = 0$

Therefore, the interval of convergence is $-\infty < x < \infty$.

(b)
$$J_0 = \sum_{k=0}^{\infty} (-1)^k \frac{x^{2k}}{4^k (k!)^2}$$

$$J_0' = \sum_{k=1}^{\infty} (-1)^k \frac{2k x^{2k-1}}{4^k (k!)^2} = \sum_{k=0}^{\infty} (-1)^{k+1} \frac{(2k+2) x^{2k+1}}{4^{k+1} [(k+1)!]^2}$$

$$J_0'' = \sum_{k=1}^{\infty} (-1)^k \frac{2k(2k-1) x^{2k-2}}{4^k (k!)^2} = \sum_{k=0}^{\infty} (-1)^{k+1} \frac{(2k+2)(2k+1) x^{2k}}{4^{k+1} [(k+1)!]^2}$$

$$x^2 J_0'' + x J_0' + x^2 J_0 = \sum_{k=0}^{\infty} (-1)^{k+1} \frac{2(2k+1) x^{2k+2}}{4^{k+1}(k+1)! k!} + \sum_{k=0}^{\infty} (-1)^{k+1} \frac{2 x^{2k+2}}{4^{k+1}(k+1)! k!} + \sum_{k=0}^{\infty} (-1)^k \frac{x^{2k+2}}{4^k (k!)^2}$$

$$= \sum_{k=0}^{\infty} \frac{(-1)^k x^{2k+2}}{4^k (k!)^2} \left[(-1) \frac{2(2k+1)}{4(k+1)} + (-1) \frac{2}{4(k+1)} + 1 \right]$$

$$= \sum_{k=0}^{\infty} \frac{(-1)^k x^{2k+2}}{4^k (k!)^2} \left[\frac{-4k-2}{4k+4} - \frac{2}{4k+4} + \frac{4k+4}{4k+4} \right] = 0$$

(c) $P_6(x) = 1 - \dfrac{x^2}{4} + \dfrac{x^4}{64} - \dfrac{x^6}{2304}$

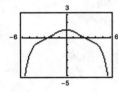

(d) $\displaystyle\int_0^1 J_0 \, dx = \int_0^1 \sum_{k=0}^{\infty} \frac{(-1)^k x^{2k}}{4^k (k!)^2} \, dx = \sum_{k=0}^{\infty} \frac{(-1)^k x^{2k+1}}{4^k (k!)^2 (2k+1)} \Big|_0^1$

$$= \sum_{k=0}^{\infty} \frac{(-1)^k}{4^k (k!)^2 (2k+1)} = 1 - \frac{1}{12} + \frac{1}{320} \approx 0.92$$

(exact integral is 0.9197304101)

45. $f(x) = \sum_{n=0}^{\infty} (-1)^n \frac{x^{2n}}{(2n)!} = \cos x$

(See Exercise 39.)

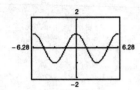

47. $f(x) = \sum_{n=0}^{\infty} (-1)^n x^n = \sum_{n=0}^{\infty} (-x)^n$

$$= \frac{1}{1-(-x)} = \frac{1}{1+x} \text{ for } -1 < x < 1$$

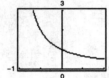

49. $\sum_{n=0}^{\infty} \left(\frac{x}{2}\right)^n$

(a) $\sum_{n=0}^{\infty} \left(\frac{3/4}{2}\right)^n = \sum_{n=0}^{\infty} \left(\frac{3}{8}\right)^n$

$$= \frac{1}{1-(3/8)} = \frac{8}{5} = 1.6$$

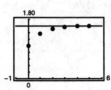

(c) The alternating series converges more rapidly. The partial sums of the series of positive terms approach the sum from below. The partial sums of the alternating series alternate sides of the horizontal line representing the sum.

(b) $\sum_{n=0}^{\infty} \left(\frac{-3/4}{2}\right)^n = \sum_{n=0}^{\infty} \left(-\frac{3}{8}\right)^n$

$$= \frac{1}{1-(-3/8)} = \frac{8}{11} \approx 0.7272$$

(d) $\sum_{n=0}^{N} \left(\frac{3}{2}\right)^n > M$

M	10	100	1000	10,000
N	4	9	15	21

51. False;

$$\sum_{n=0}^{\infty} \frac{(-1)^n x^n}{n2^n}$$

converges for $x = 2$ but diverges for $x = -2$.

53. True; the radius of convergence is $R = 1$ for both series.

Section 8.9   Representation of Functions by Power Series

1. (a) $\frac{1}{2-x} = \frac{1/2}{1-(x/2)} = \frac{a}{1-r}$

$$= \sum_{n=0}^{\infty} \frac{1}{2}\left(\frac{x}{2}\right)^n = \sum_{n=0}^{\infty} \frac{x^n}{2^{n+1}}$$

This series converges on $(-2, 2)$.

(b)
$$
\begin{array}{r}
\frac{1}{2} + \frac{x}{4} + \frac{x^2}{8} + \frac{x^3}{16} + \cdots \\
\hline
2-x \,)\,1 \\
1 - \frac{x}{2} \\
\hline
\frac{x}{2} \\
\frac{x}{2} - \frac{x^2}{4} \\
\hline
\frac{x^2}{4} \\
\frac{x^2}{4} - \frac{x^3}{8} \\
\hline
\frac{x^3}{8} \\
\frac{x^3}{8} - \frac{x^4}{16} \\
\hline
\vdots
\end{array}
$$

3. (a) $\dfrac{1}{2+x} = \dfrac{1/2}{1-(-x/2)} = \dfrac{a}{1-r}$

$$= \sum_{n=0}^{\infty} \frac{1}{2}\left(-\frac{x}{2}\right)^n = \sum_{n=0}^{\infty} \frac{(-1)^n x^n}{2^{n+1}}$$

This series converges on $(-2, 2)$.

(b)

$$\frac{1}{2} - \frac{x}{4} + \frac{x^2}{8} - \frac{x^3}{16} + \cdots$$

$$2+x\,\overline{)\,1}$$

$$\frac{1 + \dfrac{x}{2}}{-\dfrac{x}{2}}$$

$$\frac{-\dfrac{x}{2} - \dfrac{x^2}{4}}{\dfrac{x^2}{4}}$$

$$\frac{\dfrac{x^2}{4} + \dfrac{x^3}{8}}{-\dfrac{x^3}{8}}$$

$$\frac{-\dfrac{x^3}{8} - \dfrac{x^4}{16}}{\vdots}$$

5. $f(x) = \dfrac{1}{2-x}$

Writing $f(x)$ in the form $a/(1-r)$, we have

$$\frac{1}{2-x} = \frac{1}{-3-x+5} = \frac{-1/3}{1-[(x-5)/(-3)]} = \frac{a}{1-r}$$

which implies that $a = -1/3$ and $r = (x-5)/(-3)$. Therefore,

$$\frac{1}{2-x} = \sum_{n=0}^{\infty} ar^n = -\frac{1}{3}\sum_{n=0}^{\infty}\left(\frac{x-5}{-3}\right)^n = \sum_{n=0}^{\infty}\frac{(x-5)^n}{(-3)^{n+1}}.$$

Since

$$\lim_{n\to\infty}\left|\frac{u_{n+1}}{u_n}\right| = \lim_{n\to\infty}\left|\frac{(x-5)^{n+1}}{(-3)^{n+2}}\cdot\frac{(-3)^{n+1}}{(x-5)^n}\right| = \left|\frac{x-5}{3}\right|,$$

the radius of convergence is $R = 3$. Since the series is centered at $c = 5$, it converges in the interval $(2, 8)$. Finally, since the series diverges at both endpoints, the interval of convergence is $2 < x < 8$.

7. Writing $f(x)$ in the form $a/(1-r)$, we have

$$\frac{3}{2x-1} = \frac{-3}{1-2x} = \frac{a}{1-r}$$

which implies that $a = -3$ and $r = 2x$.

Therefore, the power series for $f(x)$ is given by

$$\frac{3}{2x-1} = \sum_{n=0}^{\infty} ar^n = \sum_{n=0}^{\infty}(-3)(2x)^n$$

$$= -3\sum_{n=0}^{\infty}(2x)^n, \; |2x| < 1 \text{ or } -\frac{1}{2} < x < \frac{1}{2}.$$

9. Writing $f(x)$ in the form $a/(1-r)$, we have

$$\frac{1}{2x-5} = \frac{-1}{11-2(x+3)}$$

$$= \frac{-1/11}{1-(2/11)(x+3)} = \frac{a}{1-r}$$

which implies that $a = -1/11$ and $r = (2/11)(x+3)$.
Therefore, the power series for $f(x)$ is given by

$$\frac{1}{2x-5} = \sum_{n=0}^{\infty} ar^n = \sum_{n=0}^{\infty}\left(-\frac{1}{11}\right)\left[\frac{2}{11}(x+3)\right]^n$$

$$= -\sum_{n=0}^{\infty}\frac{2^n(x+3)^n}{11^{n+1}},$$

$$|x+3| < \frac{11}{2} \text{ or } -\frac{17}{2} < x < \frac{5}{2}.$$

11. Writing $f(x)$ in the form $a/(1 - r)$, we have

$$\frac{3}{x + 2} = \frac{3}{2 + x} = \frac{3/2}{1 + (1/2)x} = \frac{a}{1 - r}$$

which implies that $a = 3/2$ and $r = (-1/2)x$. Therefore, the power series for $f(x)$ is given by

$$\frac{3}{x + 2} = \sum_{n=0}^{\infty} ar^n = \sum_{n=0}^{\infty} \frac{3}{2}\left(-\frac{1}{2}x\right)^n = 3 \sum_{n=0}^{\infty} \frac{(-1)^n x^n}{2^{n+1}} = \frac{3}{2} \sum_{n=0}^{\infty} \left(-\frac{x}{2}\right)^n,$$

$|x| < 2$ or $-2 < x < 2$.

13. $f(x) = \dfrac{3x}{x^2 + x - 2}$

Using the method for finding partial fractions (Section 7.5), we have

$$\frac{3x}{x^2 + x - 2} = \frac{2}{x + 2} + \frac{1}{x - 1} = \frac{1}{1 - [-x/2]} - \frac{1}{1 - x}.$$

Therefore, we have the difference of the sum of two geometric series. Using the fact that

$$\sum_{n=0}^{\infty} ar^n = \frac{a}{1 - r},$$

we can write

$$\frac{1}{1 - [-x/2]} - \frac{1}{1 - x} = \sum_{n=0}^{\infty} \left(\frac{x}{-2}\right)^n - \sum_{n=0}^{\infty} x^n = \sum_{n=0}^{\infty} \left[\frac{x^n}{(-2)^n} - x^n\right] = \sum_{n=0}^{\infty} \left[\frac{1}{(-2)^n} - 1\right]x^n.$$

By the Ratio Test

$$\lim_{n \to \infty} \left|\frac{u_{n+1}}{u_n}\right| = \lim_{n \to \infty} \left|\frac{[1/(-2)^{n+1}] - 1}{[1/(-2)^n] - 1} \cdot \frac{x^{n+1}}{x_n}\right| = |x|,$$

and the series converges if $|x| < 1$. Finally, when $x = \pm 1$,

$$\lim_{n \to \infty} a_n = \lim_{n \to \infty} \left[\frac{1}{(-2)^n} - 1\right] \neq 0.$$

Thus, the series diverges when $x = \pm 1$ and the interval of convergence is $-1 < x < 1$.

15. $f(x) = \dfrac{2}{1 - x^2}$

Letting $u = x^2$,

$$\frac{2}{1 - x^2} = \frac{2}{1 - u} = 2 \sum_{n=0}^{\infty} u^n = 2 \sum_{n=0}^{\infty} (x^2)^n = 2 \sum_{n=0}^{\infty} x^{2n}.$$

The series will converge if $x^2 < 1$ or $-1 < x < 1$.

17. $\dfrac{1}{1 + x} = \sum_{n=0}^{\infty} (-1)^n x^n$

$$\frac{1}{1 - x} = \sum_{n=0}^{\infty} (-1)^n (-x)^n = \sum_{n=0}^{\infty} (-1)^{2n} x^n = \sum_{n=0}^{\infty} x^n$$

$$h(x) = \frac{-2}{x^2 - 1} = \frac{1}{1 + x} + \frac{1}{1 - x} = \sum_{n=0}^{\infty} (-1)^n x^n + \sum_{n=0}^{\infty} x^n = \sum_{n=0}^{\infty} [(-1)^n + 1]x^n$$

$$= 2 + 0x + 2x^2 + 0x^3 + 2x^4 + 0x^5 + 2x^6 + \cdots = \sum_{n=0}^{\infty} 2x^{2n}, \ -1 < x < 1 \text{ (See Exercise 15.)}$$

19. By taking the first derivative, we have $\dfrac{d}{dx}\left[\dfrac{1}{x+1}\right] = \dfrac{-1}{(x+1)^2}$. Therefore,

$$\frac{-1}{(x+1)^2} = \frac{d}{dx}\left[\sum_{n=0}^{\infty}(-1)^n x^n\right] = \sum_{n=1}^{\infty}(-1)^n n x^{n-1}$$

$$= \sum_{n=0}^{\infty}(-1)^{n+1}(n+1)x^n,\ -1 < x < 1.$$

21. $f(x) = \ln(x+1)$

Since

$$\int \frac{1}{x+1}\,dx = \ln(x+1) + C,$$

integrate the power series for $1/(x+1)$ to obtain the series for $\ln(x+1)$.

$$\frac{1}{x+1} = \sum_{n=0}^{\infty}(-1)^n x^n$$

$$\ln(x+1) = \sum_{n=0}^{\infty}\frac{(-1)^n x^{n+1}}{n+1} + C$$

Substituting $x = 0$ on both sides of this equation, yields $C = 0$. Furthermore, by the Ratio Test

$$\lim_{n\to\infty}\left|\frac{u_{n+1}}{u_n}\right| = \lim_{n\to\infty}\left|\frac{x^{n+2}}{n+2}\cdot\frac{n+1}{x^{n+1}}\right| = |x|,$$

and the series converges if $|x| < 1$. At $x = -1$ we have the divergent series

$$\sum_{n=0}^{\infty}\frac{(-1)^{2n+1}}{n+1} = -\sum_{n=0}^{\infty}\frac{1}{n+1}.$$

At $x = 1$ we have the convergent alternating series

$$\sum_{n=0}^{\infty}\frac{(-1)^n}{n+1}.$$

Therefore,

$$\ln(x+1) = \sum_{n=0}^{\infty}\frac{(-1)^n x^{n+1}}{n+1},\ \text{for } -1 < x \le 1.$$

23. $\dfrac{1}{x^2+1} = \displaystyle\sum_{n=0}^{\infty}(-1)^n\,(x^2)^n = \sum_{n=0}^{\infty}(-1)^n x^{2n},\ -1 < x < 1$

25. Since, $\dfrac{1}{x+1} = \displaystyle\sum_{n=0}^{\infty}(-1)^n x^n$, we have $\dfrac{1}{4x^2+1} = \displaystyle\sum_{n=0}^{\infty}(-1)^n(4x^2)^n = \sum_{n=0}^{\infty}(-1)^n\,4^n x^{2n} = \sum_{n=0}^{\infty}(-1)^n(2x)^{2n},\ -\dfrac{1}{2} < x < \dfrac{1}{2}.$

27. $x - \dfrac{x^2}{2} \le \ln(x+1) \le x - \dfrac{x^2}{2} + \dfrac{x^3}{3}$

x	0.0	0.2	0.4	0.6	0.8	1.0
$x - \dfrac{x^2}{2}$	0.000	0.180	0.320	0.420	0.480	0.500
$\ln(x+1)$	0.000	0.180	0.336	0.470	0.588	0.693
$x - \dfrac{x^2}{2} + \dfrac{x^3}{3}$	0.000	0.183	0.341	0.492	0.651	0.833

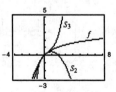

29. $g(x) = x$, line, Matches (c)

31. $g(x) = x - \dfrac{x^3}{3} + \dfrac{x^5}{5}$, Matches (a)

33. $f(x) = \arctan x$ is an odd function (symmetric to the origin)

In Exercises 35 and 37, $\arctan x = \displaystyle\sum_{n=0}^{\infty}(-1)^n \frac{x^{2n+1}}{2n+1}.$

35. $\arctan \dfrac{1}{4} = \displaystyle\sum_{n=0}^{\infty}(-1)^n \frac{(1/4)^{2n+1}}{2n+1} = \sum_{n=0}^{\infty} \frac{(-1)^n}{(2n+1)4^{2n+1}} = \frac{1}{4} - \frac{1}{192} + \frac{1}{5120} + \cdots$

Since $\frac{1}{5120} < 0.001$, we can approximate the series by its first two terms: $\arctan \frac{1}{4} \approx \frac{1}{4} - \frac{1}{192} \approx 0.245.$

37. From Example 5,

$$\arctan x = \sum_{n=0}^{\infty} \frac{(-1)^n x^{2n+1}}{2n+1}.$$

Therefore,

$$\arctan x^2 = \sum_{n=0}^{\infty} \frac{(-1)^n (x^2)^{(2n+1)}}{2n+1} = \sum_{n=0}^{\infty} \frac{(-1)^n x^{(4n+2)}}{2n+1}$$

and

$$\frac{\arctan x^2}{x} = \sum_{n=0}^{\infty} \frac{(-1)^n x^{4n+1}}{2n+1}.$$

Thus,

$$\int_0^{1/2} \frac{\arctan x^2}{x}\,dx = \left[\sum_{n=0}^{\infty} \frac{(-1)^n x^{4n+2}}{(2n+1)(4n+2)}\right]_0^{1/2} = \sum_{n=0}^{\infty} \frac{(-1)^n (1/2)^{4n+2}}{(2n+1)(4n+2)} \approx \left(\frac{1}{2}\right)\left(\frac{1}{2}\right)^2 = \frac{1}{8}.$$

Note that the second term of the series is

$$-\left(\frac{1}{18}\right)\left(\frac{1}{2}\right)^6 < 0.001.$$

Therefore, by the Alternating Series Remainder Theorem, one term is sufficient to approximate the integral.

In Exercises 39 and 41, $\dfrac{1}{1-x} = \displaystyle\sum_{n=0}^{\infty} x^n.$

39. $\dfrac{1}{(1-x)^2} = \dfrac{d}{dx}\left[\dfrac{1}{1-x}\right] = \dfrac{d}{dx}\left[\displaystyle\sum_{n=0}^{\infty} x^n\right] = \displaystyle\sum_{n=1}^{\infty} nx^{n-1}, \quad -1 < x < 1$

41. The following geometric series converges when $|x| < 1$.

$$\sum_{n=0}^{\infty} x^n = \frac{1}{1-x}$$

$$\frac{1}{(1-x)^2} = \frac{d}{dx}\left[\frac{1}{1-x}\right] = \frac{d}{dx}\left[\sum_{n=0}^{\infty} x^n\right] = \sum_{n=1}^{\infty} nx^{n-1}$$

$$E(n) = \sum_{n=1}^{\infty} n\,P(n) = \sum_{n=1}^{\infty} n\left(\frac{1}{2}\right)^n$$

$$= \frac{1}{2}\sum_{n=1}^{\infty} n\left(\frac{1}{2}\right)^{n-1} = \frac{1}{2}\frac{1}{[1-(1/2)]^2} = 2$$

The probability of obtaining a head on a single toss is $\frac{1}{2}$, and on average, a head will be obtained in two tosses.

43. Let $\arctan x + \arctan y = \theta$. Then,

$$\tan(\arctan x + \arctan y) = \tan\theta$$

$$\frac{\tan(\arctan x) + \tan(\arctan y)}{1 - \tan(\arctan x)\tan(\arctan y)} = \tan\theta$$

$$\frac{x + y}{1 - xy} = \tan\theta$$

$$\arctan\left(\frac{x + y}{1 - xy}\right) = \theta.$$

Therefore, $\arctan x + \arctan y = \arctan\left(\dfrac{x + y}{1 - xy}\right)$ for $xy \neq 1$.

45. (a) $2\arctan\dfrac{1}{2} = \arctan\dfrac{1}{2} + \arctan\dfrac{1}{2} = \arctan\left[\dfrac{2(1/2)}{1 - (1/2)^2}\right] = \arctan\dfrac{4}{3}$

$2\arctan\dfrac{1}{2} - \arctan\dfrac{1}{7} = \arctan\dfrac{4}{3} + \arctan\left(-\dfrac{1}{7}\right) = \arctan\left[\dfrac{(4/3) - (1/7)}{1 + (4/3)(1/7)}\right] = \arctan\dfrac{25}{25} = \arctan 1 = \dfrac{\pi}{4}$

(b) $\pi = 8\arctan\dfrac{1}{2} - 4\arctan\dfrac{1}{7} \approx 8\left[\dfrac{1}{2} - \dfrac{(0.5)^3}{3} + \dfrac{(0.5)^5}{5} - \dfrac{(0.5)^7}{7}\right] - 4\left[\dfrac{1}{7} - \dfrac{(1/7)^3}{3} + \dfrac{(1/7)^5}{5} - \dfrac{(1/7)^7}{7}\right] \approx 3.14$

47. From Exercise 21, we have

$$\ln(x + 1) = \sum_{n=0}^{\infty}\frac{(-1)^n x^{n+1}}{n + 1} = \sum_{n=1}^{\infty}\frac{(-1)^{n-1}x^n}{n} = \sum_{n=1}^{\infty}\frac{(-1)^{n+1}x^n}{n}.$$

Thus, $\displaystyle\sum_{n=1}^{\infty}(-1)^{n+1}\frac{1}{2^n n} = \sum_{n=1}^{\infty}\frac{(-1)^{n+1}(1/2)^n}{n} = \ln\left(\frac{1}{2} + 1\right) = \ln\frac{3}{2} \approx 0.4055$

49. In Example 4 it was shown that

$$\ln x = \sum_{n=0}^{\infty}(-1)^n\frac{(x-1)^{n+1}}{n+1} = \sum_{n=1}^{\infty}(-1)^{n-1}\frac{(x-1)^n}{n}.$$

Letting $x = \frac{7}{5}$ in the series yields

$$\sum_{n=1}^{\infty}(-1)^{n-1}\frac{([7/5]-1)^n}{n} = \sum_{n=1}^{\infty}(-1)^{n-1}\frac{(2/5)^n}{n}$$

$$= \sum_{n=1}^{\infty}(-1)^{n-1}\frac{2^n}{5^n n}.$$

Therefore, the sum of the series is

$$\ln\frac{7}{5} \approx 0.3365.$$

51. From Exercise 50, we have

$$\sum_{n=0}^{\infty}(-1)^n\frac{1}{2^{2n+1}(2n+1)} = \sum_{n=0}^{\infty}(-1)^n\frac{(1/2)^{2n+1}}{2n+1}$$

$$= \arctan\frac{1}{2} \approx 0.4636.$$

53. The series in Exercise 50 converges to its sum at a slower rate because its terms approach 0 at a much slower rate.

55. $f(x) = \displaystyle\sum_{n=1}^{\infty}(-1)^{n+1}\frac{(x-1)^n}{n}$, $0 < x \leq 2$

$$f(0.5) = \sum_{n=1}^{\infty}(-1)^{n+1}\frac{(-0.5)^n}{n} = \sum_{n=1}^{\infty}-\frac{(1/2)^n}{n}$$

$$\sum_{n=1}^{\infty}-\frac{(1/2)^n}{n} = -0.6931$$

Section 8.10   Taylor and Maclaurin Series

1. For $c = 0$, we have:

$$f(x) = e^{2x}$$

$$f^{(n)}(x) = 2^n e^{2x} \Rightarrow f^{(n)}(0) = 2^n$$

$$e^{2x} = 1 + 2x + \frac{4x^2}{2!} + \frac{8x^3}{3!} + \frac{16x^4}{4!} + \ldots = \sum_{n=0}^{\infty} \frac{(2x)^n}{n!}$$

3. For $c = \pi/4$, we have:

$$f(x) = \cos(x) \qquad f\left(\frac{\pi}{4}\right) = \frac{\sqrt{2}}{2}$$

$$f'(x) = -\sin(x) \qquad f'\left(\frac{\pi}{4}\right) = -\frac{\sqrt{2}}{2}$$

$$f''(x) = -\cos(x) \qquad f''\left(\frac{\pi}{4}\right) = -\frac{\sqrt{2}}{2}$$

$$f'''(x) = \sin(x) \qquad f'''\left(\frac{\pi}{4}\right) = \frac{\sqrt{2}}{2}$$

$$f^{(4)}(x) = \cos(x) \qquad f^{(4)}\left(\frac{\pi}{4}\right) = \frac{\sqrt{2}}{2}$$

and so on. Therefore we have

$$\cos x = \sum_{n=0}^{\infty} \frac{f^{(n)}(\pi/4)[x - (\pi/4)]^n}{n!}$$

$$= \frac{\sqrt{2}}{2}\left[1 - \left(x - \frac{\pi}{4}\right) - \frac{[x - (\pi/4)]^2}{2!} + \frac{[x - (\pi/4)]^3}{3!} + \frac{[x - (\pi/4)]^4}{4!} - \ldots\right]$$

$$= \frac{\sqrt{2}}{2}\sum_{n=0}^{\infty} \frac{(-1)^{n(n+1)/2}[x - (\pi/4)]^n}{n!}.$$

[**Note:** $(-1)^{n(n+1)/2} = 1, -1, -1, 1, 1, -1, -1, 1, \ldots$]

5. For $c = 1$, we have,

$$f(x) = \ln x \qquad f(1) = 0$$

$$f'(x) = \frac{1}{x} \qquad f'(1) = 1$$

$$f''(x) = -\frac{1}{x^2} \qquad f''(1) = -1$$

$$f'''(x) = \frac{2}{x^3} \qquad f'''(1) = 2$$

$$f^{(4)}(x) = -\frac{6}{x^4} \qquad f^{(4)}(1) = -6$$

$$f^{(5)}(x) = \frac{24}{x^5} \qquad f^{(5)}(1) = 24$$

and so on. Therefore, we have:

$$\ln x = \sum_{n=0}^{\infty} \frac{f^{(n)}(1)(x - 1)^n}{n!}$$

$$= 0 + (x - 1) - \frac{(x - 1)^2}{2!} + \frac{2(x - 1)^3}{3!} - \frac{6(x - 1)^4}{4!} + \frac{24(x - 1)^5}{5!} - \ldots$$

$$= (x - 1) - \frac{(x - 1)^2}{2} + \frac{(x - 1)^3}{3} - \frac{(x - 1)^4}{4} + \frac{(x - 1)^5}{5} - \ldots = \sum_{n=0}^{\infty}(-1)^n \frac{(x - 1)^{n+1}}{n + 1}$$

7. $f(x) = \sin 2x$

Since

$$f(x) = \sin 2x \qquad\qquad f(0) = 0$$
$$f'(x) = 2\cos 2x \qquad\qquad f'(0) = 2$$
$$f''(x) = -4\sin 2x \qquad\qquad f''(0) = 0$$
$$f'''(x) = -8\cos 2x \qquad\qquad f'''(0) = -8 = -2^3$$
$$f^{(4)}(x) = 16\sin 2x \qquad\qquad f^{(4)}(0) = 0$$
$$f^{(5)}(x) = 32\cos 2x \qquad\qquad f^{(5)}(0) = 32 = 2^5,$$

we can see that the signs alternate and that $\left|f^{(n)}(0)\right| = 2^n$ if n is odd. Therefore, the Taylor Series is

$$\sin 2x = f(0) + f'(0)x + \frac{f''(0)x^2}{2!} + \frac{f'''(0)x^3}{3!} + \frac{f^{(4)}(0)x^4}{4!} + \cdots$$

$$= \frac{2x}{1!} - \frac{2^3 x^3}{3!} + \frac{2^5 x^5}{5!} - \cdots + \frac{(-1)^n (2x)^{2n+1}}{(2n+1)!} + \cdots$$

$$= \sum_{n=0}^{\infty} \frac{(-1)^n (2x)^{2n+1}}{(2n+1)!}$$

Note that we could have arrived at the same result by substituting $2x$ into the series for $\sin x$ as follows:

$$\sin x = x - \frac{x^3}{3!} + \frac{x^5}{5!} - \frac{x^7}{7!} + \cdots$$

$$\sin(2x) = (2x) - \frac{(2x)^3}{3!} + \frac{(2x)^5}{5!} - \frac{(2x)^7}{7!} + \cdots$$

$$= \sum_{n=0}^{\infty} \frac{(-1)^n (2x)^{2n+1}}{(2n+1)!}$$

9. For $c = 0$, we have:

$$f(x) = \sec(x) \qquad\qquad\qquad\qquad f(0) = 1$$
$$f'(x) = \sec(x)\tan(x) \qquad\qquad\qquad\qquad f'(0) = 0$$
$$f''(x) = \sec^3(x) + \sec(x)\tan^2(x) \qquad\qquad\qquad\qquad f''(0) = 1$$
$$f'''(x) = 5\sec^3(x)\tan(x) + \sec(x)\tan^3(x) \qquad\qquad\qquad\qquad f'''(0) = 0$$
$$f^{(4)}(x) = 5\sec^5(x) + 18\sec^3(x)\tan^2(x) + \sec(x)\tan^4(x) \qquad\qquad f^{(4)}(0) = 5$$

$$\sec(x) = \sum_{n=0}^{\infty} \frac{f^{(n)}(0)x^n}{n!} = 1 + \frac{x^2}{2!} + \frac{5x^4}{4!} + \cdots$$

11. Since $(1 + x)^{-k} = 1 - kx + \dfrac{k(k+1)x^2}{2!} - \dfrac{k(k+1)(k+2)x^3}{3!} + \cdots$, we have

$$(1 + x)^{-2} = 1 - 2x + \frac{2(3)x^2}{2!} - \frac{2(3)(4)x^3}{3!} + \frac{2(3)(4)(5)x^4}{5!} - \cdots = 1 - 2x + 3x^2 - 4x^3 + 5x^4 - \cdots$$

$$= \sum_{n=0}^{\infty} (-1)^n (n+1)x^n.$$

13. $f(x) = \dfrac{1}{\sqrt{4 + x^2}}$

Consider f in the form

$$f(x) = \frac{1}{\sqrt{4 + x^2}} = \frac{1}{2\sqrt{1 + (x/2)^2}} = \frac{1}{2}\left[1 + \left(\frac{x}{2}\right)^2\right]^{-1/2}$$

which is similar to the binomial form $(1 + x)^{-k}$. Since

$$(1 + x)^{-k} = 1 - kx + \frac{k(k + 1)x^2}{2!} - \frac{k(k + 1)(k + 2)x^3}{3!} + \cdots$$

we have, for $k = \dfrac{1}{2}$,

$$(1 + x)^{-1/2} = 1 - \frac{1}{2}x + \frac{(1/2)(3/2)x^2}{2!} - \frac{(1/2)(3/2)(5/2)x^3}{3!} + \cdots$$

$$= 1 - \frac{x}{2} + \frac{1 \cdot 3x^2}{2^2 2!} - \frac{1 \cdot 3 \cdot 5x^3}{2^3 3!} + \cdots$$

$$= 1 + \sum_{n=1}^{\infty} \frac{(-1)^n 1 \cdot 3 \cdot 5 \cdots (2n - 1)x^n}{2^n n!}.$$

Now substituting $(x/2)^2$ for x, yields

$$f(x) = \frac{1}{\sqrt{4 + x^2}} = \frac{1}{2}\left[1 + \left(\frac{x}{2}\right)^2\right]^{-1/2}$$

$$= \frac{1}{2}\left[1 + \sum_{n=1}^{\infty} \frac{(-1)^n 1 \cdot 3 \cdot 5 \cdots (2n - 1)(x/2)^{2n}}{2^n n!}\right]$$

$$= \frac{1}{2} + \sum_{n=1}^{\infty} \frac{(-1)^n 1 \cdot 3 \cdot 5 \cdots (2n - 1)x^{2n}}{2^{3n+1} n!}$$

$$= \frac{1}{2}\left[1 + \sum_{n=1}^{\infty} \frac{(-1)^n 1 \cdot 3 \cdot 5 \cdots (2n - 1)x^{2n}}{2^{3n} n!}\right].$$

15. Since $(1 + x)^{1/2} = 1 + \dfrac{x}{2} + \displaystyle\sum_{n=2}^{\infty} \frac{(-1)^{n+1} 1 \cdot 3 \cdot 5 \cdots (2n - 3)x^n}{2^n n!}$ (Exercise 14)

we have $(1 + x^2)^{1/2} = 1 + \dfrac{x^2}{2} + \displaystyle\sum_{n=2}^{\infty} \frac{(-1)^{n+1} 1 \cdot 3 \cdot 5 \cdots (2n - 3)x^{2n}}{2^n n!}.$

17. $f(x) = e^{x^2/2}$

Since

$$e^x = 1 + x + \frac{x^2}{2!} + \frac{x^3}{3!} + \frac{x^4}{4!} + \frac{x^5}{5!} + \cdots,$$

we can substitute $x^2/2$ for x and obtain the series

$$e^{x^2/2} = 1 + \frac{x^2}{2} + \frac{(x^2/2)^2}{2!} + \frac{(x^2/2)^3}{3!} + \frac{(x^2/2)^4}{4!} + \cdots$$

$$= 1 + \frac{x^2}{2} + \frac{x^4}{2^2 2!} + \frac{x^6}{2^3 3!} + \frac{x^8}{2^4 4!} + \cdots$$

$$= \sum_{n=0}^{\infty} \frac{x^{2n}}{2^n n!}$$

19. $\sin x = \displaystyle\sum_{n=0}^{\infty} \frac{(-1)^n x^{2n+1}}{(2n + 1)!} = x - \frac{x^3}{3!} + \frac{x^5}{5!} - \frac{x^7}{7!} + \cdots$

$\sin 2x = \displaystyle\sum_{n=0}^{\infty} \frac{(-1)^n(2x)^{2n+1}}{(2n + 1)!} = \sum_{n=0}^{\infty} \frac{(-1)^n 2^{2n+1}x^{2n+1}}{(2n + 1)!} = 2x - \frac{8x^3}{3!} + \frac{32x^5}{5!} - \frac{128x^7}{7!} + \cdots$

21. $\cos x = \displaystyle\sum_{n=0}^{\infty} \frac{(-1)^n x^{2n}}{(2n)!} = 1 - \frac{x^2}{2!} + \frac{x^4}{4!} - \cdots$

$\cos x^{3/2} = \displaystyle\sum_{n=0}^{\infty} \frac{(-1)^n (x^{3/2})^{2n}}{(2n)!} = \sum_{n=0}^{\infty} \frac{(-1)^n x^{3n}}{(2n)!} = 1 - \frac{x^3}{2!} + \frac{x^6}{4!} - \cdots$

23. $f(x) = \dfrac{\sin x}{x}$

Since

$$\sin x = x - \frac{x^3}{3!} + \frac{x^5}{5!} - \frac{x^7}{7!} + \frac{x^9}{9!} - \cdots,$$

we can divide by x to obtain

$$\frac{\sin x}{x} = 1 - \frac{x^2}{3!} + \frac{x^4}{5!} - \frac{x^6}{7!} + \frac{x^8}{9!} - \cdots$$

$$= \sum_{n=0}^{\infty} \frac{(-1)^n x^{2n}}{(2n+1)!}$$

25. $e^x = 1 + x + \dfrac{x^2}{2!} + \dfrac{x^3}{3!} + \dfrac{x^4}{4!} + \dfrac{x^5}{5!} + \cdots$

$e^{-x} = 1 - x + \dfrac{x^2}{2!} - \dfrac{x^3}{3!} + \dfrac{x^4}{4!} - \dfrac{x^5}{5!} + \cdots$

$e^x - e^{-x} = 2x + \dfrac{2x^3}{3!} + \dfrac{2x^5}{5!} + \dfrac{2x^7}{7!} + \cdots$

$\sinh(x) = \dfrac{1}{2}(e^x - e^{-x}) = x + \dfrac{x^3}{3!} + \dfrac{x^5}{5!} + \dfrac{x^7}{7!} + \cdots = \displaystyle\sum_{n=0}^{\infty} \frac{x^{2n+1}}{(2n+1)!}$

27. $\cos^2(x) = \dfrac{1}{2}[1 + \cos(2x)] = \dfrac{1}{2}\left[1 + 1 - \dfrac{(2x)^2}{2!} + \dfrac{(2x)^4}{4!} - \dfrac{(2x)^6}{6!} - \cdots\right] = \dfrac{1}{2}\left[1 + \displaystyle\sum_{n=0}^{\infty} \frac{(-1)^n (2x)^{2n}}{(2n)!}\right]$

29. Observe the following powers of i:

$i = \sqrt{-1}$ $i^5 = i^4 \cdot i = 1$

$i^2 = -1$ $i^6 = i^4 \cdot i^2 = -1$

$i^3 = i^2 \cdot i = -i$ $i^7 = i^4 \cdot i^3 = -i$

$i^4 = i^2 \cdot i^2 = 1$ $i^8 = 1^4 \cdot i^4 = 1$

Since

$$e^x = 1 + x + \frac{x^2}{2!} + \frac{x^3}{3!} + \frac{x^4}{4!} + \frac{x^5}{5!} + \cdots,$$

we can substitute (ix) and $(-ix)$ for x and obtain the series for e^{ix} and e^{-ix}.

$$e^{ix} = 1 + (ix) + \frac{(ix)^2}{2!} + \frac{(ix)^3}{3!} + \frac{(ix)^4}{4!} + \frac{(ix)^5}{5!} + \cdots$$

$$= 1 + ix - \frac{x^2}{2!} - \frac{ix^3}{3!} + \frac{x^4}{4!} + \frac{ix^5}{5!} - \cdots$$

$$e^{-ix} = 1 + (-ix) + \frac{(-ix)^2}{2!} + \frac{(-ix)^3}{3!} + \frac{(-ix)^4}{4!} + \frac{(-ix)^5}{5!} + \cdots$$

$$= 1 - ix - \frac{x^2}{2!} + \frac{ix^3}{3!} + \frac{x^4}{4!} - \frac{ix^5}{5!} - \cdots$$

—CONTINUED—

29. —CONTINUED—

Therefore, subtracting the series for e^{ix} and e^{-ix} yields

$$e^{ix} - e^{-ix} = 2ix - \frac{2ix^3}{3!} + \frac{2ix^5}{5!} - \cdots \quad \text{and}$$

$$\frac{e^{ix} - e^{-ix}}{2i} = x - \frac{x^3}{3!} + \frac{x^5}{5!} - \cdots$$

$$= \sum_{n=0}^{\infty} \frac{(-1)^n x^{2n+1}}{(2n+1)} = \sin x.$$

31. $f(x) = e^x \sin x$

$$= \left(1 + x + \frac{x^2}{2} + \frac{x^3}{6} + \frac{x^4}{24} + \cdots\right)\left(x - \frac{x^3}{6} + \frac{x^5}{120} - \cdots\right)$$

$$= x + x^2 + \left(\frac{x^3}{2} - \frac{x^3}{6}\right) + \left(\frac{x^4}{6} - \frac{x^4}{6}\right) + \left(\frac{x^5}{120} - \frac{x^5}{12} + \frac{x^5}{24}\right) + \cdots$$

$$= x + x^2 + \frac{x^3}{3} - \frac{x^5}{30} + \cdots$$

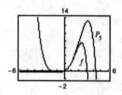

33. $h(x) = \cos x \ln(1 + x)$

$$= \left(1 - \frac{x^2}{2} + \frac{x^4}{24} - \cdots\right)\left(x - \frac{x^2}{2} + \frac{x^3}{3} - \frac{x^4}{4} + \frac{x^5}{5} - \cdots\right)$$

$$= x - \frac{x^2}{2} + \left(\frac{x^3}{3} - \frac{x^3}{2}\right) + \left(\frac{x^4}{4} - \frac{x^4}{4}\right) + \left(\frac{x^5}{5} - \frac{x^5}{6} + \frac{x^5}{24}\right) + \cdots$$

$$= x - \frac{x^2}{2} - \frac{x^3}{6} + \frac{3x^5}{40} + \cdots$$

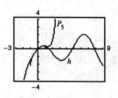

35. $g(x) = \frac{\sin x}{1 + x} = x - x^2 + \frac{5x^3}{6} - \frac{5x^4}{6} + \cdots$ The graph is shown in the figure.

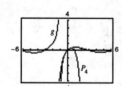

$$
\begin{array}{r}
x - x^2 + \dfrac{5x^3}{6} - \dfrac{5x^4}{6} + \cdots \\[1ex]
1 + x \overline{\smash{\big)}\; x + 0x^2 - \dfrac{x^3}{6} + 0x^4 + \dfrac{x^5}{120} + \cdots} \\[1ex]
\underline{x + x^2} \\[1ex]
-x^2 - \dfrac{x^3}{6} \\[1ex]
\underline{-x^2 - x^3} \\[1ex]
\dfrac{5x^3}{6} + 0x^4 \\[1ex]
\underline{\dfrac{5x^3}{6} + \dfrac{5x^4}{6}} \\[1ex]
-\dfrac{5x^4}{6} + \dfrac{x^5}{120} \\[1ex]
\underline{-\dfrac{5x^4}{6} - \dfrac{5x^5}{6}} \\[1ex]
\vdots
\end{array}
$$

37. $y = x^2 - \dfrac{x^4}{3!} = x\left(x - \dfrac{x^3}{3!}\right) \approx x \sin x.$

Matches (a)

39. $y = x + x^2 + \dfrac{x^3}{2!} = x\left(1 + x + \dfrac{x^2}{2!}\right) \approx xe^x.$

Matches (c)

41. $f(x) = \displaystyle\int_0^x (e^{-t^2} - 1)\, dt = \int_0^x \left[\left(\sum_{n=0}^{\infty} \frac{(-1)^n t^{2n}}{n!}\right) - 1\right] dt = \int_0^x \left[\sum_{n=0}^{\infty} \frac{(-1)^{n+1} t^{2n+2}}{(n+1)!}\right] dt$

$= \left[\displaystyle\sum_{n=0}^{\infty} \frac{(-1)^{n+1} t^{2n+3}}{(2n+3)(n+1)!}\right]_0^x = \sum_{n=0}^{\infty} \frac{(-1)^{n+1} x^{2n+3}}{(2n+3)(n+1)!}$

43. Since $\ln x = \displaystyle\sum_{n=0}^{\infty} \frac{(-1)^n (x-1)^{n+1}}{n+1} = (x-1) - \frac{(x-1)^2}{2} + \frac{(x-1)^3}{3} - \frac{(x-1)^4}{4} + \cdots$, we have

$\ln 2 = 1 - \dfrac{1}{2} + \dfrac{1}{3} - \dfrac{1}{4} + \cdots = \displaystyle\sum_{n=1}^{\infty} (-1)^{n+1} \frac{1}{n} \approx 0.6931.$ (10,001 terms)

45. Since $e^x = \displaystyle\sum_{n=0}^{\infty} \frac{x^n}{n!} = 1 + x + \frac{x^2}{2!} + \frac{x^3}{3!} + \cdots,$, we have

$e^2 = 1 + 2 + \dfrac{2^2}{2!} + \dfrac{2^3}{3!} + \cdots = \displaystyle\sum_{n=0}^{\infty} \frac{2^n}{n!} \approx 7.3891.$ (12 terms)

47. Since

$\cos x = \displaystyle\sum_{n=0}^{\infty} \frac{(-1)^n x^{2n}}{(2n)!} = 1 - \frac{x^2}{2!} + \frac{x^4}{4!} - \frac{x^6}{6!} + \frac{x^8}{8!} - \cdots$

$1 - \cos x = \dfrac{x^2}{2!} - \dfrac{x^4}{4!} + \dfrac{x^6}{6!} - \dfrac{x^8}{8!} + \cdots = \displaystyle\sum_{n=0}^{\infty} \frac{(-1)^n x^{2n+2}}{(2n+2)!}$

$\dfrac{1 - \cos}{x} = \dfrac{x}{2!} - \dfrac{x^3}{4!} + \dfrac{x^5}{6!} - \dfrac{x^7}{8!} + \cdots = \displaystyle\sum_{n=0}^{\infty} \frac{(-1)^n x^{2n+1}}{(2n+2)!}$, we have $\displaystyle\lim_{x \to 0} \frac{1 - \cos x}{x} = \lim_{x \to 0} \sum_{n=0}^{\infty} \frac{(-1)x^{2n+1}}{(2n+2)!} = 0.$

49. From Exercise 23 we have

$\dfrac{\sin x}{x} = \displaystyle\sum_{n=0}^{\infty} \frac{(-1)^n x^{2n}}{(2n+1)!}.$

Therefore,

$\displaystyle\int_0^1 \frac{\sin x}{x}\, dx = \left[\sum_{n=0}^{\infty} \frac{(-1)^n x^{2n+1}}{(2n+1)(2n+1)!}\right]_0^1 = \sum_{n=0}^{\infty} \frac{(-1)^n}{(2n+1)(2n+1)!} = 1 - \frac{1}{3 \cdot 3!} + \frac{1}{5 \cdot 5!} \approx 0.9461.$

By the Alternating Series Remainder Theorem, we have

$|R_3| \leq a_4 = \dfrac{1}{7 \cdot 7!} \approx 0.00003 < 0.0001.$

51. $\displaystyle\int_0^{\pi/2} \sqrt{x} \cos x\, dx = \int_0^{\pi/2} \left[\sum_{n=0}^{\infty} \frac{(-1)^n x^{(4n+1)/2}}{(2n)!}\right] dx = \left[\sum_{n=0}^{\infty} \frac{(-1)^n x^{(4n+3)/2}}{\left(\frac{4n+3}{2}\right)(2n)!}\right]_0^{\pi/2} = \left[\sum_{n=0}^{\infty} \frac{(-1)^n 2x^{(4n+3)/2}}{(4n+3)(2n)!}\right]_0^{\pi/2}$

Since $(\pi/2)^{19/2}/766{,}080 < 0.0001$, we have

$\displaystyle\int_0^1 \sqrt{x} \cos x\, dx = 2\left[\frac{(\pi/2)^{3/2}}{3} - \frac{(\pi/2)^{7/2}}{14} + \frac{(\pi/2)^{11/2}}{264} - \frac{(\pi/2)^{15/2}}{10{,}800} + \frac{(\pi/2)^{19/2}}{766{,}080}\right] \approx 0.7040.$

53. $\int_{0.1}^{0.3} \sqrt{1 + x^3}\, dx = \int_{0.1}^{0.3} \left(1 + \frac{x^3}{2} - \frac{x^6}{8} + \frac{x^9}{16} - \frac{5x^{12}}{128} + \cdots\right) dx = \left[x + \frac{x^4}{8} - \frac{x^7}{56} + \frac{x^{10}}{160} - \frac{5x^{13}}{1664} + \cdots\right]_{0.1}^{0.3}$

Since $\frac{1}{56}(0.3^7 - 0.1^7) < 0.0001$, we have

$$\int_{0.1}^{0.3} \sqrt{1 + x^3}\, dx = \left[(0.3 - 0.1) + \frac{1}{8}(0.3^4 - 0.1^4) - \frac{1}{56}(0.3^7 - 0.1^7)\right] \approx 0.2010.$$

55. From Exercise 17, we have

$$\frac{1}{\sqrt{2\pi}}\int_0^1 e^{-x^2/2}\, dx = \frac{1}{\sqrt{2\pi}}\int_0^1 \sum_{n=0}^{\infty} \frac{(-1)^n x^{2n}}{2^n n!}\, dx$$

$$= \frac{1}{\sqrt{2\pi}}\left[\sum_{n=0}^{\infty} \frac{(-1)^n x^{2n+1}}{2^n n!(2n+1)}\right]_0^1$$

$$= \frac{1}{\sqrt{2\pi}}\sum_{n=0}^{\infty} \frac{(-1)^n}{2^n n!(2n+1)}$$

$$\approx \frac{1}{\sqrt{2\pi}}\left[1 - \frac{1}{2 \cdot 1 \cdot 3} + \frac{1}{2^2 \cdot 2! \cdot 5} - \frac{1}{2^3 \cdot 3! \cdot 7}\right] \approx 0.3413.$$

57. $f(x) = x \cos 2x = \sum_{n=0}^{\infty} \frac{(-1)^n 4^n x^{2n+1}}{(2n)!}$

$P_5(x) = x - 2x^3 + \frac{2x^5}{3}$

The polynomial is a reasonable approximation on the interval $\left[-\frac{3}{4}, \frac{3}{4}\right]$.

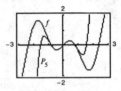

59. $f(x) = \sqrt{x} \ln x,\ c = 1$

$P_5(x) = (x - 1) - \frac{(x-1)^3}{24} + \frac{(x-1)^4}{24} - \frac{71(x-1)^5}{1920}$

The polynomial is a reasonable approximation on the interval $\left[\frac{1}{4}, 2\right]$.

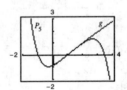

61. $y = \left(\tan\theta - \dfrac{g}{kv_0 \cos\theta}\right)x - \dfrac{g}{k^2}\ln\left(1 - \dfrac{kx}{v_0 \cos\theta}\right)$

$= (\tan\theta)x - \dfrac{gx}{kv_0 \cos\theta} - \dfrac{g}{k^2}\left[-\dfrac{kx}{v_0 \cos\theta} - \dfrac{1}{2}\left(\dfrac{kx}{v_0 \cos\theta}\right)^2 - \dfrac{1}{3}\left(\dfrac{kx}{v_0 \cos\theta}\right)^3 - \dfrac{1}{4}\left(\dfrac{kx}{v_0 \cos\theta}\right)^4 - \cdots\right]$

$= (\tan\theta)x - \dfrac{gx}{kv_0 \cos\theta} + \dfrac{gx}{kv_0 \cos\theta} + \dfrac{gx^2}{2v_0^2 \cos^2\theta} + \dfrac{gkx^3}{3v_0^3 \cos^3\theta} + \dfrac{gk^2x^4}{4v_0^4 \cos^4\theta} + \cdots$

$= (\tan\theta)x + \dfrac{gx^2}{2v_0^2 \cos^2\theta} + \dfrac{kgx^3}{3v_0^3 \cos^3\theta} + \dfrac{k^2gx^4}{4v_0^4 \cos^4\theta} + \cdots$

63. $f(x) = \begin{cases} e^{-1/x^2}, & x \neq 0 \\ 0, & x = 0 \end{cases}$

(a)

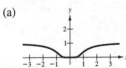

(b) $f'(0) = \lim_{x \to 0} \dfrac{f(x) - f(0)}{x - 0} = \lim_{x \to 0} \dfrac{e^{-1/x^2} - 0}{x}$

Let $y = \lim_{x \to 0} \dfrac{e^{-1/x^2}}{x}$. Then

$\ln y = \lim_{x \to 0} \ln\left(\dfrac{e^{-1/x^2}}{x}\right) = \lim_{x \to 0^+}\left[-\dfrac{1}{x^2} - \ln x\right]$

(c) $\sum_{n=0}^{\infty} \dfrac{f^{(n)}(0)}{n!}x^n = f(0) + \dfrac{f'(0)x}{1!} + \dfrac{f''(0)x^2}{2!} + \cdots$

$= 0 \neq f(x)$

This series converges to f at $x = 0$ only.

$= \lim_{x \to 0^+}\left[\dfrac{-1 - x^2 \ln x}{x^2}\right] = -\infty.$

Thus, $y = e^{-\infty} = 0$ and we have $f'(0) = 0$.

65. By the Ratio Test:

$$\lim_{n \to \infty} \left| \frac{x^{n+1}}{(n+1)!} \cdot \frac{n!}{x^n} \right| = \lim_{n \to \infty} \frac{|x|}{n+1} = 0 \text{ which shows that } \sum_{n=0}^{\infty} \frac{x^n}{n!} \text{ converges for all } x.$$

Review Exercises for Chapter 8

1. $a_n = \dfrac{1}{n!}$

3. $a_n = 4 + \dfrac{2}{n}$: $6, 5, 4.67, \ldots$

    Matches (a)

5. $a_n = 10(0.3)^{n-1}$: $10, 3, \ldots$

    Matches (d)

7. $a_n = \dfrac{5n+2}{n}$

The sequence seems to converge to 5.

$$\lim_{n \to \infty} a_n = \lim_{n \to \infty} \frac{5n+2}{n} = \lim_{n \to \infty} \left(5 + \frac{2}{n} \right) = 5$$

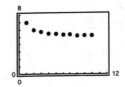

9. $\displaystyle \lim_{n \to \infty} \frac{n+1}{n^2} = 0$

    Converges

11. $\displaystyle \lim_{n \to \infty} \frac{n^3}{n^2+1} = \infty$

    Diverges

13. $a_n = \sqrt{n+1} - \sqrt{n}$

$$\lim_{n \to \infty} = \lim_{n \to \infty} \left[\sqrt{n+1} - \sqrt{n} \right]$$

$$= \lim_{n \to \infty} \left[\left(\sqrt{n+1} - \sqrt{n} \right) \frac{\sqrt{n+1} + \sqrt{n}}{\sqrt{n+1} + \sqrt{n}} \right]$$

$$= \lim_{n \to \infty} \frac{1}{\sqrt{n+1} + \sqrt{n}} = 0$$

The sequence converges to 0.

15. $\displaystyle \lim_{n \to \infty} \frac{\sin(n)}{\sqrt{n}} = 0$

    Converges

17. $A_n = 5000 \left(1 + \dfrac{0.05}{4} \right)^n = 5000(1.0125)^n$

$n = 1, 2, 3$

  (a) $A_1 = 5062.50$ $A_5 \approx 5320.41$

        $A_2 \approx 5125.78$ $A_6 \approx 5386.92$

        $A_3 \approx 5189.85$ $A_7 \approx 5454.25$

        $A_4 \approx 5254.73$ $A_8 \approx 5522.43$

  (b) $A_{40} \approx 8218.10$

19. (a)

k	5	10	15	20	25
S_k	13.2	113.3	873.8	6448.5	50,500.3

(b)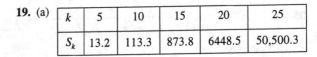

(c) The series diverges $\left(\text{geometric } r = \frac{3}{2} > 1 \right)$

21. (a) $\displaystyle \sum_{n=1}^{\infty} \frac{(-1)^{n+1}}{(2n)!}$

n	5	10	15	20	25
S_n	0.4597	0.4597	0.4597	0.4597	0.4597

(b) The graph is shown in the figure.

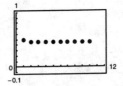

—CONTINUED—

21. —CONTINUED—

(c) Observe that $\lim\limits_{n\to\infty} a_n = \lim\limits_{n\to\infty} \dfrac{1}{(2n)!} = 0$ and

$$a_{n+1} = \frac{1}{[2(n+1)]!} < \frac{1}{(2n)!} = a_n$$

for all n. Therefore, by the Alternating Series Test, the series converges.

23. $\displaystyle\sum_{n=0}^{\infty}\left(\frac{2}{3}\right)^n$

Geometric series with $a = 1$ and $r = \frac{2}{3}$.

$$S = \frac{a}{1-r} = \frac{1}{1-(2/3)} = \frac{1}{1/3} = 3$$

25. $\displaystyle\sum_{n=0}^{\infty}\left(\frac{1}{2^n} - \frac{1}{3^n}\right)$

Write the series as the difference of two geometric series.

$$\sum_{n=0}^{\infty}\left(\frac{1}{2^n} - \frac{1}{3^n}\right) = \sum_{n=0}^{\infty}\left(\frac{1}{2}\right)^n - \sum_{n=0}^{\infty}\left(\frac{1}{3}\right)^n$$

Since these two geometric series have the values $a = 1$, $r = \frac{1}{2}$, and $r = \frac{1}{3}$, respectively, it follows that

$$\sum_{n=0}^{\infty}\left(\frac{1}{2^n} - \frac{1}{3^n}\right) = \frac{1}{1-(1/2)} - \frac{1}{1-(1/3)}$$

$$= 2 - \frac{3}{2} = \frac{1}{2}.$$

27. $0.\overline{09} = 0.09 + 0.0009 + 0.000009 + \cdots = 0.09(1 + 0.01 + 0.0001 + \cdots) = \displaystyle\sum_{n=0}^{\infty}(0.09)(0.01)^n = \dfrac{0.09}{1-0.01} = \dfrac{1}{11}$

29. $D_1 = 8$

$D_2 = 0.7(8) + 0.7(8) = 16(0.7)$

$\vdots$

$D = 8 + 16(0.7) + 16(0.7)^2 + \cdots + 16(0.7)^n + \cdots$

$= -8 + \displaystyle\sum_{n=0}^{\infty} 16(0.7)^n = -8 + \dfrac{16}{1-0.7} = 45\frac{1}{3}$ meters

31. See Exercise 76 in Section 8.2.

$$A = \frac{P(e^{rt} - 1)}{e^{r/12} - 1}$$

$$= \frac{200(e^{(0.06)(2)} - 1)}{e^{0.06/12} - 1}$$

$$\approx \$5087.14$$

33. (a) Ratio Test: $\lim\limits_{n\to\infty}\left|\dfrac{a_{n+1}}{a_n}\right| = \lim\limits_{n\to\infty}\dfrac{(n+1)(3/5)^{n+1}}{n(3/5)^n} = \lim\limits_{n\to\infty}\left(\dfrac{n+1}{n}\right)\left(\dfrac{3}{5}\right) = \dfrac{3}{5} < 1$

Converges

(b)

x	5	10	15	20	25
S_n	2.8752	3.6366	3.7377	3.7488	3.7499

(c)

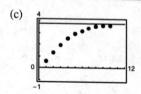

(d) The sum is approximately 3.75.

35. $\displaystyle\sum_{n=1}^{\infty} \frac{2^n}{n^3}$

$$\lim_{n\to\infty} \left|\frac{a_{n+1}}{a_n}\right| = \lim_{n\to\infty} \left|\frac{2^{n+1}}{(n+1)^3} \cdot \frac{n^3}{2^n}\right|$$

$$= \lim_{n\to\infty} \frac{2n^3}{(n+1)^3} = 2$$

Therefore, by the Ratio Test, the series diverges.

37. $\displaystyle\sum_{n=1}^{\infty} \frac{1}{\sqrt{n^3 + 2n}}$

$$\sum_{n=1}^{\infty} \frac{1}{\sqrt{n^3 + 2n}} < \sum_{n=1}^{\infty} \frac{1}{\sqrt{n^3}} = \sum_{n=1}^{\infty} \frac{1}{n^{3/2}}$$

Since

$$\sum_{n=1}^{\infty} \frac{1}{n^{3/2}}$$

is a p-series with $p > 1$, it converges. Therefore, by the Comparison Test, the given series converges.

39. $\displaystyle\sum_{n=1}^{\infty} \frac{n}{e^{n^2}}$

$$\lim_{n\to\infty} \left|\frac{a_{n+1}}{a_n}\right| = \lim_{n\to\infty} \left|\frac{n+1}{e^{(n+1)^2}} \cdot \frac{e^{n^2}}{n}\right| = \lim_{n\to\infty} \left|\frac{e^{n^2}(n+1)}{e^{n^2+2n+1}n}\right|$$

$$= \lim_{n\to\infty} \left(\frac{1}{e^{2n+1}}\right)\left(\frac{n+1}{n}\right)$$

$$= (0)(1) = 0 < 1$$

By the Ratio Test, the series converges.

41. $\displaystyle\sum_{n=1}^{\infty} \frac{(-1)^n n}{\ln(n)}$

$$\lim_{n\to\infty} \frac{n}{\ln(n)} = \infty \neq 0$$

The series diverges by the nth term test.

43. $\displaystyle\sum_{n=1}^{\infty} \left(\frac{1}{n^2} - \frac{1}{n}\right) = \sum_{n=1}^{\infty} \frac{1}{n^2} - \sum_{n=1}^{\infty} \frac{1}{n}$

Since the second series is a divergent p-series while the first series is a convergent p-series, the difference diverges.

45. $\displaystyle\sum_{n=1}^{\infty} \frac{1 \cdot 3 \cdot 5 \cdots (2n-1)}{2 \cdot 4 \cdot 6 \cdots (2n)}$

$$a_n = \frac{1 \cdot 3 \cdot 5 \cdots (2n-1)}{2 \cdot 4 \cdot 6 \cdots (2n)} = \left(\frac{3}{2} \cdot \frac{5}{4} \cdots \frac{2n-1}{2n-2}\right)\frac{1}{2n} > \frac{1}{2n}$$

Since $\displaystyle\sum_{n=1}^{\infty} \frac{1}{2n} = \frac{1}{2}\sum_{n=1}^{\infty} \frac{1}{n}$ diverges (harmonic series), so does the original series.

47. (a) $\displaystyle\int_N^{\infty} \frac{1}{x^2}\, dx = \left[-\frac{1}{x}\right]_N^{\infty} = \frac{1}{N}$

N	5	10	20	30	40
$\displaystyle\sum_{n=1}^{N} \frac{1}{n^2}$	1.4636	1.5498	1.5962	1.6122	1.6202
$\displaystyle\int_N^{\infty} \frac{1}{x^2}\, dx$	0.2000	0.1000	0.0500	0.0333	0.0250

(b) $\displaystyle\int_N^{\infty} \frac{1}{x^5}\, dx = \left[-\frac{1}{4x^4}\right]_N^{\infty} = \frac{1}{4N^4}$

N	5	10	20	30	40
$\displaystyle\sum_{n=1}^{N} \frac{1}{n^5}$	1.0367	1.0369	1.0369	1.0369	1.0369
$\displaystyle\int_N^{\infty} \frac{1}{x^5}\, dx$	0.0004	0.0000	0.0000	0.0000	0.0000

The series in part (b) converges more rapidly. The integral values represent the remainders of the partial sums.

49. $\displaystyle\sum_{n=0}^{\infty} \left(\frac{x}{10}\right)^n$

The series is geometric with common ratio $r = x/10$. Therefore, it converges only if

$$\left|\frac{x}{10}\right| < 1 \implies -10 < x < 10.$$

51. $\displaystyle\sum_{n=0}^{\infty} \frac{(-1)^n(x - 2)^n}{(n + 1)^2}$

$$\lim_{n\to\infty} \left|\frac{u_{n+1}}{u_n}\right| = \lim_{n\to\infty} \left|\frac{(-1)^{n+1}(x - 2)^{n+1}}{(n + 2)^2} \cdot \frac{(n + 1)^2}{(-1)^n(x - 2)^n}\right|$$

$$= |x - 2|$$

$R = 1$
Center: 2

Since the series converges when $x = 1$ and when $x = 3$, the interval of convergence is $1 \le x \le 3$.

53. $\displaystyle\sum_{n=0}^{\infty} n!(x - 2)^n$

Since

$$\lim_{n\to\infty} \left|\frac{u_{n+1}}{u_n}\right| = \lim_{n\to\infty} \left|\frac{(n + 1)!(x - 2)^{n+1}}{n!(x - 2)^2}\right|$$

$$= \lim_{n\to\infty} |(n + 1)(x - 2)| = \infty$$

for all $x \ne 2$, it follows that the radius of convergence is $R = 0$, the series will converge only at $x = 2$.

55. $f(x) = \sin(x)$

$f'(x) = \cos(x)$

$f''(x) = -\sin(x)$

$f'''(x) = -\cos(x), \cdots$

$$\sin(x) = \sum_{n=0}^{\infty} \frac{f^{(n)}(x)[x - (3\pi/4)]^n}{n!} = \frac{\sqrt{2}}{2} - \frac{\sqrt{2}}{2}\left(x - \frac{3\pi}{4}\right) - \frac{\sqrt{2}}{2 \cdot 2!}\left(x - \frac{3\pi}{4}\right)^2 + \cdots = \frac{\sqrt{2}}{2}\sum_{n=0}^{\infty} \frac{(-1)^{n(n+1)/2}[x - (3\pi/4)]^n}{n!}$$

57. Since $3^x = e^{\ln(3^x)} = e^{x(\ln 3)}$, we can substitute $x(\ln 3)$ for x in the series

$$e^x = 1 + x + \frac{x^2}{2!} + \frac{x^3}{3!} + \frac{x^4}{4!} + \cdots$$

to obtain

$$3^x = e^{x(\ln 3)}$$

$$= 1 + (\ln 3)x + \frac{(\ln 3)^2 x^2}{2!} + \frac{(\ln 3)^3 x^3}{3!} + \frac{(\ln 3)^4 x^4}{4!} + \cdots$$

$$= \sum_{n=0}^{\infty} \frac{(x \ln 3)^n}{n!}.$$

59. $f(x) = \dfrac{1}{x}$

$f'(x) = -\dfrac{1}{x^2}$

$f''(x) = \dfrac{2}{x^3}$

$f'''(x) = -\dfrac{6}{x^4}, \cdots$

$$\frac{1}{x} = \sum_{n=0}^{\infty} \frac{f^{(n)}(-1)(x + 1)^n}{n!} = \sum_{n=0}^{\infty} \frac{-n!(x + 1)^n}{n!} = -\sum_{n=0}^{\infty} (x + 1)^n$$

61. $\displaystyle g(x) = \frac{2}{3 - x} = \frac{2/3}{1 - (x/3)} = \sum_{n=0}^{\infty} \frac{2}{3}\left(\frac{x}{3}\right)^n = \sum_{n=0}^{\infty} \frac{2x^n}{3^{n+1}}$

63. $\ln x = \sum_{n=1}^{\infty} (-1)^{n+1} \frac{(x-1)^n}{n}, \quad 0 < x \le 2$

$\ln\left(\frac{5}{4}\right) = \sum_{n=1}^{\infty} (-1)^{n+1} \left(\frac{(5/4)-1}{n}\right)^n$

$= \sum_{n=1}^{\infty} (-1)^{n+1} \frac{1}{4^n n} \approx 0.2231$

65. $\sum_{n=0}^{\infty} \frac{1}{2^n n!}$

$e^x = 1 + x + \frac{x^2}{2!} + \frac{x^3}{3!} + \frac{x^4}{4!} + \cdots = \sum_{n=0}^{\infty} \frac{x^n}{n!}$

Substituting $x = \frac{1}{2}$ into the series yields

$\sum_{n=0}^{\infty} \frac{(1/2)^n}{n!} = \sum_{n=0}^{\infty} \frac{1}{2^n n!} = e^{1/2} \approx 1.6487.$

67. $\cos x = \sum_{n=0}^{\infty} (-1)^n \frac{x^{2n}}{(2n)!}, \quad -\infty < x < \infty$

$\cos\left(\frac{2}{3}\right) = \sum_{n=0}^{\infty} (-1)^n \frac{2^{2n}}{3^{2n}(2n)!} \approx 0.7859$

69. The series for Exercise 37 converges very slowly because the terms approach 0 at a slow rate.

71. (a) $f(x) = e^{2x}$ $f(0) = 1$

$f'(x) = 2e^{2x}$ $f'(0) = 2$

$f''(x) = 4e^{2x}$ $f''(0) = 4$

$f'''(x) = 8e^{2x}$ $f'''(0) = 8$

$e^{2x} = 1 + 2x + \frac{4x^2}{2!} + \frac{8x^3}{3!} + \cdots$

$= 1 + 2x + 2x^2 + \frac{4}{3}x^3 + \cdots$

(b) $e^x = \sum_{n=0}^{\infty} \frac{x^n}{n!}$

$e^{2x} = \sum_{n=0}^{\infty} \frac{(2x)^n}{n!} = 1 + 2x + \frac{4x^2}{2!} + \frac{8x^3}{3!} + \cdots$

$= 1 + 2x + 2x^2 + \frac{4}{3}x^3 + \cdots$

(c) $e^{2x} = e^x \cdot e^x = \left(1 + x + \frac{x^2}{2} + \frac{x^3}{6} + \cdots\right)\left(1 + x + \frac{x^2}{2} + \frac{x^3}{6} + \cdots\right)$

$= 1 + (x + x) + \left(x^2 + \frac{x^2}{2} + \frac{x^2}{2}\right) + \left(\frac{x^3}{6} + \frac{x^3}{6} + \frac{x^3}{2} + \frac{x^3}{2}\right) + \cdots = 1 + 2x + 2x^2 + \frac{4}{3}x^3 + \cdots$

73. $1 + \frac{2}{3}x + \frac{4}{9}x^2 + \frac{8}{27}x^3 + \cdots$

is a geometric series with $r = 2x/3$. Therefore, it converges if

$\left|\frac{2x}{2}\right| < 1 \implies -\frac{3}{2} < x < \frac{3}{2}.$

Using the formula for the sum of a convergent geometric series we have

$1 + \frac{2}{3}x + \frac{4}{9}x^2 + \frac{8}{27}x^3 + \cdots = \sum_{n=0}^{\infty} \left(\frac{2x}{3}\right)^n$

$= \frac{1}{1-(2x/3)} = \frac{3}{3-2x}, \quad -\frac{3}{2} < x < \frac{3}{2}.$

75. $\sin t = \sum_{n=0}^{\infty} \frac{(-1)^n t^{2n+1}}{(2n+1)!}$

$\frac{\sin t}{t} = \sum_{n=0}^{\infty} \frac{(-1)^n t^{2n}}{(2n+1)!}$

$\int_0^x \frac{\sin t}{t} dt = \left[\sum_{n=0}^{\infty} \frac{(-1)^n t^{2n+1}}{(2n+1)(2n+1)!}\right]_0^x$

$= \sum_{n=0}^{\infty} \frac{(-1)^n x^{2n+1}}{(2n+1)(2n+1)!}$

77. $\frac{1}{1+t} = \sum_{n=0}^{\infty} (-1)^n t^n$

$\ln(1+t) = \int \frac{1}{1+t} dt = \sum_{n=0}^{\infty} \frac{(-1)^n t^{n+1}}{n+1}$

$\frac{\ln(t+1)}{t} = \sum_{n=0}^{\infty} \frac{(-1)^n t^n}{n+1}$

$\int_0^x \frac{\ln(t+1)}{t} dt = \left[\sum_{n=0}^{\infty} \frac{(-1)^n t^{n+1}}{(n+1)^2}\right]_0^x = \sum_{n=0}^{\infty} \frac{(-1)^n x^{n+1}}{(n+1)^2}$

79. $\arctan x = x - \dfrac{x^3}{3} + \dfrac{x^5}{5} - \dfrac{x^7}{7} + \dfrac{x^9}{9} - \cdots$

$\dfrac{\arctan x}{\sqrt{x}} = \sqrt{x} - \dfrac{x^{5/2}}{3} + \dfrac{x^{9/2}}{5} - \dfrac{x^{13/2}}{7} + \dfrac{x^{17/2}}{9} - \cdots$

$\displaystyle\lim_{x \to 0} \dfrac{\arctan x}{\sqrt{x}} = 0$

By L'Hôpital's Rule, $\displaystyle\lim_{x \to 0} \dfrac{\arctan x}{\sqrt{x}} = \lim_{x \to 0} \dfrac{\left(\dfrac{1}{1+x^2}\right)}{\left(\dfrac{1}{2\sqrt{x}}\right)} = \lim_{x \to 0} \dfrac{2\sqrt{x}}{1+x^2} = 0.$

81.

$$y = \sum_{n=0}^{\infty} \dfrac{(-1)^n x^{2n}}{4^n (n!)^2}$$

$$y' = \sum_{n=1}^{\infty} \dfrac{(-1)^n (2n) x^{2n-1}}{4^n (n!)^2} = \sum_{n=0}^{\infty} \dfrac{(-1)^{n+1}(2n+2) x^{2n+1}}{4^{n+1}[(n+1)!]^2}$$

$$y'' = \sum_{n=0}^{\infty} \dfrac{(-1)^{n+1}(2n+2)(2n+1) x^{2n}}{4^{n+1}[(n+1)!]^2}$$

$$x^2 y'' + xy' + x^2 y = \sum_{n=0}^{\infty} \dfrac{(-1)^{n+1}(2n+2)(2n+1) x^{2n+2}}{4^{n+1}[(n+1)!]^2} + \sum_{n=0}^{\infty} \dfrac{(-1)^{n+1}(2n+2) x^{2n+2}}{4^{n+1}[(n+1)!]^2} + \sum_{n=0}^{\infty} \dfrac{(-1)^n x^{2n+2}}{4^n (n!)^2}$$

$$= \sum_{n=0}^{\infty} \left[\dfrac{(-1)^{n+1}(2n+2)(2n+1)}{4^{n+1}[(n+1)!]^2} + \dfrac{(-1)^{n+1}(2n+2)}{4^{n+1}[(n+1)!]^2} + \dfrac{(-1)^n}{4^n (n!)^2} \right] x^{2n+2}$$

$$= \sum_{n=0}^{\infty} \left[\dfrac{(-1)^{n+1} 4(n+1)^2}{4^{n+1}[(n+1)!]^2} - \dfrac{(-1)^{n+1}}{4^n (n!)^2} \right] x^{2n+2}$$

$$= \sum_{n=0}^{\infty} \left[\dfrac{(-1)^{n+1}}{4^n (n!)^2} - \dfrac{(-1)^{n+1}}{4^n (n!)^2} \right] x^{2n+2} = 0$$

83. $\sin(95°) = \sin\left(\dfrac{95\pi}{180}\right) \approx \dfrac{95\pi}{180} - \dfrac{(95\pi)^3}{180^3 3!} + \dfrac{(95\pi)^5}{180^5 5!} - \dfrac{(95\pi)^7}{180^7 7!} + \dfrac{(95\pi)^9}{180^9 9!} \approx 0.996$

85. $\ln(1.75) \approx (0.75) - \dfrac{(0.75)^2}{2} + \dfrac{(0.75)^3}{3} - \dfrac{(0.75)^4}{4} + \dfrac{(0.75)^5}{5} - \dfrac{(0.75)^6}{6} + \cdots + \dfrac{(0.75)^{15}}{15} \approx 0.560$

87. $f(x) = \cos x, \ c = 0$

$R_n(x) = \dfrac{f^{(n+1)}(z)}{(n+1)!} x^{n+1}$

$|f^{(n+1)}(z)| \le 1 \implies R_n(x) \le \dfrac{x^{n+1}}{(n+1)!}$

(a) $R_n(x) \le \dfrac{(0.5)^{n+1}}{(n+1)!} < 0.001$

This inequality is true for $n = 4$.

(b) $R_n(x) \le \dfrac{(1)^{n+1}}{(n+1)!} < 0.001$

This inequality is true for $n = 6$.

(c) $R_n(x) \le \dfrac{(0.5)^{n+1}}{(n+1)!} < 0.0001$

This inequality is true for $n = 5$.

(d) $R_n(x) \le \dfrac{2^{n+1}}{(n+1)!} < 0.0001$

This inequality is true for $n = 10$.

CHAPTER 9
Conics, Parametric Equations, and Polar Coordinates

CHAPTER 9
Conics, Parametric Equations, and Polar Coordinates

Section 9.1   Conics and Calculus

Solutions to Odd-Numbered Exercises

1. $y^2 = 4x$

   Vertex: $(0, 0)$

   $p = 1 > 0$

   Opens to the right
   Matches graph (h).

3. $(x + 3)^2 = -2(y - 2)$

   Vertex: $(-3, 2)$

   $p = -\frac{1}{2} < 0$

   Opens downward
   Matches graph (e).

5. $\dfrac{x^2}{9} + \dfrac{y^2}{4} = 1$

   Center: $(0, 0)$
   Ellipse
   Matches (f)

7. $\dfrac{y^2}{16} - \dfrac{x^2}{1} = 1$

   Hyperbola

   Center: $(0, 0)$

   Vertical transverse axis.
   Matches (c)

9. $y^2 = -6x$

   Write the equation in standard form.

$$(y - k)^2 = 4p(x - h)$$
$$y^2 = -6x$$
$$(y - 0)^2 = 4\left(-\tfrac{3}{2}\right)(x - 0)$$

   Thus, $k = 0$, $h = 0$, and $p = -\frac{3}{2}$. It follows that:

   Vertex, (h, k): $(0, 0)$

   Focus, $(h + p, k)$: $\left(-\tfrac{3}{2}, 0\right)$

   Directrix, $(x = h - p)$: $x = \tfrac{3}{2}$

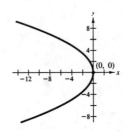

11. $(x + 3) + (y - 2)^2 = 0$

$$(y - 2)^2 = 4\left(-\tfrac{1}{4}\right)(x + 3)$$

   Vertex: $(-3, 2)$

   Focus: $(-3.25, 2)$

   Directrix: $x = -2.75$

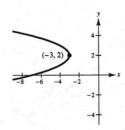

476

13. $y^2 - 4y - 4x = 0$

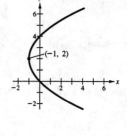

Write the equation in standard form.

$$(y - k)^2 = 4p(x - h)$$

$$y^2 - 4y = 4x$$

$$y^2 - 4y + 4 = 4x + 4$$

$$(y - 2)^2 = 4(1)(x + 1)$$

Thus, $h = -1, k = 2$, and $p = 1$.

Vertex, (h, k): $(-1, 2)$

Focus, $(h + p, k)$: $(0, 2)$

Directrix, $(x = h - p)$: $x = -2$

15. $x^2 + 4x + 4y - 4 = 0$

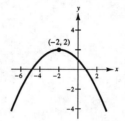

$$x^2 + 4x + 4 = -4y + 4 + 4$$

$$(x + 2)^2 = 4(-1)(y - 2)$$

Vertex: $(-2, 2)$

Focus: $(-2, 1)$

Directrix: $y = 3$

17. $y^2 + x + y = 0$

$$y^2 + y + \tfrac{1}{4} = -x + \tfrac{1}{4}$$

$$\left(y + \tfrac{1}{2}\right)^2 = 4\left(-\tfrac{1}{4}\right)\left(x - \tfrac{1}{4}\right)$$

Vertex: $\left(\tfrac{1}{4}, -\tfrac{1}{2}\right)$

Focus: $\left(0, -\tfrac{1}{2}\right)$

Directrix: $x = \tfrac{1}{2}$

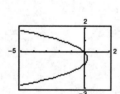

19. $y^2 - 4x - 4 = 0$

$$y^2 = 4x + 4$$

$$= 4(1)(x + 1)$$

Vertex: $(-1, 0)$

Focus: $(0, 0)$

Directrix: $x = -2$

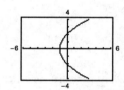

21. The vertex and focus of the parabola are $(3, 2)$ and $(1, 2)$, respectively. Since the vertex and focus lie on a horizontal line, the axis of this parabola must be horizontal and its standard form is $(y - k)^2 = 4p(x - h)$. Since the vertex is at $(3, 2)$, $h = 3$ and $k = 2$. Furthermore, the *directed distance* from the focus to the vertex is $p = 1 - 3 = -2$. Thus,

$$(y - 2)^2 = 4(-2)(x - 3)$$

$$y^2 - 4y + 4 = -8x + 24$$

$$y^2 - 4y + 8x - 20 = 0.$$

23. $(x - h)^2 = 4p(y - k)$

$$x^2 = 4(6)(y - 4)$$

$$x^2 - 24y + 96 = 0$$

25. $y = 4 - x^2$

$$x^2 + y - 4 = 0$$

27. Since the axis of the parabola is vertical, the standard form is

$$(x - h)^2 = 4p(y - k).$$

For this exercise, a more convenient form for this equation is

$$y = ax^2 + bx + c.$$

Substituting the values of the coordinates of the points $(0, 3)$, $(3, 4)$, and $(4, 11)$ into this equation, yields the following three equations.

(i) $\quad 3 = a(0)^2 + b(0) + c$

(ii) $\quad 4 = a(3)^2 + b(3) + c$

(iii) $\quad 11 = a(4)^2 + b(4) + c$

Simplification yields:

(i) $\quad 3 = c$

(ii) $\quad 4 = 9a + 3b + c \implies 1 = 9a + 3b$

(iii) $\quad 11 = 16a + 4b + c \implies 8 = 16a + 4b$

Solving (ii) and (iii) for a and b yields:

(ii) $\quad 9a + 3b = 1 \implies 9a + 3b = 1$

(iii) $\quad 4a + b = 2 \implies \underline{12a + 3b = 6}$

$$-3a \qquad = -5$$

$$a = \tfrac{5}{3}$$

$$b = -\tfrac{14}{3}$$

Finally,

$$y = ax^2 + bx + c$$

$$y = \tfrac{5}{3}x^2 - \tfrac{14}{3}x + 3$$

$$3y = 5x^2 - 14x + 9$$

$$5x^2 - 14x - 3y + 9 = 0.$$

29. Assume that the vertex is at the origin.

$$x^2 = 4py$$

$$(3)^2 = 4p(1)$$

$$\tfrac{9}{4} = p$$

The pipe is located $\tfrac{9}{4}$ meters from the vertex.

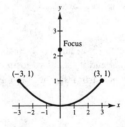

31. $y = ax^2$

$y' = 2ax$

The equation of the tangent line is

$$y - ax_0^2 = 2ax_0(x - x_0) \text{ or } y = 2ax_0x - ax_0^2.$$

Let $y = 0$. Then:

$$-ax_0^2 = 2ax_0x - 2ax_0^2$$

$$ax_0^2 = 2ax_0x$$

Therefore, $\dfrac{x_0}{2} = x$ is the x-intercept.

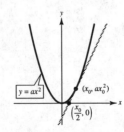

33. (a) Consider the parabola $x^2 = 4py$. Let m_0 be the slope of the one tangent line at (x_1, y_1) and therefore, $-1/m_0$ is the slope of the second at (x_2, y_2). From the derivative given in Exercise 32 we have:

$$m_0 = \frac{1}{2p}x_1 \text{ or } x_1 = 2pm_0$$

$$\frac{-1}{m_0} = \frac{1}{2p}x_2 \text{ or } x_2 = \frac{-2p}{m_0}$$

Substituting these values of x into the equation $x^2 = 4py$, we have the coordinates of the points of tangency $(2pm_0, pm_0{}^2)$ and $(-2p/m_0, p/m_0{}^2)$ and the equations of the tangent lines are

$$(y - pm_0{}^2) = m_0(x - 2pm_0) \quad \text{and} \quad \left(y - \frac{p}{m_0{}^2}\right) = \frac{-1}{m_0}\left(x + \frac{2p}{m_0}\right).$$

The point of intersection of these lines is

$$\left(\frac{p(m_0{}^2 - 1)}{m_0}, -p\right) \text{ and is on the directrix, } y = -p.$$

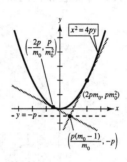

(b) $x^2 - 4x - 4y + 8 = 0$

$$(x - 2)^2 = 4(y - 1). \text{ Vertex } (2, 1)$$

$$2x - 4 - 4\frac{dy}{dx} = 0$$

$$\frac{dy}{dx} = \frac{1}{2}x - 1$$

At $(-2, 5)$, $dy/dx = -2$. At $\left(3, \frac{5}{4}\right)$, $dy/dx = \frac{1}{2}$.

Tangent line at $(-2, 5)$: $y - 5 = -2(x + 2) \Rightarrow 2x + y - 1 = 0$.

Tangent line at $\left(3, \frac{5}{4}\right)$: $y - \frac{5}{4} = \frac{1}{2}(x - 3) \Rightarrow 2x - 4y - 1 = 0$.

Since $m_1 m_2 = (-2)\left(\frac{1}{2}\right) = -1$, the lines are perpendicular.

Point of intersection: $-2x + 1 = \frac{1}{2}x - \frac{1}{4}$

$$-\frac{5}{2}x = -\frac{5}{4}$$

$$x = \frac{1}{2}$$

$$y = 0$$

Directrix: $y = 0$ and the point of intersection $\left(\frac{1}{2}, 0\right)$ lies on this line.

35. The position of the receiver is the x-intercept of the tangent line to the curve $y = x - x^2$ that passes through the point $(-1, 1)$ (see figure). The point of tangency has coordinates $(x, y) = (x, x - x^2)$. The slope of the tangent line can be calculated in two ways. First, use the formula for the slope of a line through two points and obtain

$$m = \frac{(x - x^2) - 1}{x - (-1)} = \frac{x - x^2 - 1}{x + 1}.$$

The slope of the line is also given by $y' = 1 - 2x$. Equating these two expressions for the slope of the tangent line and solving the resulting equation gives the x-coordinate of the point of tangency.

$$\frac{x - x^2 - 1}{x + 1} = 1 - 2x$$

$$x - x^2 - 1 = (1 - 2x)(1 + x)$$

$$x^2 + 2x - 2 = 0 \Rightarrow x = \sqrt{3} - 1$$

—CONTINUED—

35. —CONTINUED—

The value of the derivative at this value of x is

$$y' = 1 - 2(\sqrt{3} - 1) = 3 - 2\sqrt{3},$$

and the equation of the tangent line is

$$y - 1 = (3 - 2\sqrt{3})[x - (\sqrt{3} - 1)]$$
$$y = (3 - 2\sqrt{3})x + 2(2 - \sqrt{3}).$$

Since the receiver is located at the x-intercept of the line, set $y = 0$ and solve for x to obtain

$$x_0 = x = \frac{2\sqrt{3}}{3}.$$

The distance between the base of the hill and the receiver is

$$\frac{2\sqrt{3}}{3} - 1 \approx 0.155.$$

37. Parabola
Vertex: $(0, 4)$

$$x^2 = 4p(y - 4)$$
$$4^2 = 4p(0 - 4)$$
$$p = -1$$
$$x^2 = -4(y - 4)$$
$$y = 4 - \frac{x^2}{4}$$

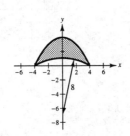

Circle
Center: $(0, k)$
Radius: 8

$$x^2 + (y - k)^2 = 64$$
$$4^2 + (0 - k)^2 = 64$$
$$k^2 = 48$$
$$k = -4\sqrt{3} \quad \text{(Center is on the negative y-axis.)}$$
$$x^2 + (y + 4\sqrt{3})^2 = 64$$
$$y = -4\sqrt{3} \pm \sqrt{64 - x^2}$$

Since the y value is positive when $x = 0$, we have $y = -4\sqrt{3} + \sqrt{64 - x^2}$.

$$A = 2\int_0^4 \left[\left(4 - \frac{x^2}{4}\right) - \left(-4\sqrt{3} + \sqrt{64 - x^2}\right) \right] dx$$

$$= 2\left[4x - \frac{x^3}{12} + 4\sqrt{3}x - \frac{1}{2}\left(x\sqrt{64 - x^2} + 64 \arcsin\frac{x}{8}\right) \right]_0^4$$

$$= 2\left[16 - \frac{64}{12} + 16\sqrt{3} - 2\sqrt{48} - 32 \arcsin\frac{1}{2} \right]$$

$$= \frac{16(4 + 3\sqrt{3} - 2\pi)}{3} \approx 15.536 \text{ square feet}$$

39. (a) Place the coordinate axes so that the standard form of the equation of the parabola is $x^2 = 4py$ (see figure). Since the parabola passes through the point $(60, 20)$,

$$60^2 = 4p(20) \quad \text{or} \quad 45 = p.$$

Therefore, $x^2 = 4(45)y$ or $y = \frac{1}{180}x^2$.

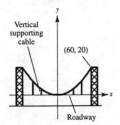

(b) $y' = \frac{1}{90}x$

$$s = \int_{-60}^{60} \sqrt{1 + (y')^2}\, dx$$

$$= 2\int_0^{60} \sqrt{1 + \left(\frac{x}{90}\right)^2}\, dx$$

$$= \frac{1}{45}\int_0^{60} \sqrt{90^2 + x^2}\, dx$$

$$= \frac{1}{90}\left[x\sqrt{90^2 + x^2} + 90^2 \ln\left(x + \sqrt{90^2 + x^2}\right) \right]_0^{60}$$

$$= 10\left[2\sqrt{13} + 9 \ln\left(\frac{2 + \sqrt{13}}{3}\right) \right] \approx 128.4 \text{ meters}$$

41. $x^2 + 4y^2 = 4$

Write the equation in standard form.

$$x^2 + 4y^2 = 4$$

$$\frac{x^2}{4} + y^2 = 1$$

$$\frac{(x-0)^2}{2^2} + \frac{(y-0)^2}{1^2} = 1$$

$$\frac{(x-h)^2}{a^2} + \frac{(y-k)^2}{b^2} = 1$$

Thus, $h = 0$, $k = 0$, $a = 2$, $b = 1$, and $c = \sqrt{2^2 - 1^2} = \sqrt{3}$.

Center, (h, k): $(0, 0)$

Foci, $(h \pm c, k)$: $(\pm\sqrt{3}, 0)$

Vertices, $(h \pm a, k)$: $(\pm 2, 0)$

$$e = \frac{c}{a} = \frac{\sqrt{3}}{2}$$

43. $\dfrac{(x-1)^2}{9} + \dfrac{(y-5)^2}{25} = 1$

$a^2 = 25$, $b^2 = 9$, $c^2 = 16$

Center: $(1, 5)$

Foci: $(1, 9), (1, 1)$

Vertices: $(1, 10), (1, 0)$

$$e = \frac{4}{5}$$

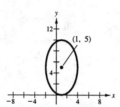

45. $9x^2 + 4y^2 + 36x - 24y + 36 = 0$

Write the equation in standard form.

$$9x^2 + 4y^2 + 36x - 24y + 36 = 0$$

$$9x^2 + 36x + 4y^2 - 24y = -36$$

$$9(x^2 + 4x + 4) + 4(y^2 - 6y + 9) = -36 + 36 + 36$$

$$9(x + 2)^2 + 4(y - 3)^2 = 36$$

$$\frac{(x + 2)^2}{4} + \frac{(y - 3)^2}{9} = 1$$

$$\frac{(x + 2)^2}{2^2} + \frac{(y - 3)^2}{3^2} = 1$$

$$\frac{(x - h)^2}{b^2} + \frac{(y - k)^2}{a^2} = 1$$

Thus, $h = -2$, $k = 3$, $a = 3$, $b = 2$, and $c = \sqrt{3^2 - 2^2} = \sqrt{5}$.

Center, (h, k): $(-2, 3)$

Foci, $(h, k \pm c)$: $\left(-2, 3 \pm \sqrt{5}\right)$

Vertices, $(h, k \pm a)$: $(-2, 3 \pm 3)$

$$e = \frac{c}{a} = \frac{\sqrt{5}}{3}$$

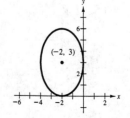

47. $12x^2 + 20y^2 - 12x + 40y - 37 = 0$

$$12\left(x^2 - x + \frac{1}{4}\right) + 20(y^2 + 2y + 1) = 37 + 3 + 20$$

$$= 60$$

$$\frac{[x - (1/2)]^2}{5} + \frac{(y + 1)^2}{3} = 1$$

$a^2 = 5, b^2 = 3, c^2 = 2$

Center: $\left(\frac{1}{2}, -1\right)$

Foci: $\left(\frac{1}{2} \pm \sqrt{2}, -1\right)$

Vertices: $\left(\frac{1}{2} \pm \sqrt{5}, -1\right)$

Solve for y:

$$20(y^2 + 2y + 1) = -12x^2 + 12x + 37 + 20$$

$$(y + 1)^2 = \frac{57 + 12x - 12x^2}{20}$$

$$y = -1 \pm \sqrt{\frac{57 + 12x - 12x^2}{20}}$$

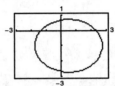

(Graph each of these separately.)

49. $x^2 + 2y^2 - 3x + 4y + 0.25 = 0$

$$\left(x^2 - 3x + \frac{9}{4}\right) + 2(y^2 + 2y + 1) = -\frac{1}{4} + \frac{9}{4} + 2 = 4$$

$$\frac{[x - (3/2)]^2}{4} + \frac{(y + 1)^2}{2} = 1$$

$a^2 = 4, b^2 = 2, c^2 = 2$

Center: $\left(\frac{3}{2}, -1\right)$

Foci: $\left(\frac{3}{2} \pm \sqrt{2}, -1\right)$

Vertices: $\left(-\frac{1}{2}, -1\right), \left(\frac{7}{2}, -1\right)$

Solve for y: $2(y^2 + 2y + 1) = -x^2 + 3x - \frac{1}{4} + 2$

$$(y + 1)^2 = \frac{1}{2}\left(\frac{7}{4} + 3x - x^2\right)$$

$$y = -1 \pm \sqrt{\frac{7 + 12x - 4x^2}{8}}$$

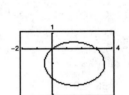

(Graph each of these separately.)

51. Center: $(0, 0)$
Focus: $(2, 0)$
Vertex: $(3, 0)$
Horizontal major axis

$a = 3, c = 2 \implies b = \sqrt{5}$

$$\frac{x^2}{9} + \frac{y^2}{5} = 1$$

53. Vertices: $(3, 1)$, $(3, 9)$

Minor axis length: 6

Since the vertices lie on a vertical line (see figure), the standard form of the equation of the ellipse is

$$\frac{(x - h)^2}{b^2} + \frac{(y - k)^2}{a^2} = 1.$$

Since the center of the ellipse is the midpoint of the line segment connecting the vertices, we have

$$(h, k) = \left(\frac{3 + 3}{2}, \frac{1 + 9}{2}\right) = (3, 5).$$

The length of the major axis is $2a = 8$, and therefore, $a = 4$. Furthermore, since the length of the minor axis is 6, $2b = 6$ or $b = 3$. Finally, the equation is

$$\frac{(x - 3)^2}{9} + \frac{(y - 5)^2}{16} = 1.$$

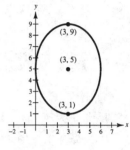

55. Center: $(0, 0)$
Horizontal major axis
Points on ellipse: $(3, 1), (4, 0)$

Since the major axis is horizontal,

$$\left(\frac{x^2}{a^2}\right) + \left(\frac{y^2}{b^2}\right) = 1.$$

Substituting the values of the coordinates of the given points into this equation, we have

$$\left(\frac{9}{a^2}\right) + \left(\frac{1}{b^2}\right) = 1, \text{ and } \frac{16}{a^2} = 1.$$

The solution to this system is $a^2 = 16$, $b^2 = 16/7$.
Therefore,

$$\frac{x^2}{16} + \frac{y^2}{16/7} = 1, \frac{x^2}{16} + \frac{7y^2}{16} = 1.$$

57.

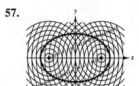

59. Since the height of the fireplace arch is 2 feet, $b = 2$ (see figure). Since the width of the arch is 5 feet, $a = \frac{5}{2}$. Therefore,

$$c^2 = a^2 - b^2 = \frac{25}{4} - 4 = \frac{9}{4} \implies c = \frac{3}{2}.$$

Hence, the tacks should be placed $c = 1.5$ feet from the center, and the length of the string should be $2a = 5$ feet.

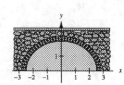

61. $e = \dfrac{c}{a}$

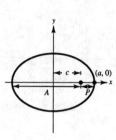

$A + P = 2a$

$a = \dfrac{A + P}{2}$

$c = a - P = \dfrac{A + P}{2} - P = \dfrac{A - P}{2}$

$e = \dfrac{c}{a} = \dfrac{(A - P)/2}{(A + P)/2} = \dfrac{A - P}{A + P}$

63. $e = \dfrac{A - P}{A + P} = \dfrac{35.34au - 0.59au}{35.34au + 0.59au} \approx 0.9672$

65. $16x^2 + 9y^2 + 96x + 36y + 36 = 0$

$32x + 18yy' + 96 + 36y' = 0$

$y'(18y + 36) = -(32x + 96)$

$y' = \dfrac{-(32x + 96)}{18y + 36}$

$y' = 0$ when $x = -3$. y' is undefined when $y = -2$.

At $x = -3$, $y = 2$ or -6.

Endpoints of major axis: $(-3, 2)$, $(-3, -6)$

At $y = -2$, $x = 0$ or -6.

Endpoints of minor axis: $(0, -2)$, $(-6, -2)$

Note: Equation of ellipse is $\dfrac{(x + 3)^2}{9} + \dfrac{(y + 2)^2}{16} = 1$

67. $\dfrac{x^2}{10^2} + \dfrac{y^2}{5^2} = 1$

$\dfrac{2x}{10^2} + \dfrac{2yy'}{5^2} = 0$

$y' = \dfrac{-5^2x}{10^2y} = \dfrac{-x}{4y}$

At $(-8, 3)$: $y' = \dfrac{8}{12} = \dfrac{2}{3}$

The equation of the tangent line is $y - 3 = \frac{2}{3}(x + 8)$. It will cross the y-axis when $x = 0$ and $y = \frac{2}{3}(8) + 3 = \frac{25}{3}$.

69. $\dfrac{x^2}{4} + \dfrac{y^2}{1} = 1$

(a) Using the symmetry of the region and trigonometric substitution to evaluate the integral, we have

$$\text{Area} = 4\int_0^2 \sqrt{1 - \dfrac{x^2}{4}}\, dx$$

$$= 2\int_0^2 \sqrt{4 - x^2}\, dx$$

$$= \left[x\sqrt{4 - x^2} + 4\arcsin\dfrac{x}{2} \right]_0^2$$

$$= 4\arcsin 1 = 2\pi.$$

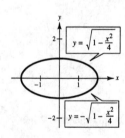

—CONTINUED—

69. —**CONTINUED**—

(b) Using the Disc Method and the symmetry of the region, yields

$$V = 2\pi \int_0^2 \left(\sqrt{1 - \frac{x^2}{4}} \right)^2 dx = \frac{\pi}{2} \int_0^2 (4 - x^2)\, dx = \frac{\pi}{2}\left[4x - \frac{1}{3}x^3 \right]_0^2 = \frac{8\pi}{3}.$$

$$\sqrt{1 + \left(\frac{dy}{dx}\right)^2} = \sqrt{1 + \left(\frac{x}{2\sqrt{4 - x^2}}\right)^2} = \frac{\sqrt{16 - 3x^2}}{2\sqrt{4 - x^2}} = \frac{\sqrt{16 - 3x^2}}{4y}$$

$$S = 2(2\pi) \int_0^2 y \sqrt{1 + \left(\frac{dy}{dx}\right)^2}\, dx$$

$$= 4\pi \int_0^2 y \frac{\sqrt{16 - 3x^2}}{4y}\, dx$$

$$= \pi \int_0^2 \sqrt{4^2 - \left(\sqrt{3}x\right)^2}\, dx$$

$$= \frac{\pi}{2\sqrt{3}} \left[\sqrt{3}x\sqrt{16 - 3x^2} + 16 \arcsin\left(\frac{\sqrt{3}x}{4}\right) \right]_0^2$$

$$= \frac{2\pi}{9}\left(9 + 4\sqrt{3}\pi\right) \approx 21.48$$

(c) Using the Shell Method and the symmetry of the region we have

$$V = 2(2\pi) \int_0^2 x\left(\frac{1}{2}\sqrt{4 - x^2}\right) dx = 2\pi\left(-\frac{1}{2}\right) \int_0^2 (4 - x^2)^{1/2}(-2x)\, dx = -\frac{2\pi}{3}\left[(4 - x^2)^{3/2} \right]_0^2 = \frac{16\pi}{3}.$$

Since $x = 2\sqrt{1 - y^2}$, the derivative of x with respect to y is

$$\frac{dx}{dy} = \frac{-2y}{\sqrt{1 - y^2}}.$$

Therefore,

$$\sqrt{1 + \left(\frac{dx}{dy}\right)^2} = \sqrt{1 + \frac{4y^2}{1 - y^2}} = \frac{\sqrt{1 + 3y^2}}{\sqrt{1 - y^2}} = \frac{2\sqrt{1 + 3y^2}}{x}$$

and

$$S = 2(2\pi) \int_0^1 x \sqrt{1 + \left(\frac{dx}{dy}\right)^2}\, dy$$

$$= 4\pi \int_0^1 x \frac{2\sqrt{1 + 3y^2}}{x}\, dy$$

$$= 8\pi \int_0^1 \sqrt{1 + 3y^2}\, dy$$

$$= \frac{8\pi}{2\sqrt{3}} \left[\sqrt{3}y\sqrt{1 + 3y^2} + \ln\left| \sqrt{3}y + \sqrt{1 + 3y^2} \right| \right]_0^1$$

$$= \frac{4\pi}{3}\left[6 + \sqrt{3}\ln\left(2 + \sqrt{3}\right) \right] \approx 34.69.$$

71. From Example 5 we have

$$C = 4a \int_0^{\pi/2} \sqrt{1 - e^2 \sin^2 \theta}\, d\theta.$$

For $(x^2/9) + (y^2/16) = 1$ we have

$$a = 4,\, b = 3,\, c = \sqrt{7},\, e = \frac{\sqrt{7}}{4},\, C = 4(4) \int_0^{\pi/2} \sqrt{1 - \left(\frac{7}{16}\right) \sin^2 \theta}\, d\theta.$$

Applying Simpson's Rule with $n = 12$, or the integration capability of a graphing utility, produces $C \approx 22.10$.

73. Area circle $= \pi r^2 = 100\pi$

Area ellipse $= \pi ab = \pi a(10)$

$$2(100\pi) = 10\pi a \implies a = 20$$

Hence, the length of the major axis is $2a = 40$.

75.
$$y^2 - \frac{x^2}{4} = 1$$

$$\frac{(y-0)^2}{1^2} - \frac{(x-0)^2}{2^2} = 1$$

$$\frac{(y-k)^2}{a^2} - \frac{(x-h)^2}{b^2} = 1$$

Thus, $h = 0$, $k = 0$, $a = 1$, $b = 2$, and $c = \sqrt{1^2 + 2^2} = \sqrt{5}$.

Center, (h, k): $(0, 0)$

Vertices, $(h, k \pm a)$: $(0, \pm 1)$

Foci, $(h, k \pm c)$: $\left(0, \pm \sqrt{5}\right)$

Finally, the asymptotes are given by

$$y = k \pm \frac{a}{b}(x - h) = \pm \frac{x}{2}.$$

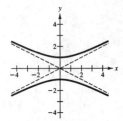

77. $\frac{(x-1)^2}{4} - \frac{(y+2)^2}{1} = 1$

$$\frac{(x-h)^2}{a^2} - \frac{(y+k)^2}{b^2} = 1$$

Thus, $h = 1$, $k = -2$, $a = 2$, $b = 1$, and $c = \sqrt{4+1} = \sqrt{5}$.

Center, (h, k): $(1, -2)$

Vertices, $(h \pm a, k)$: $(-1, -2), (3, -2)$

Foci, $(h \pm c, k)$: $\left(1 \pm \sqrt{5}, -2\right)$

Finally, the asymptotes are

$$y = k \pm \frac{b}{a}(x - h) = -2 \pm \frac{1}{2}(x - 1)$$

$$y = \frac{1}{2}x - \frac{5}{2} \text{ and } y = -\frac{1}{2}x - \frac{3}{2}.$$

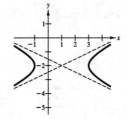

79. $9x^2 - y^2 - 36x - 6y + 18 = 0$

Write the equation in standard form.

$$9x^2 - y^2 - 36x - 6y + 18 = 0$$

$$9x^2 - 36x - (y^2 + 6y) = -18$$

$$9(x^2 - 4x + 4) - (y^2 + 6y + 9) = -18 + 36 - 9$$

$$9(x - 2)^2 - (y + 3)^2 = 9$$

$$\frac{(x-2)^2}{1^2} - \frac{(y+3)^2}{3^2} = 1$$

Thus, $h = 2$, $k = -3$, $a = 1$, $b = 3$, and $c = \sqrt{1^2 + 3^2} = \sqrt{10}$.

Center, (h, k): $(2, -3)$

Vertices, $(h \pm a, k)$: $(1, -3)$ and $(3, -3)$

Foci, $(h \pm c, k)$: $\left(2 \pm \sqrt{10}, -3\right)$

Finally, the asymptotes are

$$y = k \pm \frac{b}{a}(x - h) = -3 \pm \frac{3}{1}(x - 2)$$

$$y = 3x - 9 \text{ and } y = -3x + 3.$$

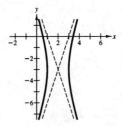

81. $x^2 - 9y^2 + 2x - 54y - 80 = 0$

$(x^2 + 2x + 1) - 9(y^2 + 6y + 9) = 80 + 1 - 81 = 0$

$(x + 1)^2 - 9(y + 3)^2 = 0$

$$y + 3 = \pm\frac{1}{3}(x + 1)$$

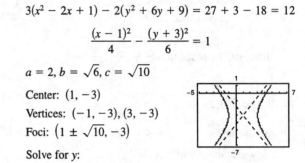

Degenerate hyperbola is two lines intersecting at $(-1, -3)$.

83. $9y^2 - x^2 + 2x + 54y + 62 = 0$

$9(y^2 + 6y + 9) - (x^2 - 2x + 1) = -62 - 1 + 81 = 18$

$$\frac{(y + 3)^2}{2} - \frac{(x - 1)^2}{18} = 1$$

$a = \sqrt{2}, b = 3\sqrt{2}, c = 2\sqrt{5}$

Center: $(1, -3)$

Vertices: $\left(1, -3 \pm \sqrt{2}\right)$

Foci: $\left(1, -3 \pm 2\sqrt{5}\right)$

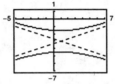

Solve for y:

$9(y^2 + 6y + 9) = x^2 - 2x - 62 + 81$

$$(y + 3)^2 = \frac{x^2 - 2x + 19}{9}$$

$$y = -3 \pm \frac{1}{3}\sqrt{x^2 - 2x + 19}$$

(Graph each curve separately.)

85. $3x^2 - 2y^2 - 6x - 12y - 27 = 0$

$3(x^2 - 2x + 1) - 2(y^2 + 6y + 9) = 27 + 3 - 18 = 12$

$$\frac{(x - 1)^2}{4} - \frac{(y + 3)^2}{6} = 1$$

$a = 2, b = \sqrt{6}, c = \sqrt{10}$

Center: $(1, -3)$

Vertices: $(-1, -3), (3, -3)$

Foci: $\left(1 \pm \sqrt{10}, -3\right)$

Solve for y:

$2(y^2 + 6y + 9) = 3x^2 - 6x - 27 + 18$

$$(y + 3)^2 = \frac{3x^2 - 6x - 9}{2}$$

$$y = -3 \pm \sqrt{\frac{3(x^2 - 2x - 3)}{2}}$$

(Graph each curve separately.)

87. Vertices: $(-1, 0), (1, 0)$

Asymptotes: $y = \pm 3x$

Since the vertices lie on a horizontal line, the standard form is

$$\frac{(x - h)^2}{a^2} - \frac{(y - k)^2}{b^2} = 1.$$

The center of the hyperbola lies at the midpoint of the line segment connecting the vertices. Thus,

$$(h, k) = \left(\frac{1 + (-1)}{2}, \frac{0 + 0}{2}\right) = (0, 0)$$

and we have $h = 0$ and $k = 0$. Since the asymptotes are of the form

$$y = k \pm \frac{b}{a}(x - h) = \pm 3x$$

we have

$$\pm\frac{b}{a} = \pm 3 \text{ or } b = 3a.$$

The distance from the center to the vertices is $a = 1$. Therefore, $b = 3$ and the equation is

$$\frac{x^2}{1^2} - \frac{y^2}{3^2} = 1 \text{ or } x^2 - \frac{y^2}{9} = 1.$$

89. Vertices: $(2, \pm 3)$
Point on graph: $(0, 5)$
Vertical transverse axis
Center: $(2, 0)$

$a = 3$

Therefore, the equation is of the form

$$\frac{y^2}{9} - \frac{(x-2)^2}{b^2} = 1.$$

Substituting the coordinates of the point $(0, 5)$, we have

$$\frac{25}{9} - \frac{4}{b^2} = 1 \quad \text{or} \quad b^2 = \frac{9}{4}.$$

Therefore, the equation is $\dfrac{y^2}{9} - \dfrac{(x-2)^2}{9/4} = 1.$

91. Center: $(0, 0)$
Vertex: $(0, 2)$
Focus: $(0, 4)$
Vertical transverse axis

$a = 2, c = 4, b^2 = c^2 - a^2 = 12$

Therefore, $\dfrac{y^2}{4} - \dfrac{x^2}{12} = 1.$

93. Vertices: $(0, 2), (6, 2)$

Asymptotes: $y = \dfrac{2}{3}x, y = 4 - \dfrac{2}{3}x$

Horizontal transverse axis

Center: $(3, 2)$

$a = 3$

Slopes of asymptotes: $\pm\dfrac{b}{a} = \pm\dfrac{2}{3}$

Thus, $b = 2$. Therefore, $\dfrac{(x-3)^2}{9} - \dfrac{(y-2)^2}{4} = 1.$

95. The points $(2, 2)$ and $(10, 2)$ are the foci of the hyperbola. From the figure and the distance formula we have

$$d_1 - d_2 = 6$$

$$\sqrt{(x-2)^2 + (y-2)^2} - \sqrt{(x-10)^2 + (y-2)^2} = 6.$$

Isolate the radicals one at a time, square each member of the resulting equation, and simplify.

$$\sqrt{(x-2)^2 + (y-2)^2} = 6 + \sqrt{(x-10)^2 + (y-2)^2}$$

$$(x-2)^2 + (y-2)^2 = 36 + 12\sqrt{(x-10)^2 + (y-2)^2} + (x-10)^2 + (y-2)^2$$

$$(x-2)^2 - (x-10)^2 - 36 = 12\sqrt{(x-10)^2 + (y-2)^2}$$

$$4x - 33 = 3\sqrt{(x-10)^2 + (y-2)^2}$$

$$16x^2 - 264x + 1089 = 9(x^2 - 20x + 100 + y^2 - 4y + 4)$$

$$7x^2 - 9y^2 - 84x + 36y + 153 = 0$$

$$7(x^2 - 12x) - 9(y^2 - 4y) = -153$$

$$7(x-6)^2 - 9(y-2)^2 = 63$$

$$\frac{(x-6)^2}{9} - \frac{(y-2)^2}{7} = 1$$

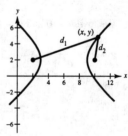

97. The transverse axis is vertical since $(-3, 0)$ and $(-3, 3)$ are the foci.

Center: $\left(-3, \dfrac{3}{2}\right)$

$c = \dfrac{3}{2}, \ 2a = 2, \ b^2 = c^2 - a^2 = \dfrac{5}{4}$

Therefore, the equation is $\dfrac{[y - (3/2)]^2}{1} - \dfrac{(x + 3)^2}{5/4} = 1.$

99. Time for sound of bullet hitting target to reach (x, y): $\dfrac{2c}{v_m} + \dfrac{\sqrt{(x - c)^2 + y^2}}{v_s}$

Time for sound of rifle to reach (x, y): $\dfrac{\sqrt{(x + c)^2 + y^2}}{v_s}$

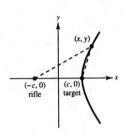

Since the times are the same, we have:

$$\dfrac{2c}{v_m} + \dfrac{\sqrt{(x - c)^2 + y^2}}{v_s} = \dfrac{\sqrt{(x + c)^2 + y^2}}{v_s}$$

$$\dfrac{4c^2}{v_m^{\,2}} + \dfrac{4c}{v_m v_s}\sqrt{(x - c)^2 + y^2} + \dfrac{(x - c)^2 + y^2}{v_s^{\,2}} = \dfrac{(x + c)^2 + y^2}{v_s^{\,2}}$$

$$\sqrt{(x - c)^2 + y^2} = \dfrac{v_m^{\,2}x - v_s^{\,2}c}{v_s v_m}$$

$$\left(1 - \dfrac{v_m^{\,2}}{v_s^{\,2}}\right)x^2 + y^2 = \left(\dfrac{v_s^{\,2}}{v_m^{\,2}} - 1\right)c^2$$

$$\dfrac{x^2}{c^2 v_s^{\,2}/v_m^{\,2}} - \dfrac{y^2}{c^2(v_m^{\,2} - v_s^{\,2})/v_m^{\,2}} = 1$$

101. Let (x, y) be a point on the hyperbola and the line through the points $(0, 10)$ and $(10, 0)$. The equation of the line is $y = 10 - x$. Substituting this expression for y into the equation of the hyperbola yields

$$\dfrac{x^2}{36} - \dfrac{y^2}{64} = 1$$

$$\dfrac{x^2}{36} - \dfrac{(10 - x)^2}{64} = 1$$

$$16x^2 - 9(10 - x)^2 = 576$$

$$7x^2 + 180x - 1476 = 0.$$

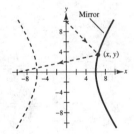

Using the Quadratic Formula yields

$$x = \dfrac{-180 \pm \sqrt{180^2 - 4(7)(-1476)}}{2(7)} = \dfrac{-180 \pm 192\sqrt{2}}{14} = \dfrac{-90 \pm 96\sqrt{2}}{7}.$$

Choosing the positive value for x, we have

$$x = \dfrac{-90 \pm 96\sqrt{2}}{7} \approx 6.538 \text{ and } y = 10 - x = \dfrac{160 - 96\sqrt{2}}{7} \approx 3.462.$$

103. (a) $\dfrac{y^2}{4} - \dfrac{x^2}{2} = 1$, $y^2 - 2x^2 = 4$, $2yy' - 4x = 0$,

$$y' = \frac{4x}{2y} = \frac{2x}{y}$$

At $x = 4$: $y = \pm 6$, $y' = \dfrac{\pm 2(4)}{6} = \pm\dfrac{4}{3}$

At $(4, 6)$: $y - 6 = -\dfrac{4}{3}(x - 4)$ or $4x - 3y + 2 = 0$

At $(4, -6)$: $y + 6 = -\dfrac{4}{3}(x - 4)$ or $4x + 3y + 2 = 0$

(b) From part (a) we know that the slopes of the normal lines must be $\mp 3/4$.

At $(4, 6)$: $y - 6 = -\dfrac{3}{4}(x - 4)$ or $3x + 4y - 36 = 0$

At $(4, -6)$: $y + 6 = \dfrac{3}{4}(x - 4)$ or $3x - 4y - 36 = 0$

105.

$$\frac{x^2}{a^2} + \frac{2y^2}{b^2} = 1 \implies \frac{2y^2}{b^2} = 1 - \frac{x^2}{a^2}, c^2 = a^2 - b^2$$

$$\frac{x^2}{a^2 - b^2} - \frac{2y^2}{b^2} = 1 \implies \frac{2y^2}{b^2} = \frac{x^2}{a^2 - b^2} - 1$$

$$1 - \frac{x^2}{a^2} = \frac{x^2}{a^2 - b^2} - 1 \implies 2 = x^2\left(\frac{1}{a^2} + \frac{1}{a^2 - b^2}\right)$$

$$x^2 = \frac{2a^2(a^2 - b^2)}{2a^2 - b^2} \implies x = \pm\frac{\sqrt{2}a\sqrt{a^2 - b^2}}{\sqrt{2a^2 - b^2}} = \pm\frac{\sqrt{2}ac}{\sqrt{2a^2 - b^2}}$$

$$\frac{2y^2}{b^2} = 1 - \frac{1}{a^2}\left(\frac{2a^2c^2}{2a^2 - b^2}\right) \implies \frac{2y^2}{b^2} = \frac{b^2}{2a^2 - b^2}$$

$$y^2 = \frac{b^4}{2(2a^2 - b^2)} \implies y = \pm\frac{b^2}{\sqrt{2}\sqrt{2a^2 - b^2}}$$

There are four points of intersection: $\left(\dfrac{\sqrt{2}ac}{\sqrt{2a^2 - b^2}}, \pm\dfrac{b^2}{\sqrt{2}\sqrt{2a^2 - b^2}}\right), \left(-\dfrac{\sqrt{2}ac}{\sqrt{2a^2 - b^2}}, \pm\dfrac{b^2}{\sqrt{2}\sqrt{2a^2 - b^2}}\right)$

$$\frac{x^2}{a^2} + \frac{2y^2}{b^2} = 1 \implies \frac{2x}{a^2} + \frac{4yy'}{b^2} = 0 \implies y'_e = -\frac{b^2x}{2a^2y}$$

$$\frac{x^2}{a^2 - b^2} - \frac{2y^2}{b^2} = 1 \implies \frac{2x}{c^2} - \frac{4yy'}{b^2} = 0 \implies y'_h = \frac{b^2x}{2c^2y}$$

At $\left(\dfrac{\sqrt{2}ac}{\sqrt{2a^2 - b^2}}, \dfrac{b^2}{\sqrt{2}\sqrt{2a^2 - b^2}}\right)$, the slopes of the tangent lines are:

$$y'_e = \frac{-b^2\left(\dfrac{\sqrt{2}ac}{\sqrt{2a^2 - b^2}}\right)}{2a^2\left(\dfrac{b^2}{\sqrt{2}\sqrt{2a^2 - b^2}}\right)} = -\frac{c}{a} \quad \text{and} \quad y'_h = \frac{b^2\left(\dfrac{\sqrt{2}ac}{\sqrt{2a^2 - b^2}}\right)}{2c^2\left(\dfrac{b^2}{\sqrt{2}\sqrt{2a^2 - b^2}}\right)} = \frac{a}{c}$$

Since the slopes are negative reciprocals, the tangent lines are perpendicular. Similarly, the curves are perpendicular at the other three points of intersection.

107. True

109. False. The y^4 term should be y^2.

111. True

113.
$$Ax^2 + Cy^2 + Dx + Ey + F = 0 \quad \text{(Assume } A \neq 0 \text{ and } C \neq 0; \text{ see (b) below)}$$

$$A\left(x^2 + \frac{D}{A}x\right) + C\left(y^2 + \frac{E}{C}y\right) = -F$$

$$A\left(x^2 + \frac{D}{A}x + \frac{D^2}{4A^2}\right) + C\left(y^2 + \frac{E}{C}y + \frac{E^2}{4C^2}\right) = -F + \frac{D^2}{4A} + \frac{E^2}{4C} = R$$

$$\frac{\left[x + \left(\dfrac{D}{2A}\right)\right]^2}{C} + \frac{\left[y + \left(\dfrac{E}{2C}\right)\right]^2}{A} = \frac{R}{AC}$$

(a) If $A = C$, we have

$$\left(x + \frac{D}{2A}\right)^2 + \left(y + \frac{E}{2C}\right)^2 = \frac{R}{A}$$

which is the standard equation of a circle.

(b) If $C = 0$, we have

$$A\left(x + \frac{D}{2A}\right)^2 = -F - Ey + \frac{D^2}{4A}.$$

If $A = 0$, we have

$$C\left(y + \frac{E}{2C}\right)^2 = -F - Dx + \frac{E^2}{4C}.$$

These are the equations of parabolas.

(c) If $AC > 0$, we have

$$\frac{\left[x + \left(\dfrac{D}{2A}\right)\right]^2}{\left|\dfrac{R}{A}\right|} + \frac{\left[y + \left(\dfrac{E}{2C}\right)\right]^2}{\left|\dfrac{R}{C}\right|} = 1$$

which is the equation of an ellipse.

(d) If $AC < 0$, we have

$$\frac{\left[x + \left(\dfrac{D}{2A}\right)\right]^2}{\left|\dfrac{R}{A}\right|} - \frac{\left[y + \left(\dfrac{E}{2C}\right)\right]^2}{\left|\dfrac{R}{C}\right|} = \pm 1$$

which is the equation of a hyperbola.

115. $4x^2 - y^2 - 4x - 3 = 0$

$A = 4, C = -1$

$AC < 0$

Hyperbola

117. $25x^2 - 10x - 200y - 119 = 0$

$A = 25, C = 0$

Parabola

119. $y^2 - x - 4y - 5 = 0$

$A = 0, C = 1$

Parabola

121.
$$2x^2 - 2xy = 3y - y^2 - 2xy$$

$$2x^2 + y^2 - 3y = 0$$

$A = 2, C = 1, AC > 0$

Ellipse

123.
$$9x^2 + 54x + 81 = 36 - 4(y^2 - 4y + 4)$$

$$9x^2 + 4y^2 + 54x - 16y + 61 = 0$$

$A = 9, C = 4, AC > 0$

Ellipse

Section 9.2   Plane Curves and Parametric Equations

1. $x = \sqrt{t},\ y = 1 - t$

(a)

t	0	1	2	3	4
x	0	1	$\sqrt{2}$	$\sqrt{3}$	2
y	1	0	-1	-2	-3

(b)

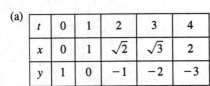

(c)

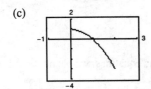

(d) $x^2 = t$

$y = 1 - x^2,\ x \geq 0$

3. $x = 3t - 1$

$y = 2t + 1$

$y = 2\left(\dfrac{x + 1}{3}\right) + 1$

$2x - 3y + 5 = 0$

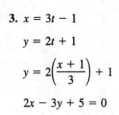

5. $x = t + 1$

$y = t^2$

$y = (x - 1)^2$

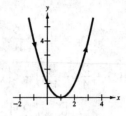

7. $x = t^3, \; y = \dfrac{t^2}{2}$

t	$-\frac{3}{2}$	-1	$-\frac{1}{2}$	0	$\frac{1}{2}$	1	$\frac{3}{2}$
x	$-\frac{27}{8}$	-1	$-\frac{1}{8}$	0	$\frac{1}{8}$	1	$\frac{27}{8}$
y	$\frac{9}{8}$	$\frac{1}{2}$	$\frac{1}{8}$	0	$\frac{1}{8}$	$\frac{1}{2}$	$\frac{9}{8}$

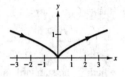

By plotting these points in the order of increasing t and using the continuity of the parametric equation, we obtain the curve shown in the figure. Since $x = t^3$ and $y = t^2/2$, we have

$$t = x^{1/3} \quad \text{or} \quad y = \frac{1}{2}(x^{1/3})^2 = \frac{1}{2}x^{2/3}.$$

9. $x = t - 1$

$y = \dfrac{t}{t - 1}$

$y = \dfrac{x + 1}{x}$

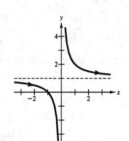

11. $x = 2t$

$y = |t - 2|$

$y = \left|\dfrac{x}{2} - 2\right| = \dfrac{|x - 4|}{2}$

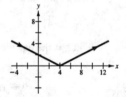

13. $x = \sec \theta$

 $y = \cos \theta$

 $0 \le \theta < \dfrac{\pi}{2}, \; \dfrac{\pi}{2} < \theta \le \pi$

 $xy = 1$

 $y = \dfrac{1}{x}$

 $|x| \ge 1, \; |y| \le 1$

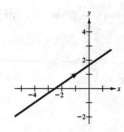

15. $x = 3 \cos \theta, \; y = 3 \sin \theta$

t	0	$\frac{\pi}{4}$	$\frac{\pi}{2}$	$\frac{3\pi}{4}$	π	$\frac{5\pi}{4}$	$\frac{3\pi}{2}$	$\frac{7\pi}{4}$
x	3	$\frac{3\sqrt{2}}{2}$	0	$-\frac{3\sqrt{2}}{2}$	-3	$-\frac{3\sqrt{2}}{2}$	0	$\frac{3\sqrt{2}}{2}$
y	0	$\frac{3\sqrt{2}}{2}$	3	$\frac{3\sqrt{2}}{2}$	0	$-\frac{3\sqrt{2}}{2}$	-3	$-\frac{3\sqrt{2}}{2}$

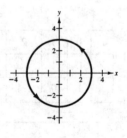

By plotting these points in order of increasing θ and by using the continuity of the parametric equations, we obtain the curve shown in the figure. To eliminate the parameter, use the identity $\sin^2 \theta + \cos^2 \theta = 1$.

$$x^2 + y^2 = 9 \cos^2 \theta + 9 \sin^2 \theta = 9(\cos^2 \theta + \sin^2 \theta) = 9$$

The graph of the equation is a circle centered at the origin with radius 3.

17.
$$x = 4 \sin 2\theta$$
$$y = 2 \cos 2\theta$$
$$\frac{x^2}{16} = \sin^2 2\theta$$
$$\frac{y^2}{4} = \cos^2 2\theta$$
$$\frac{x^2}{16} + \frac{y^2}{4} = 1$$

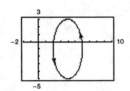

19.
$$x = 4 + 2 \cos \theta$$
$$y = -1 + \sin \theta$$
$$\frac{(x-4)^2}{4} = \cos^2 \theta$$
$$\frac{(y+1)^2}{1} = \sin^2 \theta$$
$$\frac{(x-4)^2}{4} + \frac{(y+1)^2}{1} = 1$$

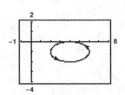

21.
$$x = 4 + 2 \cos \theta$$
$$y = -1 + 4 \sin \theta$$
$$\frac{(x-4)^2}{4} = \cos^2 \theta$$
$$\frac{(y+1)^2}{16} = \sin^2 \theta$$
$$\frac{(x-4)^2}{4} + \frac{(y+1)^2}{16} = 1$$

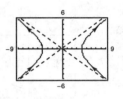

23. $x = 4 \sec \theta, \ y = 3 \tan \theta$

θ	$-\dfrac{\pi}{3}$	$-\dfrac{\pi}{6}$	0	$\dfrac{\pi}{6}$	$\dfrac{\pi}{3}$	$\dfrac{\pi}{2}$	$\dfrac{2\pi}{3}$	$\dfrac{5\pi}{6}$	π	$\dfrac{7\pi}{6}$	$\dfrac{4\pi}{3}$
x	8	$\dfrac{8}{\sqrt{3}}$	4	$\dfrac{8}{\sqrt{3}}$	8	undef.	-8	$-\dfrac{8}{\sqrt{3}}$	-4	$-\dfrac{8}{\sqrt{3}}$	-8
y	$-3\sqrt{3}$	$-\sqrt{3}$	0	$\sqrt{3}$	$3\sqrt{3}$	undef.	$-3\sqrt{3}$	$-\sqrt{3}$	0	$\sqrt{3}$	$3\sqrt{3}$

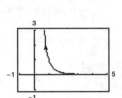

By plotting these points in order of increasing θ we obtain the curve shown in the figure. Since the parametric equations involve secants and tangents, use the identity $\sec^2 \theta - \tan^2 \theta = 1$. Therefore,

$$\frac{x}{4} = \sec \theta \quad \text{and} \quad \frac{y}{3} = \tan \theta \quad \text{or} \quad \frac{x^2}{16} - \frac{y^2}{9} = \sec^2 \theta - \tan^2 \theta = 1.$$

The graph of this equation is a hyperbola centered at the origin with vertices $(\pm 4, 0)$.

25. $x = t^3$
$$y = 3 \ln t$$
$$y = 3 \ln \sqrt[3]{x} = \ln x$$

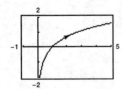

27.
$$x = e^{-t}$$
$$y = e^{3t}$$
$$e^t = \frac{1}{x}$$
$$e^t = \sqrt[3]{y}$$
$$\sqrt[3]{y} = \frac{1}{x}$$
$$y = \frac{1}{x^3}$$
$$x > 0$$
$$y > 0$$

29. By eliminating the parameter in each part of this exercise, we get $y = 2x + 1$. The graphs differ in their orientation and domains. In each case the derivatives of $x = f(t)$ and $y = g(t)$ are continuous and not simultaneously zero. Therefore, the graphs are smooth.

(a) $x = t$
$\quad -\infty < x < \infty$

$\quad y = 2t + 1$
$\quad -\infty < y < \infty$

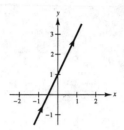

(b) $x = \cos \theta$
$\quad -1 \le x \le 1$

$\quad y = 2 \cos \theta + 1$
$\quad -1 \le y \le 3$

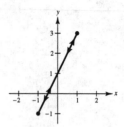

(c) $x = e^{-t}$
$\quad x > 0$

$\quad y = 2e^{-t} + 1$
$\quad y > 1$

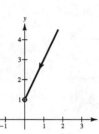

(d) $x = e^t$
$\quad x > 0$

$\quad y = 2e^t + 1$
$\quad y > 1$

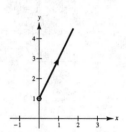

31. The curves are identical on $0 < \theta < \pi$. They are both smooth.

33. (a)

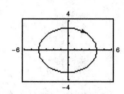

(b) The orientation of the second curve is reversed.

(c) The orientation will be reversed.

(d) Many answers possible. For example, $x = 1 + t$, $y = 1 + 2t$, and $x = 1 - t$, $x = 1 - 2t$.

35.
$$x = x_1 + t(x_2 - x_1)$$
$$y = y_1 + t(y_2 - y_1)$$
$$\frac{x - x_1}{x_2 - x_1} = t$$
$$y = y_1 + \left(\frac{x - x_1}{x_2 - x_1}\right)(y_2 - y_1)$$
$$y - y_1 = \frac{y_2 - y_1}{x_2 - x_1}(x - x_1)$$
$$y - y_1 = m(x - x_1)$$

37. Since the parametric equations involve sines and cosines, use the identity $\sin^2 \theta + \cos^2 \theta = 1$.

$$x = h + a \cos \theta \qquad y = k + b \sin \theta$$

$$\frac{x - h}{a} = \cos \theta \qquad \frac{y - k}{b} = \sin \theta$$

$$\frac{(x - h)^2}{a^2} = \cos^2 \theta \qquad \frac{(y - k)^2}{b^2} = \sin^2 \theta$$

$$\frac{(x - h)^2}{a^2} + \frac{(y - k)^2}{b^2} = \cos^2 \theta + \sin^2 \theta = 1$$

$$\frac{(x - h)^2}{a^2} + \frac{(y - k)^2}{b^2} = 1$$

39. From Exercise 35 we have

$$x = 5t$$

$$y = -2t.$$

Solution not unique

41. From Exercise 36 we have

$$x = 2 + 4 \cos \theta$$

$$y = 1 + 4 \sin \theta.$$

Solution not unique

43. From Exercise 37 we have

$$a = 5, c = 4 \implies b = 3$$

$$x = 5 \cos \theta$$

$$y = 3 \sin \theta.$$

Center: $(0, 0)$
Solution not unique

45. The midpoint of the line segment joining the vertices is the center of the hyperbola. Therefore, $(h, k) = (0, 0)$. The transverse axis of the hyperbola is horizontal with $a = 4$ and $c = 5$. Since $b^2 = c^2 - a^2$, we have $b = 3$. Using the result of Exercise 38 a set of parametric equations are

$$x = h + a \sec \theta \quad y = k + b \tan \theta$$

$$x = 4 \sec \theta, \qquad y = 3 \tan \theta.$$

47. $y = 3x - 2$

Example

$$x = t, \qquad y = 3t - 2$$

$$x = t - 3, \quad y = 3t - 11$$

49. $y = x^3$

Example

$$x = t, \qquad y = t^3$$

$$x = \sqrt[3]{t}, \qquad y = t$$

$$x = \tan t, \qquad y = \tan^3 t$$

51. $x = 2(\theta - \sin \theta)$

$$y = 2(1 - \cos \theta)$$

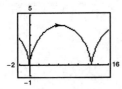

Not smooth at $\theta = 2n\pi$

53. $x = \theta - \frac{3}{2} \sin \theta, y = 1 - \frac{3}{2} \cos \theta$

Select the parametric equations mode of your graphing utility and enter the parametric equations. The parametric mode may require the parameter t rather than θ. A graph of the curve is shown in the figure. The curve is smooth for all values of θ.

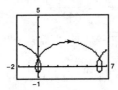

55. $x = 3 \cos^3 \theta$

$$y = 3 \sin^3 \theta$$

Not smooth at $(x, y) = (\pm 3, 0)$ and $(0, \pm 3)$, or $\theta = \frac{1}{2} n\pi$.

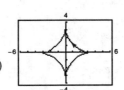

57. $x = 2 \cot \theta$

$$y = 2 \sin^2 \theta$$

Smooth everywhere

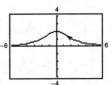

59. $x = 4 \cos \theta$

$$y = 2 \sin 2\theta$$

Matches (d)

61. $x = \cos \theta + \theta \sin \theta$

$$y = \sin \theta - \theta \cos \theta$$

Matches (b)

63. When the circle has rolled θ radians, we know that the center is at $(a\theta, a)$.

$$\sin \theta = \sin(180° - \theta) = \frac{|AC|}{b} = \frac{|BD|}{b} \quad \text{or} \quad |BD| = b \sin \theta$$

$$\cos \theta = -\cos(180° - \theta) = \frac{|AP|}{-b} \quad \text{or} \quad |AP| = -b \cos \theta$$

Therefore, $x = a\theta - b \sin \theta$ and $y = a - b \cos \theta$.

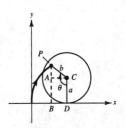

65. True

67. False. Let $x = t^2$ and $y = t$. Then $x = y^2$ and y is not a function of x.

69. $x = (v_0 \cos \theta)t,\ y = h + (v_0 \sin \theta)t - 16t^2$

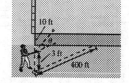

(a) Since the ball is hit 3 feet above the ground, $h = 3$. Since the initial velocity is 100 miles per hour we have

$$v_0 = 100 \text{ mi/hr} = \frac{100(5280)}{3600} = \frac{440}{3} \text{ ft/sec.}$$

Therefore,

$$x = \left(\frac{440}{3} \cos \theta\right)t,\ y = 3 + \left(\frac{440}{3} \sin \theta\right)t - 16t^2.$$

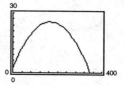

(b) When $\theta = 15°$, the parametric equations are

$$x = \left(\frac{440}{3} \cos 15°\right)t,\ y = 3 + \left(\frac{440}{3} \sin 15°\right)t - 16t^2,$$

and the graph of the curve is given in the figure. It is not a home run, since the ball drops to the ground in front of the fence which is 400 feet from the home plate.

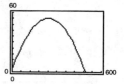

(c) When $\theta = 23°$, the parametric equations are

$$x = \left(\frac{440}{3} \cos 23°\right)t,\ y = 3 + \left(\frac{440}{3} \sin 23°\right)t - 16t^2,$$

and the graph of the curve is given in the figure. By using the trace feature of the graphing utility we observe that $y \approx 32$ feet when $x = 400$ feet. Therefore, it is a home run.

(d) For the hit to be a home run, y must be at least 10 when x is 400. When $x = 400$, we have

$$\left(\frac{440}{3} \cos \theta\right)t = 400 \Rightarrow t = \frac{1200}{440 \cos \theta}.$$

Substituting this expression for t into the parametric equation for y when $y = 10$ yields

$$y = 3 + \left(\frac{440}{3} \sin \theta\right)t - 16t^2$$

$$10 = 3 + \left(\frac{440}{3} \sin \theta\right) \cdot \frac{1200}{440 \cos \theta} - 16\left(\frac{1200}{440 \cos \theta}\right)^2$$

$$0 = -7 + 400 \tan \theta - 16\left(\frac{30}{11} \sec \theta\right)^2.$$

Using the root-finding capabilities of a graphing utility yields the root

$$\theta \approx 0.3383 \text{ radians} = 0.3383\left(\frac{180}{\pi}\right) \approx 19.4°.$$

71. $x = \dfrac{1 - t^2}{1 + t^2}$ and $y = \dfrac{2t}{1 + t^2}$

The graph is the circle $x^2 + y^2 = 1$ except the point $(-1, 0)$. Thus,

$$\left(\frac{1 - t^2}{1 + t^2}\right)^2 + \left(\frac{2t}{1 + t^2}\right)^2 = 1$$

$$(1 - t^2)^2 + (2t)^2 = (1 + t^2)^2.$$

When $t = 2$: $(-3)^2 + (4)^2 = (5)^2$

When $t = 3$: $(-8)^2 + (6)^2 = (10)^2$

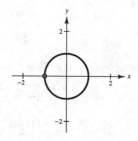

Section 9.3   Parametric Equations and Calculus

1. Since $x = 2t$ and $y = 3t - 1$, you have

$$\frac{dy}{dx} = \frac{dy/dt}{dx/dt} = \frac{3}{2} \text{ for all values of } t$$

and $\dfrac{d^2y}{dx^2} = \dfrac{d[dy/dx]/dt}{dx/dt} = \dfrac{0}{2} = 0$ for all values of t.

3. $x = t + 1$, $y = t^2 + 3t$

$$\frac{dy}{dx} = \frac{2t + 3}{1} = 1 \text{ when } t = -1.$$

$$\frac{d^2y}{dx^2} = 2$$

5. $x = 2 \cos \theta$, $y = 2 \sin \theta$

$$\frac{dy}{dx} = \frac{2 \cos \theta}{-2 \sin \theta} = -\cot \theta = -1 \text{ when } \theta = \frac{\pi}{4}.$$

$$\frac{d^2y}{dx^2} = \frac{\csc^2 \theta}{-2 \sin \theta} = \frac{-\csc^3 \theta}{2} = -\sqrt{2} \text{ when } \theta = \frac{\pi}{4}.$$

7. Since $x = 2 + \sec \theta$ and $y = 1 + 2 \tan \theta$, we have

$$\frac{dy}{dx} = \frac{dy/d\theta}{dx/d\theta} = \frac{2 \sec^2 \theta}{\sec \theta \tan \theta} = \frac{2 \sec \theta}{\tan \theta} = 2 \csc \theta$$

$$\frac{d^2y}{dx^2} = \frac{d[dy/dx]/d\theta}{dx/d\theta} = \frac{-2 \csc \theta \cot \theta}{\sec \theta \tan \theta} = -2 \cot^3 \theta.$$

At $\theta = \pi/6$,

$$\frac{dy}{dx} = 2 \csc \frac{\pi}{6} = 2(2) = 4$$

$$\frac{d^2y}{dx^2} = -2 \cot^3 \frac{\pi}{6} = -2(\sqrt{3})^3 = -6\sqrt{3}.$$

9. $x = \cos^3 \theta$, $y = \sin^3 \theta$

$$\frac{dy}{dx} = \frac{3 \sin^2 \theta \cos \theta}{-3 \cos^2 \theta \sin \theta}$$

$$= -\tan \theta = -1 \text{ when } \theta = \frac{\pi}{4}.$$

$$\frac{d^2y}{dx^2} = \frac{-\sec^2 \theta}{-3 \cos^2 \theta \sin \theta} = \frac{1}{3 \cos^4 \theta \sin \theta}$$

$$= \frac{\sec^4 \theta \csc \theta}{3} = \frac{4\sqrt{2}}{3} \text{ when } \theta = \frac{\pi}{4}.$$

11. $x = 2 \cot \theta$, $y = 2 \sin^2 \theta$

$$\frac{dy}{dx} = \frac{dy/d\theta}{dx/d\theta} = \frac{4 \sin \theta \cos \theta}{-2 \csc^2 \theta} = -2 \sin^3 \theta \cos \theta$$

At the point $\left(-\dfrac{2}{\sqrt{3}}, \dfrac{3}{2}\right)$, $\theta = \dfrac{2\pi}{3}$. When $\theta = \dfrac{2\pi}{3}$, $\dfrac{dy}{dx} = -2 \sin^3 \dfrac{2\pi}{3} \cos \dfrac{2\pi}{3} = -2\left(\dfrac{\sqrt{3}}{2}\right)^3\left(-\dfrac{1}{2}\right) = \dfrac{3\sqrt{3}}{8}$.

Therefore, the equation of the tangent line is

$$y - \frac{3}{2} = \frac{3\sqrt{3}}{8}\left(x + \frac{2}{\sqrt{3}}\right)$$

$$3\sqrt{3}x - 8y + 18 = 0.$$

At the point $(0, 2)$, $\theta = \dfrac{\pi}{2}$. When $\theta = \dfrac{\pi}{2}$, $\dfrac{dy}{dx} = -2 \sin^3 \dfrac{\pi}{2} \cos \dfrac{\pi}{2} = -2(1)^3(0) = 0$.

Therefore, the equation of the tangent line is

$$y - 2 = 0(x - 0)$$

$$y - 2 = 0.$$

At the point $\left(2\sqrt{3}, \dfrac{1}{2}\right)$, $\theta = \dfrac{\pi}{6}$. When $\theta = \dfrac{\pi}{6}$, $\dfrac{dy}{dx} = -2 \sin^3 \dfrac{\pi}{6} \cos \dfrac{\pi}{6} = -2\left(\dfrac{1}{2}\right)^3\left(\dfrac{\sqrt{3}}{2}\right) = -\dfrac{\sqrt{3}}{8}$.

Therefore, the equation of the tangent line is

$$y - \frac{1}{2} = -\frac{\sqrt{3}}{8}(x - 2\sqrt{3})$$

$$\sqrt{3}x + 8y - 10 = 0.$$

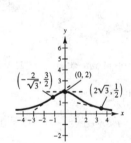

13. $x = 2t$, $y = t^2 - 1$, $t = 2$

(a)

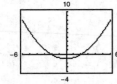

(b) At $t = 2$, $(x, y) = (4, 3)$, and $\dfrac{dx}{dt} = 2$, $\dfrac{dy}{dt} = 4$, $\dfrac{dy}{dx} = 2$

(d)

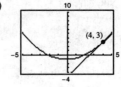

(c) $\dfrac{dy}{dx} = 2$. At $(4, 3)$, $y - 3 = 2(x - 4)$

$$y = 2x - 5$$

15. $x = t^2 - t + 2$, $y = t^3 - 3t$, $t = -1$

(a)

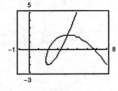

(b) At $t = -1$, $(x, y) = (4, 2)$, and

$$\frac{dx}{dt} = -3, \quad \frac{dy}{dt} = 0, \quad \frac{dy}{dx} = 0$$

(d)

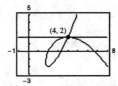

(c) $\dfrac{dy}{dx} = 0$. At $(4, 2)$, $y - 2 = 0(x - 4)$

$$y = 2$$

17. $x = \cos\theta + \theta\sin\theta$, $y = \sin\theta - \theta\cos\theta$

Horizontal tangents: $\dfrac{dy}{d\theta} = \theta\sin\theta = 0$ when $\theta = 0,\ \pi,\ 2\pi,\ 3\pi, \ldots$.

Points: $(-1, [2n - 1]\pi)$, $(1, 2n\pi)$ where n is an integer.

Points shown: $(1, 0)$, $(-1, \pi)$, $(1, -2\pi)$

Vertical tangents: $\dfrac{dx}{d\theta} = \theta\cos\theta = 0$ when $\theta = \dfrac{\pi}{2}, \dfrac{3\pi}{2}, \dfrac{5\pi}{2}, \ldots$.

Points: $\left(\dfrac{(-1)^{n+1}(2n - 1)\pi}{2}, (-1)^{n+1}\right)$

Points shown: $\left(\dfrac{\pi}{2}, 1\right)$, $\left(-\dfrac{3\pi}{2}, -1\right)$, $\left(\dfrac{5\pi}{2}, 1\right)$

19. $x = 1 - t$, $y = t^2$

Horizontal tangents: $\dfrac{dy}{dt} = 2t = 0$ when $t = 0$.

Point: $(1, 0)$

Vertical tangents: $\dfrac{dx}{dt} = -1 \neq 0$; none

21. $x = 1 - t$, $y = t^3 - 3t$

Since

$$\frac{dy}{dx} = \frac{dy/dt}{dx/dt} = \frac{3t^2 - 3}{-1} = 3 - 3t^2,$$

the horizontal tangents occur when $3 - 3t^2 = 0$ or $t = \pm 1$. The corresponding points are $(0, -2)$, and $(2, 2)$. Since dy/dx is never undefined, there are no points of vertical tangency.

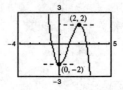

23. $x = 3 \cos \theta, y = 3 \sin \theta$

Horizontal tangents: $\dfrac{dy}{d\theta} = 3 \cos \theta = 0$ when $\theta = \dfrac{\pi}{2}, \dfrac{3\pi}{2}$.

Points: $(0, 3), (0, -3)$

Vertical tangents: $\dfrac{dx}{d\theta} = -3 \sin \theta = 0$ when $\theta = 0, \pi$.

Points: $(3, 0), (-3, 0)$

25. $x = 4 + 2 \cos \theta, y = -1 + \sin \theta$

Horizontal tangents: $\dfrac{dy}{d\theta} = \cos \theta = 0$ when $\theta = \dfrac{\pi}{2}, \dfrac{3\pi}{2}$.

Points: $(4, 0), (4, -2)$

Vertical tangents: $\dfrac{dx}{d\theta} = -2 \sin \theta = 0$ when $x = 0, \pi$.

Points: $(6, -1), (2, -1)$

27. $x = \sec \theta, \ y = \tan \theta$

Horizontal tangents: $\dfrac{dy}{d\theta} = \sec^2 \theta \neq 0$; none

Vertical tangents: $\dfrac{dx}{d\theta} = \sec \theta \tan \theta = 0$ when $x = 0, \pi$.

Points: $(1, 0), (-1, 0)$

29. One possible answer is the graph given by

$$x = t, y = -t.$$

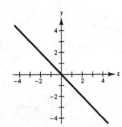

31.
$$x = e^{-t} \cos t$$

$$\frac{dx}{dt} = -e^{-t}(\sin t + \cos t)$$

$$\left(\frac{dx}{dt}\right)^2 = e^{-2t}(\sin^2 t + 2 \sin t \cos t + \cos^2 t) = e^{-2t}(1 + \sin 2t)$$

$$y = e^{-t} \sin t$$

$$\frac{dy}{dt} = e^{-t}(\cos t - \sin t)$$

$$\left(\frac{dy}{dt}\right)^2 = e^{-2t}(\cos^2 t - 2 \sin t \cos t + \sin^2 t) = e^{-2t}(1 - \sin 2t)$$

$$\left(\frac{dx}{dt}\right)^2 + \left(\frac{dy}{dt}\right)^2 = 2e^{-2t}$$

Therefore,

$$s = \int_0^{\pi/2} \sqrt{\left(\frac{dx}{dt}\right)^2 + \left(\frac{dy}{dt}\right)^2}\, dt = \int_0^{\pi/2} \sqrt{2e^{-2t}}\, dt$$

$$= -\sqrt{2} \int_0^{\pi/2} e^{-t}(-1)\, dt = -\sqrt{2}\left[e^{-t}\right]_0^{\pi/2} = \sqrt{2}(1 - e^{-\pi/2}) \approx 1.12.$$

33. $x = t^2, y = 2t, 0 \le t \le 2$

$$\frac{dx}{dt} = 2t, \frac{dy}{dt} = 2, \left(\frac{dx}{dt}\right)^2 + \left(\frac{dy}{dt}\right)^2 = 4t^2 + 4 = 4(t^2 + 1)$$

$$s = 2 \int_0^2 \sqrt{t^2 + 1}\, dt$$

$$= \left[t\sqrt{t^2 + 1} + \ln\left|t + \sqrt{t^2 + 1}\right|\right]_0^2$$

$$= 2\sqrt{5} + \ln\left(2 + \sqrt{5}\right) \approx 5.916$$

35. $x = \sqrt{t},\ y = 3t - 1,\ \dfrac{dx}{dt} = \dfrac{1}{2\sqrt{t}},\ \dfrac{dy}{dt} = 3$

$$S = \int_0^1 \sqrt{\frac{1}{4t} + 9}\, dt = \frac{1}{2} \int_0^1 \frac{\sqrt{1 + 36t}}{\sqrt{t}}\, dt$$

$$= \frac{1}{6} \int_0^6 \sqrt{1 + u^2}\, du$$

$$= \frac{1}{12}\left[\ln\left(\sqrt{1 + u^2} + u\right) + u\sqrt{1 + u^2}\right]_0^6$$

$$= \frac{1}{12}\left[\ln\left(\sqrt{37} + 6\right) + 6\sqrt{37}\right] \approx 3.249$$

$$u = 6\sqrt{t}, \ du = \frac{3}{\sqrt{t}}\, dt$$

37. $x = a \cos^3 \theta, y = a \sin^3 \theta$

Using $dx/d\theta = -3a \cos^2 \theta \sin \theta$, $dy/d\theta = 3a \sin^2 \theta \cos \theta$, and the symmetry of the graph, the perimeter is given by

$$s = 4 \int_0^{\pi/2} \sqrt{\left(\frac{dx}{d\theta}\right)^2 + \left(\frac{dy}{d\theta}\right)^2} \, d\theta = 4 \int_0^{\pi/2} \sqrt{9a^2 \cos^4 \theta \sin^2 \theta + 9a^2 \sin^4 \theta \cos^2 \theta} \, d\theta$$

$$= 4 \int_0^{\pi/2} \sqrt{9a^2 \sin^2 \theta \cos^2 \theta (\cos^2 \theta + \sin^2 \theta)} \, d\theta$$

$$= 4 \int_0^{\pi/2} 3a \sin \theta \cos \theta \, d\theta = 12a \left[\frac{\sin^2 \theta}{2}\right]_0^{\pi/2} = 6a.$$

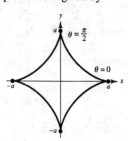

39. $x = a(\theta - \sin \theta)$, $y = a(1 - \cos \theta)$, $\dfrac{dx}{d\theta} = a(1 - \cos \theta)$,

$\dfrac{dy}{d\theta} = a \sin \theta$

$$S = 2 \int_0^{\pi} \sqrt{a^2 (1 - \cos \theta)^2 + a^2 \sin^2 \theta} \, d\theta$$

$$= 2\sqrt{2}a \int_0^{\pi} \sqrt{1 - \cos \theta} \, d\theta$$

$$= 2\sqrt{2}a \int_0^{\pi} \frac{\sin \theta}{\sqrt{1 + \cos \theta}} \, d\theta$$

$$= \left[-4\sqrt{2}a \sqrt{1 + \cos \theta}\right]_0^{\pi} = 8a$$

41. $x = (90 \cos 30°)t$, $y = (90 \sin 30°)t - 16t^2$

(a)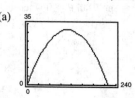

(b) Range: 219.2 ft

(c) $\dfrac{dx}{dt} = 90 \cos 30°$, $\dfrac{dy}{dt} = 90 \sin 30° - 32t$.

$y = 0$ for $t = \dfrac{45}{16}$.

$$s = \int_0^{45/16} \sqrt{(90 \cos 30°)^2 + (90 \sin 30° - 32t)^2} \, dt$$

$$= 230.8 \text{ ft}$$

43. (a) $x = t - \sin t$ $x = 2t - \sin(2t)$

   $y = 1 - \cos t$ $y = 1 - \cos(2t)$

   $0 \le t \le 2\pi$ $0 \le t \le \pi$

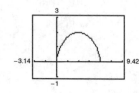

(b) The average speed of the particle on the second path is twice the average speed of a particle on the first path.

(c) $x = \frac{1}{2}t - \sin\left(\frac{1}{2}t\right)$

$y = 1 - \cos\left(\frac{1}{2}t\right)$

The time required for the particle to traverse the same path is $t = 4\pi$.

45. $x = t$, $y = 2t$, $\dfrac{dx}{dt} = 1$, $\dfrac{dy}{dt} = 2$

(a) $S = 2\pi \int_0^4 2t \sqrt{1 + 4} \, dt = 4\sqrt{5}\pi \int_0^4 t \, dt$

$$= \left[2\sqrt{5}\pi t^2\right]_0^4 = 32\pi\sqrt{5}$$

(b) $S = 2\pi \int_0^4 t \sqrt{1 + 4} \, dt = 2\sqrt{5}\pi \int_0^4 t \, dt$

$$= \left[\sqrt{5}\pi t^2\right]_0^4 = 16\pi\sqrt{5}$$

47. $x = 4 \cos \theta$, $y = 4 \sin \theta$, $\dfrac{dx}{d\theta} = -4 \sin \theta$, $\dfrac{dy}{d\theta} = 4 \cos \theta$

$$S = 2\pi \int_0^{\pi/2} 4 \cos \theta \sqrt{(-4 \sin \theta)^2 + (4 \cos \theta)^2} \, d\theta$$

$$= 32\pi \int_0^{\pi/2} \cos \theta \, d\theta = \left[32\pi \sin \theta\right]_0^{\pi/2} = 32\pi$$

49. $x = a \cos^3 \theta$, $y = a \sin^3 \theta$

$$\frac{dx}{d\theta} = -3a \cos^2 \theta \sin \theta, \frac{dy}{d\theta} = 3a \sin^2 \theta \cos \theta$$

Using the integral for surface area and the symmetry of the graph shown in the figure, we have

$$S = 2\pi \int_a^b g(\theta) \sqrt{\left(\frac{dx}{d\theta}\right)^2 + \left(\frac{dy}{d\theta}\right)^2} \, d\theta$$

$$= 4\pi \int_0^{\pi/2} a \sin^3 \theta \sqrt{9a^2 \cos^4 \theta \sin^2 \theta + 9a^2 \sin^4 \theta \cos^2 \theta} \, d\theta$$

$$= 12a^2\pi \int_0^{\pi/2} \sin^4 \theta \cos \theta \, d\theta$$

$$= 4 \frac{12a^2\pi}{5} \left[\sin^5 \theta \right]_0^{\pi/2} = \frac{12}{5} \pi a^2.$$

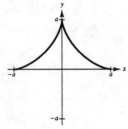

51. The sphere is formed by revolving a circle of radius r about the x-axis. We represent the circle by

$$x = f(\phi) = r \cos \phi \qquad y = g(\phi) = r \sin \phi$$

$$\frac{dx}{d\phi} = -r \sin \phi \qquad \frac{dy}{d\phi} = r \cos \phi.$$

From the integrals of Theorem 9.9 and the accompanying figure, we have

$$S = 2\pi \int_0^\theta g(\phi) \sqrt{\left(\frac{dx}{d\phi}\right)^2 + \left(\frac{dy}{d\phi}\right)^2} \, d\phi$$

$$= 2\pi \int_0^\theta r \sin \phi \sqrt{r^2 \sin^2 \phi + r^2 \cos^2 \phi} \, d\phi$$

$$= 2\pi r^2 \int_0^\theta \sin \phi \, d\phi = -2\pi r^2 \left[\cos \phi \right]_0^\theta$$

$$= 2\pi r^2 (1 - \cos \theta).$$

53. $x = \sqrt{t}$, $y = 4 - t$, $0 \le t \le 4$

$$A = \int_0^4 (4 - t) \frac{1}{2\sqrt{t}} \, dt = \frac{1}{2} \int_0^4 (4t^{-1/2} - t^{1/2}) \, dt = \left[\frac{1}{2} \left(8\sqrt{t} - \frac{2}{3} t \sqrt{t} \right) \right]_0^4 = \frac{16}{3}$$

$$\bar{x} = \frac{3}{16} \int_0^4 (4 - t) \sqrt{t} \left(\frac{1}{2\sqrt{t}} \right) dt = \frac{3}{32} \int_0^4 (4 - t) \, dt = \left[\frac{3}{32} \left(4t - \frac{t^2}{2} \right) \right]_0^4 = \frac{3}{4}$$

$$\bar{y} = \frac{3}{32} \int_0^4 (4 - t)^2 \frac{1}{2\sqrt{t}} \, dt = \frac{3}{64} \int_0^4 [16t^{-1/2} - 8t^{1/2} + t^{3/2}] \, dt = \frac{3}{64} \left[32\sqrt{t} - \frac{16}{3} t \sqrt{t} + \frac{2}{5} t^2 \sqrt{t} \right]_0^4 = \frac{8}{5}$$

$$(\bar{x}, \bar{y}) = \left(\frac{3}{4}, \frac{8}{5} \right)$$

55. $x = 3 \cos \theta$, $y = 3 \sin \theta$, $\frac{dx}{d\theta} = -3 \sin \theta$

$$V = 2\pi \int_{\pi/2}^0 (3 \sin \theta)^2 (-3 \sin \theta) \, d\theta$$

$$= -54\pi \int_{\pi/2}^0 \sin^3 \theta \, d\theta$$

$$= -54\pi \int_{\pi/2}^0 (1 - \cos^2 \theta) \sin \theta \, d\theta$$

$$= -54\pi \left[-\cos \theta + \frac{\cos^3 \theta}{3} \right]_{\pi/2}^0 = 36\pi$$

57. $x = 2\sin^2\theta$, $y = 2\sin^2\theta\tan\theta$

From Exercise 52, we have the following convergent improper integral:

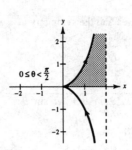

$$A = \int_0^2 y\,dx = \int_0^{\pi/2} y\frac{dx}{d\theta}\,d\theta$$

$$= \int_0^{\pi/2} 2\sin^2\theta\tan\theta(4\sin\theta\cos\theta)\,d\theta$$

$$= 8\int_0^{\pi/2} \sin^4\theta\,d\theta$$

$$= 8\int_0^{\pi/2} \left(\frac{1-\cos 2\theta}{2}\right)^2 d\theta$$

$$= 2\int_0^{\pi/2} (1 - 2\cos 2\theta + \cos^2 2\theta)\,d\theta$$

$$= 2\int_0^{\pi/2} \left(1 - 2\cos 2\theta + \frac{1 + \cos 4\theta}{2}\right) d\theta$$

$$= 2\int_0^{\pi/2} \left(\frac{3}{2} - 2\cos 2\theta + \frac{1}{2}\cos 4\theta\right) d\theta$$

$$= 2\left[\frac{3}{2}\theta - \sin 2\theta + \frac{1}{8}\sin 4\theta\right]_0^{\pi/2} = 2\left(\frac{3\pi}{4}\right) = \frac{3\pi}{2}$$

59. πab is area of ellipse (d). **61.** $6\pi a^2$ is area of cardioid (f). **63.** $\frac{8}{3}ab$ is area of hourglass (a).

65. (a) $x = \dfrac{1 - t^2}{1 + t^2}$, $y = \dfrac{2t}{1 + t^2}$, $-20 \le t \le 20$

The graph is the circle $x^2 + y^2 = 1$, except the point $(-1, 0)$.

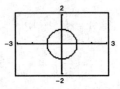

Verify: $x^2 + y^2 = \left(\dfrac{1 - t^2}{1 + t^2}\right)^2 + \left(\dfrac{2t}{1 + t^2}\right)^2 = \dfrac{1 - 2t^2 + t^4 + 4t^2}{(1 + t^2)^2} = \dfrac{(1 + t^2)^2}{(1 + t^2)^2} = 1$

(b) As t increases from -20 to 0, the speed increases, and as t increases from 0 to 20, the speed decreases.

67. (a) Let d_1 be the distance between point P and the plane flying 375 miles per hour (see figure). Therefore,

$$d_1 = 150 - 375t$$

where t is time in hours. If (x_1, y_1) are the coordinates of the position of this plane, then we obtain the required parametric equations in the following manner.

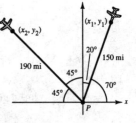

$$\cos 70° = \frac{x_1}{150 - 375t} \implies x_1 = \cos 70°(150 - 375t)$$

$$\sin 70° = \frac{y_2}{150 - 375t} \implies y_1 = \sin 70°(150 - 375t)$$

Let d_2 be the distance between the point P and the plane flying 450 miles per hour. Therefore,

$$d_2 = 190 - 450t$$

where t is time in hours. If (x_2, y_2) are the coordinates of the position of this plane, then we obtain the required parametric equations in the following manner.

$$\cos 45° = \frac{-x_2}{190 - 450t} \implies x_2 = -\cos 45°(190 - 450t)$$

$$\sin 45° = \frac{y_2}{190 - 450t} \implies y_2 = \sin 45°(190 - 450t)$$

—CONTINUED—

67. **—CONTINUED—**

(b) The distance d between the planes is

$$d = \sqrt{(x_2 - x_1)^2 + (y_2 - y_1)^2}$$

$$= \sqrt{[-\cos 45°(190 - 450t) - \cos 70°(150 - 375t)]^2 + [\sin 45°(190 - 450t) - \sin 70°(150 - 375t)]^2}.$$

(c) The graph of the distance function of part (b) is shown in the figure. Using the capabilities of finding extrema on a graphing utility yields a minimum separation of the planes of 7.59 miles when $t \approx 0.4145$. This meets regulations requiring a minimum separation of at least 3 miles.

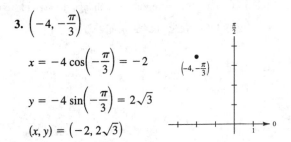

69. False

$$\frac{d^2y}{dx^2} = \frac{\dfrac{d}{dt}\left[\dfrac{g'(t)}{f'(t)}\right]}{f'(t)} = \frac{f'(t)g''(t) - g'(t)f''(t)}{[f'(t)]^3}$$

Section 9.4   Polar Coordinates and Polar Graphs

1. $\left(4, \dfrac{\pi}{2}\right)$

$x = 4\cos\left(\dfrac{\pi}{2}\right) = 0$

$y = 4\sin\left(\dfrac{\pi}{2}\right) = 4$

$(x, y) = (0, 4)$

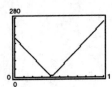

3. $\left(-4, -\dfrac{\pi}{3}\right)$

$x = -4\cos\left(-\dfrac{\pi}{3}\right) = -2$

$y = -4\sin\left(-\dfrac{\pi}{3}\right) = 2\sqrt{3}$

$(x, y) = \left(-2, 2\sqrt{3}\right)$

5. Using the conversion from polar to rectangular coordinates, you have

$x = r\cos\theta = \sqrt{2}\cos(2.36) \approx -1.004$

$y = r\sin\theta = \sqrt{2}\sin(2.36) \approx 0.996$.

Therefore the rectangular coordinates are $(1.004, 0.996)$.

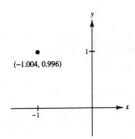

7. $(r, \theta) = \left(5, \dfrac{3\pi}{4}\right)$

$(x, y) = (-3.5355, 3.5355)$

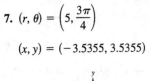

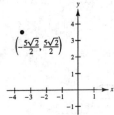

9. $(r, \theta) = (-3.5, 2.5)$

$(x, y) = (2.804, -2.095)$

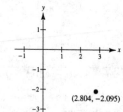

(2.804, -2.095)

11. $(x, y) = (1, 1)$

$r = \pm\sqrt{2}$

$\tan \theta = 1$

$\theta = \dfrac{\pi}{4}, \dfrac{5\pi}{4}, \left(\sqrt{2}, \dfrac{\pi}{4}\right), \left(-\sqrt{2}, \dfrac{5\pi}{4}\right)$

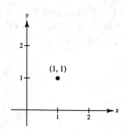

(1, 1)

13. First,

$$r = \pm\sqrt{x^2 + y^2} = \pm\sqrt{(-3)^2 + 4^2} = \pm 5$$

$$\tan \theta = -\tfrac{4}{3} \text{ and } \arctan\left(-\tfrac{4}{3}\right) \approx -0.9273.$$

Since $(-3, 4)$ lies in the second quadrant, let $\theta = \pi - 0.9273 = 2.214$. Thus one polar representation is

$(5, 2.214) \quad (r > 0, 0 \le \theta < 2\pi)$.

To obtain the second representation, change the sign of r and increase θ by π radians to obtain

$(-5, 5.356) \quad (r < 0, 0 \le \theta < 2\pi)$.

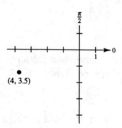

15. $(x, y) = (3, -2)$

$(r, \theta) = (3.606, -0.588)$

17. $(x, y) = \left(\tfrac{5}{2}, \tfrac{4}{3}\right)$

$(r, \theta) = (2.833, 0.490)$

19. (a) $(x, y) = (4, 3.5)$

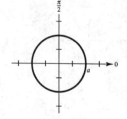

(4, 3.5)

(b) $(r, \theta) = (4, 3.5)$

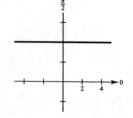

(4, 3.5)

21. $x^2 + y^2 = a^2$

$r = a$

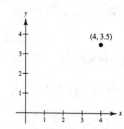

23. $\quad y = 4$

$r \sin \theta = 4$

$r = 4 \csc \theta$

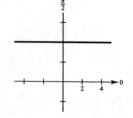

25. Since $x = r \cos \theta$ and $y = r \sin \theta$, we have

$$3x - y + 2 = 0$$
$$3(r \cos \theta) - r \sin \theta + 2 = 0$$
$$r(3 \cos \theta - \sin \theta) = -2$$
$$r = \frac{-2}{3 \cos \theta - \sin \theta}.$$

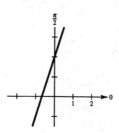

27. $\quad y^2 = 9x$

$$r^2 \sin^2 \theta = 9r \cos \theta$$
$$r = \frac{9 \cos \theta}{\sin^2 \theta}$$
$$r = 9 \csc^2 \theta \cos \theta$$

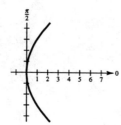

29. $\quad r = 3$

$$r^2 = 9$$
$$x^2 + y^2 = 9$$

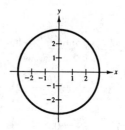

31. Since

$$r^2 = x^2 + y^2 \text{ and } y = r \sin \theta,$$

we begin by multiplying both members of the polar equation by r to obtain

$$r = \sin \theta$$
$$r^2 = r \sin \theta$$
$$x^2 + y^2 = y$$
$$x^2 + y^2 - y = 0$$
$$x^2 + \left(y^2 - y + \tfrac{1}{4}\right) = \tfrac{1}{4}$$
$$x^2 + \left(y - \tfrac{1}{2}\right)^2 = \left(\tfrac{1}{2}\right)^2.$$

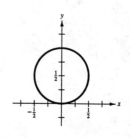

Therefore, the graph is a circle of radius $\frac{1}{2}$ centered at $\left(0, \frac{1}{2}\right)$.

33. $\quad r = \theta$

$$\tan r = \tan \theta$$
$$\tan \sqrt{x^2 + y^2} = \frac{y}{x}$$
$$\sqrt{x^2 + y^2} = \arctan \frac{y}{x}$$

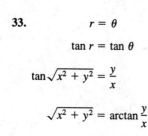

35. $\quad r = 3 \sec \theta$

$$r \cos \theta = 3$$
$$x = 3$$
$$x - 3 = 0$$

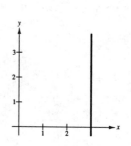

37.
$$r = 2(h \cos \theta + k \sin \theta)$$
$$r^2 = 2r(h \cos \theta + k \sin \theta)$$
$$r^2 = 2[h(r \cos \theta) + k(r \sin \theta)]$$
$$x^2 + y^2 = 2(hx + ky)$$
$$x^2 + y^2 - 2hx - 2ky = 0$$
$$(x^2 - 2hx + h^2) + (y^2 - 2ky + k^2) = 0 + h^2 + k^2$$
$$(x - h)^2 + (y - k)^2 = h^2 + k^2$$

Radius: $\sqrt{h^2 + k^2}$

Center: (h, k)

39. $\left(4, \dfrac{2\pi}{3}\right), \left(2, \dfrac{\pi}{6}\right)$

$$d = \sqrt{r_1{}^2 + r_2{}^2 - 2r_1 r_2 \cos(\theta_1 - \theta_2)}$$

$$= \sqrt{4^2 + 2^2 - 2(4)(2) \cos\left(\dfrac{2\pi}{3} - \dfrac{\pi}{6}\right)}$$

$$= \sqrt{20 - 16 \cos\dfrac{\pi}{2}} = 2\sqrt{5} \approx 4.5$$

41. $(2, 0.5), (7, 1.2)$

$$d = \sqrt{2^2 + 7^2 - 2(2)(7) \cos(0.5 - 1.2)}$$

$$= \sqrt{53 - 28 \cos(-0.7)} \approx 5.6$$

43. $r = 2 + 3 \sin \theta$

$$\frac{dy}{dx} = \frac{3 \cos \theta \sin \theta + \cos \theta(2 + 3 \sin \theta)}{3 \cos \theta \cos \theta - \sin \theta(2 + 3 \sin \theta)}$$

$$= \frac{2 \cos \theta(3 \sin \theta + 1)}{3 \cos 2\theta - 2 \sin \theta} = \frac{2 \cos \theta(3 \sin \theta + 1)}{6 \cos^2 \theta - 2 \sin \theta - 3}$$

At $\left(5, \dfrac{\pi}{2}\right)$, $\dfrac{dy}{dx} = 0$.

At $(2, \pi)$, $\dfrac{dy}{dx} = -\dfrac{2}{3}$.

At $\left(-1, \dfrac{3\pi}{2}\right)$, $\dfrac{dy}{dx} = 0$.

45. $r = 3(1 - \cos \theta)$

(a) The graph is shown in the figure.

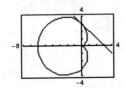

(b) The graph of the tangent line when $\theta = \pi/2$ is shown on the graph of part (a),

(c) $f(\theta) = 3(1 - \cos \theta)$

$f'(\theta) = 3 \sin \theta$

$$\frac{dy}{dx} = \frac{f'(\theta) \sin \theta + f(\theta) \cos \theta}{f'(\theta) \cos \theta - f(\theta) \sin \theta}$$

$$= \frac{(3 \sin \theta) \sin \theta + 3(1 - \cos \theta) \cos \theta}{(3 \sin \theta) \cos \theta - 3(1 - \cos \theta) \sin \theta}$$

$$= \frac{\sin^2 \theta + \cos \theta - \cos^2 \theta}{\sin \theta(2 \cos \theta - 1)}$$

$$= \frac{(1 + 2 \cos \theta)(1 - \cos \theta)}{\sin \theta(2 \cos \theta - 1)}$$

When $\theta = \pi/2$, the slope is

$$\frac{dy}{dx} = \frac{(1 + 0)(1 - 0)}{1(0 - 1)} = -1.$$

47. (a), (b) $r = 3 \sin \theta$

(c) At $\theta = \dfrac{\pi}{3}$, $\dfrac{dy}{dx} = -\sqrt{3} \approx 1.732$.

$(r, \theta) = \left(\dfrac{3\sqrt{3}}{2}, \dfrac{\pi}{3}\right) \implies (x, y) = \left(\dfrac{3\sqrt{3}}{4}, \dfrac{9}{4}\right)$

Tangent line: $y - \dfrac{9}{4} = -\sqrt{3}\left(x - \dfrac{3\sqrt{3}}{4}\right)$

$$y = -\sqrt{3}x + \dfrac{9}{2}$$

49. Since $f(\theta) = 1 + \sin\theta$ and $f'(\theta) = \cos\theta$, we have

$$\frac{dy}{dx} = \frac{f'(\theta)\sin\theta + f(\theta)\cos\theta}{f'(\theta)\cos\theta - f(\theta)\sin\theta}$$

$$= \frac{\cos\theta\sin\theta + (1 + \sin\theta)\cos\theta}{\cos^2\theta - (1 + \sin\theta)\sin\theta}$$

$$= \frac{\cos\theta(1 + 2\sin\theta)}{1 - \sin\theta - 2\sin^2\theta}$$

$$= \frac{\cos\theta(1 + 2\sin\theta)}{(1 - 2\sin\theta)(1 + \sin\theta)}.$$

Since $dy/dx = 0$ when $\cos\theta(1 + 2\sin\theta) = 0$ or $\theta = \pi/2, 7\pi/6, 11\pi/6$, there are horizontal tangents at the points

$$\left(2, \frac{\pi}{2}\right), \left(\frac{1}{2}, \frac{7\pi}{6}\right), \text{ and } \left(\frac{1}{2}, \frac{11\pi}{6}\right).$$

Since dy/dx is undefined when $(1 - 2\sin\theta)(1 + \sin\theta) = 0$ or $\theta = \pi/6, 5\pi/6, 3\pi/2$, there are vertical tangents at the points

$$\left(\frac{3}{2}, \frac{\pi}{6}\right) \text{ and } \left(\frac{3}{2}, \frac{5\pi}{6}\right).$$

51. $r = 2\csc\theta + 3$

$$\frac{dy}{d\theta} = (2\csc\theta + 3)\cos\theta + (-2\csc\theta\cot\theta)\sin\theta$$

$$= 3\cos\theta = 0$$

$$\theta = \frac{\pi}{2}, \frac{3\pi}{2}$$

Horizontal: $\left(5, \dfrac{\pi}{2}\right), \left(1, \dfrac{3\pi}{2}\right)$

53. $r = 4\sin\theta\cos^2\theta$

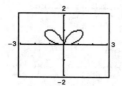

Horizontal tangents:

$(0, 0), (1.4142, 0.7854), (1.4142, 2.3562)$

55. $r = 2\csc\theta + 5$

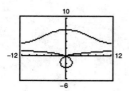

Horizontal tangents: $\left(7, \dfrac{\pi}{2}\right), \left(3, \dfrac{3\pi}{2}\right)$

57.
$$r = 3\sin\theta$$
$$r^2 = 3r\sin\theta$$
$$x^2 + y^2 = 3y$$
$$x^2 + \left(y - \tfrac{3}{2}\right)^2 = \tfrac{9}{4}$$

Circle $r = \tfrac{3}{2}$

Center: $\left(0, \tfrac{3}{2}\right)$

Tangent at the pole: $\theta = 0$

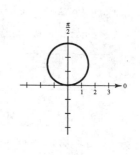

59. The equation has the form $r = a\cos(n\theta) = 2\cos 3\theta$ where n is odd. This means the graph is a *rose curve* with $n = 3$ petals. The curve has polar axis symmetry. The relative extrema of r are $(2, 0), (-2, \pi/3)$, and $(2, 2\pi/3)$. Since $r = 0$ and $dr/d\theta \neq 0$ when $\theta = \pi/6, \theta = \pi/2$, and $\theta = 5\pi/6$, we have tangents at the pole for these values of θ.

θ	0	$\dfrac{\pi}{12}$	$\dfrac{\pi}{6}$	$\dfrac{\pi}{3}$	$\dfrac{\pi}{2}$	$\dfrac{2\pi}{3}$
r	2	$\sqrt{2}$	0	-2	0	2

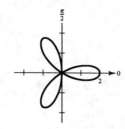

61. $r = 3 \sin 2\theta$

Rose curve with four petals

Symmetric to the polar axis, $\theta = \dfrac{\pi}{2}$, and pole

Relative extrema: $\left(\pm 3, \dfrac{\pi}{4}\right), \left(\pm 3, \dfrac{5\pi}{4}\right)$

Tangents at the pole: $\theta = 0, \dfrac{\pi}{2}$

($\theta = \pi$, $3\pi/2$ give the same tangents.)

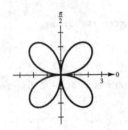

63. $r = 3 - 2 \cos \theta$

Limaçon

Symmetric to polar axis

θ	0	$\dfrac{\pi}{3}$	$\dfrac{\pi}{2}$	$\dfrac{2\pi}{3}$	π
r	1	2	3	4	5

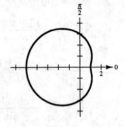

65. $r = 3 \csc \theta$

$r \sin \theta = 3$

$y = 3$

Horizontal line

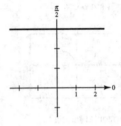

67. $r = 2\theta$

Spiral of Archimedes

Symmetric to $\theta = \pi/2$

θ	0	$\dfrac{\pi}{4}$	$\dfrac{\pi}{2}$	$\dfrac{3\pi}{4}$	π	$\dfrac{5\pi}{4}$	$\dfrac{3\pi}{2}$
r	2	$\dfrac{\pi}{2}$	π	$\dfrac{3\pi}{2}$	2π	$\dfrac{5\pi}{2}$	3π

Tangent at the pole: $\theta = 0$

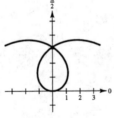

69. $r^2 = 4 \cos(2\theta)$

Lemniscate

Symmetric to the polar axis, $\theta = \dfrac{\pi}{2}$, and pole

Relative extrema: $(\pm 2, 0)$

θ	0	$\dfrac{\pi}{6}$	$\dfrac{\pi}{4}$
r	± 2	$\pm \sqrt{2}$	0

Tangents at the pole: $\theta = \dfrac{\pi}{4}, \dfrac{3\pi}{4}$

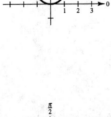

71. $r = 3 - 4 \cos \theta$

$0 \le \theta < 2\pi$

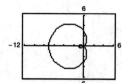

73. $r = 2 + \sin \theta$

$0 \le \theta < 2\pi$

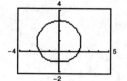

75. $r = \dfrac{2}{1 + \cos \theta}$

Traced out once on
$-\pi < \theta < \pi$

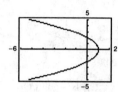

77. $r = 2 \cos\left(\dfrac{3\theta}{2}\right)$

$0 \le \theta < 4\pi$

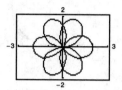

79. Before using the graphing utility to obtain the graph of the polar equation, observe that the equation has the form

$$r^2 = a^2 \sin 2\theta = 4 \sin 2\theta$$

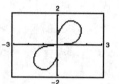

and is a *leminscate* with symmetry with respect to the pole. (If your graphing utility doesn't have a polar mode, but does have a parametric mode, you can sketch the graph of $r = f(\theta)$ by writing the equation as $x = f(\theta) \cos \theta$ and $y = f(\theta) \sin \theta$.) The entire graph will be traced for $0 \le \theta \le \pi$. Also, the tangents at the pole are $\theta = 0$ and $\theta = \pi/2$ since $r = 0$ and $dr/d\theta \ne 0$ at these values.

81. The graph of the polar equation obtained by a graphing utility is shown in the figure. To locate the vertical asymptote, note that

$$r \to -\infty \text{ as } \theta \to \frac{\pi^-}{2} \qquad \text{and} \qquad r \to \infty \text{ as } \theta \to \frac{\pi^+}{2}.$$

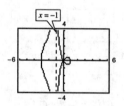

To see that the vertical asymptote is located at $x = -1$, write

$$r = 2 - \frac{1}{\cos \theta} = 2 - \frac{r}{r \cos \theta} = 2 - \frac{r}{x}$$

$$rx = 2x - r$$

$$r(1 + x) = 2x$$

$$r = \frac{2x}{1 + x}.$$

Thus, $r \to \pm\infty$ as $x \to -1$.

83. $r = \dfrac{2}{\theta}$

Hyperbolic spiral

$r \Rightarrow \infty$ as $\theta \Rightarrow 0$

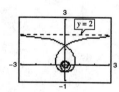

$$r = \frac{2}{\theta} \Rightarrow \theta = \frac{2}{r} = \frac{2 \sin \theta}{r \sin \theta} = \frac{2 \sin \theta}{y}$$

$$y = \frac{2 \sin \theta}{\theta}$$

$$\lim_{\theta \to 0} \frac{2 \sin \theta}{\theta} = \lim_{\theta \to 0} \frac{2 \cos \theta}{1} = 2$$

85. $r = 4 \sin \theta$

(a) $0 \leq \theta \leq \dfrac{\pi}{2}$

(b) $\dfrac{\pi}{2} \leq \theta \leq \pi$

(c) $-\dfrac{\pi}{2} \leq \theta \leq \dfrac{\pi}{2}$

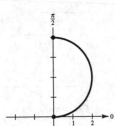

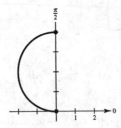

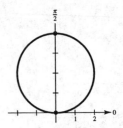

87. Let the curve $r = f(\theta)$ be rotated by ϕ to form the curve $r = g(\theta)$. If (r_1, θ_1) is a point on $r = f(\theta)$, then $(r_1, \theta_1 + \phi)$ is on $r = g(\theta)$. That is,

$$g(\theta_1 + \phi) = r_1 = f(\theta_1).$$

Letting $\theta = \theta_1 + \phi$, or $\theta_1 = \theta - \phi$, we see that

$$g(\theta) = g(\theta_1 + \phi) = f(\theta_1) = f(\theta - \phi).$$

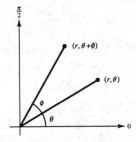

89. $r = 2 - \sin \theta$

(a) $r = 2 - \sin\left(\theta - \dfrac{\pi}{4}\right) = 2 - \dfrac{\sqrt{2}}{2}(\sin \theta - \cos \theta)$

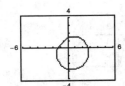

(b) $r = 2 - (-\cos \theta) = 2 + \cos \theta$

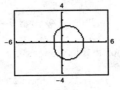

(c) $r = 2 - (-\sin \theta) = 2 + \sin \theta$

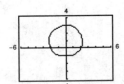

(d) $r = 2 - \cos \theta$

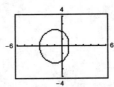

91. (a) $r = 1 - \sin \theta$

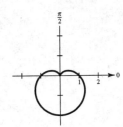

(b) $r = 1 - \sin\left(\theta - \dfrac{\pi}{4}\right)$

Rotate the graph of $r = 1 - \sin \theta$ through the angle $\pi/4$.

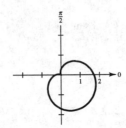

93. $\tan \psi = \dfrac{r}{dr/d\theta} = \dfrac{2(1 - \cos \theta)}{2 \sin \theta}$

At $\theta = \pi$, $\tan \psi$ is undefined $\implies \psi = \dfrac{\pi}{2}$.

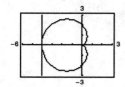

95. $\tan \psi = \dfrac{r}{dr/d\theta} = \dfrac{2 \cos 3\theta}{-6 \sin 3\theta}$

At $\theta = \dfrac{\pi}{6}$, $\tan \psi = 0 \implies \psi = 0$.

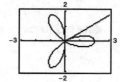

97. $f(\theta) = r = \dfrac{6}{1 - \cos \theta}$

$f'(\theta) = \dfrac{-6 \sin \theta}{(1 - \cos \theta)^2}$

From the definition of the angle ψ between the radial line and the tangent line (see Exercise 92), we have

$$\tan \psi = \left| \frac{f(\theta)}{f'(\theta)} \right| = \left| \frac{6/(1 - \cos \theta)}{-6 \sin \theta/(1 - \cos \theta)^2} \right| = \left| \frac{1 - \cos \theta}{-\sin \theta} \right|.$$

At $\theta = 2\pi/3$,

$$\tan \psi = \left| \frac{1 - (-1/2)}{-\sqrt{3}/2} \right| = \left| \frac{3/2}{-\sqrt{3}/2} \right| = \sqrt{3}.$$

Therefore, $\psi = \pi/3$. The graph is shown in the figure.

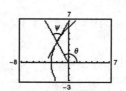

99. The curve is produced over the interval $0 \le \theta \le 9\pi$.

101. True

103. True

Section 9.5   Area and Arc Length in Polar Coordinates

1. (a) $r = 8 \sin \theta$

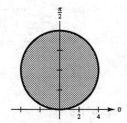

$A = \pi(4)^2 = 16\pi$

(b) $A = 2\left(\dfrac{1}{2}\right) \displaystyle\int_0^{\pi/2} \left[8 \sin \theta \right]^2 d\theta$

$\quad = 64 \displaystyle\int_0^{\pi/2} \sin^2 \theta \, d\theta$

$\quad = 32 \displaystyle\int_0^{\pi/2} (1 - \cos 2\theta) \, d\theta$

$\quad = 32 \left[\theta - \dfrac{\sin 2\theta}{2} \right]_0^{\pi/2} = 16\pi$

3. The graph of $r = 2 \cos 3\theta$ is shown in the figure. Use symmetry to find the area of one petal.

$$A = 2\left[\frac{1}{2} \int_0^{\pi/6} (2 \cos 3\theta)^2 \, d\theta \right]$$

$$= \int_0^{\pi/6} 4\left(\frac{1 + \cos 6\theta}{2} \right) d\theta$$

$$= 2\left[\theta + \frac{1}{6} \sin 6\theta \right]_0^{\pi/6} = \frac{\pi}{3}$$

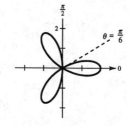

5. $A = 2\left[\dfrac{1}{2}\displaystyle\int_0^{\pi/4} (\cos 2\theta)^2\, d\theta\right]$

$= \dfrac{1}{2}\left[\theta + \dfrac{1}{4}\sin 4\theta\right]_0^{\pi/4} = \dfrac{\pi}{8}$

7. $A = 2\left[\dfrac{1}{2}\displaystyle\int_{-\pi/2}^{\pi/2} (1 - \sin\theta)^2\, d\theta\right]$

$= \left[\dfrac{3}{2}\theta + 2\cos\theta - \dfrac{1}{4}\sin 2\theta\right]_{-\pi/2}^{\pi/2} = \dfrac{3\pi}{2}$

9. Solving the equation $r = 0$ to find the tangents at the pole we have,

$$1 + 2\cos\theta = 0$$

$$\cos\theta = -\dfrac{1}{2}$$

$$\theta = \dfrac{2\pi}{3} \text{ or } \dfrac{4\pi}{3}.$$

Therefore, the lower half of the inner loop is generated when θ is in the interval $2\pi/3 \le \theta \le \pi$. From the symmetry of the graph in the figure, the area of the inner loop is given by

$$2\int_{2\pi/3}^{\pi} \dfrac{1}{2}r^2\, d\theta = \int_{2\pi/3}^{\pi} (1 + 2\cos\theta)^2\, d\theta$$

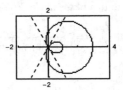

$$= \int_{2\pi/3}^{\pi} (1 + 4\cos\theta + 4\cos^2\theta)\, d\theta$$

$$= \int_{2\pi/3}^{\pi}\left(1 + 4\cos\theta + 4\dfrac{1 + \cos 2\theta}{2}\right) d\theta$$

$$= \int_{2\pi/3}^{\pi} (3 + 4\cos\theta + 2\cos 2\theta)\, d\theta$$

$$= \left[3\theta + 4\sin\theta + \sin 2\theta\right]_{2\pi/3}^{\pi}$$

$$= \pi - \dfrac{3\sqrt{3}}{2} = \dfrac{2\pi - 3\sqrt{3}}{2}.$$

11. From the symmetry of the graph given in the figure, the area of the region inside the outer loop is

$$2\int_0^{2\pi/3} \dfrac{1}{2}r^2\, d\theta = \int_0^{2\pi/3} (1 + 2\cos\theta)^2\, d\theta$$

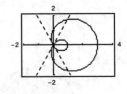

$$= \left[3\theta + 4\sin\theta + \sin 2\theta\right]_0^{2\pi/3} \qquad \text{From Exercise 9}$$

$$= 2\pi + 2\sqrt{3} - \dfrac{\sqrt{3}}{2} = 2\pi + \dfrac{3\sqrt{3}}{2}.$$

From Exercise 9, we see that the area of the inner loop is given by $\pi - (3\sqrt{3}/2)$. Finally, the area of the region between the two loops is

$$A = \left(2\pi + \dfrac{3\sqrt{3}}{2}\right) - \left(\pi - \dfrac{3\sqrt{3}}{2}\right) = \pi + 3\sqrt{3}.$$

13. $r = 1 + \cos \theta$

$r = 1 - \cos \theta$

Solving simultaneously,

$$1 + \cos \theta = 1 - \cos \theta$$

$$2 \cos \theta = 0$$

$$\theta = \frac{\pi}{2}, \frac{3\pi}{2}.$$

Replacing r by $-r$ and θ by $\theta + \pi$ in the first equation and solving, $-1 + \cos \theta = 1 - \cos \theta$, $\cos \theta = 1$, $\theta = 0$. Both curves pass through the pole, $(0, \pi)$, and $(0, 0)$, respectively.

Points of intersection: $\left(1, \dfrac{\pi}{2}\right), \left(1, \dfrac{3\pi}{2}\right), (0, 0)$

15. $r = 1 + \cos \theta$

$r = 1 - \sin \theta$

Solving simultaneously,

$$1 + \cos \theta = 1 - \sin \theta$$

$$\cos \theta = -\sin \theta$$

$$\tan \theta = -1$$

$$\theta = \frac{3\pi}{4}, \frac{7\pi}{4}.$$

Replacing r by $-r$ and θ by $\theta + \pi$ in the first equation and solving, $-1 + \cos \theta = 1 - \sin \theta$, $\sin \theta + \cos \theta = 2$, which has no solution. Both curves pass through the pole, $(0, \pi)$, and $(0, \pi/2)$, respectively.

Points of intersection: $\left(\dfrac{2 - \sqrt{2}}{2}, \dfrac{3\pi}{4}\right), \left(\dfrac{2 + \sqrt{2}}{2}, \dfrac{7\pi}{4}\right), (0, 0)$

17. From Section 9.4 we know the graph of $r = 4 - 5 \sin \theta$ is a limaçon and the graph of $r = 3 \sin \theta$ is a circle (see figure). Solving the two equations simultaneously, yields

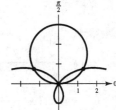

$$4 - 5 \sin \theta = 3 \sin \theta$$

$$8 \sin \theta = 4$$

$$\sin \theta = \frac{1}{2}$$

$$\theta = \frac{\pi}{6}, \frac{5\pi}{6} \quad (0 \le \theta < 2\pi).$$

From these values we obtain the points $(3/2, \pi/6)$ and $(3/2, 5\pi/6)$. To test additional points of intersection, replace r by $-r$ and θ by $\pi + \theta$ in $r = 4 - 5 \sin \theta$ to obtain $-r = 4 - 5 \sin(\pi + \theta) = 4 + 5 \sin \theta$. Solving this equation simultaneously with $r = 3 \sin \theta$, yields

$$-4 - 5 \sin \theta = 3 \sin \theta$$

$$8 \sin \theta = -4$$

$$\sin \theta = -\frac{1}{2}$$

$$\theta = \frac{7\pi}{6}, \frac{11\pi}{6}.$$

The corresponding points are $(-3/2, 7\pi/6)$ and $(-3/2, 11\pi/6)$. However, these two points coincide with the previous two points. Finally, observe that both curves pass through the pole. Hence there are three points of intersection, $(3/2, \pi/6)$, $(3/2, 5\pi/6)$, and $(0, 0)$ as seen in the figure.

19. $r = \dfrac{\theta}{2}$

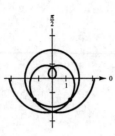

$r = 2$

Solving simultaneously, we have

$\theta/2 = 2, \; \theta = 4.$

Points of intersection:

$(2, 4), (-2, -4)$

21. From Section 9.4, we know the graph of $r = 4 \sin 2\theta$ is a rose curve with 4 petals and is symmetric to the polar axis, the vertical axis and the pole. Also, the graph of $r = 2$ is a circle of radius 2 centered at the pole. Solving the two equations simultaneously, yields

$4 \sin 2\theta = 2$

$\sin 2\theta = \dfrac{1}{2}$

$2\theta = \dfrac{\pi}{6}, \dfrac{5\pi}{6}$

$\theta = \dfrac{\pi}{12}, \dfrac{5\pi}{12}.$

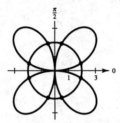

Therefore, the points of intersection for one petal are $(2, \pi/12)$ and $(2, 5\pi/12)$. By symmetry, the other points of intersection are $(2, 7\pi/12)$, $(2, 11\pi/12)$, $(2, 13\pi/12)$, $(2, 17\pi/12)$, $(2, 19\pi/12)$, and $(2, 23\pi/12)$.

23. $r = 2 + 3 \cos \theta$

$r = \dfrac{\sec \theta}{2}$

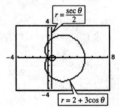

The graph of $r = 2 + 3 \cos \theta$ is a limaçon with an inner loop $(b > a)$ and is symmetric to the polar axis. The graph of $r = (\sec \theta)/2$ is the vertical line $x = 1/2$. Therefore, there are four points of intersection. Solving simultaneously,

$2 + 3 \cos \theta = \dfrac{\sec \theta}{2}$

$6 \cos^2 \theta + 4 \cos \theta - 1 = 0$

$\cos \theta = \dfrac{-2 \pm \sqrt{10}}{6}$

$\theta = \arccos\left(\dfrac{-2 + \sqrt{10}}{6}\right) \approx 1.376$

$\theta = \arccos\left(\dfrac{-2 - \sqrt{10}}{6}\right) \approx 2.6068.$

Points of intersection: $(-0.581, \pm 2.607), (2.581, \pm 1.376)$

25. $r = \cos \theta$

$r = 2 - 3 \sin \theta$

Points of intersection: $(0, 0), (0.935, 0.363), (0.535, -1.006)$

The graphs reach the pole at different times (θ values).

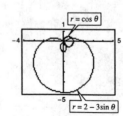

27. From the graph we see that we need only consider the region common to both curves in one petal of the rose curve and multiply the result by four. From Exercise 21 the points of intersection on the first petal occur when $\theta = \pi/12$ and $5\pi/12$. There are three subregions within one petal with the following bounds.

(a) for $0 \le \theta \le \dfrac{\pi}{12}$, $r = 4 \sin 2\theta$

(b) for $\dfrac{\pi}{12} \le \theta \le \dfrac{5\pi}{12}$, $r = 2$

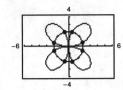

(c) for $\dfrac{5\pi}{12} \le \theta \le \dfrac{\pi}{2}$, $r = 4 \sin 2\theta$

Therefore, the area within one petal is

$$A = \int_0^{\pi/12} \frac{1}{2}(4 \sin 2\theta)^2 \, d\theta + \int_{\pi/12}^{5\pi/12} \frac{1}{2}(2)^2 \, d\theta + \int_{5\pi/12}^{\pi/2} \frac{1}{2}(4 \sin 2\theta)^2 \, d\theta.$$

By the symmetry of the petal, the first and third integrals are equal. Thus,

$$A = 2\int_0^{\pi/12} \frac{1}{2}(4 \sin 2\theta)^2 \, d\theta + \int_{\pi/12}^{5\pi/12} \frac{1}{2}(2)^2 \, d\theta$$

$$= 16 \int_0^{\pi/12} \sin^2 2\theta \, d\theta + 2 \int_{\pi/12}^{5\pi/12} d\theta$$

$$= 8 \int_0^{\pi/12} (1 - \cos 4\theta) \, d\theta + 2 \int_{\pi/12}^{5\pi/12} d\theta$$

$$= 8\left[\theta - \frac{1}{4} \sin 4\theta \right]_0^{\pi/12} + \left[2\theta \right]_{\pi/12}^{5\pi/12}$$

$$= \frac{2\pi}{3} - \frac{2\sqrt{3}}{2} + \frac{2\pi}{3} = \frac{4\pi}{3} - \sqrt{3}.$$

Finally, multiplying by 4, we obtain the total area of $\frac{4}{3}\left(4\pi - 3\sqrt{3}\right)$.

29. $A = 4\left[\dfrac{1}{2} \displaystyle\int_0^{\pi/2} (3 - 2 \sin \theta)^2 \, d\theta \right]$

$$= 2\left[11\theta + 12 \cos \theta - \sin(2\theta) \right]_0^{\pi/2} = 11\pi - 24$$

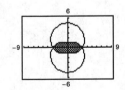

31. $A = 2\left[\dfrac{1}{2} \displaystyle\int_0^{\pi/6} (4 \sin \theta)^2 \, d\theta + \dfrac{1}{2} \displaystyle\int_{\pi/6}^{\pi/2} (2)^2 \, d\theta \right]$

$$= 16\left[\frac{1}{2} \theta - \frac{1}{4} \sin(2\theta) \right]_0^{\pi/6} + \left[4\theta \right]_{\pi/6}^{\pi/2}$$

$$= \frac{8\pi}{3} - 2\sqrt{3} = \frac{2}{3}\left(4\pi - 3\sqrt{3} \right)$$

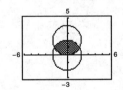

33. The graphs of $r = a(1 + \cos \theta)$ and $r = a \cos \theta$ are symmetric to the polar axis (see figure). Therefore, double the area of the top half of the cardiod and subtract the area of the circle of radius $a/2$.

$$A = 2\left[\frac{1}{2}\int_0^\pi [a(1 + \cos \theta)]^2\right] - \frac{\pi a^2}{4}$$

$$= a^2 \int_0^\pi (1 + 2\cos \theta + \cos^2 \theta)\,d\theta - \frac{\pi a^2}{4}$$

$$= a^2 \int_0^\pi \left(1 + 2\cos \theta + \frac{1 + \cos 2\theta}{2}\right) d\theta - \frac{\pi a^2}{4}$$

$$= a^2 \int_0^\pi \left(\frac{3}{2} + 2\cos \theta + \frac{1}{2}\cos 2\theta\right) d\theta - \frac{\pi a^2}{4}$$

$$= a^2 \left[\frac{3}{2}\theta + 2\sin \theta + \frac{1}{4}\sin 2\theta\right]_0^\pi - \frac{\pi a^2}{4}$$

$$= \frac{3\pi a^2}{2} - \frac{\pi a^2}{4} = \frac{5\pi a^2}{4}$$

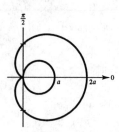

35. $A = \dfrac{\pi a^2}{8} + \dfrac{1}{2}\displaystyle\int_{\pi/2}^\pi [a(1 + \cos \theta)]^2\,d\theta$

$$= \frac{\pi a^2}{8} + \frac{a^2}{2}\int_{\pi/2}^\pi \left(\frac{3}{2} + 2\cos \theta + \frac{\cos 2\theta}{2}\right) d\theta$$

$$= \frac{\pi a^2}{8} + \frac{a^2}{2}\left[\frac{3}{2}\theta + 2\sin \theta + \frac{\sin 2\theta}{4}\right]_{\pi/2}^\pi$$

$$= \frac{\pi a^2}{8} + \frac{a^2}{2}\left[\frac{3\pi}{2} - \frac{3\pi}{4} - 2\right] = \frac{a^2}{2}[\pi - 2]$$

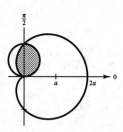

37. (a) $r = a\cos^2 \theta$

$r^3 = ar^2\cos^2 \theta$

$(x^2 + y^2)^{3/2} = ax^2$

(b)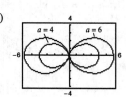

(c) $A = 4\left(\dfrac{1}{2}\right)\displaystyle\int_0^{\pi/2} [(6\cos^2 \theta)^2 - (4\cos^2 \theta)^2]\,d\theta = 40\int_0^{\pi/2}\cos^4 \theta\,d\theta = 10\int_0^{\pi/2}(1 + \cos 2\theta)^2\,d\theta$

$$= 10\int_0^{\pi/2}\left(1 + 2\cos 2\theta + \frac{1 - \cos 4\theta}{2}\right) d\theta = 10\left[\frac{3}{2}\theta + \sin 2\theta + \frac{1}{8}\sin 4\theta\right]_0^{\pi/2} = \frac{15\pi}{2}$$

39. $r = a\cos(n\theta)$

For $n = 1$:

$r = a\cos \theta$

$A = \pi\left(\dfrac{a}{2}\right)^2 = \dfrac{\pi a^2}{4}$

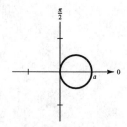

For $n = 2$:

$r = a\cos 2\theta$

$A = 8\left(\dfrac{1}{2}\right)\displaystyle\int_0^{\pi/4}(a\cos 2\theta)^2\,d\theta = \dfrac{\pi a^2}{2}$

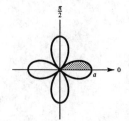

—CONTINUED—

39. —CONTINUED—

For $n = 3$:

$r = a \cos 3\theta$

$$A = 6\left(\frac{1}{2}\right)\int_0^{\pi/6} (a \cos 3\theta)^2 \, d\theta = \frac{\pi a^2}{4}$$

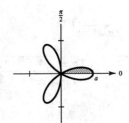

For $n = 4$:

$r = a \cos 4\theta$

$$A = 16\left(\frac{1}{2}\right)\int_0^{\pi/8} (a \cos 4\theta)^2 \, d\theta = \frac{\pi a^2}{2}$$

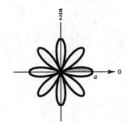

In general, the area of the region enclosed by $r = a \cos(n\theta)$ for $n = 1, 2, 3, \ldots$ is $(\pi a^2)/4$ if n is odd and is $(\pi a^2)/2$ if n is even.

41. $r = a$

$r' = 0$

$$s = \int_0^{2\pi} \sqrt{a^2 + 0^2} \, d\theta = \Big[a\theta \Big]_0^{2\pi} = 2\pi a$$

(circumference of circle of radius a)

43. $r = 1 + \sin \theta, 0 \le \theta \le 2\pi$

$$\frac{dr}{d\theta} = \cos \theta$$

The graph of the polar equation is symmetric to $\theta = \pi/2$. Therefore, double the arc length for $-\pi/2 \le \theta \le \pi/2$.

$$s = \int_\alpha^\beta \sqrt{r^2 + \left(\frac{dr}{d\theta}\right)^2} \, d\theta$$

$$= 2\int_{-\pi/2}^{\pi/2} \sqrt{(1 + \sin \theta)^2 + (\cos \theta)^2} \, d\theta$$

$$= 2\int_{-\pi/2}^{\pi/2} \sqrt{1 + 2 \sin \theta + \sin^2 \theta + \cos^2 \theta} \, d\theta$$

$$= 2\int_{-\pi/2}^{\pi/2} \sqrt{2(1 + \sin \theta)} \, d\theta$$

$$= 2\sqrt{2}\int_{-\pi/2}^{\pi/2} \frac{\cos \theta}{\sqrt{1 - \sin \theta}} \, d\theta$$

$$= -4\sqrt{2}\Big[\sqrt{1 - \sin \theta} \Big]_{-\pi/2}^{\pi/2}$$

$$= -4\sqrt{2}\left(0 - \sqrt{2}\right) = 8$$

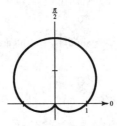

45. $r = 2\theta, 0 \leq \theta \leq \dfrac{\pi}{2}$

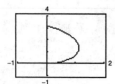

Length ≈ 4.16

47. $s = \displaystyle\int_\alpha^\beta \sqrt{[f(\theta)]^2 + [f'(\theta)]^2}\, d\theta$

$\qquad = \displaystyle\int_\pi^{2\pi} \sqrt{\left(\dfrac{1}{\theta}\right)^2 + \left(\dfrac{-1}{\theta^2}\right)^2}\, d\theta$

$\qquad = \displaystyle\int_\pi^{2\pi} \dfrac{1}{\theta^2}\sqrt{\theta^2 + 1}\, d\theta$

$\qquad = \left[-\dfrac{\sqrt{\theta^2 + 1}}{\theta} + \ln\left|\theta + \sqrt{\theta^2 + 1}\right| \right]_\pi^{2\pi}$

$\qquad = \dfrac{2\sqrt{\pi^2 + 1} - \sqrt{4\pi^2 + 1}}{2\pi} + \ln\left|\dfrac{2\pi + \sqrt{4\pi^2 + 1}}{\pi + \sqrt{\pi^2 + 1}}\right|$

$\qquad \approx 0.7112$

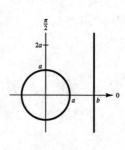

49. $r = \sin(3\cos\theta), 0 \leq \theta \leq \pi$

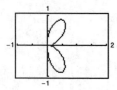

Length ≈ 4.39

51. $r = 2\cos\theta$

$\qquad r' = -2\sin\theta$

$\qquad S = 2\pi \displaystyle\int_0^{\pi/2} 2\cos\theta \sin\theta \sqrt{4\cos^2\theta + 4\sin^2\theta}\, d\theta$

$\qquad = 8\pi \displaystyle\int_0^{\pi/2} \sin\theta\cos\theta\, d\theta = \left[4\pi\sin^2\theta\right]_0^{\pi/2} = 4\pi$

53. $S = 2\pi \displaystyle\int_\alpha^\beta f(\theta)\cos\theta \sqrt{[f(\theta)]^2 + [f'(\theta)]^2}\, d\theta$

$\qquad = 2\pi \displaystyle\int_0^{\pi/2} e^{a\theta}(\cos\theta)\sqrt{(e^{a\theta})^2 + (ae^{a\theta})^2}\, d\theta$

$\qquad = 2\pi \displaystyle\int_0^{\pi/2} \cos\theta e^{a\theta}\sqrt{e^{2a\theta}(1 + a^2)}\, d\theta$

$\qquad = 2\pi\sqrt{1 + a^2} \displaystyle\int_0^{\pi/2} \cos\theta e^{2a\theta}\, d\theta$

$\qquad = 2\pi\sqrt{1 + a^2}\left[\dfrac{e^{2a\theta}}{4a^2 + 1}(2a\cos\theta + \sin\theta) \right]_0^{\pi/2}$ (Integration by Parts)

$\qquad = \dfrac{2\pi\sqrt{1 + a^2}}{4a^2 + 1}(e^{\pi a} - 2a)$

55. $r = 4\cos 2\theta$

$\qquad r' = -8\sin 2\theta$

$\qquad S = 2\pi \displaystyle\int_0^{\pi/4} 4\cos 2\theta \sin\theta\sqrt{16\cos^2 2\theta + 64\sin^2 2\theta}\, d\theta = 32\pi \displaystyle\int_0^{\pi/4} \cos 2\theta \sin\theta\sqrt{\cos^2 2\theta + 4\sin^2 2\theta}\, d\theta \approx 21.87$

57. Revolve $r = a$ about the line $r = b\sec\theta$ where $b > a > 0$.

$\qquad f(\theta) = a$

$\qquad f'(\theta) = 0$

$\qquad S = 2\pi \displaystyle\int_0^{2\pi} [b - a\cos\theta]\sqrt{a^2 + 0^2}\, d\theta$

$\qquad = 2\pi a\left[b\theta - a\sin\theta \right]_0^{2\pi}$

$\qquad = 2\pi a(2\pi b) = 4\pi^2 ab$

59. $r = 8 \cos \theta, 0 \le \theta \le \pi$

(a) $A = \dfrac{1}{2} \int_0^\pi r^2 \, d\theta = \dfrac{1}{2} \int_0^\pi 64 \cos^2 \theta \, d\theta = 32 \int_0^\pi \dfrac{1 + \cos 2\theta}{2} \, d\theta = 16 \left[\theta + \dfrac{\sin 2\theta}{2} \right]_0^\pi = 16 \pi$

(Area circle $= \pi r^2 = \pi 4^2 = 16\pi$)

(b)

θ	0.2	0.4	0.6	0.8	1.0	1.2	1.4
A	6.32	12.14	17.06	20.80	23.27	24.60	25.08

(c), (d) For $\frac{1}{4}$ of area $(4\pi \approx 12.57)$: 0.42

For $\frac{1}{2}$ of area $(8\pi \approx 25.13)$: 1.57 $(\pi/2)$

For $\frac{3}{4}$ of area $(12\pi \approx 37.70)$: 2.73

(e) No, it does not depend on the radius.

61. False. $f(\theta) = 1$ and $g(\theta) = -1$ have the same graphs.

63. True. The area enclosed by $r = \sin(n\theta)$ is $\pi/2$ and the area enclosed by $r = \sin[(n + 1)\theta]$ is $\pi/4$.

Section 9.6 Polar Equations of Conics and Kepler's Laws

1. $r = \dfrac{2e}{1 + e \cos \theta}$

(a) $e = 1, r = \dfrac{2}{1 + \cos \theta}$, parabola

(b) $e = 0.5, r = \dfrac{1}{1 + 0.5 \cos \theta} = \dfrac{2}{2 + \cos \theta}$, ellipse

(c) $e = 1.5, r = \dfrac{3}{1 + 1.5 \cos \theta} = \dfrac{6}{2 + 3 \cos \theta}$, hyperbola

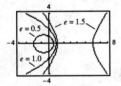

3. $r = \dfrac{2e}{1 - e \sin \theta}$

(a) $e = 1, r = \dfrac{2}{1 - \sin \theta}$, parabola

(b) $e = 0.5, r = \dfrac{1}{1 - 0.5 \sin \theta} = \dfrac{2}{2 - \sin \theta}$, ellipse

(c) $e = 1.5, r = \dfrac{3}{1 - 1.5 \sin \theta} = \dfrac{6}{2 - 3 \sin \theta}$, hyperbola

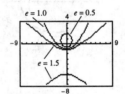

5. $r = \dfrac{4}{1 + e \sin \theta}$

(a)

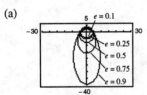

(b)

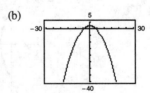

The conic is an ellipse. As $e \to 1^-$, the ellipse becomes more elliptical, and as $e \to 0^+$, it becomes more circular.

The conic is a parabola.

(c)

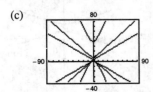

The conic is a hyperbola. As $e \to 1^+$, the hyperbolas opens more slowly, and as $e \to \infty$, they open more rapidly.

7. Parabola; Matches (c)   **9.** Hyperbola; Matches (a)   **11.** Ellipse; Matches (b)

13. From the form of the equation we have

$$r = \frac{-1}{1 - \sin \theta} = \frac{ed}{1 - e \sin \theta}.$$

We can conclude that the graph of the equation is a parabola ($e = 1$). Sketch the left half of the parabola by plotting points in the table. Then using symmetry with respect to $\theta = \pi/2$, sketch the right half.

θ	$-\dfrac{\pi}{2}$	$-\dfrac{\pi}{3}$	$-\dfrac{\pi}{4}$	$-\dfrac{\pi}{6}$	0	$\dfrac{\pi}{6}$	$\dfrac{\pi}{4}$	$\dfrac{\pi}{3}$	$\dfrac{\pi}{2}$
r	-0.50	-0.54	-0.59	-0.67	-1	-2	-3.41	-7.46	Undefined

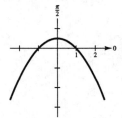

15. $r = \dfrac{6}{2 + \cos \theta}$

$= \dfrac{3}{1 + (1/2) \cos \theta}$

Ellipse since $e = \dfrac{1}{2} < 1$

Vertices: $(2, 0), (6, \pi)$

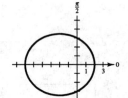

17. $r(2 + \sin \theta) = 4$

$r = \dfrac{4}{2 + \sin \theta}$

$= \dfrac{2}{1 + (1/2) \sin \theta}$

Ellipse since $e = \dfrac{1}{2} < 1$

Vertices: $\left(\dfrac{4}{3}, \dfrac{\pi}{2}\right), \left(4, \dfrac{3\pi}{2}\right)$

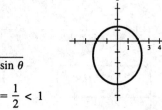

19. $r = \dfrac{5}{-1 + 2 \cos \theta} = \dfrac{-5}{1 - 2 \cos \theta}$

Hyperbola since $e = 2 > 1$

Vertices: $(5, 0), \left(-\dfrac{5}{3}, \pi\right)$

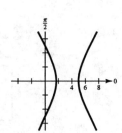

21. To determine the type of conic, rewrite the equation as

$$r = \frac{3}{2 + 6 \sin \theta} = \frac{3/2}{1 + 3 \sin \theta} = \frac{ed}{1 - e \sin \theta}.$$

From this form we can conclude that the graph is a hyperbola with $e = 3$. Since $r = f(\sin \theta)$, its graph is symmetric to $\theta = \pi/2$. Therefore, the entries of the table are solution points of the equation for the right half of the hyperbola. Plot these points and sketch the right half and then sketch the other half by symmetry.

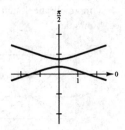

θ	0	$\dfrac{\pi}{6}$	$\dfrac{\pi}{3}$	$\dfrac{\pi}{2}$	$\dfrac{7\pi}{6}$	$\dfrac{4\pi}{3}$	$\dfrac{3\pi}{2}$
r	1.500	0.600	0.417	0.125	-3.000	-0.417	-0.750

23.

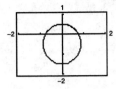

Ellipse

25.

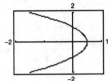

Parabola

27. $r = \dfrac{-1}{1 - \sin\left(\theta - \dfrac{\pi}{4}\right)}$

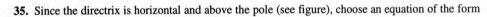

Rotate the graph of

$$r = \dfrac{-1}{1 - \sin\theta}$$

counterclockwise through the angle $\dfrac{\pi}{4}$.

29. $r = \dfrac{6}{2 + \cos\left(\theta + \dfrac{\pi}{6}\right)}$

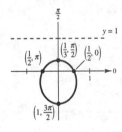

Rotate the graph of

$$r = \dfrac{6}{2 + \cos\theta}$$

clockwise through the angle $\dfrac{\pi}{6}$.

31. Change θ to $\theta + \dfrac{\pi}{4}$: $r = \dfrac{5}{5 + 3\cos\left(\theta + \dfrac{\pi}{4}\right)}$.

33. Parabola

$e = 1, x = -1, d = 1$

$$r = \dfrac{ed}{1 - e\cos\theta} = \dfrac{1}{1 - \cos\theta}$$

35. Since the directrix is horizontal and above the pole (see figure), choose an equation of the form

$$r = \dfrac{ed}{1 + e\sin\theta}.$$

Moreover, since the eccentricity of the ellipse is $\frac{1}{2}$ and the directed distance from the focus to the directrix is $d = 1$, we have the equation

$$r = \dfrac{1/2}{1 + (1/2)\sin\theta} = \dfrac{1}{2 + \sin\theta}.$$

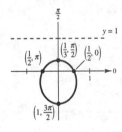

37. Hyperbola

$e = 2, x = 1, d = 1$

$$r = \dfrac{ed}{1 + e\cos\theta} = \dfrac{2}{1 + 2\cos\theta}$$

39. Since the directrix is horizontal and below the pole (see figure), choose an equation of the form

$$r = \dfrac{ed}{1 - e\sin\theta}.$$

Moreover, since the eccentricity of a parabola is $e = 1$ and the distance from the focus to the directrix is $d = 2$, we have the equation

$$r = \dfrac{2}{1 - \sin\theta}.$$

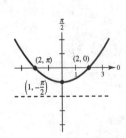

41. Ellipse

Vertices: $(2, 0)$, $(8, \pi)$

$e = \dfrac{3}{5}, d = \dfrac{16}{3}$

$r = \dfrac{ed}{1 + e \cos \theta}$

$ = \dfrac{16/5}{1 + (3/5) \cos \theta}$

$ = \dfrac{16}{5 + 3 \cos \theta}$

43. Hyperbola

Vertices: $\left(1, \dfrac{3\pi}{2}\right), \left(9, \dfrac{3\pi}{2}\right)$

$e = \dfrac{5}{4}, d = \dfrac{9}{5}$

$r = \dfrac{ed}{1 - e \sin \theta}$

$ = \dfrac{9/4}{1 - (5/4) \sin \theta}$

$ = \dfrac{9}{4 - 5 \sin \theta}$

45.

$$\dfrac{x^2}{a^2} + \dfrac{y^2}{b^2} = 1$$

$$x^2 b^2 + y^2 a^2 = a^2 b^2$$

$$b^2 r^2 \cos^2 \theta + a^2 r^2 \sin^2 \theta = a^2 b^2$$

$$r^2 [b^2 \cos^2 \theta + a^2 (1 - \cos^2 \theta)] = a^2 b^2$$

$$r^2 [a^2 + \cos^2 \theta (b^2 - a^2)] = a^2 b^2$$

$$r^2 = \dfrac{a^2 b^2}{a^2 + (b^2 - a^2) \cos^2 \theta} = \dfrac{a^2 b^2}{a^2 - c^2 \cos^2 \theta}$$

$$ = \dfrac{b^2}{1 - (c/a)^2 \cos^2 \theta} = \dfrac{b^2}{1 - e^2 \cos^2 \theta}$$

47. $a = 5, c = 4, e = \dfrac{4}{5}, b = 3$

$$r^2 = \dfrac{9}{1 - (16/25) \cos^2 \theta}$$

49. The polar equation for the hyperbola

$\dfrac{x^2}{a^2} - \dfrac{y^2}{b^2} = 1$ is $r^2 = \dfrac{-b^2}{1 - e^2 \cos^2 \theta}$ (see Exercise 46).

For the hyperbola $\dfrac{x^2}{9} - \dfrac{y^2}{16} = 1$, we have

$$a = 3, b = 4, c = \sqrt{a^2 + b^2} = 5, \text{ and } e = \dfrac{c}{a} = \dfrac{5}{3}.$$

Therefore, $r^2 = \dfrac{-16}{1 - (25/9) \cos^2 \theta} = \dfrac{-144}{9 - 25 \cos^2 \theta}$.

51. $A = 2 \left[\dfrac{1}{2} \displaystyle\int_0^\pi \left(\dfrac{3}{2 - \cos \theta} \right)^2 d\theta \right] = 9 \displaystyle\int_0^\pi \dfrac{1}{(2 - \cos \theta)^2} d\theta \approx 10.88$

53. Vertices: $(126,000, 0)$, $(4119, \pi)$

$a = \dfrac{126,000 + 4119}{2} = 65,059.5, c = 65,059.5 - 4119 = 60,940.5, e = \dfrac{c}{a} = \dfrac{40,627}{43,373}, d = 4119 \left(\dfrac{84,000}{40,627} \right)$

$r = \dfrac{ed}{1 - e \cos \theta} = \dfrac{4119(84,000/43,373)}{1 - (40,627/43,373) \cos \theta} = \dfrac{345,996,000}{43,373 - 40,627 \cos \theta}$

When $\theta = 60°$, $r = \dfrac{345,996,000}{23,059.5} \approx 15,004.49$.

Distance between the surface of the earth and the satellite is $r - 4000 = 11,004.49$ miles.

55. $a = 92.957 \times 10^6$ mi, $e = 0.0167$

$$r = \frac{(1 - e^2)a}{1 - e \cos \theta} = \frac{92,931,075.2223}{1 - 0.0167 \cos \theta}$$

Perihelion distance: $a(1 - e) \approx 91,4$

Aphelion distance: $a(1 + e) \approx 94,509,382$ mi

57. $a = 5.900 \times 10^9$ km, $e = 0.2481$

$$r = \frac{(1 - e^2)a}{1 - e \cos\theta} \approx \frac{5.537 \times 10^9}{1 - 0.2481 \cos \theta}$$

Perihelion distance: $a(1 - e) = 4.436 \times 10^9$ km

Aphelion distance: $a(1 + e) = 7.364 \times 10^9$ km

59. $r = \dfrac{5.537 \times 10^9}{1 - 0.2481 \cos \theta}$

(a) $A = \dfrac{1}{2} \displaystyle\int_0^{\pi/9} \left[\dfrac{5.537 \times 10^9}{1 - 0.2481 \cos \theta} \right]^2 d\theta \approx 9.341 \times 10^{18} \text{ km}^2$

$$248 \left[\frac{\dfrac{1}{2} \displaystyle\int_0^{\pi/9} \left[\dfrac{5.537 \times 10^9}{1 - 0.2481 \cos \theta} \right]^2 d\theta}{\dfrac{1}{2} \displaystyle\int_0^{2\pi} \left[\dfrac{5.537 \times 10^9}{1 - 0.2481 \cos \theta} \right]^2 d\theta} \right] \approx 21.867 \text{ yr}$$

(b) $\dfrac{1}{2} \displaystyle\int_\pi^{\alpha - \pi} \left[\dfrac{5.537 \times 10^9}{1 - 0.2481 \cos \theta} \right]^2 d\theta = 9.341 \times 10^{18}$

$\alpha \approx \pi + 0.8995$ rad

In part (a) the ray swept through a smaller angle to generate the same area since the length of the ray is longer than in part (b).

(c) $r' = \dfrac{(-5.537 \times 10^9)(0.2481 \sin \theta)}{(1 - 0.2481 \cos \theta)^2}$

$$s = \int_0^{\pi/9} \sqrt{\left(\frac{5.537 \times 10^9}{1 - 0.2481 \cos \theta} \right)^2 + \left[\frac{-1.3737297 \times 10^9 \sin \theta}{(1 - 0.2481 \cos \theta)^2} \right]^2} \, d\theta \approx 2.559 \times 10^9 \text{ km}$$

$\dfrac{2.559 \times 10^9 \text{ km}}{21.867 \text{ yr}} \approx 1.17 \times 10^8$ km/yr

$$s = \int_\pi^{\pi + 0.899} \sqrt{\left(\frac{5.537 \times 10^9}{1 - 0.2481 \cos \theta} \right)^2 + \left[\frac{-1.3737297 \times 10^9 \sin \theta}{(1 - 0.2481 \cos \theta)^2} \right]^2} \, d\theta \approx 4.119 \times 10^9 \text{ km}$$

$\dfrac{4.119 \times 10^9 \text{ km}}{21.867 \text{ yr}} \approx 1.88 \times 10^8$ km/yr

61. $r_1 = \dfrac{ed}{1 + \sin \theta}$ and $r_2 = \dfrac{ed}{1 - \sin \theta}$

Points of intersection: $(ed, 0), (ed, \pi)$

$$r_1: \frac{dy}{dx} = \frac{\left(\dfrac{ed}{1 + \sin \theta} \right)(\cos \theta) + \left(\dfrac{-ed \cos \theta}{(1 + \sin \theta)^2} \right)(\sin \theta)}{\left(\dfrac{-ed}{1 + \sin \theta} \right)(\sin \theta) + \left(\dfrac{-ed \cos \theta}{(1 + \sin \theta)^2} \right)(\cos \theta)}$$

At $(ed, 0), \dfrac{dy}{dx} = -1$. At $(ed, \pi), \dfrac{dy}{dx} = 1$.

$$r_2: \frac{dy}{dx} = \frac{\left(\dfrac{ed}{1 - \sin \theta} \right)(\cos \theta) + \left(\dfrac{ed \cos \theta}{(1 - \sin \theta)^2} \right)(\sin \theta)}{\left(\dfrac{-ed}{1 - \sin \theta} \right)(\sin \theta) + \left(\dfrac{ed \cos \theta}{(1 - \sin \theta)^2} \right)(\cos \theta)}$$

At $(ed, 0), \dfrac{dy}{dx} = 1$. At $(ed, \pi), \dfrac{dy}{dx} = -1$.

Therefore, at $(ed, 0)$ we have $m_1 m_2 = (-1)(1) = -1$, and at (ed, π) we have $m_1 m_2 = 1(-1) = -1$. The curves intersect at right angles.

Review Exercises for Chapter 9

1. Matches (d); ellipse

3. Matches (a); parabola

5. $16x^2 + 16y^2 - 16x + 24y - 3 = 0$

$$\left(x^2 - x + \frac{1}{4}\right) + \left(y^2 + \frac{3}{2}y + \frac{9}{16}\right) = \frac{3}{16} + \frac{1}{4} + \frac{9}{16}$$

$$\left(x - \frac{1}{2}\right)^2 + \left(y + \frac{3}{4}\right)^2 = 1$$

Circle

Center: $\left(\frac{1}{2}, -\frac{3}{4}\right)$

Radius: 1

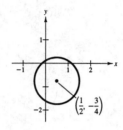

7. $3x^2 - 2y^2 + 24x + 12y + 24 = 0$

$$3(x^2 + 8x + 16) - 2(y^2 - 6y + 9) = -24 + 48 - 18$$

$$\frac{(x + 4)^2}{2} - \frac{(y - 3)^2}{3} = 1$$

Hyperbola

Center: $(-4, 3)$

Vertices: $(-4 \pm \sqrt{2}, 3)$

Asymptotes:

$$y = 3 \pm \sqrt{\tfrac{3}{2}}(x + 4)$$

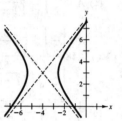

9. $3x^2 + 2y^2 - 12x + 12y + 29 = 0$

Write the standard form of the equation.

$$3x^2 + 2y^2 - 12x + 12y + 29 = 0$$

$$3(x^2 - 4x) + 2(y^2 + 6y) = -29$$

$$3(x^2 - 4x + 4) + 2(y^2 + 6y + 9) = -29 + 12 + 18$$

$$3(x - 2)^2 + 2(y + 3)^2 = 1$$

$$\frac{(x - 2)^2}{(1/\sqrt{3})^2} + \frac{(y + 3)^2}{(1/\sqrt{2})^2} = 1$$

The graph is an ellipse where $h = 2, k = -3, a = 1/\sqrt{2}, b = 1/\sqrt{3}$, and $c = \sqrt{(1/2) - (1/3)} = 1/\sqrt{6}$.

Center, (h, k): $(2, -3)$

Vertices, $(h, k \pm a)$: $\left(2, -3 \pm \frac{\sqrt{2}}{2}\right)$

Foci, $(h, k \pm c)$: $\left(2, -3 \pm \frac{\sqrt{6}}{6}\right)$

11. Since the directrix $(x = -3)$ is vertical, the axis of the parabola is horizontal and its standard form is

$$(y - k)^2 = 4p(x - h).$$

Since the vertex $(0, 2)$ is to the right of the directrix, the parabola opens to the right and $p > 0$. Therefore, $p = 3$ (the distance between the vertex and directrix), $h = 0$, and $k = 2$.

$$(y - 2)^2 = 4(3)(x - 0)$$

$$y^2 - 4y + 4 = 12x$$

$$y^2 - 4y - 12x + 4 = 0$$

13. Vertices: $(-3, 0), (7, 0)$

Foci: $(0, 0), (4, 0)$

Horizontal major axis

Center: $(2, 0)$

$a = 5, c = 2, b = \sqrt{21}$

$$\frac{(x - 2)^2}{25} + \frac{y^2}{21} = 1$$

15. $\dfrac{x^2}{9} + \dfrac{y^2}{4} = 1, a = 3, b = 2, c = \sqrt{5}, e = \dfrac{\sqrt{5}}{3}$

By Example 5 of Section 9.1,

$$C = 12 \int_0^{\pi/2} \sqrt{1 - \left(\dfrac{5}{9}\right) \sin^2 \theta} \, d\theta \approx 15.87.$$

17. $y = x - 2$ has a slope of 1. The perpendicular slope is -1.

$$y = x^2 - 2x + 2$$

$\dfrac{dy}{dx} = 2x - 2 = -1$ when $x = \dfrac{1}{2}$ and $y = \dfrac{5}{4}$.

Perpendicular line: $\qquad y - \dfrac{5}{4} = -1\left(x - \dfrac{1}{2}\right)$

$$4x + 4y - 7 = 0$$

19. (a) The volume of the tank is the area of the ellipse times the length of the tank.

$$\dfrac{x^2}{16} + \dfrac{y^2}{9} = 1 \implies x = \dfrac{4}{3}\sqrt{9 - y^2}$$

Using the symmetry of the ellipse (see figure) and trigonometric substitution to evaluate the integral, the area is

$$A = 4 \int_0^3 \dfrac{4}{3}\sqrt{9 - y^2} \, dy$$

$$= \dfrac{16}{3}\left(\dfrac{1}{2}\right)\left[y\sqrt{9 - y^2} + 9 \arcsin \dfrac{y}{3}\right]_0^3 = 12\pi.$$

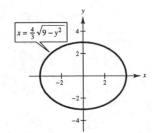

Therefore, the volume of the tank is $16(12\pi) = 192\pi$ cubic feet.

(b) The force against a representative rectangle of length $2x$ is

$$\Delta F = (\text{density})(\text{depth})(\text{area})$$

$$= 62.4(3 - y)(2x \, \Delta y)$$

$$= 62.4(3 - y)(2)\left(\dfrac{4}{3}\sqrt{9 - y^2}\right) \Delta y = 166.4(3 - y)\sqrt{9 - y^2} \, \Delta y.$$

The total force is

$$F = 166.4 \int_{-3}^3 (3 - y)(9 - y^2)^{1/2} \, dy = 166.4(3) \int_{-3}^3 \sqrt{9 - y^2} \, dy - 166.4 \int_{-3}^3 3y\sqrt{9 - y^2} \, dy.$$

The second integral is 0 since the integrand is an odd function and it is evaluated over the interval $[-3, 3]$. The first integral is the area of a semicircle of radius 3. Therefore, $F = 166.4(3)\left(\dfrac{1}{2}\right)(\pi)(3^2) \approx 7057.3$ pounds.

(c) The truck will be carrying $\dfrac{3}{4}$ of its total capacity when the water covers $\dfrac{3}{4}$ of the area of a cross section of the tank. One-half of this area will be below the major axis and $\dfrac{1}{4}$ above the major axis of the ellipse

$$\dfrac{x^2}{16} + \dfrac{y^2}{9} = 1.$$

One-fourth the total area is 3π [see part (a)]. From the figure we have

$$\int_0^h 2\left(\dfrac{4}{3}\sqrt{9 - y^2}\right) dy = 3\pi$$

$$\int_0^y \sqrt{3^2 - y^2} \, dy = \dfrac{9\pi}{8}$$

$$\dfrac{1}{2}\left[y\sqrt{9 - y^2} + 9 \arcsin \dfrac{y}{3}\right]_0^h = \dfrac{9\pi}{8}$$

$$h\sqrt{9 - h^2} + 9 \arcsin \dfrac{h}{3} = \dfrac{9\pi}{4}.$$

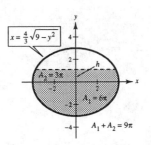

Find h such that $f(h) = \sqrt{9 - h^2} + \arcsin\left(\dfrac{h}{3}\right) - \dfrac{9\pi}{4} - 0$.

Using the root finding capabilities of a graphing utility yields $h \approx 1.212$ and therefore the total height of the water in the tank is $3 + 1.212 = 4.212$ feet.

—CONTINUED—

19. —CONTINUED—

(d) To approximate the surface area of the tank, multiply the perimeter of an elliptical cross section by the length of the tank and add the area of the ends of the tank [see part (a)]. Using rectangular coordinates yields the following improper integral. (Observe that the integrand is undefined when $x = 4$.)

$$\frac{x^2}{16} + \frac{y^2}{9} = 1$$

$$y = \frac{3}{4}\sqrt{16 - x^2}$$

$$\frac{dy}{dx} = \frac{-3x}{4\sqrt{16 - x^2}}$$

$$s = 4\int_0^4 \sqrt{1 + \left(\frac{dy}{dx}\right)^2}\, dx = 4\int_0^4 \sqrt{1 + \frac{9x^2}{16(16 - x^2)}}\, dx$$

If we use parametric equations to represent the ellipse, we have

$$x = 4\cos\theta \quad \text{and} \quad y = 3\sin\theta.$$

Using symmetry and the integration capabilities of a graphing utility we approximate the perimeter of an elliptical cross section of the tank.

$$S = 4\int_0^{\pi/2} \sqrt{\left(\frac{dx}{d\theta}\right)^2 + \left(\frac{dy}{d\theta}\right)^2}\, d\theta = 4\int_0^{\pi/2}\sqrt{(-4\sin\theta)^2 + (3\cos\theta)^2}\, d\theta = 4\int_0^{\pi/2}\sqrt{16\sin^2\theta + 9\cos^2\theta}\, d\theta \approx 22.1$$

Therefore, $S \approx 22.1(16) + 2(12\pi) \approx 429$ square feet.

21. $x = 1 + 4t$

$y = 2 - 3t$

(a) $\dfrac{dy}{dx} = -\dfrac{3}{4}$

No horizontal tangents

(b) $t = \dfrac{x - 1}{4}$

$y = 2 - \dfrac{3}{4}(x - 1) = \dfrac{-3x + 11}{4}$

(c)

23. $x = \dfrac{1}{t}$

$y = 2t + 3$

(a) $\dfrac{dy}{dx} = \dfrac{2}{-1/t^2} = -2t^2$

No horizontal tangents $(t \neq 0)$

(b) $t = \dfrac{1}{x}$

$y = \dfrac{2}{x} + 3$

(c)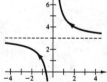

25. $x = \dfrac{1}{2t + 1}$

$y = \dfrac{1}{t^2 - 2t}$

(a) $\dfrac{dy}{dx} = \dfrac{\dfrac{-(2t - 2)}{(t^2 - 2t)^2}}{\dfrac{-2}{(2t + 1)^2}} = \dfrac{(t - 1)(2t + 1)^2}{t^2(t - 2)^2} = 0$ when $t = 1$.

Point of horizontal tangency: $\left(\frac{1}{3}, -1\right)$

(c)

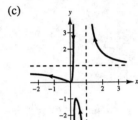

(b) $2t + 1 = \dfrac{1}{x} \Rightarrow t = \dfrac{1}{2}\left(\dfrac{1}{x} - 1\right)$

$y = \dfrac{1}{\dfrac{1}{2}\left(\dfrac{1 - x}{x}\right)\left[\dfrac{1}{2}\left(\dfrac{1 - x}{x}\right) - 2\right]}$

$= \dfrac{4x^2}{(1 - x)^2 - 4x(1 - x)} = \dfrac{4x^2}{(5x - 1)(x - 1)}$

27. (a) Since $x = 3 + 2\cos\theta$ and $y = 2 + 5\sin\theta$, we have

$$\frac{dy}{dx} = \frac{dy/d\theta}{dx/d\theta} = \frac{5\cos\theta}{-2\sin\theta} = -\frac{5}{2}\cot\theta.$$

The points of horizontal tangency occur at $\theta = \pi/2$ and $\theta = 3\pi/2$. Substituting these values of θ into the set of parametric equations yields the points $(3, 7)$ and $(3, -3)$.

(b) To eliminate the parameter, consider the identity $\sin^2\theta + \cos^2\theta = 1$ and write the parametric equations in the form

$$\frac{x - 3}{2} = \cos\theta, \quad \frac{y - 2}{5} = \sin\theta.$$

By squaring and adding these equations, we obtain

$$\frac{(x - 3)^2}{4} + \frac{(y - 2)^2}{25} = \sin^2\theta + \cos^2\theta = 1$$

which is an equation for the ellipse centered at $(3, 2)$ with vertices at $(3, -3)$ and $(3, 7)$.

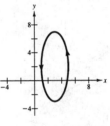

29. $x = \cos^3\theta$

$y = 4\sin^3\theta$

(a) $\dfrac{dy}{dx} = \dfrac{12\sin^2\theta\cos\theta}{3\cos^2\theta(-\sin\theta)} = \dfrac{-4\sin\theta}{\cos\theta} = -4\tan\theta = 0$ when $\theta = 0, \pi$.

But, $\dfrac{dy}{dt} = \dfrac{dx}{dt} = 0$ at $\theta = 0, \pi$. Hence no points of horizontal tangency.

(b) $x^{2/3} + \left(\dfrac{y}{4}\right)^{2/3} = 1$

(c)

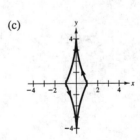

31. $x = \cot\theta$

$y = \sin 2\theta = 2\sin\theta\cos\theta$

(a), (c)

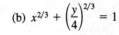

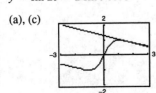

(b) At $\theta = \dfrac{\pi}{6}, \dfrac{dx}{d\theta} = -4, \dfrac{dy}{d\theta} = 1,$ and $\dfrac{dy}{dx} = -\dfrac{1}{4}$

33. $x = 3 + (3 - (-2))t = 3 + 5t$

   $y = 2 + (2 - 6)t = 2 - 4t$

   (other answers possible)

35. Semi-major axis: $a = 4$
   Semi-minor axis: $b = 3$
   Center: $(h, k) = (-3, 4)$

   The parametric equations for an ellipse with horizontal major axis is

   $$x = h + a \cos \theta = -3 + 4 \cos \theta$$
   $$y = k + b \sin \theta = 4 + 3 \sin \theta.$$

37. $x = \cos 3\theta + 5 \cos \theta$

   $y = \sin 3\theta + 5 \sin \theta$

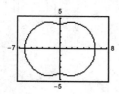

39. $x = a(\theta - \sin \theta)$

   $y = a(1 - \cos \theta)$

   $\cos \theta = \dfrac{a - y}{a}$

   $\theta = \arccos\left(\dfrac{a - y}{a}\right)$

   $x = a \arccos\left(\dfrac{a - y}{a}\right) - a \sin\left[\arccos\left(\dfrac{a - y}{a}\right)\right]$

   $\quad = a \arccos\left(\dfrac{a - y}{a}\right) \pm \sqrt{2ay - y^2}$

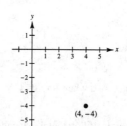

41. $x = r(\cos \theta + \theta \sin \theta)$ $y = r(\sin \theta - \theta \cos \theta)$

   $\dfrac{dx}{d\theta} = r\theta \cos \theta$ $\dfrac{dy}{d\theta} = r\theta \sin \theta$

   $$s = \int_0^\pi \sqrt{\left(\dfrac{dx}{d\theta}\right)^2 + \left(\dfrac{dy}{d\theta}\right)^2}\, d\theta$$

   $$\quad = \int_0^\pi \sqrt{(r\theta \cos \theta)^2 + (r\theta \sin \theta)^2}\, d\theta$$

   $$\quad = r \int_0^\pi \theta\, d\theta = r\left[\dfrac{\theta^2}{2}\right]_0^\pi = \dfrac{1}{2}\pi^2 r$$

43. $(x, y) = (4, -4)$

   $r = \sqrt{4^2 + (-4)^2} = 4\sqrt{2}$

   $\theta = 7\dfrac{\pi}{4}$

   $(r, \theta) = \left(4\sqrt{2}, \dfrac{7\pi}{4}\right), \left(-4\sqrt{2}, \dfrac{3\pi}{4}\right)$

(4, −4)

45. $r = 3 \cos \theta$

   $r^2 = 3r \cos \theta$

   $x^2 + y^2 = 3x$

   $x^2 + y^2 - 3x = 0$

47. $r = -2(1 + \cos \theta)$

   $r^2 = -2r(1 + \cos \theta)$

   $x^2 + y^2 = -2\left(\pm\sqrt{x^2 + y^2}\right) - 2x$

   $(x^2 + y^2 + 2x)^2 = 4(x^2 + y^2)$

49. $r^2 = \cos 2\theta = \cos^2 \theta - \sin^2 \theta$

   $r^4 = r^2 \cos^2 \theta - r^2 \sin^2 \theta$

   $(x^2 + y^2)^2 = x^2 - y^2$

51. First, replace $\cos 2\theta$ by $2\cos^2\theta - 1$ and $\sec\theta$ by $1/\cos\theta$ to obtain

$$r = 4\cos 2\theta \sec\theta = 4(2\cos^2\theta - 1)\frac{1}{\cos\theta}$$

$$r\cos\theta = 8\cos^2\theta - 4.$$

Now since $x = r\cos\theta$ and $r^2 = x^2 + y^2$, we have

$$x = 8\left(\frac{x^2}{r^2}\right) - 4 = \frac{8x^2 - 4(x^2 + y^2)}{x^2 + y^2}$$

$$x^3 + xy^2 = 4x^2 - 4y^2$$

$$(4 + x)y^2 = (x^2)(4 - x)$$

$$y^2 = x^2\left(\frac{4 - x}{4 + x}\right).$$

53. $(x^2 + y^2)^2 = ax^2 y$

$$r^4 = a(r^2\cos^2\theta)(r\sin\theta)$$

$$r = a\cos^2\theta\sin\theta$$

55. Since $r^2 = x^2 + y^2$ and $\theta = \arctan(y/x)$, we have

$$x^2 + y^2 = a^2\left(\arctan\frac{y}{x}\right)^2$$

$$r^2 = a^2\theta^2.$$

57. $r = 4$

Circle of radius 4

Centered at the pole

Symmetric to polar axis,

$\theta = \pi/2$, and pole

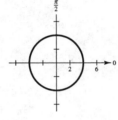

59. $r = -\sec\theta = \dfrac{-1}{\cos\theta}$

$r\cos\theta = -1, x = -1$

Vertical line

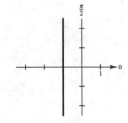

61. $r = -2(1 + \cos\theta)$

Cardioid

Symmetric to
polar axis

θ	0	$\dfrac{\pi}{3}$	$\dfrac{\pi}{2}$	$\dfrac{2\pi}{3}$	π
r	-4	-3	-2	-1	0

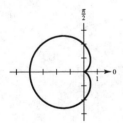

63. $r = 4 - 3\cos\theta$

Limaçon

Symmetric to
polar axis

θ	0	$\dfrac{\pi}{3}$	$\dfrac{\pi}{2}$	$\dfrac{2\pi}{3}$	π
r	1	$\dfrac{5}{2}$	4	$\dfrac{11}{2}$	7

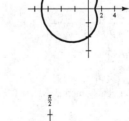

65. $r = -3\cos(2\theta)$

Rose curve with four petals

Symmetric to polar axis, $\theta = \dfrac{\pi}{2}$, and pole

Relative extrema: $(-3, 0), \left(3, \dfrac{\pi}{2}\right), (-3, \pi), \left(3, \dfrac{3\pi}{2}\right)$

Tangents at the pole: $\theta = \dfrac{\pi}{4}, \dfrac{3\pi}{4}$

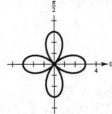

67. Given the polar equation $r^2 = 4 \sin^2 2\theta$, we have $r = \pm 2 \sin 2\theta$.

Type of curve: Rose curve with four petals
Symmetry: With respect to the pole, polar axis, and $\theta = \pi/2$.
Extrema of r: $(\pm 2, \pi/4)$, $(\pm 2, 3\pi/4)$
Tangents at the pole: $\theta = 0, \pi/2$

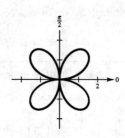

θ	0	$\dfrac{\pi}{12}$	$\dfrac{\pi}{8}$	$\dfrac{\pi}{6}$	$\dfrac{\pi}{4}$	$\dfrac{\pi}{3}$	$\dfrac{3\pi}{8}$	$\dfrac{5\pi}{12}$	$\dfrac{\pi}{2}$
r	0	± 1	$\pm\sqrt{2}$	$\pm\sqrt{3}$	± 2	$\pm\sqrt{3}$	$\pm\sqrt{2}$	± 1	0

69. $r = \dfrac{2}{1 - \sin\theta}$

Parabola

Focus at the pole

Vertex: $\left(1, \dfrac{3\pi}{2}\right)$

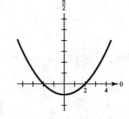

71. $r = \dfrac{3}{\cos[\theta - (\pi/4)]}$

Graph of $r = 3 \sec\theta$ rotated through an angle of $\pi/4$

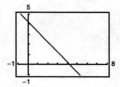

73. $r = 4 \cos 2\theta \sec\theta$

Strophoid

Symmetric to the polar axis

$r \Longrightarrow -\infty$ as $\theta \Longrightarrow \dfrac{\pi^-}{2}$

$r \Longrightarrow -\infty$ as $\theta \Longrightarrow \dfrac{-\pi^+}{2}$

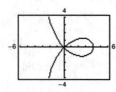

75. (a) The graph has polar axis symmetry and the tangents at the pole are $\theta = \pi/3$ and $\theta = -\pi/3$.

(b) To find the points of vertical or horizontal tangency, note that $f'(\theta) = 2 \sin\theta$ and find dy/dx as follows:

$$\frac{dy}{dx} = \frac{f'(\theta) \sin\theta + f(\theta) \cos\theta}{f'(\theta) \cos\theta - f(\theta) \sin\theta}$$

$$= \frac{2 \sin^2\theta + (1 - 2\cos\theta) \cos\theta}{2 \sin\theta \cos\theta - (1 - 2\cos\theta) \sin\theta}$$

$$= \frac{2 \sin^2\theta + \cos\theta - 2\cos^2\theta}{4 \sin\theta \cos\theta - \sin\theta}$$

$$= \frac{2(1 - \cos^2\theta) + \cos\theta - 2\cos^2\theta}{\sin\theta(4\cos\theta - 1)}$$

$$= \frac{2 + \cos\theta - 4\cos^2\theta}{\sin\theta(4\cos\theta - 1)}$$

The graph has horizontal tangents when $dy/dx = 0$, and this occurs when

$$-4\cos^2\theta + \cos\theta + 2 = 0$$

$$\cos\theta = \frac{-1 \pm \sqrt{1 + 32}}{-8} = \frac{1 \mp \sqrt{33}}{8}.$$

When $\cos\theta = \left(1 \mp \sqrt{33}\right)/8$,

$$r = 1 - 2\left(\frac{1 \mp \sqrt{33}}{8}\right) = \frac{3 \pm \sqrt{33}}{4}.$$

—CONTINUED—

75. **—CONTINUED—**

Therefore, the points of horizontal tangency are

$$\left(\frac{3 - \sqrt{33}}{4}, \arccos\left[\frac{1 + \sqrt{33}}{8}\right]\right) \approx (-0.686, 0.586)$$

$$\left(\frac{3 - \sqrt{33}}{4}, -\arccos\left[\frac{1 + \sqrt{33}}{8}\right]\right) \approx (-0.686, -0.568)$$

$$\left(\frac{3 + \sqrt{33}}{4}, \arccos\left[\frac{1 - \sqrt{33}}{8}\right]\right) \approx (2.186, 2.206)$$

$$\left(\frac{3 + \sqrt{33}}{4}, -\arccos\left[\frac{1 - \sqrt{33}}{8}\right]\right) \approx (2.186, -2.206).$$

The graph has vertical tangents when

$$\sin\theta(4\cos\theta - 1) = 0$$

$$\theta = 0, \pi, \text{ or } \pm\arccos\frac{1}{4}.$$

When $\cos\theta = 1/4$, $r = 1 - 2(1/4) = 1/2$. Thus, the points of vertical tangency are

$$(-1, 0), \ (3, \pi), \ \text{and} \ \left(\frac{1}{2}, \pm\arccos\frac{1}{4}\right) \approx (0.5, \pm1.318).$$

(c) The graph is shown in the figure.

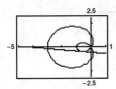

77. $r = 1 + \cos\theta, r = 1 - \cos\theta$

The points $(1, \pi/2)$ and $(1, 3\pi/2)$ are the two points of intersection (other than the pole). The slope of the graph of $r = 1 + \cos\theta$ is

$$m_1 = \frac{dy}{dx} = \frac{r'\sin\theta + r\cos\theta}{r'\cos\theta - r\sin\theta} = \frac{-\sin^2\theta + \cos\theta(1 + \cos\theta)}{-\sin\theta\cos\theta - \sin\theta(1 + \cos\theta)}.$$

At $(1, \pi/2), m_1 = -1/-1 = 1$ and at $(1, 3\pi/2), m_1 = -1/1 = -1$. The slope of the graph of $r = 1 - \cos\theta$ is

$$m_2 = \frac{dy}{dx} = \frac{\sin^2\theta + \cos\theta(1 - \cos\theta)}{\sin\theta\cos\theta - \sin\theta(1 - \cos\theta)}.$$

At $(1, \pi/2), m_2 = 1/-1 = -1$ and at $(1, 3\pi/2), m_2 = 1/1 = 1$. In both cases, $m_1 = -1/m_2$ and we conclude that the graphs are orthogonal at $(1, \pi/2)$ and $(1, 3\pi/2)$.

79. Circle: $r = 3\sin\theta$

$$\frac{dy}{dx} = \frac{3\cos\theta\sin\theta + 3\sin\theta\cos\theta}{3\cos\theta\cos\theta - 3\sin\theta\sin\theta} = \frac{\sin 2\theta}{\cos^2\theta - \sin^2\theta} = \tan 2\theta \text{ at } \theta = \frac{\pi}{6}, \frac{dy}{dx} = \sqrt{3}$$

Limaçon: $r = 4 - 5\sin\theta$

$$\frac{dy}{dx} = \frac{-5\cos\theta\sin\theta + (4 - 5\sin\theta)\cos\theta}{-5\cos\theta\cos\theta - (4 - 5\sin\theta)\sin\theta} \text{ at } \theta = \frac{\pi}{6}, \frac{dy}{dx} = \frac{\sqrt{3}}{9}$$

Let α be the angle between the curves:

$$\tan\alpha = \frac{\sqrt{3} - \left(\sqrt{3}/9\right)}{1 + (1/3)} = \frac{2\sqrt{3}}{3}.$$

Therefore, $\alpha = \arctan\left(\frac{2\sqrt{3}}{3}\right) \approx 49.1°.$

81. $r = 2 + \cos\theta$

$$A = 2\left[\frac{1}{2}\int_0^{\pi} (2 + \cos\theta)^2 \, d\theta\right] \approx 14.14 \quad \left(\frac{9\pi}{2}\right)$$

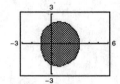

83. $r = \sin\theta \cdot \cos^2\theta$

$$A = 2\left[\frac{1}{2}\int_0^{\pi/2} (\sin\theta\cos^2\theta)^2 \, d\theta\right] \approx 0.10 \quad \left(\frac{\pi}{32}\right)$$

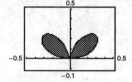

85. $r^2 = 4\sin 2\theta$

$$A = 2\left[\frac{1}{2}\int_0^{\pi/2} 4\sin 2\theta \, d\theta\right] = 4$$

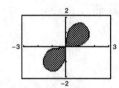

87. The graphs of the polar equations are shown in the figure. To find the area of the common interior of the two curves, we must first find their points of intersection by solving the two equations simultaneously.

$$4\cos\theta = 2$$

$$\cos\theta = \frac{1}{2} \implies \theta = \pm\frac{\pi}{3}$$

Using symmetry and the integration capabilities of a graphing utility, we have

$$A = 2\left[\frac{1}{2}\int_0^{\pi/3} 2^2 \, d\theta + \frac{1}{2}\int_{\pi/3}^{\pi/2} (4\cos\theta)^2 \, d\theta\right] = \frac{8\pi - 6\sqrt{3}}{3} \approx 4.91.$$

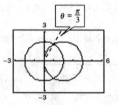

89. $s = 2\displaystyle\int_0^{\pi} \sqrt{a^2(1 - \cos\theta)^2 + a^2\sin^2\theta} \, d\theta$

$$= 2\sqrt{2}\,a\int_0^{\pi} \sqrt{1 - \cos\theta} \, d\theta = 2\sqrt{2}\,a\int_0^{\pi} \frac{\sin\theta}{\sqrt{1 + \cos\theta}} \, d\theta = \left[-4\sqrt{2}\,a(1 + \cos\theta)^{1/2}\right]_0^{\pi} = 8a$$

91. Circle

Center: $\left(5, \dfrac{\pi}{2}\right) = (0, 5)$ in rectangular coordinates

Solution point: $(0, 0)$

$$x^2 + (y - 5)^5 = 25$$

$$x^2 + y^2 - 10y = 0$$

$$r^2 - 10r\sin\theta = 0$$

$$r = 10\sin\theta$$

93. Parabola

Vertex: $(2, \pi)$

Focus: $(0, 0)$

Since the vertex is 2 units to the left of the pole, the parabola opens to the right, is symmetric to the polar axis, the distance between the focus and directrix is $d = 4$, and the eccentricity is $e = 1$. The polar equation of the parabola is

$$r = \frac{ed}{1 \pm e\cos\theta} = \frac{4}{1 - \cos\theta}.$$

95. Ellipse

Vertices: $(5, 0), (1, \pi)$

Focus: $(0, 0)$

$$a = 3, c = 2, e = \frac{2}{3}, d = \frac{5}{2}$$

$$r = \frac{\left(\frac{2}{3}\right)\left(\frac{5}{2}\right)}{1 - \left(\frac{2}{3}\right)\cos\theta} = \frac{5}{3 - 2\cos\theta}$$

C H A P T E R 1 0
Vectors and the Geometry of Space

CHAPTER 10
Vectors and the Geometry of Space

Section 10.1   Vectors in the Plane

Solutions to Odd-Numbered Exercises

1. (a) $\mathbf{v} = \langle 5 - 1, 3 - 1 \rangle = \langle 4, 2 \rangle$

(b)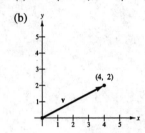

3. (a) $\mathbf{v} = \langle -4 - 3, -2 - (-2) \rangle$

$= \langle -7, 0 \rangle$

(b)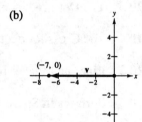

5. (a) The sketch of the directed line is shown in the figure.

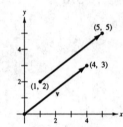

(b) We let $P = (1, 2) = (p_1, p_2)$ and $Q = (5, 5) = (q_1, q_2)$. Then the components of $\mathbf{v} = \langle v_1, v_2 \rangle$ are given by

$$v_1 = q_1 - p_1 = 5 - 1 = 4$$

$$v_2 = q_2 - p_2 = 5 - 2 = 3.$$

Thus, $\mathbf{v} = \langle 4, 3 \rangle$.

(c) The sketch of the vector $\mathbf{v}$ is shown in the figure.

7. (b) $\mathbf{v} = \langle 6 - 10, -1 - 2 \rangle$

$= \langle -4, -3 \rangle$

(a) and (c).

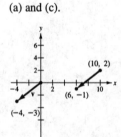

9. (b) $\mathbf{v} = \langle 6 - 6, 6 - 2 \rangle = \langle 0, 4 \rangle$

(a) and (c).

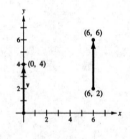

11. (b) $\mathbf{v} = \langle \frac{1}{2} - \frac{3}{2}, 3 - \frac{4}{3} \rangle = \langle -1, \frac{5}{3} \rangle$

(a) and (c).

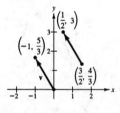

13. (a) $2\mathbf{v} = \langle 4, 6 \rangle$

(b) $-3\mathbf{v} = \langle -6, -9 \rangle$

(c) $\frac{7}{2}\mathbf{v} = \langle 7, \frac{21}{2} \rangle$

(d) $\frac{2}{3}\mathbf{v} = \langle \frac{4}{3}, 2 \rangle$

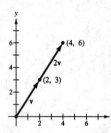

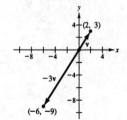

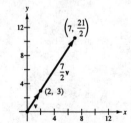

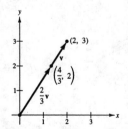

534

15.

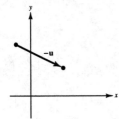

17.

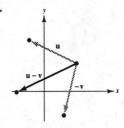

19. $v = \frac{3}{2}(2i - j) = 3i - \frac{3}{2}j$

$\qquad = \langle 3, -\frac{3}{2} \rangle$

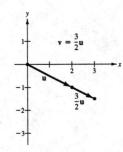

21. Since $u = 2i - j$ and $2w = 2(i + 2j) = 2i + 4j$, we have

$\qquad v = u + 2w$

$\qquad\qquad = (2i - j) + (2i + 4j)$

$\qquad\qquad = (2 + 2)i + (4 - 1)j = 4i + 3j = \langle 4, 3 \rangle.$

Geometrically, this sum is illustrated in the figure.

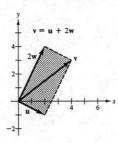

For Exercises 23–27, $au + bw = a(i + 2j) + b(i - j) = (a + b)i + (2a - b)j.$

23. $v = 2i + j.$ Therefore, $a + b = 2, 2a - b = 1.$ Solving simultaneously, we have $a = 1, b = 1.$

25. $v = au + bw$

$\quad 3i = a(i + 2j) + b(i - j) = (a + b)i + (2a - b)j$

Equating coefficients yields

$\qquad a + b = 3 \text{ and } 2a - b = 0.$

Solving the system of equations simultaneously we obtain $a = 1$ and $b = 2.$

27. $v = i + j.$ Therefore, $a + b = 1, 2a - b = 1.$ Solving simultaneously, we have $a = \frac{2}{3}, b = \frac{1}{3}.$

29. $u_1 - 4 = -1$

$\quad u_2 - 2 = 3$

$\qquad u_1 = 3$

$\qquad u_2 = 5$

$\qquad Q = (3, 5)$

31. $\|v\| = \sqrt{16 + 9} = 5$

33. The magnitude (length) of the vector $v = v_1 i + v_2 j$ is

$\qquad \|v\| = \sqrt{v_1^2 + v_2^2}.$

The magnitude of the vector $v = 6i - 5j$ is

$\qquad \|v\| = \sqrt{6^2 + (-5)^2} = \sqrt{61} \approx 7.81.$

35. $\|v\| = \sqrt{0 + 16} = 4$

37. $\|\mathbf{u}\| = \langle 1, -1 \rangle, \mathbf{v} = \langle -1, 2 \rangle$

   (a) $\|\mathbf{u}\| = \sqrt{1 + 1} = \sqrt{2}$

   (b) $\|\mathbf{v}\| = \sqrt{1 + 4} = \sqrt{5}$

   (c) $\mathbf{u} + \mathbf{v} = \langle 0, 1 \rangle$

       $\|\mathbf{u} + \mathbf{v}\| = \sqrt{0 + 1} = 1$

   (d) $\dfrac{\mathbf{u}}{\|\mathbf{u}\|} = \dfrac{1}{\sqrt{2}} \langle 1, -1 \rangle$

       $\left\| \dfrac{\mathbf{u}}{\|\mathbf{u}\|} \right\| = 1$

   (e) $\dfrac{\mathbf{v}}{\|\mathbf{v}\|} = \dfrac{1}{\sqrt{5}} \langle -1, 2 \rangle$

       $\left\| \dfrac{\mathbf{v}}{\|\mathbf{v}\|} \right\| = 1$

   (f) $\dfrac{\mathbf{u} + \mathbf{v}}{\|\mathbf{u} + \mathbf{v}\|} = \langle 0, 1 \rangle$

       $\left\| \dfrac{\mathbf{u} + \mathbf{v}}{\|\mathbf{u} + \mathbf{v}\|} \right\| = 1$

39. $\mathbf{u} = \left\langle 1, \dfrac{1}{2} \right\rangle, \mathbf{v} = \langle 2, 3 \rangle$

   (a) $\|\mathbf{u}\| = \sqrt{1 + \dfrac{1}{4}} = \dfrac{\sqrt{5}}{2}$

   (b) $\|\mathbf{v}\| = \sqrt{4 + 9} = \sqrt{13}$

   (c) $\mathbf{u} + \mathbf{v} = \left\langle 3, \dfrac{7}{2} \right\rangle$

       $\|\mathbf{u} + \mathbf{v}\| = \sqrt{9 + \dfrac{49}{4}} = \dfrac{\sqrt{85}}{2}$

   (d) $\dfrac{\mathbf{u}}{\|\mathbf{u}\|} = \dfrac{2}{\sqrt{5}} \left\langle 1, \dfrac{1}{2} \right\rangle$

       $\left\| \dfrac{\mathbf{u}}{\|\mathbf{u}\|} \right\| = 1$

   (e) $\dfrac{\mathbf{v}}{\|\mathbf{v}\|} = \dfrac{1}{\sqrt{13}} \langle 2, 3 \rangle$

       $\left\| \dfrac{\mathbf{v}}{\|\mathbf{v}\|} \right\| = 1$

   (f) $\dfrac{\mathbf{u} + \mathbf{v}}{\|\mathbf{u} + \mathbf{v}\|} = \dfrac{2}{\sqrt{85}} \left\langle 3, \dfrac{7}{2} \right\rangle$

       $\left\| \dfrac{\mathbf{u} + \mathbf{v}}{\|\mathbf{u} + \mathbf{v}\|} \right\| = 1$

41. $\|\mathbf{u}\| = \sqrt{2^2 + 1^2} = \sqrt{5}$

   $\|\mathbf{v}\| = \sqrt{5^2 + 4^2} = \sqrt{41}$

   Since $\mathbf{u} + \mathbf{v} = \langle 2, 1 \rangle + \langle 5, 4 \rangle = \langle 7, 5 \rangle$, we have

   $\|\mathbf{u} + \mathbf{v}\| = \sqrt{7^2 + 5^2} = \sqrt{74}.$

   Therefore,

       $\|\mathbf{u} + \mathbf{v}\| = \sqrt{74} \approx 8.602 \leq 2.236 + 6.403$

                         $\approx \sqrt{5} + \sqrt{41} = \|\mathbf{u}\| + \|\mathbf{v}\|.$

43. $\mathbf{v} = (\text{magnitude of } \mathbf{v})(\text{unit vector in the direction of } \mathbf{v})$

   $= 4 \left(\dfrac{\mathbf{u}}{\|\mathbf{u}\|} \right)$

   $= 4 \left(\dfrac{\mathbf{u}}{\sqrt{2}} \right) = 2\sqrt{2}\mathbf{u} = \langle 2\sqrt{2}, 2\sqrt{2} \rangle$

45. $\dfrac{\mathbf{u}}{\|\mathbf{u}\|} = \dfrac{1}{2\sqrt{3}} \langle \sqrt{3}, 3 \rangle$

   $2 \left(\dfrac{\mathbf{u}}{\|\mathbf{u}\|} \right) = \dfrac{1}{\sqrt{3}} \langle \sqrt{3}, 3 \rangle$

       $\mathbf{v} = \langle 1, \sqrt{3} \rangle$

47. (a) At $(1, 1)$ the slope of the tangent line is $f'(1) = 3$. Therefore a vector $\mathbf{v} = x\mathbf{i} + y\mathbf{j}$ parallel to the tangent line must have a slope of 3 (see figure) and $y = 3x$. Since $\mathbf{v}$ is a unit vector, $x^2 + y^2 = 1$. Thus,

       $x^2 + (3x)^2 = 1$

           $10x^2 = 1$

            $x = \pm \dfrac{1}{\sqrt{10}}$ and $y = \pm \dfrac{3}{\sqrt{10}}.$

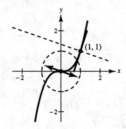

      Finally, we conclude that $\mathbf{v} = \dfrac{1}{\sqrt{10}}\mathbf{i} + \dfrac{3}{\sqrt{10}}\mathbf{j} = \left\langle \dfrac{1}{\sqrt{10}}, \dfrac{3}{\sqrt{10}} \right\rangle$

      or $\mathbf{v} = -\dfrac{1}{\sqrt{10}}\mathbf{i} - \dfrac{3}{\sqrt{10}}\mathbf{j} = \left\langle -\dfrac{1}{\sqrt{10}}, -\dfrac{3}{\sqrt{10}} \right\rangle.$

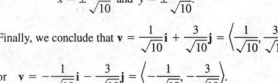

—CONTINUED—

47. **—CONTINUED—**

(b) Similarly, a vector $\mathbf{v} = x\mathbf{i} + y\mathbf{j}$ normal to the tangent line must have a slope of $-\frac{1}{3}$ (see figure), and $x = -3y$. Since $\mathbf{v}$ is a unit vector, $x^2 + y^2 = 1$. Thus,

$$(-3y)^2 + y^2 = 1$$

$$10y^2 = 1$$

$$y = \pm\frac{1}{\sqrt{10}} \text{ and } x = \pm\frac{3}{\sqrt{10}}.$$

Finally, we conclude that $\mathbf{v} = \frac{3}{\sqrt{10}}\mathbf{i} - \frac{1}{\sqrt{10}}\mathbf{j} = \left\langle \frac{3}{\sqrt{10}}, -\frac{1}{\sqrt{10}} \right\rangle$ or $\mathbf{v} = \frac{-3}{\sqrt{10}}\mathbf{i} + \frac{1}{\sqrt{10}}\mathbf{j} = \left\langle -\frac{3}{\sqrt{10}}, \frac{1}{\sqrt{10}} \right\rangle.$

49. $f(x) = \sqrt{25 - x^2}$

$$f'(x) = \frac{-x}{\sqrt{25 - x^2}} = \frac{-3}{4} \text{ at } x = 3.$$

(a) $m = -\frac{3}{4}$. Let $\mathbf{w} = \langle -4, 3 \rangle$, then

$$\frac{\mathbf{w}}{\|\mathbf{w}\|} = \pm\frac{1}{5}\langle -4, 3 \rangle.$$

(b) $m = \frac{4}{3}$. Let $\mathbf{w} = \langle 3, 4 \rangle$, then

$$\frac{\mathbf{w}}{\|\mathbf{w}\|} = \pm\frac{1}{5}\langle 3, 4 \rangle$$

51. $\mathbf{v} = 3[(\cos 0°)\mathbf{i} + (\sin 0°)\mathbf{j}] = 3\mathbf{i} = \langle 3, 0 \rangle$

53. Begin by finding a unit vector $\mathbf{u}$ making an angle of $150°$ with the positive x-axis. Since $\mathbf{u}$ is a unit vector, consider it as the radius of a unit circle as shown in the figure. Therefore, $x = \cos\theta$ and $y = \sin\theta$, and the component form for $\mathbf{u}$ is

$$\mathbf{u} = x\mathbf{i} + y\mathbf{j} = (\cos 150°)\mathbf{i} + (\sin 150°)\mathbf{j} = \left\langle -\frac{\sqrt{3}}{2}, \frac{1}{2} \right\rangle.$$

Since $\mathbf{v} = 2\mathbf{u}$, we have $\mathbf{v} = \left\langle -\sqrt{3}, 1 \right\rangle.$

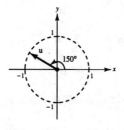

55. $\mathbf{u} = \mathbf{i}$

$$\mathbf{v} = \frac{3\sqrt{2}}{2}\mathbf{i} + \frac{3\sqrt{2}}{2}\mathbf{j}$$

$$\mathbf{u} + \mathbf{v} = \left(\frac{2 + 3\sqrt{2}}{2} \right)\mathbf{i} + \frac{3\sqrt{2}}{2}\mathbf{j}$$

57. $\mathbf{u} = 2(\cos 4)\mathbf{i} + 2(\sin 4)\mathbf{j}$

$$\mathbf{v} = (\cos 2)\mathbf{i} + (\sin 2)\mathbf{j}$$

$$\mathbf{u} + \mathbf{v} = (2\cos 4 + \cos 2)\mathbf{i} + (2\sin 4 + \sin 2)\mathbf{j}$$

59. For any nonzero vector $\mathbf{w}$ making an angle θ with the positive x-axis can be written as

$$\mathbf{w} = \|\mathbf{w}\|(\cos\theta\,\mathbf{i} + \sin\theta\,\mathbf{j}).$$

Since $\|\mathbf{u}\| = 1$ and $\theta = 45°$,

$$\mathbf{u} = 1(\cos 45°\,\mathbf{i} + \sin 45°\,\mathbf{j}) = \frac{\sqrt{2}}{2}\mathbf{i} + \frac{\sqrt{2}}{2}\mathbf{j}.$$

Since $\|\mathbf{u} + \mathbf{v}\| = \sqrt{2}$ and $\theta = 90°$,

$$\mathbf{u} + \mathbf{v} = \sqrt{2}(\cos 90°\mathbf{i} + \sin 90°\,\mathbf{j}) = \sqrt{2}\mathbf{j}.$$

Therefore,

$$\mathbf{v} = (\mathbf{u} + \mathbf{v}) - \mathbf{u}$$

$$= \sqrt{2}\mathbf{j} - \left(\frac{\sqrt{2}}{2}\mathbf{i} + \frac{\sqrt{2}}{2}\mathbf{j} \right) = -\frac{\sqrt{2}}{2}\mathbf{i} + \frac{\sqrt{2}}{2}\mathbf{j}.$$

61. Programs will vary.

63. $\|\mathbf{F}_1\| = 2,\ \theta_{\mathbf{F}_1} = 33°$

$\|\mathbf{F}_2\| = 3,\ \theta_{\mathbf{F}_2} = -125°$

$\|\mathbf{F}_3\| = 2.5,\ \theta_{\mathbf{F}_3} = 110°$

$\|\mathbf{R}\| = \|\mathbf{F}_1 + \mathbf{F}_2 + \mathbf{F}_3\| \approx 1.33$

$\theta_{\mathbf{R}} = \theta_{\mathbf{F}_1 + \mathbf{F}_2 + \mathbf{F}_3} \approx 132.5°$

65. (a) The forces act along the same direction. $\theta = 0°$.

(b) The forces cancel out each other. $\theta = 180°$.

(c) No, the magnitude of the resultant can not be greater than the sum.

67. (a) $180(\cos 30\mathbf{i} + \sin 30\mathbf{j}) + 275\mathbf{i} = 430.88\mathbf{i} + 90\mathbf{j}$

Direction: $\alpha = \arctan\left(\dfrac{90}{430.88}\right) = 0.206(= 11.8°)$

Magnitude: $\sqrt{430.88^2 + 90^2} = 440.18$ newtons

(b) $M = \sqrt{(275 + 180 \cos \theta)^2 + (180 \sin \theta)^2}$

$\alpha = \arctan\left[\dfrac{180 \sin \theta}{275 + 180 \cos \theta}\right]$

(c)

θ	0°	30°	60°	90°	120°	150°	180°
M	455	440.2	396.9	328.7	241.9	149.3	95
α	0°	11.8°	23.1°	33.2°	40.1°	37.1°	0

(d)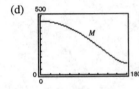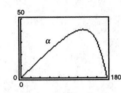

(e) M decreases because the forces change from acting in the same direction to acting in the opposite direction as θ increases from 0° to 180°.

69. Let the three forces be represented by $\mathbf{F}_1$, $\mathbf{F}_2$, and $\mathbf{F}_3$ respectively.

$$\mathbf{F}_1 = 75(\cos 30° \mathbf{i} + \sin 30° \mathbf{j}) = \frac{75\sqrt{3}}{2}\mathbf{i} + \frac{75}{2}\mathbf{j}$$

$$\mathbf{F}_2 = 100(\cos 45° \mathbf{i} + \sin 45° \mathbf{j}) = 50\sqrt{2}\mathbf{i} + 50\sqrt{2}\mathbf{j}$$

$$\mathbf{F}_3 = 125(\cos 120° \mathbf{i} + \sin 120° \mathbf{j}) = -\frac{125}{2}\mathbf{i} + \frac{125\sqrt{3}}{2}\mathbf{j}$$

$$\mathbf{F}_1 + \mathbf{F}_2 + \mathbf{F}_3 = \left(\frac{75\sqrt{3}}{2} + 50\sqrt{2} - \frac{125}{2}\right)\mathbf{i} + \left(\frac{75}{2} + 50\sqrt{2} + \frac{125\sqrt{3}}{2}\right)\mathbf{j}$$

$$\|\mathbf{F}_1 + \mathbf{F}_2 + \mathbf{F}_3\| = \sqrt{\left(\frac{75\sqrt{3}}{2} + 50\sqrt{2} - \frac{125}{2}\right)^2 + \left(\frac{75}{2} + 50\sqrt{2} + \frac{125\sqrt{3}}{2}\right)^2} \approx 228.5 \text{ pounds}$$

$$\theta_{\mathbf{F}_1 + \mathbf{F}_2 + \mathbf{F}_3} = \arctan\left(\dfrac{\dfrac{75\sqrt{3}}{2} + 50\sqrt{2} - \dfrac{125}{2}}{\dfrac{75}{2} + 50\sqrt{2} + \dfrac{125\sqrt{3}}{2}}\right) \approx 71.3°$$

71. $(-4, -1), (6, 5), (10, 3)$

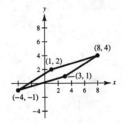 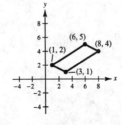 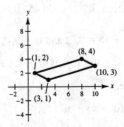

73. (a) Consider the vectors, **T**, **u**, and **v** where **T** is the force in the rope from the pole to the tether ball, **u** is the horizontal force pulling the ball away from the pole, and **v** represents the weight of the ball (see figure).

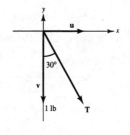

$$\mathbf{u} = \|\mathbf{u}\|\mathbf{i}$$

$$\mathbf{v} = -\mathbf{j}$$

$$\mathbf{T} = \|\mathbf{T}\|(\sin 30°)\mathbf{i} + \|\mathbf{T}\|(-\cos 30°)\mathbf{j}$$

Also, $\mathbf{T} = \mathbf{u} + \mathbf{v} = \|\mathbf{u}\|\mathbf{i} - \mathbf{j}$. Therefore,

$$-1 = \|\mathbf{T}\|(-\cos 30°)$$

$$\text{Tension} = \|\mathbf{T}\| = \frac{2}{\sqrt{3}} \approx 1.1547 \text{ pounds,}$$

and

$$\|\mathbf{u}\| = \|\mathbf{T}\|(\sin 30°) = \left(\frac{2}{\sqrt{3}}\right)\left(\frac{1}{2}\right) \approx 0.5774 \text{ pounds.}$$

(b) Replacing 30° with θ in part (a) yields

$$-1 = \|\mathbf{T}\|(-\cos \theta).$$

$$\text{Tension} = T = \|\mathbf{T}\| = \frac{1}{\cos \theta} = \sec \theta,$$

and

$$\|\mathbf{u}\| = \|\mathbf{T}\| \sin \theta = \sec \theta \sin \theta = \tan \theta.$$

(c)

θ	0°	10°	20°	30°	40°	50°	60°
T	1	1.0154	1.0642	1.1547	1.3054	1.5557	2
$\|\mathbf{u}\|$	0	0.1763	0.3640	0.5774	0.8391	1.1918	1.7321

(d) The graph is shown in the figure.

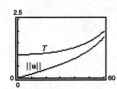

(e) Both are increasing functions for $0° \leq \theta \leq 60°$.

(f) $\displaystyle\lim_{\theta \to \pi/2} T = \lim_{\theta \to \pi/2} \sec \theta = \infty$

$\displaystyle\lim_{\theta \to \pi/2} \|\mathbf{u}\| = \lim_{\theta \to \pi/2} \tan \theta = \infty$

These results are expected. The forces increase without bound as the rope between the pole and the tether ball approaches the horizontal.

75. Horizontal component $= \|\mathbf{v}\| \cos \theta = 1200 \cos 6° \approx 1193.43$ ft/sec

Vertical component $= \|\mathbf{v}\| \sin \theta = 1200 \sin 6° \approx 125.43$ ft/sec

77. Let **u** represent the air speed and direction of the plane, and let **v** represent the speed and direction of the wind.

$$\mathbf{u} = 900[(-\cos 32°)\mathbf{i} + (\sin 32°)\mathbf{j}]$$

$$\mathbf{v} = 100[(\cos 45°)\mathbf{i} + (\sin 45°)\mathbf{j}]$$

$$\mathbf{u} + \mathbf{v} = (-900 \cos 32° + 100 \cos 45°)\mathbf{i} + (900 \sin 32° + 100 \sin 45°)\mathbf{j} \approx -692.53\mathbf{i} + 547.64\mathbf{j}$$

The speed of the plane is

$$\|\mathbf{u} + \mathbf{v}\| = \sqrt{(-692.53)^2 + 547.64^2} \approx 882.90 \text{ kilometers per hour.}$$

The true direction on the plane North of West is

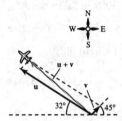

$$\cos \theta = \frac{(\mathbf{u} + \mathbf{v}) \cdot (-\mathbf{i})}{\|\mathbf{u} + \mathbf{v}\|} \approx \frac{692.53}{882.90} \approx 0.7844$$

$$\theta \approx \arccos(0.7844) \approx 38.3° \text{ North of West.}$$

79. $\mathbf{F}_1 = \mathbf{F}_2 + \mathbf{F}_3 = 0$

$$-3600\mathbf{j} + T_2(\cos 35°\mathbf{i} - \sin 35° \,\mathbf{j}) + T_3(\cos 92°\mathbf{i} + \sin 92°\mathbf{j}) = 0$$

$$T_2 \cos 35° + T_3 \cos 92° = 0$$

$$-T_2 \cos 35° + T_3 \sin 92° = 3600$$

$$T_2 = \frac{-T_3 \cos 92°}{\cos 35°} \implies \frac{T_3 \cos 92°}{\cos 35°} \sin 35° + T_3 \sin 92° = 3600 \text{ and } T_3(0.97495) = 3600 \implies T_3 \approx 3692.48$$

Finally, $T_2 = 157.32$

81. Let the triangle have vertices at $(0, 0)$, $(a, 0)$, and (b, c). Let **u** be the vector joining $(0, 0)$ and (b, c), as indicated in the figure. Then **v**, the vector joining the midpoints, is

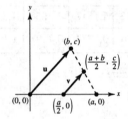

$$\mathbf{v} = \left(\frac{a + b}{2} - \frac{a}{2}\right)\mathbf{i} + \frac{c}{2}\mathbf{j}$$

$$= \frac{b}{2}\mathbf{i} + \frac{c}{2}\mathbf{j} = \frac{1}{2}(b\mathbf{i} + c\mathbf{j}) = \frac{1}{2}\mathbf{u}$$

83. $\mathbf{w} = \|\mathbf{u}\|\mathbf{v} + \|\mathbf{v}\|\mathbf{u}$

$$= \|\mathbf{u}\|[\|\mathbf{v}\| \cos \theta_v\mathbf{i} + \|\mathbf{v}\| \sin \theta_v\mathbf{j}] + \|\mathbf{v}\|[\|\mathbf{u}\| \cos \theta_u\mathbf{i} + \|\mathbf{u}\| \sin \theta_u\mathbf{j}] = \|\mathbf{u}\| \|\mathbf{v}\|[(\cos \theta_u + \cos \theta_v)\mathbf{i} + (\sin \theta_u + \sin \theta_v)\mathbf{j}]$$

$$= 2\|\mathbf{u}\| \|\mathbf{v}\|\left[\cos\left(\frac{\theta_u + \theta_v}{2}\right)\cos\left(\frac{\theta_u - \theta_v}{2}\right)\mathbf{i} + \sin\left(\frac{\theta_u + \theta_v}{2}\right)\cos\left(\frac{\theta_u - \theta_v}{2}\right)\mathbf{j}\right]$$

$$\tan \theta_w = \frac{\sin\left(\dfrac{\theta_u + \theta_v}{2}\right)\cos\left(\dfrac{\theta_u - \theta_v}{2}\right)}{\cos\left(\dfrac{\theta_u + \theta_v}{2}\right)\cos\left(\dfrac{\theta_u - \theta_v}{2}\right)} = \tan\left(\frac{\theta_u + \theta_v}{2}\right)$$

Thus, $\theta_w = (\theta_u + \theta_v)/2$ and **w** bisects the angle between **u** and **v**.

85. True

87. False

$$a = b = 0$$

89. True

Section 10.2   Space Coordinates and Vectors in Space

1.
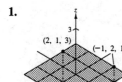

3.
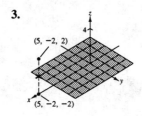

5. $A(2, 3, 4)$

$B(-1, -2, 2)$

7. $x = -3, y = 4, z = 5$: $(-3, 4, 5)$

9. $y = z = 0, x = 10$: $(10, 0, 0)$

11. The z-coordinate is 0.

13. The point (x, y, z) is below the xy-plane, and below either quadrant I or III.

15. The point could be above the xy-plane and thus above quadrants II or IV, or below the xy-plane, and thus below quadrants I or III.

17. $A(0, 0, 0), B(2, 2, 1), C(2, -4, 4)$

$$|AB| = \sqrt{4 + 4 + 1} = 3$$

$$|AC| = \sqrt{4 + 16 + 16} = 6$$

$$|BC| = \sqrt{0 + 36 + 9} = 3\sqrt{5}$$

$$|BC|^2 = |AB|^2 + |AC|^2$$

Right triangle

19. Given the three points $A(1, -3, -2), B(5, -1, 2)$, and $C(-1, 1, 2)$, we have

$$|AB| = \sqrt{(5 - 1)^2 + (-1 + 3)^2 + (2 + 2)^2}$$

$$= \sqrt{16 + 4 + 16} = \sqrt{36} = 6$$

$$|AC| = \sqrt{(-1 - 1)^2 + (1 + 3)^2 + (2 + 2)^2}$$

$$= \sqrt{4 + 16 + 16} = \sqrt{36} = 6$$

$$|BC| = \sqrt{(-1 - 5)^2 + (1 + 1)^2 + (2 - 2)^2}$$

$$= \sqrt{36 + 4} = \sqrt{40} = 2\sqrt{10}.$$

Since two sides have equal lengths, the triangle is isosceles.

21. The z-coordinate is changed by 5 units:

$$(0, 0, 5), (2, 2, 6), (2, -4, 9)$$

23. $\left(\dfrac{5 + (-2)}{2}, \dfrac{-9 + 3}{2}, \dfrac{7 + 3}{2} \right) = \left(\dfrac{3}{2}, -3, 5 \right)$

25. Center: $(0, 2, 5)$

Radius: 2

$$(x - 0)^2 + (y - 2)^2 + (z - 5)^2 = 4$$

$$x^2 + y^2 + z^2 - 4y - 10z + 25 = 0$$

27. The center of the circle is the midpoint of the endpoints of the diameter $(2, 0, 0)$ and $(0, 6, 0)$.

Center: $\left(\dfrac{2 + 0}{2}, \dfrac{0 + 6}{2}, \dfrac{0 + 0}{2} \right) = (1, 3, 0)$

The radius is the distance from the center to one of the endpoints of a diameter.

Radius: $\sqrt{(1 - 2)^2 + (3 - 0)^2 + (0 - 0)^2} = \sqrt{10}$

Since the center is $(x_0, y_0, z_0) = (1, 3, 0)$, we have

$$(x - x_0)^2 + (y - y_0)^2 + (z - z_0)^2 = r^2$$

$$(x - 1)^2 + (y - 3)^2 + (z - 0)^2 = 10.$$

29. Writing the equation in standard form yields

$$x^2 + y^2 + z^2 - 2x + 6y + 8z + 1 = 0$$

$$(x^2 - 2x) + (y^2 + 6y) + (z^2 + 8z) = -1$$

$$(x^2 - 2x + 1) + (y^2 + 6y + 9) + (z^2 + 8z + 16) = -1 + 1 + 9 + 16$$

$$(x - 1)^2 + (y + 3)^2 + (z + 4)^2 = 25.$$

Thus, the sphere is centered at $(1, -3, -4)$ with radius 5.

31. $9x^2 + 9y^2 + 9z^2 - 6x + 18y + 1 = 0$

$$x^2 + y^2 + z^2 - \frac{2}{3}x + 2y + \frac{1}{9} = 0$$

$$\left(x^2 - \frac{2}{3}x + \frac{1}{9}\right) + (y^2 + 2y + 1) + z^2 = -\frac{1}{9} + \frac{1}{9} + 1$$

$$\left(x - \frac{1}{3}\right)^2 + (y + 1)^2 + (z - 0)^2 = 1$$

Center: $\left(\frac{1}{3}, -1, 0\right)$; Radius: 1

33. (a) $\mathbf{v} = (2 - 4)\mathbf{i} + (4 - 2)\mathbf{j} + (3 - 1)\mathbf{k}$

$\qquad = -2\mathbf{i} + 2\mathbf{j} + 2\mathbf{k} = \langle -2, 2, 2 \rangle$

(b)

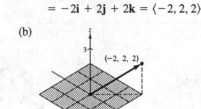

35. (a) $\mathbf{v} = (0 - 3)\mathbf{i} + (3 - 3)\mathbf{j} + (3 - 0)\mathbf{k}$

$\qquad = -3\mathbf{i} + 3\mathbf{k} = \langle -3, 0, 3 \rangle$

(b)

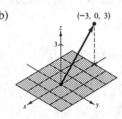

37. (a) and (c)

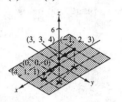

(b) $\mathbf{v} = (3 + 1)\mathbf{i} + (3 - 2)\mathbf{j} + (4 - 3)\mathbf{k}$

$\qquad = 4\mathbf{i} + \mathbf{j} + \mathbf{k} = \langle 4, 1, 1 \rangle$

39. The initial point is $P = (0, 6, 2)$ and the terminal point is $Q = (q_1, q_2, q_3)$. Then

$\qquad \mathbf{v} = \langle 3, -5, 6 \rangle = \langle q_1 - 0, q_2 - 6, q_3 - 2 \rangle$.

Therefore,

$\qquad q_1 - 0 = 3 \quad \Rightarrow q_1 = 3$

$\qquad q_2 - 6 = -5 \Rightarrow q_2 = 1$

$\qquad q_3 - 2 = 6 \quad \Rightarrow q_1 = 8,$

and the coordinates of the terminal point are $(3, 1, 8)$.

41. (a) $2\mathbf{v} = \langle 2, 4, 4 \rangle$ (b) $-\mathbf{v} = \langle -1, -2, -2 \rangle$ (c) $\frac{3}{2}\mathbf{v} = \langle \frac{3}{2}, 3, 3 \rangle$ (d) $0\mathbf{v} = \langle 0, 0, 0 \rangle$

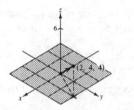 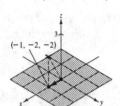 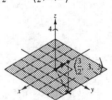 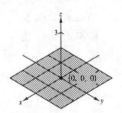

43. $\mathbf{z} = \mathbf{u} - \mathbf{v} = \langle 1, \qquad\qquad 2, 3 \rangle - \langle 2$

45. $\mathbf{z} = 2\mathbf{u} + 4\mathbf{v} - \mathbf{w} = \langle 2, 4, 6 \rangle + \langle 8, 8, -4 \rangle - \langle 4, 0, -4 \rangle = \langle 6, 12, 6 \rangle$

47. $\mathbf{u} = \langle 1, 2, 3 \rangle, \mathbf{w} = \langle 4, 0, -4 \rangle$

$\qquad 2\mathbf{z} - 3\mathbf{u} = \mathbf{w}$

$\qquad\quad 2\mathbf{z} = 3\mathbf{u} + \mathbf{w}$

$\qquad\qquad = 3(\mathbf{i} + 2\mathbf{j} + 3\mathbf{k}) + (4\mathbf{i} - 4\mathbf{k})$

$\qquad\qquad = 3\mathbf{i} + 6\mathbf{j} + 9\mathbf{k} + 4\mathbf{i} - 4\mathbf{k}$

$\qquad\qquad = 7\mathbf{i} + 6\mathbf{j} + 5\mathbf{k}$

$\qquad\quad \mathbf{z} = \frac{7}{2}\mathbf{i} + 3\mathbf{j} + \frac{5}{2}\mathbf{k} = \langle \frac{7}{2}, 3, \frac{5}{2} \rangle$

49. (a) and (b) are parallel since

$\qquad \langle -6, -4, 10 \rangle = -2\langle 3, 2, -5 \rangle$

and

$\qquad \langle 2, \frac{4}{3}, -\frac{10}{3} \rangle = \frac{2}{3}\langle 3, 2, -5 \rangle.$

51. $\mathbf{z} = -3\mathbf{i} + 4\mathbf{j} + 2\mathbf{k}$

    (a) is parallel since $-6\mathbf{i} + 8\mathbf{j} + 4\mathbf{k} = 2\mathbf{z}$.

53. Given the points $A(0, -2, -5)$, $B(3, 4, 4)$, and $C(2, 2, 1)$, we have

$$\overrightarrow{AB} = (3 - 0)\mathbf{i} + (4 + 2)\mathbf{j} + (4 + 5)\mathbf{k} = 3\mathbf{i} + 6\mathbf{j} + 9\mathbf{k}$$

$$\overrightarrow{AC} = (2 - 0)\mathbf{i} + (2 + 2)\mathbf{j} + (1 + 5)\mathbf{k} = 2\mathbf{i} + 4\mathbf{j} + 6\mathbf{k}$$

$$= \tfrac{2}{3}(3\mathbf{i} + 6\mathbf{j} + 9\mathbf{k}) = \tfrac{2}{3}\overrightarrow{AB}.$$

Since $\overrightarrow{AC}$ is a scaler multiple of $\overrightarrow{AB}$, the three points lie on a straight line.

55. $P(1, 2, 4)$, $Q(2, 5, 0)$, $R(0, 1, 5)$

$$\overrightarrow{PQ} = \langle 1, 3, -4 \rangle$$

$$\overrightarrow{PR} = \langle -1, -1, 1 \rangle$$

Since $\overrightarrow{PQ}$ and $\overrightarrow{PR}$ are not parallel, the points are not collinear.

57. $A(2, 9, 1)$, $B(3, 11, 4)$, $C(0, 10, 2)$, $D(1, 12, 5)$

$$\overrightarrow{AB} = \langle 1, 2, 3 \rangle$$

$$\overrightarrow{CD} = \langle 1, 2, 3 \rangle$$

$$\overrightarrow{AC} = \langle -2, 1, 1 \rangle$$

$$\overrightarrow{BD} = \langle -2, 1, 1 \rangle$$

Since $\overrightarrow{AB} = \overrightarrow{CD}$ and $\overrightarrow{AC} = \overrightarrow{BD}$, the given points form the vertices of a parallelogram.

59. $\|\mathbf{v}\| = 0$

61. $\mathbf{v} = \langle 1, -2, -3 \rangle$

$$\|\mathbf{v}\| = \sqrt{1 + 4 + 9} = \sqrt{14}$$

63. $\mathbf{v} = \langle 0, 3, -5 \rangle$

$$\|\mathbf{v}\| = \sqrt{0 + 9 + 25} = \sqrt{34}$$

65. $\mathbf{u} = \langle 2, -1, 2 \rangle$

    (a) Since the magnitude of $\mathbf{u}$ is

$$\|\mathbf{u}\| = \sqrt{2^2 + (-1)^2 + 2^2} = \sqrt{9} = 3,$$

    the unit vector in the direction of $\mathbf{u}$ is

$$\frac{\mathbf{u}}{\|\mathbf{u}\|} = \frac{1}{3}\langle 2, -1, 2 \rangle.$$

    (b) Since the unit vector in the opposite direction is obtained by multiplying by the scalar -1, we have

$$(-1)\frac{\mathbf{u}}{\|\mathbf{u}\|} = -\frac{1}{3}\langle 2, -1, 2 \rangle.$$

67. $\mathbf{u} = \langle 3, 2, -5 \rangle$

$$\|\mathbf{u}\| = \sqrt{9 + 4 + 25} = \sqrt{38}$$

    (a) $\dfrac{\mathbf{u}}{\|\mathbf{u}\|} = \dfrac{1}{\sqrt{38}}\langle 3, 2, -5 \rangle$

    (b) $-\dfrac{\mathbf{u}}{\|\mathbf{u}\|} = -\dfrac{1}{\sqrt{38}}\langle 3, 2, -5 \rangle$

69. Programs will vary.

71. $c\mathbf{v} = \langle 2c, 2c, -c \rangle$

$$\|c\mathbf{v}\| = \sqrt{4c^2 + 4c^2 + c^2} = 5$$

$$9c^2 = 25$$

$$c = \pm\frac{5}{3}$$

73. $\mathbf{v} = 10\dfrac{\mathbf{u}}{\|\mathbf{u}\|} = 10\left\langle 0, \dfrac{1}{\sqrt{2}}, \dfrac{1}{\sqrt{2}} \right\rangle = \left\langle 0, \dfrac{5}{\sqrt{2}}, \dfrac{5}{\sqrt{2}} \right\rangle$

$$= \left\langle 0, \dfrac{5\sqrt{2}}{2}, \dfrac{5\sqrt{2}}{2} \right\rangle$$

75. $\mathbf{u} = \langle 2, -2, 1 \rangle$

$\|\mathbf{u}\| = \sqrt{2^2 + (-2)^2 + 1^2} = \sqrt{9} = 3$

Hence, the unit vector in the direction of $\mathbf{u}$ is

$$\frac{\mathbf{u}}{\|\mathbf{u}\|} = \frac{1}{3}\langle 2, -2, 1 \rangle.$$

The vector $\mathbf{v}$ of length $\frac{3}{2}$ in the direction of $\mathbf{u}$ is $\frac{3}{2}$ times the unit vector in the direction of $\mathbf{u}$. Therefore,

$$\mathbf{v} = \frac{3}{2}\left[\frac{1}{3}\langle 2, -2, 1 \rangle\right] = \frac{1}{2}\langle 2, -2, 1 \rangle = \left\langle 1, -1, \frac{1}{2}\right\rangle.$$

77. $\mathbf{v} = 2[\cos(\pm 30°)\mathbf{j} + \sin(\pm 30°)\mathbf{k}]$

$= \sqrt{3}\mathbf{j} \pm \mathbf{k} = \langle 0, \sqrt{3}, \pm 1 \rangle$

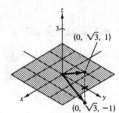

79. Consider the points $P(4, 3, 0)$ and $Q(1, -3, 3)$. By finding the component form of the vector from P to Q, we have

$$\overrightarrow{PQ} = \langle 1 - 4, -3 - 3, 3 - 0 \rangle = \langle -3, -6, 3 \rangle.$$

Let $R = (x, y, z)$ be a point on the line segment two-thirds of the way from P to Q (see figure). Then

$$\overrightarrow{PR} = \langle x - 4, y - 3, z - 0 \rangle = \langle x - 4, y - 3, z \rangle$$

and

$$\frac{2}{3}\overrightarrow{PQ} = \frac{2}{3}\langle -3, -6, 3 \rangle$$

$$= \langle -2, -4, 2 \rangle = \langle x - 4, y - 3, z \rangle = \overrightarrow{PR}.$$

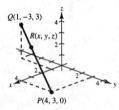

Therefore,

$$x - 4 = -2 \implies x = 2$$

$$y - 3 = -4 \implies y = -1$$

$$z = 2,$$

and the required point is $(2, -1, 2)$.

81. $\mathbf{u} = \mathbf{i} + \mathbf{j}, \mathbf{v} = \mathbf{j} + \mathbf{k}$

(a) See the figure.

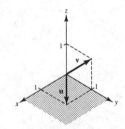

(b) $\mathbf{w} = a(\mathbf{i} + \mathbf{j}) + b(\mathbf{j} + \mathbf{k}) = \mathbf{0}$

$\quad a\mathbf{i} + (a + b)\mathbf{j} + b\mathbf{k} = 0\mathbf{i} + 0\mathbf{j} + 0\mathbf{k}$

Therefore, $a = b = 0$.

(c) $\mathbf{w} = a(\mathbf{i} + \mathbf{j}) + b(\mathbf{j} + \mathbf{k}) = \mathbf{i} + 2\mathbf{j} + \mathbf{k}$

$\quad a\mathbf{i} + (a + b)\mathbf{j} + b\mathbf{k} = \mathbf{i} + 2\mathbf{j} + \mathbf{k}$

Therefore, $a = b = 1$.

(d) $\mathbf{w} = a(\mathbf{i} + \mathbf{j}) + b(\mathbf{j} + \mathbf{k}) = \mathbf{i} + 2\mathbf{j} + 3\mathbf{k}$

$\quad a\mathbf{i} + (a + b)\mathbf{j} + b\mathbf{k} = \mathbf{i} + 2\mathbf{j} + 3\mathbf{k}$

Therefore, $a = 1, b = 3$, and $a + b = 2$, which is a contradiction.

83. (a) From the Pythagorean Theorem, the distance from the center of a disk to the support in the ceiling is $\sqrt{L^2 - 18^2}$. Thus, the coordinates of the points P and Q in the figure are $(0, 18, 0)$ and $\left(0, 0, \sqrt{L^2 - 18^2}\right)$, respectively, and the vector from P to Q is $\left\langle 0, -18, \sqrt{L^2 - 18^2} \right\rangle$. The force $\mathbf{F}$ in one of the supporting wires must be a scalar multiple c of the vector from P to Q, or

$$\mathbf{F} = \left\langle 0, -18c, c\sqrt{L^2 - 18^2} \right\rangle.$$

Since there are three supporting wires, the vertical component of the force vector in one wire must be one-third the weight of the light. Therefore,

$$c\sqrt{L^2 - 18^2} = \frac{24}{3} \implies c = \frac{8}{\sqrt{L^2 - 18^2}} \quad \text{and} \quad \mathbf{F} = \left\langle 0, \frac{-8 \cdot 18}{\sqrt{L^2 - 18^2}}, 8 \right\rangle.$$

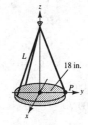

The tension T in each wire is

$$T = \|\mathbf{F}\| = 8\sqrt{\frac{18^2}{L^2 - 18^2} + 1} = \frac{8L}{\sqrt{L^2 - 18^2}}.$$

(b)

L	20	25	30	35	40	45	50
T	18.4	11.5	10.0	9.3	9.0	8.7	8.6

(c) The graph of the tension is shown in the figure.

Vertical asymptote: $L = 18$

Horizontal asymptote: $T = 8$

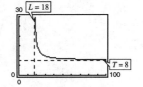

(d) $\displaystyle \lim_{L \to 18^+} \frac{8L}{\sqrt{L^2 - 18^2}} = \infty$

For $L > 0$, we can write $L = \sqrt{L^2}$. Thus, dividing the numerator and denominator by L produces

$$\lim_{L \to \infty} \frac{8L}{\sqrt{L^2 - 18^2}} = \lim_{L \to \infty} \frac{\dfrac{8L}{L}}{\dfrac{\sqrt{L^2 - 18^2}}{\sqrt{L^2}}}$$

$$= \lim_{x \to 0} \frac{8}{\sqrt{1 - \dfrac{18^2}{L^2}}} = 8.$$

(e) Since the tension in the equation must not exceed 10 pounds, solve the following inequality.

$$\frac{8L}{\sqrt{L^2 - 18^2}} \le 10$$

$$8L \le 10\sqrt{L^2 - 18^2}$$

$$64L^2 \le 100(L^2 - 18^2)$$

$$100(18^2) \le 36L^2$$

$$\frac{100(18^2)}{36} \le L^2 \implies 30 \le L$$

Each wire must be at least 30 inches long.

85. Let α be the angle between $\mathbf{v}$ and the coordinate axes.

$$\mathbf{v} = (\cos \alpha)\mathbf{i} + (\cos \alpha)\mathbf{j} + (\cos \alpha)\mathbf{k}$$

$$\|\mathbf{v}\| = \sqrt{3}\cos \alpha = 1$$

$$\cos \alpha = \frac{1}{\sqrt{3}} = \frac{\sqrt{3}}{3}$$

$$\mathbf{v} = \frac{\sqrt{3}}{3}(\mathbf{i} + \mathbf{j} + \mathbf{k}) = \frac{\sqrt{3}}{3}\langle 1, 1, 1 \rangle$$

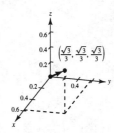

87. $\overrightarrow{AB} = \langle 0, 70, 115 \rangle$, $\mathbf{F}_1 = C_1 \langle 0, 70, 115 \rangle$

$\overrightarrow{AC} = \langle -60, 0, 115 \rangle$, $\mathbf{F}_2 = C_2 \langle -60, 0, 115 \rangle$

$\overrightarrow{AD} = \langle 45, -65, 115 \rangle$, $\mathbf{F}_3 = C_3 \langle 45, -65, 115 \rangle$

$\mathbf{F} = \mathbf{F}_1 + \mathbf{F}_2 + \mathbf{F}_3 = \langle 0, 0, -500 \rangle$

Thus:

$$-60C_2 + 45C_3 = 0$$
$$70C_1 \quad - 65C_3 = 0$$
$$115(C_1 + C_2 + C_3) = -500$$

Solving this system yields $C_1 = -\frac{104}{69}$, $C_2 = -\frac{28}{23}$ and $C_3 = -\frac{112}{69}$. Thus:

$\|\mathbf{F}_1\| \approx 202.919N$

$\|\mathbf{F}_2\| \approx 157.909N$

$\|\mathbf{F}_3\| \approx 226.521N$

89. $d(AP) = 2d(BP)$

$$\sqrt{x^2 + (y+1)^2 + (z-1)^2} = 2\sqrt{(x-1)^2 + (y-2)^2 + z^2}$$

$$x^2 + y^2 + z^2 + 2y - 2z + 2 = 4(x^2 + y^2 + z^2 - 2x - 4y + 5)$$

$$0 = 3x^2 + 3y^2 + 3z^2 - 8x - 18y + 2z + 18$$

$$-6 + \frac{16}{9} + 9 + \frac{1}{9} = \left(x^2 - \frac{8}{3}x + \frac{16}{9}\right) + (y^2 - 6y + 9) + \left(z^2 + \frac{2}{3}z + \frac{1}{9}\right)$$

$$\frac{44}{9} = \left(x - \frac{4}{3}\right)^2 + (y-3)^2 + \left(z + \frac{1}{3}\right)^2$$

Sphere; center: $\left(\frac{4}{3}, 3, -\frac{1}{3}\right)$, radius: $\frac{2\sqrt{11}}{3}$

Section 10.3   The Dot Product of Two Vectors

1. $\mathbf{u} = \langle 3, 4 \rangle$, $\mathbf{v} = \langle 2, -3 \rangle$

(a) $\mathbf{u} \cdot \mathbf{v} = 3(2) + 4(-3) = -6$

(b) $\mathbf{u} \cdot \mathbf{u} = 3(3) + 4(4) = 25$

(c) $\|\mathbf{u}\|^2 = 25$

(d) $(\mathbf{u} \cdot \mathbf{v})\mathbf{v} = -6\langle 2, -3 \rangle = \langle -12, 18 \rangle$

(e) $\mathbf{u} \cdot (2\mathbf{v}) = 2(\mathbf{u} \cdot \mathbf{v}) = 2(-6) = -12$

3. $\mathbf{u} = \langle 2, -3, 4 \rangle$, $\mathbf{v} = \langle 0, 6, 5 \rangle$

(a) For the vectors $\mathbf{u} = \langle u_1, u_2, u_3 \rangle$ and $\mathbf{v} = \langle v_1, v_2, v_3 \rangle$,

$$\mathbf{u} \cdot \mathbf{v} = u_1 v_1 + u_2 v_2 + u_3 v_3$$
$$= 2(0) + (-3)(6) + 4(5) = 2.$$

(b) $\mathbf{u} \cdot \mathbf{u} = 2(2) + (-3)(-3) + 4(4) = 29$

(c) $\|\mathbf{u}\|^2 = 2^2 + (-3)^2 + 4^2 = 29 = \mathbf{u} \cdot \mathbf{u}$

(d) From part (a) we have $\mathbf{u} \cdot \mathbf{v} = 2$. Therefore,

$$(\mathbf{u} \cdot \mathbf{v})\mathbf{v} = 2\mathbf{v} = \langle 0, 12, 10 \rangle.$$

(e) From part (a) we have

$$\mathbf{u} \cdot (2\mathbf{v}) = 2(\mathbf{u} \cdot \mathbf{v}) = 2(2) = 4.$$

5. $\mathbf{u} = 2\mathbf{i} - \mathbf{j} + \mathbf{k}$, $\mathbf{v} = \mathbf{i} - \mathbf{k}$

(a) $\mathbf{u} \cdot \mathbf{v} = 2(1) + (-1)(0) + 1(-1) = 1$

(b) $\mathbf{u} \cdot \mathbf{u} = 2(2) + (-1)(-1) + (1)(1) = 6$

(c) $\|\mathbf{u}\|^2 = 6$

(d) $(\mathbf{u} \cdot \mathbf{v})\mathbf{v} = \mathbf{v} = \mathbf{i} - \mathbf{k}$

(e) $\mathbf{u} \cdot (2\mathbf{v}) = 2(\mathbf{u} \cdot \mathbf{v}) = 2$

7. $\mathbf{u} = \langle 3240, 1450, 2235 \rangle$

$\mathbf{v} = \langle 2.22, 1.85, 3.25 \rangle$

$\mathbf{u} \cdot \mathbf{v} = \$17,139.05$

This gives the total amount that the person earned on his products.

9. $\mathbf{u} \cdot \mathbf{v} = \|\mathbf{u}\| \|\mathbf{v}\| \cos \theta = (8)(5) \cos \dfrac{\pi}{3} = 40\left(\dfrac{1}{2}\right) = 20$

11. $\mathbf{u} = \langle 1, 1 \rangle, \mathbf{v} = \langle 2, -2 \rangle$

$$\cos \theta = \frac{\mathbf{u} \cdot \mathbf{v}}{\|\mathbf{u}\| \|\mathbf{v}\|} = \frac{0}{\sqrt{2}\sqrt{8}} = 0$$

$$\theta = \frac{\pi}{2}$$

13. $\mathbf{u} = 3\mathbf{i} + \mathbf{j}, \mathbf{v} = -2\mathbf{i} + 4\mathbf{j}$

$$\cos \theta = \frac{\mathbf{u} \cdot \mathbf{v}}{\|\mathbf{u}\| \|\mathbf{v}\|} = \frac{-2}{\sqrt{10}\sqrt{20}} = \frac{-1}{5\sqrt{2}}$$

$$\theta = \arccos\left(-\frac{1}{5\sqrt{2}}\right) \approx 98.1°$$

15. $\mathbf{u} = \langle 1, 1, 1 \rangle, \mathbf{v} = \langle 2, 1, -1 \rangle$

$$\cos \theta = \frac{\mathbf{u} \cdot \mathbf{v}}{\|\mathbf{u}\| \|\mathbf{v}\|} = \frac{2}{\sqrt{3}\sqrt{6}} = \frac{\sqrt{2}}{3}$$

$$\theta = \arccos \frac{\sqrt{2}}{3} \approx 61.9°$$

17. $\mathbf{u} = 3\mathbf{i} + 4\mathbf{j}, \mathbf{v} = -2\mathbf{j} + 3\mathbf{k}$

Since

$$\cos \theta = \frac{\mathbf{u} \cdot \mathbf{v}}{\|\mathbf{u}\| \|\mathbf{v}\|},$$

we have

$$\cos \theta = \frac{0 - 8 + 0}{\sqrt{25}\sqrt{13}} = \frac{-8\sqrt{13}}{65}$$

and

$$\theta = \arccos\left(\frac{-8\sqrt{13}}{65}\right) \approx 116.3°.$$

19. Programs will vary.

21. $\mathbf{u} = \langle 4, 0 \rangle, \mathbf{v} = \langle 1, 1 \rangle$

$\mathbf{u} \neq c\mathbf{v} \implies$ not parallel

$\mathbf{u} \cdot \mathbf{v} = 4 \neq 0 \implies$ not orthogonal

Neither

23. $\mathbf{u} = \langle 4, 3 \rangle, \mathbf{v} = \left\langle \frac{1}{2}, -\frac{2}{3} \right\rangle$

$\mathbf{u} \cdot \mathbf{v} = 4\left(\frac{1}{2}\right) + 3\left(-\frac{2}{3}\right) = 2 - 2 = 0$

Therefore, $\mathbf{u}$ and $\mathbf{v}$ are orthogonal.

25. $\mathbf{u} = \mathbf{j} + 6\mathbf{k}, \mathbf{v} = \mathbf{i} - 2\mathbf{j} - \mathbf{k}$

$\mathbf{u} \neq c\mathbf{v} \implies$ not parallel

$\mathbf{u} \cdot \mathbf{v} = -8 \neq 0 \implies$ not orthogonal

Neither

27. $\mathbf{u} = \langle 2, -3, 1 \rangle, \mathbf{v} = \langle -1, -1, -1 \rangle$

$\mathbf{u} \neq c\mathbf{v} \implies$ not parallel

$\mathbf{u} \cdot \mathbf{v} = 0 \implies$ orthogonal

29. In a rhombus, $\|\mathbf{u}\| = \|\mathbf{v}\|$. The diagonals are $\mathbf{u} + \mathbf{v}$ and $\mathbf{u} - \mathbf{v}$.

$$(\mathbf{u} + \mathbf{v}) \cdot (\mathbf{u} - \mathbf{v}) = (\mathbf{u} + \mathbf{v}) \cdot \mathbf{u} - (\mathbf{u} + \mathbf{v}) \cdot \mathbf{v}$$

$$= \mathbf{u} \cdot \mathbf{u} + \mathbf{v} \cdot \mathbf{u} - \mathbf{u} \cdot \mathbf{v} - \mathbf{v} \cdot \mathbf{v}$$

$$= \|\mathbf{u}\|^2 - \|\mathbf{v}\|^2 = 0$$

Therefore, the diagonals are orthogonal.

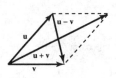

31. Assuming that $\mathbf{u}$ and $\mathbf{v}$ are nonzero vectors and $\mathbf{u} \cdot \mathbf{v} = \|\mathbf{u}\| \|\mathbf{v}\| \cos \theta$, we have the following:

(a) $\mathbf{u} \cdot \mathbf{v} = 0$ implies that $\cos \theta = 0$, or $\theta = \pi/2$.

(b) $\mathbf{u} \cdot \mathbf{v} > 0$ implies that $\cos \theta > 0$, or $0 \leq \theta < \pi/2$.

(c) $\mathbf{u} \cdot \mathbf{v} < 0$ implies that $\cos \theta < 0$, or $\pi/2 < \theta \leq \pi$.

33. $\mathbf{u} = \langle \cos \alpha, \sin \alpha, 0 \rangle$, $\mathbf{v} = \langle \cos \beta, \sin \beta, 0 \rangle$

The angle between $\mathbf{u}$ and $\mathbf{v}$ is $\alpha - \beta$.
(Assuming that $\alpha > \beta$). Also,

$$\cos(\alpha - \beta) = \frac{\mathbf{u} \cdot \mathbf{v}}{\|\mathbf{u}\| \, \|\mathbf{v}\|}$$

$$= \frac{\cos \alpha \cos \beta + \sin \alpha \sin \beta}{(1)(1)}$$

$$= \cos \alpha \cos \beta + \sin \alpha \sin \beta.$$

35. $\mathbf{u} = \mathbf{i} + 2\mathbf{j} + 2\mathbf{k}$

Given a vector $\mathbf{u} = u_1\mathbf{i} + u_2\mathbf{j} + u_3\mathbf{k}$, the direction cosines are

$$\cos \alpha = \frac{u_1}{\|\mathbf{u}\|}, \cos \beta = \frac{u_2}{\|\mathbf{u}\|}, \cos \gamma = \frac{u_3}{\|\mathbf{u}\|}.$$

Therefore, for the given vector, we have

$$\cos \alpha = \frac{1}{\sqrt{1^2 + 2^2 + 2^2}} = \frac{1}{\sqrt{9}} = \frac{1}{3}$$

$$\cos \beta = \frac{2}{\sqrt{1^2 + 2^2 + 2^2}} = \frac{2}{\sqrt{9}} = \frac{2}{3}$$

$$\cos \gamma = \frac{2}{\sqrt{1^2 + 2^2 + 2^2}} = \frac{2}{\sqrt{9}} = \frac{2}{3}.$$

The sum of the squares of the direction cosines is

$$\cos^2 \alpha + \cos^2 \beta + \cos^2 \gamma = \left(\frac{1}{3}\right)^2 + \left(\frac{2}{3}\right)^2 + \left(\frac{2}{3}\right)^2 = 1.$$

37. $\mathbf{u} = \langle 0, 6, -4 \rangle$, $\|\mathbf{u}\| = \sqrt{52} = 2\sqrt{13}$

$$\cos \alpha = 0$$

$$\cos \beta = \frac{3}{\sqrt{13}}$$

$$\cos \gamma = -\frac{2}{\sqrt{13}}$$

$$\cos^2 \alpha + \cos^2 \beta + \cos^2 \gamma = 0 + \frac{9}{13} + \frac{4}{13} = 1$$

39. $\mathbf{F}_1$: $C_1 = \dfrac{50}{\|\mathbf{F}_1\|} \approx 4.3193$

$\mathbf{F}_2$: $C_2 = \dfrac{80}{\|\mathbf{F}_2\|} \approx 5.4183$

$\mathbf{F} = \mathbf{F}_1 + \mathbf{F}_2$

$\approx 4.3193\langle 10, 5, 3 \rangle + 5.4183\langle 12, 7, -5 \rangle$

$= \langle 108.2126, 59.5246, -14.1336 \rangle$

$\|\mathbf{F}\| \approx 124.310 \text{ lb}$

$\cos \alpha \approx \dfrac{108.2126}{\|\mathbf{F}\|} \Longrightarrow \alpha \approx 29.48°$

$\cos \beta \approx \dfrac{59.5246}{\|\mathbf{F}\|} \Longrightarrow \beta \approx 61.39°$

$\cos \gamma \approx \dfrac{-14.1336}{\|\mathbf{F}\|} \Longrightarrow \gamma \approx 96.53°$

41. Let s = length of a side.

$$\mathbf{v} = \langle s, s, s \rangle$$

$$\|\mathbf{v}\| = s\sqrt{3}$$

$$\cos \alpha = \cos \beta = \cos \gamma = \frac{s}{s\sqrt{3}} = \frac{1}{\sqrt{3}}$$

$$\alpha = \beta = \gamma = \arccos\left(\frac{1}{\sqrt{3}}\right) \approx 54.7°$$

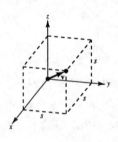

43. $\overrightarrow{OA} = \langle 0, 10, 10 \rangle$

$$\cos \alpha = \frac{0}{\sqrt{0^2 + 10^2 + 10^2}} = 0 \Rightarrow \alpha = 90°$$

$$\cos \beta = \cos \gamma = \frac{10}{\sqrt{0^2 + 10^2 + 10^2}}$$

$$= \frac{1}{\sqrt{2}} \Rightarrow \beta = \gamma = 45°$$

45. $\mathbf{u} = \langle 2, 3 \rangle$, $\mathbf{v} = \langle 5, 1 \rangle$

(a) $\mathbf{w}_1 = \left(\dfrac{\mathbf{u} \cdot \mathbf{v}}{\|\mathbf{v}\|^2}\right)\mathbf{v} = \dfrac{13}{26}\langle 5, 1 \rangle = \left\langle \dfrac{5}{2}, \dfrac{1}{2} \right\rangle$

(b) $\mathbf{w}_2 = \mathbf{u} - \mathbf{w}_1 = \left\langle -\dfrac{1}{2}, \dfrac{5}{2} \right\rangle$

47. (a) The projection of $\mathbf{u} = \langle 2, 1, 2 \rangle$ onto $\mathbf{v} = \langle 0, 3, 4 \rangle$ is

$$\mathbf{w}_1 = \left(\frac{\mathbf{u} \cdot \mathbf{v}}{\|\mathbf{v}\|^2} \right) \mathbf{v}$$

$$= \frac{11}{25} \langle 0, 3, 4 \rangle = \left\langle 0, \frac{33}{25}, \frac{44}{25} \right\rangle.$$

(b) The vector component of $\mathbf{u}$ orthogonal to $\mathbf{v}$ is

$$\mathbf{w}_2 = \mathbf{u} = \mathbf{w}_1 = \left\langle 2, -\frac{8}{25}, \frac{6}{25} \right\rangle.$$

49. Programs will vary.

51. Because $\mathbf{u}$ appears to be perpendicular to $\mathbf{v}$, the projection of $\mathbf{u}$ onto $\mathbf{v}$ is $\mathbf{0}$. Analytically,

$$\text{proj}_\mathbf{v} \mathbf{u} = \frac{\mathbf{u} \cdot \mathbf{v}}{\|\mathbf{v}\|^2} \mathbf{v} = \frac{\langle 2, -3 \rangle \cdot \langle 6, 4 \rangle}{\|\langle 6, 4 \rangle\|^2} \langle 6, 4 \rangle = 0\langle 6, 4 \rangle = \mathbf{0}.$$

53. (a) $\left(\dfrac{\mathbf{u} \cdot \mathbf{v}}{\|\mathbf{v}\|^2} \right) \mathbf{v} = \mathbf{u} \implies \mathbf{u} = c\mathbf{v} \implies \mathbf{u}$ and $\mathbf{v}$ are parallel.

(b) $\left(\dfrac{\mathbf{u} \cdot \mathbf{v}}{\|\mathbf{v}\|^2} \right) \mathbf{v} = \mathbf{0} \implies \mathbf{u} \cdot \mathbf{v} = 0 \implies \mathbf{u}$ and $\mathbf{v}$ are orthogonal.

55. $\mathbf{u} = \dfrac{1}{2}\mathbf{i} - \dfrac{2}{3}\mathbf{j}$. Want $\mathbf{u} \cdot \mathbf{v} = 0$.

$\mathbf{v} = 8\mathbf{i} + 6\mathbf{j}$ and $-\mathbf{v} = -8\mathbf{i} - 6\mathbf{j}$ are orthogonal to $\mathbf{u}$.

57. Let $\mathbf{v} = \langle v_1, v_2, v_3 \rangle$ be a vector orthogonal to $\mathbf{u} = \langle 3, 1, -2 \rangle$. Then

$$\mathbf{u} \cdot \mathbf{v} = 3v_1 + v_2 - 2v_3 = 0.$$

Solving the equation for v_2 produces

$$v_2 = 2v_3 - 3v_1.$$

If we let $v_1 = 1$ and $v_3 = 2$, then $v_2 = 1$. Therefore, a vector orthogonal to $\mathbf{u}$ is $\mathbf{v} = \langle 1, 1, 2 \rangle$. A vector in the opposite direction is $-\mathbf{v} = \langle -1, -1, -2 \rangle$. (Note that the answers are not unique since our choices for v_1 and v_3 in the equation above were arbitrary.)

59. (a) Gravitational force $\mathbf{F} = -32,000\mathbf{j}$

$$\mathbf{v} = \cos 15°\mathbf{i} + \sin 15°\mathbf{j}$$

$$\mathbf{w}_1 = \frac{\mathbf{F} \cdot \mathbf{v}}{\|\mathbf{v}\|^2} \mathbf{v} = (\mathbf{F} \cdot \mathbf{v})\mathbf{v} = (-32,000)(\sin 15°)\mathbf{v} \approx -8282.2(\cos 15°\mathbf{i} + \sin 15°\mathbf{j})$$

$$\|\mathbf{w}_1\| \approx 8282.2 \text{ lb}$$

(b) $\mathbf{w}_2 = \mathbf{F} - \mathbf{w}_1 = -32,000\mathbf{j} + 8282.2(\cos 15°\mathbf{i} + \sin 15°\mathbf{j})$

$$\|\mathbf{w}_2\| \approx 30,909.6 \text{ lb}$$

61. The work done by a constant force $\mathbf{F}$ as its point of application moves along the vector $\overrightarrow{PQ}$ is given by

$$W = \mathbf{F} \cdot \overrightarrow{PQ}.$$

From the figure it follows that

$$\mathbf{F} = 85[(\cos 60°)\mathbf{i} + (\sin 60°)\mathbf{j}]$$

and

$$\overrightarrow{PQ} = 10\mathbf{i}.$$

Therefore,

$$W = 85[(\cos 60°)(10) + (\sin 60°)(0)] = 425 \text{ ft} \cdot \text{lb}.$$

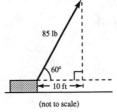

63. $\overrightarrow{PQ} = \langle 4, 7, 5 \rangle$

$\mathbf{v} = \langle 1, 4, 8 \rangle$

$W = \overrightarrow{PQ} \cdot \mathbf{v} = 72$

65. $\|\mathbf{u} - \mathbf{v}\|^2 = (\mathbf{u} - \mathbf{v}) \cdot (\mathbf{u} - \mathbf{v})$

$= (\mathbf{u} - \mathbf{v}) \cdot \mathbf{u} - (\mathbf{u} - \mathbf{v}) \cdot \mathbf{v}$

$= \mathbf{u} \cdot \mathbf{u} - \mathbf{v} \cdot \mathbf{u} - \mathbf{u} \cdot \mathbf{v} + \mathbf{v} \cdot \mathbf{v}$

$= \|\mathbf{u}\|^2 - \mathbf{u} \cdot \mathbf{v} - \mathbf{u} \cdot \mathbf{v} + \|\mathbf{v}\|^2$

$= \|\mathbf{u}\|^2 + \|\mathbf{v}\|^2 - 2\mathbf{u} \cdot \mathbf{v}$

67. $\|\mathbf{u} + \mathbf{v}\|^2 = (\mathbf{u} + \mathbf{v}) \cdot (\mathbf{u} + \mathbf{v})$

$= (\mathbf{u} + \mathbf{v}) \cdot \mathbf{u} + (\mathbf{u} + \mathbf{v}) \cdot \mathbf{v}$

$= \mathbf{u} \cdot \mathbf{u} + \mathbf{v} \cdot \mathbf{u} + \mathbf{u} \cdot \mathbf{v} + \mathbf{v} \cdot \mathbf{v}$

$= \|\mathbf{u}\|^2 + 2\mathbf{u} \cdot \mathbf{v} + \|\mathbf{v}\|^2$

$\leq \|\mathbf{u}\|^2 + 2\|\mathbf{u}\| \|\mathbf{v}\| + \|\mathbf{v}\|^2$ from Exercise 66

$\leq (\|\mathbf{u}\| + \|\mathbf{v}\|)^2$

Therefore, $\|\mathbf{u} + \mathbf{v}\| \leq \|\mathbf{u}\| + \|\mathbf{v}\|$.

Section 10.4   The Cross Product of Two Vectors in Space

1. $\mathbf{j} \times \mathbf{i} = \begin{vmatrix} \mathbf{i} & \mathbf{j} & \mathbf{k} \\ 0 & 1 & 0 \\ 1 & 0 & 0 \end{vmatrix} = -\mathbf{k}$

3. $\mathbf{j} \times \mathbf{k} = \begin{vmatrix} \mathbf{i} & \mathbf{j} & \mathbf{k} \\ 0 & 1 & 0 \\ 0 & 0 & 1 \end{vmatrix} = \mathbf{i}$

5. $\mathbf{i} \times \mathbf{k} = \begin{vmatrix} \mathbf{i} & \mathbf{j} & \mathbf{k} \\ 1 & 0 & 0 \\ 0 & 0 & 1 \end{vmatrix} = -\mathbf{j}$

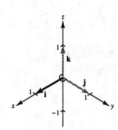

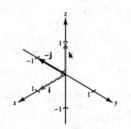

7. $\mathbf{u} = \langle 2, -3, 1 \rangle, \mathbf{v} = \langle 1, -2, 1 \rangle$

$\mathbf{u} \times \mathbf{v} = \begin{vmatrix} \mathbf{i} & \mathbf{j} & \mathbf{k} \\ 2 & -3 & 1 \\ 1 & -2 & 1 \end{vmatrix} = -\mathbf{i} - \mathbf{j} - \mathbf{k} = \langle -1, -1, -1 \rangle$

$\mathbf{u} \cdot (\mathbf{u} \times \mathbf{v}) = 2(-1) + (-3)(-1) + (1)(-1) = 0 \implies \mathbf{u} \perp \mathbf{u} \times \mathbf{v}$

$\mathbf{v} \cdot (\mathbf{u} \times \mathbf{v}) = 1(-1) + (-2)(-1) + (1)(-1) = 0 \implies \mathbf{v} \perp \mathbf{u} \times \mathbf{v}$

9. $\mathbf{u} = \langle 12, -3, 0 \rangle, \mathbf{v} = \langle -2, 5, 0 \rangle$

$\mathbf{u} \times \mathbf{v} = \begin{vmatrix} \mathbf{i} & \mathbf{j} & \mathbf{k} \\ 12 & -3 & 0 \\ -2 & 5 & 0 \end{vmatrix} = 54\mathbf{k} = \langle 0, 0, 54 \rangle$

$\mathbf{u} \cdot (\mathbf{u} \times \mathbf{v}) = 12(0) + (-3)(0) + 0(54)$

$= 0 \implies \mathbf{u} \perp \mathbf{u} \times \mathbf{v}$

$\mathbf{v} \cdot (\mathbf{u} \times \mathbf{v}) = -2(0) + 5(0) + 0(54)$

$= 0 \implies \mathbf{v} \perp \mathbf{u} \times \mathbf{v}$

11. u $= \langle 1, 1, 1 \rangle$, **v** $= \langle 2, 1, -1 \rangle$

The cross product is given by

$$\mathbf{u} \times \mathbf{v} = \begin{vmatrix} \mathbf{i} & \mathbf{j} & \mathbf{k} \\ 1 & 1 & 1 \\ 2 & 1 & -1 \end{vmatrix} = \mathbf{i} \begin{vmatrix} 1 & 1 \\ 1 & -1 \end{vmatrix} - \mathbf{j} \begin{vmatrix} 1 & 1 \\ 2 & -1 \end{vmatrix} + \mathbf{k} \begin{vmatrix} 1 & 1 \\ 2 & 1 \end{vmatrix}$$

$$= (-1 - 1)\mathbf{i} - (-1 - 2)\mathbf{j} + (1 - 2)\mathbf{k}$$

$$= -2\mathbf{i} + 3\mathbf{j} - \mathbf{k} = \langle -2, 3, -1 \rangle.$$

Using the dot product yields

$$\mathbf{u} \cdot (\mathbf{u} \times \mathbf{v}) = (\mathbf{i} + \mathbf{j} + \mathbf{k}) \cdot (-2\mathbf{i} + 3\mathbf{j} - \mathbf{k}) = -2 + 3 - 1 = 0$$

and

$$\mathbf{v} \cdot (\mathbf{u} \times \mathbf{v}) = (2\mathbf{i} + \mathbf{j} - \mathbf{k}) \cdot (-2\mathbf{i} + 3\mathbf{j} - \mathbf{k}) = -4 + 3 + 1 = 0.$$

Therefore $\mathbf{u} \times \mathbf{v}$ is orthogonal to both **u** and **v**.

13.

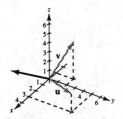

15.

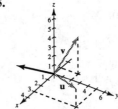

17. u $= \langle 4, -3.5, 7 \rangle$

v $= \langle -1, 8, 4 \rangle$

$$\mathbf{u} \times \mathbf{v} = \left\langle -70, -23, \frac{57}{2} \right\rangle$$

$$\frac{\mathbf{u} \times \mathbf{v}}{\|\mathbf{u} \times \mathbf{v}\|} = \left\langle \frac{-140}{\sqrt{24,965}}, \frac{-46}{\sqrt{24,965}}, \frac{57}{\sqrt{24,965}} \right\rangle$$

19. u $= -3\mathbf{i} + 2\mathbf{j} - 5\mathbf{k}$

$$\mathbf{v} = \frac{1}{2}\mathbf{i} - \frac{3}{4}\mathbf{j} + \frac{1}{10}\mathbf{k}$$

$$\mathbf{u} \times \mathbf{v} = \left\langle -\frac{71}{20}, -\frac{11}{5}, \frac{5}{4} \right\rangle$$

$$\frac{\mathbf{u} \times \mathbf{v}}{\|\mathbf{u} \times \mathbf{v}\|} = \frac{20}{\sqrt{7602}} \left\langle -\frac{71}{20}, -\frac{11}{5}, \frac{5}{4} \right\rangle$$

$$= \left\langle -\frac{71}{\sqrt{7602}}, -\frac{44}{\sqrt{7602}}, \frac{25}{\sqrt{7602}} \right\rangle$$

21. Programs will vary.

23. The area of the parallelogram with adjacent sides $\mathbf{u} = \mathbf{j}$ and $\mathbf{v} = \mathbf{j} + \mathbf{k}$ is the magnitude of their cross product.

$$\mathbf{u} \times \mathbf{v} = \begin{vmatrix} \mathbf{i} & \mathbf{j} & \mathbf{k} \\ 0 & 1 & 0 \\ 0 & 1 & 1 \end{vmatrix} = \mathbf{i}$$

$$A = \|\mathbf{u} \times \mathbf{v}\| = \|\mathbf{i}\| = 1$$

25. u $= \langle 3, 2, -1 \rangle$

v $= \langle 1, 2, 3 \rangle$

$$\mathbf{u} \times \mathbf{v} = \begin{vmatrix} \mathbf{i} & \mathbf{j} & \mathbf{k} \\ 3 & 2 & -1 \\ 1 & 2 & 3 \end{vmatrix} = \langle 8, -10, 4 \rangle$$

$$A = \|\mathbf{u} \times \mathbf{v}\| = \|\langle 8, -10, 4 \rangle\| = \sqrt{180} = 6\sqrt{5}$$

27. If you denote the four given points by $A(1, 1, 1)$, $B(2, 3, 4)$, $C(6, 5, 2)$, and $D(7, 7, 5)$, respectively, the vectors representing the sides of the quadrilateral are

$$\overrightarrow{AB} = (2 - 1)\mathbf{i} + (3 - 1)\mathbf{j} + (4 - 1)\mathbf{k} = \mathbf{i} + 2\mathbf{j} + 3\mathbf{k}$$

$$\overrightarrow{AC} = (6 - 1)\mathbf{i} + (5 - 1)\mathbf{j} + (2 - 1)\mathbf{k} = 5\mathbf{i} + 4\mathbf{j} + \mathbf{k}$$

$$\overrightarrow{CD} = (7 - 6)\mathbf{i} + (7 - 5)\mathbf{j} + (5 - 2)\mathbf{k} = \mathbf{i} + 2\mathbf{j} + 3\mathbf{k}$$

$$\overrightarrow{DB} = (7 - 2)\mathbf{i} + (7 - 3)\mathbf{j} + (5 - 4)\mathbf{k} = 5\mathbf{i} + 4\mathbf{j} + \mathbf{k}$$

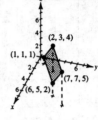

Since $\overrightarrow{AB} = \overrightarrow{CD}$ and $\overrightarrow{AC} = \overrightarrow{DB}$, the quadrilateral is a parallelogram. The area of the parallelogram is given by $\|\overrightarrow{AB} \times \overrightarrow{AC}\|$.

$$\overrightarrow{AB} \times \overrightarrow{AC} = \begin{vmatrix} \mathbf{i} & \mathbf{j} & \mathbf{k} \\ 1 & 2 & 3 \\ 5 & 4 & 1 \end{vmatrix} = \begin{vmatrix} 2 & 3 \\ 4 & 1 \end{vmatrix}\mathbf{i} - \begin{vmatrix} 1 & 3 \\ 5 & 1 \end{vmatrix}\mathbf{j} + \begin{vmatrix} 1 & 2 \\ 5 & 4 \end{vmatrix}\mathbf{k}$$

$$= -10\mathbf{i} + 14\mathbf{j} - 6\mathbf{k} = 2(-5\mathbf{i} + 7\mathbf{j} - 3\mathbf{k})$$

$$\|\overrightarrow{AB} \times \overrightarrow{AC}\| = 2\sqrt{25 + 49 + 9} = 2\sqrt{83}.$$

29. $A(0, 0, 0)$, $B(1, 2, 3)$, $C(-3, 0, 0)$

$$\overrightarrow{AB} = \langle 1, 2, 3 \rangle, \overrightarrow{AC} = \langle -3, 0, 0 \rangle$$

$$\overrightarrow{AB} \times \overrightarrow{AC} = \begin{vmatrix} \mathbf{i} & \mathbf{j} & \mathbf{k} \\ 1 & 2 & 3 \\ -3 & 0 & 0 \end{vmatrix} = -9\mathbf{j} + 6\mathbf{k}$$

$$A = \frac{1}{2}\|\overrightarrow{AB} \times \overrightarrow{AC}\| = \frac{1}{2}\sqrt{117} = \frac{3}{2}\sqrt{13}$$

31. $A(1, 3, 5)$, $B(3, 3, 0)$, $C(-2, 0, 5)$

$$\overrightarrow{AB} = \langle 2, 0, -5 \rangle, \overrightarrow{AC} = \langle -3, -3, 0 \rangle$$

$$\overrightarrow{AB} \times \overrightarrow{AC} = \begin{vmatrix} \mathbf{i} & \mathbf{j} & \mathbf{k} \\ 2 & 0 & -5 \\ -3 & -3 & 0 \end{vmatrix} = -15\mathbf{i} + 15\mathbf{j} - 6\mathbf{k}$$

$$A = \frac{1}{2}\|\overrightarrow{AB} \times \overrightarrow{AC}\| = \frac{1}{2}\sqrt{486} = \frac{9}{2}\sqrt{6}$$

33. $\mathbf{u} \cdot (\mathbf{v} \times \mathbf{w}) = \begin{vmatrix} 1 & 0 & 0 \\ 0 & 1 & 0 \\ 0 & 0 & 1 \end{vmatrix} = 1$

35. $\mathbf{u} = \langle 2, 0, 1 \rangle$, $\mathbf{v} = \langle 0, 3, 0 \rangle$, $\mathbf{w} = \langle 0, 0, 1 \rangle$

$$\mathbf{v} \times \mathbf{w} = \begin{vmatrix} \mathbf{i} & \mathbf{j} & \mathbf{k} \\ 0 & 3 & 0 \\ 0 & 0 & 1 \end{vmatrix}$$

$$= \mathbf{i}\begin{vmatrix} 3 & 0 \\ 0 & 1 \end{vmatrix} - \mathbf{j}\begin{vmatrix} 0 & 0 \\ 0 & 1 \end{vmatrix} + \mathbf{k}\begin{vmatrix} 0 & 3 \\ 0 & 0 \end{vmatrix} = 3\mathbf{i}$$

Therefore, the triple scalar product is

$$\mathbf{u} \cdot (\mathbf{v} \times \mathbf{w}) = 2(3) + 0(0) + 1(0) = 6.$$

37. $\mathbf{u} \cdot (\mathbf{v} \times \mathbf{w}) = \begin{vmatrix} 1 & 1 & 0 \\ 0 & 1 & 1 \\ 1 & 0 & 1 \end{vmatrix} = 2$

$$V = |\mathbf{u} \cdot (\mathbf{v} \times \mathbf{w})| = 2$$

39. The vertices of a parallelepiped are $(0, 0, 0)$, $(3, 0, 0)$, $(0, 5, 1)$ $(3, 5, 1)$, $(2, 0, 5)$, $(5, 0, 5)$, $(2, 5, 6)$, and $(5, 5, 6)$. From the figure, it can be seen that three adjacent sides of the parallelepiped are given by $\mathbf{u}$, $\mathbf{v}$, and $\mathbf{w}$ where

$$\mathbf{u} = 3\mathbf{i}, \mathbf{v} = 5\mathbf{j} + \mathbf{k}, \text{ and } \mathbf{w} = 2\mathbf{i} + 5\mathbf{k}.$$

Since the volume of the parallelepiped is the absolute value of the triple scalar product $\mathbf{u} \cdot (\mathbf{v} \times \mathbf{w})$, we have

$$\mathbf{v} \times \mathbf{w} = \begin{vmatrix} \mathbf{i} & \mathbf{j} & \mathbf{k} \\ 0 & 5 & 1 \\ 2 & 0 & 5 \end{vmatrix} = \begin{vmatrix} 5 & 1 \\ 0 & 5 \end{vmatrix}\mathbf{i} - \begin{vmatrix} 0 & 1 \\ 2 & 5 \end{vmatrix}\mathbf{j} + \begin{vmatrix} 0 & 5 \\ 2 & 0 \end{vmatrix}\mathbf{l}$$

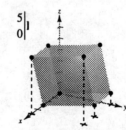

$$= 25\mathbf{i} + 2\mathbf{j} - 10\mathbf{k}$$

$$|\mathbf{u} \cdot (\mathbf{v} \times \mathbf{w})| = |3(25) + 0(2) + 0(-10)| = 75.$$

41. If we represent the 20 pound force as $\mathbf{F} = -20\mathbf{k}$ and the lever of length one-half foot as

$$\mathbf{v} = \tfrac{1}{2}(\cos 40°\,\mathbf{j} + \sin 40°\,\mathbf{k}),$$

then the moment of $\mathbf{F}$ about P is given by

$$\mathbf{M} = \mathbf{v} \times \mathbf{F} = \begin{vmatrix} \mathbf{i} & \mathbf{j} & \mathbf{k} \\ 0 & \tfrac{1}{2}\cos 40° & \tfrac{1}{2}\sin 40° \\ 0 & 0 & -20 \end{vmatrix}$$

$$= -10 \cos 40°\,\mathbf{i}.$$

The torque is the magnitude of this moment. Thus, torque $= \|\mathbf{M}\| = 10 \cos 40° \approx 7.66$ foot-pounds.

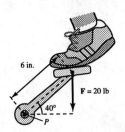

6 in.

$F = 20$ lb

40°

P

43. (a) B is $-\frac{15}{12} = -\frac{5}{4}$ to the left of A, and one foot upwards:

$$\overrightarrow{AB} = \tfrac{-5}{4}\mathbf{j} + \mathbf{k}$$

$$\mathbf{F} = -200(\cos \theta\mathbf{j} + \sin \theta\mathbf{k})$$

(b) $\overrightarrow{AB} \times \mathbf{F} = \begin{vmatrix} \mathbf{i} & \mathbf{j} & \mathbf{k} \\ 0 & -5/4 & 1 \\ 0 & -200\cos\theta & -200\sin\theta \end{vmatrix}$

$$= (250 \sin \theta + 200 \cos \theta)\mathbf{i}$$

$$\|\overrightarrow{AB} \times \mathbf{F}\| = |250 \sin \theta + 200 \cos \theta|$$

$$= 25(10 \sin \theta + 8 \cos \theta)$$

(c) For $\theta = 30°$,

$$\|\overrightarrow{AB} \times \mathbf{F}\| = 25\left(10\left(\tfrac{1}{2}\right) + 8\left(\tfrac{\sqrt{3}}{2}\right)\right)$$

$$= 25\left(5 + 4\sqrt{3}\right) \approx 298.2.$$

(d) If $T = \|\overrightarrow{AB} \times \mathbf{F}\|$,

$$\frac{dT}{d\theta} = 25(10 \cos \theta - 8 \sin \theta) = 0 \implies \tan \theta = \frac{5}{4}$$

$$\implies \theta \approx 51.34°.$$

The vectors are orthogonal.

(e) The zero is $\theta \approx 141.34°$, the angle making $\overrightarrow{AB}$ parallel to $\mathbf{F}$.

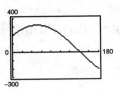

400

0   180

−300

45. $\mathbf{u} = \langle u_1, u_2, u_3 \rangle,\ \mathbf{v} = \langle v_1, v_2, v_3 \rangle,\ \mathbf{w} = \langle w_1, w_2, w_3 \rangle$

$$\mathbf{u} \times (\mathbf{v} + \mathbf{w}) = \begin{vmatrix} \mathbf{i} & \mathbf{j} & \mathbf{k} \\ u_1 & u_2 & u_3 \\ v_1 + w_1 & v_2 + w_2 & v_3 + w_3 \end{vmatrix}$$

$$= [u_2(v_3 + w_3) - u_3(v_2 + w_2)]\mathbf{i} - [u_1(v_3 + w_3) - u_3(v_1 + w_1)]\mathbf{j} + [u_1(v_2 + w_2) - u_2(v_1 + w_1)]\mathbf{k}$$

$$= (u_2 v_3 - u_3 v_2)\mathbf{i} - (u_1 v_3 - u_3 v_1)\mathbf{j} + (u_1 v_2 - u_2 v_1)\mathbf{k} + (u_2 w_3 - u_3 w_2)\mathbf{i} - (u_1 w_3 - u_3 w_1)\mathbf{j} + (u_1 w_2 - u_2 w_1)\mathbf{k}$$

$$= (\mathbf{u} \times \mathbf{v}) + (\mathbf{u} \times \mathbf{w})$$

47. $\mathbf{u} = \langle u_1, u_2, u_3 \rangle$

$$\mathbf{u} \times \mathbf{u} = \begin{vmatrix} \mathbf{i} & \mathbf{j} & \mathbf{k} \\ u_1 & u_2 & u_3 \\ u_1 & u_2 & u_3 \end{vmatrix} = (u_2 u_3 - u_3 u_2)\mathbf{i} - (u_1 u_3 - u_3 u_1)\mathbf{j} + (u_1 u_2 - u_2 u_1)\mathbf{k} = \mathbf{0}$$

49. $\mathbf{u} \times \mathbf{v} = (u_2 v_3 - u_3 v_2)\mathbf{i} - (u_1 v_3 - u_3 v_1)\mathbf{j} + (u_1 v_2 - u_2 v_1)\mathbf{k}$

$(\mathbf{u} \times \mathbf{v}) \cdot \mathbf{u} = (u_2 v_3 - u_3 v_2)u_1 + (u_3 v_1 - u_1 v_3)u_2 + (u_1 v_2 - u_2 v_1)u_3 = 0$

$(\mathbf{u} \times \mathbf{v}) \cdot \mathbf{v} = (u_2 v_3 - u_3 v_2)v_1 + (u_3 v_1 - u_1 v_3)v_2 + (u_1 v_2 - u_2 v_1)v_3 = 0$

Thus, $\mathbf{u} \times \mathbf{v} \perp \mathbf{u}$ and $\mathbf{u} \times \mathbf{v} \perp \mathbf{v}$.

51. $\|\mathbf{u} \times \mathbf{v}\| = \|\mathbf{u}\| \|\mathbf{v}\| \sin \theta$

If $\mathbf{u}$ and $\mathbf{v}$ are orthogonal, $\theta = \pi/2$ and $\sin \theta = 1$. Therefore, $\|\mathbf{u} \times \mathbf{v}\| = \|\mathbf{u}\| \|\mathbf{v}\|$.

53. $\mathbf{u} = \langle u_1, u_2, u_3 \rangle$, $\mathbf{v} = \langle v_1, v_2, v_3 \rangle$, $\mathbf{w} = \langle w_1, w_2, w_3 \rangle$

$\mathbf{u} = u_1 \mathbf{i} + u_2 \mathbf{j} + u_3 \mathbf{k}$

$\mathbf{v} \times \mathbf{w} = (v_2 w_3 - v_3 w_2)\mathbf{i} - (v_1 w_3 - v_3 w_1)\mathbf{j} + (v_1 w_2 - v_2 w_1)\mathbf{k}$

$\mathbf{u} \cdot (\mathbf{v} + \mathbf{w}) = u_1(v_2 w_3 - v_3 w_2) - u_2(v_1 w_3 - v_3 w_1) + u_3(v_1 w_2 - v_2 w_1) = \begin{vmatrix} u_1 & u_2 & u_3 \\ v_1 & v_2 & v_3 \\ w_1 & w_2 & w_3 \end{vmatrix}$

55. Form the vectors for two sides of the triangle, and compute their cross product:

$$\langle x_2 - x_1, y_2 - y_1, z_2 - z_1 \rangle \times \langle x_3 - x_1, y_3 - y_1, z_3 - z_1 \rangle$$

57. Let $\theta = \alpha - \beta$, the angle between $\mathbf{u}$ and $\mathbf{v}$. Then

$$\sin(\alpha - \beta) = \frac{\|\mathbf{u} \times \mathbf{v}\|}{\|\mathbf{u}\| \|\mathbf{v}\|} = \frac{\|\mathbf{v} \times \mathbf{u}\|}{\|\mathbf{u}\| \|\mathbf{v}\|}.$$

For $\mathbf{u} = \langle \cos \alpha, \sin \alpha, 0 \rangle$ and $\mathbf{v} = \langle \cos \beta, \sin \beta, 0 \rangle$, $\|\mathbf{u}\| = \|\mathbf{v}\| = 1$ and

$$\mathbf{v} \times \mathbf{u} = \begin{vmatrix} \mathbf{i} & \mathbf{j} & \mathbf{k} \\ \cos \beta & \sin \beta & 0 \\ \cos \alpha & \sin \alpha & 0 \end{vmatrix} = (\sin \alpha \cos \beta - \cos \alpha \sin \beta)\mathbf{k}.$$

Thus, $\sin(\alpha - \beta) = \|\mathbf{v} \times \mathbf{u}\| = \sin \alpha \cos \beta - \cos \alpha \sin \beta$.

Section 10.5   Lines and Planes in Space

1. $x = 1 + 3t$, $y = 2 - t$, $z = 2 + 5t$

(a)

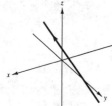

(c) $y = 0$ when $t = 2$. Thus, $x = 7$ and $z = 12$. Point: $(7, 0, 12)$

$x = 0$ when $t = -\frac{1}{3}$. Point: $\left(0, \frac{7}{3}, \frac{1}{3}\right)$

$z = 0$ when $t = -\frac{2}{5}$. Point: $\left(-\frac{1}{5}, \frac{12}{5}, 0\right)$

(b) When $t = 0$ we have $P = (1, 2, 2)$. When $t = 3$ we have $Q = (10, -1, 17)$.

$\overrightarrow{PQ} = \langle 9, -3, 15 \rangle$

The components of the vector and the coefficients of t are proportional since the line is parallel to $\overrightarrow{PQ}$.

3. Point: $(0, 0, 0)$

Direction vector: $\mathbf{v} = \langle 1, 2, 3 \rangle$

Direction numbers: $1, 2, 3$

(a) Parametric: $x = t$, $y = 2t$, $z = 3t$

(b) Symmetric: $x = \frac{y}{2} = \frac{z}{3}$

5. Point: $(-2, 0, 3)$

Direction vector: $\mathbf{v} = \langle 2, 4, -2 \rangle$

Direction numbers: $2, 4, -2$

(a) Parametric: $x = -2 + 2t$, $y = 4t$, $z = 3 - 2t$

(b) Symmetric: $\frac{x + 2}{2} = \frac{y}{4} = \frac{z - 3}{-2}$

7. Point: $(1, 0, 1)$

Direction vector: $\mathbf{v} = 3\mathbf{i} - 2\mathbf{j} + \mathbf{k}$

Direction numbers: $3, -2, 1$

(a) Parametric: $x = 1 + 3t, y = -2t, z = 1 + t$

(b) Symmetric: $\dfrac{x - 1}{3} = \dfrac{y}{-2} = \dfrac{z - 1}{1}$

9. (a) If $A\left(-\frac{2}{3}, \frac{2}{3}, 1\right)$ and $B(5, -3, -2)$, then a direction vector for the line passing through these points is given by

$$\overrightarrow{AB} = \frac{17}{3}\mathbf{i} - \frac{11}{3}\mathbf{j} - 3\mathbf{k} = \frac{1}{3}(17\mathbf{i} - 11\mathbf{j} - 9\mathbf{k})$$

and a set of direction numbers for the line is $a = 17$, $b = -11$, and $c = -9$. Using the form

$$x = x_1 + at, \ y = y_1 + bt, \ z = z_1 + ct$$

with $(x_1, y_1, z_1) = (5, -3, -2)$, a set of parametric equation for the line is

$$x = 5 + 17t, \ y = -3 - 11t, \ z = -2 - 9t.$$

(b) Solving for t in each equation of part (a) yields

$$t = \frac{x - 5}{17} = \frac{y + 3}{-11} = \frac{z + 2}{-9}.$$

Consequently, the symmetric form is

$$\frac{x - 5}{17} = \frac{y + 3}{-11} = \frac{z + 2}{-9}.$$

11. Point: $(2, 3, 4)$

Direction vector: $\mathbf{v} = \mathbf{k}$

Direction numbers: $0, 0, 1$

Parametric: $x = 2, y = 3, z = 4 + t$

13. Point: $(-2, 3, 1)$

Direction vector: $\mathbf{v} = 4\mathbf{i} - \mathbf{k}$

Direction numbers: $4, 0, -1$

Parametric: $x = -2 + 4t, y = 3, z = 1 - t$

Symmetric: $\dfrac{x + 2}{4} = \dfrac{z - 1}{-1}, y = 3$

(a) On line

(b) On line

(c) Not on line $(y \neq 3)$

(d) Not on line $\left(\dfrac{6 + 2}{4} \neq \dfrac{-2 - 1}{-1}\right)$

15. $x = 4t + 2 \qquad x = 2s + 2$

$ y = 3 \qquad\qquad y = 2s + 3$

$ z = -t + 1 \qquad z = s + 1$

At the point of intersection, the coordinates for one line equal the corresponding coordinates for the other line. Thus, we have three equations.

(1) $\qquad 4t + 2 = 2s + 2$

(2) $\qquad\qquad 3 = 2s + 3$

(3) $\qquad -t + 1 = s + 1$

From equation (2) it follows that $s = 0$ and consequently, from equation (3), $t = 0$. Letting $s = t = 0$, equation (1) is satisfied and we can conclude that the two lines intersect. Substituting zero for s or for t, we obtain the point $(2, 3, 1)$.

—CONTINUED—

15. —CONTINUED—

To find the cosine of the angle of intersection, consider the vectors

$$\mathbf{u} = 4\mathbf{i} - \mathbf{k} \quad \text{and} \quad \mathbf{v} = 2\mathbf{i} + 2\mathbf{j} + \mathbf{k}$$

that have the respective directions of the two given lines. Therefore,

$$\cos\theta = \frac{|\mathbf{u} \cdot \mathbf{v}|}{\|\mathbf{u}\|\|\mathbf{v}\|} = \frac{8-1}{\sqrt{17}\sqrt{9}} = \frac{7}{3\sqrt{17}} = \frac{7\sqrt{17}}{51}.$$

17. Writing the equations of the lines in parametric form we have

$$x = 3t \qquad y = 2 - t \qquad z = -1 + t$$

$$x = 1 + 4s \qquad y = -2 + s \qquad z = -3 - 3s.$$

For the coordinates to be equal, $3t = 1 + 4s$ and $2 - t = -2 + s$. Solving this system yields $t = \frac{17}{7}$ and $s = \frac{11}{7}$. When using these values for s and t, the z coordinates are not equal. The lines do not intersect.

19. $x = 2t + 3 \qquad x = -2s + 7$

$y = 5t - 2 \qquad y = s + 8$

$z = -t + 1 \qquad z = 2s - 1$

Point of intersection: $(7, 8, -1)$

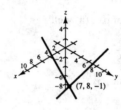

21. $4x - 3y - 6z = 6$

(a) $P = (0, 0, -1), Q = (0, -2, 0), R = (3, 4, -1)$

$\overrightarrow{PQ} = \langle 0, -2, 1 \rangle, \overrightarrow{PR} = \langle 3, 4, 0 \rangle$

(b) $\overrightarrow{PQ} \times \overrightarrow{PR} = \begin{vmatrix} \mathbf{i} & \mathbf{j} & \mathbf{k} \\ 0 & -2 & 1 \\ 3 & 4 & 0 \end{vmatrix} = \langle -4, 3, 6 \rangle$

The components of the cross product are proportional to the coefficients of the variables in the equation. The cross product is parallel to the normal vector.

23. Point: $(2, 1, 2)$

$\mathbf{n} = \mathbf{i} = \langle 1, 0, 0 \rangle$

$1(x - 2) + 0(y - 1) + 0(z - 2) = 0$

$x - 2 = 0$

25. The plane containing the point (x_1, y_1, z_1) and having a normal vector $\mathbf{n} = a\mathbf{i} + b\mathbf{j} + c\mathbf{k}$ can be represented by the equation

$$a(x - x_1) + b(y - y_1) + c(z - z_1) = 0.$$

Point: $(x_1, y_1, z_1) = (3, 2, 2)$

Normal vector: $\mathbf{n} = a\mathbf{i} + b\mathbf{j} + c\mathbf{k} = 2\mathbf{i} + 3\mathbf{j} - \mathbf{k}$

Therefore, the equation of the plane is

$$2(x - 3) + 3(y - 2) - 1(z - 2) = 0$$

$$2x + 3y - z = 10.$$

27. Point: $(0, 0, 6)$

Normal vector: $\mathbf{n} = -\mathbf{i} + \mathbf{j} - 2\mathbf{k}$

$$-1(x - 0) + 1(y - 0) - 2(z - 6) = 0$$

$$-x + y - 2z + 12 = 0$$

$$x - y + 2z = 12$$

29. $(0, 0, 0), (1, 2, 3), (-2, 3, 3)$

To use the form

$$a(x - x_1) + b(y - y_1) + c(z - z_1) = 0$$

we need to know a point in the plane and a vector **n** that is normal to the plane. To obtain a normal vector, use the cross product of the vectors $\mathbf{v}_1$ and $\mathbf{v}_2$ from the point $(0, 0, 0)$ to $(1, 2, 3)$ and to $(-2, 3, 3)$, respectively. We have

$$\mathbf{v}_1 = \mathbf{i} + 2\mathbf{j} + 3\mathbf{k} \quad \text{and} \quad \mathbf{v}_2 = -2\mathbf{i} + 3\mathbf{j} + 3\mathbf{k}.$$

Thus, the vector

$$\mathbf{n} = \mathbf{v}_1 \times \mathbf{v}_2 = \begin{vmatrix} \mathbf{i} & \mathbf{j} & \mathbf{k} \\ 1 & 2 & 3 \\ -2 & 3 & 3 \end{vmatrix} = -3\mathbf{i} - 9\mathbf{j} + 7\mathbf{k}$$

is normal to the given plane. Using the direction numbers from **n** and the point $(0, 0, 0)$ in the plane, we have

$$-3(x - 0) - 9(y - 0) + 7(z - 0) = 0$$
$$3x + 9y - 7z = 0.$$

31. Let **u** be the vector from $(1, 2, 3)$ to $(3, 2, 1)$: $\mathbf{u} = 2\mathbf{i} - 2\mathbf{k}$

Let **v** be the vector from $(1, 2, 3)$ to $(-1, -2, 2)$: $\mathbf{v} = -2\mathbf{i} - 4\mathbf{j} - \mathbf{k}$

Normal vector: $\left(\frac{1}{2}\mathbf{u}\right) \times (-\mathbf{v}) = \begin{vmatrix} \mathbf{i} & \mathbf{j} & \mathbf{k} \\ 1 & 0 & -1 \\ 2 & 4 & 1 \end{vmatrix} = 4\mathbf{i} - 3\mathbf{j} + 4\mathbf{k}$

$$4(x - 1) - 3(y - 2) + 4(z - 3) = 0$$
$$4x - 3y + 4z = 10$$

33. $(1, 2, 3)$, Normal vector: $\mathbf{v} = \mathbf{k}, 1(z - 3) = 0, z = 3$

35. $\dfrac{x - 1}{-2} = y - 4 = z$ and $\dfrac{x - 2}{-3} = \dfrac{y - 1}{4} = \dfrac{z - 2}{-1}$.

Writing the equation of the lines in parametric form, we have

$$x = 1 - 2t \qquad x = 2 - 3s$$
$$y = 4 + t \qquad y = 1 + 4s$$
$$z = t \qquad z = 2 - s$$

To find the point of intersection of the lines, we equate the expressions for the respective values of x, y, and z, and solve the resulting equations. The solution is $t = s = 1$, and the point of intersection is $(-1, 5, 1)$. Since the direction vectors of the lines are

$$\mathbf{v}_1 = -2\mathbf{i} + \mathbf{j} + \mathbf{k} \quad \text{and} \quad \mathbf{v}_2 = -3\mathbf{i} + 4\mathbf{j} - \mathbf{k},$$

the vector **n** normal to the plane is

$$\mathbf{n} = \mathbf{v}_1 \times \mathbf{v}_2 = \begin{vmatrix} \mathbf{i} & \mathbf{j} & \mathbf{k} \\ -2 & 1 & 1 \\ -3 & 4 & -1 \end{vmatrix} = -5(\mathbf{i} + \mathbf{j} + \mathbf{k}).$$

Therefore, the equation of the plane is

$$1(x + 1) + 1(y - 5) + 1(z - 1) = 0$$
$$x + y + z = 5.$$

37. Let **v** be the vector from $(-1, 1, -1)$ to $(2, 2, 1)$, let **n** be a vector normal to the plane $2x - 3y + z = 3$. Then **v** and **n** both lie in the required plane, where

$$\mathbf{v} = 3\mathbf{i} + \mathbf{j} + 2\mathbf{k} \quad \text{and} \quad \mathbf{n} = 2\mathbf{i} - 3\mathbf{j} + \mathbf{k}.$$

The vector

$$\mathbf{v} \times \mathbf{n} = \begin{vmatrix} \mathbf{i} & \mathbf{j} & \mathbf{k} \\ 3 & 1 & 2 \\ 2 & -3 & 1 \end{vmatrix} = 7\mathbf{i} + \mathbf{j} - 11\mathbf{k}$$

is normal to the required plane. Finally, since the point $(2, 2, 1)$ lies in the plane, an equation for the plane is

$$7(x - 2) + 1(y - 2) - 11(z - 1) = 0$$
$$7x + y - 11z = 5.$$

39. Let $\mathbf{u} = \mathbf{i}$ and let $\mathbf{v}$ be the vector from $(1, -2, -1)$ to $(2, 5, 6)$: $\mathbf{v} = \mathbf{i} + 7\mathbf{j} + 7\mathbf{k}$

Since $\mathbf{u}$ and $\mathbf{v}$ both lie in the plane P, the normal vector to P is:

$$\mathbf{u} \times \mathbf{v} = \begin{vmatrix} \mathbf{i} & \mathbf{j} & \mathbf{k} \\ 1 & 0 & 0 \\ 1 & 7 & 7 \end{vmatrix} = -7\mathbf{j} + 7\mathbf{k} = -7(\mathbf{j} - \mathbf{k})$$

$[y - (-2)] - [z - (-1)] = 0$

$y - z = -1$

41. The normal vectors to the planes are

$$\mathbf{n}_1 = \langle 5, -3, 1 \rangle, \mathbf{n}_2 = \langle 1, 4, 7 \rangle, \cos\theta = \frac{|\mathbf{n}_1 \cdot \mathbf{n}_2|}{\|\mathbf{n}_1\| \, \|\mathbf{n}_2\|} = 0.$$

Thus, $\theta = \pi/2$ and the planes are orthogonal.

43. Vectors normal to the planes $x - 3y + 6z = 4$ and $5x + y - z = 4$ are $\mathbf{n}_1 = \langle 1, -3, 6 \rangle$ and $\mathbf{n}_2 = \langle 5, 1, -1 \rangle$, respectively. Since there is no scalar c such that $\mathbf{n}_1 = c\mathbf{n}_2$, the vectors, and thus the planes, are not parallel. Also, since $\mathbf{n}_1 \cdot \mathbf{n}_2 \neq 0$, the vectors, and thus the planes, are not orthogonal. The cosine of the angle θ between the two planes is given by

$$\cos \theta = \frac{|\mathbf{n}_1 \cdot \mathbf{n}_2|}{\|\mathbf{n}_1\| \|\mathbf{n}_2\|} = \frac{|5 - 3 - 6|}{\sqrt{46}\sqrt{27}} = \frac{4\sqrt{138}}{414}.$$

Therefore,

$$\theta = \arccos\left(\frac{4\sqrt{138}}{414}\right) \approx 83.5°.$$

45. The normal vectors to the planes are $\mathbf{n}_1 = \langle 1, -5, -1 \rangle$ and $\mathbf{n}_2 = \langle 5, -25, -5 \rangle$. Since $\mathbf{n}_2 = 5\mathbf{n}_1$, the planes are parallel, but not equal.

47. $4x + 2y + 6z = 12$

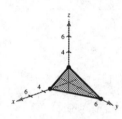

49. $2x - y + 3z = 4$

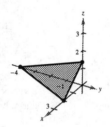

51. $y + z = 5$

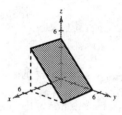

53. $2x + y - z = 6$

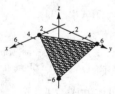

55. $-5x + 4y - 6z + 8 = 0$

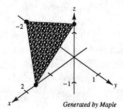

Generated by Maple

57. $3x + 2y - z = 7, \ x - 4y + 2z = 0$

Let $\mathbf{n}_1 = 3\mathbf{i} + 2\mathbf{j} - \mathbf{k}$ and $\mathbf{n}_2 = \mathbf{i} - 4\mathbf{j} + 2\mathbf{k}$ be the normal vectors to the respective planes. The line of intersection of the two planes will have the same direc-tion as the vector $\mathbf{n}_1 \times \mathbf{n}_2$. Since

$$\mathbf{n}_1 \times \mathbf{n}_2 = \begin{vmatrix} \mathbf{i} & \mathbf{j} & \mathbf{k} \\ 3 & 2 & -1 \\ 1 & -4 & 2 \end{vmatrix}$$

$$= 0\mathbf{i} - 7\mathbf{j} - 14\mathbf{k} = -7(0\mathbf{i} + \mathbf{j} + 2\mathbf{k}),$$

a set of direction numbers for the line of intersections is 0, 1, and 2. By solving the equations for the two planes simultaneously, we can find points on the line of intersection.

—CONTINUED—

57. —CONTINUED—

$$3x + 2y - z = 7, \quad x - 4y + 2z = 0$$

$$3x + 2y - z = 7 \implies 6x + 4y - 2z = 14$$

$$x - 4y + 2z = 0 \implies x - 4y + 2z = 0$$

$$7x = 14 \text{ or } x = 2$$

By substituting 2 for x, we obtain the equation $2y - z = 1$. If we let $y = 1$, then $z = 1$. Thus, $(2, 1, 1)$ lies on the line of intersection, and we conclude that a set of parametric equations for the line of intersection is

$$x = 2, \quad y = 1 + t, \quad z = 1 + 2t.$$

59. Line: $\dfrac{x - (1/2)}{1} = \dfrac{y + (3/2)}{-1} = \dfrac{z + 1}{2}$

Plane: $2x - 2y + z = 12$

The parametric equations for the line are

$$x = \frac{1}{2} + t, \quad y = \frac{-3}{2} - t, \quad z = -1 + 2t.$$

If the line intersects the plane, then the expressions for x, y, and z from the line must satisfy the equation of the plane. Thus,

$$2x - 2y + z = 12$$

$$2\left(\frac{1}{2} + t\right) - 2\left(\frac{-3}{2} - t\right) + (-1 + 2t) = 12$$

$$6t + 3 = 12$$

$$6t = 9 \implies t = \frac{3}{2}$$

and we conclude that the point of intersection occurs when $t = \frac{3}{2}$. This yields the point $(2, -3, 2)$.

61. Writing the equation of the line in parametric form and substituting into the equation of the plane we have:

$$x = 1 + 3t, \quad y = -1 - 2t, \quad z = 3 + t$$

$$2(1 + 3t) + 3(-1 - 2t) = 10, \quad -1 = 10,$$

contradiction

Therefore, the line does not intersect the plane.

63. Point: $Q(0, 0, 0)$

Plane: $2x + 3y + z - 12 = 0$

Normal to plane: $\mathbf{n} = \langle 2, 3, 1 \rangle$

Point in plane: $P(6, 0, 0)$

Vector $\overrightarrow{PQ} = \langle -6, 0\ 0 \rangle$

$$D = \frac{|\overrightarrow{PQ} \cdot \mathbf{n}|}{\|\mathbf{n}\|} = \frac{|-12|}{\sqrt{14}} = \frac{6\sqrt{14}}{7}$$

65. The normal vectors to the planes are $\mathbf{n}_1 = \langle 1, -3, 4 \rangle$ and $\mathbf{n}_2 = \langle 1, -3, 4 \rangle$. Since $\mathbf{n}_1 = \mathbf{n}_2$, the planes are parallel. Choose a point in each plane.

$P = (10, 0, 0)$ is a point in $x - 3y + 4z = 10$.
$Q = (6, 0, 0)$ is a point in $x - 3y + 4z = 6$.

$$\overrightarrow{PQ} = \langle -4, 0, 0 \rangle, \quad D = \frac{|\overrightarrow{PQ} \cdot \mathbf{n}_1|}{\|\mathbf{n}_1\|} = \frac{4}{\sqrt{26}} = \frac{2\sqrt{26}}{13}$$

67. The distance between a point Q and a line in space is

$$D = \frac{\|\overrightarrow{PQ} \times \mathbf{u}\|}{\|\mathbf{u}\|}$$

where $\mathbf{u}$ is the direction vector for the line and P is a point on the line. For the line $x = 4t - 2$, $y = 3$, and $z = -t + 1$, the direction vector is $\mathbf{u} = \langle 4, 0, -1 \rangle$ and a point P on the line is $(-2, 3, 1)$ when $t = 0$. Since $Q = (1, 5, -2)$,

$$\overrightarrow{PQ} = \langle 3, 2, -3 \rangle.$$

$$\overrightarrow{PQ} \times \mathbf{u} = \begin{vmatrix} \mathbf{i} & \mathbf{j} & \mathbf{k} \\ 3 & 2 & -3 \\ 4 & 0 & -1 \end{vmatrix} = \langle -2, -9, -8 \rangle$$

$$D = \frac{\|\overrightarrow{PQ} \times \mathbf{u}\|}{\|\mathbf{u}\|} = \frac{\sqrt{(-2)^2 + (-9)^2 + (-8)^2}}{\sqrt{4^2 + 0^2 + (-1)^2}} = \frac{\sqrt{2533}}{17} \approx 2.96$$

69. (a) $z = 276 - 0.987x - 1.71y$

Year	1970	1975	1980	1985	1990	1991	1992	1993
z (approx.)	213.6	173.7	144.7	121.1	85.3	81.9	81.4	83.6

(b) An increase in x or y will cause a decrease in z. In fact, any increase in two variables will cause a decrease in the third.

(c)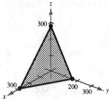

71. (a) Sphere

$$(x - 3)^2 + (y + 2)^2 + (z - 5)^2 = 16$$
$$x^2 + y^2 + z^2 - 6x + 4y - 10z + 22 = 0$$

73. Vectors for two adjacent edges of one side of the chute shown in the figure are $\langle 6, 0, 0 \rangle$ and $\langle -1, -1, 8 \rangle$, and a normal vector to the side is

$$\mathbf{n}_1 = \begin{vmatrix} \mathbf{i} & \mathbf{j} & \mathbf{k} \\ 6 & 0 & 0 \\ -1 & -1 & 8 \end{vmatrix} = -48\mathbf{j} - 6\mathbf{k}.$$

Vectors for two adjacent edges of the adjacent side of the chute shown in the figure are $\langle 0, 6, 0 \rangle$ and $\langle -1, -1, 8 \rangle$, and a normal vector to the side is

$$\mathbf{n}_2 = \begin{vmatrix} \mathbf{i} & \mathbf{j} & \mathbf{k} \\ 0 & 6 & 0 \\ -1 & -1 & 8 \end{vmatrix} = 48\mathbf{i} + 6\mathbf{k}.$$

The angle θ between the two adjacent sides is the angle between their normal vectors.

$$\cos \theta = \frac{|\mathbf{n}_1 \cdot \mathbf{n}_2|}{\|\mathbf{n}_1\| \|\mathbf{n}_2\|} = \frac{36}{2340} = \frac{1}{65}$$

$$\theta = \arccos \frac{1}{65} \approx 89.1°$$

75. True

77. From Theorem 10.13 and Theorem 10.7 (6) we have

$$D = \frac{|\overrightarrow{PQ} \cdot \mathbf{n}|}{\|\mathbf{n}\|} = \frac{|\mathbf{w} \cdot (\mathbf{u} \times \mathbf{v})|}{\|\mathbf{u} \times \mathbf{v}\|} = \frac{|(\mathbf{u} \times \mathbf{v}) \cdot \mathbf{w}|}{\|\mathbf{u} \times \mathbf{v}\|} = \frac{|\mathbf{u} \cdot (\mathbf{v} \times \mathbf{w})|}{\|\mathbf{u} \times \mathbf{v}\|}.$$

Section 10.6   Surfaces in Space

1. Ellipsoid

Matches graph (c)

3. Hyperboloid of one sheet

Matches graph (f)

5. Elliptic paraboloid

Matches graph (d)

7. $z = 3$

Plane parallel to the xy-coordinate plane

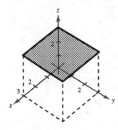

9. $y^2 + z^2 = 9$

The x-coordinate is missing so we have a cylindrical surface with rulings parallel to the x-axis. The generating curve is a circle.

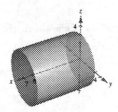

11. $x_2 - y = 0$

Since the z-coordinate is missing in the equation, the surface is a cylindrical surface with rulings parallel to the z-axis. The generating curve is the parabola $y = x^2$ and the surface is called a *parabolic cylinder*. (see figure.)

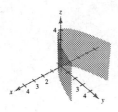

13. $4x^2 + y^2 = 4$

$$\frac{x^2}{1} + \frac{y^2}{4} = 1$$

The z-coordinate is missing so we have a cylindrical surface with rulings parallel to the z-axis. The generating curve is an ellipse.

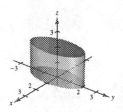

15. $z = \sin y$

The x-coordinate is missing so we have a cylindrical surface with rulings parallel to the x-axis. The generating curve is the sine curve.

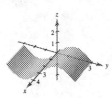

17. $x = x^2 + y^2$

(a) You are viewing the paraboloid from the x-axis: $(20, 0, 0)$

(b) You are viewing the paraboloid from above, but not on the z-axis: $(10, 10, 20)$

(c) You are viewing the paraboloid from the z-axis: $(0, 0, 20)$

(d) You are viewing the paraboloid from the y-axis: $(0, 20, 0)$

19. $\dfrac{x^2}{1} + \dfrac{y^2}{4} + \dfrac{z^2}{1} = 1$

Ellipsoid

xy-trace: $\dfrac{x^2}{1} + \dfrac{y^2}{4} = 1$

xz-trace: $x^2 + z^2 = 1$

yz-trace: $\dfrac{y^2}{4} + \dfrac{z^2}{1} = 1$

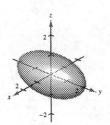

21. $16x^2 - y^2 + 16z^2 = 4$

The equation has the form

$$\frac{x^2}{1/4} - \frac{y^2}{4} + \frac{z^2}{1/4} = 1$$

which is the form for a **hyperboloid of one sheet.** The axis of the hyperboloid is the y-axis. The xz-trace $(y = 0)$ is the circle

$$\frac{x^2}{1/4} + \frac{z^2}{1/4} = 1$$

and the xy- and yz- traces are the hyperbolas

$$\frac{x^2}{1/4} - \frac{y^2}{4} = 1 \quad \text{and} \quad \frac{z^2}{1/4} - \frac{y^2}{4} = 1. \quad \text{(see figure)}$$

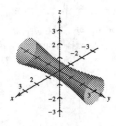

23. $x^2 - y + z^2 = 0$

Elliptic paraboloid

xy-trace: $y = x^2$

xz-trace: $x^2 + z^2 = 0$,

   point $(0, 0, 0)$

yz-trace: $y = z^2$

$y = 1$: $x^2 + z^2 = 1$

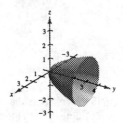

25. $x^2 - y^2 + z = 0$

The given equation can be written as

$$z = -\frac{x^2}{1} + \frac{y^2}{1}$$

which is the form for a **hyperbolic paraboloid.**

   xy-trace $(z = 0)$: $y = \pm x$ (intersecting lines)

   xz-trace $(y = 0)$: $z = -x^2$ (parabola opening downward)

   yz-trace $(x = 0)$: $z = 13y^2$ (parabola opening upward)

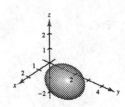

Traces parallel to the xy-coordinate plane are hyperbolas. For example, when $z = 1$, we have $y^2 - x^2 = 1$.

27. $z^2 = x^2 + \frac{y^2}{4}$

Elliptic Cone

xy-trace: point $(0, 0, 0)$

xz-trace: $z = \pm x$

yz-trace: $z = \frac{\pm 1}{2}y$

$z = \pm 1$: $x^2 + \frac{y^2}{4} = 1$

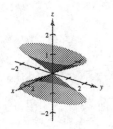

29. $16x^2 + 9y^2 + 16z^2 - 32x - 36y + 36 = 0$

$$16(x^2 - 2x + 1) + 9(y^2 - 4y + 4) + 16z^2 = -36 + 16 + 36$$

$$16(x - 1)^2 + 9(y - 2)^2 + 16z^2 = 16$$

$$\frac{(x - 1)^2}{1} + \frac{(y - 2)^2}{16/9} + \frac{z^2}{1} = 1$$

Ellipsoid with center $(1, 2, 0)$.

31. $z = 2 \sin x$

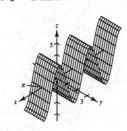

33. $z^2 = x^2 + 4y^2$

$z = \pm\sqrt{x^2 + 4y^2}$

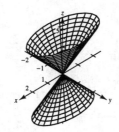

35. $x^2 + y^2 = \left(\dfrac{2}{z}\right)^2$

$y = \pm\sqrt{\dfrac{4}{z^2} - x^2}$

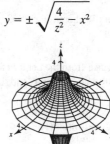

37. $z = 4 - \sqrt{|xy|}$

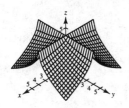

39. $4x^2 - y^2 + 4z^2 = -16$

$z = \pm\sqrt{\dfrac{y^2}{4} - x^2 - 4}$

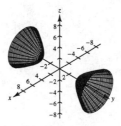

41. The surface $z = 2\sqrt{x^2 + y^2}$ is a cone and the graph of $z = 2$ is a plane 2 units above the xy-plane. The intersection of the surfaces is a circle of radius 1.

$$2\sqrt{x^2 + y^2} = 2$$
$$\sqrt{x^2 + y^2} = 1$$
$$x^2 + y^2 = 1$$

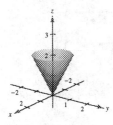

43. $x^2 + y^2 = 1$

$x + z = 2$

$z = 0$

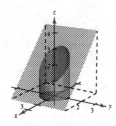

45. $x^2 + z^2 = [r(y)]^2$ and $z = r(y) = \pm 2\sqrt{y}$; therefore, $x^2 + z^2 = 4y$.

47. Since we are revolving the curve $z = 2y$ in the yz-plane about the z-axis, the equation for the surface of revolution has the form $x^2 + y^2 = [a(z)]^2$ where $y = a(z) = z/2$. Therefore, the equation is

$$x^2 + y^2 = \dfrac{z^2}{4} \quad \text{or} \quad 4x^2 + 4y^2 = z^2.$$

49. $y^2 + z^2 = [r(x)]^2$ and $y = r(x) = \dfrac{2}{x}$; therefore,

$$y^2 + z^2 = \left(\dfrac{2}{x}\right)^2, \, y^2 + z^2 = \dfrac{4}{x^2}.$$

51. $x^2 + y^2 - 2z = 0$

$x^2 + y^2 = \left(\sqrt{2z}\right)^2$

Equation of generating curve: $y = \sqrt{2z}$ or $x = \sqrt{2z}$

53. The distance from the center of the rectangle to the axis of revolution is $p(x) = x$, and the height of the rectangle is $h(x) = 4x - x^2$.

$$V = 2\pi \int_a^b p(x)h(x)\, dx$$

$$= 2\pi \int_0^4 x(4x - x^2)\, dx$$

$$= 2\pi \int_0^4 (4x^2 - x^3)\, dx = 2\pi \left[\frac{4}{3}x^3 - \frac{1}{4}x^4\right]_0^4 = \frac{128\pi}{3}$$

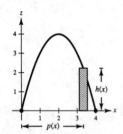

55. $z = \dfrac{x^2}{2} + \dfrac{y^2}{4}$

(a) When $z = 2$ we have $2 = \dfrac{x^2}{2} + \dfrac{y^2}{4}$, or $1 = \dfrac{x^2}{4} + \dfrac{y^2}{8}$

Major axis: $2\sqrt{8} = 4\sqrt{2}$ or 1

Minor axis: $2\sqrt{4} = 4$

$$c^2 = a^2 - b^2, c^2 = 4, c = 2$$

Foci: $(0, \pm 2, 2)$

(b) When $z = 8$ we have $8 = \dfrac{x^2}{2} + \dfrac{y^2}{4}$, or $1 = \dfrac{x^2}{16} + \dfrac{y^2}{32}$.

Major axis: $2\sqrt{32} = 8\sqrt{2}$

Minor axis: $2\sqrt{16} = 8$

$$c^2 = 32 - 16 = 16, c = 4$$

Foci: $(0, \pm 4, 8)$

57. $\dfrac{x^2}{3963^2} + \dfrac{y^2}{3963^2} + \dfrac{z^2}{3942^2} = 1$

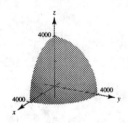

59. $z = \dfrac{y^2}{b^2} - \dfrac{x^2}{a^2}, z = bx + ay$

$$bx + ay = \frac{y^2}{b^2} - \frac{x^2}{a^2}$$

$$\frac{1}{a^2}\left(x^2 + a^2 bx + \frac{a^4 b^2}{4}\right) = \frac{1}{b^2}\left(y^2 - ab^2 y + \frac{a^2 b^4}{4}\right)$$

$$\frac{\left(x + \dfrac{a^2 b}{2}\right)^2}{a^2} = \frac{\left(y - \dfrac{ab^2}{2}\right)^2}{b^2}$$

$$y = \pm \frac{b}{a}\left(x + \frac{a^2 b}{2}\right) + \frac{ab^2}{2}$$

Letting $x = at$, you obtain the two intersecting lines $x = at, y = -bt, z = 0$ and $x = at, y = bt + ab^2$ $z = 2abt + a^2 b^2$.

Section 10.7   Cylindrical and Spherical Coordinates

1. $(0, 5, 1)$, rectangular

$r = \sqrt{(0)^2 + (5)^2} = 5$

$\theta = \arctan \dfrac{5}{0} = \dfrac{\pi}{2}$

$z = 1$

$\left(5, \dfrac{\pi}{2}, 1\right)$, cylindrical

3. $\left(1, \sqrt{3}, 4\right)$, rectangular

$r = \sqrt{1^2 + \left(\sqrt{3}\right)^2} = 2$

$\theta = \arctan \sqrt{3} = \dfrac{\pi}{3}$

$z = 4$

$\left(2, \dfrac{\pi}{3}, 4\right)$, cylindrical

5. Rectangular coordinates: $(2, -2, -4)$

Since $x = 2$, $y = -2$, and $z = -4$, we have

$$r = \pm\sqrt{x^2 + y^2} = \pm\sqrt{4 + 4} = \pm 2\sqrt{2}$$

$$\theta = \arctan\frac{y}{x} = \arctan\frac{-2}{2} = \arctan(-1) = -\frac{\pi}{4} \text{ or } \frac{3\pi}{4}$$

$$z = -4.$$

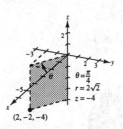

Therefore, one set of corresponding cylindrical coordinates for the given point is $(r, \theta, z) = \left(2\sqrt{2}, -\pi/4, -4\right)$. (see figure.)
Another set of cylindrical coordinates for the given point is $\left(-2\sqrt{2}, 3\pi/4, -4\right)$.

7. $(5, 0, 2)$, cylindrical

$x = 5\cos 0 = 5$

$y = 5\sin 0 = 0$

$z = 2$

$(5, 0, 2)$, rectangular

9. $\left(2, \dfrac{\pi}{3}, 2\right)$, cylindrical

$x = 2\cos\dfrac{\pi}{3} = 1$

$y = 2\sin\dfrac{\pi}{3} = \sqrt{3}$

$z = 2$

$\left(1, \sqrt{3}, 2\right)$, rectangular

11. Cylindrical coordinates: $\left(4, \dfrac{7\pi}{6}, 3\right)$

Since $\left(4, \dfrac{7\pi}{6}, 3\right) = (r, \theta, z)$ we have

$$x = r\cos\theta = 4\cos\frac{7\pi}{6} = -2\sqrt{3}$$

$$y = r\sin\theta = 4\sin\frac{7\pi}{6} = -2$$

$$z = 3.$$

Therefore, in rectangular coordinates, the point is
$\left(-2\sqrt{3}, -2, 3\right)$.

13. $r = 2$

$\sqrt{x^2 + y^2} = 2$

$x^2 + y^2 = 4$

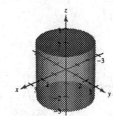

15. $\theta = \dfrac{\pi}{6}$

$$\tan\frac{\pi}{6} = \frac{y}{x}$$

$$\frac{1}{\sqrt{3}} = \frac{y}{x}$$

$$x = \sqrt{3}\,y$$

$$x - \sqrt{3}\,y = 0$$

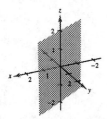

17. Cylindrical coordinates: $r = 2\sin\theta$

Since $x^2 + y^2 = r^2$ and $y = r\sin\theta$, we have

$$r = 2\sin\theta$$

$$r^2 = 2r\sin\theta$$

$$x^2 + y^2 = 2y$$

$$x^2 + y^2 - 2y + 1 = 1$$

$$x^2 + (y - 1)^2 = 1.$$

Therefore, the graph of the equation is a circular cylinder
with rulings parallel to the z-axis.

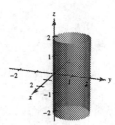

19. $r^2 + z^2 = 4$

$x^2 + y^2 + z^2 = 4$

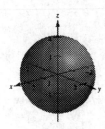

21. $(4, 0, 0)$, rectangular

$\rho = \sqrt{4^2 + 0^2 + 0^2} = 4$

$\theta = \arctan 0 = 0$

$\phi = \arccos 0 = \dfrac{\pi}{2}$

$\left(4, 0, \dfrac{\pi}{2}\right)$, spherical

23. Rectangular coordinates: $\left(-2, 2\sqrt{3}, 4\right)$

Since $\left(-2, 2\sqrt{3}, 4\right) = (x, y, z)$, we have

$$\rho = \sqrt{x^2 + y^2 + z^2} = \sqrt{4 + 12 + 16} = 4\sqrt{2}$$

$$\theta = \arctan \frac{y}{x} = \arctan \frac{2\sqrt{3}}{-2} = \frac{2\pi}{3}$$

$$\phi = \arccos \frac{z}{\rho} = \arccos \frac{4}{4\sqrt{2}} = \frac{\pi}{4}.$$

Therefore, in spherical coordinates, the point is

$\left(4\sqrt{2}, \dfrac{2\pi}{3}, \dfrac{\pi}{4}\right).$

25. $\left(\sqrt{3}, 1, 2\sqrt{3}\right)$, rectangular

$\rho = \sqrt{3 + 1 + 12} = 4$

$\theta = \arctan \dfrac{1}{\sqrt{3}} = \dfrac{\pi}{6}$

$\phi = \arccos \dfrac{\sqrt{3}}{2} = \dfrac{\pi}{6}$

$\left(4, \dfrac{\pi}{6}, \dfrac{\pi}{6}\right)$, spherical

27. Spherical coordinates: $\left(4, \dfrac{\pi}{6}, \dfrac{\pi}{4}\right)$

Since $\left(4, \dfrac{\pi}{6}, \dfrac{\pi}{4}\right) = (\rho, \theta, \phi)$, we have

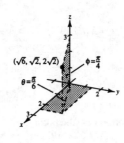

$$x = \rho \sin \phi \cos \theta = 4 \sin \frac{\pi}{4} \cos \frac{\pi}{6} = 4\left(\frac{\sqrt{2}}{2}\right)\left(\frac{\sqrt{3}}{2}\right) = \sqrt{6}$$

$$y = \rho \sin \phi \sin \theta = 4 \sin \frac{\pi}{4} \sin \frac{\pi}{6} = 4\left(\frac{\sqrt{2}}{2}\right)\left(\frac{1}{2}\right) = \sqrt{2}$$

$$z = \rho \cos \phi = 4 \cos \frac{\pi}{4} = 4\left(\frac{\sqrt{2}}{2}\right) = 2\sqrt{2}.$$

Therefore, in rectangular coordinates, the point is $\left(\sqrt{6}, \sqrt{2}, 2\sqrt{2}\right)$.

29. $\left(12, \dfrac{-\pi}{4}, 0\right)$, spherical

$x = 12 \sin 0 \cos\left(\dfrac{-\pi}{4}\right) = 0$

$y = 12 \sin 0 \sin\left(\dfrac{-\pi}{4}\right) = 0$

$z = 12 \cos 0 = 12$

$(0, 0, 12)$, rectangular

31. $\left(5, \dfrac{\pi}{4}, \dfrac{3\pi}{4}\right)$, spherical

$x = 5 \sin \dfrac{3\pi}{4} \cos \dfrac{\pi}{4} = \dfrac{5}{2}$

$y = 5 \sin \dfrac{3\pi}{4} \sin \dfrac{\pi}{4} = \dfrac{5}{2}$

$z = 5 \cos \dfrac{3\pi}{4} = -\dfrac{5\sqrt{2}}{2}$

$\left(\dfrac{5}{2}, \dfrac{5}{2}, -\dfrac{5\sqrt{2}}{2}\right)$, rectangular

33. (a) Programs will vary.

(b) $(x, y, z) = (3, -4, 2)$

$(\rho, \theta, \phi) = (5.385, -0.927, 1.190)$

35. $\rho = 2$

$x^2 + y^2 + z^2 = 4$

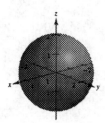

37. $\phi = \dfrac{\pi}{6}$

$\cos \phi = \dfrac{z}{\sqrt{x^2 + y^2 + z^2}}$

$\dfrac{\sqrt{3}}{2} = \dfrac{z}{\sqrt{x^2 + y^2 + z^2}}$

$\dfrac{3}{4} = \dfrac{z^2}{x^2 + y^2 + z^2}$

$3x^2 + 3y^2 - z^2 = 0$

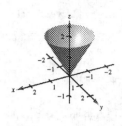

39. Spherical coordinates: $\rho = 4 \cos \phi$

Since

$$\cos \phi = \frac{z}{\sqrt{x^2 + y^2 + z^2}},$$

write

$$\frac{\rho}{4} = \cos \phi = \frac{z}{\sqrt{x^2 + y^2 + z^2}}.$$

Furthermore, since $\rho = \sqrt{x^2 + y^2 + z^2}$, it follows that

$$\frac{\sqrt{x^2 + y^2 + z^2}}{4} = \frac{z}{\sqrt{x^2 + y^2 + z^2}}$$

$$x^2 + y^2 + z^2 = 4z$$

$$x^2 + y^2 + z^2 - 4z = 0.$$

Completing the square on variable z yields the equation

$$x^2 + y^2 + (z - 2)^2 = 4$$

which represents a sphere of radius 2, centered at $(0, 0, 2)$.

41. $\rho = \csc \phi$

$\rho \sin \phi = 1$

$\sqrt{x^2 + y^2} = 1$

$x^2 + y^2 = 1$

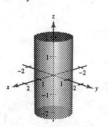

43. $\left(4, \dfrac{\pi}{4}, 0\right)$, cylindrical

$\rho = \sqrt{4^2 + 0^2} = 4$

$\theta = \dfrac{\pi}{4}$

$\phi = \arccos 0 = \dfrac{\pi}{2}$

$\left(4, \dfrac{\pi}{4}, \dfrac{\pi}{2}\right)$, spherical

45. Cylindrical coordinates: $\left(4, -\dfrac{\pi}{6}, 6\right)$

Since $\left(4, -\dfrac{\pi}{6}, 6\right) = (r, \theta, z)$, we have

$$\rho^2 = x^2 + y^2 + z^2 = r^2 + z^2 = 16 + 36 = 52$$

or

$$\rho = 2\sqrt{13} > 0.$$

Furthermore,

$$\cos \phi = \frac{z}{\sqrt{x^2 + y^2 + z^2}}$$

$$= \frac{z}{\sqrt{r^2 + z^2}} = \frac{6}{\sqrt{52}} = \frac{3}{\sqrt{13}}$$

or

$$\phi = \arccos \frac{3}{\sqrt{13}}.$$

Therefore, in spherical coordinates, the point is

$$\left(2\sqrt{13}, -\frac{\pi}{6}, \arccos \frac{3}{\sqrt{13}}\right).$$

47. $(12, \pi, 5)$, cylindrical

$\rho = \sqrt{12^2 + 5^2} = 13$

$\theta = \pi$

$\phi = \arccos \dfrac{5}{13}$

$\left(13, \pi, \arccos \dfrac{5}{13}\right)$, spherical

49. $\left(10, \dfrac{\pi}{6}, \dfrac{\pi}{2}\right)$, spherical

$r = 10 \sin \dfrac{\pi}{2} = 10$

$\theta = \dfrac{\pi}{6}$

$z = 10 \cos \dfrac{\pi}{2} = 0$

$\left(10, \dfrac{\pi}{6}, 0\right)$, cylindrical

51. $\left(6, -\dfrac{\pi}{6}, \dfrac{\pi}{3}\right)$, spherical

$r = 6 \sin \dfrac{\pi}{3} = 3\sqrt{3}$

$\theta = -\dfrac{\pi}{6}$

$z = 6 \cos \dfrac{\pi}{3} = 3$

$\left(3\sqrt{3}, -\dfrac{\pi}{6}, 3\right)$, cylindrical

53. Spherical coordinates: $(\rho, \theta, \phi) = \left(8, \dfrac{7\pi}{6}, \dfrac{\pi}{6}\right)$

$r = \rho \sin \phi = 8 \sin \dfrac{\pi}{6} = 4$

$\theta = \dfrac{7\pi}{6}$

$z = \rho \cos \phi = 8 \cos \dfrac{\pi}{6} = \dfrac{8\sqrt{3}}{2} = 4\sqrt{3}$

Cylindrical coordinates: $\left(4, \dfrac{7\pi}{6}, 4\sqrt{3}\right)$

Rectangular	*Cylindrical*	*Spherical*
55. $(4, 6, 3)$	$(7.211, 0.983, 3)$	$(7.810, 0.983, 1.177)$
57. $(4.698, 1.710, 8)$	$\left(5, \dfrac{\pi}{9}, 8\right)$	$(9.434, 0.349, 0.559)$
59. $(-7.071, 12.247, 14.142)$	$(14.142, 2.094, 14.142)$	$\left(20, \dfrac{2\pi}{3}, \dfrac{\pi}{4}\right)$
61. $(3, -2, 2)$	$(3.606, -0.588, 2)$	$(4.123, -0.588, 1.064)$
63. $\left(\dfrac{5}{2}, \dfrac{4}{3}, \dfrac{-3}{2}\right)$	$(2.833, 0.490, -1.5)$	$(3.206, 0.490, 2.058)$

[**Note:** Use the cylindrical coordinates $(3.5, 5.642, 6)$]

65. Cylindrical coordinates: $(r, \theta, z) = \left(5, \dfrac{3\pi}{4}, -5\right)$

First we convert to rectangular coordinates.

$x = r \cos \theta = 5 \cos \dfrac{3\pi}{4} \approx -3.536$

$y = r \sin \theta = 5 \sin \dfrac{3\pi}{4} \approx 3.536$

$z = -5$

Rectangular coordinates: $(-3.536, 3.536, -5)$

—CONTINUED—

65. **—CONTINUED—**

Converting from cylindrical coordinates to spherical coordinates, we have the following.

$$\rho = \sqrt{r^2 + z^2} = \sqrt{5^2 + (-5)^2} = 5\sqrt{2} \approx 7.071$$

$$\theta = \frac{3\pi}{4} \approx 2.356$$

$$\phi = \arccos\left(\frac{z}{\sqrt{r^2 + z^2}}\right)$$

$$= \arccos\left(\frac{-5}{5\sqrt{2}}\right) = \arccos\left(-\frac{1}{\sqrt{2}}\right) = \frac{3\pi}{4} \approx 2.356$$

Spherical coordinates: $(7.071, 2.356, 2.356)$

Rectangular	*Cylindrical*	*Spherical*
67. $(2.804, -2.095, 6)$	$(-3.5, 2.5, 6)$	$(6.946, 5.642, 0.528)$

[**Note:** Use the cylindrical coordinates $(3.5, 5.642, 6)$]

69. $r = 5$

Cylinder

Matches graph (d)

71. $\rho = 5$

Sphere

Matches graph (c)

73. $r^2 = z, x^2 + y^2 = z$

Paraboloid

Matches graph (f)

75. $x^2 + y^2 + z^2 = 16$

(a) $r^2 + z^2 = 16$

(b) $\rho^2 = 16, \rho = 4$

77. $x^2 + y^2 + z^2 - 2z = 0$

(a) $r^2 + z^2 - 2z = 0, r^2 + (z - 1)^2 = 1$

(b) $\rho^2 - 2\rho \cos \phi = 0, \rho(\rho - 2 \cos \phi) = 0,$

$\rho = 2 \cos \phi$

79. Rectangular coordinates: $x^2 + y^2 = 4y$

(a) Since $x^2 + y^2 = r^2$ and $y = 4 \sin \theta$, the equation in cylindrical coordinates is

$$x^2 + y^2 = 4y$$

$$r^2 = 4r \sin \theta \implies r = 4 \sin \theta.$$

(b) In spherical coordinates, since $x^2 + y^2 = r^2 = \rho^2 \sin^2 \phi$ and $y = \rho \sin \phi \sin \theta$, we have

$$x^2 + y^2 = 4y$$

$$\rho^2 \sin^2 \phi = 4\rho \sin \phi \sin \theta$$

$$\rho \sin \phi = 4 \sin \theta$$

$$\rho = 4 \sin \theta \csc \phi.$$

81. $x^2 - y^2 = 9$

(a) $r^2 \cos^2 \theta - r^2 \sin^2 \theta = 9,$

$$r^2 = \frac{9}{\cos^2 \theta - \sin^2 \theta}$$

(b) $\rho^2 \sin^2 \phi \cos^2 \theta - \rho^2 \sin^2 \phi \sin^2 \theta = 9,$

$$\rho^2 \sin^2 \phi = \frac{9}{\cos^2 \theta - \sin^2 \theta},$$

$$\rho^2 = \frac{9 \csc^2 \phi}{\cos^2 \theta - \sin^2 \theta}$$

83. $0 \le \theta \le \dfrac{\pi}{2}$

$0 \le r \le 2$

$0 \le z \le 4$

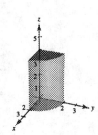

85. $0 \le \theta \le 2\pi$

$0 \le r \le a$

$r \le z \le a$

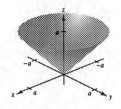

87. Spherical coordinates: $0 \le \theta \le 2\pi$, $0 \le \phi \le \pi/6$,
$$0 \le \rho \le a \sec \phi$$

From the constraint $0 \le \rho \le a \sec \phi$, we have

$$0 \le \rho \le a\left(\frac{1}{\cos \phi}\right)$$

$$0 \le \rho \cos \phi \le a$$

$$0 \le z \le a$$

89. Rectangular

$$0 \le x \le 10$$
$$0 \le y \le 10$$
$$0 \le z \le 10$$

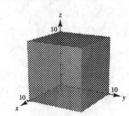

91. Spherical

$$4 \le \rho \le 6$$

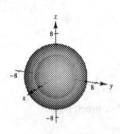

93. $z = \sin \theta$, $r = 1$

$$z = \frac{y}{r} = \frac{y}{1} = y$$

The curve of intersection is the ellipse formed by the intersection of the plane $z = y$ and the cylinder $r = 1$.

Review Exercises for Chapter 10

1. $P = (1, 2)$, $Q = (4, 1)$, $R = (5, 4)$

(a) $\mathbf{u} = \overrightarrow{PQ} = \langle 3, -1 \rangle = 3\mathbf{i} - \mathbf{j}$,

$\quad \mathbf{v} = \overrightarrow{PR} = \langle 4, 2 \rangle = 4\mathbf{i} + 2\mathbf{j}$

(b) $\|\mathbf{v}\| = \sqrt{4^2 + 2^2} = 2\sqrt{5}$

(c) $\mathbf{u} \cdot \mathbf{v} = 3(4) + (-1)(2) = 10$

(d) $2\mathbf{u} + \mathbf{v} = \langle 6, -2 \rangle + \langle 4, 2 \rangle = \langle 10, 0 \rangle = 10\mathbf{i}$

(e) $\mathbf{w}_1 = \text{proj}_{\mathbf{v}}(\mathbf{u}) = \left(\frac{\mathbf{u} \cdot \mathbf{v}}{\|\mathbf{v}\|^2}\right)\mathbf{v} = \frac{10}{(2\sqrt{5})^2}(4\mathbf{i} + 2\mathbf{j}) = 2\mathbf{i} + \mathbf{j}$

(f) $\mathbf{w}_2 = \mathbf{u} - \mathbf{w}_1 = (3\mathbf{i} - \mathbf{j}) - (2\mathbf{i} + \mathbf{j}) = \mathbf{i} - 2\mathbf{j}$

3. $z = 0$, $y = 4$, $x = -5$: $(-5, 4, 0)$

5. Looking down from the positive x-axis towards the yz-plane, the point is either in the first quadrant $(y > 0, z > 0)$ or in the third quadrant $(y < 0, z < 0)$. The x-coordinate can be any number.

7. $(x - 3)^2 + (y + 2)^2 + (z - 6)^2 = \left(\dfrac{15}{2}\right)^2$

9.
$$x^2 + y^2 + z^2 - 4x - 6y + 4 = 0$$
$$(x^2 - 4x + \underline{}) + (y^2 - 6y + \underline{}) + z^2 = -4 + \underline{} + \underline{}$$
$$(x^2 - 4x + 4) + (y^2 - 6y + 9) + z^2 = -4 + 4 + 9$$
$$(x - 2)^2 + (y - 3)^2 + (z - 0)^2 = 9$$

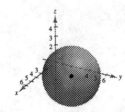

The last equation is the standard form of the equation of a sphere with center $(2, 3, 0)$ and radius 3. The graph of the sphere is given in the figure.

11. $P(5, 0, 0), Q(4, 4, 0), R(2, 0, 6)$

(a) $\mathbf{u} = \overrightarrow{PQ} = \langle 4 - 5, 4 - 0, 0 - 0 \rangle = \langle -1, 4, 0 \rangle$

$\mathbf{v} = \overrightarrow{PR} = \langle 2 - 5, 0 - 0, 6 - 0 \rangle = \langle -3, 0, 6 \rangle$

(c) $\mathbf{u} \times \mathbf{v} = \begin{vmatrix} \mathbf{i} & \mathbf{j} & \mathbf{k} \\ -1 & 4 & 0 \\ -3 & 0 & 6 \end{vmatrix} = 24\mathbf{i} + 6\mathbf{j} + 12\mathbf{k}$

$\qquad\qquad = 6(4\mathbf{i} + \mathbf{j} + 2\mathbf{k})$

(e) Since the direction of the line is determined by $\mathbf{u} = \langle -1, 4, 0 \rangle$ [see part (a)], a set of parametric equations of the line passing through the point $(4, 4, 0)$ is

$x = 4 - t, \ y = 4 + 4t, \ z = 0.$

Note that when $t = -1, x = 5, y = 0,$ and $z = 0.$ Thus, the line passes through the point P.

(b) $\mathbf{u} \cdot \mathbf{v} = (-1)(-3) + (4)(0) + (0)(6) = 3$

(d) A vector normal to the plane is

$\frac{1}{6}(\mathbf{u} \times \mathbf{v}) = 4\mathbf{i} + \mathbf{j} + 2\mathbf{k}$ See part (c)

Therefore, using $(5, 0, 0)$ as a point in the plane, an equation of the plane is

$4(x - 5) + 1(y - 0) + 2(z - 0) = 0$

$4x + y + 2z = 20.$

13. $\mathbf{u} = \langle 7, -2, 3 \rangle, \ \mathbf{v} = \langle -1, 4, 5 \rangle$

Since $\mathbf{u} \cdot \mathbf{v} = 0,$ the vectors are orthogonal.

15. $\mathbf{u} = 5\left(\cos \frac{3\pi}{4}\mathbf{i} + \sin \frac{3\pi}{4}\mathbf{j} \right) = \frac{5\sqrt{2}}{2}[-\mathbf{i} + \mathbf{j}]$

$\mathbf{v} = 2\left(\cos \frac{2\pi}{3}\mathbf{i} + \sin \frac{2\pi}{3}\mathbf{j} \right) = -\mathbf{i} + \sqrt{3}\mathbf{j}$

$\mathbf{u} \cdot \mathbf{v} = \frac{5\sqrt{2}}{2}(1 + \sqrt{3})$

$\|\mathbf{u}\| = 5$

$\|\mathbf{v}\| = 2$

$\cos \theta = \frac{|\mathbf{u} \cdot \mathbf{v}|}{\|\mathbf{u}\| \, \|\mathbf{v}\|} = \frac{(5\sqrt{2}/2)(1 + \sqrt{3})}{5(2)} = \frac{\sqrt{2} + \sqrt{6}}{4}$

$\theta = \arccos \frac{\sqrt{2} + \sqrt{6}}{4} = 15°$

17. $\mathbf{u} = \langle 10, -5, 15 \rangle, \mathbf{v} = \langle -2, 1, -3 \rangle$

Since $\mathbf{u} = -5\mathbf{v}, \mathbf{u}$ is parallel to $\mathbf{v}$ and in the opposite direction. Therefore, $\theta = \pi.$ A second method for solving the problem is the following.

$\cos \theta = \frac{\mathbf{u} \cdot \mathbf{v}}{\|\mathbf{u}\|\|\mathbf{v}\|} = \frac{-70}{5\sqrt{14}\sqrt{14}} = -1$

Since $\cos \theta = -1, \theta = \arccos(-1) = \pi.$

19. $\mathbf{u} = 4[(\cos 135°)\mathbf{i} + (\sin 135°)\mathbf{j}]$

$= 4\left[-\frac{\sqrt{2}}{2}\mathbf{i} + \frac{\sqrt{2}}{2}\mathbf{j} \right] = -2\sqrt{2}\mathbf{i} + 2\sqrt{2}\mathbf{j}$

21. $\mathbf{v} = \mathbf{i} - 3\mathbf{j} + 4\mathbf{k}$

$\mathbf{u} = 3\left(\frac{\mathbf{v}}{\|\mathbf{v}\|} \right) = 3\left(\frac{\mathbf{i} - 3\mathbf{j} + 4\mathbf{k}}{\sqrt{26}} \right) = \frac{3}{\sqrt{26}}\mathbf{i} - \frac{9}{\sqrt{26}}\mathbf{j} + \frac{12}{\sqrt{26}}\mathbf{k}$

In Exercises 23–31, $\mathbf{u} = \langle 3, -2, 1 \rangle, \quad \mathbf{v} = \langle 2, -4, -3 \rangle, \quad \mathbf{w} = \langle -1, 2, 2 \rangle.$

23. $\|\mathbf{u}\| = \sqrt{3^2 + (-2)^2 + 1^2} = \sqrt{14}$

25. $\mathbf{u} \cdot \mathbf{u} = 3(3) + (-2)(-2) + (1)(1) = 14 = \left(\sqrt{14} \right)^2 = \|\mathbf{u}\|^2$

27. $\mathbf{u} = \langle 3, -2, 1 \rangle, \mathbf{w} = \langle -1, 2, 2 \rangle$

$\text{proj}_{\mathbf{u}}\mathbf{w} = \left(\frac{\mathbf{u} \cdot \mathbf{w}}{\|\mathbf{u}\|^2} \right)\mathbf{u} = -\frac{5}{14}\langle 3, -2, 1 \rangle$

$= \left\langle -\frac{15}{14}, \frac{10}{14}, -\frac{5}{14} \right\rangle$

29. $\mathbf{u} \cdot (\mathbf{v} + \mathbf{w}) = \langle 3, -2, 1 \rangle \cdot \langle 1, -2, -1 \rangle = 6$

$\mathbf{u} \cdot \mathbf{v} + \mathbf{u} \cdot \mathbf{w} = \langle 3, -2, 1 \rangle \cdot \langle 2, -4, -3 \rangle + \langle 3, -2, 1 \rangle \cdot \langle -1, 2, 2 \rangle = 11 + (-5) = 6$

Thus, $\mathbf{u} \cdot (\mathbf{v} + \mathbf{w}) = \mathbf{u} \cdot \mathbf{v} + \mathbf{u} \cdot \mathbf{w}$.

31. $V = |\mathbf{u} \cdot (\mathbf{v} \times \mathbf{w})|$

$= |\langle 3, -2, 1 \rangle \cdot \langle -2, -1, 0 \rangle| = |-4| = 4$

33. $\|AC\| \cos 40° - \|BC\| \cos 20° = 0$

$\|AC\| \sin 40° + \|BC\| \sin 20° = 20$

$\|AC\| = \dfrac{\|BC\| \cos 20°}{\cos 40°}$

By substitution, we have:

$\|BC\|(\cos 20° \tan 40° + \sin 20°) = 20$

$\|BC\| \approx 17.7 \, \text{N}$

$\|AC\| \approx 21.7 \, \text{N}$

$\|BC\|(\cos 20° + \tan 40° + \sin 20°) = 20$

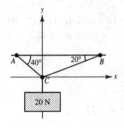

35. $\mathbf{F} = c(\cos 20°\mathbf{j} + \sin 20°\mathbf{k})$

$\overrightarrow{PQ} = 2\mathbf{k}$

$\overrightarrow{PQ} \times \mathbf{F} = \begin{vmatrix} \mathbf{i} & \mathbf{j} & \mathbf{k} \\ 0 & 0 & 2 \\ 0 & c\cos 20° & c\sin 20° \end{vmatrix} = -2c\cos 20°\mathbf{i}$

$200 = \|\overrightarrow{PQ} \times \mathbf{F}\| = 2c\cos 20°$

$c = \dfrac{100}{\cos 20°}$

$\mathbf{F} = \dfrac{100}{\cos 20°}(\cos 20°\mathbf{j} + \sin 20°\mathbf{k}) = 100(\mathbf{j} + \tan 20°\mathbf{k})$

$\|\mathbf{F}\| = 100\sqrt{1 + \tan^2 20°} = 100 \sec 20° \approx 106.4 \, \text{lb}$

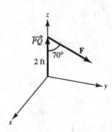

37. (a) Any line perpendicular to the xz-plane must have the direction of the vector $\mathbf{v} = 0\mathbf{i} + \mathbf{j} + 0\mathbf{k}$. Thus, direction numbers for the required line are 0, 1, 0. Since the line passes through the point $(1, 2, 3)$, the parametric equations are

$x = 1 + (0)t = 1$

$y = 2 + t$

$z = 3 + (0)t = 3.$

(b) Since two of the direction numbers are zero, there is no symmetric form.

39. $3x - 3y - 7z = -4, \ x - y + 2z = 3$

Solving simultaneously, we have $z = 1$. Substituting $z = 1$ into the second equation we have $y = x - 1$. Substituting for x in this equation we obtain two points on the line of intersection, $(0, -1, 1), (1, 0, 1)$. The direction vector of the line of intersection is $\mathbf{v} = \mathbf{i} + \mathbf{j}$.

(a) $x = t, \ y = -1 + t, \ z = 1$

(b) $x = y + 1, \ z = 1$

41. $\dfrac{x-1}{-2} = y = z + 1, \dfrac{x+1}{-2} = y - 1 = z - 2$

We first observe that the lines are parallel since they have the same direction numbers, $-2, 1, 1$. Therefore, a vector parallel to the plane is $\mathbf{u} = \langle -2, 1, 1 \rangle$. A point on the first line is $(1, 0, -1)$ and a point on the second line is $(-1, 1, 2)$. The vector $\mathbf{v} = \langle 2, -1, -3 \rangle$ connecting these two points is also parallel to the plane. Thus, a normal vector to the plane is

$$\mathbf{u} \times \mathbf{v} = \begin{vmatrix} \mathbf{i} & \mathbf{j} & \mathbf{k} \\ -2 & 1 & 1 \\ 2 & -1 & -3 \end{vmatrix} = -2(\mathbf{i} + 2\mathbf{j}).$$

Therefore, an equation of the plane is

$$1(x - 1) + 2(y - 0) + 0(z + 1) = 0$$
$$x + 2y = 1.$$

43. $Q = (1, 0, 2)$

$2x - 3y + 6z = 6$

A point P on the plane is $(3, 0, 0)$.

$\overrightarrow{PQ} = \langle -2, 0, 2 \rangle$

$\mathbf{n} = \langle 2, -3, 6 \rangle$

$D = \dfrac{|\overrightarrow{PQ} \cdot \mathbf{n}|}{\|\mathbf{n}\|} = \dfrac{8}{7}$

45. Line 1: $\dfrac{x}{1} = \dfrac{y}{2} = \dfrac{z}{3}$

Line 2: $\dfrac{x+1}{-1} = \dfrac{y}{3} = \dfrac{z+2}{2}$

Direction vectors for the two lines:

$\mathbf{u} = \langle 1, 2, 3 \rangle, \mathbf{v} = \langle -1, 3, 2 \rangle$

A vector perpendicular to the two lines:

$$\mathbf{u} \times \mathbf{v} = \begin{vmatrix} \mathbf{i} & \mathbf{j} & \mathbf{k} \\ 1 & 2 & 3 \\ -1 & 3 & 2 \end{vmatrix} = \langle -5, -5, 5 \rangle$$

Point on Line 1: $(1, 2, 3)$

Point on Line 2: $(0, -3, -4)$

The vector connecting the two points:

$\mathbf{w} = \langle -1, -5, -7 \rangle$

$D = \dfrac{|\mathbf{w} \cdot (\mathbf{u} \times \mathbf{v})|}{\|\mathbf{u} \times \mathbf{v}\|} = \dfrac{5}{5\sqrt{3}} = \dfrac{\sqrt{3}}{3}$

47. $x + 2y + 3z = 6$

Plane

Intercepts: $(6, 0, 0), (0, 3, 0), (0, 0, 2)$

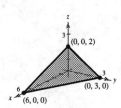

49. $y = \frac{1}{2}z$

Plane with rulings parallel to the x-axis

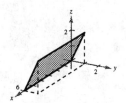

51. $\dfrac{x^2}{16} + \dfrac{y^2}{9} + z^2 = 1$

Ellipsoid

xy-trace: $\dfrac{x^2}{16} + \dfrac{y^2}{9} = 1$

xz-trace: $\dfrac{x^2}{16} + z^2 = 1$

yz-trace: $\dfrac{y^2}{9} + z^2 = 1$

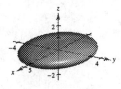

53. $\dfrac{x^2}{16} - \dfrac{y^2}{9} + z^2 = -1$

Hyperboloid of two sheets

xy-trace: $\dfrac{y^2}{4} - \dfrac{x^2}{16} = 1$

xz-trace: None

yz-trace: $\dfrac{y^2}{9} - z^2 = 1$

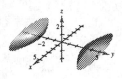

55. (a) $z = \frac{1}{2}y^2 + 1 \quad (0 \le y \le 2)$

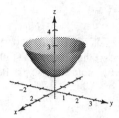

$2z = y^2 + 2$

$y = \sqrt{2z - 2} = \sqrt{2(z - 1)}$

The equation of the surface generated by revolving the curve about the z-axis is given by

$$x^2 + y^2 = [r(z)]^2 = \left[\sqrt{2(z - 1)}\right]^2$$

$$x^2 + y^2 - 2z + 2 = 0.$$

(b) $V = 2\pi \int_0^2 x\left[3 - \left(\frac{1}{2}x^2 + 1\right)\right] dx$

$$= 2\pi \int_0^2 \left(2x - \frac{1}{2}x^3\right) dx$$

$$= 2\pi \left[x^2 - \frac{x^4}{8}\right]_0^2$$

$$= 4\pi \approx 12.6 \text{ cubic centimeters}$$

(c) $V = 2\pi \int_{1/2}^2 x\left[3 - \left(\frac{1}{2}x^2 + 1\right)\right] dx$

$$= 2\pi \int_{1/2}^2 \left(2x - \frac{1}{2}x^3\right) dx$$

$$= 2\pi \left[x^2 - \frac{x^4}{8}\right]_{1/2}^2$$

$$= 4\pi - \frac{31\pi}{64} = \frac{225\pi}{64} \approx 11.0 \text{ cubic centimeters}$$

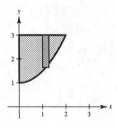

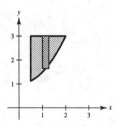

57. $\left(-2\sqrt{2}, 2\sqrt{2}, 2\right)$, rectangular

(a) $r = \sqrt{\left(-2\sqrt{2}\right)^2 + \left(2\sqrt{2}\right)^2} = 4,$

$\theta = \arctan(-1) = \frac{3\pi}{4},$

$z = 2,$

$\left(4, \frac{3\pi}{4}, 2\right)$, cylindrical

(b) $\rho = \sqrt{\left(-2\sqrt{2}\right)^2 + \left(2\sqrt{2}\right)^2 + (2)^2} = 2\sqrt{5},$

$\theta = \frac{3\pi}{4},$

$\phi = \arccos\frac{2}{2\sqrt{5}} = \arccos\frac{1}{\sqrt{5}},$

$\left(2\sqrt{5}, \frac{3\pi}{4}, \arccos\frac{\sqrt{5}}{5}\right)$, spherical

59. $x^2 - y^2 = 2z$

(a) Cylindrical: $r^2 \cos^2 \theta - r^2 \sin^2 \theta = 2z,$

$r^2 \cos 2\theta = 2z$

(b) Spherical: $\rho^2 \sin^2 \phi \cos^2 \theta - \rho^2 \sin^2 \phi \sin^2 \theta = 2\rho \cos \phi,$

$\rho \sin^2 \phi \cos 2\theta - 2 \cos \phi = 0,$

$\rho = 2 \sec 2\theta \cos \phi \csc^2 \phi$

C H A P T E R   11
Vector-Valued Functions

CHAPTER 11
Vector-Valued Functions

Section 11.1   Vector-Valued Functions

Solutions to Odd-Numbered Exercises

1. $\mathbf{r}(t) = 5t\mathbf{i} - 4t\mathbf{j} - \dfrac{1}{t}\mathbf{k}$

Component functions: $f(t) = 5t$

$$g(t) = -4t$$

$$h(t) = -\frac{1}{t}$$

Domain: $(-\infty, 0) \cup (0, \infty)$

3. $\mathbf{r}(t) = \ln t\mathbf{i} - e^t\mathbf{j} - t\mathbf{k}.$

The component functions of the vector-valued function

$$\mathbf{r}(t) = f(t)\mathbf{i} + g(t)\mathbf{j} + h(t)\mathbf{k}$$

are the real-valued functions f, g, and h. Given the vector-valued function $\mathbf{r}(t) = \ln t\mathbf{i} - e^t\mathbf{j} - t\mathbf{k}$ the component functions and their domains are:

$$f(t) = \ln t, \qquad 0 < t < \infty$$

$$g(t) = -e^t, \qquad -\infty < t < \infty$$

$$h(t) = -t, \qquad -\infty < t < \infty.$$

The intersection of the domains of f, g, and h, is the interval $(0, \infty)$, the domain of $\mathbf{r}$.

5. $\mathbf{r}(t) = \mathbf{F}(t) + \mathbf{G}(t) = \left(\cos t\mathbf{i} - \sin t\mathbf{j} + \sqrt{t}\mathbf{k}\right) + \left(\cos t\mathbf{i} + \sin t\mathbf{j}\right) = 2\cos t\mathbf{i} + \sqrt{t}\mathbf{k}$

Component functions: $f(t) = 2\cos t$

$$g(t) = 0$$

$$h(t) = \sqrt{t}$$

Domain: $[0, \infty)$

7. $\mathbf{r}(t) = \mathbf{F}(t) \times \mathbf{G}(t) = \begin{vmatrix} \mathbf{i} & \mathbf{j} & \mathbf{k} \\ \sin t & \cos t & 0 \\ 0 & \sin t & \cos t \end{vmatrix} = \cos^2 t\mathbf{i} - \sin t\cos t\mathbf{j} + \sin^2 t\mathbf{k}$

Component functions: $f(t) = \cos^2 t$

$$g(t) = -\sin t\cos t$$

$$h(t) = \sin^2 t$$

Domain: $(-\infty, \infty)$

9. $\mathbf{r}(t) = \frac{1}{2}t^2\mathbf{i} - (t - 1)\mathbf{j}$

(a) $\mathbf{r}(1) = \frac{1}{2}\mathbf{i}$

(b) $\mathbf{r}(0) = \mathbf{j}$

(c) $\mathbf{r}(s + 1) = \frac{1}{2}(s + 1)^2\mathbf{i} - (s + 1 - 1)\mathbf{j} = \frac{1}{2}(s + 1)^2\mathbf{i} - s\mathbf{j}$

(d) $\mathbf{r}(2 + \Delta t) - \mathbf{r}(2) = \frac{1}{2}(2 + \Delta t)^2\mathbf{i} - (2 + \Delta t - 1)\mathbf{j} - (2\mathbf{i} - \mathbf{j})$

$$= \left(2 + 2\Delta t + \frac{1}{2}(\Delta t)^2\right)\mathbf{i} - (1 + \Delta t)\mathbf{j} - 2\mathbf{i} + \mathbf{j} = \left(2\Delta t + \frac{1}{2}(\Delta t)^2\right)\mathbf{i} - (\Delta t)\mathbf{j}$$

11. $\mathbf{r}(t) = \ln t\mathbf{i} + \frac{1}{t}\mathbf{j} + 3t\mathbf{k}$

(a) $\mathbf{r}(2) = \ln 2\mathbf{i} + \frac{1}{2}\mathbf{j} + 6\mathbf{k}$

(b) $\mathbf{r}(-3)$ is not defined. ($\ln(-3)$ does not exist.)

(c) $\mathbf{r}(t - 4) = \ln(t - 4)\mathbf{i} + \frac{1}{t - 4}\mathbf{j} + 3(t - 4)\mathbf{k}$

(d) $\mathbf{r}(1 + \Delta t) - \mathbf{r}(1) = \ln(1 + \Delta t)\mathbf{i} + \frac{1}{1 + \Delta t}\mathbf{j} + 3(1 + \Delta t)\mathbf{k} - (0\mathbf{i} + \mathbf{j} + 3\mathbf{k})$

$$= \ln(1 + \Delta t)\mathbf{i} + \left(\frac{1}{1 + \Delta t} - 1\right)\mathbf{j} + (3\Delta t)\mathbf{k}$$

13. $\mathbf{r}(t) = \sin 3t\mathbf{i} + \cos 3t\mathbf{j} + t\mathbf{k}$

$\|\mathbf{r}(t)\| = \sqrt{(\sin 3t)^2 + (\cos 3t)^2 + t^2} = \sqrt{(\sin^2 3t + \cos^2 3t) + t^2} = \sqrt{1 + t^2}$

15. $\mathbf{r}(t) \cdot \mathbf{u}(t) = (3t - 1)(t^2) + \left(\frac{1}{4}t^3\right)(-8) + 4(t^3)$

$\qquad\qquad = 3t^3 - t^2 - 2t^3 + 4t^3 = 5t^3 - t^2$, a scalar.

The dot product is a scalar-valued function.

17. $\mathbf{r}(t) = t\mathbf{i} + 2t\mathbf{j} + t^2\mathbf{k}, \ -2 \le t \le 2$

$x = t, y = 2t, z = t^2$

Thus, $z = x^2$. Matches (b)

19. $\mathbf{r}(t) = t\mathbf{i} + t^2\mathbf{j} + e^{0.75t}\mathbf{k}, \ -2 \le t \le 2$

$x = t, y = t^2, z = e^{0.75t}$

Thus, $y = x^2$. Matches (d)

21. (a) View from the negative x-axis: $(-20, 0, 0)$

(b) View from above the first octant: $(10, 20, 10)$

(c) View from the z-axis: $(0, 0, 20)$

(d) View from the positive x-axis: $(20, 0, 0)$

23. $x = 3t$

$\quad y = t - 1$

$\quad y = \dfrac{x}{3} - 1$

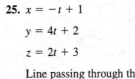

25. $x = -t + 1$

$\quad y = 4t + 2$

$\quad z = 2t + 3$

Line passing through the points:

$\qquad (0, 6, 5), \ (1, 2, 3)$

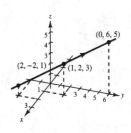

27. $\mathbf{r}(t) = 2\cos t\mathbf{i} + 2\sin t\mathbf{j} + t\mathbf{k}$

From the first two parametric equations $x = 2\cos t$ and $y = 2\sin t$, we obtain

$$x^2 + y^2 = 4\cos^2 t + 4\sin^2 t = 4.$$

This means that the curve lies on a right circular cylinder of radius 2 centered about the z-axis. To locate the curve on this cylinder, use the third parametric equation $z = t$. Thus the graph of the vector-valued function spirals counterclockwise up the cylinder to produce a circular helix.

29. $x = 2 \sin t, \ y = 2 \cos t, \ z = e^{-t}$

$x^2 + y^2 = 4$

$z = e^{-t}$

31. $\mathbf{r}(t) = \left\langle t, t^2, \frac{2}{3}t^3 \right\rangle$

$x = t, y = t^2, z = \frac{2}{3}t^3$

From the first two parametric equations, we obtain $y = x^2$. This means that the space curve lies on the cylinder $y = x^2$ and the vertical position of each point is determined by $z = \frac{2}{3}x^3$.

t	-2	-1	0	1	2
x	-2	-1	0	1	2
y	4	1	0	1	4
z	$-\frac{16}{3}$	$-\frac{2}{3}$	0	$\frac{2}{3}$	$\frac{16}{3}$

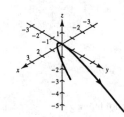

33. $\mathbf{r}(t) = -\frac{1}{2}t^2\mathbf{i} + t\mathbf{j} - \frac{\sqrt{3}}{2}t^2\mathbf{k}$

Parabola

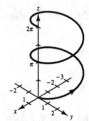

35. $\mathbf{r}(t) = \sin t\mathbf{i} + \left(\frac{\sqrt{3}}{2}\cos t - \frac{1}{2}t \right)\mathbf{j} + \left(\frac{1}{2}\cos t + \frac{\sqrt{3}}{2} \right)\mathbf{k}$

Helix

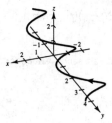

37.

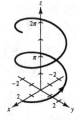

(a)

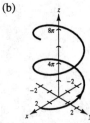

The helix is translated 2 units back on the x-axis.

(b)

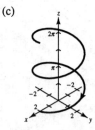

The height of the helix increases at a faster rate.

(c)

The orientation of the helix is reversed.

(d)

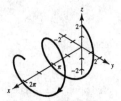

The axis of the helix is the x-axis.

(e)

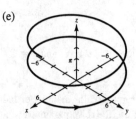

The radius of the helix is increased from 2 to 6.

39. $y = 4 - x$

Let $x = t$, then $y = 4 - t$.

$\mathbf{r}(t) = t\mathbf{i} + (4 - t)\mathbf{j}$

41. The graph of the equation $x^2 + y^2 = 25$ is a circle with center at the origin and radius 5. Let (x, y) be any point on the circumference of the circle (see figure). Then

$\cos \theta = \dfrac{x}{5} \implies x = 5 \cos \theta$

$\sin \theta = \dfrac{y}{5} \implies y = 5 \sin \theta$

and $\mathbf{r}(\theta) = (5 \cos \theta)\mathbf{i} + (5 \sin \theta)\mathbf{j}$.

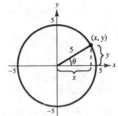

43. The parametric equations for the line are $x = 2 - 2t$, $y = 3 + 5t$, $z = 8t$.
One possible answer is $\mathbf{r}(t) = (2 - 2t)\mathbf{i} + (3 + 5t)\mathbf{j} + 8t\mathbf{k}$.

45. Label the sides of the triangle as shown in the figure. Note that $y = 0$ on C_1. Therefore, C_1 can be represented by the vector-valued function $\mathbf{r}_1(t) = t\mathbf{i}$, $0 \le t \le 4$. The line segment C_2 has slope $m = -\frac{3}{2}$ and y-intercept $(0, 6)$. Hence, the rectangular form of the equation is $y = -\frac{3}{2}x + 6$. Letting $x = 2t$ and substituting this expression for x in the rectangular equation of the line yields $y = -3t + 6$. However, for increasing values of the parameter, x increases and y decreases which is the incorrect orientation. Replacing t by $2 - t$ reverses the orientation and produces

$x = 2(2 - t) = 4 - 2t$ and $y = -3(2 - t) + 6 = 3t$.

Therefore,

$\mathbf{r}_2(t) = (4 - 2t)\mathbf{i} + 3t\mathbf{j}, 0 \le t \le 2$.

Note that $x = 0$ on C_3. Since y is decreasing on C_3, a vector-valued function for C_3 is

$\mathbf{r}_3(t) = (6 - t)\mathbf{j}, 0 \le t \le 6$.

(Observe that there are many correct answers for this problem.)

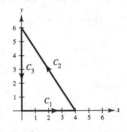

47. $\mathbf{r}_1(t) = t\mathbf{i} + t^2\mathbf{j}$, $0 \le t \le 2$ $(y = x^2)$

$\mathbf{r}_2(t) = (2 - t)\mathbf{i}$, $0 \le t \le 2$

$\mathbf{r}_3(t) = (4 - t)\mathbf{j}$, $0 \le t \le 4$

(Other answers possible)

49. $z = x^2 + y^2$, $x + y = 0$

Let $x = t$, then $y = -x = -t$ and $z = x^2 + y^2 = 2t^2$.
Therefore, $x = t$, $y = -t$, $z = 2t^2$.

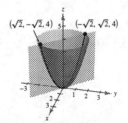

51. $x^2 + y^2 = 4$, $z = x^2$

$x = 2 \sin t$, $y = 2 \cos t$

$z = x^2 = 4 \sin^2 t$

t	0	$\dfrac{\pi}{6}$	$\dfrac{\pi}{4}$	$\dfrac{\pi}{2}$	$\dfrac{3\pi}{4}$	π
x	0	1	$\sqrt{2}$	2	$\sqrt{2}$	0
y	2	$\sqrt{3}$	$\sqrt{2}$	0	$-\sqrt{2}$	-2
z	0	1	2	4	2	0

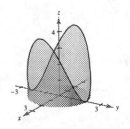

53. The equation $x^2 + y^2 + z^2 = 4$ represents a sphere of radius 2 centered at the origin.
The equation $x + z = 2$ represents a plane. If we let $x = 1 + \sin t$, then

$$z = 2 - x = 1 - \sin t.$$

Substituting into the equation of the sphere, we have

$$x^2 + y^2 + z^2 = 4$$

$$(1 + \sin t)^2 + y^2 + (1 - \sin t)^2 = 4$$

$$2 + 2\sin^2 t + y^2 = 4$$

$$y^2 = 2 - 2\sin^2 t$$

$$y^2 = 2\cos^2 t$$

$$y = \pm\sqrt{2}\cos t.$$

Therefore, $x = 1 + \sin t$, $y = \pm\sqrt{2}\cos t$, $z = 1 - \sin t$ and the
two vector-valued functions are

$$\mathbf{r}(t) = (1 + \sin t)\mathbf{i} + \left(\sqrt{2}\cos t\right)\mathbf{j} + (1 - \sin t)\mathbf{k}$$

and

$$\mathbf{r}(t) = (1 + \sin t)\mathbf{i} - \left(\sqrt{2}\cos t\right)\mathbf{j} + (1 - \sin t)\mathbf{k}.$$

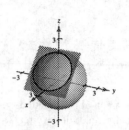

t	$-\dfrac{\pi}{2}$	$-\dfrac{\pi}{6}$	0	$\dfrac{\pi}{6}$	$\dfrac{\pi}{2}$
x	0	$\dfrac{1}{2}$	1	$\dfrac{3}{2}$	2
y	0	$\pm\dfrac{\sqrt{6}}{2}$	$\pm\sqrt{2}$	$\pm\dfrac{\sqrt{6}}{2}$	0
z	2	$\dfrac{3}{2}$	1	$\dfrac{1}{2}$	0

55. The equation $x^2 + z^2 = 4$ represents a cylinder of radius 2 with its axis along the y-axis, while the equation $y^2 + z^2 = 4$
represents a cylinder of radius 2 with its axis along the x-axis. Thus the curve of intersection lies along both cylinders, as
shown in the sketch. Two points on the curve are $(2, 2, 0)$ and $(0, 0, 2)$. To find a set of parametric equations for the curve of
intersection, subtract the second equation from the first to obtain

$$x^2 + z^2 = 4$$
$$\underline{-(y^2 + z^2 = 4)}$$
$$x^2 - y^2 = 0 \text{ or } y = \pm x.$$

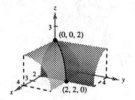

Therefore, in the first octant, if we let $x = t(t > 0)$, then parametric equations for the curve are

$$x = t, \, y = t, \, z = \sqrt{4 - t^2}$$

and the vector-valued function is

$$\mathbf{r}(t) = t\mathbf{i} + t\mathbf{j} + \sqrt{4 - t^2}\mathbf{k}.$$

57. $\displaystyle\lim_{t \to 2}\left[t\mathbf{i} + \frac{t^2 - 4}{t^2 - 2t}\mathbf{j} + \frac{1}{t}\mathbf{k}\right] = 2\mathbf{i} + 2\mathbf{j} + \frac{1}{2}\mathbf{k}$ since $\displaystyle\lim_{t \to 2}\frac{t^2 - 4}{t^2 - 2t} = \lim_{t \to 2}\frac{2t}{2t - 2} = 2.$ (L'Hôpital's Rule)

59. $\displaystyle\lim_{t \to 0}\left(t^2\mathbf{i} + 3t\mathbf{j} + \frac{1 - \cos t}{t}\mathbf{k}\right) = \left[\lim_{t \to 0}t^2\right]\mathbf{i} + \left[\lim_{t \to 0}3t\right]\mathbf{j} + \left[\lim_{t \to 0}\frac{1 - \cos t}{t}\right]\mathbf{k}$

$$= 0\mathbf{i} + 0\mathbf{j} + 0\mathbf{k} = \mathbf{0}$$

61. $\displaystyle\lim_{t \to 0}\left[\frac{1}{t}\mathbf{i} + \cos t\mathbf{j} + \sin t\mathbf{k}\right]$

does not exist since $\displaystyle\lim_{t \to 0}\frac{1}{t}$ does not exist.

63. $\mathbf{r}(t) = t\mathbf{i} + \dfrac{1}{t}\mathbf{j}$

Continuous on $(-\infty, 0)$, $(0, \infty)$

65. $\mathbf{r}(t) = t\mathbf{i} + \arcsin t\mathbf{j} + (t - 1)\mathbf{k}$

is continuous on $[-1, 1]$. This interval is the domain of $\mathbf{r}$ since it is the domain of the arcsine function.

67. $\mathbf{r}(t) = \langle e^{-t}, t^2, \tan t \rangle$

Discontinuous at $t = \dfrac{\pi}{2} + n\pi$

Continuous on $\left(-\dfrac{\pi}{2} + n\pi, \dfrac{\pi}{2} + n\pi \right)$

69. Let $\mathbf{r}(t) = x_1(t) + y_1(t)\mathbf{j} + z_1(t)\mathbf{k}$ and $\mathbf{u}(t) = x_2(t)\mathbf{i} + y_2(t)\mathbf{j} + z_2(t)\mathbf{k}$. Then:

$$\lim_{t \to c} [\mathbf{r}(t) \times \mathbf{u}(t)] = \lim_{t \to c} \{ [y_1(t)z_2(t) - y_2(t)z_1(t)]\mathbf{i} - [x_1(t)z_2(t) - x_2(t)z_1(t)]\mathbf{j} + [x_1(t)y_2(t) - x_2(t)y_1(t)]\mathbf{k} \}$$

$$= \left[\lim_{t \to c} y_1(t) \lim_{t \to c} z_2(t) - \lim_{t \to c} y_2(t) \lim_{t \to c} z_1(t) \right]\mathbf{i} - \left[\lim_{t \to c} x_1(t) \lim_{t \to c} z_2(t) - \lim_{t \to c} x_2(t) \lim_{t \to c} z_1(t) \right]\mathbf{j}$$

$$+ \left[\lim_{t \to c} x_1(t) \lim_{t \to c} y_2(t) - \lim_{t \to c} x_2(t) \lim_{t \to c} y_1(t) \right]\mathbf{k}$$

$$= \left[\lim_{t \to c} x_1(t)\mathbf{i} + \lim_{t \to c} y_1(t)\mathbf{j} + \lim_{t \to c} z_1(t)\mathbf{k} \right] \times \left[\lim_{t \to c} x_2(t)\mathbf{i} + \lim_{t \to c} y_2(t)\mathbf{j} + \lim_{t \to c} z_2(t)\mathbf{k} \right]$$

$$= \lim_{t \to c} \mathbf{r}(t) \times \lim_{t \to c} \mathbf{u}(t)$$

71. Let $\mathbf{r}(t) = x(t)\mathbf{i} + y(t)\mathbf{j} + z(t)\mathbf{k}$. Since $\mathbf{r}$ is continuous at $t = c$, then li

$$\mathbf{r}(c) = x(c)\mathbf{i} + y(c)\mathbf{j} + z(c)\mathbf{k} \implies x(c), \ y(c), \ z(c)$$

are defined at c.

$$\|\mathbf{r}\| = \sqrt{(x(t))^2 + (y(t))^2 + (z(t))^2}$$

$$\lim_{t \to c} \|\mathbf{r}\| = \sqrt{(x(c))^2 + (y(c))^2 + (z(c))^2} = \|\mathbf{r}(c)\|$$

Therefore, $\|\mathbf{r}\|$ is continuous at c.

73. True

Section 11.2   Differentiation and Integration of Vector-Valued Functions

1. $\mathbf{r}(t) = t^2\mathbf{i} + t\mathbf{j}, \ t_0 = 2$

$x(t) = t^2, \ y(t) = t$

$x = y^2$

$\quad \mathbf{r}(2) = 4\mathbf{i} + 2\mathbf{j}$

$\quad \mathbf{r}'(t) = 2t\mathbf{i} + \mathbf{j}$

$\quad \mathbf{r}'(2) = 4\mathbf{i} + \mathbf{j}$

$\mathbf{r}'(t_0)$ is tangent to the curve.

3. $\mathbf{r}(t) = \cos t\mathbf{i} + \sin t\mathbf{j}$

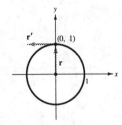

(a) Eliminating the parameter from the parametric equations $x = \cos t$ and $y = \sin t$, we have

$$x^2 + y^2 = \cos^2 t + \sin^2 t = 1.$$

Therefore, the vector-valued function represents a circle of radius 1 center at the origin. (See the figure.)

(b) $\mathbf{r}(t) = \cos t\mathbf{i} + \sin t\mathbf{j} \implies \mathbf{r}\left(\dfrac{\pi}{2} \right) = \mathbf{j}$

$\mathbf{r}'(t) = -\sin t\mathbf{i} + \cos t\mathbf{j} \implies \mathbf{r}'\left(\dfrac{\pi}{2} \right) = -\mathbf{i}$

5. $\mathbf{r}(t) = t\mathbf{i} + t^2\mathbf{j}$

(a)

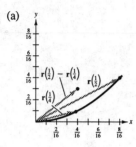

(b) $\qquad \mathbf{r}\left(\dfrac{1}{4}\right) = \dfrac{1}{4}\mathbf{i} + \dfrac{1}{16}\mathbf{j}$

$\qquad \mathbf{r}\left(\dfrac{1}{2}\right) = \dfrac{1}{2}\mathbf{i} + \dfrac{1}{4}\mathbf{j}$

$\mathbf{r}\left(\dfrac{1}{2}\right) - \mathbf{r}\left(\dfrac{1}{4}\right) = \dfrac{1}{4}\mathbf{i} + \dfrac{3}{16}\mathbf{j}$

(c) $\qquad\qquad \mathbf{r}'(t) = \mathbf{i} + 2t\mathbf{j}$

$\qquad\qquad \mathbf{r}'\left(\dfrac{1}{4}\right) = \mathbf{i} + \dfrac{1}{2}\mathbf{j}$

$\dfrac{\mathbf{r}(1/2) - \mathbf{r}(1/4)}{(1/2) - (1/4)} = \dfrac{(1/4)\mathbf{i} + (3/16)\mathbf{j}}{1/4} = \mathbf{i} + \dfrac{3}{4}\mathbf{j}$

This vector approximates $\mathbf{r}'\left(\tfrac{1}{4}\right)$.

7. $\mathbf{r}(t) = 2\cos t\mathbf{i} + 2\sin t\mathbf{j} + t\mathbf{k},\ t_0 = \dfrac{3\pi}{2}$

$x^2 + y^2 = 4,\ z = t$

$\qquad \mathbf{r}'(t) = -2\sin t\mathbf{i} + 2\cos t\mathbf{j} + \mathbf{k}$

$\qquad \mathbf{r}\left(\dfrac{3\pi}{2}\right) = -2\mathbf{j} + \dfrac{3\pi}{2}\mathbf{k}$

$\qquad \mathbf{r}'\left(\dfrac{3\pi}{2}\right) = 2\mathbf{i} + \mathbf{k}$

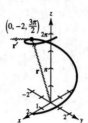

9. $\qquad \mathbf{r}(t) = \cos(\pi t)\mathbf{i} + \sin(\pi t)\mathbf{j} + t^2\mathbf{k},\ t_0 = -\dfrac{1}{4}$

$\qquad \mathbf{r}'(t) = -\pi\sin(\pi t)\mathbf{i} + \pi\cos(\pi t)\mathbf{j} + 2t\mathbf{k}$

$\mathbf{r}'\left(-\dfrac{1}{4}\right) = \dfrac{\sqrt{2}\pi}{2}\mathbf{i} + \dfrac{\sqrt{2}\pi}{2}\mathbf{j} - \dfrac{1}{2}\mathbf{k}$

$\left\|\mathbf{r}'\left(\dfrac{1}{4}\right)\right\| = \sqrt{\left(\dfrac{\sqrt{2}\pi}{2}\right)^2 + \left(\dfrac{\sqrt{2}\pi}{2}\right)^2 + \left(-\dfrac{1}{2}\right)^2} = \sqrt{\pi^2 + \dfrac{1}{4}} = \dfrac{\sqrt{4\pi^2 + 1}}{2}$

$\dfrac{\mathbf{r}'(-1/4)}{\|\mathbf{r}'(-1/4)\|} = \dfrac{1}{\sqrt{4\pi^2 + 1}}(\sqrt{2}\pi\mathbf{i} + \sqrt{2}\pi\mathbf{j} - \mathbf{k})$

$\qquad \mathbf{r}''(t) = -\pi^2\cos(\pi t)\mathbf{i} - \pi^2\sin(\pi t)\mathbf{j} + 2\mathbf{k}$

$\mathbf{r}''\left(-\dfrac{1}{4}\right) = -\dfrac{\sqrt{2}\pi^2}{2}\mathbf{i} + \dfrac{\sqrt{2}\pi^2}{2}\mathbf{j} + 2\mathbf{k}$

$\left\|\mathbf{r}''\left(-\dfrac{1}{4}\right)\right\| = \sqrt{\left(-\dfrac{\sqrt{2}\pi^2}{2}\right)^2 + \left(\dfrac{\sqrt{2}\pi^2}{2}\right)^2 + (2)^2} = \sqrt{\pi^4 + 4}$

$\dfrac{\mathbf{r}''(-1/4)}{\|\mathbf{r}'(-1/4)\|} = \dfrac{1}{2\sqrt{\pi^4 + 4}}(-\sqrt{2}\pi^2\mathbf{i} + \sqrt{2}\pi^2\mathbf{j} + 4\mathbf{k})$

11. $\mathbf{r}(t) = 6t\mathbf{i} - 7t^2\mathbf{j} + t^3\mathbf{k}$

$\mathbf{r}'(t) = \dfrac{d}{dt}[6t]\mathbf{i} + \dfrac{d}{dt}[-7t^2]\mathbf{j} + \dfrac{d}{dt}[t^3]\mathbf{k}$

$\qquad = 6\mathbf{i} - 14t\mathbf{j} + 3t^2\mathbf{k}$

13. $\mathbf{r}(t) = a\cos^3 t\mathbf{i} + a\sin^3 t\mathbf{j} + \mathbf{k}$

$\qquad \mathbf{r}'(t) = -3a\cos^2 t\sin t\mathbf{i} + 3a\sin^2 t\cos t\mathbf{j}$

15. $\mathbf{r}(t) = e^{-t}\mathbf{i} + 4\mathbf{j}$

$\quad\mathbf{r}'(t) = -e^{-t}\mathbf{i}$

17. $\mathbf{r}(t) = \langle t \sin t, t \cos t, t \rangle$

$\quad\mathbf{r}'(t) = \left\langle \dfrac{d}{dt}[t \sin t], \dfrac{d}{dt}[t \cos t], \dfrac{d}{dt}[t] \right\rangle$

$\qquad\ = \langle t \cos t + \sin t, -t \sin t + \cos t, 1 \rangle$

19. $\mathbf{r}(t) = t\mathbf{i} + 3t\mathbf{j} + t^2\mathbf{k}, \mathbf{u}(t) = 4t\mathbf{i} + t^2\mathbf{j} + t^3\mathbf{k}$

   (a) Differentiating in a component-by-component basis produces

$\qquad\mathbf{r}'(t) = \mathbf{i} + 3\mathbf{j} + 2t\mathbf{k}.$

   (c) $\mathbf{r}(t) \cdot \mathbf{u}(t) = t(4t) + 3t(t^2) + t^2(t^3)$

$\qquad\qquad\qquad\ = 4t^2 + 3t^3 + t^5$

$\qquad D_t[\mathbf{r}(t) \cdot \mathbf{u}(t)] = 8t + 9t^2 + 5t^4$

   (e) $\mathbf{r}(t) \times \mathbf{u}(t) = \begin{vmatrix} \mathbf{i} & \mathbf{j} & \mathbf{k} \\ t & 3t & t^2 \\ 4t & t^2 & t^3 \end{vmatrix}$

$\qquad\qquad\ = \begin{vmatrix} 3t & t^2 \\ t^2 & t^3 \end{vmatrix}\mathbf{i} - \begin{vmatrix} t & t^2 \\ 4t & t^3 \end{vmatrix}\mathbf{j} + \begin{vmatrix} t & 3t \\ 4t & t^2 \end{vmatrix}\mathbf{k}$

$\qquad\qquad\ = 2t^4\mathbf{i} - (t^4 - 4t^3)\mathbf{j} + (t^3 - 12t^2)\mathbf{k}$

$\qquad D_t[\mathbf{r}(t) \times \mathbf{u}(t)] = 8t^3\mathbf{i} + (12t^2 - 4t^3)\mathbf{j} + (3t^2 - 24t)\mathbf{k}$

   (b) Differentiating $\mathbf{r}'(t)$ in a component-by-component basis produces

$\qquad\mathbf{r}''(t) = 2\mathbf{k}.$

   (d) $3\mathbf{r}(t) - \mathbf{u}(t) = 3(t\mathbf{i} + 3t\mathbf{j} + t^2\mathbf{k}) - (4t\mathbf{i} + t^2\mathbf{j} + t^3\mathbf{k})$

$\qquad\qquad\qquad\qquad = -t\mathbf{i} + (9t - t^2)\mathbf{j} + (3t^2 - t^3)\mathbf{k}$

$\qquad D_t[3\mathbf{r}(t) - \mathbf{u}(t)] = -\mathbf{i} + (9 - 2t)\mathbf{j} + (6t - 3t^2)\mathbf{k}$

   (f) $\|r(t)\| = \sqrt{t^2 + (3t)^2 + (t^2)^2}$

$\qquad\qquad\ = \sqrt{10t^2 + t^4}$

$\qquad D_t[\|\mathbf{r}(t)\|] = \dfrac{1}{2}(10t^2 + t^4)^{-1/2}(20t + 4t^3)$

$\qquad\qquad\qquad\ = \dfrac{10t + 2t^3}{\sqrt{10t^2 + t^4}} = \dfrac{10 + 2t^2}{\sqrt{10 + t^2}}$

21. $\qquad\mathbf{r}(t) = 3 \sin t\mathbf{i} + 4 \cos t\mathbf{j}$

$\qquad\quad\mathbf{r}'(t) = 3 \cos t\mathbf{i} - 4 \sin t\mathbf{j}$

$\mathbf{r}(t) \cdot \mathbf{r}'(t) = 9 \sin t \cos t - 16 \cos t \sin t = -7 \sin t \cos t$

$\qquad\cos \theta = \dfrac{\mathbf{r}(t) \cdot \mathbf{r}'(t)}{\|\mathbf{r}(t)\|\,\|\mathbf{r}'(t)\|} = \dfrac{-7 \sin t \cos t}{\sqrt{9 \sin^2 t + 16 \cos^2 t}\sqrt{9 \cos^2 t + 16 \sin^2 t}}$

$\qquad\qquad\theta = \arccos\left[\dfrac{-7 \sin t \cos t}{\sqrt{(9 \sin^2 t + 16 \cos^2 t)(9 \cos^2 t + 16 \sin^2 t)}}\right]$

$\theta = 1.855$ maximum at $t = 3.927\left(\dfrac{5\pi}{4}\right)$ and $t = 0.785\left(\dfrac{\pi}{4}\right).$

$\theta = 1.287$ minimum at $t = 2.356\left(\dfrac{3\pi}{4}\right)$ and $t = 5.498\left(\dfrac{7\pi}{4}\right).$

$\theta = \dfrac{\pi}{2}(1.571)$ for $t = n\dfrac{\pi}{2}, n = 0, 1, 2, 3, \ldots$

23. $\mathbf{r}(t) = t^2\mathbf{i} + t^3\mathbf{j}$

$\quad\mathbf{r}'(t) = 2t\mathbf{i} + 3t^2\mathbf{j}$

$\quad\mathbf{r}'(0) = \mathbf{0}$

Smooth on $(-\infty, 0), (0, \infty)$

25. $\qquad\mathbf{r}(\theta) = 2 \cos^3 \theta\mathbf{i} + 3 \sin^3 \theta\mathbf{j}$

$\qquad\quad\mathbf{r}'(\theta) = -6 \cos^2 \theta \sin \theta\mathbf{i} + 9 \sin^2 \theta \cos \theta\mathbf{j}$

$\qquad\quad\mathbf{r}'\left(\dfrac{n\pi}{2}\right) = \mathbf{0}$

Smooth on $\left(\dfrac{n\pi}{2}, \dfrac{(n + 1)\pi}{2}\right), n$ any integer.

27. $\mathbf{r}(\theta) = (\theta - 2\sin\theta)\mathbf{i} + (1 - 2\cos\theta)\mathbf{j}$

$\mathbf{r}'(\theta) = (1 - 2\cos\theta)\mathbf{i} + (1 + 2\sin\theta)\mathbf{j}$

$\mathbf{r}'(\theta) \neq \mathbf{0}$ for any value of θ

Smooth on $(-\infty, \infty)$

29. $\mathbf{r}(t) = (t - 1)\mathbf{i} + \dfrac{1}{t}\mathbf{j} - t^2\mathbf{k}$

$\mathbf{r}'(t) = \mathbf{i} - \dfrac{1}{t^2}\mathbf{j} - 2t\mathbf{k}$

$\mathbf{r}$ is not continuous at $t = 0$ and $\mathbf{r}'(t) \neq \mathbf{0}$ for all t in the domain of $\mathbf{r}$. Therefore, the curve is smooth on $(-\infty, 0)$ and $(0, \infty)$.

31. $\mathbf{r}(t) = t\mathbf{i} - 3t\mathbf{j} + \tan t\mathbf{k}$

$\mathbf{r}'(t) = \mathbf{i} - 3\mathbf{j} + \sec^2 t\mathbf{k} \neq \mathbf{0}$

$\mathbf{r}$ is smooth for all $t \neq \dfrac{\pi}{2} + n\pi = \dfrac{2n+1}{2}\pi$.

Smooth on intervals of form $\left(-\dfrac{\pi}{2} + n\pi, \dfrac{\pi}{2} + n\pi\right)$

33. $\mathbf{r}'(t) = \lim\limits_{\Delta t \to 0} \dfrac{\mathbf{r}(t + \Delta t) - \mathbf{r}(t)}{\Delta t}$

$= \lim\limits_{\Delta t \to 0} \dfrac{[3(t + \Delta t) + 2]\mathbf{i} + [1 - (t + \Delta t)^2]\mathbf{j} - (3t + 2)\mathbf{i} - (1 - t^2)\mathbf{j}}{\Delta t}$

$= \lim\limits_{\Delta t \to 0} \dfrac{(3\Delta t)\mathbf{i} - (2t(\Delta t) + (\Delta t)^2)\mathbf{j}}{\Delta t}$

$= \lim\limits_{\Delta t \to 0} 3\mathbf{i} - (2t + \Delta t)\mathbf{j} = 3\mathbf{i} - 2t\mathbf{j}$

35. At $t = t_0$, the graph of $\mathbf{u}(t)$ is increasing in the x, y, and z directions simultaneously.

37. $\displaystyle\int (2t\mathbf{i} + \mathbf{j} + \mathbf{k})\, dt = t^2\mathbf{i} + t\mathbf{j} + t\mathbf{k} + \mathbf{C}$

39. $\displaystyle\int \left(\dfrac{1}{t}\mathbf{i} + \mathbf{j} - t^{3/2}\mathbf{k}\right) dt = \left[\int \dfrac{1}{t}\, dt\right]\mathbf{i} + \left[\int dt\right]\mathbf{j} + \left[\int -t^{3/2}\, dt\right]\mathbf{k}$

$= \ln|t|\mathbf{i} + t\mathbf{j} - \dfrac{2}{5}t^{5/2}\mathbf{k} + \mathbf{C}$

41. $\displaystyle\int \left[(2t - 1)\mathbf{i} + 4t^3\mathbf{j} + 3\sqrt{t}\mathbf{k}\right] dt = (t^2 - t)\mathbf{i} + t^4\mathbf{j} + 2t^{3/2}\mathbf{k} + \mathbf{C}$

43. $\displaystyle\int \left[\sec^2 t\mathbf{i} + \dfrac{1}{1 + t^2}\mathbf{j}\right] dt = \tan t\mathbf{i} + \arctan t\mathbf{j} + \mathbf{C}$

45. $\mathbf{r}'(t) = 4e^{2t}\mathbf{i} + 3e^t\mathbf{j}$, $\mathbf{r}(0) = 2\mathbf{i}$

$\mathbf{r}(t) = \mathbf{i}\displaystyle\int 4e^{2t}\, dt + \mathbf{j}\int 3e^t\, dt = \mathbf{i}[2e^{2t} + c_1] + \mathbf{j}[3e^t + c_2]$

$\mathbf{r}(0) = \mathbf{i}[2 + c_1] + \mathbf{j}[3 + c_2] = 2\mathbf{i}$

Therefore, $2 + c_1 = 2$, or $c_1 = 0$. Also, $3 + c_2 = 0$, or $c_2 = -3$. Thus,

$\mathbf{r}(t) = 2e^{2t}\mathbf{i} + (3e^t - 3)\mathbf{j} = 2e^{2t}\mathbf{i} + 3(e^t - 1)\mathbf{j}$.

47. $\mathbf{r}'(t) = \displaystyle\int -32\mathbf{j}\, dt = -32t\mathbf{j} + \mathbf{C}_1$

$\mathbf{r}'(0) = \mathbf{C}_1 = 600\sqrt{3}$

$\mathbf{r}'(t) = 600\sqrt{3}\mathbf{i} + (600 - 32t)\mathbf{j}$

$\mathbf{r}(t) = \displaystyle\int \left[600\sqrt{3}\mathbf{i} + (600 - 32t)\mathbf{j}\right] dt$

$= 600\sqrt{3}\, t\mathbf{i} + (600t - 16t^2)\mathbf{j} + \mathbf{C}$

$\mathbf{r}(0) = \mathbf{C} = \mathbf{0}$

$\mathbf{r}(t) = 600\sqrt{3}\, t\mathbf{i} + (600t - 16t^2)\mathbf{j}$

49. $\mathbf{r}(t) = \displaystyle\int (te^{-t^2}\mathbf{i} - e^{-t}\mathbf{j} + \mathbf{k})\,dt = -\dfrac{1}{2}e^{-t^2}\mathbf{i} + e^{-t}\mathbf{j} + t\mathbf{k} + \mathbf{C}$

$\mathbf{r}(0) = -\dfrac{1}{2}\mathbf{i} + \mathbf{j} + \mathbf{C} = \dfrac{1}{2}\mathbf{i} - \mathbf{j} + \mathbf{k} \implies \mathbf{C} = \mathbf{i} - 2\mathbf{j} + \mathbf{k}$

$\mathbf{r}(t) = \left(1 - \dfrac{1}{2}e^{-t^2}\right)\mathbf{i} + (e^{-t} - 2)\mathbf{j} + (t + 1)\mathbf{k} = \left(\dfrac{2 - e^{-t^2}}{2}\right)\mathbf{i} + (e^{-t} - 2)\mathbf{j} + (t + 1)\mathbf{k}$

51. $\displaystyle\int_0^1 (8t\mathbf{i} + t\mathbf{j} - \mathbf{k})\,dt = \mathbf{i}\int_0^1 8t\,dt + \mathbf{j}\int_0^1 t\,dt - \mathbf{k}\int_0^1 dt$

$\qquad = \left[4t^2\right]_0^1\mathbf{i} + \left[\dfrac{1}{2}t^2\right]_0^1\mathbf{j} - \left[t\right]_0^1\mathbf{k}$

$\qquad = 4\mathbf{i} + \dfrac{1}{2}\mathbf{j} - \mathbf{k}$

53. $\displaystyle\int_0^{\pi/2} [(a\cos t)\mathbf{i} + (a\sin t)\mathbf{j} + \mathbf{k}]\,dt = \left[a\sin t\,\mathbf{i}\right]_0^{\pi/2} - \left[a\cos t\,\mathbf{j}\right]_0^{\pi/2} + \left[t\mathbf{k}\right]_0^{\pi/2} = a\mathbf{i} + a\mathbf{j} + \dfrac{\pi}{2}\mathbf{k}$

55. Let $\mathbf{r}(t) = x(t)\mathbf{i} + y(t)\mathbf{j} + z(t)\mathbf{k}$. Then $c\mathbf{r}(t) = cx(t)\mathbf{i} + cy(t)\mathbf{j} + cz(t)\mathbf{k}$ and

$D_t[c\mathbf{r}(t)] = cx'(t)\mathbf{i} + cy'(t)\mathbf{j} + cz'(t)\mathbf{k}$

$\qquad = c[x'(t)\mathbf{i} + y'(t)\mathbf{j} + z'(t)\mathbf{k}] = c\mathbf{r}'(t).$

57. Let $\mathbf{r}(t) = x(t)\mathbf{i} + y(t)\mathbf{j} + z(t)\mathbf{k}$, then $f(t)\mathbf{r}(t) = f(t)x(t)\mathbf{i} + f(t)y(t)\mathbf{j} + f(t)z(t)\mathbf{k}$.

$D_t[f(t)\mathbf{r}(t)] = [f(t)x'(t) + f'(t)x(t)]\mathbf{i} + [f(t)y'(t) + f'(t)y(t)]\mathbf{j} + [f(t)z'(t) + f'(t)z(t)]\mathbf{k}$

$\qquad = f(t)[x'(t)\mathbf{i} + y'(t)\mathbf{j} + z'(t)\mathbf{k}] + f'(t)[x(t)\mathbf{i} + y(t)\mathbf{j} + z(t)\mathbf{k}]$

$\qquad = f(t)\mathbf{r}'(t) + f'(t)\mathbf{r}(t)$

59. Let $\mathbf{r}(t) = x(t)\mathbf{i} + y(t)\mathbf{j} + z(t)\mathbf{k}$. Then $\mathbf{r}(f(t)) = x(f(t))\mathbf{i} + y(f(t))\mathbf{j} + z(f(t))\mathbf{k}$ and

$D_t[\mathbf{r}(f(t))] = x'(f(t))f'(t)\mathbf{i} + y'(f(t))f'(t)\mathbf{j} + z'(f(t))f'(t)\mathbf{k}$ (Chain Rule)

$\qquad = f'(t)[x'(f(t))\mathbf{i} + y'(f(t))\mathbf{j} + z'(f(t))\mathbf{k}] = f'(t)\mathbf{r}'(f(t)).$

61. Let $\mathbf{r}(t) = x_1(t)\mathbf{i} + y_1(t)\mathbf{j} + z_1(t)\mathbf{k}$, $\mathbf{u}(t) = x_2(t)\mathbf{i} + y_2(t)\mathbf{j} + z_2(t)\mathbf{k}$, and $\mathbf{v}(t) = x_3(t)\mathbf{i} + y_3(t)\mathbf{j} + z_3(t)\mathbf{k}$. Then:

$\mathbf{r}(t) \cdot [\mathbf{u}(t) \times \mathbf{v}(t)] = x_1(t)[y_2(t)z_3(t) - z_2(t)y_3(t)] - y_1(t)[x_2(t)z_3(t) - z_2(t)x_3(t)] + z_1(t)[x_2(t)y_3(t) - y_2(t)x_3(t)]$

$D_t[\mathbf{r}(t) \cdot (\mathbf{u}(t) \times \mathbf{v}(t))] = x_1(t)y_2(t)z_3'(t) + x_1(t)y_2'(t)z_3(t) + x_1'(t)y_2(t)z_3(t) - x_1(t)y_3(t)z_2'(t) -$

$\qquad x_1(t)y_3'(t)z_2(t) - x_1'(t)y_3(t)z_2(t) - y_1(t)x_2(t)z_3'(t) - y_1(t)x_2'(t)z_3(t) - y_1'(t)x_2(t)z_3(t) +$

$\qquad y_1(t)z_2(t)x_3'(t) + y_1(t)z_2'(t)x_3(t) + y_1'(t)z_2(t)x_3(t) + z_1(t)x_2(t)y_3'(t) + z_1(t)x_2'(t)y_3(t) +$

$\qquad z_1'(t)x_2(t)y_3(t) - z_1(t)y_2(t)x_3'(t) - z_1(t)y_2'(t)x_3(t) - z_1'(t)y_2(t)x_3(t)$

$\qquad = \{x_1'(t)[y_2(t)z_3(t) - y_3(t)z_2(t)] + y_1'(t)[-x_2(t)z_3(t) + z_2(t)x_3(t)] + z_1'(t)[x_2(t)y_3(t) - y_2(t)x_3(t)]\} +$

$\qquad \{x_1(t)[y_2'(t)z_3(t) - y_3(t)z_2'(t)] + y_1(t)[-x_2'(t)z_3(t) + z_2'(t)x_3(t)] + z_1(t)[x_2'(t)y_3(t) - y_2'(t)x_3(t)]\} +$

$\qquad \{x_1(t)[y_2(t)z_3'(t) - y_3'(t)z_2(t)] + y_1(t)[-x_2(t)z_3'(t) + z_2(t)x_3'(t)] + z_1(t)[x_2(t)y_3'(t) - y_2(t)x_3'(t)]\}$

$\qquad = \mathbf{r}'(t) \cdot [\mathbf{u}(t) \times \mathbf{v}(t)] + \mathbf{r}(t) \cdot [\mathbf{u}'(t) \times \mathbf{v}(t)] + \mathbf{r}(t) \cdot [\mathbf{u}(t) \times \mathbf{v}'(t)]$

63. False. Let $\mathbf{r}(t) = \cos t\mathbf{i} + \sin t\mathbf{j} + \mathbf{k}$.

$$\|\mathbf{r}(t)\| = \sqrt{2}$$

$$\frac{d}{dt}[\|\mathbf{r}(t)\|] = 0$$

$$\mathbf{r}'(t) = -\sin t\mathbf{i} + \cos t\mathbf{j}$$

$$\|\mathbf{r}'(t)\| = 1$$

Section 11.3   Velocity and Acceleration

1. $\mathbf{r}(t) = 3t\mathbf{i} + (t-1)\mathbf{j}$

$\mathbf{v}(t) = \mathbf{r}'(t) = 3\mathbf{i} + \mathbf{j}$

$\mathbf{a}(t) = \mathbf{r}''(t) = \mathbf{0}$

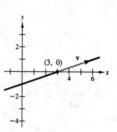

$x = 3t,\ y = t-1,\ y = \dfrac{x}{3} - 1$

At $(3, 0)$, $t = 1$.

$\mathbf{v}(1) = 3\mathbf{i} + \mathbf{j},\ \mathbf{a}(1) = \mathbf{0}$

3. $\mathbf{r}(t) = t^2\mathbf{i} + t\mathbf{j}$

Eliminating the parameter from the parametric equations $x = t^2$ and $y = t$, we obtain the rectangular equation $x = y^2$. Therefore, the object is moving in a parabolic path. (See the figure.) The velocity is given by

$$\mathbf{v}(t) = \mathbf{r}'(t) = 2t\mathbf{i} + \mathbf{j}$$

and the acceleration is given by

$$\mathbf{a}(t) = \mathbf{r}''(t) = 2\mathbf{i}.$$

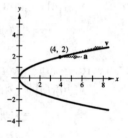

At the point $(4, 2)$, $t = 2$. Thus, $\mathbf{v}(2) = 4\mathbf{i} + \mathbf{j}$ and $\mathbf{a}(2) = 2\mathbf{i}$.

5. $\mathbf{r}(t) = 2\cos t\mathbf{i} + 2\sin t\mathbf{j}$

$\mathbf{v}(t) = \mathbf{r}'(t) = -2\sin t\mathbf{i} + 2\cos t\mathbf{j}$

$\mathbf{a}(t) = \mathbf{r}''(t) = -2\cos t\mathbf{i} - 2\sin t\mathbf{j}$

$x = 2\cos t,\ y = 2\sin t,\ x^2 + y^2 = 4$

At $\left(\sqrt{2}, \sqrt{2}\right)$, $t = \dfrac{\pi}{4}$.

$\mathbf{v}\left(\dfrac{\pi}{4}\right) = -\sqrt{2}\mathbf{i} + \sqrt{2}\mathbf{j}$

$\mathbf{a}\left(\dfrac{\pi}{4}\right) = -\sqrt{2}\mathbf{i} - \sqrt{2}\mathbf{j}$

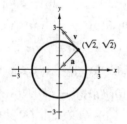

7. $\mathbf{r}(t) = \langle t - \sin t, 1 - \cos t \rangle$

$\mathbf{v}(t) = \mathbf{r}'(t) = \langle 1 - \cos t, \sin t \rangle$

$\mathbf{a}(t) = \mathbf{r}''(t) = \langle \sin t, \cos t \rangle$

$x = t - \sin t,\ y = 1 - \cos t$ (cycloid)

At $(\pi, 2)$, $t = \pi$.

$\mathbf{v}(\pi) = \langle 2, 0 \rangle = 2\mathbf{i}$

$\mathbf{a}(\pi) = \langle 0, -1 \rangle = -\mathbf{j}$

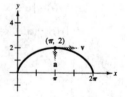

9. $\mathbf{r}(t) = t\mathbf{i} + (2t - 5)\mathbf{j} + 3t\mathbf{k}$

$\mathbf{v}(t) = \mathbf{i} + 2\mathbf{j} + 3\mathbf{k}$

$s(t) = \|\mathbf{v}(t)\| = \sqrt{1 + 4 + 9} = \sqrt{14}$

$\mathbf{a}(t) = \mathbf{0}$

11. $\mathbf{r}(t) = t\mathbf{i} + t^2\mathbf{j} + \dfrac{t^2}{2}\mathbf{k}$

$\mathbf{v}(t) = \mathbf{i} + 2t\mathbf{j} + t\mathbf{k}$

$s(t) = \sqrt{1 + 4t^2 + t^2} = \sqrt{1 + 5t^2}$

$\mathbf{a}(t) = 2\mathbf{j} + \mathbf{k}$

13. $\mathbf{r}(t) = t\mathbf{i} + t\mathbf{j} + \sqrt{9 - t^2}\mathbf{k}$

$$\mathbf{v}(t) = \mathbf{i} + \mathbf{j} - \frac{t}{\sqrt{9 - t^2}}\mathbf{k}$$

$$s(t) = \sqrt{1 + 1 + \frac{t^2}{9 - t^2}} = \sqrt{\frac{18 - t^2}{9 - t^2}}$$

$$\mathbf{a}(t) = -\frac{9}{(9 - t^2)^{3/2}}\mathbf{k}$$

15. Since $\mathbf{r}(t) = \langle 4t, 3 \cos t, 3 \sin t \rangle$, we have

$$\mathbf{v}(t) = \mathbf{r}'(t) = \langle 4, -3 \sin t, 3 \cos t \rangle,$$

$$\text{speed} = \|\mathbf{v}(t)\| = \sqrt{16 + 9(\sin^2 t + \cos^2 t)}$$

$$= \sqrt{25} = 5,$$

and $\mathbf{a}(t) = \mathbf{r}''(t) = \langle 0, -3 \cos t, -3 \sin t \rangle$.

17. (a) $\mathbf{r}(t) = \left\langle t, -t^2, \dfrac{t^3}{4} \right\rangle, t_0 = 1$

$$\mathbf{r}'(t) = \left\langle 1, -2t, \frac{3t^2}{4} \right\rangle$$

$$\mathbf{r}'(1) = \left\langle 1, -2, \frac{3}{4} \right\rangle$$

$$x = 1 + t, \ y = -1 - 2t, \ z = \frac{1}{4} + \frac{3}{4}t$$

(b) $\mathbf{r}(1 + 0.1) \approx \left\langle 1 + 0.1, -1 - 2(0.1), \dfrac{1}{4} + \dfrac{3}{4}(0.1) \right\rangle$

$$= \langle 1.100, -1.200, 0.325 \rangle$$

19. $\mathbf{a}(t) = \mathbf{i} + \mathbf{j} + \mathbf{k}, \mathbf{v}(0) = \mathbf{0}, \mathbf{r}(0) = \mathbf{0}$

$$\mathbf{v}(t) = \int (\mathbf{i} + \mathbf{j} + \mathbf{k}) \, dt = t\mathbf{i} + t\mathbf{j} + t\mathbf{k} + \mathbf{C}$$

$$\mathbf{v}(0) = \mathbf{C} = \mathbf{0}, \mathbf{v}(t) = t\mathbf{i} + t\mathbf{j} + t\mathbf{k}, \mathbf{v}(t) = t(\mathbf{i} + \mathbf{j} + \mathbf{k})$$

$$\mathbf{r}(t) = \int (t\mathbf{i} + t\mathbf{j} + t\mathbf{k}) \, dt = \frac{t^2}{2}(\mathbf{i} + \mathbf{j} + \mathbf{k}) + \mathbf{C}$$

$$\mathbf{r}(0) = \mathbf{C} = \mathbf{0}, \mathbf{r}(t) = \frac{t^2}{2}(\mathbf{i} + \mathbf{j} + \mathbf{k}),$$

$$\mathbf{r}(2) = 2(\mathbf{i} + \mathbf{j} + \mathbf{k}) = 2\mathbf{i} + 2\mathbf{j} + 2\mathbf{k}$$

21. $\mathbf{a}(t) = t\mathbf{j} + t\mathbf{k}, \mathbf{v}(1) = 5\mathbf{j}, \mathbf{r}(1) = \mathbf{0}$

$$\mathbf{v}(t) = \int \mathbf{a}(t) \, dt + \mathbf{C} = \int (t\mathbf{j} + t\mathbf{k}) \, dt + \mathbf{C} = \frac{1}{2}t^2\mathbf{j} + \frac{1}{2}t^2\mathbf{k} + C_1\mathbf{i} + C_2\mathbf{j} + C_3\mathbf{k}$$

$$\mathbf{v}(1) = C_1\mathbf{i} + \left(\frac{1}{2} + C_2\right)\mathbf{j} + \left(\frac{1}{2} + C_3\right)\mathbf{k} = 5\mathbf{j}$$

Therefore,

$$C_1 = 0$$

$$\frac{1}{2} + C_2 = 5 \implies C_2 = \frac{9}{2}$$

$$\frac{1}{2} + C_3 = 0 \implies C_3 = -\frac{1}{2}.$$

Thus, the velocity vector is

$$\mathbf{v}(t) = \left(\frac{t^2}{2} + \frac{9}{2}\right)\mathbf{j} + \left(\frac{t^2}{2} - \frac{1}{2}\right)\mathbf{k}$$

$$\mathbf{r}(t) = \int \mathbf{v}(t) \, dt + \mathbf{C} = \int \left(\frac{t^2}{2} + \frac{9}{2}t\right) dt \, \mathbf{j} + \int \left(\frac{t^2}{2} - \frac{1}{2}\right) dt \, \mathbf{k} + \mathbf{C} = \left(\frac{t^3}{6} + \frac{9}{2}t\right)\mathbf{j} + \left(\frac{t^3}{6} - \frac{1}{2}t\right)\mathbf{k} + C_4\mathbf{i} + C_5\mathbf{j} + C_6\mathbf{k}$$

$$\mathbf{r}(1) = C_4\mathbf{i} + \left(\frac{1}{6} + \frac{9}{2} + C_5\right)\mathbf{j} + \left(\frac{1}{6} - \frac{1}{2} + C_6\right)\mathbf{k} = C_4\mathbf{i} + \left(\frac{14}{3} + C_5\right)\mathbf{j} + \left(-\frac{1}{3} + C_6\right)\mathbf{k} = \mathbf{0}.$$

This implies that

$$C_4 = 0, C_5 = \frac{-14}{3}, \text{ and } C_6 = \frac{1}{3}.$$

Thus, the position vector is

$$\mathbf{r}(t) = \left(\frac{t^3}{6} + \frac{9}{2}t - \frac{14}{3}\right)\mathbf{j} + \left(\frac{t^3}{6} - \frac{1}{2}t + \frac{1}{3}\right)\mathbf{k} \text{ and } \mathbf{r}(2) = \frac{17}{3}\mathbf{j} + \frac{2}{3}\mathbf{k}.$$

23. $\mathbf{r}(t) = (88 \cos 30°)t\mathbf{i} + [10 + (88 \sin 30°)t - 16t^2]\mathbf{j}$

$\qquad = 44\sqrt{3}\, t\mathbf{i} + (10 + 44t - 16t^2)\mathbf{j}$

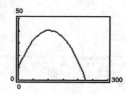

25. The path of the ball is given by

$\qquad \mathbf{r}(t) = (v_0 \cos 45°)t\mathbf{i} + [3 + (v_0 \sin 45°)t - 16t^2]\mathbf{j}$

$\qquad\qquad = \left(\dfrac{tv_0}{\sqrt{2}}\right)\mathbf{i} + \left(3 + \dfrac{tv_0}{\sqrt{2}} - 16t^2\right)\mathbf{j}.$

We know that the horizontal component is 300 when the vertical component is three. Thus,

$\qquad \dfrac{tv_0}{\sqrt{2}} = 300 \quad \text{and} \quad 3 + \dfrac{tv_0}{\sqrt{2}} - 16t^2 = 3.$

From the first equation we obtain $t = 300\sqrt{2}/v_0$. Substituting this expression into the second equation yields

$\qquad \dfrac{300\sqrt{2}}{v_0}\left(\dfrac{v_0}{\sqrt{2}}\right) - 16\left(\dfrac{300\sqrt{2}}{v_0}\right)^2 = 0$

$\qquad\qquad\qquad 300 = \dfrac{16(300^2)(2)}{v_0{}^2}$

$\qquad\qquad\qquad v_0{}^2 = 32(300)$

$\qquad\qquad\qquad v_0 = \sqrt{9600} = 40\sqrt{6} \approx 97.98 \text{ ft/sec.}$

The maximum height is reached when the derivative of the vertical component is zero. Thus,

$\qquad y(t) = 3 + \dfrac{tv_0}{\sqrt{2}} - 16t^2 = 3 + \dfrac{t(40\sqrt{6})}{\sqrt{2}} - 16t^2 = 3 + 40\sqrt{3}\,t - 16t^2$

$\qquad y'(t) = 40\sqrt{3} - 32t = 0$

$\qquad\qquad t = \dfrac{40\sqrt{3}}{32} = \dfrac{5\sqrt{3}}{4}.$

Finally, the maximum height is

$\qquad y\left(\dfrac{5\sqrt{3}}{4}\right) = 3 + 40\sqrt{3}\left(\dfrac{5\sqrt{3}}{4}\right) - 16\left(\dfrac{5\sqrt{3}}{4}\right)^2$

$\qquad\qquad\qquad = 3 + 150 - 75 = 78 \text{ ft.}$

27. $h = 7$ feet, $\theta = 35°$, 30 yards $= 90$ feet

$\qquad \mathbf{r}(t) = (v_0 \cos 35°)t\mathbf{i} + [7 + (v_0 \sin 35°)t - 16t^2]\mathbf{j}$

(a) $v_0 \cos 35°\, t = 90$ when $7 + (v_0 \sin 35°)t - 16t^2 = 4$

$\qquad\qquad\qquad t = \dfrac{90}{v_0 \cos 35°}$

$\qquad 7 + (v_0 \sin 35°)\left(\dfrac{90}{v_0 \cos 35°}\right) - 16\left(\dfrac{90}{v_0 \cos 35°}\right)^2 = 4$

$\qquad\qquad\qquad 90 \tan 35° + 3 = \dfrac{129,600}{v_0{}^2 \cos^2 35°}$

$\qquad\qquad\qquad v_0{}^2 = \dfrac{129,600}{\cos^2 35°(90 \tan 35° + 3)}$

$\qquad\qquad\qquad v_0 \approx 54.088 \text{ feet per second}$

—CONTINUED—

27. —CONTINUED—

(b) The maximum height occurs when

$$y'(t) = v_0 \sin 35° - 32t = 0.$$

$$t = \frac{v_0 \sin 35°}{32} \approx 0.969 \text{ second}$$

At this time, the height is $y(0.969) \approx 22.0$ feet.

(c) $x(t) = 90 \implies (v_0 \cos 35°)t = 90$

$$t = \frac{90}{54.088 \cos 35°} \approx 2.0 \text{ seconds}$$

29. If we place the origin of the coordinate system at the ejector on the baler (see figure), then

$$\mathbf{r}(t) = (v \cos \theta)t\mathbf{i} + [(v \sin \theta)t - 16t^2]\mathbf{j}.$$

Since the bale must be thrown to the position (16, 8), we have

$$16 = (v \cos \theta)t \implies t = \frac{16}{v \cos \theta}$$

$$8 = (v \sin \theta)t - 16t^2.$$

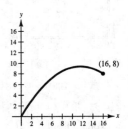

Substituting into the second equation and solving for v, we obtain the following.

$$8 = (v \sin \theta)\left(\frac{16}{v \cos \theta}\right) - 16\left(\frac{16}{v \cos \theta}\right)^2$$

$$1 = \frac{2 \sin \theta}{\cos \theta} - \frac{512}{v^2 \cos^2 \theta}$$

$$\frac{512}{v^2 \cos^2 \theta} = \frac{2 \sin \theta}{\cos \theta} - 1$$

$$\frac{1}{v^2} = \left(\frac{2 \sin \theta}{\cos \theta} - 1\right)\left(\frac{\cos^2 \theta}{512}\right) = \frac{2 \sin \theta \cos \theta - \cos^2 \theta}{512}$$

$$v^2 = \frac{512}{2 \sin \theta \cos \theta - \cos^2 \theta}$$

We now must minimize $f(\theta) = \dfrac{512}{2 \sin \theta \cos \theta - \cos^2 \theta}$.

$$f'(\theta) = \frac{-512(2 \cos^2 \theta - 2 \sin^2 \theta + 2 \sin \theta \cos \theta)}{(2 \sin \theta \cos \theta - \cos^2 \theta)^2}$$

$$= \frac{-512(2 \cos 2\theta + \sin 2\theta)}{(2 \sin \theta \cos \theta - \cos^2 \theta)^2}$$

$$f'(\theta) = 0 \implies 2 \cos 2\theta + \sin 2\theta = 0$$

$$\tan 2\theta = -2$$

$$\theta \approx 1.01722 \approx 58.28°$$

Substituting this into the equation for v yields $v \approx 28.78$ feet per second.

31. $\mathbf{r}(t) = (v_0 \cos \theta)t\mathbf{i} + [(v_0 \sin \theta)t - 16t^2]\mathbf{j}$

$(v_0 \sin \theta)t - 16t^2 = 0$ when $t = 0$ and $t = \dfrac{v_0 \sin \theta}{16}$.

The range is

$$x = (v_0 \cos \theta)t = (v_0 \cos \theta)\frac{v_0 \sin \theta}{16} = \frac{v_0^2}{32} \sin 2\theta.$$

Hence,

$$x = \frac{1200^2}{32} \sin(2\theta) = 3000 \implies \sin 2\theta = \frac{1}{15} \implies \theta \approx 1.91°.$$

33. (a) $\theta = 10°$, $v_0 = 66$ ft/sec

$\mathbf{r}(t) = (66 \cos 10°)t\mathbf{i} + [0 + (66 \sin 10°)t - 16t^2]\mathbf{j}$

$\mathbf{r}(t) \approx (65t)\mathbf{i} + (11.46t - 16t^2)\mathbf{j}$

Maximum height: 2.052 feet

Range: 46.557 feet

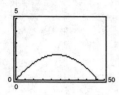

(c) $\theta = 45°$, $v_0 = 66$ ft/sec

$\mathbf{r}(t) = (66 \cos 45°)t\mathbf{i} + [0 + (66 \sin 45°)t - 16t^2]\mathbf{j}$

$\mathbf{r}(t) \approx (46.67t)\mathbf{i} + (46.67t - 16t^2)\mathbf{j}$

Maximum height: 34.031 feet

Range: 136.125 feet

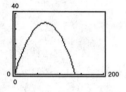

(e) $\theta = 60°$, $v_0 = 66$ ft/sec

$\mathbf{r}(t) = (66 \cos 60°)t\mathbf{i} + [0 + (66 \sin 60°)t - 16t^2]\mathbf{j}$

$\mathbf{r}(t) \approx (33t)\mathbf{i} + (57.16t - 16t^2)\mathbf{j}$

Maximum height: 51.074 feet

Range: 117.888 feet

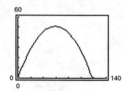

(b) $\theta = 10°$, $v_0 = 146$ ft/sec

$\mathbf{r}(t) = (146 \cos 10°)t\mathbf{i} + [0 + (146 \sin 10°)t - 16t^2]\mathbf{j}$

$\mathbf{r}(t) \approx (143.78t)\mathbf{i} + (25.35t - 16t^2)\mathbf{j}$

Maximum height: 10.043 feet

Range: 227.828 feet

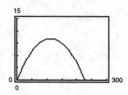

(d) $\theta = 45°$, $v_0 = 146$ ft/sec

$\mathbf{r}(t) = (146 \cos 45°)t\mathbf{i} + [0 + (146 \sin 45°)t - 16t^2]\mathbf{j}$

$\mathbf{r}(t) \approx (103.24t)\mathbf{i} + (103.24t - 16t^2)\mathbf{j}$

Maximum height: 166.531 feet

Range: 666.125 feet

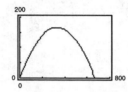

(f) $\theta = 60°$, $v_0 = 146$ ft/sec

$\mathbf{r}(t) = (146 \cos 60°)t\mathbf{i} + [0 + (146 \sin 60°)t - 16t^2]\mathbf{j}$

$\mathbf{r}(t) \approx (73t)\mathbf{i} + (126.44t - 16t^2)\mathbf{j}$

Maximum height: 249.797 feet

Range: 576.881 feet

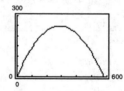

35. $y = x - 0.005x^2$; From Exercise 34 we know that $\tan \theta$ is the coefficient of x. Therefore, $\tan \theta = 1$, $\theta = (\pi/4)$ rad $= 45°$. Also:

$$\frac{16}{v_0^2} \sec^2 \theta = \text{negative of coefficient of } x^2$$

$$\frac{16}{v_0^2}(2) = 0.005 \text{ or } v_0 = 80 \text{ ft/sec}$$

$\mathbf{r}(t) = \left(40\sqrt{2}t\right)\mathbf{i} + \left(40\sqrt{2}t - 16t^2\right)\mathbf{j}$ Position function

When $40\sqrt{2}t = 60$:

$$t = \frac{60}{40\sqrt{2}} = \frac{3\sqrt{2}}{4}$$

$\mathbf{v}(t) = 40\sqrt{2}\mathbf{i} + \left(40\sqrt{2} - 32t\right)\mathbf{j}$

$\mathbf{v}\left(\dfrac{3\sqrt{2}}{4}\right) = 40\sqrt{2}\mathbf{i} + \left(40\sqrt{2} - 24\sqrt{2}\right)\mathbf{j} = 8\sqrt{2}(5\mathbf{i} + 2\mathbf{j})$ direction

$\text{Speed} = \left\| \mathbf{v}\left(\dfrac{3\sqrt{2}}{4}\right) \right\| = 8\sqrt{2}\sqrt{25 + 4} = 8\sqrt{58}$ ft/sec

37. $\mathbf{r}(t) = (v_0 \cos \theta)t\mathbf{i} + [h + (v_0 \sin \theta)t - 4.9t^2]\mathbf{j}$

$\qquad = (100 \cos 30°)t\mathbf{i} + [1.5 + (100 \sin 30°)t - 4.9t^2]\mathbf{j}$

The projectile hits the ground when $-4.9t^2 + 100\left(\frac{1}{2}\right)t + 1.5 = 0 \Rightarrow t \approx 10.234$ seconds.

The range is therefore $(100 \cos 30°)(10.234) \approx 886.3$ meters.

The maximum height occurs when $dy/dt = 0$.

$\qquad 100 \sin 30 = 9.8t \Rightarrow t \approx 5.102$ sec

The maximum height is $y = 1.5 + (100 \sin 30°)(5.102) - 4.9(5.102)^2 \approx 129.1$ meters.

39.
$\mathbf{r}(t) = b(\omega t - \sin \omega t)\mathbf{i} + b(1 - \cos \omega t)\mathbf{j}$

$\mathbf{r}'(t) = \mathbf{v}(t) = b(\omega - \omega \cos \omega t)\mathbf{i} + b\omega \sin \omega t\,\mathbf{j}$

$\text{speed} = \|\mathbf{v}(t)\|$

$\qquad = \sqrt{[b(\omega - \omega \cos \omega t)]^2 + [b\omega \sin \omega t]^2}$

$\qquad = b\omega\sqrt{1 - 2 \cos \omega t + \cos^2 \omega t + \sin^2 \omega t}$

$\qquad = b\omega\sqrt{2 - 2 \cos \omega t} = \sqrt{2}b\omega\sqrt{1 - \cos \omega t}$

(a) When $\omega t = 0, 2\pi, 4\pi, \ldots, 1 - \cos \omega t = 0$, and therefore, $\|\mathbf{v}(t)\| = 0$. Hence, the speed is zero when the point contacts the surface on which the circle is rolling.

(b) When $\omega t = \pi, 3\pi, \ldots, 1 - \cos \omega t = 2$, and therefore, $\|\mathbf{v}(t)\| = 2b\omega$, its maximum value. Hence, the speed is maximum when the point is at the top of cycloidal arch.

41. $\mathbf{r}(t) = b \cos \omega t\mathbf{i} + b \sin \omega t\mathbf{j}$

The velocity vector is

$\qquad \mathbf{v}(t) = \mathbf{r}'(t) = -b\omega \sin \omega t\mathbf{i} + b\omega \cos \omega t\mathbf{j}$

and since

$\qquad \mathbf{r}(t) \cdot \mathbf{v}(t) = -b^2\omega \sin \omega t \cos \omega t + b^2\omega \sin \omega t \cos \omega t$

$\qquad\qquad = 0,$

it follows that $\mathbf{r}(t)$ and $\mathbf{v}(t)$ are orthogonal.

43. $\mathbf{r}(t) = b \cos \omega t\mathbf{i} + b \sin \omega t\mathbf{j}$

$\mathbf{r}'(t) = -b\omega \sin \omega t\mathbf{i} + b\omega \cos \omega t\mathbf{j}$

$\mathbf{a}(t) = \mathbf{r}''(t) = [-b\omega^2 \cos \omega t]\mathbf{i} - [b\omega^2 \sin \omega t]\mathbf{j}$

$\qquad = -b\omega^2[\cos \omega t\mathbf{i} + \sin \omega t\mathbf{j}]$

$\qquad = -\omega^2\,\mathbf{r}(t)$

Therefore, $\mathbf{a}(t)$ is a negative multiple of a unit vector from $(0, 0)$ to $(\cos \omega t, \sin \omega t)$, and thus $\mathbf{a}(t)$ is directed toward the origin.

45. $\|\mathbf{a}(t)\| = \omega^2 b$

$1 = m(32)$

$F = m(\omega^2 b) = \dfrac{1}{32}(2\omega^2) = 10$

$\omega = 4\sqrt{10}$ rad/sec

$\|\mathbf{v}(t)\| = b\omega = 8\sqrt{10}$ ft/sec

47. To find the range, set $y(t) = h + (v_0 \sin \theta)t - \frac{1}{2}gt^2 = 0$ then $0 = \left(\frac{1}{2}g\right)t^2 - (v_0 \sin \theta)t - h$. By the Quadratic Formula, (discount the negative value)

$$t = \frac{v_0 \sin \theta + \sqrt{(-v_0 \sin \theta)^2 - 4[(1/2)g](-h)}}{2[(1/2)g]} = \frac{v_0 \sin \theta + \sqrt{v_0^2 \sin^2 \theta + 2gh}}{g}.$$

At this time,

$$x(t) = v_0 \cos \theta\left(\frac{v_0 \sin \theta + \sqrt{v_0^2 \sin^2 \theta + 2gh}}{g}\right) = \frac{v_0 \cos \theta}{g}\left(v_0 \sin \theta + \sqrt{v_0^2\left(\sin^2 \theta + \frac{2gh}{v_0^2}\right)}\right)$$

$$= \frac{v_0^2 \cos \theta}{g}\left(\sin \theta + \sqrt{\sin^2 \theta + \frac{2gh}{v_0^2}}\right) >$$

49. $\mathbf{r}(t) = x(t)\mathbf{i} + y(t)\mathbf{j} + z(t)\mathbf{k}$ Position vector

$\mathbf{v}(t) = x'(t)\mathbf{i} + y'(t)\mathbf{j} + z'(t)\mathbf{k}$ Velocity vector

$\mathbf{a}(t) = x''(t)\mathbf{i} + y''(t)\mathbf{j} + z''(t)\mathbf{k}$ Acceleration vector

Speed $= \|\mathbf{v}(t)\| = \sqrt{(x'(t)^2 + y'(t)^2 + z'(t)^2}) = C$, C is a constant.

$$\frac{d}{dt}[x'(t)^2 + y'(t)^2 + z'(t)^2] = 0$$

$$2x'(t)x''(t) + 2y'(t)y''(t) + 2z'(t)z''(t) = 0$$

$$2[x'(t)x''(t) + y'(t)y''(t) + z'(t)z''(t)] = 0$$

$$\mathbf{v}(t) \cdot \mathbf{a}(t) = 0$$

Orthogonal

51. $\mathbf{r}(t) = 6\cos t\mathbf{i} + 3\sin t\mathbf{j}$

(a) $\mathbf{v}(t) = \mathbf{r}'(t) = -6\sin t\mathbf{i} + 3\cos t\mathbf{j}$

$\|\mathbf{v}(t)\| = \sqrt{36\sin^2 t + 9\cos^2 t}$

$\quad\quad\quad = 3\sqrt{4\sin^2 t + \cos^2 t}$

$\quad\quad\quad = 3\sqrt{3\sin^2 t + 1}$

$\mathbf{a}(t) = \mathbf{v}'(t) = -6\cos t\mathbf{i} - 3\sin t\mathbf{j}$

(c)

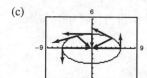

(b)

t	0	$\dfrac{\pi}{4}$	$\dfrac{\pi}{2}$	$\dfrac{2\pi}{3}$	π
Speed	3	$\dfrac{3}{2}\sqrt{10}$	6	$\dfrac{3}{2}\sqrt{13}$	3

(d) The speed is increasing when the angle between $\mathbf{v}$ and $\mathbf{a}$ is in the interval

$$\left[0, \frac{\pi}{2}\right).$$

The speed is decreasing when the angle is in the interval

$$\left(\frac{\pi}{2}, \pi\right].$$

Section 11.4   Tangent Vectors and Normal Vectors

1. $\mathbf{r}(t) = t\mathbf{i} + t^2\mathbf{j} + t\mathbf{k}$

$\mathbf{r}'(t) = \mathbf{i} + 2t\mathbf{j} + \mathbf{k}$

When $t = 0$, $\mathbf{r}'(0) = \mathbf{i} + \mathbf{k}$, $[t = 0$ at $(0, 0, 0)]$.

$$\mathbf{T}(0) = \frac{\mathbf{r}'(0)}{\|\mathbf{r}'(0)\|} = \frac{\sqrt{2}}{2}(\mathbf{i} + \mathbf{k})$$

Direction numbers: $a = 1$, $b = 0$, $c = 1$

Parametric equations: $x = t$, $y = 0$, $z = t$

3. $\mathbf{r}(t) = 2\cos t\mathbf{i} + 2\sin t\mathbf{j} + t\mathbf{k}$

$\mathbf{r}'(t) = -2\sin t\mathbf{i} + 2\cos t\mathbf{j} + \mathbf{k}$

The unit tangent vector is

$$\mathbf{T}(t) = \frac{\mathbf{r}'(t)}{\|\mathbf{r}'(t)\|} = \frac{-2\sin t\mathbf{i} + 2\cos t\mathbf{j} + \mathbf{k}}{\sqrt{(-2\sin t)^2 + (2\cos t)^2 + 1}}$$

$$= \frac{1}{\sqrt{5}}(-2\sin t\mathbf{i} + 2\cos t\mathbf{j} + \mathbf{k}).$$

Since $t = 0$ at the point $(2, 0, 0)$, the direction vector for the line is given by $\mathbf{r}'(0) = 2\mathbf{j} + \mathbf{k}$, and the parametric representation of the line is $x = 2$, $y = 2s$, $z = s$.

5. $\mathbf{r}(t) = \langle 2\cos t, 2\sin t, 4\rangle$

$\mathbf{r}'(t) = \langle -2\sin t, 2\cos t, 0\rangle$

When $t = \dfrac{\pi}{4}$, $\mathbf{r}'\!\left(\dfrac{\pi}{4}\right) = \langle -\sqrt{2}, \sqrt{2}, 0\rangle$, $\left[t = \dfrac{\pi}{4} \text{ at } \left(\sqrt{2}, \sqrt{2}, 4\right)\right]$.

$$\mathbf{T}\!\left(\frac{\pi}{4}\right) = \frac{\mathbf{r}'(\pi/4)}{\|\mathbf{r}'(\pi/4)\|} = \frac{1}{2}\langle -\sqrt{2}, \sqrt{2}, 0\rangle$$

Direction numbers: $a = -\sqrt{2}$, $b = \sqrt{2}$, $c = 0$

Parametric equations: $x = -\sqrt{2}t + \sqrt{2}$, $y = \sqrt{2}t + \sqrt{2}$, $z = 4$

7. $\mathbf{r}(t) = \left\langle t, t^2, \dfrac{2}{3}t^3 \right\rangle$

$\mathbf{r}'(t) = \langle 1, 2t, 2t^2 \rangle$

When $t = 3$, $\mathbf{r}'(3) = \langle 1, 6, 18 \rangle$, $[t = 3$ at $(3, 9, 18)]$.

$$\mathbf{T}(3) = \dfrac{\mathbf{r}'(3)}{\|\mathbf{r}'(3)\|} = \dfrac{1}{19}\langle 1, 6, 18 \rangle$$

Direction numbers: $a = 1$, $b = 6$, $c = 18$

Parametric equations: $x = t + 3$, $y = 6t + 9$, $z = 18t + 18$

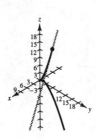

9. $\mathbf{r}(t) = t\mathbf{i} + \ln t\mathbf{j} + \sqrt{t}\mathbf{k}$, $t_0 = 1$

$\mathbf{r}'(t) = \mathbf{i} + \dfrac{1}{t}\mathbf{j} + \dfrac{1}{2\sqrt{t}}\mathbf{k} \cdot \mathbf{r}'(1) = \mathbf{i} + \mathbf{j} + \dfrac{1}{2}\mathbf{k}$

$$\mathbf{T}(1) = \dfrac{\mathbf{r}'(t)}{\|\mathbf{r}'(t)\|} = \dfrac{\mathbf{i} + \mathbf{j} + (1/2)\mathbf{k}}{\sqrt{1 + 1 + (1/4)}} = \dfrac{2}{3}\mathbf{i} + \dfrac{2}{3}\mathbf{j} + \dfrac{1}{3}\mathbf{k}$$

Tangent line: $x = 1 + t$, $y = t$, $z = 1 + \dfrac{1}{2}t$

$\mathbf{r}(t_0 + 0.1) = \mathbf{r}(1.1) \approx 1.1\mathbf{i} + 0.1\mathbf{j} + 1.05\mathbf{k} = \langle 1.1, 0.1, 1.05 \rangle$

11. $\mathbf{r}(t) = \left\langle t - 2, t^2, \dfrac{1}{2}t \right\rangle$, $\mathbf{u}(s) = \left\langle \dfrac{1}{4}s, 2s, \sqrt[3]{s} \right\rangle$

The space curves intersect since

$$\mathbf{r}(4) = \langle 2, 16, 2 \rangle = \mathbf{u}(8).$$

Now determine the tangent vectors at the specified values of the parameters.

$\mathbf{r}'(t) = \left\langle 1, 2t, \dfrac{1}{2} \right\rangle$

$\mathbf{r}'(4) = \left\langle 1, 2, \dfrac{1}{2} \right\rangle$

$\mathbf{u}'(s) = \left\langle \dfrac{1}{4}, 2, \dfrac{1}{3s^{2/3}} \right\rangle$

$\mathbf{u}'(8) = \left\langle \dfrac{1}{4}, 2, \dfrac{1}{12} \right\rangle$

The angle θ between the tangent vectors to the curves at the point of intersection is

$$\theta = \arccos\left(\dfrac{\mathbf{r}'(4) \cdot \mathbf{u}'(8)}{\|\mathbf{r}'(4)\|\|\mathbf{u}'(8)\|} \right) = \arccos\left(\dfrac{\dfrac{391}{24}}{\dfrac{3\sqrt{29}}{2} \cdot \dfrac{\sqrt{586}}{12}} \right) \approx \arccos(0.9998) \approx 0.0206 \approx 1.2°.$$

13. $\mathbf{r}(t) = 4t\mathbf{i}$

$\mathbf{v}(t) = 4\mathbf{i}$

$\mathbf{a}(t) = \mathbf{O}$

$\mathbf{T}(t) = \dfrac{\mathbf{v}(t)}{\|\mathbf{v}(t)\|} = \dfrac{4\mathbf{i}}{4} = \mathbf{i}$

$\mathbf{T}'(t) = \mathbf{O}$

$\mathbf{N}(t) = \dfrac{\mathbf{T}'(t)}{\|\mathbf{T}'(t)\|}$ is undefined.

The path is a line and the speed is constant.

15. $\mathbf{r}(t) = 4t^2\mathbf{i}$

$\mathbf{v}(t) = 8t\mathbf{i}$

$\mathbf{a}(t) = 8\mathbf{i}$

$\mathbf{T}(t) = \dfrac{\mathbf{v}(t)}{\|\mathbf{v}(t)\|} = \dfrac{8t\mathbf{i}}{8t} = \mathbf{i}$

$\mathbf{T}'(t) = \mathbf{O}$

$\mathbf{N}(t) = \dfrac{\mathbf{T}'(t)}{\|\mathbf{T}'(t)\|}$ is undefined.

The path is a line and the speed is variable.

17. $\mathbf{r}(t) = t\mathbf{i} + \dfrac{1}{t}\mathbf{j}$

$\mathbf{v}(t) = \mathbf{r}'(t) = \mathbf{i} - \dfrac{1}{t^2}\mathbf{j}$

$\mathbf{a}(t) = \mathbf{r}''(t) = \dfrac{2}{t^3}\mathbf{j}$

At $t = 1$, we have $\mathbf{v}(1) = \mathbf{i} - \mathbf{j}$, $\|\mathbf{v}(1)\| = \sqrt{2}$, and $\mathbf{a}(1) = 2\mathbf{j}$. Therefore, when $t = 1$,

$$\mathbf{T}(1) = \frac{\mathbf{v}(1)}{\|\mathbf{v}(1)\|} = \frac{\mathbf{i}}{\sqrt{2}} - \frac{\mathbf{j}}{\sqrt{2}} = \frac{\sqrt{2}}{2}(\mathbf{i} - \mathbf{j}).$$

Since $\mathbf{N}(1)$ points toward the concave side of the curve (see figure),

$$\mathbf{N}(1) = \frac{\mathbf{i}}{\sqrt{2}} + \frac{\mathbf{j}}{\sqrt{2}} = \frac{\sqrt{2}}{2}(\mathbf{i} + \mathbf{j}).$$

It follows that

$$a_{\mathbf{T}} = \mathbf{a}(1) \cdot \mathbf{T}(1) = (2\mathbf{j}) \cdot \left(\frac{\mathbf{i}}{\sqrt{2}} - \frac{\mathbf{j}}{\sqrt{2}}\right) = \frac{-2}{\sqrt{2}} = -\sqrt{2}$$

and

$$a_{\mathbf{N}} = \mathbf{a}(1) \cdot \mathbf{N}(1) = (2\mathbf{j}) \cdot \left(\frac{\mathbf{i}}{\sqrt{2}} + \frac{\mathbf{j}}{\sqrt{2}}\right) = \frac{2}{\sqrt{2}} = \sqrt{2}.$$

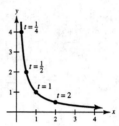

19. $\mathbf{r}(t) = e^t \cos t\,\mathbf{i} + e^t \sin t\,\mathbf{j}$

$\mathbf{v}(t) = \mathbf{r}'(t) = e^t(\cos t - \sin t)\mathbf{i} + e^t(\cos t + \sin t)\mathbf{j}$

$\mathbf{a}(t) = \mathbf{r}''(t) = e^t(-\sin t - \cos t + \cos t - \sin t)\mathbf{i} + e^t(-\sin t + \cos t + \cos t + \sin t)\mathbf{j}$

$\quad = e^t(-2\sin t)\mathbf{i} + e^t(2\cos t)\mathbf{j}$

At $t = \pi/2$, we have

$$\mathbf{v}\left(\frac{\pi}{2}\right) = -e^{\pi/2}\mathbf{i} + e^{\pi/2}\mathbf{j}$$

$$\left\|\mathbf{v}\left(\frac{\pi}{2}\right)\right\| = e^{\pi/2}\sqrt{2}$$

$$\mathbf{a}\left(\frac{\pi}{2}\right) = -2e^{\pi/2}\mathbf{i}.$$

Therefore, at $t = \pi/2$,

$$\mathbf{T}\left(\frac{\pi}{2}\right) = \frac{\mathbf{v}(\pi/2)}{\|\mathbf{v}(\pi/2)\|} = \frac{-\mathbf{i}}{\sqrt{2}} + \frac{\mathbf{j}}{\sqrt{2}} = \frac{\sqrt{2}}{2}(-\mathbf{i} + \mathbf{j}),$$

and since $\mathbf{N}(\pi/2)$ points toward the concave side of the curve, (see figure)

$$\mathbf{N}\left(\frac{\pi}{2}\right) = -\frac{\sqrt{2}}{2}(\mathbf{i} + \mathbf{j}).$$

It follows that

$$a_{\mathbf{T}} = \mathbf{a}\left(\frac{\pi}{2}\right) \cdot \mathbf{T}\left(\frac{\pi}{2}\right) = (-2e^{\pi/2}\mathbf{i}) \cdot \frac{(-\mathbf{i} + \mathbf{j})}{\sqrt{2}} = \sqrt{2}e^{\pi/2}$$

$$a_{\mathbf{N}} = \mathbf{a}\left(\frac{\pi}{2}\right) \cdot \mathbf{N}\left(\frac{\pi}{2}\right) = (-2e^{\pi/2}\mathbf{i}) \cdot \frac{(-\mathbf{i} - \mathbf{j})}{\sqrt{2}} = \sqrt{2}e^{\pi/2}.$$

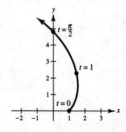

21. $\mathbf{r}(t_0) = (\cos \omega t_0 + \omega t_0 \sin \omega t_0)\mathbf{i} + (\sin \omega t_0 - \omega t_0 \cos \omega t_0)\mathbf{j}$

$\mathbf{v}(t_0) = (\omega^2 t_0 \cos \omega t_0)\mathbf{i} + (\omega^2 t_0 \sin \omega t_0)\mathbf{j}$

$\mathbf{a}(t_0) = \omega^2[(\cos \omega t_0 - \omega t_0 \sin \omega t_0)\mathbf{i} + (\omega t_0 \cos \omega t_0 + \sin \omega t_0)\mathbf{j}]$

$\mathbf{T}(t_0) = \dfrac{\mathbf{v}}{\|\mathbf{v}\|} = (\cos \omega t_0)\mathbf{i} + (\sin \omega t_0)\mathbf{j}$

Motion along **r** is counterclockwise. Therefore:

$\mathbf{N}(t_0) = (-\sin \omega t_0)\mathbf{i} + (\cos \omega t_0)\mathbf{j}.$

$a_{\mathbf{T}} = \mathbf{a} \cdot \mathbf{T} = \omega^2$

$a_{\mathbf{N}} = \mathbf{a} \cdot \mathbf{N} = \omega^2(\omega t_0) = \omega^3 t_0$

23. $\mathbf{r}(t) = a \cos(\omega t)\mathbf{i} + a \sin(\omega t)\mathbf{j}$

$\mathbf{v}(t) = -a\omega \sin(\omega t)\mathbf{i} + a\omega \cos(\omega t)\mathbf{j}$

$\mathbf{a}(t) = -a\omega^2 \cos(\omega t)\mathbf{i} - a\omega^2 \sin(\omega t)\mathbf{j}$

$\mathbf{T}(t) = \dfrac{\mathbf{v}(t)}{\|\mathbf{v}(t)\|} = -\sin(\omega t)\mathbf{i} + \cos(\omega t)\mathbf{j}$

$\mathbf{N}(t) = \dfrac{\mathbf{T}'(t)}{\|\mathbf{T}'(t)\|} = -\cos(\omega t)\mathbf{i} - \sin(\omega t)\mathbf{j}$

$a_{\mathbf{T}} = \mathbf{a} \cdot \mathbf{T} = 0$

$a_{\mathbf{N}} = \mathbf{a} \cdot \mathbf{N} = a\omega^2$

25. Speed: $\|\mathbf{v}(t)\| = a\omega$

The speed is constant since $a_{\mathbf{T}} = 0$.

27. $\mathbf{r}(t) = t\mathbf{i} + \dfrac{1}{t}\mathbf{j}, \ t_0 = 2$

$x = t, \ y = \dfrac{1}{t} \implies xy = 1$

$\mathbf{r}'(t) = \mathbf{i} - \dfrac{1}{t^2}\mathbf{j}$

$\mathbf{T}(t) = \dfrac{t^2\mathbf{i} - \mathbf{j}}{\sqrt{t^4 + 1}}$

$\mathbf{N}(t) = \dfrac{\mathbf{i} + t^2\mathbf{j}}{\sqrt{t^4 + 1}}$

$\mathbf{r}(2) = 2\mathbf{i} + \dfrac{1}{2}\mathbf{j}$

$\mathbf{T}(2) = \dfrac{\sqrt{17}}{17}(4\mathbf{i} - \mathbf{j})$

$\mathbf{N}(2) = \dfrac{\sqrt{17}}{17}(\mathbf{i} + 4\mathbf{j})$

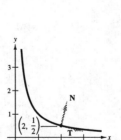

29. (a) $\mathbf{r}(t) = \langle \pi t - \sin \pi t, 1 - \cos \pi t \rangle$

$\mathbf{v}(t) = \langle \pi - \pi \cos \pi t, \pi \sin \pi t \rangle$

$\mathbf{a}(t) = \langle \pi^2 \sin \pi t, \pi^2 \cos \pi t \rangle$

$\mathbf{T}(t) = \dfrac{\mathbf{v}(t)}{\|\mathbf{v}(t)\|} = \dfrac{1}{\sqrt{2(1 - \cos \pi t)}} \langle 1 - \cos \pi t, \sin \pi t \rangle$

$\mathbf{N}(t) = \dfrac{\mathbf{T}'(t)}{\|\mathbf{T}'(t)\|} = \dfrac{1}{\sqrt{2(1 - \cos \pi t)}} \langle \sin \pi t, -1 + \cos \pi t \rangle$

$a_{\mathbf{T}} = \mathbf{a} \cdot \mathbf{T} = \dfrac{1}{\sqrt{2(1 - \cos \pi t)}}[\pi^2 \sin \pi t(1 - \cos \pi t) + \pi^2 \cos \pi t \sin \pi t] = \dfrac{\pi^2 \sin \pi t}{\sqrt{2(1 - \cos \pi t)}}$

$a_{\mathbf{N}} = \mathbf{a} \cdot \mathbf{N} = \dfrac{1}{\sqrt{2(1 - \cos \pi t)}}[\pi^2 \sin^2 \pi t + \pi^2 \cos \pi t(-1 + \cos \pi t)] = \dfrac{\pi^2(1 - \cos \pi t)}{\sqrt{2(1 - \cos \pi t)}} = \dfrac{\pi^2 \sqrt{2(1 - \cos \pi t)}}{2}$

When $t = \dfrac{1}{2}$: $a_{\mathbf{T}} = \dfrac{\pi^2}{\sqrt{2}} = \dfrac{\sqrt{2}\pi^2}{2}, a_{\mathbf{N}} = \dfrac{\sqrt{2}\pi^2}{2}$

When $t = 1$: $a_{\mathbf{T}} = 0, a_{\mathbf{N}} = \pi^2$

When $t = \dfrac{3}{2}$: $a_{\mathbf{T}} = -\dfrac{\sqrt{2}\pi^2}{2}, a_{\mathbf{N}} = \dfrac{\sqrt{2}\pi^2}{2}$

(b) Speed: $\quad s = \|\mathbf{v}(t)\| = \pi\sqrt{2(1 - \cos \pi t)}$

$\dfrac{ds}{dt} = \dfrac{\pi^2 \sin \pi t}{\sqrt{2(1 - \cos \pi t)}} = a_{\mathbf{T}}$

When $t = \dfrac{1}{2}$: $a_{\mathbf{T}} = \dfrac{\sqrt{2}\pi^2}{2} > 0 \Rightarrow$ the speed is increasing.

When $t = 1$: $a_{\mathbf{T}} = 0 \Rightarrow$ the speed is maximum.

When $t = \dfrac{3}{2}$: $a_{\mathbf{T}} = -\dfrac{\sqrt{2}\pi^2}{2} < 0 \Rightarrow$ the speed is decreasing.

When the sign of $a_{\mathbf{T}}$ and $a_{\mathbf{N}}$ are the same, the speed increases, and when they have opposite signs, the speed decreases.

31. $\mathbf{r}(t) = t\mathbf{i} + 2t\mathbf{j} - 3t\mathbf{k}$

$\mathbf{v}(t) = \mathbf{i} + 2\mathbf{j} - 3\mathbf{k}$

$\mathbf{a}(t) = \mathbf{0}$

$\mathbf{T}(t) = \dfrac{\mathbf{v}}{\|\mathbf{v}\|} = \dfrac{1}{\sqrt{14}}(\mathbf{i} + 2\mathbf{j} - 3\mathbf{k}) = \dfrac{\sqrt{14}}{14}(\mathbf{i} + 2\mathbf{j} - 3\mathbf{k})$

$\mathbf{N}(t) = \dfrac{\mathbf{T}'}{\|\mathbf{T}'\|}$ is undefined.

$a_{\mathbf{T}}, a_{\mathbf{N}}$ are not defined.

33. $\mathbf{r}(t) = t\mathbf{i} + t^2\mathbf{j} + \dfrac{t^2}{2}\mathbf{k}$

$\mathbf{v}(t) = \mathbf{i} + 2t\mathbf{j} + t\mathbf{k}$

$\mathbf{v}(1) = \mathbf{i} + 2\mathbf{j} + \mathbf{k}$

$\mathbf{a}(t) = 2\mathbf{j} + \mathbf{k}$

$\mathbf{T}(t) = \dfrac{\mathbf{v}}{\|\mathbf{v}\|} = \dfrac{1}{\sqrt{1 + 5t^2}}(\mathbf{i} + 2t\mathbf{j} + t\mathbf{k})$

$\mathbf{T}(1) = \dfrac{\sqrt{6}}{6}(\mathbf{i} + 2\mathbf{j} + \mathbf{k})$

$\mathbf{N}(t) = \dfrac{\mathbf{T}'}{\|\mathbf{T}'\|} = \dfrac{\dfrac{-5t\mathbf{i} + 2\mathbf{j} + \mathbf{k}}{(1 + 5t^2)^{3/2}}}{\dfrac{\sqrt{5}}{1 + 5t^2}} = \dfrac{-5t\mathbf{i} + 2\mathbf{j} + \mathbf{k}}{\sqrt{5}\sqrt{1 + 5t^2}}$

$\mathbf{N}(1) = \dfrac{\sqrt{30}}{30}(-5\mathbf{i} + 2\mathbf{j} + \mathbf{k})$

$a_{\mathbf{T}} = \mathbf{a} \cdot \mathbf{T} = \dfrac{5\sqrt{6}}{6}$

$a_{\mathbf{N}} = \mathbf{a} \cdot \mathbf{N} = \dfrac{\sqrt{30}}{6}$

35. $\mathbf{r}(t) = 4t\mathbf{i} + 3\cos t\mathbf{j} + 3\sin t\mathbf{k}$

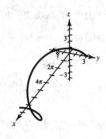

$\mathbf{v}(t) = \mathbf{r}'(t) = 4\mathbf{i} - 3\sin t\mathbf{j} + 3\cos t\mathbf{k}$

$\|\mathbf{v}(t)\| = \sqrt{16 + 9(\sin^2 t + \cos^2 t)} = \sqrt{25} = 5$

$\mathbf{a}(t) = \mathbf{r}''(t) = -3\cos t\mathbf{j} - 3\sin t\mathbf{k}$

$\mathbf{T}(t) = \dfrac{\mathbf{v}(t)}{\|\mathbf{v}(t)\|} = \dfrac{1}{5}[4\mathbf{i} - 3\sin t\mathbf{j} + 3\cos t\mathbf{k}]$

$\mathbf{N}(t) = \dfrac{\mathbf{T}'(t)}{\|\mathbf{T}'(t)\|} = \dfrac{(1/5)[-3\cos t\mathbf{j} - 3\sin t\mathbf{k}]}{(1/5)\sqrt{9(\cos^2 t + \sin^2 t)}} = \dfrac{(-3/5)[(\cos t)\mathbf{j} + (\sin t)\mathbf{k}]}{3/5} = -\cos t\mathbf{j} - \sin t\mathbf{k}$

Therefore

$$\mathbf{a}\left(\frac{\pi}{2}\right) = -3\mathbf{k},\ \mathbf{T}\left(\frac{\pi}{2}\right) = \frac{1}{5}[4\mathbf{i} - 3\mathbf{j}],\ \text{and}\ \mathbf{N}\left(\frac{\pi}{2}\right) = -\mathbf{k}.$$

Thus,

$$a_\mathbf{T} = \mathbf{a}\left(\frac{\pi}{2}\right) \cdot \mathbf{T}\left(\frac{\pi}{2}\right) = 0\ \text{and}\ a_\mathbf{N} = \mathbf{a}\left(\frac{\pi}{2}\right) \cdot \mathbf{N}\left(\frac{\pi}{2}\right) = 3.$$

37. $\mathbf{r}(t) = 2\cos t\mathbf{i} + 2\sin t\mathbf{j} + \dfrac{t}{2}\mathbf{k},\ t_0 = \dfrac{\pi}{2}$

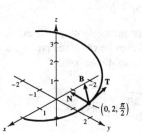

$\mathbf{r}'(t) = -2\sin t\mathbf{i} + 2\cos t\mathbf{j} + \dfrac{1}{2}\mathbf{k}$

$\mathbf{T}(t) = \dfrac{2\sqrt{17}}{17}\left(-2\sin t\mathbf{i} + 2\cos t\mathbf{j} + \dfrac{1}{2}\mathbf{k}\right)$

$\mathbf{N}(t) = -\cos t\mathbf{i} - \sin t\mathbf{j}$

$\mathbf{r}\left(\dfrac{\pi}{2}\right) = 2\mathbf{j} + \dfrac{\pi}{4}\mathbf{k}$

$\mathbf{T}\left(\dfrac{\pi}{2}\right) = \dfrac{2\sqrt{17}}{17}\left(-2\mathbf{i} + \dfrac{1}{2}\mathbf{k}\right) = \dfrac{\sqrt{17}}{17}(-4\mathbf{i} + \mathbf{k})$

$\mathbf{N}\left(\dfrac{\pi}{2}\right) = -\mathbf{j}$

$\mathbf{B}\left(\dfrac{\pi}{2}\right) = \mathbf{T}\left(\dfrac{\pi}{2}\right) \times \mathbf{N}\left(\dfrac{\pi}{2}\right) = \begin{vmatrix} \mathbf{i} & \mathbf{j} & \mathbf{k} \\ -\dfrac{4\sqrt{17}}{17} & 0 & \dfrac{\sqrt{17}}{17} \\ 0 & -1 & 0 \end{vmatrix} = \dfrac{\sqrt{17}}{17}\mathbf{i} + \dfrac{4\sqrt{17}}{17}\mathbf{k} = \dfrac{\sqrt{17}}{17}(\mathbf{i} + 4\mathbf{k})$

39. $\mathbf{r}(t) = \langle 10\cos 10\pi t,\ 10\sin 10\pi t,\ 4 + 4t \rangle,\ 0 \le t \le \dfrac{1}{20}$

(a) $\mathbf{r}'(t) = \langle -100\pi \sin(10\pi t),\ 100\pi \cos(10\pi t),\ 4 \rangle$

$\|\mathbf{r}'(t)\| = \sqrt{(100\pi)^2 \sin^2(10\pi t) + (100\pi)^2 \cos^2(10\pi t) + 16}$

$= \sqrt{(100\pi)^2 + 16} = 4\sqrt{625\pi^2 + 1} \approx 314\ \text{mi/hr}$

(b) $a_\mathbf{T} = 0$ and $a_\mathbf{N} = 1000\pi^2$

$a_\mathbf{T} = 0$ because the speed is constant.

41. $\mathbf{r}(t) = (v_0 t \cos \theta)\mathbf{i} + (h + v_0 t \sin \theta - 16t^2)\mathbf{j}$

$\mathbf{v}(t) = (v_0 \cos \theta)\mathbf{i} + (v_0 \sin \theta - 32t)\mathbf{j}$

$\mathbf{a}(t) = -32\mathbf{j}$

$\mathbf{T}(t) = \dfrac{\mathbf{v}(t)}{\|\mathbf{v}(t)\|} = \dfrac{(v_0 \cos \theta)\mathbf{i} + (v_0 \sin \theta - 32t)\mathbf{j}}{\sqrt{v_0^2 \cos^2 \theta + (v_0 \sin \theta - 32t)^2}}$

Since the path of a projectile is concave downward,

$$\mathbf{N}(t) = \dfrac{(v_0 \sin \theta - 32t)\mathbf{i} + (-v_0 \cos \theta)\mathbf{j}}{\sqrt{v_0^2 \cos^2 \theta + (v_0 \sin \theta - 32t)^2}}.$$

Therefore,

$$a_{\mathbf{T}} = \dfrac{-32(v_0 \sin \theta - 32t)}{\sqrt{v_0^2 \cos^2 \theta + (v_0 \sin \theta - 32t)^2}}$$

$$a_{\mathbf{N}} = \dfrac{32 v_0 \cos \theta}{\sqrt{v_0^2 \cos^2 \theta + (v_0 \sin \theta - 32t)^2}}.$$

The projectile will reach its maximum height when the vertical component of velocity is zero, or

$$v_0 \sin \theta - 32t = 0.$$

Hence, at the maximum height $a_{\mathbf{T}} = 0$ and $a_{\mathbf{N}} = 32$. Thus at the maximum height of the projectile, all the acceleration is normal to the path.

43. $\mathbf{r}(t) = a \cos(\omega t)\mathbf{i} + a \sin(\omega t)\mathbf{j}$

$\mathbf{v}(t) = -a\omega \sin(\omega t)\mathbf{i} + a\omega \cos(\omega t)\mathbf{j}$

$\mathbf{a}(t) = -a\omega^2 \cos(\omega t)\mathbf{i} - a\omega^2 \sin(\omega t)\mathbf{j}$

$\mathbf{T}(t) = \dfrac{\mathbf{v}(t)}{\|\mathbf{v}(t)\|} = -\sin(\omega t)\mathbf{i} + \cos(\omega t)\mathbf{j}$

$\mathbf{N}(t) = \dfrac{\mathbf{T}'(t)}{\|\mathbf{T}'(t)\|} = -\cos(\omega t)\mathbf{i} - \sin(\omega t)\mathbf{j}$

$a_{\mathbf{T}} = \mathbf{a} \cdot \mathbf{T} = 0$

$a_{\mathbf{N}} = \mathbf{a} \cdot \mathbf{N} = a\omega^2$

(a) If $\omega_0 = 2\omega$, then

$$\mathbf{a} \cdot \mathbf{N} = a\omega_0^2 = a(2\omega)^2 = 4a\omega^2.$$

Therefore, the centripetal acceleration is increased by a factor of 4 when the velocity is doubled.

(b) If $a_0 = a/2$, then

$$\mathbf{a} \cdot \mathbf{N} = a_0\omega^2 = \frac{a}{2}(\omega^2) = \frac{1}{2}a\omega^2.$$

Therefore, the centripetal acceleration is halved when the radius is halved.

45. $v = \sqrt{\dfrac{9.56 \times 10^4}{4100}} \approx 4.83 \text{ mi/sec}$

47. $v = \sqrt{\dfrac{9.56 \times 10^4}{4385}} \approx 4.67 \text{ mi/sec}$

49. Let $\mathbf{T}(t) = \cos \phi \mathbf{i} + \sin \phi \mathbf{j}$ be the unit tangent vector. Then

$$\mathbf{T}'(t) = \frac{d\mathbf{T}}{dt} = \frac{d\mathbf{T}}{d\phi}\frac{d\phi}{dt} = -(\sin \phi \mathbf{i} + \cos \phi \mathbf{j})\frac{d\phi}{dt} = \mathbf{M}\frac{d\phi}{dt}.$$

$\mathbf{M} = -\sin \phi \mathbf{i} + \cos \phi \mathbf{j} = \cos[\phi + (\pi/2)]\mathbf{i} + \sin[\phi + (\pi/2)]\mathbf{j}$ and is rotated counterclockwise through an angle of $\pi/2$ from $\mathbf{T}$.

If $d\phi/dt > 0$, then the curve bends to the left and $\mathbf{M}$ has the same direction as $\mathbf{T}'$. Thus, $\mathbf{M}$ has the same direction as

$$\mathbf{N} = \frac{\mathbf{T}'}{\|\mathbf{T}'\|},$$

which is toward the concave side of the curve.

If $d\phi/dt < 0$, then the curve bends to the right and $\mathbf{M}$ has the opposite direction as $\mathbf{T}'$. Thus,

$$\mathbf{N} = \frac{\mathbf{T}'}{\|\mathbf{T}'\|}$$

again points to the concave side of the curve.

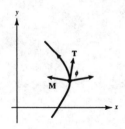

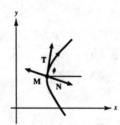

51. Using $\mathbf{a} = a_{\mathbf{T}}\mathbf{T} + a_{\mathbf{N}}\mathbf{N}$, $\mathbf{T} \times \mathbf{T} = \mathbf{O}$, and $\|\mathbf{T} \times \mathbf{N}\| = 1$, we have:

$$\mathbf{v} \times \mathbf{a} = \|\mathbf{v}\|\mathbf{T} \times (a_{\mathbf{T}}\mathbf{T} + a_{\mathbf{N}}\mathbf{N}) = \|\mathbf{v}\|a_{\mathbf{T}}(\mathbf{T} \times \mathbf{T}) + \|\mathbf{v}\|a_{\mathbf{N}}(\mathbf{T} \times \mathbf{N}) = \|\mathbf{v}\|a_{\mathbf{N}}(\mathbf{T} \times \mathbf{N})$$

$$\|\mathbf{v} \times \mathbf{a}\| = \|\mathbf{v}\|a_{\mathbf{N}}\|\mathbf{T} \times \mathbf{N}\| = \|\mathbf{v}\|a_{\mathbf{N}}$$

Thus, $a_{\mathbf{N}} = \dfrac{\|\mathbf{v} \times \mathbf{a}\|}{\|\mathbf{v}\|}$.

Section 11.5   Arc Length and Curvature

1. $\mathbf{r}(t) = t\mathbf{i} + 3t\mathbf{j}$

$$\frac{dx}{dt} = 1, \frac{dy}{dt} = 3, \frac{dz}{dt} = 0$$

$$s = \int_0^4 \sqrt{1+9}\,dt$$

$$= \sqrt{10}\int_0^4 dt$$

$$= \left[\sqrt{10}\,t\right]_0^4 = 4\sqrt{10}$$

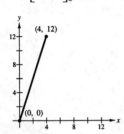

3. $\mathbf{r}(t) = a\cos^3 t\mathbf{i} + a\sin^3 t\mathbf{j}$

$$\frac{dx}{dt} = -3a\cos^2 t\sin t, \frac{dy}{dt} = 3a\sin^2 t\cos t$$

$$s = 4\int_0^{\pi/2} \sqrt{[3a\cos^2 t(-\sin t)]^2 + [3a\sin^2 t\cos t]^2}\,dt$$

$$= 12a\int_0^{\pi/2} \sin t\cos t\,dt$$

$$= 3a\int_0^{\pi/2} 2\sin 2t\,dt = \left[-3a\cos 2t\right]_0^{\pi/2} = 6a$$

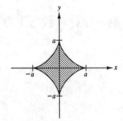

5. $\mathbf{r}(t) = 2t\mathbf{i} - 3t\mathbf{j} + t\mathbf{k}$

$$\frac{dx}{dt} = 2, \frac{dy}{dt} = -3, \frac{dz}{dt} = 1$$

$$s = \int_0^2 \sqrt{2^2 + (-3)^2 + 1^2}\,dt$$

$$= \int_0^2 \sqrt{14}\,dt = \left[\sqrt{14}\,t\right]_0^2$$

$$= 2\sqrt{14}$$

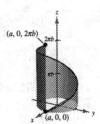

7. $\mathbf{r}(t) = a\cos t\mathbf{i} + a\sin t\mathbf{j} + bt\mathbf{k}$

The graph is a circular helix of radius a (see figure). Since

$$\mathbf{r}'(t) = -a\sin t\mathbf{i} + a\cos t\mathbf{j} + b\mathbf{k},$$

the arc length on the interval $[0, 2\pi]$ is

$$s = \int_0^{2\pi} \|\mathbf{r}'(t)\|\,dt$$

$$= \int_0^{2\pi} \sqrt{(-a\sin t)^2 + (a\cos t)^2 + b^2}\,dt$$

$$= \int_0^{2\pi} \sqrt{a^2(\sin^2 t + \cos^2 t) + b^2}\,dt$$

$$= \int_0^{2\pi} \sqrt{a^2 + b^2}\,dt = \left[\sqrt{a^2 + b^2}\,t\right]_0^{2\pi} = 2\pi\sqrt{a^2 + b^2}.$$

9. $\mathbf{r}(t) = t^2\mathbf{i} + t\mathbf{j} + \ln t\mathbf{k}$

$$\frac{dx}{dt} = 2t, \frac{dy}{dt} = 1, \frac{dz}{dt} = \frac{1}{t}$$

$$s = \int_1^3 \sqrt{(2t)^2 + (1)^2 + \left(\frac{1}{t}\right)^2}\, dt$$

$$= \int_1^3 \sqrt{\frac{4t^4 + t^2 + 1}{t^2}}\, dt$$

$$= \int_1^3 \frac{\sqrt{4t^4 + t^2 + 1}}{t}\, dt \approx 8.37$$

11. $\mathbf{r}(t) = t\mathbf{i} + (4 - t^2)\mathbf{j} + t^3\mathbf{k}, \quad 0 \le t \le 2$

(a) $\mathbf{r}(0) = \langle 0, 4, 0 \rangle, \mathbf{r}(2) = \langle 2, 0, 8 \rangle$

distance $= \sqrt{2^2 + 4^2 + 8^2} = \sqrt{84} = 2\sqrt{21} \approx 9.165$

(b) $\mathbf{r}(0) = \langle 0, 4, 0 \rangle$

$\mathbf{r}(0.5) = \langle 0.5, 3.75, .125 \rangle$

$\mathbf{r}(1) = \langle 1, 3, 1 \rangle$

$\mathbf{r}(1.5) = \langle 1.5, 1.75, 3.375 \rangle$

$\mathbf{r}(2) = \langle 2, 0, 8 \rangle$

distance $\approx \sqrt{(0.5)^2 + (.25)^2 + (.125)^2} + \sqrt{(.5)^2 + (.75)^2 + (.875)^2} + \sqrt{(0.5)^2 + (1.25)^2 + (2.375)^2} +$

$\sqrt{(0.5)^2 + (1.75)^2 + (4.625)^2}$

$\approx 0.5728 + 1.2562 + 2.7300 + 4.9702 \approx 9.529$

(c) Increase the number of line segments.

(d) Using a graphing utility, you obtain 9.57057.

13. $\mathbf{r}(t) = \langle 2 \cos t, 2 \sin t, t \rangle$

(a) Since $x'(t) = -2 \sin t$, $y'(t) = 2 \cos t$, and $z'(t) = 1$, we have

$$s = \int_0^t \sqrt{[x'(\tau)]^2 + [y'(\tau)]^2 + [z'(\tau)]^2}\, d\tau = \int_0^t \sqrt{(-2 \sin \tau)^2 + (2 \cos \tau)^2 + (1)^2}\, d\tau$$

$$= \int_0^t \sqrt{5}\, d\tau = \sqrt{5}\Big[\tau\Big]_0^t = \sqrt{5}t.$$

(b) Since $s = \sqrt{5}t$, we have $t = s/\sqrt{5}$. Therefore, the parameterization of th curve in terms of s is

$$r(s) = \left\langle 2 \cos \frac{s}{\sqrt{5}}, 2 \sin \frac{s}{\sqrt{5}}, \frac{s}{\sqrt{5}} \right\rangle.$$

(c) $\mathbf{r}(\sqrt{5}) = \langle 2 \cos 1, 2 \sin 1, 1 \rangle \approx \langle 1.081, 1.683, 1 \rangle$

and

$$\mathbf{r}(4) = \left\langle 2 \cos \frac{4}{\sqrt{5}}, 2 \sin \frac{4}{\sqrt{5}}, 1 \right\rangle \approx \langle -0.433, 1.953, 1.789 \rangle.$$

(d) $\mathbf{r}'(s) = \left\langle -\frac{2}{\sqrt{5}} \sin \frac{s}{\sqrt{5}}, \frac{2}{\sqrt{5}} \cos \frac{s}{\sqrt{5}}, \frac{1}{\sqrt{5}} \right\rangle$

$$\|\mathbf{r}'(s)\| = \sqrt{\left(-\frac{2}{\sqrt{5}} \sin \frac{s}{\sqrt{5}}\right)^2 + \left(\frac{2}{\sqrt{5}} \cos \frac{s}{\sqrt{5}}\right)^2 + \left(\frac{1}{\sqrt{5}}\right)^2} = \sqrt{\frac{4}{5} + \frac{1}{5}} = 1$$

15. $\mathbf{r}(s) = \left(1 + \dfrac{\sqrt{2}}{2}s\right)\mathbf{i} + \left(1 - \dfrac{\sqrt{2}}{2}s\right)\mathbf{j}$

  $\mathbf{r}'(s) = \dfrac{\sqrt{2}}{2}\mathbf{i} - \dfrac{\sqrt{2}}{2}\mathbf{j}$ and $\|\mathbf{r}'(s)\| = \sqrt{\dfrac{1}{2} + \dfrac{1}{2}} = 1$

  $\mathbf{T}(s) = \dfrac{\mathbf{r}'(s)}{\|\mathbf{r}'(s)\|} = \mathbf{r}'(s)$

  $\mathbf{T}'(s) = \mathbf{0} \Rightarrow K = \|\mathbf{T}'(s)\| = 0$ (The curve is a line.)

17. $\mathbf{r}(s) = 2\cos\left(\dfrac{s}{\sqrt{5}}\right)\mathbf{i} + 2\sin\left(\dfrac{s}{\sqrt{5}}\right)\mathbf{j} + \dfrac{s}{\sqrt{5}}\mathbf{k}$

  $\mathbf{T}(s) = \mathbf{r}'(s) = -\dfrac{2}{\sqrt{5}}\sin\left(\dfrac{s}{\sqrt{5}}\right)\mathbf{i} + \dfrac{2}{\sqrt{5}}\cos\left(\dfrac{s}{\sqrt{5}}\right)\mathbf{j} + \dfrac{1}{\sqrt{5}}\mathbf{k}$

  $\mathbf{T}'(s) = -\dfrac{2}{5}\cos\left(\dfrac{s}{\sqrt{5}}\right)\mathbf{i} - \dfrac{2}{5}\sin\left(\dfrac{s}{\sqrt{5}}\right)\mathbf{j}$

  $K = \|\mathbf{T}'(s)\| = \dfrac{2}{5}$

19. $\mathbf{r}(t) = 4t\mathbf{i} - 2t\mathbf{j}$

  $\mathbf{v}(t) = 4\mathbf{i} - 2\mathbf{j}$

  $\mathbf{T}(t) = \dfrac{1}{\sqrt{5}}(2\mathbf{i} - \mathbf{j})$

  $\mathbf{T}'(t) = \mathbf{0}$

  $K = \dfrac{\|\mathbf{T}'(t)\|}{\|\mathbf{r}'(t)\|} = 0$ (The curve is a line.)

21. $\mathbf{r}(t) = t\mathbf{i} + \dfrac{1}{t}\mathbf{j}$

  From Exercise 17, Section 11.4, we have

  $\mathbf{a}(1) \cdot \mathbf{N}(1) = \sqrt{2}$ and $\|\mathbf{v}(1)\|^2 = 2$.

  Therefore, the curvature is

  $K = \dfrac{\mathbf{a}(1) \cdot \mathbf{N}(1)}{\|\mathbf{v}(1)\|^2} = \dfrac{\sqrt{2}}{2} \approx 0.707.$

23. $\mathbf{r}(t) = 4\cos(2\pi t)\mathbf{i} + 4\sin(2\pi t)\mathbf{j}$

  $\mathbf{r}'(t) = -8\pi\sin(2\pi t)\mathbf{i} + 8\pi\cos(2\pi t)\mathbf{j}$

  $\mathbf{T}(t) = -\sin(2\pi t)\mathbf{i} + \cos(2\pi t)\mathbf{j}$

  $\mathbf{T}'(t) = -2\pi\cos(2\pi t)\mathbf{i} - 2\pi\sin(2\pi t)\mathbf{j}$

  $K = \dfrac{\|\mathbf{T}'(t)\|}{\|\mathbf{r}'(t)\|} = \dfrac{2\pi}{8\pi} = \dfrac{1}{4}$

25. $\mathbf{r}(t) = a\cos(\omega t)\mathbf{i} + a\sin(\omega t)\mathbf{j}$

  $\mathbf{r}'(t) = -a\omega\sin(\omega t)\mathbf{i} + a\omega\cos(\omega t)\mathbf{j}$

  $\mathbf{T}(t) = -\sin(\omega t)\mathbf{i} + \cos(\omega t)\mathbf{j}$

  $\mathbf{T}'(t) = -\omega\cos(\omega t)\mathbf{i} - \omega\sin(\omega t)\mathbf{j}$

  $K = \dfrac{\|\mathbf{T}'(t)\|}{\|\mathbf{r}'(t)\|} = \dfrac{\omega}{a\omega} = \dfrac{1}{a}$

27. $\mathbf{r}(t) = e^t\cos t\,\mathbf{i} + e^t\sin t\,\mathbf{j}$

  $\mathbf{r}'(t) = e^t(\cos t - \sin t)\mathbf{i} + e^t(\cos t + \sin t)\mathbf{j}$

  $\|\mathbf{r}'(t)\| = e^t\sqrt{(\cos t - \sin t)^2 + (\cos t + \sin t)^2} = \sqrt{2}e^t$

  $\mathbf{T}(t) = \dfrac{\mathbf{r}'(t)}{\|\mathbf{r}'(t)\|} = \dfrac{1}{\sqrt{2}}[(\cos t - \sin t)\mathbf{i} + (\cos t + \sin t)\mathbf{j}]$

  $\mathbf{T}'(t) = \dfrac{1}{\sqrt{2}}[(-\sin t - \cos t)\mathbf{i} + (-\sin t + \cos t)\mathbf{j}]$

  $\|\mathbf{T}'(t)\| = \dfrac{1}{\sqrt{2}}\sqrt{(-\sin t - \cos t)^2 + (-\sin t + \cos t)^2} = 1$

  $K = \dfrac{\|\mathbf{T}'(t)\|}{\|\mathbf{r}'(t)\|} = \dfrac{1}{\sqrt{2}e^t} = \dfrac{\sqrt{2}}{2}e^{-t}$

29. $\mathbf{r}(t) = \langle \cos\omega t + \omega t\sin\omega t,\ \sin\omega t - \omega t\cos\omega t \rangle$

  From Exercise 21, Section 11.4, we have:

  $\mathbf{a} \cdot \mathbf{N} = \omega^3 t$

  $K = \dfrac{\mathbf{a}(t) \cdot \mathbf{N}(t)}{\|\mathbf{v}\|^2} = \dfrac{\omega^3 t}{\omega^4 t^2} = \dfrac{1}{\omega t}$

31. $\mathbf{r}(t) = t\mathbf{i} + t^2\mathbf{j} + \dfrac{t^2}{2}\mathbf{k}$

  $\mathbf{r}'(t) = \mathbf{i} + 2t\mathbf{j} + t\mathbf{k}$

  $\mathbf{T}(t) = \dfrac{\mathbf{i} + 2t\mathbf{j} + t\mathbf{k}}{\sqrt{1 + 5t^2}}$

  $\mathbf{T}'(t) = \dfrac{-5t\mathbf{i} + 2\mathbf{j} + \mathbf{k}}{(1 + 5t^2)^{3/2}}$

  $K = \dfrac{\|\mathbf{T}'(t)\|}{\|\mathbf{r}'(t)\|} = \dfrac{\dfrac{\sqrt{5}}{(1 + 5t^2)}}{\sqrt{1 + 5t^2}} = \dfrac{\sqrt{5}}{(1 + 5t^2)^{3/2}}$

33. $\mathbf{r}(t) = 4t\mathbf{i} + 3\cos t\,\mathbf{j} + 3\sin t\,\mathbf{k}$

  From Exercise 35, Section 11.4, we have

  $\|\mathbf{T}'(t)\| = \dfrac{3}{5}$ and $\|\mathbf{r}'(t)\| = 5$.

  Therefore, the curvature is

  $K = \dfrac{\|\mathbf{T}'(t)\|}{\|\mathbf{r}'(t)\|} = \dfrac{3/5}{5} = \dfrac{3}{25}.$

35. $y = 3x - 2$

Since $y'' = 0$, $K = 0$, and the radius of curvature is undefined.

37. $y = 2x^2 + 3$, $y' = 4x$, $y'' = 4$

$$K = \left| \frac{y''}{[1 + (y')^2]^{3/2}} \right| = \frac{4}{[1 + (4x)^2]^{3/2}}$$

When $x = -1$, the curvature is

$$K = \frac{4}{(1 + 16)^{3/2}} = \frac{4}{17^{3/2}} \approx 0.057$$

and the radius of curvature when $x = -1$ is

$$r = \frac{1}{K} = \frac{17^{3/2}}{4} \approx 17.523.$$

39. $y = \sqrt{a^2 - x^2}$

$$y' = \frac{-x}{\sqrt{a^2 - x^2}}$$

$$y'' = \frac{-(2x^2 - a^2)}{(a^2 - x^2)^{3/2}}$$

At $x = 0$: $\quad y' = 0$

$$y'' = \frac{1}{a}$$

$$K = \frac{1/a}{(1 + 0^2)^{3/2}} = \frac{1}{a}$$

$$\frac{1}{K} = a \quad \text{(radius of curvature)}$$

41. (a) Point on circle: $\left(\frac{\pi}{2}, 1 \right)$

Center: $\left(\frac{\pi}{2}, 0 \right)$

Equation: $\left(x - \frac{\pi}{2} \right)^2 + y^2 = 1$

(b) The circles have different radii since the curvature is different and

$$r = \frac{1}{K}.$$

43. $f(x) = x + \dfrac{1}{x}$, $f'(x) = 1 - \dfrac{1}{x^2} = \dfrac{x^2 - 1}{x^2}$, $f''(x) = \dfrac{2}{x^3}$

At the point $(1, 2)$, $f'(1) = 0$, and $f''(1) = 2$. Thus at $(1, 2)$ the curvature is

$$K = \left| \frac{2}{(1 + 0^2)^{3/2}} \right| = 2$$

and the radius of curvature is

$$r = \frac{1}{K} = \frac{1}{2}.$$

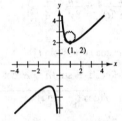

Since the slope of the tangent line to the graph of the function is 0 at the point $(1, 2)$, the normal line is vertical and the center of the closest circular approximation is $\left(1, \frac{5}{2} \right)$ (see figure). Finally, the equation of the closest circular approximation is

$$(x - 1)^2 + \left(y - \frac{5}{2} \right)^2 = \left(\frac{1}{2} \right)^2.$$

45. $\quad y = e^x, \qquad x = 0$

$\quad y' = e^x, \qquad y'' = e^x$

$y'(0) = 1, \qquad y''(0) = 1$

$$K = \frac{1}{(1 + 1^2)^{3/2}} = \frac{1}{2^{3/2}} = \frac{1}{2\sqrt{2}}, \quad r = \frac{1}{K} = 2\sqrt{2}$$

—CONTINUED—

45. —CONTINUED—

The slope of the tangent line at $(0, 1)$ is $y'(0) = 1$. The slope of the normal line is -1. The equation of the normal line is $y - 1 = -x$ or $y = -x + 1$ The center of the circle is on the normal line $2\sqrt{2}$ units away from the point $(0, 1)$.

$$\sqrt{(0 - x)^2 + (1 - y)^2} = 2\sqrt{2}$$

$$x^2 + x^2 = 8$$

$$x^2 = 4$$

$$x = \pm 2$$

Since the circle is above the curve, $x = -2$ and $y = 3$.

Center of circle: $(-2, 3)$

Equation of circle: $(x + 2)^2 + (y - 3)^2 = 8$

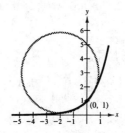

47. $y = (x - 1)^2 + 3$, $y' = 2(x - 1)$, $y'' = 2$

$$K = \frac{2}{(1 + [2(x - 1)]^2)^{3/2}} = \frac{2}{[1 + 4(x - 1)^2]^{3/2}}$$

(a) K is maximum when $x = 1$ or at the vertex $(1, 3)$.

(b) $\lim\limits_{x \to \infty} K = 0$

49. $y = x^{2/3}$, $y' = \frac{2}{3}x^{-1/3}$, $y'' = -\frac{2}{9}x^{-4/3}$

$$K = \left| \frac{(-2/9)x^{-4/3}}{[1 + (4/9)x^{-2/3}]^{3/2}} \right| = \left| \frac{6}{x^{1/3}(9x^{2/3} + 4)^{3/2}} \right|$$

(a) $K \Rightarrow \infty$ as $x \Rightarrow 0$. No maximum

(b) $\lim\limits_{x \to \infty} K = 0$

51. $y = (x - 1)^3 + 3$, $y' = 3(x - 1)^2$, $y'' = 6(x - 1)$

$$K = \left| \frac{6(x - 1)}{[1 + 9(x - 1)^4]^{3/2}} \right|$$

$K = 0$ when $x = 1$.

Point: $(1, 3)$

53. $x^2 + 4y^2 = 4$

The endpoints of the major axis are $(\pm 2, 0)$ and the endpoints of the minor axis are $(0, \pm 1)$.

$$x^2 + 4y^2 = 4$$

$$2x + 8yy' = 0$$

$$y' = \frac{-x}{4y}$$

$$y'' = \frac{(4y)(-1) - (-x)(4y')}{16y^2} = \frac{-4y - (x^2/y)}{16y^2} = \frac{-(4y^2 + x^2)}{16y^3}$$

$$= \frac{-4}{16y^3} = \frac{-1}{4y^3}$$

The curvature is given by

$$K = \left| \frac{-1/4y^3}{[1 + (-x/4y)^2]^{3/2}} \right| = \left| \frac{-1}{4y^3[(16y^2 + x^2)/16y^2]^{3/2}} \right| = \left| \frac{-16}{(16y^2 + x^2)^{3/2}} \right|$$

$$= \frac{16}{(12y^2 + 4y^2 + x^2)^{3/2}} = \frac{16}{(12y^2 + 4)^{3/2}}.$$

Since $-1 \le y \le 1$, K is greatest when $y = 0$ and smallest when $y = \pm 1$.

55. $f(x) = x^4 - x^2$

(a) $K = \dfrac{2|6x^2 - 1|}{[16x^6 - 16x^4 + 4x^2 + 1]^{3/2}}$

(b) For $x = 0$, $K = 2$. $f(0) = 0$. At $(0, 0)$, the circle of curvature has radius $\frac{1}{2}$. Using the symmetry of the graph of f, you obtain

$$x^2 + \left(y + \frac{1}{2}\right)^2 = \frac{1}{4}.$$

For $x = 1$, $K = \left(2\sqrt{5}\right)/5$. $f(1) = 0$. At $(1, 0)$, the circle of curvature has radius

$$\frac{\sqrt{5}}{2} = \frac{1}{K}.$$

Using the graph of f, you see that the center of curvature is $\left(0, \frac{1}{2}\right)$. Thus,

$$x^2 + \left(y - \frac{1}{2}\right)^2 = \frac{5}{4}.$$

To graph these circles, use

$$y = -\frac{1}{2} \pm \sqrt{\frac{1}{4} - x^2} \quad \text{and} \quad y = \frac{1}{2} \pm \sqrt{\frac{5}{4} - x^2}.$$

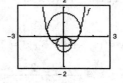

(c) The curvature tends to be greatest near the extrema of f, and K decreases as $x \to \pm\infty$. However, f and K do not have the same critical numbers.

Critical numbers of f: $x = 0, \pm\dfrac{\sqrt{2}}{2} \approx \pm0.7071$

Critical numbers of K: $x = 0, \pm.7647, \pm0.4082$

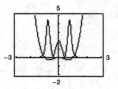

57. (a) Imagine dropping the circle $x^2 + (y - k)^2 = 16$ into the parabola $y = x^2$. The circle will drop to the point where the tangents to the circle and parabola are equal.

$$y = x^2 \quad \text{and} \quad x^2 + (y - k)^2 = 16 \implies x^2 + (x^2 - k)^2 = 16$$

Taking derivatives, $2x + 2(y - k)y' = 0$ and $y' = 2x$. Hence,

$$(y - k)y' = -x \implies y' = \frac{-x}{y - k}.$$

Thus,

$$\frac{-x}{y - k} = 2x \implies -x = 2x(y - k) \implies -1 = 2(x^2 - k) \implies x^2 - k = -\frac{1}{2}.$$

Thus,

$$x^2 + (x^2 - k)^2 = x^2 + \left(-\frac{1}{2}\right)^2 = 16 \implies x^2 = 15.75.$$

Finally, $k = x^2 + \frac{1}{2} = 16.25$, and the center of the circle is 16.25 units from the vertex of the parabola. Since the radius of the circle is 4, the circle is 12.25 units from the vertex.

(b) In 2-space, the parabola $z = y^2$ (or $z = x^2$) has a curvature of $K = 2$ at $(0, 0)$. The radius of the largest sphere that will touch the vertex has radius $= 1/K = \frac{1}{2}$.

59. $K = \dfrac{|y''|}{[1 + (y')^2]^{3/2}}$

At the smooth relative extremum $y' = 0$, so $K = |y''|$. Yes, for example, $y = x^4$ has a curvature of 0 at its relative minimum $(0, 0)$. The curvature is positive for any other point of the curvature.

61. Given $y = f(x)$: $K = \dfrac{|y''|}{(1 + [y']^2)^{3/2}}$

$$R = \frac{1}{K}$$

The center of the circle is on the normal line at a distance of R from (x, y).

Equation of normal line: $y - y_0 = -\dfrac{1}{y'}(x - x_0)$

$$\sqrt{(x - x_0)^2 + \left[-\frac{1}{y'}(x - x_0)\right]^2} = \frac{(1 + [y']^2)^{3/2}}{|y''|}$$

$$(x - x_0)^2\left[1 + \frac{1}{(y')^2}\right] = \frac{(1 + [y']^2)^3}{(y'')^2}$$

$$(x - x_0)^2 = \frac{(y')^2(1 + [y']^2)^2}{(y'')^2}$$

$$x - x_0 = \frac{y'(1 + [y']^2)}{y''} = y'z$$

$$x_0 = x - y'z$$

$$y - y_0 = -\frac{1}{y'}(x - (x - y'z)) = -z$$

$$y_0 = y + z$$

Thus, $(x_0, y_0) = (x - y'z, y + z)$.

For $y = e^x$, $y' = e^x$, $y'' = e^x$, $z = \dfrac{1 + e^{2x}}{e^x} = e^{-x} + e^x$.

When $x = 0$: $x_0 = x - y'z = 0 - (1)(2) = -2$

 $y_0 = y + z = 1 + 2 = 3$

Center of curvature: $(-2, 3)$

(See Exercise 45.)

---

63. $r = 1 + \sin \theta$

$r' = \cos \theta$

$r'' = -\sin \theta$

$K = \dfrac{|2(r')^2 - rr'' + r^2|}{[(r')^2 + r^2]^{3/2}}$

$= \dfrac{|2\cos^2 \theta - (1 + \sin \theta)(-\sin \theta) + (1 + \sin \theta)^2|}{\sqrt{[\cos^2 \theta + (1 + \sin \theta)^2]^3}}$

$= \dfrac{3(1 + \sin \theta)}{\sqrt{8(1 + \sin \theta)^3}} = \dfrac{3}{2\sqrt{2(1 + \sin \theta)}}$

65. $r = a \sin \theta$

$r' = a \cos \theta$

$r'' = -a \sin \theta$

$K = \dfrac{|2(r\omega)^2 - rr'' + r^2|}{[(r')^2 + r^2]^{3/2}}$

$= \dfrac{|2a^2 \cos^2 \theta + a^2 \sin^2 \theta + a^2 \sin^2 \theta|}{\sqrt{[a^2 \cos^2 \theta + a^2 \sin^2 \theta]^3}}$

$= \dfrac{2a^2}{a^3} = \dfrac{2}{a}, a > 0$

67. $r = e^{a\theta}, a > 0$

$r' = ae^{a\theta}$

$r'' = a^2 e^{a\theta}$

$K = \dfrac{|2(r')^2 - rr'' + r^2|}{[(r')^2 + r^2]^{3/2}} = \dfrac{|2a^2 e^{2a\theta} - a^2 e^{2a\theta} + e^{2a\theta}|}{[a^2 e^{2a\theta} + e^{2a\theta}]^{3/2}} = \dfrac{1}{e^{a\theta}\sqrt{a^2 + 1}}$

(a) As $\theta \Rightarrow \infty$, $K \Rightarrow 0$.

(b) As $a \Rightarrow \infty$, $K \Rightarrow 0$.

69. $r = 4 \sin 2\theta$

$r' = 8 \cos 2\theta$

At the pole: $K = \dfrac{2}{|r'(0)|} = \dfrac{2}{8} = \dfrac{1}{4}$

71. $x = f(t)$

$y = g(t)$

$y' = \dfrac{dy}{dx} = \dfrac{\dfrac{dy}{dt}}{\dfrac{dx}{dt}} = \dfrac{g'(t)}{f'(t)}$

$y'' = \dfrac{\dfrac{d}{dt}\left[\dfrac{g'(t)}{f'(t)}\right]}{\dfrac{dx}{dt}} = \dfrac{\dfrac{f'(t)g''(t) - g'(t)f''(t)}{[f'(t)]^2}}{f'(t)} = \dfrac{f'(t)g''(t) - g'(t)f''(t)}{[f'(t)]^3}$

$K = \dfrac{|y''|}{[1 + (y')^2]^{3/2}} = \dfrac{\left|\dfrac{f'(t)g''(t) - g'(t)f''(t)}{[f'(t)]^3}\right|}{\left[1 + \left(\dfrac{g'(t)}{f'(t)}\right)^2\right]^{3/2}} = \dfrac{\left|\dfrac{f'(t)g''(t) - g'(t)f''(t)}{[f'(t)]^3}\right|}{\sqrt{\left\{\dfrac{[f'(t)]^2 + [g'(t)]^2}{[f'(t)]^2}\right\}^3}} = \dfrac{|f'(t)g''(t) - g'(t)f''(t)|}{([f'(t)]^2 + [g'(t)]^2)^{3/2}}$

73. $x(\theta) = a(\theta - \sin\theta), y(\theta) = a(1 - \cos\theta)$

$x'(\theta) = a(1 - \cos\theta), y'(\theta) = a\sin\theta$

$x''(\theta) = a\sin\theta, y'' = a\cos\theta$

$K = \dfrac{|x'(\theta)y''(\theta) - y'(\theta)x''(\theta)|}{\{[x'(\theta)]^2 + [y'(\theta)]^2\}^{3/2}}$

$= \dfrac{|a(1 - \cos\theta)(a\cos\theta) - (a\sin\theta)(a\sin\theta)|}{\{[a(1 - \cos\theta)]^2 + [a\sin\theta]^2\}^{3/2}}$

$= \dfrac{\sqrt{2}}{4a\sqrt{1 - \cos\theta}} = \dfrac{1}{4a}\left|\csc\dfrac{\theta}{2}\right|$

The minimum curvature is $K = 1/(4a)$ when $\theta = \pi$.
There is no maximum since $K \to \infty$ as θ approaches even
multiples of π.

75. $a_N = mK\left(\dfrac{ds}{dt}\right)^2$

$= \left(\dfrac{4000 \text{ lb}}{32 \text{ ft/sec}^2}\right)\left(\dfrac{1}{100 \text{ ft}}\right)\left(\dfrac{30(5280) \text{ ft}}{3600 \text{ sec}}\right)^2 = 2420 \text{ lb}$

77. Let $\mathbf{r} = x(t)\mathbf{i} + y(t)\mathbf{j} + z(t)\mathbf{k}$. Then $r = \|\mathbf{r}\| = \sqrt{[x(t)]^2 + [y(t)]^2 + [z(t)]^2}$ and $\mathbf{r}' = x'(t)\mathbf{i} + y'(t)\mathbf{j} + z'(t)\mathbf{k}$. Then,

$r\left(\dfrac{dr}{dt}\right) = \sqrt{[x(t)]^2 + [y(t)]^2 + [z(t)]^2}\left[\dfrac{1}{2}\{[x(t)]^2 + [y(t)]^2 + [z(t)]^2\}^{-1/2} \cdot (2x(t)x'(t) + 2y(t)y'(t) + 2z(t)z'(t))\right]$

$= x(t)x'(t) + y(t)y'(t) + z(t)z'(t) = \mathbf{r} \cdot \mathbf{r}'.$

79. Let $\mathbf{r} = x\mathbf{i} + y\mathbf{j} + z\mathbf{k}$ where $x, y,$ and z are functions of t, and $r = \|\mathbf{r}\|$.

$\dfrac{d}{dt}\left[\dfrac{\mathbf{r}}{r}\right] = \dfrac{r\mathbf{r}' - \mathbf{r}(dr/dt)}{r^2} = \dfrac{r\mathbf{r}' - \mathbf{r}[(\mathbf{r} \cdot \mathbf{r}')/r]}{r^2} = \dfrac{r^2\mathbf{r}' - (\mathbf{r} \cdot \mathbf{r}')\mathbf{r}}{r^3}$ (using Exercise 77)

$= \dfrac{(x^2 + y^2 + z^2)(x'\mathbf{i} + y'\mathbf{j} + z'\mathbf{k}) - (xx' + yy' + zz')(x\mathbf{i} + y\mathbf{j} + z\mathbf{k})}{r^3}$

$= \dfrac{1}{r^3}[(x'y^2 + x'z^2 - xyy' - xzz')\mathbf{i} + (x^2y' + z^2y' - xx'y - zz'y)\mathbf{j} + (x^2z' + y^2z' - xx'z - yy'z)\mathbf{k}]$

$= \dfrac{1}{r^3}\begin{vmatrix} \mathbf{i} & \mathbf{j} & \mathbf{k} \\ yz' - y'z & -(xz' - x'z) & xy' - x'y \\ x & y & z \end{vmatrix} = \dfrac{1}{r^3}\{[\mathbf{r} \times \mathbf{r}'] \times \mathbf{r}\}$

81. From Exercise 78, we have concluded that planetary motion is planar. Assume that the planet moves in the xy-plane with the sun at the origin. From Exercise 80, we have

$$\mathbf{r}' \times \mathbf{L} = GM\left(\frac{\mathbf{r}}{r} + \mathbf{e}\right).$$

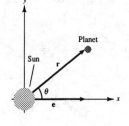

Since $\mathbf{r}' \times \mathbf{L}$ and $\mathbf{r}$ are both perpendicular to $\mathbf{L}$, so is $\mathbf{e}$. Thus, $\mathbf{e}$ lies in the xy-plane. Situate the coordinate system so that $\mathbf{e}$ lies along the positive x-axis and θ is the angle between $\mathbf{e}$ and $\mathbf{r}$. Let $e = \|\mathbf{e}\|$. Then $\mathbf{r} \cdot \mathbf{e} = \|\mathbf{r}\| \|\mathbf{e}\| \cos \theta = re \cos \theta$. Also,

$$\|\mathbf{L}\|^2 = \mathbf{L} \cdot \mathbf{L} = (\mathbf{r} \times \mathbf{r}') \cdot \mathbf{L}$$

$$= \mathbf{r} \cdot (\mathbf{r}' \times \mathbf{L}) = \mathbf{r} \cdot \left[GM\left(\mathbf{e} + \frac{\mathbf{r}}{r}\right)\right] = GM\left[\mathbf{r} \cdot \mathbf{e} + \frac{\mathbf{r} \cdot \mathbf{r}}{r}\right] = GM[re \cos \theta + r]$$

Thus,

$$\frac{\|\mathbf{L}\|^2/GM}{1 + e \cos \theta} = r$$

and the planetary motion is a conic section. Since the planet returns to its initial position periodically, the conic is an ellipse.

83. $A = \dfrac{1}{2}\displaystyle\int_\alpha^\beta r^2\, d\theta$

Thus,

$$\frac{dA}{dt} = \frac{dA}{d\theta}\frac{d\theta}{dt} = \frac{1}{2}r^2\frac{d\theta}{dt} = \frac{1}{2}\|\mathbf{L}\|$$

and $\mathbf{r}$ sweeps out area at a constant rate.

85. s is the arc length parameter.

(a) $s = \displaystyle\int_0^a \sqrt{\left(\cos\frac{\pi s^2}{2}\right)^2 + \left(\sin\frac{\pi s^2}{2}\right)^2}\, ds = a$

(b) $\mathbf{r}'(s) = \left(\cos\dfrac{\pi s^2}{2}\right)\mathbf{i} + \left(\sin\dfrac{\pi s^2}{2}\right)\mathbf{j}$

$$\mathbf{r}''(s) = -s\pi\left(\sin\frac{\pi s^2}{2}\right)\mathbf{i} + s\pi\left(\cos\frac{\pi s^2}{2}\right)\mathbf{j}$$

$$K = \|\mathbf{r}''(s)\| = \pi s$$

When $s = a$: $K = \pi a$

(c) $K = \pi a$

Review Exercises for Chapter 11

1. $\mathbf{r}(t) = t\mathbf{i} + \csc t\,\mathbf{k}$

  (a) Domain: $t \neq n\pi$, n an integer

  (b) Continuous except at $t = n\pi$, n an integer

3. $\mathbf{r}(t) = \ln t\mathbf{i} + t\mathbf{j} + t\mathbf{k}$

  (a) Domain: $(0, \infty)$

  (b) Continuous for all $t > 0$

5. (a) $\mathbf{r}(0) = \mathbf{i}$

  (b) $\mathbf{r}(-2) = -3\mathbf{i} + 4\mathbf{j} + \frac{8}{3}\mathbf{k}$

  (c) $\mathbf{r}(c - 1) = (2(c - 1) + 1)\mathbf{i} + (c - 1)^2\mathbf{j} - \frac{1}{3}(c - 1)^3\mathbf{k}$

      $= (2c - 1)\mathbf{i} + (c - 1)^2\mathbf{j} - \frac{1}{3}(c - 1)^3\mathbf{k}$

  (d) $\mathbf{r}(1 + \Delta t) - \mathbf{r}(1) = ([2(1 + \Delta t) + 1]\mathbf{i} + [1 + \Delta t]^2\mathbf{j} - \frac{1}{3}[1 + \Delta t]^3\mathbf{k}) - (3\mathbf{i} + \mathbf{j} - \frac{1}{3}\mathbf{k})$

      $= 2\Delta t\mathbf{i} + \Delta t(\Delta t + 2)\mathbf{j} - \frac{1}{3}(\Delta t^3 + 3\Delta t^2 + 3)\mathbf{k}$

7. $\mathbf{r}(t) = \tan t\mathbf{i} - \sec t\mathbf{j} + (1 - t)\mathbf{k}$

  $\mathbf{u}(t) = 2\cos t\mathbf{i} + 3\sin t\cos t\mathbf{j} + \mathbf{k}$

    $\mathbf{r}(t) \cdot \mathbf{u}(t) = (\tan t)(2\cos t) + (-\sec t)(3\sin t\cos t) + (1 - t)(1)$

      $= 2\sin t - 3\sin t + 1 - t = 1 - t - \sin t$

  The dot product of two vector-valued functions is a scalar function.

9. $\mathbf{r}(t) = \cos t\mathbf{i} + 2\sin^2 t\mathbf{j}$

$x(t) = \cos t,\ y(t) = 2\sin^2 t$

$x^2 + \dfrac{y}{2} = 1$

$y = 2(1 - x^2)$

$-1 \leq x \leq 1$

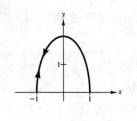

11. $\mathbf{r}(t) = \mathbf{i} + t\mathbf{j} + t^2\mathbf{k}$

$x = 1$

$y = t$

$z = t^2 \implies z = y^2$

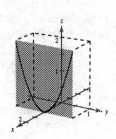

13. $\mathbf{r}(t) = \mathbf{i} + \sin t\mathbf{j} + \mathbf{k}$

$x = 1,\ y = \sin t,\ z = 1$

t	0	$\dfrac{\pi}{2}$	π	$\dfrac{3\pi}{2}$
x	1	1	1	1
y	0	1	0	-1
z	1	1	1	1

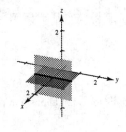

15. $\mathbf{r}(t) = t\mathbf{i} + \ln t\mathbf{j} + \frac{1}{2}t^2\mathbf{k}$

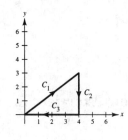

17. Label the sides of the triangle as shown in the figure. The line segment C_1 has slope $m = \frac{3}{4}$ and y-intercept $(0, 0)$. Hence, the rectangular form of the equation is

$y = \frac{3}{4}x.$

Letting $x = 4t$ and substituting this expression for x in the rectangular equation of the line yields $y = 3t$. Therefore,

$\mathbf{r}_1(t) = 4t\mathbf{i} + 3t\mathbf{j},\ 0 \leq t \leq 1.$

Note that $x = 4$ on C_2. Since y is decreasing on C_2, a vector-valued function for C_2 is

$\mathbf{r}_2(t) = 4\mathbf{i} - (3 - t)\mathbf{j},\ 0 \leq t \leq 3.$

Observe that $y = 0$ on C_3. Since x is decreasing on C_3, a vector-valued function for C_3 is

$\mathbf{r}_3(t) = (4 - t)\mathbf{i},\ 0 \leq t \leq 4.$

(Observe that there are many correct answers for this problem.)

19. The vector joining the points is $\langle 7, 4, -10 \rangle$. One path is $\mathbf{r}(t) = \langle -2 + 7t, -3 + 4t, 8 - 10t \rangle$.

21. $z = x^2 + y^2,\ x + y = 0,\ t = x$

$x = t,\ y = -t,\ z = 2t^2$

$\mathbf{r}(t) = t\mathbf{i} - t\mathbf{j} + 2t^2\mathbf{k}$

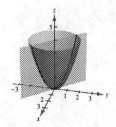

23. $\lim\limits_{t \to 2^-} (t^2\mathbf{i} + \sqrt{4 - t^2}\mathbf{j} + \mathbf{k}) = 4\mathbf{i} + \mathbf{k}$

25. $\mathbf{r}(t) = 3t\mathbf{i} + (t - 1)\mathbf{j},\ \mathbf{u}(t) = t\mathbf{i} + t^2\mathbf{j} + \dfrac{2}{3}t^3\mathbf{k}$

(a) $\mathbf{r}'(t) = 3\mathbf{i} + \mathbf{j}$

(b) $\mathbf{r}''(t) = \mathbf{0}$

(c) $\mathbf{r}(t) \cdot \mathbf{u}(t) = 3t^2 + t^2(t - 1) = t^3 + 2t^2$

$D_t[\mathbf{r}(t) \cdot \mathbf{u}(t)] = 3t^2 + 4t$

(d) $\mathbf{u}(t) - 2\mathbf{r}(t) = -5t\mathbf{i} + (t^2 - 2t + 2)\mathbf{j} + \dfrac{2}{3}t^3\mathbf{k}$

$D_t[\mathbf{u}(t) - 2\mathbf{r}(t)] = -5\mathbf{i} + (2t - 2)\mathbf{j} + 2t^2\mathbf{k}$

(e) $\|\mathbf{r}(t)\| = \sqrt{10t^2 - 2t + 1}$

$D_t[\|\mathbf{r}(t)\|] = \dfrac{10t - 1}{\sqrt{10t^2 - 2t + 1}}$

(f) $\mathbf{r}(t) \times \mathbf{u}(t) = \dfrac{2}{3}(t^4 - t^3)\mathbf{i} - 2t^4\mathbf{j} + (3t^3 - t^2 + t)\mathbf{k}$

$D_t[\mathbf{r}(t) \times \mathbf{u}(t)] = \left(\dfrac{8}{3}t^3 - 2t^2\right)\mathbf{i} - 8t^3\mathbf{j} + (9t^2 - 2t + 1)\mathbf{k}$

27. $\mathbf{r}(t) = 2\cos t\mathbf{i} + 2\sin t\mathbf{j} + t\mathbf{k}$

$\mathbf{r}\left(\dfrac{3\pi}{4}\right) = -\sqrt{2}\mathbf{i} + \sqrt{2}\mathbf{j} + \dfrac{3\pi}{4}\mathbf{k}$

$\mathbf{r}'(t) = -2\sin t\mathbf{i} + 2\cos t\mathbf{j} + \mathbf{k}$

$\mathbf{r}'\left(\dfrac{3\pi}{4}\right) = -\sqrt{2}\mathbf{i} - \sqrt{2}\mathbf{j} + \mathbf{k}$

Therefore, the tangent line must pass through the point $\left(-\sqrt{2}, \sqrt{2}, 3\pi/4\right)$ and have direction numbers $a = -\sqrt{2},\ b = -\sqrt{2},$ and $c = 1$. Thus, the parametric equations of the line are given by

$$x = -\sqrt{2} - \sqrt{2}t,\ y = \sqrt{2} - \sqrt{2}t,\ \text{and } z = \dfrac{3\pi}{4} + t.$$

29. $x(t)$ and $y(t)$ are increasing functions at $t = t_0$, and $z(t)$ is a decreasing function at $t = t_0$.

31. $\mathbf{r}(t) = \left\langle \ln(t - 3), t^2, \dfrac{1}{2}t \right\rangle,\ t_0 = 4$

$\mathbf{r}'(t) = \left\langle \dfrac{1}{t - 3}, 2t, \dfrac{1}{2} \right\rangle$

$\mathbf{r}'(4) = \left\langle 1, 8, \dfrac{1}{2} \right\rangle$ direction numbers

Since $\mathbf{r}(4) = \langle 0, 16, 2 \rangle$, the parametric equations are $x = t,\ y = 16 + 8t,\ z = 2 + \frac{1}{2}t$.

$\mathbf{r}(t_0 + 0.1) = \mathbf{r}(4.1) \approx \langle 0.1, 16.8, 2.05 \rangle$

33. $\displaystyle\int (\cos t\mathbf{i} + t\cos t\mathbf{j})\,dt = \sin t\mathbf{i} + (t\sin t + \cos t)\mathbf{j} + \mathbf{C}$

35. $\displaystyle\int \|\cos t\mathbf{i} + \sin t\mathbf{j} + t\mathbf{k}\|\,dt = \int \sqrt{\cos^2 t + \sin^2 t + t^2}\,dt$

$= \displaystyle\int \sqrt{1 + t^2}\,dt = \dfrac{1}{2}\left(t\sqrt{1 + t^2} + \ln\left|t + \sqrt{1 + t^2}\right|\right) + C$

37. $\mathbf{r}(t) = \displaystyle\int (2t\mathbf{i} + e^t\mathbf{j} + e^{-t}\mathbf{k})\,dt = t^2\mathbf{i} + e^t\mathbf{j} - e^{-t}\mathbf{k} + \mathbf{C}$

$\mathbf{r}(0) = \mathbf{j} - \mathbf{k} + \mathbf{C} = \mathbf{i} + 3\mathbf{j} - 5\mathbf{k} \Rightarrow \mathbf{C} = \mathbf{i} + 2\mathbf{j} - 4\mathbf{k}$

$\mathbf{r}(t) = (t^2 + 1)\mathbf{i} + (e^t + 2)\mathbf{j} - (e^{-t} + 4)\mathbf{k}$

39. $\displaystyle\int_{-2}^{2} (3t\mathbf{i} + 2t^2\mathbf{j} - t^3\mathbf{k})\,dt = \left[\dfrac{3t^2}{2}\mathbf{i} + \dfrac{2t^3}{3}\mathbf{j} - \dfrac{t^4}{4}\mathbf{k}\right]_{-2}^{2} = \dfrac{32}{3}\mathbf{j}$

41. $\mathbf{r}(t) = \langle \cos^3 t, \sin^3 t, 3t \rangle$

$\mathbf{v}(t) = \mathbf{r}'(t) = \langle -3 \cos^2 t \sin t, 3 \sin^2 t \cos t, 3 \rangle$

$\|\mathbf{v}(t)\| = \sqrt{9 \cos^4 t \sin^2 t + 9 \sin^4 t \cos^2 t + 9}$

$\qquad = 3 \sqrt{\cos^2 t \sin^2 t (\cos^2 t + \sin^2 t) + 1}$

$\qquad = 3 \sqrt{\cos^2 t \sin^2 t + 1}$

$\mathbf{a}(t) = \mathbf{v}'(t) = \langle -6 \cos t(-\sin^2 t) + (-3 \cos^2 t) \cos t, 6 \sin t \cos^2 t + 3 \sin^2 t(-\sin t), 0 \rangle$

$\qquad = \langle 3 \cos t(2 \sin^2 t - \cos^2 t), 3 \sin t(2 \cos^2 t - \sin^2 t), 0 \rangle$

43. $\mathbf{r}(t) = (v_0 \cos \theta)t\mathbf{i} + [(v_0 \sin \theta)t - 16t^2]\mathbf{j}$

The projectile will strike the ground when

$(v_0 \sin \theta)t - 16t^2 = 0$

$t(v_0 \sin \theta - 16t) = 0 \implies t = \dfrac{v_0 \sin \theta}{16}$.

Substituting this expression for t into the x-component of the vector-valued function will give the range.

Range: $x = v_0 \cos \theta \left(\dfrac{v_0 \sin \theta}{16} \right) = \left(\dfrac{v_0^2}{32} \right) \sin 2\theta$

When $\theta = 30°$ and $v_0 = 75$, the range is

$x = \left(\dfrac{75^2}{32} \right) \sin 60° \approx 152$ feet.

45. Range $= x = \dfrac{v_0^2}{9.8} \sin 2\theta = 80 \implies v_0 = \sqrt{\dfrac{(80)(9.8)}{\sin 40°}} \approx 34.9$ m/sec

47. $\mathbf{r}(t) = 5t\mathbf{i}$

$\mathbf{v}(t) = 5\mathbf{i}$

$\|\mathbf{v}(t)\| = 5$

$\mathbf{a}(t) = \mathbf{0}$

$\mathbf{T}(t) = \mathbf{i}$

$\mathbf{N}(t)$ does not exist

$\mathbf{a} \cdot \mathbf{T} = 0$

$\mathbf{a} \cdot \mathbf{N}$ does not exist

$K = 0$

(The curve is a line.)

49. $\mathbf{r}(t) = t\mathbf{i} + \sqrt{t}\,\mathbf{j}$

$\mathbf{v}(t) = \mathbf{i} + \dfrac{1}{2\sqrt{t}}\mathbf{j}$

$\|\mathbf{v}(t)\| = \dfrac{\sqrt{4t + 1}}{2\sqrt{t}}$

$\mathbf{a}(t) = -\dfrac{1}{4t\sqrt{t}}\mathbf{j}$

$\mathbf{T}(t) = \dfrac{\mathbf{i} + \left(1/2\sqrt{t}\right)\mathbf{j}}{\left(\sqrt{4t + 1}\right)/2\sqrt{t}} = \dfrac{2\sqrt{t}\,\mathbf{i} + \mathbf{j}}{\sqrt{4t + 1}}$

$\mathbf{N}(t) = \dfrac{\mathbf{i} - 2\sqrt{t}\,\mathbf{j}}{\sqrt{4t + 1}}$

$\mathbf{a} \cdot \mathbf{T} = \dfrac{-1}{4t\sqrt{t}\sqrt{4t + 1}}$

$\mathbf{a} \cdot \mathbf{N} = \dfrac{1}{2t\sqrt{4t + 1}}$

$K = \dfrac{2}{(4t + 1)^{3/2}}$

51. $\mathbf{r}(t) = e^t\mathbf{i} + e^{-t}\mathbf{j}$

$\mathbf{v}(t) = e^t\mathbf{i} - e^{-t}\mathbf{j}$

$\|\mathbf{v}(t)\| = \sqrt{e^{2t} + e^{-2t}}$

$\mathbf{a}(t) = e^t\mathbf{i} + e^{-t}\mathbf{j}$

$\mathbf{T}(t) = \dfrac{e^t\mathbf{i} - e^{-t}\mathbf{j}}{\sqrt{e^{2t} + e^{-2t}}}$

$\mathbf{N}(t) = \dfrac{e^{-t}\mathbf{i} + e^t\mathbf{j}}{\sqrt{e^{2t} + e^{-2t}}}$

$\mathbf{a} \cdot \mathbf{T} = \dfrac{e^{2t} - e^{-2t}}{\sqrt{e^{2t} + e^{-2t}}}$

$\mathbf{a} \cdot \mathbf{N} = \dfrac{2}{\sqrt{e^{2t} + e^{-2t}}}$

$K = \dfrac{\mathbf{a} \cdot \mathbf{N}}{\|\mathbf{v}\|^2} = \dfrac{2}{(e^{2t} + e^{-2t})^{3/2}}$

53. $\mathbf{r}(t) = t\mathbf{i} + t^2\mathbf{j} + \dfrac{1}{2}t^2\mathbf{k}$

$\mathbf{v}(t) = \mathbf{r}'(5) = \mathbf{i} + 2t\mathbf{j} + t\mathbf{k}$

$\text{speed} = \|\mathbf{v}(t)\| = \sqrt{1^2 + (2t)^2 + t^2} = \sqrt{1 + 5t^2}$

$\mathbf{a}(t) = \mathbf{r}''(t) = 2\mathbf{j} + \mathbf{k}$

$\mathbf{T}(t) = \dfrac{\mathbf{v}(t)}{\|\mathbf{v}(t)\|} = \dfrac{\mathbf{i} + 2t\mathbf{j} + t\mathbf{k}}{\sqrt{1 + 5t^2}}$

$\mathbf{T}'(t) = \dfrac{5t}{(1 + 5t^2)^{3/2}}\mathbf{i} + \dfrac{2}{(1 + 5t^2)^{3/2}}\mathbf{j} + \dfrac{1}{(1 + 5t^2)^{3/2}}\mathbf{k} = \dfrac{5t\mathbf{i} + 2\mathbf{j} + \mathbf{k}}{(1 + 5t^2)^{3/2}}$

$\|\mathbf{T}'(t)\| = \dfrac{\sqrt{(5t)^2 + 2^2 + 1^2}}{(1 + 5t^2)^{3/2}} = \dfrac{\sqrt{5}\sqrt{1 + 5t^2}}{(1 + 5t^2)^{3/2}} = \dfrac{\sqrt{5}}{1 + 5t^2}$

$\mathbf{N}(t) = \dfrac{\mathbf{T}'(t)}{\|\mathbf{T}'(t)\|} = \dfrac{5t\mathbf{i} + 2\mathbf{j} + \mathbf{k}}{\sqrt{5}\sqrt{1 + 5t^2}}$

$a_{\mathbf{T}} = \mathbf{a}(t) \cdot \mathbf{T}(t) = \dfrac{2(2t) + 1(t)}{\sqrt{1 + 5t^2}} = \dfrac{5t}{\sqrt{1 + 5t^2}}$

$a_{\mathbf{N}} = \mathbf{a}(t) \cdot \mathbf{N}(t) = \dfrac{2(2) + 1(1)}{\sqrt{5}\sqrt{1 + 5t^2}} = \dfrac{5}{\sqrt{5}\sqrt{1 + 5t^2}} = \dfrac{\sqrt{5}}{\sqrt{1 + 5t^2}}$

$K = \dfrac{\mathbf{a}(t) \cdot \mathbf{N}(t)}{\|\mathbf{v}(t)\|} = \dfrac{\dfrac{\sqrt{5}}{\sqrt{1 + 5t^2}}}{1 + 5t^2} = \dfrac{\sqrt{5}}{(1 + 5t^2)^{3/2}}$

55. $\mathbf{r}(t) = \dfrac{1}{2}t\mathbf{i} + \sin t\mathbf{j} + \cos t\mathbf{k}$

$s = \displaystyle\int_0^\pi \|\mathbf{r}'(t)\|\, dt$

$= \displaystyle\int_0^\pi \sqrt{(1/2)^2 + \cos^2 t + (-\sin t)^2}\, dt$

$= \dfrac{\sqrt{5}}{2}\displaystyle\int_0^\pi dt = \dfrac{\sqrt{5}}{2}\Big[t\Big]_0^\pi = \dfrac{\sqrt{5}\pi}{2}$

57. $v = \sqrt{\dfrac{9.56 \times 10^4}{4600}} \approx 4.56 \text{ mi/sec}$

(11.4 Exercise 44)

59. The curvature changes abruptly from zero to a nonzero constant at the points B and C.

61. $\mathbf{r}(t) = \langle t \cos \pi t, t \sin \pi t \rangle, \ 0 \le t \le 2$

(a)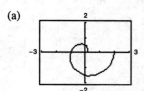

(b) Length $= \displaystyle\int_0^2 \|\mathbf{r}'(t)\| \, dt$

$$= \int_0^2 \sqrt{\pi^2 t^2 + 1} \, dt \approx 6.766 \quad \text{(graphing utility)}$$

(c) $\quad K = \dfrac{\pi(\pi^2 t^2 + 2)}{[\pi^2 t^2 + 1]^{3/2}}$

$K(0) = 2\pi$

$K(1) = \dfrac{\pi(\pi^2 + 2)}{(\pi^2 + 1)^{3/2}} \approx 1.04$

$K(2) \approx 0.51$

(d)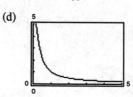

(e) $\displaystyle\lim_{t \to \infty} K = 0$

(f) As $t \to \infty$, the graph spirals outward and the curvature decreases.

C H A P T E R   1 2
Functions of Several Variables

CHAPTER 12
Functions of Several Variables

Section 12.1   Introduction to Functions of Several Variables
Solutions to Odd-Numbered Exercises

1. $x^2z + yz - xy = 10$

$z(x^2 + y) = 10 + xy$

$$z = \frac{10 + xy}{x^2 + y}$$

Yes, z is a function of x and y.

3. $\dfrac{x^2}{4} + \dfrac{y^2}{9} + z^2 = 1$

No, z is not a function of x and y. For example, $(x, y) = (0, 0)$ corresponds to both $z = \pm 1$.

5. $f(x, y) = \dfrac{x}{y}$

(a) $f(3, 2) = \dfrac{3}{2}$

(b) $f(-1, 4) = -\dfrac{1}{4}$

(c) $f(30, 5) = \dfrac{30}{5} = 6$

(d) $f(5, y) = \dfrac{5}{y}$

(e) $f(x, 2) = \dfrac{x}{2}$

(f) $f(5, t) = \dfrac{5}{t}$

7. $f(x, y) = xe^y$

(a) $f(5, 0) = 5e^0 = 5$

(b) $f(3, 2) = 3e^2$

(c) $f(2, -1) = 2e^{-1} = \dfrac{2}{e}$

(d) $f(5, y) = 5e^y$

(e) $f(x, 2) = xe^2$

(f) $f(t, t) = te^t$

9. $h(x, y, z) = \dfrac{xy}{z}$

(a) $h(2, 3, 9) = \dfrac{(2)(3)}{9} = \dfrac{2}{3}$

(b) $h(1, 0, 1) = \dfrac{(1)(0)}{1} = 0$

11. $f(x, y) = x \sin y$

(a) $f\left(2, \dfrac{\pi}{4}\right) = 2 \sin \dfrac{\pi}{4} = \sqrt{2}$

(b) $f(3, 1) = 3 \sin 1$

13. $f(x, y) = \displaystyle\int_x^y (2t - 3)\, dt = \left[t^2 - 3t \right]_x^y = (y^2 - 3y) - (x^2 - 3x)$

(a) $f(0, 4) = (16 - 12) - (0 - 0) = 4$

(b) $f(1, 4) = (16 - 12) - (1 - 3) = 6$

15. $f(x, y) = x^2 - 2y$

(a) $\dfrac{f(x + \Delta x, y) - f(x, y)}{\Delta x} = \dfrac{[(x + \Delta x)^2 - 2y] - (x^2 - 2y)}{\Delta x}$

$$= \dfrac{x^2 + 2x(\Delta x) + (\Delta x)^2 - 2y - x^2 + 2y}{\Delta x} = \dfrac{\Delta x(2x + \Delta x)}{\Delta x} = 2x + \Delta x,\ \Delta x \neq 0$$

(b) $\dfrac{f(x, y + \Delta y) - f(x, y)}{\Delta y} = \dfrac{[x^2 - 2(y + \Delta y)] - (x^2 - 2y)}{\Delta y} = \dfrac{x^2 - 2y - 2\Delta y - x^2 + 2y}{\Delta y} = \dfrac{-2\Delta y}{\Delta y} = -2,\ \Delta y \neq 0$

17. Since $f(x, y) = \sqrt{4 - x^2 - y^2}$, we have

$$4 - x^2 - y^2 \geq 0$$

$$4 \geq x^2 + y^2.$$

Therefore, the domain is the set of all points inside and on the boundary of the circle $x^2 + y^2 = 4$. The range of f is the set of all real numbers in the interval $[0, 2]$.

19. Since $z = \arcsin(x + y)$ implies that $\sin z = x + y$, we conclude that $|x + y| \leq 1$. Therefore, the domain is

$$-1 \leq x + y \leq 1$$

$$-1 - x \leq y \leq -x + 1.$$

This means that R lies on and between the parallel lines

$$y = -1 - x \quad \text{and} \quad y = -x + 1$$

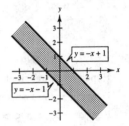

as shown in the figure. The range of the arcsine function is the set of all reals in the interval $[-\pi/2, \pi/2]$.

21. $f(x, y) = \ln(4 - x - y)$

Domain: $4 - x - y > 0$

$$x + y < 4$$

$$\{(x, y): y < -x + 4\}$$

Range: all real numbers

23. $z = \dfrac{x + y}{xy}$

Domain: $\{(x, y): x \neq 0 \text{ and } y \neq 0\}$

Range: all real numbers

25. $f(x, y) = e^{x/y}$

Domain: $\{(x, y): y \neq 0\}$

Range: $z > 0$

27. $g(x, y) = \dfrac{1}{xy}$

Domain: $\{(x, y): x \neq 0 \text{ and } y \neq 0\}$

Range: all real numbers except zero

29. $f(x, y) = \dfrac{-4x}{x^2 + y^2 + 1}$

(a) View from the positive x-axis: $(20, 0, 0)$

(b) View where x is negative, y and z are positive: $(-15, 10, 20)$

(c) View from the first octant: $(20, 15, 25)$

(d) View from the line $y = x$ in the xy-plane: $(20, 20, 0)$

31. $f(x, y) = 5$

Plane: $z = 5$

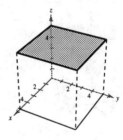

33. $f(x, y) = y^2$

Since the variable x is missing, the surface is a cylinder with rulings parallel to the x-axis. The generating curve is $z = y^2$. The domain is the entire xy-plane and the range is $z \geq 0$.

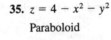

35. $z = 4 - x^2 - y^2$

Paraboloid

Domain: entire xy-plane

Range: $z \leq 4$

37. $f(x, y) = e^{-x}$

Since the variable y is missing, the surface is a cylinder with rulings parallel to the y-axis. The generating curve is $z = e^{-x}$. The domain is the entire xy-plane and the range is $z > 0$.

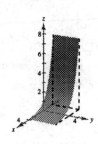

39. $z = y^2 - x^2 + 1$

Hyperbolic paraboloid

Domain: entire xy-plane

Range: $-\infty < z < \infty$

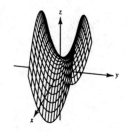

41. $f(x, y) = x^2 e^{(-xy/2)}$

43. $f(x, y) = x^2 + y^2$

(a) The surface is a paraboloid and its axis is the z-axis. Some conventional traces are

$$yz\text{-trace } (x = 0): \; z = y^2 \qquad \text{Parabola}$$

$$xz\text{-trace } (y = 0): \; z = x^2 \qquad \text{Parabola}$$

Parallel to xy-plane $(z = 4)$: $4 = x^2 + y^2$ Circle.

The domain is the entire xy-coordinate plane and the range $z \geq 0$. The surface is shown in the figure.

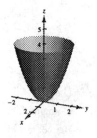

(b) The graph of g is a vertical translation of the graph of f two units upward.

(c) The graph of g is a horizontal translation of the graph of f two units to the right.

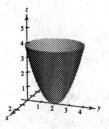

(d) The graph of g is a reflection of the graph of f in the xy-plane followed by a vertical translation four units upward.

(e) The trace parallel to the yz-coordinate plane when $x = 1$ is the parabola $z = f(1, y) = 1 + y^2$. The trace parallel to the xz-coordinate when $y = 1$ is the parabola

$$z = f(x, 1) = x^2 + 1.$$

The traces are shown in the figures.

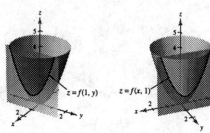

45. $z = e^{1-x^2-y^2}$

Level curves:

$$c = e^{1-x^2-y^2}$$

$$\ln c = 1 - x^2 - y^2$$

$$x^2 + y^2 = 1 - \ln c$$

Circles centered at $(0, 0)$

Matches (c)

47. $z = \ln|y - x^2|$

Level curves:

$$c = \ln|y - x^2|$$

$$\pm e^c = y - x^2$$

$$y = x^2 \pm e^c$$

Parabolas

Matches (b)

49. $z = x + y$

Level curves are parallel lines of the form $x + y = c$.

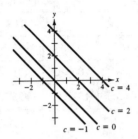

51. $f(x, y) = \sqrt{25 - x^2 - y^2}$

The level curves are of the form

$$c = \sqrt{25 - x^2 - y^2},$$

$$x^2 + y^2 = 25 - c^2.$$

Thus, the level curves are circles of radius 5 or less, centered at the origin.

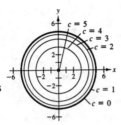

53. $f(x, y) = xy$

The level curves are hyperbolas of the form $xy = c$.

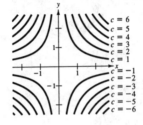

55. $f(x, y) = \dfrac{x}{x^2 + y^2}$

If $f(x, y) = c$, then the level curves are of the form

$$c = \frac{x}{x^2 + y^2}$$

$$x^2 + y^2 = \frac{x}{c}$$

$$x^2 - \frac{x}{c} + y^2 = 0$$

$$\left(x^2 - \frac{x}{c} + \frac{1}{4c^2}\right) + y^2 = \frac{1}{4c^2}$$

$$\left(x - \frac{1}{2c}\right)^2 + y^2 = \left(\frac{1}{2c}\right)^2.$$

Therefore, each level curve is a circle centered at $(1/(2c), 0)$ with radius equal to $1/(2c)$. For example, if $c = 1$, the level curve has the equation

$$\left(x - \frac{1}{2}\right)^2 + y^2 = \frac{1}{4}.$$

The required level curves are shown in the figure.

57. No. The following graphs are not hemispheres.

$$z = e^{-(x^2+y^2)}$$

$$z = x^2 + y^2$$

59. The surface is sloped like a saddle. The graph is not unique. Any vertical translation would have the same level curves. One possible function is

$$f(x, y) = x^2 - y^2.$$

61. $V(I, R) = 1000\left[\dfrac{1 + 0.10(1 - R)}{1 + I}\right]^{10}$

	Inflation Rate		
Tax Rate	0	0.03	0.05
0	2593.74	1929.99	1592.33
0.28	2004.23	1491.34	1230.42
0.35	1877.14	1396.77	1152.40

63. $f(x, y, z) = x - 2y + 3z$

   $c = 6$

   $6 = x - 2y + 3z$

   Plane

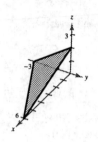

65. $f(x, y, z) = x^2 + y^2 + z^2$

   $c = 9$

   $9 = x^2 + y^2 + z^2$

   Sphere

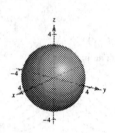

67. $f(x, y, z) = 4x^2 + 4y^2 - z^2$

   The level surface when $f(x, y, z) = 0$ is the cone

   $$4x^2 + 4y^2 - z^2 = 0$$

   $$x^2 = 4x^2 + 4y^2.$$

   xz-trace: $z = \pm 2x$

   yz-trace: $z = \pm 2y$

   $z = \pm 2$: $x^2 + y^2 = 1$

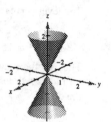

69. $N(d, L) = \left(\dfrac{d - 4}{4}\right)^2 L$

(a) $N(22, 12) = \left(\dfrac{22 - 4}{4}\right)^2 (12) = 243$ board-feet

(b) $N(30, 12) = \left(\dfrac{30 - 4}{4}\right)^2 (12) = 507$ board-feet

71. $T = 600 - 0.75x^2 - 0.75y^2$

   The level curves are of the form

   $$c = 600 - 0.75x^2 - 0.75y^2$$

   $$x^2 + y^2 = \dfrac{600 - c}{0.75}.$$

   The level curves are circles centered at the origin.

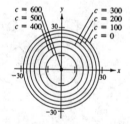

73. Assign variables to the length, width, and height of the box as shown in the figure.

   $C = $ (cost of base) $+$ (cost of front and back) $+$ (cost of two ends)

   $\quad = 0.75xy + 2(0.40)xz + 2(0.40)yz$

   $\quad = 0.75xy + 0.80(xz + yz)$

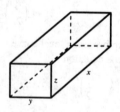

75. $PV = kT, \quad 20(2600) = k(300)$

(a) $k = \dfrac{20(2600)}{300} = \dfrac{520}{3}$

(b) $P = \dfrac{kT}{V} = \dfrac{520}{3}\left(\dfrac{T}{V}\right)$

The level curves are of the form: $c = \left(\dfrac{520}{3}\right)\left(\dfrac{T}{V}\right)$

$$V = \dfrac{520}{3c}T$$

Thus, the level curves are lines through the origin with slope $\dfrac{520}{3c}$.

77. (a) Highest pressure at C

(b) Lowest pressure at A

(c) Highest wind velocity at B

79. (a) The boundaries between colors represent level curves

(b) No, the colors represent intervals of different lengths, as indicated in the box

(c) You could use more colors, which means using smaller intervals

81. False. Let

$$f(x, y) = 2xy$$

$$f(1, 2) = f(2, 1), \text{ but } 1 \neq 2$$

83. False. Let

$$f(x, y) = 5.$$

Then, $f(2x, 2y) = 5 \neq 2^2 f(x, y)$.

Section 12.2   Limits and Continuity

1. $\lim\limits_{(x, y) \to (a, b)} [f(x, y) - g(x, y)] = \lim\limits_{(x, y) \to (a, b)} f(x, y) - \lim\limits_{(x, y) \to (a, b)} g(x, y) = 5 - 3 = 2$

3. $\lim\limits_{(x, y) \to (a, b)} [f(x, y)g(x, y)] = \left[\lim\limits_{(x, y) \to (a, b)} f(x, y)\right]\left[\lim\limits_{(x, y) \to (a, b)} g(x, y)\right] = 5(3) = 15$

5. $\lim\limits_{(x, y) \to (2, 1)} (x + 3y^2) = 2 + 3(1)^2 = 5$

Continuous everywhere

7. $\lim\limits_{(x, y) \to (2, 4)} \dfrac{x + y}{x - y} = \dfrac{2 + 4}{2 - 4} = -3$

Continuous for $x \neq y$

9. $\lim\limits_{(x, y) \to (0, 1)} \dfrac{\arcsin(x/y)}{1 + xy}$

Since the limit of a quotient is the quotient of the limits, we have

$$\lim\limits_{(x, y) \to (0, 1)} \frac{\arcsin(x/y)}{1 + xy} = \frac{\arcsin 0}{1 + 0} = \frac{0}{1} = 0.$$

A rational function is continuous at every point in its domain. Therefore, the given function is continuous for all points (x, y) in the xy-plane such that $1 + xy \neq 0$, $y \neq 0$, and $|x/y| \leq 1$.

11. $\lim\limits_{(x, y) \to (0, 0)} e^{xy} = e^0 = 1$

Continuous everywhere

13. $\lim\limits_{(x, y, z) \to (1, 2, 5)} \sqrt{x + y + z} = \sqrt{8} = 2\sqrt{2}$

Continuous for $x + y + z \geq 0$

15. $\lim\limits_{(x, y) \to (0, 0)} e^{xy} = 1$

Continuous everywhere

17. $\lim\limits_{(x, y) \to (0, 0)} \ln(x^2 + y^2) = \ln(0) = -\infty$

The limit does not exist. Continuous except at $(0, 0)$

19. $f(x, y) = \dfrac{xy}{x^2 + y^2}$

Continuous except at $(0, 0)$

Path: $y = 0$

(x, y)	$(1, 0)$	$(.5, 0)$	$(.1, 0)$	$(.01, 0)$	$(.001, 0)$
$f(x, y)$	0	0	0	0	0

Path: $y = x$

(x, y)	$(1, 1)$	$(.5, .5)$	$(.1, .1)$	$(.01, .01)$	$(.001, .001)$
$f(x, y)$	$\frac{1}{2}$	$\frac{1}{2}$	$\frac{1}{2}$	$\frac{1}{2}$	$\frac{1}{2}$

The limit does not exist because along the path $y = 0$ the function equals 0, whereas along the path $y = x$ the function equals $\frac{1}{2}$.

21. $f(x, y) = -\dfrac{xy^2}{x^2 + y^2}$

Path: $x = y^2$

x	$(1, 1)$	$(0.25, 0.5)$	$(0.01, 0.1)$	$(0.0001, 0.011)$	$(0.000001, 0.0011)$
$f(x, y)$	$-\frac{1}{2}$	$-\frac{1}{2}$	$-\frac{1}{2}$	$-\frac{1}{2}$	$-\frac{1}{2}$

$$\lim_{(x, y) \to (0, 0)} \frac{-xy^2}{x^2 + y^4} = \lim_{(y^2, y) \to (0, 0)} \frac{-y^2(y^2)}{(y^2)^2 + y^4}$$

$$= \lim_{(y^2, y) \to (0, 0)} \frac{-y^4}{y^4 + y^4} = -\frac{1}{2}$$

Path: $x = -y^2$

x	$(1, 1)$	$(-0.25, 0.5)$	$(-0.01, 0.1)$	$(-0.0001, 0.011)$	$(-0.000001, 0.0011)$
$f(x, y)$	$\frac{1}{2}$	$\frac{1}{2}$	$\frac{1}{2}$	$\frac{1}{2}$	$\frac{1}{2}$

$$\lim_{(x, y) \to (0, 0)} \frac{-xy^2}{x^2 + y^4} = \lim_{(-y2, y) \to (0, 0)} \frac{-(-y^2)(y^2)}{(-y^2)^2 + y^4}$$

$$= \lim_{(-y^2, y) \to (0, 0)} \frac{y^4}{y^4 + y^4} = \frac{1}{2}.$$

Since the limits are not the same along different paths, the limit does not exist. The function is continuous except at $(0, 0)$.

23. $\displaystyle\lim_{(x, y) \to (0, 0)} (\sin x + \sin y) = 0$

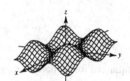

25. $\displaystyle\lim_{(x, y) \to (0, 0)} \frac{x^2 y}{x^4 + 4y^2}$

Does not exist

27. $f(x, y) = \dfrac{xy^3}{x^2 + 2y^6}$

The limit does not exist. You can see this analytically by using the paths $y = 0$ and $x = y^3$.

29. $\displaystyle\lim_{(x, y) \to (0, 0)} \frac{\sin(x^2 + y^2)}{x^2 + y^2}$

We first observe that direct substitution yields the indeterminate form $0/0$. Letting $x = r \cos \theta$, $y = r \sin \theta$, and $r^2 = x^2 + y^2$, yields

$$\lim_{(x, y) \to (0, 0)} \frac{\sin(x^2 + y^2)}{x^2 + y^2} = \lim_{r \to 0} \frac{\sin r^2}{r^2} = 1.$$

31. $\displaystyle\lim_{(x, y) \to (0, 0)} \frac{x^3 + y^3}{x^2 + y^2} = \lim_{r \to 0} \frac{r^3 (\cos^3 \theta + \sin^3 \theta)}{r^2} = \lim_{r \to 0} r(\cos^3 \theta + \sin^3 \theta) = 0$

33. $f(x, y, z) = \dfrac{1}{\sqrt{x^2 + y^2 + z^2}}$

Continuous except at $(0, 0, 0)$

35. $f(x, y, z) = \dfrac{\sin z}{e^x + e^y}$

Continuous everywhere

37. $f(t) = t^2$

$g(x, y) = 3x - 2y$

$f(g(x, y)) = f(3x - 2y)$

$\qquad = (3x - 2y)^2$

$\qquad = 9x^2 - 12xy + 4y^2$

Continuous everywhere

39. $f(t) = \dfrac{1}{t}, \; g(x, y) = 3x - 2y$

$(f \circ g)(x, y) = f[g(x, y)]$

$\qquad = \dfrac{1}{g(x, y)} = \dfrac{1}{3x - 2y}$

The composite function is continuous for $y \neq 3x/2$.

41. $f(x, y) = x^2 - 4y$

(a) $\displaystyle\lim_{\Delta x \to 0} \frac{f(x + \Delta x, y) - f(x, y)}{\Delta x} = \lim_{\Delta x \to 0} \frac{[(x + \Delta x)^2 - 4y] - (x^2 - 4y)}{\Delta x}$

$\qquad = \displaystyle\lim_{\Delta x \to 0} \frac{x^2 + 2x\Delta x + (\Delta x)^2 - 4y - x^2 + 4y}{\Delta x}$

$\qquad = \displaystyle\lim_{\Delta x \to 0} (2x + \Delta x) = 2x$

(b) $\displaystyle\lim_{\Delta y \to 0} \frac{f(x, y + \Delta y) - f(x, y)}{\Delta y} = \lim_{\Delta y \to 0} \frac{x^2 - 4(y + \Delta y) - (x^2 - 4y)}{\Delta y}$

$\qquad = \displaystyle\lim_{\Delta y \to 0} \frac{x^2 - 4y - 4\Delta y - x^2 + 4y}{\Delta y}$

$\qquad = \displaystyle\lim_{\Delta y \to 0} (-4) = -4$

43. $f(x, y) = 2x + xy - 3y$

(a) $\displaystyle\lim_{\Delta x \to 0} \frac{f(x + \Delta x, y) - f(x, y)}{\Delta x} = \lim_{\Delta x \to 0} \frac{[2(x + \Delta x) + (x + \Delta x)y - 3y] - (2x + xy - 3y)}{\Delta x}$

$\qquad = \displaystyle\lim_{\Delta x \to 0} \frac{2\Delta x + \Delta xy}{\Delta x} = \lim_{\Delta x \to 0} (2 + y) = 2 + y$

(b) $\displaystyle\lim_{\Delta y \to 0} \frac{f(x, y + \Delta y) - f(x, y)}{\Delta y} = \lim_{\Delta y \to 0} \frac{[2x + x(y + \Delta y) - 3(y + \Delta y)] - (2x + xy - 3y)}{\Delta y}$

$\qquad = \displaystyle\lim_{\Delta y \to 0} \frac{x\Delta y - 3\Delta y}{\Delta y} = \lim_{\Delta y \to 0} (x - 3) = x - 3$

45. Since $\displaystyle\lim_{(x, y) \to (a, b)} f(x, y) = L_1$, then for $\varepsilon/2 > 0$, there corresponds $\delta_1 > 0$ such that $|f(x, y) - L_1| < \varepsilon/2$ whenever

$0 < \sqrt{(x - a)^2 + (y - b)^2} < \delta_1$.

Since $\displaystyle\lim_{(x, y) \to (a, b)} g(x, y) = L_2$, then for $\varepsilon/2 > 0$, there corresponds $\delta_2 > 0$ such that $|g(x, y) - L_2| < \varepsilon/2$ whenever

$0 < \sqrt{(x - a)^2 + (y - b)^2} < \delta_2$.

Let δ be the smaller of δ_1 and δ_2. By the triangle inequality, whenever $\sqrt{(x - a)^2 + (y - b)^2} < \delta$, we have

$|f(x, y) + g(x, y) - (L_1 + L_2)| = |(f(x, y) - L_1) + (g(x, y) - L_2)|$

$\qquad\qquad \leq |f(x, y) - L_1| + |g(x, y) - L_2| < \dfrac{\varepsilon}{2} + \dfrac{\varepsilon}{2} = \varepsilon.$

Therefore, $\displaystyle\lim_{(x, y) \to (a, b)} [f(x, y) + g(x, y)] = L_1 + L_2$.

47. No.

The existence of $f(2, 3)$ has no bearing on the existence of the limit as $(x, y) \to (2, 3)$.

49. True

51. False. Let

$$f(x, y) = \begin{cases} \ln(x^2 + y^2), & (x, y) \neq (0, 0) \\ 0, & x = 0, y = 0 \end{cases}$$

See Exercise 17.

Section 12.3   Partial Derivatives

1. $f_x(4, 1) < 0$

3. $f_y(4, 1) > 0$

5. $f(x, y) = 2x - 3y + 5$

$f_x(x, y) = 2$

$f_y(x, y) = -3$

7. $z = x\sqrt{y} = xy^{1/2}$

Considering y to be a constant and differentiating with respect to x yields

$$\frac{\partial z}{\partial x} = (1)y^{1/2} = \sqrt{y}.$$

Considering x to be a constant and differentiating with respect to y yields

$$\frac{\partial z}{\partial y} = x\left(\frac{1}{2}\right)y^{-1/2} = \frac{x}{2\sqrt{y}}.$$

9. $z = x^2 e^{2y}$

$$\frac{\partial z}{\partial x} = 2xe^{2y}$$

$$\frac{\partial z}{\partial y} = 2x^2 e^{2y}$$

11. $z = \ln(x^2 + y^2)$

$$\frac{\partial z}{\partial x} = \frac{2x}{x^2 + y^2}$$

$$\frac{\partial z}{\partial y} = \frac{2y}{x^2 + y^2}$$

13. $z = \ln\dfrac{x + y}{x - y}$

Using the properties of the logarithm function, rewrite the function to obtain

$z = \ln(x + y) - \ln(x - y)$.

Considering y to be a constant and differentiating with respect to x we have

$$\frac{\partial z}{\partial x} = \frac{1}{x + y}(1) - \frac{1}{x - y}(1) = \frac{-2y}{x^2 - y^2}.$$

Now considering x to be a constant and differentiating with respect to y we have

$$\frac{\partial z}{\partial y} = \frac{1}{x + y}(1) - \frac{1}{x - y}(-1) = \frac{2x}{x^2 - y^2}.$$

15. $h(x, y) = e^{-(x^2 + y^2)}$

$h_x(x, y) = -2xe^{-(x^2 + y^2)}$

$h_y(x, y) = -2ye^{-(x^2 + y^2)}$

17. $f(x, y) = \sqrt{x^2 + y^2}$

$$f_x(x, y) = \frac{1}{2}(x^2 + y^2)^{-1/2}(2x) = \frac{x}{\sqrt{x^2 + y^2}}$$

$$f_y(x, y) = \frac{1}{2}(x^2 + y^2)^{-1/2}(2y) = \frac{y}{\sqrt{x^2 + y^2}}$$

19. $z = \tan(2x - y)$

$$\frac{\partial z}{\partial x} = 2 \sec^2(2x - y)$$

$$\frac{\partial z}{\partial y} = -\sec^2(2x - y)$$

21. $z = e^y \sin xy$

First, considering y to be constant, we have

$$\frac{\partial z}{\partial x} = e^y(\cos xy)(y) = ye^y \cos xy.$$

Now considering x to be constant and using the Product Rule, we have

$$\frac{\partial z}{\partial y} = e^y(\cos xy)(x) + (\sin xy)(e^y)(1)$$

$$= e^y(x \cos xy + \sin xy).$$

23. $f(x, y) = \displaystyle\int_x^y (t^2 - 1) \, dt$

$$= \left[\frac{t^3}{3} - t\right]_x^y = \left(\frac{y^3}{3} - y\right) - \left(\frac{x^3}{3} - x\right)$$

$$f_x(x, y) = -x^2 + 1 = 1 - x^2$$

$$f_y(x, y) = y^2 - 1$$

[You could also use the Second Fundamental Theorem of Calculus.]

25. $f(x, y) = 2x + 3y$

$$\frac{\partial f}{\partial x} = \lim_{\Delta x \to 0} \frac{f(x + \Delta x, y) - f(x, y)}{\Delta x} = \lim_{\Delta x \to 0} \frac{2(x + \Delta x) + 3y - 2x - 3y}{\Delta x} = \lim_{\Delta x \to 0} \frac{2\Delta x}{\Delta x} = 2$$

$$\frac{\partial f}{\partial y} = \lim_{\Delta y \to 0} \frac{f(x, y + \Delta y) - f(x, y)}{\Delta y} = \lim_{\Delta y \to 0} \frac{2x + 3(y + \Delta y) - 2x - 3y}{\Delta y} = \lim_{\Delta y \to 0} \frac{3\Delta y}{\Delta y} = 3$$

27. $f(x, y) = \sqrt{x + y}$

$$\frac{\partial f}{\partial x} = \lim_{\Delta x \to 0} \frac{f(x + \Delta x, y) - f(x, y)}{\Delta x} = \lim_{\Delta x \to 0} \frac{\sqrt{x + \Delta x + y} - \sqrt{x + y}}{\Delta x}$$

$$= \lim_{\Delta x \to 0} \frac{\left(\sqrt{x + \Delta x + y} - \sqrt{x + y}\right)\left(\sqrt{x + \Delta x + y} + \sqrt{x + y}\right)}{\Delta x\left(\sqrt{x + \Delta x + y} + \sqrt{x + y}\right)}$$

$$= \lim_{\Delta x \to 0} \frac{1}{\sqrt{x + \Delta x + y} + \sqrt{x + y}} = \frac{1}{2\sqrt{x + y}}$$

$$\frac{\partial f}{\partial y} = \lim_{\Delta y \to 0} \frac{f(x, y + \Delta y) - f(x, y)}{\Delta y} = \lim_{\Delta y \to 0} \frac{\sqrt{x + y + \Delta y} - \sqrt{x + y}}{\Delta y}$$

$$= \lim_{\Delta y \to 0} \frac{\left(\sqrt{x + y + \Delta y} - \sqrt{x + y}\right)\left(\sqrt{x + y + \Delta y} + \sqrt{x + y}\right)}{\Delta y\left(\sqrt{x + y + \Delta y} + \sqrt{x + y}\right)}$$

$$= \lim_{\Delta y \to 0} \frac{1}{\sqrt{x + y + \Delta y} + \sqrt{x + y}} = \frac{1}{2\sqrt{x + y}}$$

29. $g(x, y) = 4 - x^2 - y^2$

Considering y as a constant and differentiating with respect to x produces

$$g_x(x, y) = -2x.$$

Differentiating with respect to y and considering x as a constant yields

$$g_y(x, y) = -2y.$$

The slope of the surface in the x direction at $(1, 1, 2)$ is $g_x(1, 1) = -2$. The slope of the surface in the y direction at $(1, 1, 2)$ is $g_y(1, 1) = -2$.

31. $z = e^{-x} \cos y$

$$\frac{\partial z}{\partial x} = -e^{-x} \cos y$$

At $(0, 0)$: $\dfrac{\partial z}{\partial x} = -1$

$$\frac{\partial z}{\partial y} = -e^{-x} \sin y$$

At $(0, 0)$: $\dfrac{\partial z}{\partial y} = 0$

33. $f(x, y) = \arctan \dfrac{y}{x}$

First, considering y to be constant, we have

$$\frac{\partial z}{\partial x} = \frac{1}{1 + (y^2/x^2)}\left(\frac{-y}{x^2}\right) = \frac{-y}{x^2 + y^2}.$$

Now considering x to be constant, we have

$$\frac{\partial z}{\partial y} = \frac{1}{1 + (y^2/x^2)}\left(\frac{1}{x}\right) = \frac{x}{x^2 + y^2}.$$

Therefore, $f_x(2, -2) = \frac{1}{4}$ and $f_y(2, -2) = \frac{1}{4}$.

35. $f(x, y) = \dfrac{xy}{x - y}$

$$f_x(x, y) = \frac{y(x - y) - xy}{(x - y)^2} = \frac{-y^2}{(x - y)^2}$$

At $(2, -2)$: $f_x(2, -2) = -\dfrac{1}{4}$

$$f_y(x, y) = \frac{x(x - y) + xy}{(x - y)^2} = \frac{x^2}{(x - y)^2}$$

At $(2, -2)$: $f_y(2, -2) = \dfrac{1}{4}$

37. The plane $z = x + y = f(x, y)$ satisfies

$$\frac{\partial f}{\partial x} > 0 \text{ and } \frac{\partial f}{\partial y} > 0.$$

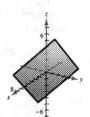

39. $z = \sqrt{49 - x^2 - y^2}$, $x = 2$, $x = 2$, $(2, 3, 6)$

Intersecting curve: $z = \sqrt{45 - y^2}$

$$\frac{\partial z}{\partial y} = \frac{-y}{\sqrt{45 - y^2}}$$

At $(2, 3, 6)$: $\dfrac{\partial z}{\partial y} = \dfrac{-3}{\sqrt{45 - 9}} = -\dfrac{1}{2}$

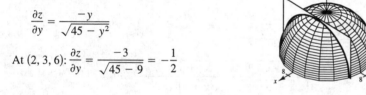

41. The graph of the equation $z = 9x^2 - y^2$ is a hyperbolic paraboloid. The xy-trace ($z = 0$), consists of the intersecting lines $y = \pm 3x$. The yz-trace ($x = 0$) is a parabola $z = -y^2$ opening downward, and the xz-trace ($y = 0$) is the parabola $z = 9x^2$ opening upward. The curve of intersection of the paraboloid and plane $y = 3$ is given by $z = 9x^2 - 9$. It is a parabola opening upward (see figure). Since y is a constant on the curve of intersection, differentiate with respect to x to obtain

$$\frac{\partial z}{\partial x} = 18x.$$

At the point $(1, 3, 0)$ the slope is

$$\frac{\partial z}{\partial x} = 18(1) = 18.$$

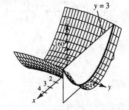

43. $f_x(x, y) = 2x + 4y - 4$, $f_y(x, y) = 4x + 2y + 16$

$f_x = f_y = 0$: $2x + 4y = 4$

$$4x + 2y = -16$$

Solving for x and y,

$$x = -6 \text{ and } y = 4.$$

45. $f_x(x, y) = -\dfrac{1}{x^2} + y$, $f_y(x, y) = -\dfrac{1}{y^2} + x$

$f_x = f_y = 0$: $-\dfrac{1}{x^2} + y = 0$ and $-\dfrac{1}{y^2} + x = 0$

$$y = \frac{1}{x^2} \text{ and } x = \frac{1}{y^2}$$

$$y = y^4 \Longrightarrow y = 1 = x$$

Points: $(1, 1)$

47. $z = x^2 - 2xy + 3y^2$

The first partials are

$$\frac{\partial z}{\partial x} = 2x - 2y \quad \text{and} \quad \frac{\partial z}{\partial y} = -2x + 6y.$$

The second partials are

$$\frac{\partial^2 z}{\partial x^2} = \frac{\partial}{\partial x}\left[\frac{\partial z}{\partial x}\right] = 2 \qquad \frac{\partial^2 z}{\partial y \partial x} = \frac{\partial}{\partial y}\left[\frac{\partial z}{\partial x}\right] = -2$$

$$\frac{\partial^2 z}{\partial y^2} = \frac{\partial}{\partial y}\left[\frac{\partial z}{\partial y}\right] = 6 \qquad \frac{\partial^2 z}{\partial x \partial y} = \frac{\partial}{\partial x}\left[\frac{\partial z}{\partial y}\right] = -2. \quad \text{(Note that the mixed partial derivatives are equal.)}$$

49. $z = \sqrt{x^2 + y^2}$

$$\frac{\partial z}{\partial x} = \frac{x}{\sqrt{x^2 + y^2}}$$

$$\frac{\partial^2 z}{\partial x^2} = \frac{y^2}{(x^2 + y^2)^{3/2}}$$

$$\frac{\partial^2 z}{\partial y \partial x} = \frac{-xy}{(x^2 + y^2)^{3/2}}$$

$$\frac{\partial z}{\partial y} = \frac{y}{\sqrt{x^2 + y^2}}$$

$$\frac{\partial^2 z}{\partial y^2} = \frac{x^2}{(x^2 + y^2)^{3/2}}$$

$$\frac{\partial^2 z}{\partial x \partial y} = \frac{-xy}{(x^2 + y^2)^{3/2}}$$

51. $z = e^x \tan y$

$$\frac{\partial z}{\partial x} = e^x \tan y$$

$$\frac{\partial^2 z}{\partial x^2} = e^x \tan y$$

$$\frac{\partial^2 z}{\partial y \partial x} = e^x \sec^2 y$$

$$\frac{\partial z}{\partial y} = e^x \sec^2 y$$

$$\frac{\partial^2 z}{\partial y^2} = 2e^x \sec^2 y \tan y$$

$$\frac{\partial^2 z}{\partial x \partial y} = e^x \sec^2 y$$

53. $z = \arctan \dfrac{y}{x}$

The first partial derivatives were found in Exercise 33.

$$\frac{\partial z}{\partial x} = \frac{-y}{x^2 + y^2} \quad \text{and} \quad \frac{\partial z}{\partial y} = \frac{x}{x^2 + y^2}$$

The second partials are

$$\frac{\partial^2 z}{\partial x^2} = \frac{\partial}{\partial x}\left[\frac{\partial z}{\partial x}\right] = \frac{(x^2 + y^2)(0) - (-y)(2x)}{(x^2 + y^2)^2} = \frac{2xy}{(x^2 + y^2)^2}$$

$$\frac{\partial^2 z}{\partial y \partial x} = \frac{\partial}{\partial y}\left[\frac{\partial z}{\partial x}\right] = \frac{(x^2 + y^2)(-1) - (-y)(2y)}{(x^2 + y^2)^2} = \frac{y^2 - x^2}{(x^2 + y^2)^2}$$

$$\frac{\partial^2 z}{\partial y^2} = \frac{\partial}{\partial y}\left[\frac{\partial z}{\partial y}\right] = \frac{(x^2 + y^2)(0) - x(2y)}{(x^2 + y^2)^2} = \frac{-2xy}{(x^2 + y^2)^2}$$

$$\frac{\partial^2 z}{\partial x \partial y} = \frac{\partial}{\partial x}\left[\frac{\partial z}{\partial y}\right] = \frac{(x^2 + y^2)(1) - x(2x)}{(x^2 + y^2)^2} = \frac{y^2 - x^2}{(x^2 + y^2)^2}. \quad \text{(Note that the mixed partial derivatives are equal.)}$$

55. $z = x \sec y$

$$\frac{\partial z}{\partial x} = \sec y$$

$$\frac{\partial^2 z}{\partial x^2} = 0$$

$$\frac{\partial^2 z}{\partial y \partial x} = \sec y \tan y$$

$$\frac{\partial z}{\partial y} = x \sec y \tan y$$

$$\frac{\partial^2 z}{\partial y^2} = x \sec y(\sec^2 y + \tan^2 y)$$

$$\frac{\partial^2 z}{\partial x \partial y} = \sec y \tan y$$

Therefore, $\dfrac{\partial^2 z}{\partial y \partial x} = \dfrac{\partial^2 z}{\partial x \partial y}$. There are no points for which

$z_x = 0 = z_y$, because $\dfrac{\partial z}{\partial x} = \sec y \neq 0$.

57. $z = \ln\left(\dfrac{x}{x^2 + y^2}\right) = \ln x - \ln(x^2 + y^2)$

$$\frac{\partial z}{\partial x} = \frac{1}{x} - \frac{2x}{x^2 + y^2} = \frac{y^2 - x^2}{x(x^2 + y^2)}$$

$$\frac{\partial^2 z}{\partial x^2} = \frac{x^4 - 4x^2 y^2 - y^4}{x^2(x^2 + y^2)^2}$$

$$\frac{\partial^2 z}{\partial y \partial x} = \frac{4xy}{(x^2 + y^2)^2}$$

$$\frac{\partial z}{\partial y} = -\frac{2y}{x^2 + y^2}$$

$$\frac{\partial^2 z}{\partial y^2} = \frac{2(y^2 - x^2)}{(x^2 + y^2)^2}$$

$$\frac{\partial^2 z}{\partial x \partial y} = \frac{4xy}{(x^2 + y^2)^2}$$

There are no points for which $z_x = z_y = 0$.

59. $w = \sqrt{x^2 + y^2 + z^2} = (x^2 + y^2 + z^2)^{1/2}$

$$\frac{\partial w}{\partial x} = \frac{1}{2}(x^2 + y^2 + z^2)^{-1/2}(2x) = \frac{x}{\sqrt{x^2 + y^2 + z^2}}$$

$$\frac{\partial w}{\partial y} = \frac{1}{2}(x^2 + y^2 + z^2)^{-1/2}(2y) = \frac{y}{\sqrt{x^2 + y^2 + z^2}}$$

$$\frac{\partial w}{\partial z} = \frac{1}{2}(x^2 + y^2 + z^2)^{-1/2}(2z) = \frac{z}{\sqrt{x^2 + y^2 + z^2}}$$

61. $F(x, y, z) = \ln \sqrt{x^2 + y^2 + z^2}$

$$= \frac{1}{2}\ln(x^2 + y^2 + z^2)$$

$$F_x(x, y, z) = \frac{x}{x^2 + y^2 + z^2}$$

$$F_y(x, y, z) = \frac{y}{x^2 + y^2 + z^2}$$

$$F_z(x, y, z) = \frac{z}{x^2 + y^2 + z^2}$$

63. $H(x, y, z) = \sin(x + 2y + 3z)$

$H_x(x, y, z) = \cos(x + 2y + 3z)$

$H_y(x, y, z) = 2\cos(x + 2y + 3z)$

$H_z(x, y, z) = 3\cos(x + 2y + 3z)$

65. $f(x, y, z) = xyz$

$f_x(x, y, z) = yz$

$f_y(x, y, z) = xz$

$f_{yy}(x, y, z) = 0$

$f_{xy}(x, y, z) = z$

$f_{yx}(x, y, z) = z$

$f_{yyx}(x, y, z) = 0$

$f_{xyy}(x, y, z) = 0$

$f_{yxy}(x, y, z) = 0$

Therefore, $f_{xyy} = f_{yxy} = f_{yyx} = 0$.

67. $f(x, y, z) = e^{-x} \sin yz$

$f_x(x, y, z) = -e^{-x} \sin yz$

$f_{xy}(x, y, z) = -e^{-x}(\cos yz)(z) = -ze^{-x} \cos yz$

$f_{xyy}(x, y, z) = -ze^{-x}(-\sin yz)(z) = z^2 e^{-x} \sin yz$

$f_y(x, y, z) = e^{-x}(\cos yz)(z) = ze^{-x} \cos yz$

$f_{yx}(x, y, z) = -ze^{-x} \cos yz$

$f_{yxy}(x, y, z) = -ze^{-x}(-\sin yz)(z) = z^2 e^{-x} \sin yz$

$f_y(x, y, z) = e^{-x}(\cos yz)(z) = ze^{-x} \cos yz$

$f_{yy}(x, y, z) = ze^{-x}(-\sin yz)(z) = -z^2 e^{-x} \sin yz$

$f_{yyx}(x, y, z) = -z^2 e^{-x}(-1) \sin yz = z^2 e^{-x} \sin yx$

Therefore,

$$f_{xyy}(x, y, z) = f_{yxy}(x, y, z) = f_{yyx}(x, y, z) = z^2 e^{-x} \sin yx.$$

69. $z = 5xy$

$\dfrac{\partial z}{\partial x} = 5y$

$\dfrac{\partial^2 z}{\partial x^2} = 0$

$\dfrac{\partial z}{\partial y} = 5x$

$\dfrac{\partial^2 z}{\partial y^2} = 0$

Therefore, $\dfrac{\partial^2 z}{\partial x^2} + \dfrac{\partial^2 z}{\partial y^2} = 0 + 0 = 0.$

71. $z = e^x \sin y$

$\dfrac{\partial z}{\partial x} = e^x \sin y$

$\dfrac{\partial^2 z}{\partial x^2} = e^x \sin y$

$\dfrac{\partial z}{\partial y} = e^x \cos y$

$\dfrac{\partial^2 z}{\partial y^2} = -e^x \sin y$

Therefore, $\dfrac{\partial^2 z}{\partial x^2} + \dfrac{\partial^2 z}{\partial y^2} = e^x \sin y - e^x \sin y = 0.$

73. $z = \sin(x - ct)$

$\dfrac{\partial z}{\partial x} = \cos(x - ct)$ and $\dfrac{\partial^2 z}{\partial x^2} = -\sin(x - ct)$

$\dfrac{\partial z}{\partial t} = -c \cos(x - ct)$ and $\dfrac{\partial^2 z}{\partial t^2} = -c^2 \sin(x - ct)$

Therefore,

$\dfrac{\partial^2 z}{\partial t^2} = -c^2 \sin(x - ct) = c^2 \dfrac{\partial^2 z}{\partial x^2}.$

75. $z = e^{-t} \cos \dfrac{x}{c}$

$\dfrac{\partial z}{\partial t} = -e^{-t} \cos \dfrac{x}{c}$

$\dfrac{\partial z}{\partial x} = -\dfrac{1}{c} e^{-t} \sin \dfrac{x}{c}$

$\dfrac{\partial^2 z}{\partial x^2} = -\dfrac{1}{c^2} e^{-t} \cos \dfrac{x}{c}$

Therefore, $\dfrac{\partial z}{\partial t} = c^2 \dfrac{\partial^2 z}{\partial x^2}.$

77. (a) $C = 32\sqrt{xy} + 175x + 205y + 1050$

$\dfrac{\partial C}{\partial x} = 16\sqrt{\dfrac{y}{x}} + 175$

$\dfrac{\partial C}{\partial x}\bigg]_{(80,\,20)} = 16\sqrt{\dfrac{1}{4}} + 175 = 183$

$\dfrac{\partial C}{\partial y} = 16\sqrt{\dfrac{x}{y}} + 205$

$\dfrac{\partial C}{\partial y}\bigg]_{(80,\,20)} = 16\sqrt{4} + 205 = 237$

(b) The fireplace-insert stove results in the cost increasing at a faster rate because $\partial C/\partial y > \partial C/\partial x$.

79. Let N be the number of applicants to a university, p the charge for food and housing, and t the tuition. Since

$$\dfrac{\partial N}{\partial p} < 0 \quad \text{and} \quad \dfrac{\partial N}{\partial t} < 0,$$

it follows that an increase in either price will cause a decrease in the number of applicants.

81. $T = 500 - 0.6x^2 - 1.5y^2$

$\dfrac{\partial T}{\partial x} = -1.2x, \dfrac{\partial T}{\partial x}(2, 3) = -2.4°/\text{m}$

$\dfrac{\partial T}{\partial y} = -3y = \dfrac{\partial T}{\partial y}(2, 3) = -9°/\text{m}$

83. $U = -5x^2 + xy - 3y^2$

(a) $U_x = -10x + y$

(b) $U_y = x - 6y$

(c) $U_x(2, 3) = -17$ and $U_y(2, 3) = -16$. The person should consume one more unit of y because the rate of decrease of satisfaction is less for y.

(d)

85. $f(x, y) = \begin{cases} \dfrac{xy(x^2 - y^2)}{x^2 + y^2}, & (x, y) \neq (0, 0) \\ 0, & (x, y) = (0, 0) \end{cases}$

(a) $f_x(x, y) = \dfrac{(x^2 + y^2)(3x^2y - y^3) - (x^3y - xy^3)(2x)}{(x^2 + y^2)^2} = \dfrac{y(x^4 + 4x^2y^2 - y^4)}{(x^2 + y^2)^2}$

$f_y(x, y) = \dfrac{(x^2 + y^2)(x^3 - 3xy^2) - (x^3y - xy^3)(2y)}{(x^2 + y^2)^2} = \dfrac{x(x^4 - 4x^2y^2 - y^4)}{(x^2 + y^2)^2}$

(b) $f_x(0, 0) = \lim\limits_{\Delta x \to 0} \dfrac{f(\Delta x, 0) - f(0, 0)}{\Delta x} = \lim\limits_{\Delta x \to 0} \dfrac{0/[(\Delta x)^2] - 0}{\Delta x} = 0$

$f_y(0, 0) = \lim\limits_{\Delta y \to 0} \dfrac{f(0, \Delta y) - f(0, 0)}{\Delta y} = \lim\limits_{\Delta y \to 0} \dfrac{0/[(\Delta y)^2] - 0}{\Delta y} = 0$

(c) $f_{xy}(0, 0) = \dfrac{\partial}{\partial y}\left(\dfrac{\partial f}{\partial x}\right)\bigg|_{(0, 0)} = \lim\limits_{\Delta y \to 0} \dfrac{f_x(0, \Delta y) - f_x(0, 0)}{\Delta y} = \lim\limits_{\Delta y \to 0} \dfrac{\Delta y(-(\Delta y)^4)}{((\Delta y)^2)^2(\Delta y)} = \lim\limits_{\Delta y \to 0} (-1) = -1$

$f_{yx}(0, 0) = \dfrac{\partial}{\partial x}\left(\dfrac{\partial f}{\partial y}\right)\bigg|_{(0, 0)} = \lim\limits_{\Delta x \to 0} \dfrac{f_y(\Delta x, 0) - f_y(0, 0)}{\Delta x} = \lim\limits_{\Delta x \to 0} \dfrac{\Delta x((\Delta x)^4)}{((\Delta x)^2)^2(\Delta x)} = \lim\limits_{\Delta x \to 0} 1 = 1$

(d) f_{yx} or f_{xy} or both are not continuous at $(0, 0)$.

87. True   **89.** True

Section 12.4   Differentials

1. $z = 3x^2y^3$

$dz = 6xy^3\, dx + 9x^2y^2\, dy$

3. $z = \dfrac{-1}{x^2 + y^2}$

$dz = \dfrac{2x}{(x^2 + y^2)^2}\, dx + \dfrac{2y}{(x^2 + y^2)^2}\, dy$

$\quad = \dfrac{2}{(x^2 + y^2)^2}(x\, dx + y\, dy)$

5. $z = x \cos y - y \cos x$

$dz = \dfrac{\partial z}{\partial x}\, dx + \dfrac{\partial z}{\partial y}\, dy$

$\quad = (\cos y + y \sin x)\, dx + (-x \sin y - \cos x)\, dy$

$\quad = (\cos y + y \sin x)\, dx - (x \sin y + \cos x)\, dy$

7. $w = 2z^3y \sin x$

$dw = 2z^3y \cos x\, dx + 2z^3 \sin x\, dy + 6z^2y \sin x\, dz$

9. Since $u = (x + y)/(z - 2y)$, we have

$du = \dfrac{\partial u}{\partial x}\, dx + \dfrac{\partial u}{\partial y}\, dy + \dfrac{\partial u}{\partial z}\, dz$

$\quad = \dfrac{1}{z - 2y}\, dx + \dfrac{(z - 2y)(1) - (x + y)(-2)}{(z - 2y)^2}\, dy + \dfrac{0 - (x + y)(1)}{(z - 2y)^2}\, dz$

$\quad = \dfrac{1}{z - 2y}\, dx + \dfrac{2x + z}{(z - 2y)^2}\, dy - \dfrac{x + y}{(z - 2y)^2}\, dz.$

11. $f(x, y) = 9 - x^2 - y^2$

(a) $f(1, 2) = 9 - 1^2 - 2^2 = 4$

$f(1.05, 2.1) = 9 - (1.05)^2 - (2.1)^2 = 3.4875$

$\Delta z = f(1.05, 2.1) - f(1, 2) = -0.5125$

(b) $dz = f_x(x, y)\, dx + f_y(x, y)\, dy = -2x\, dx - 2y\, dy$

Letting $x = 1$, $y = 2$, $dx = 0.05$, and $dy = 0.1$, yields

$dz = -2(1)(0.05) - 2(2)(0.1) = -0.5.$

13. (a) $f(1, 2) = \sin 2$

$f(1.05, 2.1) = 1.05 \sin 2.1$

$\Delta z = f(1.05, 2.1) - f(1, 2) \approx -0.00293$

(b) $dz = \sin y \, dx + x \cos y \, dy$

$= (\sin 2)(0.05) + (\cos 2)(0.1) \approx 0.00385$

15. (a) $f(1, 2) = -5$

$f(1.05, 2.1) = -5.25$

$\Delta z = -0.25$

(b) $dz = 3 \, dx - 4 \, dy$

$= 3(0.05) - 4(0.1) \approx -0.25$

17. Let $z = \sqrt{x^2 + y^2}$, $x = 5$, $y = 3$, $dx = 0.05$, and $dy = 0.1$. Then,

$$dz = \frac{\partial z}{\partial x} dx + \frac{\partial z}{\partial y} dy$$

$$= \frac{x}{\sqrt{x^2 + y^2}} dx + \frac{y}{\sqrt{x^2 + y^2}} dy$$

$$\sqrt{(5.05)^2 + (3.1)^2} - \sqrt{5^2 + 3^2} \approx \frac{5}{\sqrt{5^2 + 3^2}}(0.05) + \frac{3}{\sqrt{5^2 + 3^2}}(0.1) = \frac{0.55}{\sqrt{34}} \approx 0.094.$$

19. Let $z = (1 - x^2)/y^2$, $x = 3$, $y = 6$, $dx = 0.05$, $dy = -0.05$. Then: $dz = -\frac{2x}{y^2} dx + \frac{-2(1 - x^2)}{y^3} dy$

$$\frac{1 - (3.05)^2}{(5.95)^2} - \frac{1 - 3^2}{6^2} \approx -\frac{2(3)}{6^2}(0.05) - \frac{2(1 - 3^2)}{6^3}(-0.05) \approx -0.012$$

21. $A = lh$

$dA = l \, dh + h \, dl$

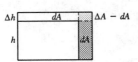

23. $V = \dfrac{\pi r^2 h}{3}$

$r = 3$

$h = 6$

$dV = \dfrac{2\pi r h}{3} dr + \dfrac{\pi r^2}{3} dh = \dfrac{\pi r}{3}(2h \, dr + r \, dh)$

Δr	Δh	dV	ΔV	$\Delta V - dV$
0.1	0.1	4.7124	4.8391	0.1267
0.1	-0.1	2.8274	2.8264	-0.0010
0.001	0.002	0.0565	0.0566	0.0001
-0.0001	0.0002	-0.0019	-0.0019	0.0000

25. First consider the relative errors in r and h as

$$\frac{dr}{r} = \pm 4\% = \pm 0.04 \quad \text{and} \quad \frac{dh}{h} = \pm 2\% = \pm 0.02.$$

Since $V = \pi r^2 h$, we have $dV = 2\pi r h \, dr + \pi r^2 \, dh$ or the relative error in V is

$$\frac{dV}{V} = \frac{2\pi r h \, dr}{\pi r^2 h} + \frac{\pi r^2 \, dh}{\pi r^2 h} = 2\frac{dr}{r} + \frac{dh}{h}$$

$$= 2(\pm 0.04) \pm 0.02 = \pm 0.10 = \pm 10\%.$$

27. $A = \frac{1}{2}ab \sin C$

$dA = \frac{1}{2}[(b \sin C) \, da + (a \sin C) \, db + (ab \cos C) \, dC]$

$= \frac{1}{2}[4(\sin 45°)(\pm\frac{1}{16}) + 3(\sin 45°)(\pm\frac{1}{16}) + 12(\cos 45°)(\pm 0.02)] \approx \pm 0.24 \text{ in.}^2$

29. $P = \dfrac{E^2}{R}$

$$dP = \frac{2E}{R}\,dE - \frac{E^2}{R^2}\,dR$$

$$\frac{dP}{P} = 2\frac{dE}{E} - \frac{dR}{R} = 2(0.02) - (-0.03) = 0.07 = 7\%$$

31. (a) Using the Law of Cosines:

$$a^2 = b^2 + c^2 - 2bc \cos A$$

$$= 330^2 + 420^2 - 2(330)(420)\cos 9°$$

$$a \approx 107.3 \text{ ft.}$$

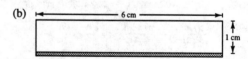
330 ft · 420 ft · 9°

(b) $a = \sqrt{b^2 + 420^2 - 2b(420)\cos\theta}$

$$da = \frac{1}{2}\Big[b^2 + 420^2 - 840b\cos\theta\Big]^{-1/2}\big[(2b - 840\cos\theta)\,db + 840b\sin\theta\,d\theta\big]$$

$$= \frac{1}{2}\Big[330^2 + 420^2 - 840(330)\Big(\cos\frac{\pi}{20}\Big)\Big]^{-1/2}\Big[\Big(2(330) - 840\cos\frac{\pi}{20}\Big)(6) + 840(330)\Big(\sin\frac{\pi}{20}\Big)\Big(\frac{\pi}{180}\Big)\Big]$$

$$\approx \frac{1}{2}[11512.79]^{-1/2}[\pm 1774.79] \approx \pm 8.27 \text{ ft}$$

33. $L = 0.00021\Big(\ln\dfrac{2h}{r} - 0.75\Big)$

Using the properties of logarithms, rewrite the function as

$$L = 0.00021[\ln(2h) - \ln r - 0.75].$$

Letting $h = 100$, $r = 2$, $dh = \pm\frac{1}{100}$, and $dr = \pm\frac{1}{16}$, the total differential is given by

$$dL = 0.00021\Big(\frac{1}{h}\,dh - \frac{1}{r}\,dr\Big)$$

$$= 0.00021\Big[\frac{1}{100}\Big(\pm\frac{1}{100}\Big) - \frac{1}{2}\Big(\pm\frac{1}{16}\Big)\Big]$$

$$\approx \pm 6.6 \times 10^{-6} \text{ microhenrys.}$$

Approximating the inductance, we have

$$L = 0.00021(\ln 200 - \ln 2 - 0.75) \pm dL$$

$$= 8.096 \times 10^{-4} \pm 6.6 \times 10^{-6}.$$

35. (a)

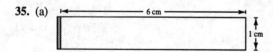
6 cm · 1 cm

(b)

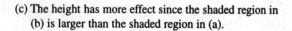
6 cm · 1 cm

(c) The height has more effect since the shaded region in (b) is larger than the shaded region in (a).

(d) $A = hl \Rightarrow dA = l\,dh + h\,dl$

If $dl = 0.01$ and $dh = 0$, then $dA = 1(0.01) = 0.01$.

If $dh = 0.01$ and $dl = 0$, then $dA = 6(0.01) = 0.06$.

37. Essay

39. $f(x, y) = x^2 - 2x + y$

$\Delta z = f(x + \Delta x, y + \Delta y) - f(x, y)$

$\qquad = (x + \Delta x)^2 - 2(x + \Delta x) + (y + \Delta y) - (x^2 - 2x + y)$

$\qquad = x^2 + 2x(\Delta x) + (\Delta x)^2 - 2x - 2\Delta x + y + \Delta y - x^2 + 2x - y$

$\qquad = (2x - 2)\Delta x + (1)\Delta y + \Delta x(\Delta x) + 0(\Delta y)$

$\qquad = f_x(x, y)\Delta x + f_y(x, y)\Delta y + \epsilon_1(\Delta x) + \epsilon_2(\Delta y)$

Therefore, $\epsilon_1 = \Delta x$ and $\epsilon_2 = 0$. As $(\Delta x, \Delta y) \to (0, 0)$, $\epsilon_1 \to 0$ and $\epsilon_2 \to 0$.

41. $z = f(x, y) = x^2 y$

$\Delta z = f(x + \Delta x, \ y + \Delta y) - f(x, y)$

$\qquad = (x^2 + 2x(\Delta x) + (\Delta x)^2)(y + \Delta y) - x^2 y$

$\qquad = 2xy(\Delta x) + y(\Delta x)^2 + x^2 \Delta y + 2x(\Delta x)(\Delta y) + (\Delta x)^2 \Delta y$

$\qquad = 2xy(\Delta x) + x^2 \Delta y + (y\Delta x)\,\Delta x + [2x\Delta x + (\Delta x)^2]\,\Delta y$

$\qquad = f_x(x, y)\,\Delta x + f_y(x, y)\,\Delta y + \epsilon_1 \Delta x + \epsilon_2 \Delta y$ where $\epsilon_1 = y(\Delta x)$ and $\epsilon_2 = 2x\Delta x + (\Delta x)^2$.

As $(\Delta x, \Delta y) \to (0, 0)$, $\epsilon_1 \to 0$ and $\epsilon_2 \to 0$.

43. $f(x, y) = \begin{cases} \dfrac{3x^2 y}{x^4 + y^2}, & (x, y) \neq (0, 0) \\ 0, & (x, y) = (0, 0) \end{cases}$

(a) $f_x(0, 0) = \lim\limits_{\Delta x \to 0} \dfrac{f(\Delta x, 0) - f(0, 0)}{\Delta x} = \lim\limits_{\Delta x \to 0} \dfrac{\frac{0}{(\Delta x)^4} - 0}{\Delta x} = 0$

$f_y(0, 0) = \lim\limits_{\Delta y \to 0} \dfrac{f(0, \Delta y) - f(0, 0)}{\Delta y} = \lim\limits_{\Delta y \to 0} \dfrac{\frac{0}{(\Delta y)^2} - 0}{\Delta y} = 0$

Thus, the partial derivatives exist at $(0, 0)$.

(b) Along the line $y = x$: $\lim\limits_{(x, y) \to (0, 0)} f(x, y) = \lim\limits_{x \to 0} \dfrac{3x^3}{x^4 + x^2} = \lim\limits_{x \to 0} \dfrac{3x}{x^2 + 1} = 0$

Along the curve $y = x^2$: $\lim\limits_{(x, y) \to (0, 0)} f(x, y) = \dfrac{3x^4}{2x^4} = \dfrac{3}{2}$

f is not continuous at $(0, 0)$. Therefore, f is not differentiable at $(0, 0)$. (See Theroem 12.5)

Section 12.5   Chain Rules for Functions of Several Variables

1. $w = x^2 + y^2$

$x = e^t$

$y = e^{-t}$

$\dfrac{dw}{dt} = 2xe^t + 2y(-e^{-t}) = 2(e^{2t} - e^{-2t})$

3. $w = x \sec y$

$x = e^t$

$y = \pi - t$

$\dfrac{dw}{dt} = (\sec y)(e^t) + (x \sec y \tan y)(-1)$

$\qquad = e^t \sec(\pi - t)[1 - \tan(\pi - t)]$

$\qquad = -e^t (\sec t + \sec t \tan t)$

5. $w = xy,\ x = 2\sin t,\ y = \cos t$

(a) $\dfrac{dw}{dt} = 2y\cos t + x(-\sin t) = 2y\cos t - x\sin t$

               $= 2(\cos^2 t - \sin^2 t) = 2\cos 2t$

(b) $w = 2\sin t\cos t = \sin 2t,\ \dfrac{dw}{dt} = 2\cos 2t$

7. $w = x^2 + y^2 + z^2$

$x = e^t\cos t$

$y = e^t\sin t$

$z = e^t$

(a) $\dfrac{dw}{dt} = 2x(-e^t\sin t + e^t\cos t) + 2y(e^t\cos t + e^t\sin t) + 2ze^t = 4e^{2t}$

(b) $w = 2e^{2t},\ \dfrac{dw}{dt} = 4e^{2t}$

9. $w = xy + xz + yz,\ x = t - 1,\ y = t^2 - 1,\ z = t$

(a) By the Chain Rule we have

$$\frac{dw}{dt} = \frac{\partial w}{\partial x}\frac{dx}{dt} + \frac{\partial w}{\partial y}\frac{dy}{dt} + \frac{\partial w}{\partial z}\frac{dz}{dt}$$

$$= (y + z)(1) + (x + z)(2t) + (x + y)(1)$$

$$= (t^2 - 1 + t)(1) + (t - 1 + t)(2t) + (t - 1 + t^2 - 1)(1)$$

$$= 6t^2 - 3 = 3(2t^2 - 1).$$

(b) By writing w as a function of t before differentiating, we have

$$w = (t - 1)(t^2 - 1) + (t - 1)t + (t^2 - 1)t = 2t^3 - 3t + 1$$

$$\frac{dw}{dt} = 6t^2 - 3 = 3(2t^2 - 1).$$

11. $w = \arctan(2xy),\ x = \cos t,\ y = \sin t,\ t = 0$

$$\frac{dw}{dt} = \frac{\partial w}{\partial x}\frac{dx}{dt} + \frac{\partial w}{\partial y}\frac{dy}{dt}$$

$$= \frac{2y}{1 + (4x^2y^2)}(-\sin t) + \frac{2x}{1 + (4x^2y^2)}(\cos t)$$

$$= \frac{2\sin t}{1 + 4\cos^2 t\sin^2 t}(-\sin t) + \frac{2\cos t}{1 + 4\cos^2 t\sin^2 t}(\cos t)$$

$$= \frac{2\cos^2 t - 2\sin^2 t}{1 + 4\cos^2 t\sin^2 t}$$

$$\frac{d^2w}{dt^2} = \frac{(1 + 4\cos^2 t\sin^2 t)(-8\cos t\sin t) - (2\cos^2 t - 2\sin^2 t)(8\cos^3 t\sin t - 8\sin^3 t\cos t)}{(1 + 4\cos^2 t\sin^2 t)}$$

At $t = 0,\ \dfrac{d^2w}{dt^2} = 0.$

13. $w = x^2 + y^2$

$x = s + t$

$y = s - t$

$\dfrac{\partial w}{\partial s} = 2x + 2y = 2(x + y) = 4s$

$\dfrac{\partial w}{\partial t} = 2x + 2y(-1) = 2(x - y) = 4t$

When $s = 2$ and $t = -1,\ \dfrac{\partial w}{\partial s} = 8$ and $\dfrac{\partial w}{\partial t} = -4.$

15. $w = x^2 - y^2, x = s \cos t, y = s \sin t$

By the Chain Rule,

$$\frac{\partial w}{\partial s} = \frac{\partial w}{\partial x}\frac{\partial x}{\partial s} + \frac{\partial w}{\partial y}\frac{\partial y}{\partial s} \quad \text{and} \quad \frac{\partial w}{\partial t} = \frac{\partial w}{\partial x}\frac{\partial x}{\partial t} + \frac{\partial w}{\partial y}\frac{\partial y}{\partial t}.$$

Therefore,

$$\frac{\partial w}{\partial s} = 2x(\cos t) + (-2y)(\sin t)$$

$$= (2s \cos t)(\cos t) - (2s \sin t)(\sin t)$$

$$= 2s(\cos^2 t - \sin^2 t) = 2s \cos 2t.$$

When $s = 3$ and $t = \pi/4$, $\partial w/\partial s = 2(3) \cos(\pi/2) = 0$. Similarly,

$$\frac{\partial w}{\partial t} = 2x(-s \sin t) - 2y(s \cos t) = 2s \cos t(-s \sin t) - 2s \sin t(s \cos t)$$

$$= -4s^2 \sin t \cos t = -2s^2 \sin 2t.$$

When $s = 3$ and $t = \pi/4$, $\partial w/\partial t = -2(9) \sin(\pi/2) = -18$.

17. $w = x^2 - 2xy + y^2, \ x = r + \theta, \ y = r - \theta$

(a) $\dfrac{\partial w}{\partial r} = (2x - 2y)(1) + (-2x + 2y)(1) = 0$

$\dfrac{\partial w}{\partial \theta} = (2x - 2y)(1) + (-2x + 2y)(-1)$

$\qquad = 4x - 4y = 4(x - y)$

$\qquad = 4[(r + \theta) - (r - \theta)] = 8\theta$

(b) $w = (r + \theta)^2 - 2(r + \theta)(r - \theta) + (r - \theta)^2$

$\qquad = (r^2 + 2r\theta + \theta^2) - 2(r^2 - \theta^2) + (r^2 - 2r\theta + \theta^2)$

$\qquad = 4\theta^2$

$\dfrac{\partial w}{\partial r} = 0$

$\dfrac{\partial w}{\partial \theta} = 8\theta$

19. $w = \arctan \dfrac{y}{x}, x = r \cos \theta, y = r \sin \theta$

(a) First calculate $\partial w/\partial x$ and $\partial w/\partial y$.

$$w = \arctan \frac{y}{x}$$

$$\frac{\partial w}{\partial x} = \frac{-y/x^2}{1 + (y^2/x^2)} = \frac{-y/x^2}{(x^2 + y^2)/x^2} = \frac{-y}{x^2 + y^2}$$

$$\frac{\partial w}{\partial y} = \frac{1/x}{1 + (y^2/x^2)} = \frac{1/x}{(x^2 + y^2)/x^2} = \frac{x}{x^2 + y^2}$$

Using the Chain Rule yields,

$$\frac{\partial w}{\partial r} = \frac{\partial w}{\partial x}\frac{\partial x}{\partial r} + \frac{\partial w}{\partial y}\frac{\partial y}{\partial r} = \frac{-y}{x^2 + y^2}(\cos \theta) + \frac{x}{x^2 + y^2}(\sin \theta)$$

$$= \frac{x \sin \theta - y \cos \theta}{x^2 + y^2} = \frac{r \cos \theta \sin \theta - r \sin \theta \cos \theta}{r^2} = 0.$$

Furthermore,

$$\frac{\partial w}{\partial \theta} = \frac{\partial w}{\partial x}\frac{\partial x}{\partial \theta} + \frac{\partial w}{\partial y}\frac{\partial y}{\partial \theta} = \frac{-y}{x^2 + y^2}(-r \sin \theta) + \frac{x}{x^2 + y^2}(r \cos \theta)$$

$$= \frac{-r \sin \theta(-r \sin \theta) + r \cos \theta(r \cos \theta)}{r^2} = \frac{r^2}{r^2} = 1.$$

—CONTINUED—

19. —CONTINUED—

(b) Since

$$w = \arctan \frac{y}{x} = \arctan\left(\frac{r \sin \theta}{r \cos \theta}\right) = \arctan(\tan \theta) = \theta + n\pi,$$

we have

$$\frac{\partial w}{\partial r} = 0 \quad \text{and} \quad \frac{\partial w}{\partial \theta} = 1.$$

21. $x^2 - 3xy + y^2 - 2x + y - 5 = 0$

$$\frac{dy}{dx} = -\frac{F_x(x, y)}{F_y(x, y)} = -\frac{2x - 3y - 2}{-3x + 2y + 1}$$

$$= \frac{3y - 2x + 2}{2y - 3x + 1}$$

23. $\ln \sqrt{x^2 + y^2} + xy = 4$

$$\frac{1}{2}\ln(x^2 + y^2) + xy - 4 = 0$$

$$\frac{dy}{dx} = -\frac{F_x(x, y)}{F_y(x, y)} = -\frac{\dfrac{x}{x^2 + y^2} + y}{\dfrac{y}{x^2 + y^2} + x} = -\frac{x + x^2y + y^3}{y + xy^2 + x^3}$$

25. $F(x, y, z) = x^2 + y^2 + z^2 - 25$

$$F_x(x, y, z) = 2x$$

$$F_y(x, y, z) = 2y$$

$$F_z(x, y, z) = 2z$$

$$\frac{\partial z}{\partial x} = -\frac{F_x(x, y, z)}{F_z(x, y, z)} = -\frac{2x}{2z} = -\frac{x}{z}$$

$$\frac{\partial z}{\partial y} = -\frac{F_y(x, y, z)}{F_z(x, y, z)} = -\frac{2y}{2z} = -\frac{y}{z}$$

27. $F(x, y, z) = \tan(x + y) + \tan(y + z) - 1$

$$F_x = \sec^2(x + y)$$

$$F_y = \sec^2(x + y) + \sec^2(y + z)$$

$$F_z = \sec^2(y + z)$$

$$\frac{\partial z}{\partial x} = -\frac{F_x}{F_z} = -\frac{\sec^2(x + y)}{\sec^2(y + z)}$$

$$\frac{\partial z}{\partial y} = -\frac{F_y}{F_z} = -\frac{\sec^2(x + y) + \sec^2(y + z)}{\sec^2(y + z)}$$

$$= -\left(\frac{\sec^2(x + y)}{\sec^2(y + z)} + 1\right)$$

29. $x^2 + 2yz + z^2 - 1 = 0$

(i) $2x + 2y\dfrac{\partial z}{\partial x} + 2z\dfrac{\partial z}{\partial x} = 0$ implies $\dfrac{\partial z}{\partial x} = -\dfrac{x}{y + z}$.

(ii) $2y\dfrac{\partial z}{\partial y} + 2z + 2z\dfrac{\partial z}{\partial y} = 0$ implies $\dfrac{\partial z}{\partial y} = -\dfrac{z}{y + z}$.

31. $F(x, y, z) = e^{xz} + xy$

$$F_x(x, y, z) = ze^{xz} + y$$

$$F_y(x, y, z) = x$$

$$F_z(x, y, z) = xe^{xz}$$

$$\frac{\partial z}{\partial x} = -\frac{F_x(x, y, z)}{F_z(x, y, z)} = -\frac{ze^{xz} + y}{xe^{xz}}$$

$$\frac{\partial z}{\partial y} = -\frac{F_y(x, y, z)}{F_z(x, y, z)} = -\frac{x}{xe^{xz}} = -e^{-xz}$$

33. $F(x, y, z, w) = xyz + xzw - yzw + w^2 - 5$

$$F_x = yz + zw$$

$$F_y = xz - zw$$

$$F_z = xy + xw - yw$$

$$F_w = xz - yz + 2w$$

$$\frac{\partial w}{\partial x} = -\frac{F_x}{F_w} = -\frac{z(y + w)}{xz - yz + 2w}$$

$$\frac{\partial w}{\partial y} = -\frac{F_y}{F_w} = -\frac{z(x - w)}{xz - yz + 2w}$$

$$\frac{\partial w}{\partial z} = -\frac{F_z}{F_w} = -\frac{xy + xw - yw}{xz - yz + 2w}$$

35. $F(x, y, z, w) = \cos xy + \sin yz + wz - 20$

$$\frac{\partial w}{\partial x} = \frac{-F_x}{F_w} = \frac{y \sin xy}{z}$$

$$\frac{\partial w}{\partial y} = \frac{-F_y}{F_w} = \frac{x \sin xy - z \cos yz}{z}$$

$$\frac{\partial w}{\partial z} = \frac{-F_z}{F_w} = -\frac{y \cos zy + w}{z}$$

37. $f(x, y) = \dfrac{xy}{\sqrt{x^2 + y^2}}$

$$f_x(x, y) = \dfrac{\sqrt{x^2 + y^2}\,(y) - xy\left(\dfrac{2x}{2\sqrt{x^2 + y^2}}\right)}{x^2 + y^2} = \dfrac{y^3}{(x^2 + y^2)^{3/2}}$$

$$f_y(x, y) = \dfrac{\sqrt{x^2 + y^2}\,(x) - xy\left(\dfrac{2y}{2\sqrt{x^2 + y^2}}\right)}{x^2 + y^2} = \dfrac{x^3}{(x^2 + y^2)^{3/2}}$$

$$f(tx, ty) = \dfrac{(tx)(ty)}{\sqrt{(tx)^2 + (ty)^2}} = t\left(\dfrac{xy}{\sqrt{x^2 + y^2}}\right) = tf(x, y)$$

Therefore, the function is homogeneous of degree 1.

$$xf_x(x, y) + yf_y(x, y) = x\left[\dfrac{y^3}{(x^2 + y^2)^{3/2}}\right] + y\left[\dfrac{x^3}{(x^2 + y^2)^{3/2}}\right] = \dfrac{xy(y^2 + x^2)}{(x^2 + y^2)^{3/2}} = \dfrac{xy}{\sqrt{x^2 + y^2}} = 1f(x, y)$$

39. $f(x, y) = e^{x/y}$

$f(tx, ty) = e^{tx/ty} = e^{x/y} = f(x, y)$

Degree: 0

$$xf_x(x, y) + yf_y(x, y) = x\left(\dfrac{1}{y}e^{x/y}\right) + y\left(-\dfrac{x}{y^2}e^{x/y}\right) = 0$$

41. From the figure we have

$$\sin\dfrac{\theta}{2} = \dfrac{b/2}{x} \implies b = 2x\sin\dfrac{\theta}{2}$$

$$\cos\dfrac{\theta}{2} = \dfrac{h}{x} \implies h = x\cos\dfrac{\theta}{2}.$$

Therefore, the area of the triangle is

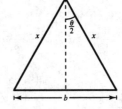

$$A = \dfrac{1}{2}bh = \dfrac{1}{2}\left(2x\sin\dfrac{\theta}{2}\right)\left(x\cos\dfrac{\theta}{2}\right) = \dfrac{1}{2}x^2\sin\theta.$$

Differentiating the area function with respect to t and substituting the given information about the triangle yields

$$\dfrac{dA}{dt} = \dfrac{\partial A}{\partial x}\dfrac{dx}{dt} + \dfrac{\partial A}{\partial \theta}\dfrac{d\theta}{dt}$$

$$= (x\sin\theta)\dfrac{dx}{dt} + \left(\dfrac{1}{2}x^2\cos\theta\right)\dfrac{d\theta}{dt}$$

$$= 6\sin\dfrac{\pi}{4}\left(\dfrac{1}{2}\right) + \left(\dfrac{1}{2}(6^2)\cos\dfrac{\pi}{4}\right)\left(\dfrac{\pi}{90}\right)$$

$$= 5\left(\dfrac{\sqrt{2}}{2}\right)\left(\dfrac{1}{2}\right) + \dfrac{1}{2}(36)\left(\dfrac{\sqrt{2}}{2}\right)\left(\dfrac{\pi}{90}\right)$$

$$= \dfrac{\sqrt{2}}{10}(15 + \pi) \text{ m}^2/\text{hr}.$$

43. (a) $V = \dfrac{1}{3}\pi r^2 h$

$$\dfrac{dV}{dt} = \dfrac{1}{3}\pi\left(2rh\dfrac{dr}{dt} + r^2\dfrac{dh}{dt}\right) = \dfrac{1}{3}\pi[2(12)(36)(6) + (12)^2(-4)] = 1536\pi \text{ in.}^3/\text{min}$$

—CONTINUED—

43. **—CONTINUED—**

(b) $S = \pi r \sqrt{r^2 + h^2} + \pi r^2$ (Surface area includes base.)

$$\frac{dS}{dt} = \pi \left[\left(\sqrt{r^2 + h^2} + \frac{r^2}{\sqrt{r^2 + h^2}} + 2r \right) \frac{dr}{dt} + \frac{rh}{\sqrt{r^2 + h^2}} \frac{dh}{dt} \right]$$

$$= \pi \left[\left(\sqrt{12^2 + 36^2} + \frac{144}{\sqrt{12^2 + 36^2}} + 2(12) \right)(6) + \frac{36(12)}{\sqrt{12^2 + 36^2}}(-4) \right]$$

$$= \pi \left[\left(12\sqrt{10} + \frac{12}{\sqrt{10}} \right)(6) + 144 + \frac{36}{\sqrt{10}}(-4) \right]$$

$$= \frac{648\pi}{\sqrt{10}} + 144\pi \text{ in.}^2/\text{min} = \frac{36\pi}{5} \left(20 + 9\sqrt{10} \right) \text{ in.}^2/\text{min}$$

45. $I = \frac{1}{2}m(r_1{}^2 + r_2{}^2)$

$$\frac{dI}{dt} = \frac{1}{2}m \left[2r_1 \frac{dr_1}{dt} + 2r_2 \frac{dr_2}{dt} \right]$$

$$= m[(6)(2) + (8)(2)] = 28m \text{ cm}^2/\text{sec}$$

47. (a) $x = (v_0 \cos \theta)t = (64 \cos 45°)t = 32\sqrt{2}t$

$y = (v_0 \sin \theta)t - 16t^2 = (64 \sin 45°)t - 16t^2 = 32\sqrt{2}t - 16t^2$

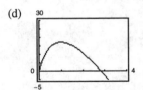

(b) $\tan \alpha = \dfrac{y}{x + 50}$

$$\alpha = \arctan\left(\frac{y}{x + 50} \right) = \arctan\left(\frac{32\sqrt{2}t - 16t^2}{32\sqrt{2}t + 50} \right)$$

(c) $\dfrac{d\alpha}{dt} = \dfrac{1}{1 + \left(\dfrac{32\sqrt{2}t - 16t^2}{32\sqrt{2}t + 50} \right)^2} \cdot \dfrac{-64\left(8\sqrt{2}t^2 + 25t - 25\sqrt{2} \right)}{\left(32\sqrt{2}t + 50 \right)^2}$

$$= \frac{-16\left(8\sqrt{2}t^2 + 25t - 25\sqrt{2} \right)}{64t^4 - 256\sqrt{2}t^3 + 1024t^2 + 800\sqrt{2}t + 625}$$

(d)

No. The rate of change of α is greatest when the projectile is closest to the camera.

(e) $\dfrac{d\alpha}{dt} = 0$ when

$$8\sqrt{2}t^2 + 25t - 25\sqrt{2} = 0$$

$$t = \frac{-25 + \sqrt{25^2 - 4\left(8\sqrt{2}\right)\left(-25\sqrt{2}\right)}}{2\left(8\sqrt{2}\right)} \approx 0.98 \text{ second.}$$

The projectile is at its maximum height when $dy/dt = 32\sqrt{2} - 32t = 0$ or $t = \sqrt{2} \approx 1.41$ seconds.

49. $g(t) = f(xt, yt) = t^n f(x, y)$

Let $u = xt$, $v = yt$, then

$$g'(t) = \frac{\partial f}{\partial u} \cdot \frac{du}{dt} + \frac{\partial f}{\partial v} \cdot \frac{dv}{dt} = \frac{\partial f}{\partial u} x + \frac{\partial f}{\partial v} y$$

and

$$g'(t) = nt^{n-1} f(x, y).$$

Now, let $t = 1$ and we have $u = x$, $v = y$. Thus,

$$\frac{\partial f}{\partial x} x + \frac{\partial f}{\partial y} y = nf(x, y).$$

51. $w = (x - y) \sin(y - x)$

$$\frac{\partial w}{\partial x} = -(x - y) \cos(y - x) + \sin(y - x)$$

$$\frac{\partial w}{\partial y} = (x - y) \cos(y - x) - \sin(y - x)$$

$$\frac{\partial w}{\partial x} + \frac{\partial w}{\partial y} = 0$$

53. $w = \arctan \frac{y}{x}$, $x = r \cos \theta$, $y = r \sin \theta$

$$= \arctan\left(\frac{r \sin \theta}{r \cos \theta}\right) = \arctan(\tan \theta) = \theta \text{ for } -\frac{\pi}{2} < \theta < \frac{\pi}{2}$$

$$\frac{\partial w}{\partial x} = \frac{-y}{x^2 + y^2}, \frac{\partial w}{\partial y} = \frac{x}{x^2 + y^2}, \frac{\partial w}{\partial r} = 0, \frac{\partial w}{\partial \theta} = 1$$

$$\left(\frac{\partial w}{\partial x}\right)^2 + \left(\frac{\partial w}{\partial y}\right)^2 = \frac{y^2}{(x^2 + y^2)^2} + \frac{x^2}{(x^2 + y^2)^2} = \frac{1}{x^2 + y^2} = \frac{1}{r^2}$$

$$\left(\frac{\partial w}{\partial r}\right)^2 + \left(\frac{1}{r^2}\right)\left(\frac{\partial w}{\partial \theta}\right)^2 = 0 + \frac{1}{r^2}(1) = \frac{1}{r^2}$$

Therefore, $\left(\frac{\partial w}{\partial x}\right)^2 + \left(\frac{\partial w}{\partial y}\right)^2 = \left(\frac{\partial w}{\partial r}\right)^2 + \frac{1}{r^2}\left(\frac{\partial w}{\partial \theta}\right)^2.$

55. Note first that

$$\frac{\partial u}{\partial x} = \frac{\partial v}{\partial y} = \frac{x}{x^2 + y^2}$$

$$\frac{\partial u}{\partial y} = -\frac{\partial v}{\partial x} = \frac{y}{x^2 + y^2}.$$

$$\frac{\partial u}{\partial r} = \frac{x}{x^2 + y^2} \cos \theta + \frac{y}{x^2 + y^2} \sin \theta = \frac{r \cos^2 \theta + r \sin^2 \theta}{r^2} = \frac{1}{r}$$

$$\frac{\partial v}{\partial \theta} = \frac{-y}{x^2 + y^2}(-r \sin \theta) + \frac{x}{x^2 + y^2}(r \cos \theta) = \frac{r^2 \sin^2 \theta + r^2 \cos^2 \theta}{r^2} = 1$$

Thus, $\frac{\partial u}{\partial r} = \frac{1}{r} \frac{\partial v}{\partial \theta}.$

$$\frac{\partial v}{\partial r} = \frac{-y}{x^2 + y^2} \cos \theta + \frac{x}{x^2 + y^2} \sin \theta = \frac{-r \sin \theta \cos \theta + r \sin \theta \cos \theta}{r^2} = 0$$

$$\frac{\partial u}{\partial \theta} = \frac{x}{x^2 + y^2}(-r \sin \theta) + \frac{y}{x^2 + y^2}(r \cos \theta) = \frac{-r^2 \sin \theta \cos \theta + r^2 \sin \theta \cos \theta}{r^2} = 0$$

Thus, $\frac{\partial v}{\partial r} = -\frac{1}{r} \frac{\partial u}{\partial \theta}.$

Section 12.6   Directional Derivatives and Gradients

1. $f(x, y) = 3x - 4xy + 5y$

$$v = \frac{1}{2}(i + \sqrt{3}j)$$

$\nabla f(x, y) = (3 - 4y)i + (-4x + 5)j$

$\nabla f(1, 2) = -5i + j$

$$u = \frac{v}{\|v\|} = \frac{1}{2}i + \frac{\sqrt{3}}{2}j$$

$D_u f(1, 2) = \nabla f(1, 2) \cdot u = \frac{1}{2}(-5 + \sqrt{3})$

3. $f(x, y) = xy$

$$v = i + j$$

$\nabla f(x, y) = yi + xj$

$\nabla f(2, 3) = 3i + 2j$

$$u = \frac{v}{\|v\|} = \frac{\sqrt{2}}{2}i + \frac{\sqrt{2}}{2}j$$

$D_u f(2, 3) = \nabla f(2, 3) \cdot u = \frac{5\sqrt{2}}{2}$

5. $g(x, y) = \sqrt{x^2 + y^2}$, $v = 3i - 4j$

The unit vector u in the direction of v is

$$u = \frac{v}{\|v\|} = \frac{3}{5}i - \frac{4}{5}j = \cos\theta i + \sin\theta j.$$

Thus, $\cos\theta = \frac{3}{5}$ and $\sin\theta = -\frac{4}{5}$.

$$D_u f(x, y) = f_x(x, y)\cos\theta + f_y(x, y)\sin\theta$$

$$= \frac{x}{\sqrt{x^2 + y^2}}\left(\frac{3}{5}\right) + \frac{y}{\sqrt{x^2 + y^2}}\left(-\frac{4}{5}\right)$$

$$= \frac{1}{5\sqrt{x^2 + y^2}}(3x - 4y)$$

Therefore, $D_u f(3, 4) = -\frac{7}{25}$. Note that $D_u f(x, y) = \nabla f(x, y) \cdot u$ where

$$\nabla f(x, y) = \frac{x}{\sqrt{x^2 + y^2}}i + \frac{y}{\sqrt{x^2 + y^2}}j.$$

7. $h(x, y) = e^x \sin y$

$$v = -i$$

$\nabla h = e^x \sin y i + e^x \cos y j$

$h\left(1, \frac{\pi}{2}\right) = ei$

$$u = \frac{v}{\|v\|} = -i$$

$D_u h\left(1, \frac{\pi}{2}\right) = \nabla h\left(1, \frac{\pi}{2}\right) \cdot u = -e$

9. $f(x, y, z) = xy + yz + xz$, $v = 2i + j - k$

We begin by finding $\nabla f(x, y, z)$ and a unit vector u in the direction of v.

$$\nabla f(x, y, z) = f_x(x, y, z)i + f_y(x, y, z)j + f_z(x, y, z)k$$

$$= (y + z)i + (x + z)j + (x + y)k$$

and

$$u = \frac{v}{\|v\|} = \frac{\sqrt{6}}{6}(2i + j - k).$$

Therefore,

$$D_u f(x, y, z) = \nabla f(x, y, z) \cdot u$$

$$= \frac{\sqrt{6}}{6}[2(y + z) + (x + z) - (x + y)]$$

$$= \frac{\sqrt{6}}{6}(y + 3z)$$

and

$$D_u f(1, 1, 1) = \frac{4\sqrt{6}}{6} = \frac{2\sqrt{6}}{3}.$$

11. $h(x, y, z) = x \arctan yz$

$$v = \langle 1, 2, -1 \rangle$$

$$\nabla h(x, y, z) = \arctan yz\, i + \frac{xz}{1 + (yz)^2}j + \frac{xy}{1 + (yz)^2}k$$

$$\nabla h(4, 1, 1) = \frac{\pi}{4}i + 2j + 2k$$

$$u = \frac{v}{\|v\|} = \left\langle \frac{1}{\sqrt{6}}, \frac{2}{\sqrt{6}}, -\frac{1}{\sqrt{6}} \right\rangle$$

$$D_u h(4, 1, 1) = \nabla h(4, 1, 1) \cdot u = \frac{\pi + 8}{4\sqrt{6}} = \frac{(\pi + 8)\sqrt{6}}{24}$$

13. $f(x, y) = x^2 + y^2$

$$\mathbf{u} = \frac{1}{\sqrt{2}}\mathbf{i} + \frac{1}{\sqrt{2}}\mathbf{j}$$

$$\nabla f = 2x\mathbf{i} + 2y\mathbf{j}$$

$$D_{\mathbf{u}}f = \nabla f \cdot \mathbf{u} = \frac{2}{\sqrt{2}}x + \frac{2}{\sqrt{2}}y = \sqrt{2}(x + y)$$

15. $f(x, y) = \sin(2x - y)$

$$\mathbf{u} = \frac{1}{2}\mathbf{i} - \frac{\sqrt{3}}{2}\mathbf{j}$$

$$\nabla f = 2\cos(2x - y)\mathbf{i} - \cos(2x - y)\mathbf{j}$$

$$D_{\mathbf{u}}f = \nabla f \cdot \mathbf{u} = \cos(2x - y) + \frac{\sqrt{3}}{2}\cos(2x - y)$$

$$= \left(\frac{2 + \sqrt{3}}{2}\right)\cos(2x - y)$$

17. $f(x, y) = x^2 + 4y^2$, $P(3, 1)$, $Q(1, -1)$

A vector in the specified direction is

$$\vec{PQ} = \mathbf{v} = (1 - 3)\mathbf{i} + (-1 - 1)\mathbf{j} = -2\mathbf{i} - 2\mathbf{j}$$

and a unit vector in this direction is

$$\mathbf{u} = \frac{\mathbf{v}}{\|\mathbf{v}\|} = \frac{-2}{\sqrt{8}}\mathbf{i} - \frac{2}{\sqrt{8}}\mathbf{j} = -\frac{1}{\sqrt{2}}\mathbf{i} - \frac{1}{\sqrt{2}}\mathbf{j}.$$

Since $\nabla f(x, y) = f_x(x, y)\mathbf{i} + f_y(x, y)\mathbf{j} = 2x\mathbf{i} + 8y\mathbf{j}$, the gradient at $(3, 1)$ is $\nabla f(3, 1) = 6\mathbf{i} + 8\mathbf{j}$. Consequently, at $(3, 1)$ the directional derivative is

$$D_{\mathbf{u}}f(3, 1) = \nabla f(3, 1) \cdot \mathbf{u}$$

$$= (6\mathbf{i} + 8\mathbf{j}) \cdot \left(-\frac{\sqrt{2}}{2}\mathbf{i} - \frac{\sqrt{2}}{2}\mathbf{j}\right)$$

$$= -3\sqrt{2} - 4\sqrt{2} = -7\sqrt{2}.$$

19. $h(x, y, z) = \ln(x + y + z)$

$$\mathbf{v} = 3\mathbf{i} + 3\mathbf{j} + \mathbf{k}$$

$$\nabla h = \frac{1}{x + y + z}(\mathbf{i} + \mathbf{j} + \mathbf{k})$$

At $(1, 0, 0)$, $\nabla h = \mathbf{i} + \mathbf{j} + \mathbf{k}$.

$$\mathbf{u} = \frac{\mathbf{v}}{\|\mathbf{v}\|} = \frac{1}{\sqrt{19}}(3\mathbf{i} + 3\mathbf{j} + \mathbf{k})$$

$$D_{\mathbf{u}}h = \nabla h \cdot \mathbf{u} = \frac{7}{\sqrt{19}} = \frac{7\sqrt{19}}{19}$$

21. (a) In the direction of the vector $-4\mathbf{i} + \mathbf{j}$.

(c) $-\nabla f = \frac{2}{5}\mathbf{i} - \frac{1}{10}\mathbf{j}$, the direction opposite that of the gradient.

(b) $\nabla f = \frac{1}{10}(2x - 3y)\mathbf{i} + \frac{1}{10}(-3x + 2y)\mathbf{j}$

$$\nabla f(1, 2) = \frac{1}{10}(-4)\mathbf{i} + \frac{1}{10}(1)\mathbf{j} = -\frac{2}{5}\mathbf{i} + \frac{1}{10}\mathbf{j}$$

(Same direction as in part (a).)

23. $f(x, y) = x^2 - y^2$, $(4, -3, 7)$

(a)

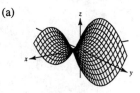

(c) Zeros: $\theta \approx 2.21, 5.36$

These are the angles θ for which $D_{\mathbf{u}}f(4, 3)$ equals zero.

(e) $\|\nabla f(4, -3)\| = \|2(4)\mathbf{i} - 2(3)\mathbf{j}\| = \sqrt{64 + 36} = 10$, the maximum value of $D_{\mathbf{u}}f(4, -3)$, at $\theta = 0.64$.

(f) $f(x, y) = x^2 - y^2 = 7$

$\nabla f(4, -3) = 8\mathbf{i} + 6\mathbf{j}$ is perpendicular to the level curve at $(4, -3)$.

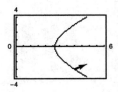

(b) $D_{\mathbf{u}}f(x, y) = \nabla f(x, y) \cdot \mathbf{u} = 2x\cos\theta - 2y\sin\theta$

$$D_{\mathbf{u}}f(4, -3) = 8\cos\theta + 6\sin\theta$$

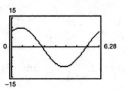

(d) $g(\theta) = D_{\mathbf{u}}f(4, -3) = 8\cos\theta + 6\sin\theta$

$g'(\theta) = -8\sin\theta + 6\cos\theta$

Critical numbers: $\theta \approx 0.64, 3.79$

These are the angles for which $D_{\mathbf{u}}f(4, -3)$ is a maximum (0.64) and minimum (3.79).

25. $h(x, y) = x \tan y$

The gradient vector is given by

$$\nabla f(x, y) = f_x(x, y)\mathbf{i} + f_y(x, y)\mathbf{j} = \tan y\mathbf{i} + x \sec^2 y\mathbf{j}.$$

At the point $P = (2, \pi/4)$ the gradient is

$$\nabla f\left(2, \frac{\pi}{4}\right) = \tan\frac{\pi}{4}\mathbf{i} + 2 \sec^2\frac{\pi}{4}\mathbf{j} = \mathbf{i} + 4\mathbf{j}.$$

Hence, it follows that the maximum value of the directional derivative at the point $P = (2, \pi/4)$ is

$$\left\| \nabla f\left(2, \frac{\pi}{4}\right) \right\| = \sqrt{17}.$$

27. $g(x, y) = \ln \sqrt[3]{x^2 + y^2} = \frac{1}{3} \ln(x^2 + y^2)$

$$\nabla g(x, y) = \frac{1}{3}\left[\frac{2x}{x^2 + y^2}\mathbf{i} + \frac{2y}{x^2 + y^2}\mathbf{j}\right]$$

$$\nabla g(1, 2) = \frac{1}{3}\left(\frac{2}{5}\mathbf{i} + \frac{4}{5}\mathbf{j}\right) = \frac{2}{15}(\mathbf{i} + 2\mathbf{j})$$

$$\|\nabla g(1, 2)\| = \frac{2\sqrt{5}}{15}$$

29. $f(x, y, z) = \sqrt{x^2 + y^2 + z^2}$

The gradient vector is given by

$$\nabla f(x, y, z) = f_x(x, y, z)\mathbf{i} + f_y(x, y, z)\mathbf{j} + f_z(x, y, z)\mathbf{k}$$

$$= \frac{x}{\sqrt{x^2 + y^2 + z^2}}\mathbf{i} + \frac{y}{\sqrt{x^2 + y^2 + z^2}}\mathbf{j} + \frac{z}{\sqrt{x^2 + y^2 + z^2}}\mathbf{k}$$

$$= \frac{x\mathbf{i} + y\mathbf{j} + z\mathbf{k}}{\sqrt{x^2 + y^2 + z^2}}.$$

At the point $(1, 4, 2)$ the gradient is

$$\nabla f(1, 4, 2) = \frac{1}{\sqrt{21}}(\mathbf{i} + 4\mathbf{j} + 2\mathbf{k}).$$

Hence, the maximum value of the directional derivative at the point $(1, 4, 2)$ is

$$\|\nabla f(1, 4, 2)\| = \frac{1}{\sqrt{21}}\sqrt{1 + 16 + 4} = 1.$$

31. $w = \dfrac{1}{\sqrt{1 - x^2 - y^2 - z^2}}$

$$\nabla w = \frac{1}{\left(\sqrt{1 - x^2 - y^2 - z^2}\right)^3}(x\mathbf{i} + y\mathbf{j} + z\mathbf{k})$$

$$\nabla w(0, 0, 0) = \mathbf{0}$$

$$\|\nabla w(0, 0, 0)\| = 0$$

For Exercises 33–39, $f(x, y) = 3 - \dfrac{x}{3} - \dfrac{y}{2}$ **and** $D_\theta f(x, y) = -\left(\dfrac{1}{3}\right)\cos\theta - \left(\dfrac{1}{2}\right)\sin\theta.$

33. $f(x, y) = 3 - \dfrac{x}{3} - \dfrac{y}{2}$

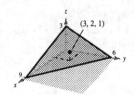

35. $f(x, y) = 3 - \dfrac{x}{3} - \dfrac{y}{2}$

    (a) The directional derivative is

$$D_{\mathbf{u}} f(x, y) = f_x(x, y) \cos \theta + f_y(x, y) \sin \theta$$

$$= -\frac{1}{3} \cos \theta - \frac{1}{2} \sin \theta.$$

For $\theta = 4\pi/3$, $x = 3$, and $y = 2$, we have

$$D_{\mathbf{u}} f(3, 2) = -\frac{1}{3} \cos \frac{4\pi}{3} - \frac{1}{2} \sin \frac{4\pi}{3}$$

$$= -\frac{1}{3}\left(-\frac{1}{2}\right) - \frac{1}{2}\left(-\frac{\sqrt{3}}{2}\right) = \frac{2 + 3\sqrt{3}}{12}.$$

    (b) For $\theta = -\pi/6$, $x = 3$, and $y = 2$, we have

$$D_{\mathbf{u}} f(3, 2) = -\frac{1}{3} \cos\left(-\frac{\pi}{6}\right) - \frac{1}{2} \sin\left(-\frac{\pi}{6}\right)$$

$$= -\frac{1}{3}\left(\frac{\sqrt{3}}{2}\right) - \frac{1}{2}\left(-\frac{1}{2}\right) = \frac{3 - 2\sqrt{3}}{12}.$$

37. $f(x, y) = 3 - \dfrac{x}{3} - \dfrac{y}{2}$

    (a) Let $\mathbf{u}$ be a unit vector in the direction of $\mathbf{v}$. Then

$$\mathbf{v} = (-2 - 1)\mathbf{i} + (6 - 2)\mathbf{j} = -3\mathbf{i} + 4\mathbf{j}$$

and $\mathbf{u} = \dfrac{\mathbf{v}}{\|\mathbf{v}\|} = \dfrac{-3\mathbf{i} + 4\mathbf{j}}{\sqrt{25}} = -\dfrac{3}{5}\mathbf{i} + \dfrac{4}{5}\mathbf{j}.$

At $(3, 2)$,

$$\nabla f(3, 2) = f_x(3, 2)\mathbf{i} + f_y(3, 2)\mathbf{j} = -\frac{1}{3}\mathbf{i} - \frac{1}{2}\mathbf{j}.$$

Therefore, the directional derivative in the direction of $\mathbf{v}$ is

$$\nabla f(3, 2) \cdot \mathbf{u} = \left(-\frac{1}{3}\right)\left(-\frac{3}{5}\right) + \left(-\frac{1}{2}\right)\left(\frac{4}{5}\right)$$

$$= \frac{1}{5} - \frac{2}{5} = -\frac{1}{5}.$$

    (b) Let $\mathbf{u}$ be a unit vector in the direction of $\mathbf{v}$. Then

$$\mathbf{v} = (4 - 3)\mathbf{i} + (5 - 2)\mathbf{j} = \mathbf{i} + 3\mathbf{j}$$

and

$$\mathbf{u} = \frac{\mathbf{v}}{\|\mathbf{v}\|} = \frac{\mathbf{i} + 3\mathbf{j}}{\sqrt{10}} = \frac{\sqrt{10}}{10}\mathbf{i} + \frac{3\sqrt{10}}{10}\mathbf{j}.$$

Therefore, the directional derivative in the direction of $\mathbf{v}$ is

$$\nabla f(3, 2) \cdot \mathbf{u} = \left(-\frac{1}{3}\right)\left(\frac{\sqrt{10}}{10}\right) + \left(-\frac{1}{2}\right)\left(\frac{3\sqrt{10}}{10}\right)$$

$$= -\frac{11\sqrt{10}}{60}.$$

39. $f(x, y) = 3 - \dfrac{x}{3} - \dfrac{y}{2}$

The maximum value of the directional derivative is $\|\nabla f(3, 2)\|$.

$$f(x, y) = 3 - \frac{x}{3} - \frac{y}{2}$$

$$\nabla f(x, y) = f_x(x, y)\mathbf{i} + f_y(x, y)\mathbf{j} = -\frac{1}{3}\mathbf{i} - \frac{1}{2}\mathbf{j}$$

Therefore, the maximum value of the directional derivative at $(3, 2)$ is $\|\nabla f(3, 2)\| = \sqrt{\dfrac{1}{9} + \dfrac{1}{4}} = \dfrac{\sqrt{13}}{6}.$

For Exercises 41 and 43, $f(x, y) = 9 - x^2 - y^2$ and $D_\theta f(x, y) = -2x \cos \theta - 2y \sin \theta = -2(x \cos \theta + y \sin \theta)$.

41. $f(x, y) = 9 - x^2 - y^2$

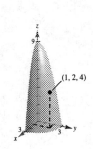

43. $\nabla f(1, 2) = -2\mathbf{i} - 4\mathbf{j}$

$$\|\nabla f(1, 2)\| = \sqrt{4 + 16} = \sqrt{20} = 2\sqrt{5}$$

45. $f(x, y) = x^2 + y^2$

$c = 25, \ P = (3, 4)$

$\nabla f(x, y) = 2x\mathbf{i} + 2y\mathbf{j}$

$x^2 + y^2 = 25$

$\nabla f(3, 4) = 6\mathbf{i} + 8\mathbf{j}$

47. $f(x, y) = \dfrac{x}{x^2 + y^2}$

The level curve for $c = \frac{1}{2}$ is given by

$$\frac{x}{x^2 + y^2} = \frac{1}{2}$$

and is shown in the figure. The normal vector to the level curve at $P(1, 1)$ is $\nabla f(1, 1)$.

$\nabla f(x, y) = f_x(x, y)\mathbf{i} + f_y(x, y)\mathbf{j}$

$\qquad = \dfrac{y^2 - x^2}{(x^2 + y^2)^2}\mathbf{i} - \dfrac{2xy}{(x^2 + y^2)^2}\mathbf{j}$

$\nabla f(1, 1) = -\dfrac{1}{2}\mathbf{j}$

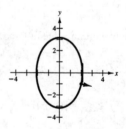

49. $4x^2 - y = 6$

$f(x, y) = 4x^2 - y$

$\nabla f(x, y) = 8x\mathbf{i} - \mathbf{j}$

$\nabla f(2, 10) = 16\mathbf{i} - \mathbf{j}$

$\dfrac{\nabla f(2, 10)}{\|\nabla f(2, 10)\|} = \dfrac{1}{\sqrt{257}}(16\mathbf{i} - \mathbf{j})$

$\qquad\qquad = \dfrac{\sqrt{257}}{257}(16\mathbf{i} - \mathbf{j})$

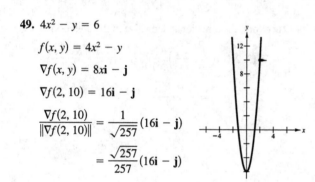

51. The ellipse given by the equation $9x^2 + 4y^2 = 40$ corresponds to the level curve with $c = 0$ to the function

$$f(x, y) = 9x^2 + 4y^2 - 40.$$

$\nabla f(x_0, y_0)$ yields a normal vector to the level curve at the point (x_0, y_0). Therefore, $\nabla f(x, y) = 18x\mathbf{i} + 8y\mathbf{j}$ and at $(2, -1)$, a normal vector is

$$\nabla f(2, -1) = 36\mathbf{i} - 8\mathbf{j} = 4(9\mathbf{i} - 2\mathbf{j}).$$

Since, $\|\nabla f(2, -1)\| = 4\sqrt{9^2 + (-2)^2} = 4\sqrt{85}$, a unit normal vector is

$$\frac{\sqrt{85}}{85}(9\mathbf{i} - 2\mathbf{j}).$$

53. $T = \dfrac{x}{x^2 + y^2}$

The direction of greatest increase in temperature at $(3, 4)$ will be the direction of the gradient $\nabla T(x, y)$ at that point. Since

$$T_x(x, y) = \frac{(x^2 + y^2)(1) - x(2x)}{(x^2 + y^2)^2} = \frac{y^2 - x^2}{(x^2 + y^2)^2}$$

$$T_y(x, y) = \frac{(x^2 + y^2)(0) - x(2y)}{(x^2 + y^2)^2} = \frac{-2xy}{(x^2 + y^2)^2},$$

the gradient at $(3, 4)$ is

$$\nabla T(3, 4) = T_x(3, 4)\mathbf{i} + T_y(3, 4)\mathbf{j} = \frac{7}{(25)^2}\mathbf{i} - \frac{24}{(25)^2}\mathbf{j} = \frac{1}{625}(7\mathbf{i} - 24\mathbf{j}).$$

55. Temperature field: $T(x, y) = 400 - 2x^2 - y^2$

Let the path be represented by the position function

$$\mathbf{r}(t) = x(t)\mathbf{i} + y(t)\mathbf{j}.$$

A tangent vector at each point $(x(t), y(t))$ is given by

$$\mathbf{r}'(t) = \frac{dx}{dt}\mathbf{i} + \frac{dy}{dt}\mathbf{j}.$$

Because the particle seeks maximum temperature increase, the direction of $\mathbf{r}'(t)$ and $\nabla T(x, y) = -4x\mathbf{i} - 2y\mathbf{j}$ are the same at each point of the path. Thus,

$$-4x = k\frac{dx}{dt} \quad \text{and} \quad -2y = k\frac{dy}{dt}$$

where k depends on t. By solving each equation for dt/k and equating the results, we have

$$\frac{dx}{-4x} = \frac{dy}{-2y}.$$

The solution of this differential equation is $y^2 = Cx$. Because the particle passes through the point $P(10, 10)$, $C = 10$. Thus, the path of the heat-seeking particle is $y^2 = 10x$.

57. (a)

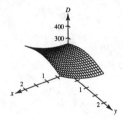

(b) The graph of $-D = -250 - 30x^2 - 50\sin(\pi y/2)$ would model the ocean floor.

(c) $D(1, 0.5) = 250 + 30(1) + 50\sin\frac{\pi}{4} \approx 315.4$ ft

(d) $\dfrac{\partial D}{\partial x} = 60x$ and $\dfrac{\partial D}{\partial x}(1, 0.5) = 60$

(e) $\dfrac{\partial D}{\partial y} = 25\pi\cos\dfrac{\pi y}{2}$ and $\dfrac{\partial D}{\partial y}(1, 0.5) = 25\pi\cos\dfrac{\pi}{4} \approx 55.5$

(f) $\nabla D = 60x\mathbf{i} + 25\pi\cos\left(\dfrac{\pi y}{2}\right)\mathbf{j}$

$\nabla D(1, 0.5) = 60\mathbf{i} + 55.5\mathbf{j}$

59. The wind speed is greatest at A.   **61.** True   **63.** True

65. Let $f(x, y, z) = e^x\cos y + \dfrac{z^2}{2} + C$. Then $\nabla f(x, y, z) = e^x\cos y\mathbf{i} - e^x\sin y\mathbf{j} + z\mathbf{k}$.

Section 12.7   Tangent Planes and Normal Lines

1. $F(x, y, z) = x + y + z - 4$

$$\nabla F = \mathbf{i} + \mathbf{j} + \mathbf{k}$$

$$\mathbf{n} = \frac{\nabla F}{\|\nabla F\|} = \frac{1}{\sqrt{3}}(\mathbf{i} + \mathbf{j} + \mathbf{k})$$

$$= \frac{\sqrt{3}}{3}(\mathbf{i} + \mathbf{j} + \mathbf{k})$$

3. $F(x, y, z) = \sqrt{x^2 + y^2} - z$

$$\nabla F(x, y, z) = \frac{x}{\sqrt{x^2 + y^2}}\mathbf{i} + \frac{y}{\sqrt{x^2 + y^2}}\mathbf{j} - \mathbf{k}$$

$$\nabla F(3, 4, 5) = \frac{3}{5}\mathbf{i} + \frac{4}{5}\mathbf{j} - \mathbf{k}$$

$$\mathbf{n} = \frac{\nabla F}{\|\nabla F\|} = \frac{5}{5\sqrt{2}}\left(\frac{3}{5}\mathbf{i} + \frac{4}{5}\mathbf{j} - \mathbf{k}\right)$$

$$= \frac{1}{5\sqrt{2}}(3\mathbf{i} + 4\mathbf{j} - 5\mathbf{k})$$

$$= \frac{\sqrt{2}}{10}(3\mathbf{i} + 4\mathbf{j} - 5\mathbf{k})$$

5. $F(x, y, z) = x^2y^4 - z$

$\nabla F(x, y, z) = 2xy^4\mathbf{i} + 4x^2y^3\mathbf{j} - \mathbf{k}$

$\nabla F(1, 2, 16) = 32\mathbf{i} + 32\mathbf{j} - \mathbf{k}$

$\mathbf{n} = \dfrac{\nabla F}{\|\nabla F\|} = \dfrac{1}{\sqrt{2049}}(32\mathbf{i} + 32\mathbf{j} - \mathbf{k})$

$\qquad = \dfrac{\sqrt{2049}}{2049}(32\mathbf{i} + 32\mathbf{j} - \mathbf{k})$

7. $z - x \sin y = 4$

Writing the equation for the surface as a function of three variables yields

$$F(x, y, z) = z - x \sin y - 4.$$

A normal vector to the surface, $F(x, y, z) = 0$, at (x_0, y_0, z_0) is given by $\nabla F(x_0, y_0, z_0)$.

$\nabla F(x, y, z) = F_x(x, y, z)\mathbf{i} + F_y(x, y, z)\mathbf{j} + F_z(x, y, z)\mathbf{k}$

$\qquad = -\sin y\mathbf{i} - x \cos y\mathbf{j} + \mathbf{k}$

$\nabla F\left(6, \dfrac{\pi}{6}, 7\right) = -\dfrac{1}{2}\mathbf{i} - 3\sqrt{3}\mathbf{j} + \mathbf{k}$

Now, the unit normal vector to the surface is

$$\dfrac{\nabla F(6, \pi/6, 7)}{\|\nabla F(6, \pi/6, 7)\|} = \dfrac{\sqrt{113}}{113}(-\mathbf{i} - 6\sqrt{3}\mathbf{j} + 2\mathbf{k}).$$

9. $F(x, y, z) = \ln\left(\dfrac{x}{y - z}\right) = \ln x - \ln(y - z)$

$\nabla F(x, y, z) = \dfrac{1}{x}\mathbf{i} - \dfrac{1}{y - z}\mathbf{j} + \dfrac{1}{y - z}\mathbf{k}$

$\nabla F(1, 4, 3) = \mathbf{i} - \mathbf{j} + \mathbf{k}$

$\mathbf{n} = \dfrac{\nabla F}{\|\nabla F\|} = \dfrac{1}{\sqrt{3}}(\mathbf{i} - \mathbf{j} + \mathbf{k}) = \dfrac{\sqrt{3}}{3}(\mathbf{i} - \mathbf{j} + \mathbf{k})$

11. $f(x, y) = 25 - x^2 - y^2$, $(3, 1, 15)$

$F(x, y, z) = 25 - x^2 - y^2 - z$

$F_x(x, y, z) = -2x \qquad\qquad F_y(x, y, z) = -2y \qquad\qquad F_z(x, y, z) = -1$

$F_x(3, 1, 15) = -6 \qquad\qquad F_y(3, 1, 15) = -2 \qquad\qquad F_z(3, 1, 15) = -1$

$-6(x - 3) - 2(y - 1) - (z - 15) = 0$

$$0 = 6x + 2y + z - 35$$

$$6x + 2y + z = 35$$

13. $f(x, y) = \dfrac{y}{x}$

Begin by writing the equation of the surface as $\dfrac{y}{x} - z = 0$. Then, considering

$$F(x, y, z) = \dfrac{y}{x} - z,$$

we have

$$F_x(x, y, z) = \dfrac{-y}{x^2}, \; F_y(x, y, z) = \dfrac{1}{x}, \text{ and } F_z(x, y, z) = -1.$$

At the point $(1, 2, 2)$, the partial derivatives are

$$F_x(1, 2, 2) = -2, \; f_y(1, 2, 2) = 1, \text{ and } F_z(1, 2, 2) = -1.$$

Therefore, the equation of the tangent plane at $(1, 2, 2)$ is

$$F_x(1, 2, 2)(x - 1) + F_y(1, 2, 2)(y - 2) + F_z(1, 2, 2)(z - 2) = 0$$

$$-2(x - 1) + 1(y - 2) - (z - 2) = 0$$

$$-2x + y - z + 2 = 0.$$

15. $g(x, y) = x^2 - y^2,\ (5, 4, 9)$

$G(x, y, z) = x^2 - y^2 - z$

$G_x(x, y, z) = 2x \qquad G_y(x, y, z) = -2y \qquad G_z(x, y, z) = -1$

$G_x(5, 4, 9) = 10 \qquad G_y(5, 4, 9) = -8 \qquad G_z(5, 4, 9) = -1$

$10(x - 5) - 8(y - 4) - (z - 9) = 0$

$10x - 8y - z = 9$

17. $z = e^x(\sin y + 1),\ \left(0, \dfrac{\pi}{2}, 2\right)$

$F(x, y, z) = e^x(\sin y + 1) - z$

$F_x(x, y, z) = e^x(\sin y + 1) \qquad F_y(x, y, z) = e^x \cos y \qquad F_z(x, y, z) = -1$

$F_x\left(0, \dfrac{\pi}{2}, 2\right) = 2 \qquad\qquad F_y\left(0, \dfrac{\pi}{2}, 2\right) = 0 \qquad\qquad F_z\left(0, \dfrac{\pi}{2}, 2\right) = -1$

$2x - z = -2$

19. $h(x, y) = \ln \sqrt{x^2 + y^2},\ (3, 4, \ln 5)$

$H(x, y, z) = \ln \sqrt{x^2 + y^2} - z = \dfrac{1}{2}\ln(x^2 + y^2) - z$

$H_x(x, y, z) = \dfrac{x}{x^2 + y^2} \qquad H_y(x, y, z) = \dfrac{y}{x^2 + y^2} \qquad H_z(x, y, z) = -1$

$H_x(3, 4, \ln 5) = \dfrac{3}{25} \qquad H_y(3, 4, \ln 5) = \dfrac{4}{25} \qquad H_z(3, 4, \ln 5) = -1$

$\dfrac{3}{25}(x - 3) + \dfrac{4}{25}(y - 4) - (z - \ln 5) = 0$

$3(x - 3) + 4(y - 4) - 25(z - \ln 5) = 0$

$3x + 4y - 25z = 25(1 - \ln 5)$

21. $x^2 + 4y^2 + z^2 = 36,\ (2, -2, 4)$

$F(x, y, z) = x^2 + 4y^2 + z^2 - 36$

$F_x(x, y, z) = 2x \qquad F_y(x, y, z) = 8y \qquad F_z(x, y, z) = 2z$

$F_x(2, -2, 4) = 4 \qquad F_y(2, -2, 4) = -16 \qquad F_z(2, -2, 4) = 8$

$4(x - 2) - 16(y + 2) + 8(z - 4) = 0$

$(x - 2) - 4(y + 2) + 2(z - 4) = 0$

$x - 4y + 2z = 18$

23. $xy^2 + 3x - z^2 = 4$

Let $F(x, y, z) = xy^2 + 3x - z^2 - 4$. Then $\nabla F(2, 1, -2)$ is normal to the tangent plane at $(2, 1, -2)$.

$\nabla F(x, y, z) = F_x(x, y, z)\mathbf{i} + F_y(x, y, z)\mathbf{j} + F_z(x, y, z)\mathbf{k}$

$\qquad = (y^2 + 3)\mathbf{i} + 2xy\,\mathbf{j} - 2z\mathbf{k}$

$\nabla F(2, 1, -2) = 4\mathbf{i} + 4\mathbf{j} + 4\mathbf{k}$

Therefore, the equation of the tangent plane is

$4(x - 2) + 4(y - 1) + 4(z + 2) = 0$

$x + y + z = 1.$

25. $x^2 + y^2 + z = 9$

Let $F(x, y, z) = x^2 + y^2 + z - 9$. Then $\nabla F(1, 2, 4)$ is normal to the surface at $(1, 2, 4)$.

$\quad \nabla F(x, y, z) = F_x(x, y, z)\mathbf{i} + F_y(x, y, z)\mathbf{j} + F_z(x, y, z)\mathbf{k} = 2x\mathbf{i} + 2y\mathbf{j} + \mathbf{k}$

$\quad \nabla F(1, 2, 4) = 2\mathbf{i} + 4\mathbf{j} + \mathbf{k}$

Therefore, the equation of the tangent plane is

$\quad 2(x - 1) + 4(y - 2) + 1(z - 4) = 0$

$\qquad\qquad\qquad 2x + 4y + z = 14.$

Since the normal line to the surface at $(1, 2, 4)$ is parallel to $\nabla F(1, 2, 4)$, the direction numbers for the line are 2, 4, and 1. Therefore, symmetric equations for a normal line at $(1, 2, 4)$ are

$\quad \dfrac{x - 1}{2} = \dfrac{y - 2}{4} = \dfrac{z - 4}{1}.$

27. $xy - z = 0, \ (-2, -3, 6)$

$\quad F(x, y, z) = xy - z$

$\qquad F_x(x, y, z) = y \qquad\qquad F_y(x, y, z) = x \qquad\qquad F_z(x, y, z) = -1$

$\quad F_x(-2, -3, 6) = -3 \qquad F_y(-2, -3, 6) = -2 \qquad F_z(-2, -3, 6) = -1$

Direction numbers: 3, 2, 1

Plane: $3(x + 2) + 2(y + 3) + (z - 6) = 0, \ 3x + 2y + z = -6$

Line: $\dfrac{x + 2}{3} = \dfrac{y + 3}{2} = \dfrac{z - 6}{1}$

29. $z = \arctan \dfrac{y}{x}$

Let $F(x, y, z) = \arctan(y/x) - z$. Then,

$\quad \nabla F(x, y, z) = F_x(x, y, z)\mathbf{i} + F_y(x, y, z)\mathbf{j} + F_z(x, y, z)\mathbf{k} = \dfrac{-y}{x^2 + y^2}\mathbf{i} + \dfrac{x}{x^2 + y^2}\mathbf{j} - \mathbf{k}$

$\quad \nabla F\left(1, 1, \dfrac{\pi}{4}\right) = -\dfrac{1}{2}\mathbf{i} + \dfrac{1}{2}\mathbf{j} - \mathbf{k} = -\dfrac{1}{2}(\mathbf{i} - \mathbf{j} + 2\mathbf{k}).$

Since $\nabla F(1, 1, \pi/4)$ is normal to the surface at the point $(1, 1, \pi/4)$, an equation of the tangent plane is

$\quad (x - 1) - (y - 1) + 2\left(z - \dfrac{\pi}{4}\right) = 0$

$\qquad\qquad\qquad x - y + 2z = \dfrac{\pi}{2}$

and symmetric equations for the normal line are $\dfrac{x - 1}{1} = \dfrac{y - 1}{-1} = \dfrac{z - (\pi/4)}{2}.$

31. $z = f(x, y) = \dfrac{4xy}{(x^2 + 1)(y^2 + 1)}, \ -2 \le x \le z, \ 0 \le y \le 3$

(a) Let $F(x, y, z) = \dfrac{4xy}{(x^2 + 1)(y^2 + 1)} - z$

$\quad \nabla F(x, y, z) = \dfrac{4y}{y^2 + 1}\left(\dfrac{x^2 + 1 - 2x^2}{(x^2 + 1)^2}\right)\mathbf{i} + \dfrac{4x}{x^2 + 1}\left(\dfrac{y^2 + 1 - 2y^2}{(y^2 + 1)^2}\right)\mathbf{j} - \mathbf{k} = \dfrac{4y(1 - x^2)}{(y^2 + 1)(x^2 + 1)^2}\mathbf{i} + \dfrac{4x(1 - y^2)}{(x^2 + 1)(y^2 + 1)^2}\mathbf{j} - \mathbf{k}$

$\quad \nabla F(1, 1, 1) = -\mathbf{k}.$

Direction numbers: $0, 0, -1$.

Line: $x = 1, \ y = 1, \ z = 1 - t$

Tangent plane: $0(x - 1) + 0(y - 1) - 1(z - 1) = 0 \implies z = 1$

—CONTINUED—

31. **—CONTINUED—**

(b) $\nabla F\left(-1, 2, -\dfrac{4}{5}\right) = 0\mathbf{i} + \dfrac{-4(-3)}{(2)(5)^2}\mathbf{j} - \mathbf{k} = \dfrac{6}{25}\mathbf{j} - \mathbf{k}$

Line: $x = -1, \ y = 2 + \dfrac{6}{25}t, \ z = -\dfrac{4}{5} - t$

Plane: $0(x + 1) + \dfrac{6}{25}(y - 2) - 1\left(z + \dfrac{4}{5}\right) = 0$

$6y - 12 - 25z - 20 = 0$

$6y - 25z - 32 = 0$

(c)

 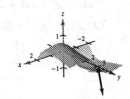

(d) At $(1, 1, 1)$, the tangent plane is parallel to the xy-plane, implying that the surface is level there. At $\left(-1, 2, -\dfrac{4}{5}\right)$, the function does not change in the x-direction.

33. $x^2 + y^2 = 5, z = x$

Let $f(x, y, z) = x^2 + y^2 - 5$ and $g(x, y, z) = x - z$. Then

$\nabla f(x, y, z) = 2x\mathbf{i} + 2y\mathbf{j} \implies \nabla f(2, 1, 2) = 4\mathbf{i} + 2\mathbf{j}$

and

$\nabla g(x, y, z) = \mathbf{i} - \mathbf{k} \implies \nabla g(2, 1, 2) = \mathbf{i} - \mathbf{k}.$

(a) Since ∇f and ∇g are each normal to their respective surfaces, the vector $\nabla f \times \nabla g$ will be tangent to both surfaces at the point $(2, 1, 2)$ on the curve of intersection. Therefore, from

$\nabla f \times \nabla g = \begin{vmatrix} \mathbf{i} & \mathbf{j} & \mathbf{k} \\ 4 & 2 & 0 \\ 1 & 0 & -1 \end{vmatrix} = -2\mathbf{i} + 4\mathbf{j} - 2\mathbf{k}$

$= -2(\mathbf{i} - 2\mathbf{j} + \mathbf{k})$

it follows that direction numbers for the tangent line are $1, -2,$ and 1. Hence, symmetric equations for the tangent line at $(2, 1, 2)$ are

$\dfrac{x - 2}{1} = \dfrac{y - 1}{-2} = \dfrac{z - 2}{1}.$

(b) The angle between ∇f and ∇g at $(2, 1, 2)$ is such that

$\cos \theta = \dfrac{\nabla f \cdot \nabla g}{\|\nabla f\| \|\nabla g\|} = \dfrac{4 + 0 - 0}{\sqrt{20}\sqrt{2}}$

$= \dfrac{4}{\sqrt{40}} = \dfrac{4}{2\sqrt{10}} = \dfrac{\sqrt{10}}{5}.$

Therefore, the surfaces are **not** orthogonal at the point of intersection.

35. $F(x, y, z) = x^2 + z^2 - 25$ $\qquad$ $G(x, y, z) = y^2 + z^2 - 25$

$\nabla F = 2x\mathbf{i} + 2z\mathbf{k}$ $\qquad\qquad$ $\nabla G = 2y\mathbf{j} + 2z\mathbf{k}$

$\nabla F(3, 3, 4) = 6\mathbf{i} + 8\mathbf{k}$ $\qquad$ $\nabla G(3, 3, 4) = 6\mathbf{j} + 8\mathbf{k}$

(a) $\nabla F \times \nabla G = \begin{vmatrix} \mathbf{i} & \mathbf{j} & \mathbf{k} \\ 6 & 0 & 8 \\ 0 & 6 & 8 \end{vmatrix} = -48\mathbf{i} - 48\mathbf{j} + 36\mathbf{k} = -12(4\mathbf{i} + 4\mathbf{j} - 3\mathbf{k})$

Direction numbers: $4, 4, -3, \quad \dfrac{x - 3}{4} = \dfrac{y - 3}{4} = \dfrac{z - 4}{-3}$

(b) $\cos \theta = \dfrac{|\nabla F \cdot \nabla G|}{\|\nabla F\| \|\nabla G\|} = \dfrac{64}{(10)(10)} = \dfrac{16}{25};$ not orthogonal

37. $F(x, y, z) = x^2 + y^2 + z^2 - 6$ $\qquad$ $G(x, y, z) = x - y - z$

$\nabla F(x, y, z) = 2x\mathbf{i} + 2y\mathbf{j} + 2z\mathbf{k}$ $\qquad$ $\nabla G(x, y, z) = \mathbf{i} - \mathbf{j} - \mathbf{k}$

$\nabla F(2, 1, 1) = 4\mathbf{i} + 2\mathbf{j} + 2\mathbf{k}$ $\qquad$ $\nabla G(2, 1, 1) = \mathbf{i} - \mathbf{j} - \mathbf{k}$

(a) $\nabla F \times \nabla G = \begin{vmatrix} \mathbf{i} & \mathbf{j} & \mathbf{k} \\ 4 & 2 & 2 \\ 1 & -1 & -1 \end{vmatrix} = 6\mathbf{j} - 6\mathbf{k} = 6(\mathbf{j} - \mathbf{k})$ $\qquad$ (b) $\cos \theta = \dfrac{|\nabla F \cdot \nabla G|}{\|\nabla F\| \|\nabla G\|} = 0;$ orthogonal

Direction numbers: $0, 1, -1, x = 2, \dfrac{y - 1}{1} = \dfrac{z - 1}{-1}$

39. $f(x, y) = 6 - x^2 - \dfrac{y^2}{4}, \ g(x, y) = 2x + y$

(a) $F(x, y, z) = z + x^2 + \dfrac{y^2}{4} - 6$ $\qquad$ $G(x, y, z) = z - 2x - y$

$\nabla F(x, y, z) = 2x\mathbf{i} + \dfrac{1}{2}y\mathbf{j} + \mathbf{k}$ $\qquad$ $\nabla G(x, y, z) = -2\mathbf{i} - \mathbf{j} + \mathbf{k}$

$\qquad\qquad\qquad\qquad\qquad\qquad\qquad$ $\nabla G(1, 2, 4) = -2\mathbf{i} - \mathbf{j} + \mathbf{k}$

$\nabla F(1, 2, 4) = 2\mathbf{i} + \mathbf{j} + \mathbf{k}$

The cross product of these gradients is parallel to the curve of intersection.

$$\nabla F(1, 2, 4) \times \nabla G(1, 2, 4) = \begin{vmatrix} \mathbf{i} & \mathbf{j} & \mathbf{k} \\ 2 & 1 & 1 \\ -2 & -1 & 1 \end{vmatrix} = 2\mathbf{i} - 4\mathbf{j}$$

Using direction numbers $1, -2, 0,$ you get $x = 1 + t, \ y = 2 - 2t, \ z = 4.$

$$\cos \theta = \frac{\nabla F \cdot \nabla G}{\|\nabla F\| \|\nabla G\|} = \frac{-4 - 1 + 1}{\sqrt{6} \sqrt{6}} = \frac{-4}{6} \implies \theta \approx 48.2°$$

(b)

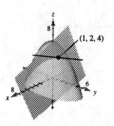

41. If we let

$$F(x, y, z) = 3x^2 + 2y^2 - z - 15$$

then the gradient of F at the point $(2, 2, 5)$ is given by

$$\nabla F(x, y, z) = 6x\mathbf{i} + 4y\mathbf{j} - \mathbf{k}$$

$$\nabla F(2, 2, 5) = 12\mathbf{i} + 8\mathbf{j} - \mathbf{k}$$

Because $\nabla F(2, 2, 5)$ is normal to the tangent plane and $\mathbf{k}$ is normal to the xy-plane, it follows that the angle of inclination of the tangent plane is given by

$$\cos \theta = \frac{|\nabla F(2, 2, 5) \cdot \mathbf{k}|}{\|\nabla F(2, 2, 5)\|}$$

$$= \frac{1}{\sqrt{12^2 + 8^2 + (-1)^2}} = \frac{1}{\sqrt{209}}$$

which implies that

$$\theta = \arccos \frac{1}{\sqrt{209}} \approx 86°.$$

43. $F(x, y, z) = x^2 - y^2 + z, \ (1, 2, 3)$

$$\nabla F(x, y, z) = 2x\mathbf{i} - 2y\mathbf{j} + \mathbf{k}$$

$$\nabla F(1, 2, 3) = 2\mathbf{i} - 4\mathbf{j} + \mathbf{k}$$

$$\cos \theta = \frac{|\nabla F(1, 2, 3) \cdot \mathbf{k}|}{\|\nabla F(1, 2, 3)\|} = \frac{1}{\sqrt{21}}$$

$$\theta = \arccos \frac{1}{\sqrt{21}} \approx 77.40°$$

45. $F(x, y, z) = 3 - x^2 - y^2 + 6y - z$

$\nabla F(x, y, z) = -2x\mathbf{i} + (-2y + 6)\mathbf{j} - \mathbf{k}$

$-2x = 0, \ x = 0$

$-2y + 6 = 0, \ y = 3$

$z = 3 - 0^2 - 3^2 + 6(3) = 12$

$(0, 3, 12)$ (vertex of paraboloid)

47. $T(x, y, z) = 400 - 2x^2 - y^2 - 4z^2, \ (4, 3, 10)$

$\dfrac{dx}{dt} = -4kx \qquad \dfrac{dy}{dt} = -2ky \qquad \dfrac{dz}{dt} = -8kz$

$x(t) = C_1 e^{-4kt} \qquad y(t) = C_2 e^{-2kt} \qquad z(t) = C_3 e^{-8kt}$

$x(0) = C_1 = 4 \qquad y(0) = C_2 = 3 \qquad z(0) = C_3 = 10$

$x = 4e^{-4kt} \qquad y = 3e^{-2kt} \qquad z = 10e^{-8kt}$

49. $\dfrac{x^2}{a^2} + \dfrac{y^2}{b^2} + \dfrac{z^2}{c^2} = 1$

We let $F(x, y, z) = \dfrac{x^2}{a^2} + \dfrac{y^2}{b^2} + \dfrac{z^2}{c^2} - 1$. Then

$\nabla F(x, y, z) = F_x(x, y, z)\mathbf{i} + F_y(x, y, z)\mathbf{j} + F_z(x, y, z)\mathbf{k}$

$\qquad = \dfrac{2x}{a^2}\mathbf{i} + \dfrac{2y}{b^2}\mathbf{j} + \dfrac{2z}{c^2}\mathbf{k}$

$\nabla F(x_0, y_0, z_0) = 2\left[\dfrac{x_0}{a^2}\mathbf{i} + \dfrac{y_0}{b^2}\mathbf{j} + \dfrac{z_0}{c^2}\mathbf{k}\right].$

Now since $\nabla F(x_0, y_0, z_0)$ is normal to the surface at the point (x_0, y_0, z_0), an equation of the tangent plane is

$$\dfrac{x_0}{a^2}(x - x_0) + \dfrac{y_0}{b^2}(y - y_0) + \dfrac{z_0}{c^2}(z - z_0) = 0$$

$$\left[\dfrac{x_0 x}{a^2} + \dfrac{y_0 y}{b^2} + \dfrac{z_0 z}{c^2}\right] - \left[\dfrac{x_0^2}{a^2} + \dfrac{y_0^2}{b^2} + \dfrac{z_0^2}{c^2}\right] = 0$$

$$\left[\dfrac{x_0 x}{a^2} + \dfrac{y_0 y}{b^2} + \dfrac{z_0 z}{c^2}\right] - 1 = 0$$

$$\dfrac{x_0 x}{a^2} + \dfrac{y_0 y}{b^2} + \dfrac{z_0 z}{c^2} = 1.$$

51. $F(x, y, z) = a^2 x^2 + b^2 y^2 - z^2$

$F_x(x, y, z) = 2a^2 x$

$F_y(x, y, z) = 2b^2 y$

$F_z(x, y, z) = -2z$

Plane: $2a^2 x_0(x - x_0) + 2b^2 y_0(y - y_0) - 2z_0(z - z_0) = 0$

$\qquad a^2 x_0 x + b^2 y_0 y - z_0 z = a^2 x_0^2 + b^2 y_0^2 - z_0^2 = 0$

Hence, the plane passes through the origin.

53. $f(x, y) = e^{x-y}$

$f_x(x, y) = e^{x-y}, \qquad\qquad f_y(x, y) = -e^{x-y}$

$f_{xx}(x, y) = e^{x-y}, \qquad\qquad f_{yy}(x, y) = e^{x-y}, \qquad\qquad f_{xy}(x, y) = -e^{x-y}$

(a) $P_1(x, y) \approx f(0, 0) + f_x(0, 0)x + f_y(0, 0)y = 1 + x - y$

(b) $P_2(x, y) \approx f(0, 0) + f_x(0, 0)x + f_y(0,0)y + \frac{1}{2}f_{xx}(0, 0)x^2 + f_{xy}(0, 0)xy + \frac{1}{2}f_{yy}(0, 0)y^2$

$\qquad = 1 + x - y + \frac{1}{2}x^2 - xy + \frac{1}{2}y^2$

(c) If $x = 0$, $P_2(0, y) = 1 - y + \frac{1}{2}y^2$. This is the second-degree Taylor polynomial for e^{-y}.

     If $y = 0$, $P_2(x, 0) = 1 + x + \frac{1}{2}x^2$. This is the second-degree Taylor polynomial for e^x.

(d)

x	y	$f(x, y)$	$P_1(x, y)$	$P_2(x, y)$
0	0	1	1	1
0	0	0.9048	0.9000	0.9050
0.2	0.1	1.1052	1.1000	1.1050
0.2	0.5	0.7408	0.7000	0.7450
1	0.5	1.6487	1.5000	1.6250

(e)

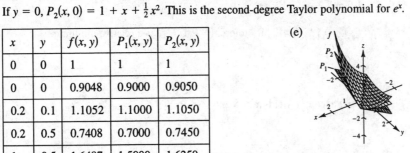

Section 12.8   Extrema of Functions of Two Variables

1. $g(x, y) = (x - 1)^2 + (y - 3)^2 \geq 0$

Relative minimum: $(1, 3, 0)$

$g_x = 2(x - 1) = 0 \implies x = 1$

$g_y = 2(y - 3) = 0 \implies y = 3$

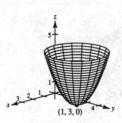

$(1, 3, 0)$

3. $f(x, y) = \sqrt{x^2 + y^2 + 1} \geq 1$

Relative minimum: $(0, 0, 1)$

Check: $f_x = \dfrac{x}{\sqrt{x^2 + y^2 + 1}} = 0 \implies x = 0$

$f_y = \dfrac{y}{\sqrt{x^2 + y^2 + 1}} = 0 \implies y = 0$

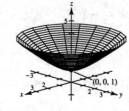

$(0, 0, 1)$

$f_{xx} = \dfrac{y^2 + 1}{(x^2 + y^2 + 1)^{3/2}}, \ f_{yy} = \dfrac{x^2 + 1}{(x^2 + y^2 + 1)^{3/2}}, \ f_{xy} = \dfrac{-xy}{(x^2 + y^2 + 1)^{3/2}}$

At the critical point $(0, 0)$, $f_{xx} > 0$ and $f_{xx} f_{yy} - (f_{xy})^2 > 0$. Therefore, $(0, 0, 1)$ is a relative minimum.

5. $f(x, y) = x^2 + y^2 + 2x - 6y + 6$

$\qquad = (x^2 + 2x + \underline{}) + (y^2 - 6y + \underline{}) + 6 - \underline{} - \underline{}$

$\qquad = (x^2 + 2x + 1) \ + (y^2 - 6y + 9) \ + 6 - 1 - 9$

$\qquad = (x + 1)^2 + (y - 3)^2 - 4 \geq -4.$

The relative minimum of f is $f(-1, 3) = -4$. Using partial derivatives to find any critical points and test for relative extrema.

$\qquad f_x(x, y) = 2x + 2 = 0$ when $x = -1$

$\qquad f_y(x, y) = 2y - 6 = 0$ when $y = 3$

$\qquad f_{xx}(x, y) = 2$

$\qquad f_{yy}(x, y) = 2$

$\qquad f_{xy}(x, y) = 0$

At the critical point $(-1, 3)$, $f_{xx} > 0$, $f_{yy} > 0$, and $f_{xx} f_{yy} - (f_{xy})^2 > 0$. Therefore, $(-1, 3, -4)$ is a relative minimum.

7. $f(x, y) = 2x^2 + 2xy + y^2 + 2x - 3$

$\left.\begin{array}{l} f_x = 4x + 2y + 2 = 0 \\ f_y = 2x + 2y = 0 \end{array}\right\}$ Solving simultaneously yields $x = -1$ and $y = 1$.

$f_{xx} = 4, \ f_{yy} = 2, \ f_{xy} = 2$

At the critical point $(-1, 1)$, $f_{xx} > 0$ and $f_{xx} f_{yy} - (f_{xy})^2 > 0$. Therefore, $(-1, 1, -4)$ is a relative minimum.

9. $f(x, y) = -5x^2 + 4xy - y^2 + 16x + 10$

$\left.\begin{array}{l} f_x = -10x + 4y + 16 = 0 \\ f_y = 4x - 2y = 0 \end{array}\right\}$ Solving simultaneously yields $x = 8$ and $y = 16$.

$f_{xx} = -10, \ f_{yy} = -2, \ f_{xy} = 4$

At the critical point $(8, 16)$, $f_{xx} < 0$ and $f_{xx} f_{yy} - (f_{xy})^2 > 0$. Therefore, $(8, 16, 74)$ is a relative maximum.

11. $f(x, y) = 2x^2 + 3y^2 - 4x - 12y + 13$

$f_x = 4x - 4 = 4(x - 1) = 0$ when $x = 1$.

$f_y = 6y - 12 = 6(y - 2) = 0$ when $y = 2$.

$f_{xx} = 4, f_{yy} = 6, f_{xy} = 0$

At the critical point $(1, 2), f_{xx} > 0$ and $f_{xx} f_{yy} - (f_{xy})^2 > 0$. Therefore, $(1, 2, -1)$ is a relative minimum.

13. $h(x, y) = x^2 - y^2 - 2x - 4y - 4$

Since $h_x(x, y) = 2x - 2 = 2(x - 1) = 0$ when $x = 1$ and $h_y(x, y) = -2y - 4 = -2(y + 2) = 0$ when $y = -2$, there is one critical point, $(1, -2)$. Since

$$h_{xx}(x, y) = 2, h_{yy}(x, y) = -2, \text{ and } h_{xy}(x, y) = 0,$$

we have

$$d = h_{xx}(1, -2)h_{yy}(1, -2) - [h_{xy}(1, -2)]^2 = -4 - 0 = -4 < 0.$$

Therefore, by part 3 of Theorem 12.17, we conclude that there is a saddle point at $(1, -2, -1)$.

15. $h(x, y) = x^2 - 3xy - y^2$

$\left. \begin{array}{l} h_x = 2x - 3y = 0 \\ h_y = -3x - 2y = 0 \end{array} \right\}$ Solving simultaneously yields $x = 0$ and $y = 0$.

$h_{xx} = 2, h_{yy} = -2, h_{xy} = -3$

At the critical point $(0, 0), h_{xx} h_{yy} - (h_{xy})^2 < 0$. Therefore, $(0, 0, 0)$ is a saddle point.

17. $f(x, y) = x^3 - 3xy + y^3$

Since $f_x(x, y) = 3x^2 - 3y$ and $f_y(x, y) = -3x + 3y^2$, any critical points must be the simultaneous solutions of the system of equations

$$3x^2 - 3y = 0 \quad \text{and} \quad 3y^2 - 3x = 0.$$

From the first equation it follows that $y = x^2$. Making this substitution for y in the second equation yields

$$3(x^2)^2 - 3x = 0$$

$$x^4 - x = 0$$

$$x(x^3 - 1) = 0.$$

Therefore, the critical points are $(0, 0)$ and $(1, 1)$. Since

$$f_{xx}(x, y) = 6x, f_{yy}(x, y) = 6y, f_{xy}(x, y) = -3,$$

we have

$$f_{xx}(0, 0) = 0 \quad \text{and} \quad d = f_{xx}(0, 0)f_{yy}(0, 0) - [f_{xy}(0, 0)]^2 = 0 - 9 < 0.$$

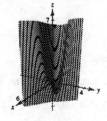

Therefore, by Theorem 12.17, we can conclude that $(0, 0, 0)$ is a saddle point of f. At $(1, 1)$ we have

$$f(1, 1) = -1, f_{xx}(1, 1) = 6 > 0, \quad \text{and} \quad d = f_{xx}(1, 1)f_{yy}(1, 1) - [f_{xy}(1, 1)]^2 = (6)(6) - 9 > 0.$$

By Theorem 12.17, the point $(1, 1, -1)$ is a relative minimum.

19. $f(x, y) = e^{-x} \sin y$

$\left. \begin{array}{l} f_x = -e^{-x} \sin y = 0 \\ f_y = e^{-x} \cos y = 0 \end{array} \right\}$ Since $e^{-x} > 0$ for all x and $\sin y$ and $\cos y$ are never both zero for a given value of y, there are no critical points.

21. $z = \dfrac{-4x}{x^2 + y^2 + 1}$

Relative minimum: $(1, 0, -2)$

Relative maximum: $(-1, 0, 2)$

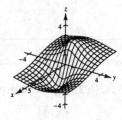

23. $f(x, y) = y^3 - 3yx^2 - 3y^2 - 3x^2 + 1$

Relative maximum: $(0, 0, 1)$

Saddle points: $(0, 2, -3), (\pm\sqrt{3}, -1, -3)$

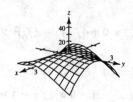

25. $f_{xx}f_{yy} - (f_{xy})^2 = (9)(4) - 6^2 = 0$

Insufficient information

27. At the critical point (x_0, y_0),

$$f_{xx}(x_0, y_0)f_{yy}(x_0, y_0) - [f_{xy}(x_0, y_0)]^2 = (-9)(6) - 10^2 < 0.$$

Therefore, $(x_0, y_0, f(x_0, y_0))$ is a saddle point.

29.

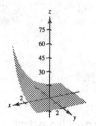

No extrema

31.

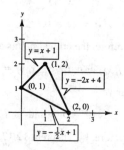

Saddle point

33. $d = f_{xx}f_{yy} - f_{xy}{}^2 = (2)(8) - f_{xy}{}^2 = 16 - f_{xy}{}^2 > 0$

$\Rightarrow f_{xy}{}^2 < 16 \Rightarrow -4 < f_{xy} < 4$

35. $f(x, y) = 12 - 3x - 2y$ has no critical points. On the line $y = x + 1, 0 \le x \le 1$,

$$f(x, y) = f(x) = 12 - 3x - 2(x + 1) = -5x + 10$$

and the maximum is 10, the minimum is 5. On the line $y = -2x + 4, 1 \le x \le 2$,

$$f(x, y) = f(x) = 12 - 3x - 2(-2x + 4) = x + 4$$

and the maximum is 6, the minimum is 5. On the line $y = -\frac{1}{2}x + 1, 0 \le x \le 2$,

$$f(x, y) = f(x) = 12 - 3x - 2\left(-\frac{1}{2}x + 1\right) = -2x + 10$$

and the maximum is 10, the minimum is 6.

Absolute maximum: 10 at $(0, 1)$

Absolute minimum: 5 at $(1, 2)$

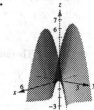

37. $f(x, y) = 3x^2 + 2y^2 - 4y$

$\left.\begin{array}{l} f_x = 6x = 0 \quad\Rightarrow x = 0 \\ f_y = 4y - 4 = 0 \Rightarrow y = 1 \end{array}\right\} f(0, 1) = -2$

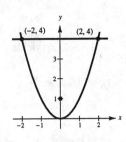

On the line $y = 4, -2 \le x \le 2$,

$$f(x, y) = f(x) = 3x^2 + 32 - 16 = 3x^2 + 16$$

and the maximum is 28, the minimum is 16. On the curve $y = x^2, -2 \le x \le 2$,

$$f(x, y) = f(x) = 3x^2 + 2(x^2)^2 - 4x^2 = 2x^4 - x^2 = x^2(2x^2 - 1)$$

and the maximum is 28, the minimum is $-\frac{1}{8}$.

Absolute maximum: 28 at $(\pm 2, 4)$

Absolute minimum: -2 at $(0, 1)$

39. $f(x, y) = x^2 + xy, R = \{(x, y): |x| \le 2, |y| \le 1\}$

$\left.\begin{array}{l} f_x = 2x + y = 0 \\ f_y = x = 0 \end{array}\right\} x = y = 0$

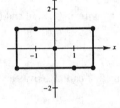

$f(0, 0) = 0$

Along $y = 1, -2 \le x \le 2, f = x^2 + x, f' = 2x + 1 = 0 \Rightarrow x = -\frac{1}{2}$.

Thus, $f(-2, 1) = 2, f\left(-\frac{1}{2}, 1\right) = -\frac{1}{4}$ and $f(2, 1) = 6$.

Along $y = -1, -2 \le x \le 2, f = x^2 - x, f' = 2x - 1 = 0 \Rightarrow x = \frac{1}{2}$.

Thus, $f(-2, -1) = 6, f\left(\frac{1}{2}, -1\right) = -\frac{1}{4}, f(2, -1) = 2$.

Along $x = 2, -1 \le y \le 1, f = 4 + 2y \Rightarrow f' = 2 \ne 0$.

Along $x = -2, -1 \le y \le 1, f = 4 - 2y \Rightarrow f' = -2 \ne 0$.

Thus, the maxima are $f(2, 1) = 6$ and $f(-2, -1) = 6$ and the minima are $f\left(-\frac{1}{2}, 1\right) = -\frac{1}{4}$ and $f\left(\frac{1}{2}, -1\right) = -\frac{1}{4}$.

41. $f(x, y) = x^2 + 2xy + y^2, R = \{(x, y): x^2 + y^2 \le 8\}$

$\left.\begin{array}{l} f_x = 2x + 2y = 0 \\ f_y = 2x + 2y = 0 \end{array}\right\} y = -x$

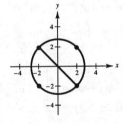

$f(x, -x) = x^2 - 2x^2 + x^2 = 0$

On the boundary $x^2 + y^2 = 8$, we have $y^2 = 8 - x^2$ and $y = \pm\sqrt{8 - x^2}$. Thus

$$f = x^2 \pm 2x\sqrt{8 - x^2} + (8 - x^2) = 8 \pm 2x\sqrt{8 - x^2}$$

$$f' = \pm(x(8 - x^2)^{-1/2}(-2x) + 2(8 - x^2)^{1/2}) = \pm\frac{16 - 4x^2}{\sqrt{8 - x^2}}.$$

Then, $f' = 0$ implies $16 = 4x^2$ or $x = \pm 2$. Thus, the maxima are $f(2, 2) = 16$ and $f(-2, -2) = 16$, and the minima are $f(x, -x) = 0, |x| \le 2$.

43. $f(x, y) = \dfrac{4xy}{(x^2 + 1)(y^2 + 1)}, R = \{(x, y): 0 \le x \le 1, 0 \le y \le 1\}$

$$f_x = \frac{4(1 - x^2)y}{(y^2 + 1)(x^2 + 1)} = 0 \Rightarrow x = 1 \text{ or } y = 0$$

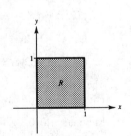

$$f_y = \frac{4(1 - y^2)x}{(x^2 + 1)(y^2 + 1)^2} \Rightarrow x = 0 \text{ or } y = 1$$

For $x = 0, y = 0$, also, and $f(0, 0) = 0$.

For $x = 1, y = 1, f(1, 1) = 1$.

The absolute maximum is $1 = f(1, 1)$.

The absolute minimum is $0 = f(0, 0)$. (In fact, $f(0, y) = f(x, 0) = 0$)

45. $f(x, y) = x^3 + y^3$

$\left.\begin{array}{l} f_x = 3x^2 = 0 \\ f_y = 3y^2 = 0 \end{array}\right\}$ Solving yields $x = y = 0$.

$f_{xx} = 6x,\ f_{yy} = 6y,\ f_{xy} = 0$

At $(0, 0), f_{xx} f_{yy} - (f_{xy})^2 = 0$ and the test fails. $(0, 0, 0)$ is a saddle point.

47. $f(x, y) = (x - 1)^2(y + 4)^2 \geq 0$

$\left.\begin{array}{l} f_x = 2(x - 1)(y + 4)^2 = 0 \\ f_y = 2(x - 1)^2(y + 4) = 0 \end{array}\right\}$ Solving yields the critical points $(1, a)$ and $(b, -4)$.

$f_{xx} = 2(y + 4)^2, f_{yy} = 2(x - 1)^2, f_{xy} = 4(x - 1)(y + 4)$

At both $(1, a)$ and $(b, -4), f_{xx} f_{yy} - (f_{xy})^2 = 0$ and the test fails.

Absolute minima: $(1, a, 0)$ and $(b, -4, 0)$

49. $f(x, y) = x^{2/3} + y^{2/3}$

From the first partial derivatives we have

$$f_x(x, y) = \frac{2}{3}x^{-1/3} = \frac{2}{3\sqrt[3]{x}} \quad \text{and} \quad f_y(x, y) = \frac{2}{3}y^{-1/3} = \frac{2}{3\sqrt[3]{y}}.$$

Since neither first partial derivative exists at $(0, 0)$, it is a critical point. Moreover,

$$f_{xx}(x, y) = -\frac{2}{9x\sqrt[3]{x}} \quad \text{and} \quad f_{yy}(x, y) = -\frac{2}{9x\sqrt[3]{x}}$$

do not exist at $(0, 0)$ and thus the Second-Partials Test fails. Since $x^{2/3} + y^{2/3} \geq 0$ for all x and y, it follows that the absolute minimum of f is $f(0, 0) = 0$.

51. $f(x, y, z) = x^2 + (y - 3)^2 + (z + 1)^2 \geq 0$

$\left.\begin{array}{l} f_x = 2x = 0 \\ f_y = 2(y - 3) = 0 \\ f_z = 2(z + 1) = 0 \end{array}\right\}$ Solving yields the critical point $(0, 3, -1)$.

Absolute minimum: $(0, 3, -1, 0)$

53. The point A will be a saddle point. The function could be $f(x, y) = x^2 - y^2$.

55. (a) When $\alpha = 1$ and $\beta = 2$, we have

$$f(x, y) = (x^2 + 2y^2)e^{-(x^2 + y^2)}$$

$$f_x(x, y) = -2xe^{-(x^2 + y^2)}(x^2 + 2y^2 - 1)$$

$$f_y(x, y) = -2ye^{-(x^2 + y^2)}(x^2 + 2y^2 - 2)$$

The critical points are $(0, 0)$, $(\pm 1, 0)$, and $(0, \pm 1)$. Using the graph of the function and the critical points, we have the following.

Minimum: $(0, 0, 0)$
Maxima: $(0, \pm 1, 2e^{-1})$
Saddle points: $(\pm 1, 0, e^{-1})$

—CONTINUED—

55. —CONTINUED—

(b) When $\alpha = -1$ and $\beta = 2$, we have

$$f(x, y) = (-x^2 + 2y^2)e^{-(x^2+y^2)}$$

$$f_x(x, y) = 2xe^{-(x^2+y^2)}(x^2 - 2y^2 - 1)$$

$$f_y(x, y) = 2ye^{-(x^2+y^2)}(x^2 - 2y^2 + 2)$$

The critical points are $(0, 0)$, $(\pm 1, 0)$, and $(0, \pm 1)$. Using the graph of the function and the critical points, we have the following.

Minima: $(\pm 1, 0, -e^{-1})$

Maxima: $(0, \pm 1, 2e^{-1})$

Saddle point: $(0, 0, 0)$

(c) $f(x, y) = (\alpha x^2 + \beta y^2)e^{-(x^2+y^2)}$

$$f_x(x, y) = -2xe^{-(x^2+y^2)}(\alpha x^2 + \beta y^2 - \alpha)$$

$$f_y(x, y) = -2ye^{-(x^2+y^2)}(\alpha x^2 + \beta y^2 - \beta)$$

$$f_{xx}(x, y) = 2e^{-(x^2+y^2)}(2\alpha x^4 + 2\beta x^2y^2 - 5\alpha x^2 - \beta y^2 + \alpha)$$

$$f_{yy}(x, y) = 2e^{-(x^2+y^2)}(2\alpha x^2y^2 - \alpha x^2 + 2\beta y^4 - 5\beta y^2 + \beta)$$

$$f_{xy}(x, y) = 4xye^{-(x^2+y^2)}(\alpha x^2 + \beta y^2 - \alpha - \beta)$$

The critical points are $(0, 0)$, $(\pm 1, 0)$, and $(0, \pm 1)$. For the case where $\alpha > 0$ and $0 < |\alpha| < \beta$, we have the following.

$f_{xx}(0, 0) = 2\alpha > 0$ $f_{xx}(0, \pm 1) = 2e^{-1}(-\beta + \alpha) < 0$

$f_{yy}(0, 0) = 2\beta > 0$ $f_{yy}(0, \pm 1) = 2e^{-1}(-2\beta) < 0$

$f_{xy}(0, 0) = 0$ $f_{xy}(0, 0) = 0$

$d = f_{xx}f_{yy} - (f_{xy})^2 > 0$ $d = f_{xx}f_{yy} - (f_{xy})^2 > 0$

Therefore, $(0, 0, 0)$ is a minimum.   Therefore, $(0, \pm 1, \beta e^{-1})$ are maxima.

$f_{xx}(\pm 1, 0) = (2e^{-1})(-2\alpha) < 0$

$f_{yy}(\pm 1, 0) = 2e^{-1}(-\alpha + \beta) > 0$

$f_{xy}(0, 0) = 0$

$d = f_{xx}f_{yy} - (f_{xy})^2 < 0$

Therefore, $(\pm 1, 0, \alpha e^{-1})$ are saddle points.

For the case where $\alpha < 0$ and $0 < |\alpha| < \beta$, we have the following.

$f_{xx}(0, 0) = 2\alpha < 0$ $f_{xx}(0, \pm 1) = 2e^{-1}(-\beta + \alpha) < 0$

$f_{yy}(0, 0) = 2\beta > 0$ $f_{yy}(0, \pm 1) = 2e^{-1}(-2\beta) < 0$

$f_{xy}(0, 0) = 0$ $f_{xy}(0, 0) = 0$

$d = f_{xx}f_{yy} - (f_{xy})^2 < 0$ $d = f_{xx}f_{yy} - (f_{xy})^2 > 0$

Therefore, $(0, 0, 0)$ is a saddle point.   Therefore, $(0, \pm 1, \beta e^{-1})$ are maxima.

$f_{xx}(\pm 1, 0) = (2e^{-1})(-2\alpha) > 0$

$f_{yy}(\pm 1, 0) = 2e^{-1}(-\alpha + \beta) > 0$

$f_{xy}(0, 0) = 0$

$d = f_{xx}f_{yy} - (f_{xy})^2 > 0$

Therefore, $(\pm 1, 0, \alpha e^{-1})$ are minima.

57. False

Let $f(x, y) = |1 - x - y|$.

$(0, 0, 1)$ is a relative maximum, but $f_x(0, 0)$ and $f_y(0, 0)$ do not exist.

59. False

Let $f(x, y) = x^4 - 2x^2 + y^2$.

Relative minima: $(\pm 1, 0, -1)$

Saddle point: $(0, 0, 0)$

Section 12.9   Applications of Extrema of Functions of Two Variables

1. A point on the plane is given by $(x, y, 12 - 2x - 3y)$. The square of the distance from the origin to this point is

$$S = x^2 + y^2 + (12 - 2x - 3y)^2$$

$$S_x = 2x + 2(12 - 2x - 3y)(-2)$$

$$S_y = 2y + 2(12 - 2x - 3y)(-3)$$

From the equations $S_x = 0$ and $S_y = 0$, we obtain the system

$$5x + 6y = 24$$

$$3x + 5y = 18.$$

Solving simultaneously, we have $x = \frac{12}{7}$, $y = \frac{18}{7}$, $z = 12 - \frac{24}{7} - \frac{54}{7} = \frac{6}{7}$. Therefore, the distance from the origin to $\left(\frac{12}{7}, \frac{18}{7}, \frac{6}{7}\right)$ is

$$\sqrt{\left(\frac{12}{7}\right)^2 + \left(\frac{18}{7}\right)^2 + \left(\frac{6}{7}\right)^2} = \frac{6\sqrt{14}}{7}.$$

3. A point on the paraboloid is given by $(x, y, x^2 + y^2)$. The square of the distance from $(5, 5, 0)$ to a point on the paraboloid is given by

$$S = (x - 5)^2 + (y - 5)^2 + (x^2 + y^2)^2$$

$$S_x = 2(x - 5) + 4x(x^2 + y^2) = 0$$

$$S_y = 2(y - 5) + 4y(x^2 + y^2) = 0.$$

From the equations $S_x = 0$ and $S_y = 0$, we obtain the system

$$2x^3 + 2xy^2 + x - 5 = 0$$

$$2y^3 + 2x^2y + y - 5 = 0$$

Multiply the first equation by y and the second equation by x, and subtract to obtain $x = y$. Then, we have $x = 1$, $y = 1$, $z = 2$ and the distance is

$$\sqrt{(1 - 5)^2 + (1 - 5)^2 + (2 - 0)^2} = 6.$$

5. Let x, y and z be the numbers. Since $x + y + z = 30$, $z = 30 - x - y$.

$$P = xyz = 30xy - x^2y - xy^2$$

$$\left. \begin{array}{l} P_x = 30y - 2xy - y^2 = y(30 - 2x - y) = 0 \\ P_y = 30x - x^2 - 2xy = x(30 - x - 2y) = 0 \end{array} \right\} \begin{array}{l} 2x + y = 30 \\ x + 2y = 30 \end{array}$$

Solving simultaneously yields $x = 10$, $y = 10$, and $z = 10$.

7. Let x, y, and z be the numbers and let $s = x^2 + y^2 + z^2$. Since $x + y + z = 30$, it is necessary to minimize

$$s = x^2 + y^2 + (30 - x - y)^2.$$

Setting the first partial derivatives equal to zero yields

$$s_x = 2x - 2(30 - x - y) = 0 \implies 2x + y = 30$$

$$s_y = 2y - 2(30 - x - y) = 0 \implies 2x + 4y = 60$$

Subtracting the first equation from the second we obtain the equation $3y = 30$ or $y = 10$. Substituting this value into the previous equations and solving yields the critical values $x = y = z = 10$. These values give us the desired minimum, since

$$s_{xx}(10, 10) = 4 > 0 \quad \text{and} \quad s_{xx}(10, 10)s_{yy}(10, 10) - [s_{xy}(10, 10)]^2 = (4)(4) - 2^2 > 0.$$

9. Let x, y, and z be the length, width, and height, respectively. Then the sum of the length and girth is given by $x + (2y + 2z) = 108$ or $x = 108 - 2y - 2z$. The volume is given by

$$V = xyz = 108zy - 2zy^2 - 2yz^2$$

$$V_y = 108z - 4yz - 2z^2 = z(108 - 4y - 2z) = 0$$

$$V_z = 108y - 2y^2 - 4yz = y(108 - 2y - 4z) = 0.$$

Solving the system $4y + 2z = 108$ and $2y + 4z = 108$, we obtain the solution $x = 36$ inches, $y = 18$ inches, and $z = 18$ inches.

11. Let $a + b + c = k$. Then

$$V = \frac{4\pi\, abc}{3} = \frac{4}{3}\pi\, ab(k - a - b) = \frac{4}{3}\pi(kab - a^2b - ab^2)$$

$$V_a = \frac{4\pi}{3}(kb - 2ab - b^2) = 0 \left.\vphantom{\frac{4\pi}{3}}\right\} \; kb - 2ab - b^2 = 0$$

$$V_b = \frac{4\pi}{3}(ka - a^2 - 2ab) = 0 \left.\vphantom{\frac{4\pi}{3}}\right\} \; ka - a^2 - 2ab = 0.$$

Solving this system simultaneously yields $a = b$ and substitution yields $b = k/3$. Therefore, the solution is $a = b = c = k/3$.

13. Let x, y, and z be the length, width, and height, respectively and let V_0 be the given volume. Then $V_0 = xyz$ and $z = V_0/xy$. The surface area is

$$S = 2xy + 2yz + 2xz = 2\left(xy + \frac{V_0}{x} + \frac{V_0}{y}\right)$$

$$S_x = 2\left(y - \frac{V_0}{x^2}\right) = 0 \left.\vphantom{\frac{V_0}{x^2}}\right\} \; x^2y - V_0 = 0$$

$$S_y = 2\left(x - \frac{V_0}{y^2}\right) = 0 \left.\vphantom{\frac{V_0}{y^2}}\right\} \; xy^2 - V_0 = 0.$$

Solving simultaneously yields $x = \sqrt[3]{V_0}$, $y = \sqrt[3]{V_0}$, and $z = \sqrt[3]{V_0}$.

15. $C = (\text{cost per mile})(\text{distance from } P \text{ to } Q) + (\text{cost per mile})(\text{distance from } Q \text{ to } R) + (\text{cost per mile})(\text{distance from } R \text{ to } S)$

$$= 3k\sqrt{x^2 + 4} + 2k\sqrt{(y - x)^2 + 1} + k(10 - y)$$

Setting the first partials equal to zero yields the system

$$\frac{\partial C}{\partial x} = k\left[\frac{3x}{\sqrt{x^2 + 4}} + \frac{-2(y - x)}{\sqrt{(y - x)^2 + 1}}\right] = 0$$

$$\frac{\partial C}{\partial y} = k\left[\frac{2(y - x)}{\sqrt{(y - x)^2 + 1}} - 1\right] = 0.$$

From the equation $\partial C/\partial y = 0$ we have,

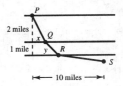

$$\frac{2(y - x)}{\sqrt{(y - x)^2 + 1}} = 1$$

$$2(y - x) = \sqrt{(y - x)^2 + 1}$$

$$4(y - x)^2 = (y - x)^2 + 1$$

$$3(y - x)^2 = 1$$

$$y - x = \pm\frac{1}{\sqrt{3}} \;\Longrightarrow\; y = x \pm \frac{1}{\sqrt{3}}.$$

Substituting the result with the positive root into the equation $\partial C/\partial x = 0$, we obtain

$$\frac{3x}{\sqrt{x^2 + 4}} = \frac{2(y - x)}{\sqrt{(y - x)^2 + 1}}$$

$$\frac{3x}{\sqrt{x^2 + 4}} = \frac{2/\sqrt{3}}{\sqrt{4/3}}$$

$$3x = \sqrt{x^2 + 4}$$

$$9x^2 = x^2 + 4$$

$$8x^2 = 4.$$

Therefore,

$$x = \frac{1}{\sqrt{2}} \approx 0.707 \text{ mile}$$

$$y = x + \frac{\sqrt{3}}{3} = \frac{3\sqrt{2} + 2\sqrt{3}}{6} \approx 1.284 \text{ miles.}$$

17. From the figure observe that the area of a trapezoidal cross section is given by

$$A = h\left[\frac{(w - 2r) + [(w - 2r) + 2x]}{2}\right]$$

$$= (w - 2r + x)h$$

where $x = r \cos\theta$ and $h = r \sin\theta$. Substituting these expressions for x and h, we have

$$A(r, \theta) = (w - 2r + r \cos\theta)(r \sin\theta)$$

$$= wr \sin\theta - 2r^2 \sin\theta + r^2 \sin\theta \cos\theta$$

$$A_r(r, \theta) = w \sin\theta - 4r \sin\theta + 2r \sin\theta \cos\theta$$

$$= \sin\theta(w - 4r + 2r \cos\theta) = 0 \Rightarrow w = r(4 - 2\cos\theta)$$

and

$$A_\theta(r, \theta) = wr \cos\theta - 2r^2 \cos\theta + r^2 \cos 2\theta = 0.$$

Substituting the expression for w from $A_r(r, \theta) = 0$ into the equation $A_\theta(r, \theta) = 0$, yields

$$r^2(4 - 2\cos\theta)\cos\theta - 2r^2 \cos\theta + r^2(2\cos^2\theta - 1) = 0$$

$$r^2(2\cos\theta - 1) = 0 \text{ or } \cos\theta = \frac{1}{2}.$$

The first partial derivatives are zero when $\theta = \pi/3$ and $r = w/3$. (Ignore the solution $r = \theta = 0$.) Thus, the trapezoid of maximum area occurs when each edge of width $w/3$ is turned up 60° from the horizontal.

19. (a) $S(x, y) = d_1 + d_2 + d_3$

$$= \sqrt{(x - 0)^2 + (y - 0)^2} + \sqrt{(x + 2)^2 + (y - 2)^2} + \sqrt{(x - 4)^2 + (y - 2)^2}$$

$$= \sqrt{x^2 + y^2} + \sqrt{(x + 2)^2 + (y - 2)^2} + \sqrt{(x - 4)^2 + (y - 2)^2}$$

From the graph we see that the surface has a minimum.

(b) $S_x(x, y) = \dfrac{x}{\sqrt{x^2 + y^2}} + \dfrac{x + 2}{\sqrt{(x + 2)^2 + (y - 2)^2}} + \dfrac{x - 4}{\sqrt{(x - 4)^2 + (y - 2)^2}}$

$S_y(x, y) = \dfrac{y}{\sqrt{x^2 + y^2}} + \dfrac{y - 2}{\sqrt{(x + 2)^2 + (y - 2)^2}} + \dfrac{y - 2}{\sqrt{(x - 4)^2 + (y - 2)^2}}$

(c) $-\nabla S(1, 1) = -S_x(1, 1)\mathbf{i} - S_y(1, 1)\mathbf{j} = -\dfrac{1}{\sqrt{2}}\mathbf{i} - \left(\dfrac{1}{\sqrt{2}} - \dfrac{2}{\sqrt{10}}\right)\mathbf{j}$

$$\tan\theta = \frac{(2/\sqrt{10}) - (1/\sqrt{2})}{-1/\sqrt{2}} = 1 - \frac{2}{\sqrt{5}} \Rightarrow \theta \approx 186.027°$$

(d) $(x_2, y_2) = (x_1 - S_x(x_1, y_1)t, \ y_1 - S_y(x_1, y_1)t) = \left(1 - \dfrac{1}{\sqrt{2}}t, \ 1 + \left(\dfrac{2}{\sqrt{10}} - \dfrac{1}{\sqrt{2}}\right)t\right)$

$$S\left(1 - \frac{1}{\sqrt{2}}t, 1 + \left(\frac{2}{\sqrt{10}} - \frac{1}{\sqrt{2}}\right)t\right) = \sqrt{2 + \left(\frac{2\sqrt{10}}{5} - 2\sqrt{2}\right)t + \left(1 - \frac{2\sqrt{5}}{5} + \frac{2}{5}\right)t^2} +$$

$$\sqrt{10 - \left(\frac{2\sqrt{10}}{5} + 2\sqrt{2}\right)t + \left(1 - \frac{2\sqrt{5}}{5} + \frac{2}{5}\right)t^2} +$$

$$\sqrt{10 - \left(\frac{2\sqrt{10}}{5} - 4\sqrt{2}\right)t + \left(1 - \frac{2\sqrt{5}}{5} + \frac{2}{5}\right)t^2}$$

Using a computer algebra system, we find that the minimum occurs when $t \approx 1.344$. Thus, $(x_2, y_2) \approx (0.05, 0.90)$.

—CONTINUED—

19. —CONTINUED—

(e) $(x_3, y_3) = (x_2 - S_x(x_2, y_2)t, y_2 - S_y(x_2, y_2)t) \approx (0.05 + 0.03t, 0.90 - 0.26t)$

$S(0.05 + 0.03t, 0.90 - 0.26t) = \sqrt{(0.05 + 0.03t)^2 + (0.90 - 0.26t)^2} + \sqrt{(2.05 + 0.03t)^2 + (-1.10 - 0.26t)^2} +$

$$\sqrt{(-3.95 + 0.03t)^2 + (-1.10 - 0.26t)^2}$$

Using a computer algebra system, we find that the minimum occurs when $t \approx 1.78$. Thus $(x_3, y_3) \approx (0.10, 0.44)$.

$(x_4, y_4) = (x_3 - S_x(x_3, y_3)t, y_3 - S_y(x_3, y_3)t) \approx (0.10 - 0.09t, 0.44 - 0.01t)$

$S(0.10 - 0.09t, 0.45 - 0.01t) = \sqrt{(0.10 - 0.09t)^2 + (0.45 - 0.01t)^2} + \sqrt{(2.10 - 0.09t)^2 + (-1.55 - 0.01t)^2} +$

$$\sqrt{(-3.90 - 0.09t)^2 + (-1.55 - 0.01t)^2}$$

Using a computer algebra system, we find that the minimum occurs when $t \approx 0.44$. Thus, $(x_4, y_4) \approx (0.06, 0.44)$.

Note: The minimum occurs at $(x, y) = (0.0555, 0.3992)$

(f) $-\nabla S(x, y)$ points in the direction that S *decreases* most rapidly. You would use $\nabla S(x, y)$ for maximization problems.

21. $P(x_1, x_2) = 15(x_1 + x_2) - C_1 - C_2$

$\qquad = 15x_1 + 15x_2 - (0.02x_1^2 + 4x_1 + 500) - (0.05x_2^2 + 4x_2 + 275)$

$\qquad = -0.02x_1^2 - 0.05x_2^2 + 11x_1 + 11x_2 - 775$

$\qquad P_{x_1} = -0.04x_1 + 11 = 0, x_1 = 275$

$\qquad P_{x_2} = -0.10x_2 + 11 = 0, x_2 = 110$

$\qquad P_{x_1 x_1} = -0.04$

$\qquad P_{x_1 x_2} = 0$

$\qquad P_{x_2 x_2} = -0.10$

$\qquad P_{x_1 x_1} < 0$ and $P_{x_1 x_1} P_{x_2 x_2} - (P_{x_1 x_2})^2 > 0$

Therefore, profit is maximized when $x_1 = 275$ and $x_2 = 110$.

23. $R(x_1, x_2) = -5x_1^2 - 8x_2^2 - 2x_1 x_2 + 42x_1 + 102x_2$

$\qquad R_{x_1} = -10x_1 - 2x_2 + 42 = 0, \ 5x_1 + x_2 = 21$

$\qquad R_{x_2} = -16x_2 - 2x_1 + 102 = 0, \ x_1 + 8x_2 = 51$

Solving this system yields $x_1 = 3$ and $x_2 = 6$.

$\qquad R_{x_1 x_1} = -10$

$\qquad R_{x_1 x_2} = -2$

$\qquad R_{x_2 x_2} = -16$

$\qquad R_{x_1 x_1} < 0$ and $R_{x_1 x_1} R_{x_2 x_2} - (R_{x_1 x_2})^2 > 0$

Thus, revenue is maximized when $x_1 = 3$ and $x_2 = 6$.

25. (a)

x	y	xy	x^2
-2	0	0	4
0	1	0	0
2	3	6	4
$\sum x_i = 0$	$\sum y_i = 4$	$\sum x_i y_i = 6$	$\sum x_i^2 = 8$

$a = \dfrac{3(6) - 0(4)}{3(8) - 0^2} = \dfrac{3}{4}, \ b = \dfrac{1}{3}\left[4 - \dfrac{3}{4}(0)\right] = \dfrac{4}{3},$

$y = \dfrac{3}{4}x + \dfrac{4}{3}$

(b) $S = \left(-\dfrac{3}{2} + \dfrac{4}{3} - 0\right)^2 + \left(\dfrac{4}{3} - 1\right)^2 + \left(\dfrac{3}{2} + \dfrac{4}{3} - 3\right)^2$

$\quad = \dfrac{1}{6}$

27. (a)

x	y	xy	x^2
0	4	0	0
1	3	3	1
1	1	1	1
2	0	0	4
$\sum x_i = 4$	$\sum y_i = 8$	$\sum x_i y_i = 4$	$\sum x_i^2 = 6$

By Theorem 12.18, we have

$$a = \frac{n \sum x_i y_i - \sum x_i \sum y_i}{n \sum x_i^2 - (\sum x_i)^2} = \frac{4(4) - 4(8)}{4(6) - 4^2} = -2$$

$$b = \frac{1}{n}\left(\sum y_i - a \sum x_i\right) = \frac{1}{4}[8 + 2(4)] = 4.$$

Therefore, the least squares regression line is
$f(x) = -2x + 4.$

(b) $S = \sum [f(x_i) - y_i]^2$

$= (4 - 4)^2 + (2 - 3)^2 + (2 - 1)^2 + (0 - 0)^2 = 2$

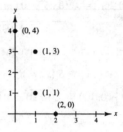

29. $(0, 0), (1, 1), (3, 4), (4, 2), (5, 5)$

$\sum x_i = 13, \qquad \sum y_i = 12,$

$\sum x_i y_i = 46, \qquad \sum x_i^2 = 51$

$a = \dfrac{5(46) - 13(12)}{5(51) - (13)^2} = \dfrac{74}{86} = \dfrac{37}{43}$

$b = \dfrac{1}{5}\left[12 - \dfrac{37}{43}(13)\right] = \dfrac{7}{43}$

$y = \dfrac{37}{43}x + \dfrac{7}{43}$

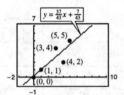

31. $(0, 6), (4, 3), (5, 0), (8, -4), (10, -5)$

$\sum x_i = 27, \qquad \sum y_i = 0,$

$\sum x_i y_i = -70, \qquad \sum x_i^2 = 205$

$a = \dfrac{5(-70) - (27)(0)}{5(205) - (27)^2} = \dfrac{-350}{296} = -\dfrac{175}{148}$

$b = \dfrac{1}{5}\left[0 - \left(-\dfrac{175}{148}\right)(27)\right] = \dfrac{945}{148}$

$y = -\dfrac{175}{148}x + \dfrac{945}{148}$

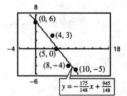

33. (a) $y = 0.03x - 6.29$

(b)

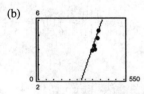

(c) If x increases 1 unit, then y increases

$(0.03)(1) = \$0.03.$

35. $(1.0, 32), (1.5, 41), (2.0, 48), (2.5, 53)$

$\sum x_i = 7, \sum y_i = 174, \sum x_i y_i = 322, \sum x_i^2 = 13.5$

$a = 14, b = 19, y = 14x + 19$

When $x = 1.6$, $y = 41.4$ bushels per acre.

37. $S(a, b, c) = \sum_{i=1}^{n} (y_i - ax_i^2 - bx_i - c)^2$

$\frac{\partial S}{\partial a} = \sum_{i=1}^{n} -2x_i^2(y_i - ax_i^2 - bx_i - c) = 0$

$\frac{\partial S}{\partial b} = \sum_{i=1}^{n} -2x_i(y_i - ax_i^2 - bx_i - c) = 0$

$\frac{\partial S}{\partial c} = -2\sum_{i=1}^{n} (y_i - ax_i^2 - bx_i - c) = 0$

$a\sum_{i=1}^{n} x_i^4 + b\sum_{i=1}^{n} x_i^3 + c\sum_{i=1}^{n} x_i^2 = \sum_{i=1}^{n} x_i^2 y_i$

$a\sum_{i=1}^{n} x_i^3 + b\sum_{i=1}^{n} x_i^2 + c\sum_{i=1}^{n} x_i = \sum_{i=1}^{n} x_i y_i$

$a\sum_{i=1}^{n} x_i^2 + b\sum_{i=1}^{n} x_i + cn = \sum_{i=1}^{n} y_i$

39. $(-2, 0), (-1, 0), (0, 1), (1, 2), (2, 5)$

$\sum x_i = 0$

$\sum y_i = 8$

$\sum x_i^2 = 10$

$\sum x_i^3 = 0$

$\sum x_i^4 = 34$

$\sum x_i y_i = 12$

$\sum x_i^2 y_i = 22$

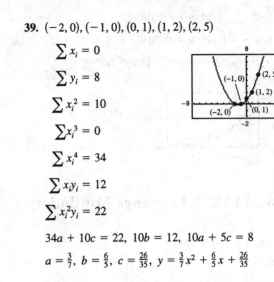

$34a + 10c = 22, \ 10b = 12, \ 10a + 5c = 8$

$a = \frac{3}{7}, \ b = \frac{6}{5}, \ c = \frac{26}{35}, \ y = \frac{3}{7}x^2 + \frac{6}{5}x + \frac{26}{35}$

41. We are given the points $(0, 0), (2, 2), (3, 6)$, and $(4, 12)$. From Exercise 37, we have that the least squares regression quadratic for the points $(x_1, y_1), (x_2, y_2), \ldots, (x_n, y_n)$ is

$y = ax^2 + bx + c$

where a, b, and c are the solutions to the system

$a\sum_{i=1}^{n} x_i^4 + b\sum_{i=1}^{n} x_i^3 + c\sum_{i=1}^{n} x_i^2 = \sum_{i=1}^{n} x_i^2 y_i$

$a\sum_{i=1}^{n} x_i^3 + b\sum_{i=1}^{n} x_i^2 + c\sum_{i=1}^{n} x_i = \sum_{i=1}^{n} x_i y_i$

$a\sum_{i=1}^{n} x_i^2 + b\sum_{i=1}^{n} x_i + cn = \sum_{i=1}^{n} y_i.$

For the given points, we have

$\sum x_i = 9, \sum x_i^2 = 29, \sum x_i^3 = 99, \sum x_i^4 = 353, \sum y_i = 20, \sum x_i y_i = 70, \sum x_i^2 y_i = 192.$

The resulting system of equations is

$353a + 99b + 29c = 192$

$99a + 29b + 9c = 70$

$29a + 9b + 4c = 20.$

Solving this system yields $a = 1$, $b = -1$, and $c = 0$. Therefore, the least squares regression quadratic is

$y = x^2 - x.$

43. $(0, 0), (2, 15), (4, 30), (6, 50), (8, 65), (10, 70)$

$\sum x_i = 30, \qquad \sum y_i = 230, \qquad \sum x_i^2 = 220, \qquad \sum x_i^3 = 1,800,$

$\sum x_i^4 = 15,664, \qquad \sum x_i y_i = 1,670, \qquad \sum x_i^2 y_i = 13,500$

$15,664a + 1,800b + 220c = 13,500$

$1,800a + 220b + 30c = 1,670$

$220a + 30b + 6c = 230$

$y = -\frac{25}{112}x^2 + \frac{541}{56}x - \frac{25}{14} \approx -0.22x^2 + 9.66x - 1.79$

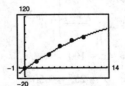

45. (a) $\ln P = -0.1499h + 9.3018$

 (b) $\ln P = -0.1499h + 9.3018$

 $P = e^{-0.1499h + 9.3018} = 10,957.7e^{-0.1499h}$

 (c)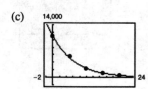

Section 12.10   Lagrange Multipliers

1. Maximize $f(x, y) = xy$.

 Constraint: $x + y = 10$

 $\nabla f = \lambda \nabla g$

 $y\mathbf{i} + x\mathbf{j} = \lambda(\mathbf{i} + \mathbf{j})$

 $\left.\begin{array}{l} y = \lambda \\ x = \lambda \end{array}\right\} x = y$

 $x + y = 10 = \implies x = y = 5$

 $f(5, 5) = 25$

3. Minimize $f(x, y) = x^2 + y^2$.

 Constraint: $x + y = 4$

 $\nabla f = \lambda \nabla g$

 $2x\mathbf{i} + 2y\mathbf{j} = \lambda\mathbf{i} + \lambda\mathbf{j}$

 $\left.\begin{array}{l} 2x = \lambda \\ 2y = \lambda \end{array}\right\} x = y$

 $x + y = 4 \implies x = y = 2$

 $f(2, 2) = 8$

5. To minimize $f(x, y) = x^2 - y^2$ subject to the constraint $x - 2y + 6 = 0$, begin by letting $g(x, y) = x - 2y + 6$. Then, since

$$\nabla f(x, y) = 2x\mathbf{i} - 2y\mathbf{j} \quad \text{and} \quad \lambda \nabla g(x, y) = \lambda(\mathbf{i} - 2\mathbf{j}),$$

we have the following system of equations.

$$\begin{array}{ll} 2x = \lambda & f_x(x, y) = \lambda g_x(x, y) \\ -2y = -2\lambda & f_y(x, y) = \lambda g_y(x, y) \\ x - 2y + 6 = 0 & \textit{Constraint} \end{array}$$

From the first equation we have $\lambda = 2x$. Substituting this result into the second equation, we have $y = 2x$. Substituting this result into the constraint yields

$$x - 2(2x) + 6 = 0$$

$$-3x = -6 \implies x = 2.$$

Since $y = 2x$, $y = 4$ and the required minimum is $f(2, 4) = 2^2 - 4^2 = -12$.

7. Maximize $f(x, y) = 2x + 2xy + y$.

 Constraint: $2x + y = 100$

 $\nabla f = \lambda \nabla g$

 $(2 + 2y)\mathbf{i} + (2x + 1)\mathbf{j} = 2\lambda\mathbf{i} + \lambda\mathbf{j}$

 $\left.\begin{array}{l} 2 + 2y = 2\lambda \implies y = \lambda - 1 \\ 2x + 1 = \lambda \quad \implies x = \dfrac{\lambda - 1}{2} \end{array}\right\} y = 2x$

 $2x + y = 100 \implies 4x = 100$

 $x = 25, \ y = 50$

 $f(25, 50) = 2600$

9. Note: $f(x, y) = \sqrt{6 - x^2 - y^2}$ is maximum when $g(x, y)$ is maximum.

 Maximize $g(x, y) = 6 - x^2 - y^2$.

 Constraint: $x + y = 2$

 $\left.\begin{array}{l} -2x = \lambda \\ -2y = \lambda \end{array}\right\} x = y$

 $x + y = 2 \implies x = y = 1$

 $f(1, 1) = \sqrt{g(1, 1)} = 2$

11. Maximize $f(x, y) = e^{xy}$.

Constraint: $x^2 + y^2 = 8$

$$\left. \begin{array}{l} ye^{xy} = 2x\lambda \\ xe^{xy} = 2y\lambda \end{array} \right\} x = y$$

$x^2 + y^2 = 8 \implies 2x^2 = 8$

$$x = y = 2$$

$f(2, 2) = e^4$

13. To minimize $f(x, y, z) = x^2 + y^2 + z^2$ subject to the constraint $x + y + z - 6 = 0$, begin by letting $g(x, y, z) = x + y + z - 6$. Since $\nabla f(x, y, z) = 2x\mathbf{i} + 2y\mathbf{j} + 2z\mathbf{k}$ and $\lambda \nabla g(x, y, z) = \lambda(\mathbf{i} + \mathbf{j} + \mathbf{k})$, we have the following system of equations.

$$2x = \lambda \qquad f_x(x, y, z) = \lambda g_x(x, y, z)$$

$$2y = \lambda \qquad f_y(x, y, z) = \lambda g_y(x, y, z)$$

$$2z = \lambda \qquad f_z(x, y, z) = \lambda g_z(x, y, z)$$

$$x + y + z - 6 = 0 \qquad \textit{Constraint}$$

From the first three equations we have $\lambda = 2x = 2y = 2z$ or $x = y = z$. Substituting x for y and z in the constraint produces $3x - 6 = 0$ or $x = 2$. Therefore, $x = 2$, $y = 2$, and $z = 2$ and the required minimum is $f(2, 2, 2) = 12$.

15. Minimize $f(x, y, z) = x^2 + y^2 + z^2$.

Constraint: $x + y + z = 1$

$$\left. \begin{array}{l} 2x = \lambda \\ 2y = \lambda \\ 2z = \lambda \end{array} \right\} x = y = z$$

$x + y + z = 1 \implies x = y = z = \frac{1}{3}$

$f\left(\frac{1}{3}, \frac{1}{3}, \frac{1}{3}\right) = \frac{1}{3}$

17. $f(x, y, z) = xyz$, $x + y + z = 32$, $x - y + z = 0$

In this case there are two constraints which we can denote by g and h.

$g(x, y, z) = x + y + z - 32$

$h(x, y, z) = x - y + z$

Since, $\nabla f(x, y, z) = yz\mathbf{i} + xz\mathbf{j} + xy\mathbf{j}$, $\lambda \nabla g(x, y, z) = \lambda\mathbf{i} + \lambda\mathbf{j} + \lambda\mathbf{k}$, and $\mu \nabla h(x, y, z) = \mu\mathbf{i} - \mu\mathbf{j} + \mu\mathbf{k}$, we have the following system of equations.

$$yz = \lambda + \mu \qquad f_x(x, y, z) = \lambda g_x(x, y, z) + \mu h_x(x, y, z)$$

$$xz = \lambda - \mu \qquad f_y(x, y, z) = \lambda g_y(x, y, z) + \mu h_y(x, y, z)$$

$$xy = \lambda + \mu \qquad f_z(x, y, z) = \lambda g_z(x, y, z) + \mu h_z(x, y, z)$$

$$x + y + z = 32 \qquad \textit{Constraint 1}$$

$$x - y + z = 0 \qquad \textit{Constraint 2}$$

From the first and third equations we have $yz = xy$ or $z = x$. Substituting this result into the second constraint, we have $y = 2x$. Finally, substituting these two results into the first constraint yields

$$4x = 32 \implies x = 8$$

$$y = 2x = 16$$

$$z = x = 8.$$

Therefore, the maximum value of f, subject to the given constraints is

$$f(8, 16, 8) = 8(16)(8) = 1024.$$

19. Maximize $f(x, y, z) = xy + yz$.

Constraints: $x + 2y = 6$

$\qquad\qquad\quad x - 3z = 0$

$\nabla f = \lambda \nabla g + \mu \nabla h$

$y\mathbf{i} + (x + z)\mathbf{j} + y\mathbf{k} = \lambda(\mathbf{i} + 2\mathbf{j}) + \mu(\mathbf{i} - 3\mathbf{k})$

$\left.\begin{array}{l} y = \lambda + \mu \\ x + z = 2\lambda \\ y = -3\mu \end{array}\right\} y = \frac{3}{4}\lambda \Rightarrow x + z = \frac{8}{3}y$

$x + 2y = 6 \Rightarrow y = 3 - \dfrac{x}{2}$

$x - 3z = 0 \Rightarrow z = \dfrac{x}{3}$

$$x + \frac{x}{3} = \frac{8}{3}\left(3 - \frac{x}{2}\right)$$

$$x = 3, y = \frac{3}{2}, z = 1$$

$f\left(3, \dfrac{3}{2}, 1\right) = 6$

21. Maximize or minimize $f(x, y) = x^2 + 3xy + y^2$.

Constraint: $x^2 + y^2 \leq 1$

Case 1: On the circle $x^2 + y^2 = 1$

$\left.\begin{array}{l} 2x + 3y = 2x\lambda \\ 3x + 2y = 2y\lambda \end{array}\right\} x^2 = y^2$

$x^2 + y^2 = 1 \Rightarrow x = \pm\dfrac{\sqrt{2}}{2}, y = \pm\dfrac{\sqrt{2}}{2}$

Maxima: $f\left(\pm\dfrac{\sqrt{2}}{2}, \pm\dfrac{\sqrt{2}}{2}\right) = \dfrac{5}{2}$

Minima: $f\left(\pm\dfrac{\sqrt{2}}{2}, \mp\dfrac{\sqrt{2}}{2}\right) = -\dfrac{1}{2}$

Case 2: Inside the circle

$\left.\begin{array}{l} f_x = 2x + 3y = 0 \\ f_y = 3x + 2y = 0 \end{array}\right\} x = y = 0$

$f_{xx} = 2, f_{yy} = 2, f_{xy} = 3, f_{xx}f_{yy} - (f_{xy})^2 \leq 0$

Saddle point: $f(0, 0) = 0$

By combining these two cases, we have a maximum of $\frac{5}{2}$ at

$$\left(\pm\frac{\sqrt{2}}{2}, \pm\frac{\sqrt{2}}{2}\right)$$

and a minimum of $-\frac{1}{2}$ at

$$\left(\pm\frac{\sqrt{2}}{2}, \mp\frac{\sqrt{2}}{2}\right).$$

23. Minimize the square of the distance $f(x, y) = x^2 + y^2$ subject to the constraint $2x + 3y = -1$.

$\left.\begin{array}{l} 2x = 2\lambda \\ 2y = 3\lambda \end{array}\right\} y = \dfrac{3x}{2}$

$2x + 3y = -1 \Rightarrow x = -\dfrac{2}{13}, y = -\dfrac{3}{13}$

The point on the line is $\left(-\frac{2}{13}, -\frac{3}{13}\right)$ and the desired distance is

$$d = \sqrt{\left(-\frac{2}{13}\right)^2 + \left(-\frac{3}{13}\right)^2} = \frac{\sqrt{13}}{13}.$$

25. $x + y + z = 1, (2, 1, 1)$

Let (x, y, z) be an arbitrary point in the given plane. Then $s = \sqrt{(x - 2)^2 + (y - 1)^2 + (z - 1)^2}$ represents the distance between $(2, 1, 1)$ and a point in the plane. To simplify our calculations, minimize s^2 rather than s. With $g(x, y, z) = x + y + z - 1$ as the constraint, we have $\nabla s^2 = 2(x - 2)\mathbf{i} + 2(y - 1)\mathbf{j} + 2(z - 1)\mathbf{k}$ and $\lambda \nabla g(x, y, z) = \lambda \mathbf{i} + \lambda \mathbf{j} + \lambda \mathbf{k}$. Therefore,

$\qquad 2(x - 2) = \lambda \qquad s_x^{\,2}(x, y, z) = \lambda g_x(x, y, z)$

$\qquad 2(y - 1) = \lambda \qquad s_y^{\,2}(x, y, z) = \lambda g_y(x, y, z)$

$\qquad 2(z - 1) = \lambda \qquad s_z^{\,2}(x, y, z) - \lambda g_z(x, y, z)$

$\quad x + y + z - 1 = 0 \qquad$ *Constraint.*

From the first three equations, we conclude that $\lambda = 2(x - 2) = 2(y - 1) = 2(z - 1)$ or that $x = y + 1$ and $z = y$. Therefore, from the constraint, we have $(y + 1) + y + y - 1 = 3y = 0$ or $y = 0$. Thus $x = 1$ and $z = 0$ and the point $(1, 0, 0)$ in the plane $x + y + z = 1$, is closest to the given point $(2, 1, 1)$. The minimum distance is $s = \sqrt{(1 - 2)^2 + (0 - 1)^2 + (0 - 1)^2} = \sqrt{3}$.

27. Maximize $f(x, y, z) = z$ subject to the constraints
$x^2 + y^2 + z^2 = 36$ and $2x + y - z = 2$.

$$\left.\begin{array}{l} 0 = 2x\lambda + 2\mu \\ 0 = 2y\lambda + \mu \\ 1 = 2z\lambda - \mu \end{array}\right\} x = 2y$$

$$x^2 + y^2 + z^2 = 36$$

$$2x + y - z = 2 \implies z = 2x + y - 2 = 5y - 2$$

$$(2y)^2 + y^2 + (5y - 2)^2 = 36$$

$$30y^2 - 20y - 32 = 0$$

$$15y^2 - 10y - 16 = 0$$

$$y = \frac{5 \pm \sqrt{265}}{15}$$

Choosing the positive value for y we have the point

$$\left(\frac{10 + 2\sqrt{265}}{15}, \frac{5 + \sqrt{265}}{15}, \frac{-1 + \sqrt{265}}{3}\right).$$

29. Maximize $V(x, y, z) = xyz$ subject to the constraint
$x + 2y + 2z = 108$.

$$\left.\begin{array}{l} yz = \lambda \\ xz = 2\lambda \\ xy = 2\lambda \end{array}\right\} y = z \text{ and } x = 2y$$

$$x + 2y + 2z = 108 \implies 6y = 108, y = 18$$

$$x = 36, y = z = 18$$

Volume is maximum when the dimensions are
$36 \times 18 \times 18$ inches.

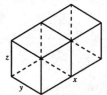

31. Letting $x, y,$ and z be the length, width, and height of the solid, respectively, it is necessary to minimize the cost function

$$C(x, y, z) = 5xy + 3(2yz + xy + 2xz)$$

$$= 8xy + 6yz + 6xz$$

subject to the constraint $xyz = 480$. First, write the constraint as $g(x, y, z) = xyz - 480$. Then, since $\nabla C(x, y, z) = (8y + 6z)\mathbf{i} + (8x + 6z)\mathbf{j} + (6y + 6x)\mathbf{k}$ and $\lambda \nabla g(x, y, z) = \lambda(yz\mathbf{i} + xz\mathbf{j} + xy\mathbf{k})$, we obtain the following system of equations.

$$8y + 6z = \lambda yz \qquad C_x(x, y, z) = \lambda g_x(x, y, z)$$

$$8x + 6z = \lambda xz \qquad C_y(x, y, z) = \lambda g_y(x, y, z)$$

$$6y + 6x = \lambda xy \qquad C_z(x, y, z) = \lambda g_z(x, y, z)$$

$$xyz - 480 = 0 \qquad \textit{Constraint}$$

We now multiply the first equation by x, the second by $-y$ and add to obtain $6xy - 6yz = 0 \implies y = x$. Next, multiply the first equation by x, the third by $-z$ and add to obtain $8xy - 6yz = 0 \implies z = \frac{4}{3}x$. Finally, substitute these results into the constraint to obtain

$$x(x)\left(\tfrac{4}{3}x\right) = 480$$

$$x^3 = 360$$

$$x = y = \sqrt[3]{360} \text{ and } z = \tfrac{4}{3}\sqrt[3]{360}.$$

33. Maximize $V(x, y, z) = (2x)(2y)(2z) = 8xyz$ subject to the constraint $\dfrac{x^2}{a^2} + \dfrac{y^2}{b^2} + \dfrac{z^2}{c^2} = 1$.

$$\left.\begin{array}{l} 8yz = \dfrac{2x}{a^2}\lambda \\[2mm] 8xz = \dfrac{2y}{b^2}\lambda \\[2mm] 8xy = \dfrac{2z}{c^2}\lambda \end{array}\right\} \dfrac{x^2}{a^2} = \dfrac{y^2}{b^2} = \dfrac{z^2}{c^2}$$

$$\frac{x^2}{a^2} + \frac{y^2}{b^2} + \frac{z^2}{c^2} = 1 \implies \frac{3x^2}{a^2} = 1, \frac{3y^2}{b^2} = 1, \frac{3z^2}{c^2} = 1$$

$$x = \frac{a}{\sqrt{3}}, y = \frac{b}{\sqrt{3}}, z = \frac{c}{\sqrt{3}}$$

Therefore, the dimensions of the box are $\dfrac{2\sqrt{3}a}{3} \times \dfrac{2\sqrt{3}b}{3} \times \dfrac{2\sqrt{3}c}{3}$.

35. Using the formula Time $= \dfrac{\text{Distance}}{\text{Rate}}$, minimize $T(x, y) = \dfrac{\sqrt{d_1^2 + x^2}}{v_1} + \dfrac{\sqrt{d_2^2 + y^2}}{v_2}$ subject to the constraint $x + y = a$.

$$\left.\begin{array}{l} \dfrac{x}{v_1\sqrt{d_2^2 + x^2}} = \lambda \\[2mm] \dfrac{y}{v_2\sqrt{d_2^2 + y^2}} = \lambda \end{array}\right\} \quad \dfrac{x}{v_1\sqrt{d_1^2 + x^2}} = \dfrac{y}{v_2\sqrt{d_2^2 + y^2}}$$

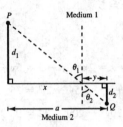

Medium 1

Medium 2

$x + y = a$

Since $\sin \theta_1 = \dfrac{x}{\sqrt{d_1^2 + x^2}}$ and $\sin \theta_2 = \dfrac{y}{\sqrt{d_2^2 + y^2}}$, we have

$$\dfrac{x/\sqrt{d_1^2 + x^2}}{v_1} = \dfrac{y/\sqrt{d_2^2 + y^2}}{v_2} \quad \text{or} \quad \dfrac{\sin \theta_1}{v_1} = \dfrac{\sin \theta_2}{v_2}.$$

37. Maximize $P(p, q, r) = 2pq + 2pr + 2qr$.

Constraint: $p + q + r = 1$

$\nabla P = \lambda \nabla g$

$$\left.\begin{array}{l} 2q + 2r = \lambda \\ 2p + 2r = \lambda \\ 2p + 2q = \lambda \end{array}\right\} \Rightarrow 3\lambda = 4(p + q + r) = 4(1)$$
$$\Rightarrow \lambda = \tfrac{4}{3}$$

$p + q + r = 1$

$$\left.\begin{array}{l} q + r = \tfrac{2}{3} \\ p + q + r = 1 \end{array}\right\} \Rightarrow p = \tfrac{1}{3}, q = \tfrac{1}{3}, r = \tfrac{1}{3}$$

$P\left(\tfrac{1}{3}, \tfrac{1}{3}, \tfrac{1}{3}\right) = 2\left(\tfrac{1}{3}\right)\left(\tfrac{1}{3}\right) + 2\left(\tfrac{1}{3}\right)\left(\tfrac{1}{3}\right) + 2\left(\tfrac{1}{3}\right)\left(\tfrac{1}{3}\right) = \tfrac{2}{3}$.

39. To maximize $P(x, y) = 100x^{0.25}y^{0.75}$ subject to the constraint $48x + 36y = 100,000$, begin by letting $g(x, y) = 48x + 36y - 100,000$. Since $\nabla P(x, y) = 25x^{-0.75}y^{0.75}\mathbf{i} + 75x^{0.25}y^{-0.25}\mathbf{j}$ and $\lambda \nabla g(x, y) = \lambda(48\mathbf{i} + 36\mathbf{j})$, we have the following system of equations.

$$25x^{-0.75}y^{0.75} = 48\lambda \qquad P_x(x, y) = \lambda g_x(x, y)$$
$$75x^{0.25}y^{-0.25} = 36\lambda \qquad P_y(x, y) = \lambda g_y(x, y)$$
$$48x + 36y - 100,000 = 0 \qquad \text{Constraint}$$

From the first equation we have

$$\left(\dfrac{y}{x}\right)^{0.75} = \dfrac{48\lambda}{25},$$

and from the second equation we have

$$\left(\dfrac{x}{y}\right)^{0.25} = \dfrac{36\lambda}{75} \quad \text{or} \quad \left(\dfrac{y}{x}\right)^{0.25} = \dfrac{75}{36\lambda}.$$

Therefore,

$$\left(\dfrac{y}{x}\right)^{0.75}\left(\dfrac{y}{x}\right)^{0.25} = \left(\dfrac{48\lambda}{25}\right)\left(\dfrac{75}{36\lambda}\right)$$

$$\dfrac{y}{x} = 4$$

$$y = 4x.$$

Substituting this expression for y into the constraint produces

$$48x + 36y = 100,000$$

$$192x = 100,000.$$

Therefore, $x = \tfrac{3125}{6}$ and $\tfrac{6250}{3}$, and the required maximum is $P\left(\tfrac{3125}{6}, \tfrac{6250}{3}\right) \approx 147,314$.

41. Minimize $C(x, y) = 48x + 36y$ subject to the constraint $100x^{0.25}y^{0.75} = 20,000$.

$$48 = 25x^{-0.75}y^{0.75}\lambda \implies \left(\frac{y}{x}\right)^{0.75} = \frac{48}{25\lambda}$$

$$36 = 75x^{0.25}y^{-0.25}\lambda \implies \left(\frac{x}{y}\right)^{0.25} = \frac{36}{75\lambda}$$

$$\left(\frac{y}{x}\right)^{0.75}\left(\frac{y}{x}\right)^{0.25} = \left(\frac{48}{25\lambda}\right)\left(\frac{75\lambda}{36}\right)$$

$$\frac{y}{x} = 4 \implies y = 4x$$

$$100x^{0.25}y^{0.75} = 20,000 \implies x^{0.25}(4x)^{0.75} = 200$$

$$x = \frac{200}{4^{0.75}} = \frac{200}{2\sqrt{2}} = 50\sqrt{2}$$

$$y = 4x = 200\sqrt{2}$$

Therefore, $C\left(50\sqrt{2}, 200\sqrt{2}\right) \approx \$13,576.45$.

43. (a) Maximize $g(\alpha, \beta, \gamma) = \cos\alpha \cos\beta \cos\gamma$ subject to the constraint $\alpha + \beta + \gamma = \pi$.

$$\left.\begin{array}{l} -\sin\alpha \cos\beta \cos\gamma = \lambda \\ -\cos\alpha \sin\beta \cos\gamma = \lambda \\ -\cos\alpha \cos\beta \sin\gamma = \lambda \end{array}\right\} \tan\alpha = \tan\beta = \tan\gamma \implies \alpha = \beta = \gamma$$

$$\alpha + \beta + \gamma = \pi \implies \alpha = \beta = \gamma = \frac{\pi}{3}$$

$$g\left(\frac{\pi}{3}, \frac{\pi}{3}, \frac{\pi}{3}\right) = \frac{1}{8}$$

(b) $\alpha + \beta + \gamma = \pi \implies \gamma = \pi - (\alpha + \beta)$

$$g(\alpha + \beta) = \cos\alpha \cos\beta \cos(\pi - (\alpha + \beta))$$

$$= \cos\alpha \cos\beta[\cos\pi\cos(\alpha + \beta) + \sin\pi\sin(\alpha + \beta)]$$

$$= -\cos\alpha \cos\beta \cos(\alpha + \beta)$$

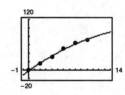

Review Exercises for Chapter 12

1. No, it is not the graph of a function.

3. $f(x, y) = e^{x^2+y^2}$

The level curves are of the form

$$c = e^{x^2+y^2}$$

$$\ln c = x^2 + y^2.$$

The level curves are circles centered at the origin.

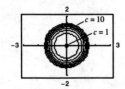

5. $f(x, y) = x^2 - y^2$

The level curves are of the form

$$c = x^2 - y^2$$

$$1 = \frac{x^2}{c} - \frac{y^2}{c}.$$

The level curves are hyperbolas.

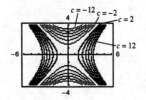

7. $f(x, y) = e^{-(x^2 + y^2)}$

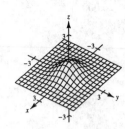

9. $\displaystyle\lim_{(x, y) \to (1, 1)} \frac{xy}{x^2 + y^2} = \frac{1}{2}$

Continuous except at $(0, 0)$.

11. $\displaystyle\lim_{(x, y) \to (0, 0)} \frac{-4x^2 y}{x^4 + y^2}$

Along the path $y = x^2$ we have

$$\lim_{(x, y) \to (0, 0)} \frac{-4x^2 y}{x^4 + y^2} = \lim_{(x, x^2) \to (0, 0)} \frac{-4x^2(x^2)}{x^4 + (x^2)^2}$$

$$= \lim_{(x, x^2) \to (0, 0)} \frac{-4x^4}{2x^4} = -2.$$

Along the path $y = -x^2$ we have

$$\lim_{(x, y) \to (0, 0)} \frac{-4x^2 y}{x^4 + y^2} = \lim_{(x, -x^2) \to (0, 0)} \frac{-4x^2(-x^2)}{x^4 + (-x^2)^2}$$

$$= \lim_{(x, -x^2) \to (0, 0)} \frac{4x^4}{2x^4} = 2.$$

Since the limits are not the same along different paths, the limit does not exist. The function is continuous except at $(0, 0)$.

13. $f(x, y) = e^x \cos y$

$$f_x = e^x \cos y$$

$$f_y = -e^x \sin y$$

15. $z = xe^y + ye^x$

$$\frac{\partial z}{\partial x} = e^y + ye^x$$

$$\frac{\partial z}{\partial y} = xe^y + e^x$$

17. $g(x, y) = \dfrac{xy}{x^2 + y^2}$

Using the Quotient Rule we have

$$g_x(x, y) = \frac{(x^2 + y^2)y - xy(2x)}{(x^2 + y^2)^2} = \frac{y(y^2 - x^2)}{(x^2 + y^2)^2}$$

$$g_y(x, y) = \frac{(x^2 + y^2)x - xy(2y)}{(x^2 + y^2)^2} = \frac{x(x^2 - y^2)}{(x^2 + y^2)^2}.$$

19. $f(x, y, z) = z \arctan \dfrac{y}{x}$

$$f_x = \frac{z}{1 + (y^2/x^2)} \left(-\frac{y}{x^2} \right) = \frac{-yz}{x^2 + y^2}$$

$$f_y = \frac{z}{1 + (y^2/x^2)} \left(\frac{1}{x} \right) = \frac{xz}{x^2 + y^2}$$

$$f_z = \arctan \frac{y}{x}$$

21. $u(x, t) = ce^{-n^2 t} \sin(nx)$

$$\frac{\partial u}{\partial x} = cne^{-n^2 t} \cos(nx)$$

$$\frac{\partial u}{\partial t} = -cn^2 e^{-n^2 t} \sin(nx)$$

23.
$$x^2y - 2yz - xz - z^2 = 0$$

$$2xy - 2y\frac{\partial z}{\partial x} - x\frac{\partial z}{\partial x} - z - 2z\frac{\partial z}{\partial x} = 0$$

$$\frac{\partial z}{\partial x} = \frac{-2xy + z}{-2y - x - 2z} = \frac{2xy - z}{x + 2y + 2z}$$

$$x^2 - 2y\frac{\partial z}{\partial y} - 2z - x\frac{\partial z}{\partial y} - 2z\frac{\partial z}{\partial y} = 0$$

$$\frac{\partial z}{\partial y} = \frac{-x^2 + 2z}{-2y - x - 2z} = \frac{x^2 - 2z}{x + 2y + 2z}$$

25. $f(x, y) = 3x^2 - xy + 2y^3$

$$f_x = 6x - y$$

$$f_y = -x + 6y^2$$

$$f_{xx} = 6$$

$$f_{yy} = 12y$$

$$f_{xy} = -1$$

$$f_{yx} = -1$$

27. Since $h(x, y) = x \sin y + y \cos x$ we have

$$h_x(x, y) = \sin y - y \sin x \qquad h_{xx}(x, y) = -y \cos x$$

$$h_y(x, y) = x \cos y + \cos x \qquad h(x, y) = -x \sin y.$$

Furthermore,

$$h_{xy}(x, y) = \cos y - \sin x$$

and

$$h_{yx}(x, y) = \cos y - \sin x.$$

29. $z = x^2 - y^2$

$$\frac{\partial z}{\partial x} = 2x$$

$$\frac{\partial^2 z}{\partial x^2} = 2$$

$$\frac{\partial z}{\partial y} = -2y$$

$$\frac{\partial^2 z}{\partial y^2} = -2$$

Therefore, $\dfrac{\partial^2 z}{\partial x^2} + \dfrac{\partial^2 z}{\partial y^2} = 0.$

31. $z = \dfrac{y}{x^2 + y^2}$

$$\frac{\partial z}{\partial x} = \frac{-2xy}{(x^2 + y^2)^2} = -2y\left[\frac{x}{(x^2 + y^2)^2}\right]$$

$$\frac{\partial^2 z}{\partial x^2} = -2y\left[\frac{(x^2 + y^2)^2 - x(2)(x^2 + y^2)(2x)}{(x^2 + y^2)^4}\right] = \frac{2y(3x^2 - y^2)}{(x^2 + y^2)^3}$$

$$\frac{\partial z}{\partial y} = \frac{(x^2 + y^2) - y(2y)}{(x^2 + y^2)^2} = \frac{x^2 - y^2}{(x^2 + y^2)^2}$$

$$\frac{\partial^2 z}{\partial y^2} = \frac{(x^2 + y^2)^2(-2y) - (x^2 - y^2)(2)(x^2 + y^2)(2y)}{(x^2 + y^2)^4} = \frac{-2y(3x^2 + y^2)}{(x^2 + y^2)^3}$$

Therefore,

$$\frac{\partial^2 z}{\partial x^2} + \frac{\partial^2 z}{\partial y^2} = \frac{2y(3x^2 - y^2)}{(x^2 + y^2)^3} + \frac{(-2y)(3x^2 - y^2)}{(x^2 + y^2)^3} = 0.$$

33. $u = x^2 + y^2 + z^2$, $x = r \cos t$, $y = r \sin t$, $z = t$

(a) By the Chain Rule

$$\frac{\partial u}{\partial r} = \frac{\partial u}{\partial x}\frac{\partial x}{\partial r} + \frac{\partial u}{\partial y}\frac{\partial y}{\partial r} + \frac{\partial u}{\partial z}\frac{\partial z}{\partial r}$$

$$= 2x(\cos t) + 2y(\sin t) + 2z(0)$$

$$= 2r \cos t(\cos t) + 2r \sin t(\sin t)$$

$$= 2r(\cos^2 t + \sin^2 t) = 2r$$

and

$$\frac{\partial u}{\partial t} = \frac{\partial u}{\partial x}\frac{\partial x}{\partial t} + \frac{\partial u}{\partial y}\frac{\partial y}{\partial t} + \frac{\partial u}{\partial z}\frac{\partial z}{\partial t}$$

$$= 2x(-r \sin t) + 2y(r \cos t) + 2z(1)$$

$$= 2r \cos t(-r \sin t) + 2r \sin t(r \cos t) + 2t$$

$$= -2r^2 \sin t \cos t + 2r^2 \sin t \cos t + 2t = 2t.$$

(b) By first substituting the expressions for x, y, and z, we have

$$u = r^2 \cos^2 t + r^2 \sin^2 t + t^2$$

$$= r^2(\cos^2 t + \sin^2 t) + t^2 = r^2 + t^2.$$

Therefore,

$$\frac{\partial u}{\partial r} = 2r \quad \text{and} \quad \frac{\partial u}{\partial t} = 2t.$$

35. $f(x, y) = x^2y$

$$\nabla f = 2xy\mathbf{i} + x^2\mathbf{j}$$

$$\nabla f(2, 1) = 4\mathbf{i} + 4\mathbf{j}$$

$$\mathbf{u} = \frac{1}{\sqrt{2}}\mathbf{v} = \frac{\sqrt{2}}{2}\mathbf{i} - \frac{\sqrt{2}}{2}\mathbf{j}$$

$$D_{\mathbf{u}}f(2, 1) = \nabla f(2, 1) \cdot \mathbf{u} = 2\sqrt{2} - 2\sqrt{2} = 0$$

37. $w = y^2 + xz$

$$\nabla w = z\mathbf{i} + 2y\mathbf{j} + x\mathbf{k}$$

$$\nabla w(1, 2, 2) = 2\mathbf{i} + 4\mathbf{j} + \mathbf{k}$$

$$\mathbf{u} = \frac{1}{3}\mathbf{v} = \frac{2}{3}\mathbf{i} - \frac{1}{3}\mathbf{j} + \frac{2}{3}\mathbf{k}$$

$$D_{\mathbf{u}}w(1, 2, 2) = \nabla w(1, 2, 2) \cdot \mathbf{u} = \frac{4}{3} - \frac{4}{3} + \frac{2}{3} = \frac{2}{3}$$

39. $f(x, y) = \dfrac{y}{x^2 + y^2}$

The gradient is given by

$$\nabla f(x, y) = f_x(x, y)\mathbf{i} + f_y(x, y)\mathbf{j}$$

$$= \frac{-2xy}{(x^2 + y^2)^2}\mathbf{i} + \frac{x^2 - y^2}{(x^2 + y^2)^2}\mathbf{j}.$$

At the point $(1, 1)$ the gradient is

$$\nabla f(1, 1) = \frac{-2(1)(1)}{(1^2 + 1^2)^2}\mathbf{i} + \frac{1^2 - 1^2}{(1^2 + 1^2)^2}\mathbf{j} = -\frac{1}{2}\mathbf{i}.$$

The maximum value of the directional derivative at the point $(1, 1)$ is given by

$$\|\nabla f(1, 1)\| = \frac{1}{2}.$$

41. $z = e^{-x} \cos y$

$$\nabla z = -e^{-x} \cos y\mathbf{i} - e^{-x} \sin y\mathbf{j}$$

$$\nabla z\left(0, \frac{\pi}{4}\right) = -\frac{\sqrt{2}}{2}\mathbf{i} - \frac{\sqrt{2}}{2}\mathbf{j} = \left\langle -\frac{\sqrt{2}}{2}, -\frac{\sqrt{2}}{2}\right\rangle$$

$$\left\|\nabla z\left(0, \frac{\pi}{4}\right)\right\| = 1$$

43. $F(x, y, z) = x^2y - z = 0$

$$\nabla F = 2xy\mathbf{i} + x^2\mathbf{j} - \mathbf{k}$$

$$\nabla F(2, 1, 4) = 4\mathbf{i} + 4\mathbf{j} - \mathbf{k}$$

Therefore, the equation of the tangent plane is $4(x - 2) + 4(y - 1) - (z - 4) = 0$ or $4x + 4y - z = 8$, and the equation of the normal line is

$$\frac{x - 2}{4} = \frac{y - 1}{4} = \frac{z - 4}{-1}.$$

45. $f(x, y) = -9 + 4x - 6y - x^2 - y^2$

We start by defining a function F and finding its first partial derivatives.

$$F(x, y, z) = z - f(x, y)$$
$$= z + 9 - 4x + 6y + x^2 + y^2$$
$$F_x(x, y, z) = -4 + 2x$$
$$F_y(x, y, z) = 6 + 2y$$
$$F_z(x, y, z) = 1$$

Then at $(2, -3, 4)$ we have $F_x(2, -3, 4) = 0$, $F_y(2, -3, 4) = 0$, and $F_z(2, -3, 4) = 1$. Therefore, an equation of the tangent plane at $(2, -3, 4)$ is

$$0(x - 2) + 0(y + 3) + 1(z - 4) = 0 \quad \text{or} \quad z = 4.$$

Furthermore, a normal line at $(2, -3, 4)$ has direction numbers 0, 0, 1 and its parametric equations are

$$x = 2, y = -3, z = 4 + t.$$

47. $F(x, y, z) = x^2 - y^2 - z = 0$
$$G(x, y, z) = 3 - z = 0$$
$$\nabla F = 2x\mathbf{i} - 2y\mathbf{j} - \mathbf{k}$$
$$\nabla G = -\mathbf{k}$$
$$\nabla F(2, 1, 3) = 4\mathbf{i} - 2\mathbf{j} - \mathbf{k}$$
$$\nabla F \times \nabla G = \begin{vmatrix} \mathbf{i} & \mathbf{j} & \mathbf{k} \\ 4 & -2 & -1 \\ 0 & 0 & -1 \end{vmatrix} = 2(\mathbf{i} + 2\mathbf{j})$$

Therefore, the equation of the tangent line is

$$\frac{x - 2}{1} = \frac{y - 1}{2}, \ z = 3.$$

49. $f(x, y) = x^3 - 3xy + y^2$
$$f_x = 3x^2 - 3y = 3(x^2 - y) = 0$$
$$f_y = -3x + 2y = 0$$
$$f_{xx} = 6x$$
$$f_{yy} = 2$$
$$f_{xy} = -3$$

From $f_x = 0$, we have $y = x^2$. Substituting this into $f_y = 0$, we have $-3x + 2x^2 = x(2x - 3) = 0$. Thus, $x = 0$ or $\frac{3}{2}$.
At the critical point $(0, 0)$, $f_{xx}f_{yy} - (f_{xy})^2 < 0$. Therefore, $(0, 0, 0)$ is a saddle point.
At the critical point $\left(\frac{3}{2}, \frac{9}{4}\right)$, $f_{xx}f_{yy} - (f_{xy})^2 > 0$ and $f_{xx} > 0$. Therefore, $\left(\frac{3}{2}, \frac{9}{4}, -\frac{27}{16}\right)$ is a relative minimum.

51. We begin by setting the first partials of f equal to zero.

$$f(x, y) = xy + \frac{1}{x} + \frac{1}{y}$$
$$f_x(x, y) = y - \frac{1}{x^2} = 0 \implies x^2 y = 1$$
$$f_y(x, y) = x - \frac{1}{y^2} = 0 \implies xy^2 = 1$$

Thus, $x^2 y = xy^2$ or $x = y$. Substituting this result into $f_x(x, y) = 0$ yields

$$f_x(x, y) = y - \frac{1}{x^2}$$
$$= x - \frac{1}{x^2}$$
$$= \frac{x^3 - 1}{x^2} = 0 \implies x = 1.$$

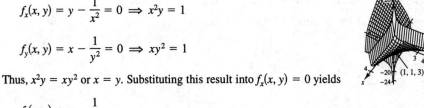

Therefore, the critical point is $(1, 1)$. We now use the Second Derivative Test and obtain

$$f_{xx}(x, y) = \frac{2}{x^3}, \ f_{xy}(x, y) = 1, \ f_{yy}(x, y) = \frac{2}{y^3}.$$

At the critical point $(1, 1)$, we have $f(1, 1) = 3$, $f_{xx}(1, 1) = 2 > 0$, and $f_{xx}(1, 2)f_{yy}(1, 1) - [f_{xy}(1, 1)]^2 = 3 > 0$. Thus, $(1, 1, 3)$ is a relative minimum.

53. The level curves are hyperbolas. There is a critical point at $(0, 0)$, but there are no relative extrema. The gradient is normal to the level curve at any given point at (x_0, y_0).

55.

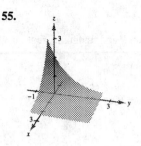

57. $z = x \sin \dfrac{y}{x}$

$$dz = \frac{\partial z}{\partial x} dx + \frac{\partial z}{\partial y} dy = \left(\sin \frac{y}{x} - \frac{y}{x} \cos \frac{y}{x} \right) dx + \left(\cos \frac{y}{x} \right) dy$$

59. $z^2 = x^2 + y^2$

$2z \, dx = 2x \, dx + 2y \, dy$

$$dz = \frac{x}{z} dx + \frac{y}{z} dy = \frac{5}{13}\left(\frac{1}{2}\right) + \frac{12}{13}\left(\frac{1}{2}\right) = \frac{17}{26} \approx 0.654 \text{ cm}$$

Percentage error: $\dfrac{dz}{z} = \dfrac{17/26}{13} \approx 0.0503 \approx 5\%$

61. Using the total differential we have

$V = \frac{1}{3}\pi r^2 h$

$dV = V_r \, dr + V_h \, dh$

$\quad = \frac{2}{3}\pi r h \, dr + \frac{1}{3}\pi r^2 \, dh.$

Now, letting $r = 2$, $h = 5$, and $dr = dh = \pm\frac{1}{8}$ we obtain the maximum approximate error.

$dV = \frac{2}{3}\pi (2)(5)\left(\pm\frac{1}{8}\right) + \frac{1}{3}\pi (2)^2\left(\pm\frac{1}{8}\right)$

$\quad = \pm\frac{5}{6}\pi \pm \frac{1}{6}\pi = \pm\pi \text{ in.}^3$

63. $P(x_1, x_2) = R - C_1 - C_2$

$\quad = [225 - 0.4(x_1 + x_2)](x_1 + x_2) - (0.05x_1^2 + 15x_1 + 5400) - (0.03x_2^2 + 15x_2 + 6100)$

$\quad = -0.45x_1^2 - 0.43x_2^2 - 0.8x_1x_2 + 210x_1 + 210x_2 - 11{,}500$

$P_{x_1} = -0.9x_1 - 0.8x_2 + 210 = 0$

$\qquad 0.9x_1 + 0.8x_2 = 210$

$P_{x_2} = -0.86x_2 - 0.8x_1 + 210 = 0$

$\qquad 0.8x_1 + 0.86x_2 = 210$

Solving this system yields $x_1 \approx 94$ and $x_2 \approx 157$.

$\qquad\qquad P_{x_1x_1} = -0.9$

$\qquad\qquad P_{x_1x_2} = -0.8$

$\qquad\qquad P_{x_2x_2} = -0.86$

$\qquad\qquad P_{x_1x_1} < 0$

$\qquad P_{x_1x_1} P_{x_2x_2} - (P_{x_1x_2})^2 > 0$

Therefore, profit is maximum when $x_1 \approx 94$ and $x_2 \approx 157$.

65. Maximize $f(x, y) = 4x + xy + 2y$ subject to the con-straint $20x + 4y = 2000$.

$$\left.\begin{array}{l} 4 + y = 20\lambda \\ x + 2 = 4\lambda \end{array}\right\} 5x - y = -6$$

$$20x + 4y = 2000 \implies \quad 5x + y = 500$$

$$\underline{ 5x - y = -6}$$

$$ 10x = 494$$

$$ x = 49.4$$

$$ y = 253$$

$$f(49.4, 253) = 13{,}201.8$$

67. (a) $y = 2.29t + 2.34$

(c) $y = 8.37 \ln t + 1.54$

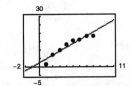

(d)
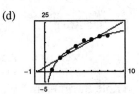

(b)
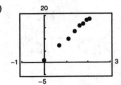

The logarithmic model is a better fit.

Yes, the data appears more linear.

69. To locate the extrema of $w = f(x, y, z) = xy + yz + xz$ subject to the constraint $x + y + z = 1$, begin by letting

$$g(x, y, z) = x + y + z - 1.$$

Since

$$\nabla f(x, y, z) = (y + z)\mathbf{i} + (x + z)\mathbf{j} + (x + y)\mathbf{k} \quad \text{and} \quad \lambda \nabla g(x, y, z) = \lambda(\mathbf{i} + \mathbf{j} + \mathbf{k}),$$

we have the following system of equations.

$$\begin{array}{ll} y + z = \lambda & f_x(x, y, z) = \lambda g_x(x, y, z) \\ x + z = \lambda & f_y(x, y, z) = \lambda g_y(x, y, z) \\ x + y = \lambda & f_z(x, y, z) = \lambda g_z(x, y, z) \\ x + y + z - 1 = 0 & \textit{Constraint} \end{array}$$

From the first three equations we have

$$\lambda = y + z = x + z = x + y \quad \text{or} \quad x = y = z.$$

Substituting x for y and z in the constraint produces $3x - 1 = 0$ or $x = \frac{1}{3}$. Therefore,

$$x = \tfrac{1}{3}, y = \tfrac{1}{3}, \text{and } z = \tfrac{1}{3}$$

and the maximum value of the function is

$$f\left(\tfrac{1}{3}, \tfrac{1}{3}, \tfrac{1}{3}\right) = \tfrac{1}{3}.$$

71. False, $\nabla F(x_0, y_0, z_0)$ is normal to the surface.

CHAPTER 13
Multiple Integration

CHAPTER 13
Multiple Integration

Section 13.1　Iterated Integrals and Area in the Plane

Solutions to Odd-Numbered Exercises

1. $\displaystyle\int_0^x (2x - y)\,dy = \left[2xy - \frac{1}{2}y^2\right]_0^x = \frac{3}{2}x^2$

3. $\displaystyle\int_1^{2y} \frac{y}{x}\,dx = \Big[y\ln x\Big]_1^{2y} = y\ln 2y - 0 = y\ln 2y$

5. $\displaystyle\int_0^{\sqrt{4-x^2}} x^2 y\,dy = \left[\frac{1}{2}x^2 y^2\right]_0^{\sqrt{4-x^2}} = \frac{4x^2 - x^4}{2}$

7. Considering y to be a constant and integrating with respect to x yields

$$\int_{e^y}^{y} y(\ln x)\left(\frac{1}{x}\right)dx = \left[\frac{y(\ln x)^2}{2}\right]_{e^y}^{y}$$

$$= \frac{y}{2}[(\ln y)^2 - (\ln e^y)^2]$$

$$= \frac{y}{2}[(\ln y)^2 - y^2].$$

9. $\displaystyle\int_0^{x^3} ye^{-y/x}\,dy = \Big[-xye^{-y/x}\Big]_0^{x^3} + x\int_0^{x^3} e^{-y/x}\,dy = -x^4 e^{-x^2} - \Big[x^2 e^{-y/x}\Big]_0^{x^3} = x^2(1 - e^{-x^2} - x^2 e^{-x^2})$

$u = y,\ du = dy,\ dv = e^{-y/x}\,dy,\ v = -xe^{-y/x}$

11. $\displaystyle\int_0^1\int_0^2 (x + y)\,dy\,dx = \int_0^1\left[xy + \frac{1}{2}y^2\right]_0^2 dx = \int_0^1 (2x + 2)\,dx = \Big[x^2 + 2x\Big]_0^1 = 3$

13. $\displaystyle\int_1^2\int_0^4 (x^2 - 2y^2 + 1)\,dx\,dy = \int_1^2\left[\frac{x^3}{3} - 2xy^2 + x\right]_0^4 dy$

$$= \int_1^2\left(\frac{64}{3} - 8y^2 + 4\right)dy = \int_1^2\left(\frac{76}{3} - 8y^2\right)dy = \frac{1}{3}\Big[76y - 8y^3\Big]_1^2 = \frac{1}{3}[152 - 64 - 76 + 8] = \frac{20}{3}$$

15. $\displaystyle\int_0^1\int_0^{\sqrt{1-y^2}} (x + y)\,dx\,dy = \int_0^1\left[\frac{1}{2}x^2 + xy\right]_0^{\sqrt{1-y^2}} dy$

$$= \int_0^1\left[\frac{1}{2}(1 - y^2) + y\sqrt{1 - y^2}\right]dy = \left[\frac{1}{2}y - \frac{1}{6}y^3 - \frac{1}{2}\left(\frac{2}{3}\right)(1 - y^2)^{3/2}\right]_0^1 = \frac{2}{3}$$

17. $\displaystyle\int_0^2\int_0^{\sqrt{4-y^2}} \frac{2}{\sqrt{4 - y^2}}\,dx\,dy = \int_0^2\left[\frac{2x}{\sqrt{4 - y^2}}\right]_0^{\sqrt{4-y^2}} dy = \int_0^2 2\,dy = \Big[2y\Big]_0^2 = 4$

19. $\displaystyle\int_0^{\pi/2}\int_0^{\sin\theta} \theta r\,dr\,d\theta = \int_0^{\pi/2}\left[\frac{\theta r^2}{2}\right]_0^{\sin\theta} d\theta = \frac{1}{2}\int_0^{\pi/2} \theta\sin^2\theta\,d\theta = \frac{1}{2}\int_0^{\pi/2}\theta\left(\frac{1 - \cos 2\theta}{2}\right)d\theta = \frac{1}{4}\int_0^{\pi/2}(\theta - \theta\cos 2\theta)\,d\theta$

Using integration by parts or a table of integrals yields

$$\int_0^{\pi/2}\int_0^{\sin\theta} \theta r\,dr\,d\theta = \frac{1}{4}\left[\frac{\theta^2}{2} - \left(\frac{1}{4}\cos 2\theta + \frac{\theta}{2}\sin 2\theta\right)\right]_0^{\pi/2} = \frac{1}{4}\left(\frac{\pi^2}{8} + \frac{1}{4} - 0 - 0 + \frac{1}{4} + 0\right) = \frac{1}{4}\left(\frac{\pi^2}{8} + \frac{1}{2}\right) = \frac{\pi^2}{32} + \frac{1}{8}.$$

21. $\int_1^\infty \int_0^{1/x} y \, dy \, dx = \int_1^\infty \left[\frac{y^2}{2} \right]_0^{1/x} dx = \frac{1}{2} \int_1^\infty \frac{1}{x^2} \, dx = \left[-\frac{1}{2x} \right]_1^\infty = 0 + \frac{1}{2} = \frac{1}{2}$

23. $\int_1^\infty \int_1^\infty \frac{1}{xy} \, dx \, dy = \int_1^\infty \lim_{b \to \infty} \int_1^b \frac{1}{xy} \, dx \, dy$

$= \int_1^\infty \lim_{b \to \infty} \left[\frac{1}{y} \ln x \right]_1^b dy$

$= \int_1^\infty \lim_{b \to \infty} \frac{1}{y} (\ln b - \ln 1) \, dy$

$= \int_1^\infty \frac{1}{y} (\infty - 0) \, dy$

The improper integral diverges.

25. $\int_0^4 \int_0^y f(x, y) \, dx \, dy, \ 0 \le x \le y, \ 0 \le y \le 4$

$= \int_0^4 \int_x^4 f(x, y) \, dy \, dx$

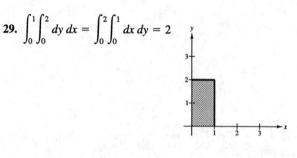

27. $\int_{-1}^1 \int_{x^2}^1 f(x, y) \, dy \, dx, \ x^2 \le y \le 1, 1 \le x \le 1$

$= \int_0^1 \int_{-\sqrt{y}}^{\sqrt{y}} f(x, y) \, dx \, dy$

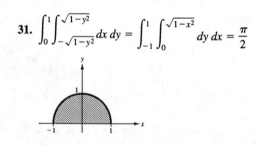

29. $\int_0^1 \int_0^2 dy \, dx = \int_0^2 \int_0^1 dx \, dy = 2$

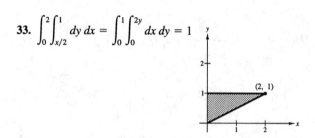

31. $\int_0^1 \int_{-\sqrt{1-y^2}}^{\sqrt{1-y^2}} dx \, dy = \int_{-1}^1 \int_0^{\sqrt{1-x^2}} dy \, dx = \frac{\pi}{2}$

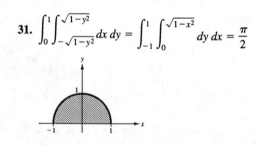

33. $\int_0^2 \int_{x/2}^1 dy \, dx = \int_0^1 \int_0^{2y} dx \, dy = 1$

35. $\int_0^1 \int_{y^2}^{\sqrt[3]{y}} dx \, dy$

From the limits of integration, we know that when $0 \le y \le 1$, then $y^2 \le x \le \sqrt[3]{y}$. This implies that the region R is bounded by the curves $x = y^2$ and $x = \sqrt[3]{y}$. Therefore, the region R can be sketched as in the figure. If we interchange the order of integration so that x is the outer variable then $0 \le x \le 1$. Solving for y in the equations $x = y^2$ and $x = \sqrt[3]{y}$, yields $y = \sqrt{x}$ and $y = x^3$. Thus $x^3 \le y \le \sqrt{x}$, and the area of R is given by the iterated integral

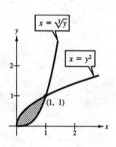

$\int_0^1 \int_{x^2}^{\sqrt{x}} dy \, dx.$

Evaluating each iterated integral, we have

$\int_0^1 \int_{y^2}^{\sqrt[3]{y}} dx \, dy = \int_0^1 (\sqrt[3]{y} - y^2) \, dy = \left[\frac{3}{4} y^{4/3} - \frac{1}{3} y^3 \right]_0^1 = \frac{5}{12}$

$\int_0^1 \int_{x^3}^{\sqrt{x}} dy \, dx = \int_0^1 (\sqrt{x} - x^3) \, dx = \left[\frac{2}{3} x^{3/2} - \frac{1}{4} x^4 \right]_0^1 = \frac{5}{12}.$

37. $A = \int_0^8 \int_0^3 dy\, dx = \int_0^8 \left[y \right]_0^3 dx = \int_0^8 3\, dx = \left[3x \right]_0^8 = 24$

$A = \int_0^3 \int_0^8 dx\, dy = \int_0^3 \left[x \right]_0^8 dy = \int_0^3 8\, dy = \left[8y \right]_0^3 = 24$

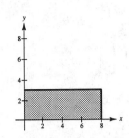

39. $A = \int_0^2 \int_0^{4-x^2} dy\, dx = \int_0^2 \left[y \right]_0^{4-x^2} dx$

$\quad = \int_0^2 (4 - x^2)\, dx$

$\quad = \left[4x - \frac{x^3}{3} \right]_0^2 = \frac{16}{3}$

$A = \int_0^4 \int_0^{\sqrt{4-y}} dx\, dy$

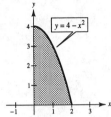

$\quad = \int_0^4 \left[x \right]_0^{\sqrt{4-y}} dy = \int_0^4 \sqrt{4-y}\, dy = -\int_0^4 (4-y)^{1/2}(-1)\, dy = \left[-\frac{2}{3}(4-y)^{3/2} \right]_0^4 = \frac{2}{3}(8) = \frac{16}{3}$

41. $A = \int_{-2}^1 \int_{x+2}^{4-x^2} dy\, dx$

$\quad = \int_{-2}^1 \left[y \right]_{x+2}^{4-x^2} dx$

$\quad = \int_{-2}^1 (4 - x^2 - x - 2)\, dx$

$\quad = \int_{-2}^1 (2 - x - x^2)\, dx$

$\quad = \left[2x - \frac{1}{2}x^2 - \frac{1}{3}x^3 \right]_{-2}^1 = \frac{9}{2}$

$A = \int_0^3 \int_{-\sqrt{4-y}}^{y-2} dx\, dy + 2\int_3^4 \int_0^{\sqrt{4-y}} dx\, dy$

$\quad = \int_0^3 \left[x \right]_{-\sqrt{4-y}}^{y-2} dy + 2\int_3^4 \left[x \right]_0^{\sqrt{4-y}} dy$

$\quad = \int_0^3 \left(y - 2 + \sqrt{4-y} \right) dy + 2\int_3^4 \sqrt{4-y}\, dy$

$\quad = \left[\frac{1}{2}y^2 - 2y - \frac{2}{3}(4-y)^{3/2} \right]_0^3 - \left[\frac{4}{3}(4-y)^{3/2} \right]_3^4 = \frac{9}{2}$

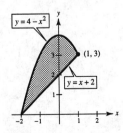

43. Solving the equation $\sqrt{x} + \sqrt{y} = 2$ for y produces $y = \left(2 - \sqrt{x} \right)^2$. The region bounded by $y = \left(2 - \sqrt{x} \right)^2$, $x = 0$, and $y = 0$ is shown in the figure.

$A = \int_0^4 \int_0^{(2-\sqrt{x})^2} dy\, dx = \int_0^4 \left[y \right]_0^{(2-\sqrt{x})^2} dx$

$\quad = \int_0^4 \left(2 - \sqrt{x} \right)^2 dx$

$\quad = \int_0^4 \left(4 - 4\sqrt{x} + x \right) dx$

$\quad = \left[4x - \frac{8}{3}x\sqrt{x} + \frac{1}{2}x^2 \right]_0^4 = \frac{8}{3}$

If the order of integration were switched, then

$A = \int_0^4 \int_0^{(2-\sqrt{y})^2} dx\, dy$

and the integration steps are similar to those above.

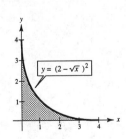

45. $A = \int_0^3 \int_0^{2x/3} dy\, dx + \int_3^5 \int_0^{5-x} dy\, dx$

$= \int_0^3 \left[y \right]_0^{2x/3} dx + \int_3^5 \left[y \right]_0^{5-x} dx$

$= \int_0^3 \frac{2x}{3}\, dx + \int_3^5 (5-x)\, dx$

$= \left[\frac{1}{3}x^2 \right]_0^3 + \left[5x - \frac{1}{2}x^2 \right]_3^5 = 5$

$A = \int_0^2 \int_{3y/2}^{5-y} dx\, dy$

$= \int_0^2 \left[x \right]_{3y/2}^{5-y} dy$

$= \int_0^2 \left(5 - y - \frac{3y}{2} \right) dy$

$= \int_2^2 \left(5 - \frac{5y}{2} \right) dy = \left[5y - \frac{5}{4}y^2 \right]_0^2 = 5$

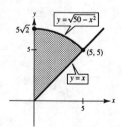

47. $\frac{A}{4} = \int_0^a \int_0^{(b/a)\sqrt{a^2-x^2}} dy\, dx = \int_0^a \left[y \right]_0^{(b/a)\sqrt{a^2-x^2}} dx$

$= \frac{b}{a} \int_0^a \sqrt{a^2 - x^2}\, dx = ab \int_0^{\pi/2} \cos^2 \theta\, d\theta$

$(x = a \sin \theta, dx = a \cos \theta\, d\theta)$

$= \frac{ab}{2} \int_0^{\pi/2} (1 + \cos 2\theta)\, d\theta = \left[\frac{ab}{2} \left(\theta + \frac{1}{2} \sin 2\theta \right) \right]_0^{\pi/2}$

$= \frac{\pi ab}{4}$

Therefore, $A = \pi ab$.

$\frac{A}{4} = \int_0^b \int_0^{(a/b)\sqrt{b^2-y^2}} dx\, dy = \frac{\pi ab}{4}$

Therefore, $A = \pi ab$. Integration steps are similar to those above.

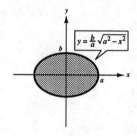

49. The first integral arises using vertical representative rectangles. The second two integrals arise using horizontal representative rectangles.

$$\int_0^5 \int_x^{\sqrt{50-x^2}} x^2 y^2\, dy\, dx = \int_0^5 \left[\frac{1}{3}x^2(50 - x^2)^{3/2} - \frac{1}{3}x^5 \right] dx$$

$$= \frac{15,625}{24}\pi$$

$$\int_0^5 \int_0^y x^2 y^2\, dx\, dy + \int_5^{5\sqrt{2}} \int_0^{\sqrt{50-y^2}} x^2 y^2\, dx\, dy = \int_0^5 \frac{1}{3}y^5\, dy + \int_5^{5\sqrt{2}} \frac{1}{3}(50 - y^2)^{3/2}\, y^2\, dy = \frac{15,625}{18} + \left(\frac{15,625}{18}\pi - \frac{15,625}{18} \right)$$

$$= \frac{15,625}{24}\pi$$

51. $\int_0^2 \int_x^2 x\sqrt{1 + y^3}\, dy\, dx = \int_0^2 \int_0^y x\sqrt{1 + y^3}\, dx\, dy = \int_0^2 \left[\sqrt{1 + y^3} \cdot \frac{x^2}{2} \right]_0^y dy$

$= \frac{1}{2} \int_0^2 \sqrt{1 + y^3}\, y^2\, dy = \left[\frac{1}{2} \cdot \frac{1}{3} \cdot \frac{2}{3}(1 + y^3)^{3/2} \right]_0^2 = \frac{1}{9}(27) - \frac{1}{9}(1) = \frac{26}{9}$

53. $\displaystyle\int_0^1 \int_y^1 \sin x^2 \, dx \, dy$

Since it is not possible to perform the inner integration, it is necessary to switch the order of integration. From the given limits of integration, it follows that

$$y \leq x \leq 1 \qquad \text{(Inner limits of integration)}$$

which means that the region R is bounded on the left by the line $x = y$ and on the right by $x = 1$. Furthermore, since

$$0 \leq y \leq 1, \qquad \text{(Outer limits of integration)}$$

it follows that R is bounded below by the x-axis as shown in the figure. Now to change the order of integration to $dy \, dx$ observe that the outer limits have the constant bounds $0 \leq x \leq 1$ and the inner limits have bounds $0 \leq y \leq x$. Therefore,

$$\int_0^1 \int_y^1 \sin x^2 \, dx \, dy = \int_0^1 \int_0^x \sin x^2 \, dy \, dx$$

$$= \int_0^1 \left[y \sin x^2 \right]_0^x dx$$

$$= \int_0^1 x \sin x^2 \, dx$$

$$= \frac{1}{2}\left[-\cos x^2 \right]_0^1 = \frac{1}{2}(1 - \cos 1) \approx 0.230.$$

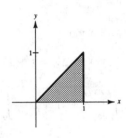

55. $\displaystyle\int_0^2 \int_{x^2}^{2x} (x^3 + 3y^2) \, dy \, dx = \frac{1664}{105} \approx 15.848$

57. $\displaystyle\int_0^4 \int_0^y \frac{2}{(x + 1)(y + 1)} \, dx \, dy = (\ln 5)^2 \approx 2.590$

59. $\displaystyle\int_0^2 \int_{y^3}^{4\sqrt{2y}} x^2 y - xy^2) \, dx \, dy$

(a) From the given limits of integration, we know that

$$y^3 \leq x \leq 4\sqrt{2y} \qquad \text{(Inner limits of integration)}$$

which means that the region R is bounded on the left by $x = y^3$ and on the right by $x = 4\sqrt{2y}$. Furthermore, since

$$0 \leq y \leq 2 \qquad \text{(Outer limits of integration)}$$

we have the region R as shown in the figure.

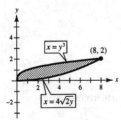

(b) To change the order of integration to $dy \, dx$, place a vertical rectangle in the region. From this you can see that the constant bounds $0 \leq x \leq 8$ serve as the outer limits of integration. By solving for y in the equations $x = y^3$ and $x = 4\sqrt{2y}$, we have $y = \sqrt[3]{x}$ and $y = x^2/32$, respectively. Therefore, the inner bounds are

$$\frac{x^2}{32} \leq y \leq \sqrt[3]{x}$$

and the required integral is

$$\int_0^8 \int_{x^2/32}^{\sqrt[3]{x}} (x^2 y - xy^2) \, dy \, dx.$$

(c) Using a symbolic integration utility to evaluate both integrals yields

$$\frac{67{,}520}{693}.$$

61. $\displaystyle\int_0^2 \int_0^{4-x^2} e^{xy} \, dy \, dx \approx 20.5648$

63. An iterated integral is a double integral of a function of two variables. First integrate with respect to one variable while holding the other variable constant. Then integrate with respect to the second variable.

65. True

Section 13.2   Double Integrals and Volume

For Exercises 1 and 3, $\Delta x_i = \Delta y_i = 1$ and the midpoints of the squares are

$$\left(\frac{1}{2}, \frac{1}{2}\right), \left(\frac{3}{2}, \frac{1}{2}\right), \left(\frac{5}{2}, \frac{1}{2}\right), \left(\frac{7}{2}, \frac{1}{2}\right), \left(\frac{1}{2}, \frac{3}{2}\right), \left(\frac{3}{2}, \frac{3}{2}\right), \left(\frac{5}{2}, \frac{3}{2}\right), \left(\frac{7}{2}, \frac{3}{2}\right).$$

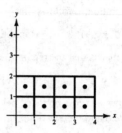

1. $f(x, y) = x + y$

$$\sum_{i=1}^{8} f(x_i, y_i)\, \Delta x_i \Delta y_i = 1 + 2 + 3 + 4 + 2 + 3 + 4 + 5 = 24$$

$$\int_0^4 \int_0^2 (x + y)\, dy\, dx = \int_0^4 \left[xy + \frac{y^2}{2}\right]_0^2 dx = \int_0^4 (2x + 2)\, dx = \left[x^2 + 2x\right]_0^4 = 24$$

3. $f(x, y) = x^2 + y^2$

$$\sum_{i=1}^{8} f(x_i, y_i)\, \Delta x_i \Delta y_i = \frac{2}{4} + \frac{10}{4} + \frac{26}{4} + \frac{50}{4} + \frac{10}{4} + \frac{18}{4} + \frac{34}{4} + \frac{58}{4} = 52$$

$$\int_0^4 \int_0^2 (x^2 + y^2)\, dy\, dx = \int_0^4 \left[x^2 y + \frac{y^3}{3}\right]_0^2 dx = \int_0^4 \left(2x^2 + \frac{8}{3}\right) dx = \left[\frac{2x^3}{3} + \frac{8x}{3}\right]_0^4 = \frac{160}{3}$$

5. $\displaystyle\int_0^2 \int_0^1 (1 + 2x + 2y)\, dy\, dx = \int_0^2 \left[y + 2xy + y^2\right]_0^1 dx$

$$= \int_0^2 (2 + 2x)\, dx$$

$$= \left[2x + x^2\right]_0^2 = 8$$

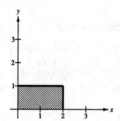

7. $\displaystyle\int_0^6 \int_{y/2}^3 (x + y)\, dx\, dy$

From the given limits of integration, it follows that

$$\frac{y}{2} \le x \le 3 \qquad \text{(Inner limits of integration)}$$

which means that the region R is bounded on the left by $x = y/2$ and on the right by $x = 3$. Furthermore, since

$$0 \le y \le 6, \qquad \text{(Outer limits of integration)}$$

it follows that R is bounded by the x-axis as shown in the figure.

$$\int_0^6 \int_{y/2}^3 (x + y)\, dx\, dy = \int_0^6 \left(\frac{1}{2}x^2 + xy\right)\Big]_{y/2}^3 dy$$

$$= \int_0^6 \left[\left(\frac{9}{2} + 3y\right) - \left(\frac{y^2}{8} + \frac{y^2}{2}\right)\right] dy$$

$$= \int_0^6 \left(\frac{9}{2} + 3y - \frac{5y^2}{8}\right) dy$$

$$= \left[\frac{9}{2}y + \frac{3}{2}y^2 - \frac{5}{24}y^3\right]_0^6 = 36$$

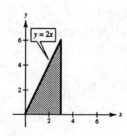

9. $\displaystyle\int_{-a}^{a}\int_{-\sqrt{a^2-x^2}}^{\sqrt{a^2-x^2}} (x+y)\,dy\,dx = \int_{-a}^{a}\left[xy+\frac{1}{2}y^2\right]_{-\sqrt{a^2-x^2}}^{\sqrt{a^2-x^2}}\,dx$

$$= \int_{-a}^{a} 2x\sqrt{a^2-x^2}\,dx$$

$$= \left[-\frac{2}{3}(a^2-x^2)^{3/2}\right]_{-a}^{a} = 0$$

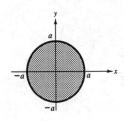

11. $\displaystyle\int_{0}^{5}\int_{0}^{3} xy\,dx\,dy = \int_{0}^{3}\int_{0}^{5} xy\,dy\,dx$

$$= \int_{0}^{3}\left[\frac{1}{2}xy^2\right]_{0}^{5}\,dx$$

$$= \frac{25}{2}\int_{0}^{3} x\,dx$$

$$= \left[\frac{25}{4}x^2\right]_{0}^{3} = \frac{225}{4}$$

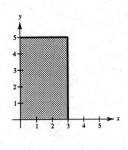

13. *R* is shown in the figure.

$$\iint_{R}\frac{y}{x^2+y^2}\,dx\,dy = \int_{0}^{2}\int_{y/2}^{y}\frac{y}{x^2+y^2}\,dx\,dy + \int_{2}^{4}\int_{y/2}^{2}\frac{y}{x^2+y^2}\,dx\,dy$$

and

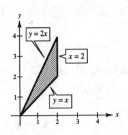

$$\iint_{R}\frac{y}{x^2+y^2}\,dy\,dx = \int_{0}^{2}\int_{x}^{2x}\frac{y}{x^2+y^2}\,dy\,dx$$

$$= \frac{1}{2}\int_{0}^{2}\left[\ln(x^2+y^2)\right]_{x}^{2x}\,dx$$

$$= \frac{1}{2}\int_{0}^{2}[\ln(5x^2) - \ln(2x^2)]\,dx$$

$$= \frac{1}{2}\int_{0}^{2}\ln\frac{5}{2}\,dx$$

$$= \frac{1}{2}\left[x\ln\frac{5}{2}\right]_{0}^{2} = \ln\frac{5}{2}$$

15. $\displaystyle\int_{0}^{4}\int_{0}^{3x/4} x\,dy\,dx + \int_{4}^{5}\int_{0}^{\sqrt{25-x^2}} x\,dy\,dx = \int_{0}^{3}\int_{4y/3}^{\sqrt{25-y^2}} x\,dx\,dy$

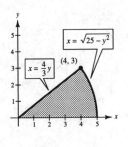

$$= \int_{0}^{3}\left[\frac{1}{2}x^2\right]_{4y/3}^{\sqrt{25-y^2}}\,dy$$

$$= \frac{25}{18}\int_{0}^{3}(9-y^2)\,dy$$

$$= \left[\frac{25}{18}\left(9y-\frac{1}{3}y^3\right)\right]_{0}^{3} = 25$$

17. $\displaystyle\int_0^4 \int_0^2 \frac{y}{2}\,dy\,dx = \int_0^4 \left[\frac{y^4}{4}\right]_0^2 dx$

$\displaystyle\qquad\qquad = \int_0^4 dx = 4$

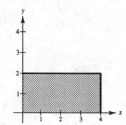

19. $\displaystyle\int_0^2 \int_0^y (6 - x - y)\,dx\,dy = \int_0^2 \left[6x - \frac{x^2}{2} - xy\right]_0^y dy$

$\displaystyle\qquad\qquad = \int_0^2 \left(6y - \frac{3}{2}y^2\right) dy$

$\displaystyle\qquad\qquad = \left[3y^2 - \frac{1}{2}y^3\right]_0^2$

$\displaystyle\qquad\qquad = 8$

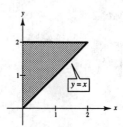

21. The solid is shown in the figure. By letting $z = 0$, if follows that the base of the solid is the triangle in the *xy*-plane bounded by the graphs of

$2x + 3y = 12,\ x = 0,$ and $y = 0.$

If the order of integration is $dy\,dx$, then the bounds of the region are

Variable bounds for y: $0 \le y \le 4 - \dfrac{2}{3}x$

Constant bounds for x: $0 \le x \le 6.$

Therefore, the volume is

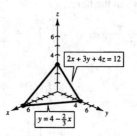

$\displaystyle V = \int_0^6 \int_0^{4-(2/3)x} \left(3 - \frac{1}{2}x - \frac{3}{4}y\right) dy\,dx$

$\displaystyle\quad = \int_0^6 \left(3y - \frac{1}{2}xy - \frac{3}{8}y^2\right)\Big|_0^{4-(2/3)x} dx$

$\displaystyle\quad = \int_0^6 \left(6 - 2x + \frac{1}{6}x^2\right) dx$

$\displaystyle\quad = \left[6x - x^2 + \frac{1}{18}x^3\right]_0^6 = 12.$

23. $\displaystyle\int_0^1 \int_0^y (1 - xy)\,dx\,dy = \int_0^1 \left[x - \frac{x^2 y}{2}\right]_0^y dy$

$\displaystyle\qquad\qquad = \int_0^1 \left(y - \frac{y^3}{2}\right) dy$

$\displaystyle\qquad\qquad = \left[\frac{y^2}{2} - \frac{y^4}{8}\right]_0^1$

$\displaystyle\qquad\qquad = \frac{3}{8}$

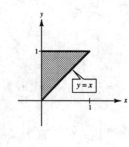

25. $\displaystyle\int_0^\infty \int_0^\infty \frac{1}{(x+1)^2(y+1)^2}\,dy\,dx = \int_0^\infty \left[-\frac{1}{(x+1)^2(y+1)}\right]_0^\infty dx = \int_0^\infty \frac{1}{(x+1)^2}\,dx = \left[-\frac{1}{(x+1)}\right]_0^\infty = 1$

27. $4\displaystyle\int_0^2 \int_0^{\sqrt{4-x^2}} (4 - x^2 - y^2)\, dy\, dx = 8\pi$

29. $V = \displaystyle\int_0^1 \int_0^x xy\, dy\, dx$

$$= \int_0^1 \left[\frac{1}{2}xy^2\right]_0^x dx = \frac{1}{2}\int_0^1 x^3\, dx$$

$$= \left[\frac{1}{8}x^4\right]_0^1 = \frac{1}{8}$$

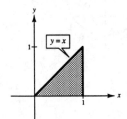

31. $V = \displaystyle\int_0^2 \int_0^4 x^2\, dy\, dx$

$$= \int_0^2 \left[x^2 y\right]_0^4 dx = \int_0^2 4x^2\, dx$$

$$= \left[\frac{4x^3}{3}\right]_0^2 = \frac{32}{3}$$

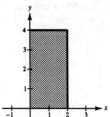

33. The figure shows the solid in the first octant. Divide this solid in two equal parts by the plane $y = x$ and find $\frac{1}{2}$ of the total volume. Therefore, integrate the function

$$z = \sqrt{1 - x^2}$$

over the triangle bounded by $y = 0$, $y = x$, and $x = 1$.

    Constant bounds for x: $0 \le x \le 1$

    Variable bounds for y: $0 \le y \le x$

$$V = 2\int_0^1 \int_0^x \sqrt{1 - x^2}\, dy\, dx$$

$$= 2\int_0^1 x\sqrt{1 - x^2}\, dx$$

$$= \left[-\frac{2}{3}(1 - x^2)^{3/2}\right]_0^1 = \frac{2}{3}.$$

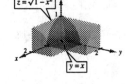

(Thus, the volume is twice that of Exercise 28.)

35. $V = \displaystyle\int_0^2 \int_0^{\sqrt{4-x^2}} (x + y)\, dy\, dx$

$$= \int_0^2 \left[xy + \frac{1}{2}y^2\right]_0^{\sqrt{4-x^2}} dx$$

$$= \int_0^2 \left(x\sqrt{4 - x^2} + 2 - \frac{1}{2}x^2\right) dx$$

$$= \left[-\frac{1}{3}(4 - x^2)^{3/2} + 2x - \frac{1}{6}x^3\right]_0^2 = \frac{16}{3}$$

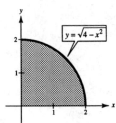

37. $V = 4\displaystyle\int_0^2 \int_0^{\sqrt{4-x^2}} (x^2 + y^2)\, dy\, dx$

$$= 4\int_0^2 \left[x^2\sqrt{4 - x^2} + \frac{1}{3}(4 - x^2)^{3/2}\right] dx, \quad x = 2\sin\theta$$

$$= 4\int_0^{\pi/2} \left(16\cos^2\theta - \frac{32}{3}\cos^4\theta\right) d\theta$$

$$= 4\left[16\left(\frac{\pi}{4}\right) - \frac{32}{3}\left(\frac{3\pi}{16}\right)\right]$$

$$= 8\pi$$

39. $z = 4 - x^2 - y^2$

Because of the symmetry of the paraboloid, find the volume of the solid in the first octant (one-fourth the total volume). Thus, you integrate over the first-quadrant portion of the circle in the figure.

Constant bounds for x: $0 \le x \le 2$

Variable bounds for y: $0 \le y \le \sqrt{4 - x^2}$

Using this information and a symbolic integration utility we have

$$V = 4 \int_0^2 \int_0^{\sqrt{4-x^2}} (4 - x^2 - y^2) \, dy \, dx = 8\pi.$$

Note that without the aid of a computer or calculator we would have the following

$$V = 4 \int_0^2 \int_0^{\sqrt{4-x^2}} (4 - x^2 - y^2) \, dy \, dx$$

$$= 4 \int_0^2 \left[4y - x^2 y - \frac{1}{3}y^3 \right]_0^{\sqrt{4-x^2}} dx$$

$$= \frac{8}{3} \int_0^2 (4 - x^2)^{3/2} \, dx$$

$$= \frac{8}{3} \int_0^{\pi/2} (2 \cos \theta)^3 (2 \cos \theta) \, d\theta \quad \text{(Let } x = 2 \sin \theta.\text{)}$$

$$= \frac{128}{3} \int_0^{\pi/2} \cos^4 \theta \, d\theta = 8\pi.$$

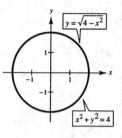

41. $V = \int_0^2 \int_0^{-0.5x+1} \dfrac{2}{1 + x^2 + y^2} \, dy \, dx \approx 1.2315$

43. f is a continuous function such that $0 \le f(x, y) \le 1$ over a region R of area 1. Let $f(m, n) = $ the minimum value of f over R and $f(M, N) = $ the maximum value of f over R. Then

$$f(m, n) \iint_R dA \le \iint_R f(x, y) \, dA \le f(M, N) \iint_R dA.$$

Since $\iint_R dA = 1$ and $0 \le f(m, n) \le f(M, N) \le 1$, we have $0 \le f(m, n)(1) \le \iint_R f(x, y) \, dA \le f(M, N)(1) \le 1$.

Therefore, $0 \le \iint_R f(x, y) \, dA \le 1$.

45. $\displaystyle \int_0^1 \int_{y/2}^{1/2} e^{-x^2} \, dx \, dy = \int_0^{1/2} \int_0^{2x} e^{-x^2} \, dy \, dx$

$$= \int_0^{1/2} 2x e^{-x^2} \, dx$$

$$= \left[-e^{-x^2} \right]_0^{1/2}$$

$$= -e^{-1/4} + 1$$

$$= 1 - e^{-1/4} \approx 0.221$$

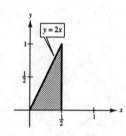

47. $\displaystyle\int_0^{\ln 10}\int_{e^x}^{10}\frac{1}{\ln y}\,dy\,dx$

Since it is not possible to perform the inner integration, it is necessary to switch the order of integration. From the given limits of integration, we know that

$e^x \le y \le 10$ $\qquad$ (Inner limits of integration)

and

$0 \le x \le \ln 10.$ $\qquad$ (Outer limits of integration)

The region R is shown in the figure. Observe from the figure that if the order of integration is reversed, the outer limits of integration are $1 \le y \le 10$ and the inner limits of integration are $0 \le x \le \ln y$. Therefore,

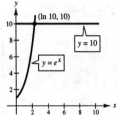

$$\int_0^{\ln 10}\int_{e^x}^{10}\frac{1}{\ln y}\,dy\,dx = \int_1^{10}\int_0^{\ln y}\frac{1}{\ln y}\,dx\,dy$$

$$= \int_1^{10}\left[\frac{x}{\ln y}\right]_0^{\ln y}dy$$

$$= \int_1^{10}1\,dy = \left[y\right]_1^{10} = 9.$$

49. Average $= \displaystyle\frac{1}{8}\int_0^4\int_0^2 x\,dy\,dx = \frac{1}{8}\int_0^4 2x\,dx = \left[\frac{x^2}{8}\right]_0^4 = 2$

51. Average $= \displaystyle\frac{1}{4}\int_0^2\int_0^2 (x^2 + y^2)\,dx\,dy$

$$= \frac{1}{4}\int_0^2\left[\frac{x^3}{3} + xy^2\right]_0^2 dy = \frac{1}{4}\int_0^2\left(\frac{8}{3} + 2y^2\right)dy$$

$$= \left[\frac{1}{4}\left(\frac{8}{3}y + \frac{2}{3}y^3\right)\right]_0^2 = \frac{8}{3}$$

53. $f(x, y) = 100x^{0.6}y^{0.4},\ 200 \le x \le 250,\ 300 \le y \le 325$

The average value of $f(x, y)$ over the region R is

$$\text{average} = \frac{1}{A}\int_R\int f(x, y)\,dA.$$

The plane region R is a rectangle bounded by $200 \le x \le 250$ and $300 \le y \le 325$. Therefore, its area is

$$A = (250 - 200)(325 - 300) = 1250$$

and the average value of f over the region is

$$\text{average} = \frac{1}{1250}\int_{300}^{325}\int_{200}^{250}100x^{0.6}y^{0.4}\,dx\,dy$$

$$= \frac{1}{1250}\int_{300}^{325}(100y^{0.4})\frac{x^{1.6}}{1.6}\bigg]_{200}^{250}dy$$

$$= \frac{128,844.1}{1250}\int_{300}^{325}y^{0.4}\,dy$$

$$= 103.075\left[\frac{y^{1.4}}{1.4}\right]_{300}^{325} \approx 25,645.$$

55. The value of $\displaystyle\int_R\int f(x, y)\,dA$ would be kB.

57. $f(x, y) \geq 0$ for all (x, y) and

$$\int_{-\infty}^{\infty} \int_{-\infty}^{\infty} f(x, y) \, dA = \int_0^5 \int_0^2 \frac{1}{10} \, dy \, dx = \int_0^5 \frac{1}{5} \, dx = 1$$

$$P(0 \leq x \leq 2, 1 \leq y \leq 2) = \int_0^2 \int_1^2 \frac{1}{10} \, dy \, dx = \int_0^2 \frac{1}{10} \, dx = \frac{1}{5}.$$

59. $f(x, y) = \begin{cases} \frac{1}{27}(9 - x - y), & 0 \leq x \leq 3, 3 \leq y \leq 6 \\ 0, & \text{elsewhere} \end{cases}$

First observe that $f(x, y) \geq 0$ for all (x, y).

$$\int_{-\infty}^{\infty} \int_{-\infty}^{\infty} f(x, y) \, dA = \int_0^3 \int_3^6 \frac{1}{27}(9 - x - y) \, dy \, dx$$

$$= \int_0^3 \frac{1}{27} \left[9y - xy - \frac{1}{2}y^2 \right]_3^6 \, dx$$

$$= \int_0^3 \left(\frac{1}{2} - \frac{1}{9}x \right) \, dx$$

$$= \left[\frac{1}{2}x - \frac{1}{18}x^2 \right]_0^3 = 1$$

Therefore, f is a joint density function. Finally, we find the specified probability.

$$P(0 \leq x \leq 1, 4 \leq y \leq 6) = \int_0^1 \int_4^6 \frac{1}{27}(9 - x - y) \, dy \, dx$$

$$= \int_0^1 \frac{1}{27} \left[9y - xy - \frac{1}{2}y^2 \right]_4^6 \, dx$$

$$= \int_0^1 \frac{2}{27}(4 - x) \, dx$$

$$= \frac{2}{27} \left[4x - \frac{1}{2}x^2 \right]_0^1 = \frac{7}{27}$$

61. Divide the base into six squares, and assume the height at the center of each square is the height of the entire square. Thus, $V \approx (4 + 3 + 6 + 7 + 3 + 2)(100) = 2500m^3$.

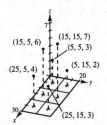

63. $\int_0^1 \int_0^2 \sin \sqrt{x + y} \, dy \, dx \quad m = 4, n = 8$

(a) 1.78435

(b) 1.7879

65. $\int_4^6 \int_0^2 y \cos \sqrt{x} \, dx \, dy \quad m = 4, n = 8$

(a) 11.0571

(b) 11.0414

67. Essay

69. $V \approx 50$

Matches a.

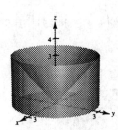

71. True

73. $\displaystyle\int_1^2 e^{-xy}\, dy = \left[-\frac{1}{x}e^{-xy} \right]_1^2 = \frac{e^{-x} - e^{-2x}}{x}$

Thus,

$$\int_0^\infty \frac{e^{-x} - e^{-2x}}{x}\, dx = \int_0^\infty \int_1^2 e^{-xy}\, dy\, dx$$

$$= \int_1^2 \int_0^\infty e^{-xy}\, dx\, dy$$

$$= \int_1^2 \left[-\frac{e^{-xy}}{y} \right]_0^\infty dy$$

$$= \int_1^2 \frac{1}{y}\, dy = \left[\ln y \right]_1^2 = \ln 2.$$

Section 13.3   Change of Variables: Polar Coordinates

1. $\displaystyle\int_0^{2\pi} \int_0^6 3r^2 \sin\theta\, dr\, d\theta = \int_0^{2\pi} \left[r^3 \sin\theta \right]_0^6 d\theta$

$$= \int_0^{2\pi} 216 \sin\theta\, d\theta$$

$$= \left[-216 \cos\theta \right]_0^{2\pi} = 0$$

3. $\displaystyle\int_0^{\pi/2} \int_2^3 \sqrt{9 - r^2}\, r\, dr\, d\theta = \int_0^{\pi/2} \left[-\frac{1}{3}(9 - r^2)^{3/2} \right]_2^3 d\theta$

$$= \left[\frac{5\sqrt{5}}{3}\theta \right]_0^{\pi/2}$$

$$= \frac{5\sqrt{5}\,\pi}{6}$$

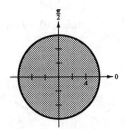

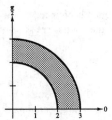

5. $\displaystyle\int_0^{\pi/2} \int_0^{1+\sin\theta} \theta r\, dr\, d\theta$

From the given limits of integration, we know that the inner limits are $0 \le r \le 1 + \sin\theta$ and the outer limits are $0 \le \theta \le \pi/2$. Hence, the region R is the first quadrant portion of the cardioid $r = 1 + \sin\theta$ as shown in the figure.

$$\int_0^{\pi/2} \int_0^{1+\sin\theta} \theta r\, dr\, d\theta = \frac{1}{2}\int_0^{\pi/2} \left[\theta r^2 \right]_0^{1+\sin\theta} d\theta$$

$$= \frac{1}{2}\int_0^{\pi/2} (\theta + 2\theta \sin\theta + \theta \sin^2\theta)\, d\theta$$

$$= \frac{1}{2}\int_0^{\pi/2} \left(\frac{3}{2}\theta + 2\theta \sin\theta - \frac{1}{2}\theta \cos 2\theta \right) d\theta = \frac{9}{8} + \frac{3\pi^2}{32}$$

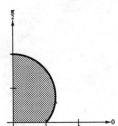

7. $A = \int_0^\pi \int_0^{6\cos\theta} r\,dr\,d\theta = \int_0^\pi 18\cos^2\theta\,d\theta = 9\int_0^\pi (1 + \cos 2\theta)\,d\theta = \left[9\left(\theta + \frac{1}{2}\sin 2\theta\right)\right]_0^\pi = 9\pi$

9. Using polar axis symmetry, we have

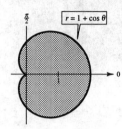

$$A = 2\int_0^\pi \int_0^{1+\cos\theta} r\,dr\,d\theta$$

$$= \int_0^\pi \left[r^2\right]_0^{1+\cos\theta} d\theta$$

$$= \int_0^\pi (1 + 2\cos\theta + \cos^2\theta)\,d\theta$$

$$= \int_0^\pi \left(\frac{3}{2} + 2\cos\theta + \frac{1}{2}\cos 2\theta\right) d\theta$$

$$= \left[\frac{3}{2}\theta + 2\sin\theta + \frac{1}{4}\sin 2\theta\right]_0^\pi = \frac{3\pi}{2}$$

11. $3\int_0^{\pi/3}\int_0^{2\sin 3\theta} r\,dr\,d\theta = \frac{3}{2}\int_0^{\pi/3} 4\sin^2 3\theta\,d\theta = 3\int_0^{\pi/3}(1 - \cos 6\theta)\,d\theta = 3\left[\theta - \frac{1}{6}\sin 6\theta\right]_0^{\pi/3} = \pi$

13. $\int_0^a \int_0^{\sqrt{a^2-y^2}} y\,dx\,dy = \int_0^{\pi/2}\int_0^a r^2\sin\theta\,dr\,d\theta = \frac{a^3}{3}\int_0^{\pi/2}\sin\theta\,d\theta = \left[\frac{a^3}{3}(-\cos\theta)\right]_0^{\pi/2} = \frac{a^3}{3}$

15. $\int_0^3 \int_0^{\sqrt{9-x^2}} (x^2 + y^2)^{3/2}\,dy\,dx = \int_0^{\pi/2}\int_0^3 r^4\,dr\,d\theta = \frac{243}{5}\int_0^{\pi/2} d\theta = \frac{243\pi}{10}$

17. $\int_0^2 \int_0^{\sqrt{2x-x^2}} xy\,dy\,dx$

From the limits of integration it follows that

$$0 \le x \le 2$$
$$0 \le y \le \sqrt{2x - x^2} = \sqrt{1 - (x-1)^2}.$$

Therefore, the region of integration is bounded by the semicircle in the first quadrant with radius 1 and center $(1, 0)$ a shown in the figure. In polar coordinates the bounds are

$$0 \le \theta \le \frac{\pi}{2}$$

$$0 \le r \le 2\cos\theta.$$

Consequently, the double integral in polar coordinates is

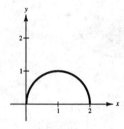

$$\int_0^{\pi/2}\int_0^{2\cos\theta} (r\cos\theta)(r\sin\theta)\,r\,dr\,d\theta = \int_0^{\pi/2}\int_0^{2\cos\theta} r^3\sin\theta\cos\theta\,dr\,d\theta$$

$$= \frac{1}{4}\int_0^{\pi/2}\left[r^4\sin\theta\cos\theta\right]_0^{2\cos\theta} d\theta$$

$$= 4\int_0^{\pi/2}\cos^5\theta\sin\theta\,d\theta$$

$$= -\frac{4}{6}\left[\cos^6\theta\right]_0^{\pi/2} = \frac{2}{3}.$$

19. $\int_0^2 \int_0^x \sqrt{x^2 + y^2}\, dy\, dx + \int_0^{2\sqrt{2}} \int_0^{\sqrt{8-x^2}} \sqrt{x^2 + y^2}\, dy\, dx$

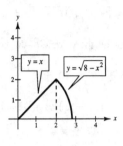

From the figure we can see that R has the bounds

$0 \le y \le x$ $0 \le x \le 2$

$0 \le y \le \sqrt{8 - x^2}$ $2 \le x \le 2\sqrt{2}$

and these bounds form a sector of a circle. In polar coordinates the bounds are

$0 \le r \le 2\sqrt{2}$ and $0 \le \theta \le \dfrac{\pi}{4}$

where the integrand is $\sqrt{x^2 + y^2} = r$. Consequently, the double integral in polar coordinates is

$$\int_0^{\pi/4} \int_0^{2\sqrt{2}} (r)r\, dr\, d\theta = \int_0^{\pi/4} \left[\frac{1}{3}r^3\right]_0^{2\sqrt{2}} d\theta = \frac{16\sqrt{2}}{3} \int_0^{\pi/4} d\theta = \frac{4\sqrt{2}\pi}{3}.$$

21. $\int_0^2 \int_0^{\sqrt{4-x^2}} (x + y)\, dy\, dx = \int_0^{\pi/2} \int_0^2 (r\cos\theta + r\sin\theta)r\, dr\, d\theta = \int_0^{\pi/2} \int_0^2 (\cos\theta + \sin\theta)r^2\, dr\, d\theta$

$$= \frac{8}{3} \int_0^{\pi/2} (\cos\theta + \sin\theta)\, d\theta = \left[\frac{8}{3}(\sin\theta - \cos\theta)\right]_0^{\pi/2} = \frac{16}{3}$$

23. $\int_0^{1/\sqrt{2}} \int_{\sqrt{1-y^2}}^{\sqrt{4-y^2}} \arctan\frac{y}{x}\, dx\, dy + \int_{1/\sqrt{2}}^{\sqrt{2}} \int_y^{\sqrt{4-y^2}} \arctan\frac{y}{x}\, dx\, dy = \int_0^{\pi/4} \int_1^2 \theta r\, dr\, d\theta$

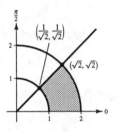

25. $V = \int_0^{\pi/2} \int_0^1 (r\cos\theta)(r\sin\theta)r\, dr\, d\theta$

$= \dfrac{1}{2} \int_0^{\pi/2} \int_0^1 r^3 \sin 2\theta\, dr\, d\theta$

$= \dfrac{1}{8} \int_0^{\pi/2} \sin 2\theta\, d\theta$

$= \left[-\dfrac{1}{16}\cos 2\theta\right]_0^{\pi/2} = \dfrac{1}{8}$

27. $V = \int_0^{2\pi} \int_0^5 r^2\, dr\, d\theta = \dfrac{250\pi}{3}$

29. Writing the equation for the cylinder in polar form we have $r = 4\cos\theta$. We can see from the figure that in polar coordinates R has the bounds

$0 \le r \le 4\cos\theta$ and $-\dfrac{\pi}{2} \le \theta \le \dfrac{\pi}{2}$

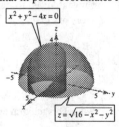

and $z = \sqrt{16 - x^2 - y^2} = \sqrt{16 - r^2}$. Since the solid is symmetric with respect to the xz-plane, the volume V is given by

$$V = 2\int_0^{\pi/2} \int_0^{4\cos\theta} \sqrt{16 - r^2}\, r\, dr\, d\theta = -\frac{2}{3}\int_0^{\pi/2} [(16 - 16\cos^2\theta)^{3/2} - 64]\, d\theta$$

$$= \frac{128}{3} \int_0^{\pi/2} (1 - \sin^3\theta)\, d\theta = \frac{64}{9}(3\pi - 4).$$

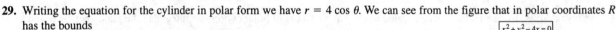

31. $V = \displaystyle\int_0^{2\pi} \int_a^4 \sqrt{16 - r^2}\, r\, dr\, d\theta = \int_0^{2\pi} \left[-\frac{1}{3}\left(\sqrt{16 - r^2}\right)^3 \right]_a^4 d\theta = \frac{1}{3}\left(\sqrt{16 - a^2}\right)^3 (2\pi)$

One-half the volume of the hemisphere is $(64\pi)/3$.

$$\frac{2\pi}{3}(16 - a^2)^{3/2} = \frac{64\pi}{3}$$

$$(16 - a^2)^{3/2} = 32$$

$$16 - a^2 = 32^{2/3}$$

$$a^2 = 16 - 32^{2/3} = 16 - 8\sqrt[3]{2}$$

$$a = \sqrt{4(4 - 2\sqrt[3]{2})} = 2\sqrt{4 - 2\sqrt[3]{2}} \approx 2.4332$$

33. Using symmetry to find the volume of the solid, we have

$$V = 4\int_0^{\pi/2} \int_0^4 25e^{-r^2/4} r\, dr\, d\theta$$

$$= -200 \int_0^{\pi/2} \int_0^4 e^{-r^2/4}\left(-\frac{r}{2}\right) dr\, d\theta$$

$$= -200 \int_0^{\pi/2} \left[e^{r^2/4} \right]_0^4 d\theta$$

$$= 200(1 - e^{-4}) \int_0^{\pi/2} d\theta = 100\pi(1 - e^{-4}).$$

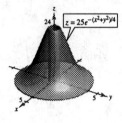

$z = 25e^{-(x^2+y^2)/4}$

Now find the radius a of the hole through the center which is one-tenth the volume of the solid.

$$10\pi(1 - e^{-4}) = 4\int_0^{\pi/2} \int_0^a 25e^{-r^2/4} r\, dr\, d\theta$$

Using the same integration steps as shown above, we have

$$10\pi(1 - e^{-4}) = 100\pi(1 - e^{-a^2/4})$$

$$1 - e^{-4} = 10 - 10e^{-a^2/4}$$

$$e^{-a^2/4} = \frac{9 + e^{-4}}{10}$$

$$-\frac{a^2}{4} = \ln\left(\frac{9 + e^{-4}}{10}\right)$$

$$a^2 = -4\ln\left(\frac{9 + e^{-4}}{10}\right)$$

$$a = \sqrt{-4\ln\left(\frac{9 + e^{-4}}{10}\right)} \approx 0.6429.$$

Therefore, the diameter of the hole is approximately $2(0.6429) = 1.2858$ units.

35. You would need to insert a factor of r because of the $r\, dr\, d\theta$ nature of polar coordinate integrals. The plane regions would be sectors of circles.

37. $\displaystyle\int_{\pi/4}^{\pi/2} \int_0^5 r\sqrt{1 + r^3}\, \sin\sqrt{\theta}\, dr\, d\theta \approx 56.051$

$$\left[\textit{Note: } \text{This integral equals} \left(\int_{\pi/4}^{\pi/2} \sin\sqrt{\theta}\, d\theta \right)\left(\int_0^5 r\sqrt{1 + r^3}\, dr \right) \right]$$

39. Volume = base × height

$$\approx 8\pi \times 12 \approx 300$$

Answer (c)

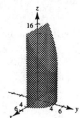

41. False

Let $f(r, \theta) = r - 1$ where R is the circular sector $0 \le r \le 6$ and $0 \le \theta \le \pi$. Then,

$$\int_R \int (r - 1)\, dA > 0 \quad \text{but} \quad r - 1 \not> 0 \text{ for all } r.$$

43. (a) $\displaystyle I^2 = \int_{-\infty}^{\infty} \int_{-\infty}^{\infty} e^{-(x^2 + y^2)/2}\, dA$

$$= 4 \int_0^{\pi/2} \int_0^{\infty} e^{-r^2/2}\, r\, dr\, d\theta$$

$$= 4 \int_0^{\pi/2} \left[-e^{-r^2/2} \right]_0^{\infty} d\theta = 4 \int_0^{\pi/2} d\theta = 2\pi$$

(b) Therefore, $I = \sqrt{2\pi}$.

45. Using the symmetry of the density function, we have the following approximation of the population P.

$$P = 4 \int_0^7 \int_0^{\sqrt{49 - x^2}} 4000 e^{-0.01(x^2 + y^2)}\, dy\, dx$$

$$= 16{,}000 \int_0^{\pi/2} \int_0^7 e^{-0.01 r^2} r\, dr\, d\theta$$

$$= 16{,}000 \int_0^{\pi/2} \left[-50 e^{-0.01 r^2} \right]_0^7 d\theta$$

$$= 800{,}000(1 - e^{-0.49}) \int_0^{\pi/2} d\theta$$

$$= 800{,}000(1 - e^{-0.49}) \frac{\pi}{2}$$

$$= 400{,}000\pi(1 - e^{-0.49}) \approx 486{,}788$$

47. (a) $\displaystyle \int_2^4 \int_{y/\sqrt{3}}^{y} f\, dx\, dy$

(b) $\displaystyle \int_{2/\sqrt{3}}^2 \int_2^{\sqrt{3}x} f\, dy\, dx + \int_2^{4/\sqrt{3}} \int_x^{\sqrt{3}x} f\, dy\, dx + \int_{4/\sqrt{3}}^4 \int_x^4 f\, dy\, dx$

(c) $\displaystyle \int_{\pi/4}^{\pi/3} \int_{2\csc\theta}^{4\csc\theta} f r\, dr\, d\theta$

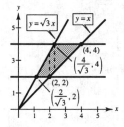

49. $\displaystyle A = \frac{\Delta\theta r_2^2}{2} - \frac{\Delta\theta r_1^2}{2} = \Delta\theta \left(\frac{r_1 + r_2}{2} \right)(r_2 - r_1) = r\Delta r\Delta\theta$

Section 13.4   Center of Mass and Moments of Inertia

1. The rectangular lamina is shown in the figure.

(a) When the lamina has uniform density $\rho = k$, we have the following.

$$m = \int_0^a \int_0^b k\, dy\, dx = kab$$

$$M_x = \int_0^a \int_0^b ky\, dy\, dx = \frac{kab^2}{2}$$

$$M_y = \int_0^a \int_0^b kx\, dy\, dx = \frac{ka^2 b}{2}$$

$$\bar{x} = \frac{M_y}{m} = \frac{ka^2 b/2}{kab} = \frac{a}{2}$$

$$\bar{y} = \frac{M_x}{m} = \frac{kab^2/2}{kab} = \frac{b}{2}$$

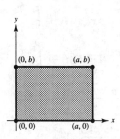

—CONTINUED—

1. —CONTINUED—

(b) When the lamina has density $\rho = ky$, we have the following.

$$m = \int_0^a \int_0^b ky \, dy \, dx = \frac{kab^2}{2}$$

$$M_x = \int_0^a \int_0^b ky^2 \, dy \, dx = \frac{kab^3}{3}$$

$$M_y = \int_0^a \int_0^b kxy \, dy \, dx = \frac{ka^2b^2}{4}$$

$$\bar{x} = \frac{M_y}{m} = \frac{ka^2b^2/4}{kab^2/2} = \frac{a}{2}$$

$$\bar{y} = \frac{M_x}{m} = \frac{kab^3/3}{kab^2/2} = \frac{2}{3}b$$

(c) When the lamina has density $\rho = kx$, we have the following.

$$m = \int_0^a \int_0^b kx \, dy \, dx = \frac{ka^2b}{2}$$

$$M_x = \int_0^a \int_0^b kxy \, dy \, dx = \frac{ka^2b^2}{4}$$

$$M_y = \int_0^a \int_0^b kx^2 \, dy \, dx = \frac{ka^3b}{3}$$

$$\bar{x} = \frac{M_y}{m} = \frac{ka^3b/3}{ka^2b/2} = \frac{2a}{3}$$

$$\bar{y} = \frac{M_x}{m} = \frac{ka^2b^2/4}{ka^2b/2} = \frac{b}{2}$$

3. (a) $m = \dfrac{k}{2}bh$

$\bar{x} = \dfrac{b}{2}$ by symmetry

$$M_x = \int_0^{b/2} \int_0^{2hx/b} ky \, dy \, dx + \int_{b/2}^b \int_0^{-2h(x-b)/b} ky \, dy \, dx = \frac{kbh^2}{12} + \frac{kbh^2}{12} = \frac{kbh^2}{6}$$

$$\bar{y} = \frac{M_x}{m} = \frac{kbh^2/6}{kbh/2} = \frac{h}{3}$$

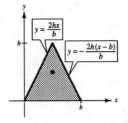

(b) $$m = \int_0^{b/2} \int_0^{2hx/b} ky \, dy \, dx + \int_{b/2}^b \int_0^{-2h(x-b)/b} ky \, dy \, dx = \frac{kbh^2}{6}$$

$$M_x = \int_0^{b/2} \int_0^{2hx/b} ky^2 \, dy \, dx + \int_{b/2}^b \int_0^{-2h(x-b)/b} ky^2 \, dy \, dx = \frac{kbh^2}{12}$$

$$M_y = \int_0^{b/2} \int_0^{2hx/b} kxy \, dy \, dx + \int_{b/2}^b \int_0^{-2h(x-b)/b} kxy \, dy \, dx = \frac{kb^2h^2}{12}$$

$$\bar{x} = \frac{M_y}{m} = \frac{kb^2h^2/12}{kbh^2/6} = \frac{b}{2}$$

$$\bar{y} = \frac{M_x}{m} = \frac{kbh^3/12}{kbh^2/6} = \frac{h}{2}$$

(c) $$m = \int_0^{b/2} \int_0^{2hx/b} kx \, dy \, dx + \int_{b/2}^b \int_0^{-2h(x-b)/b} kx \, dy \, dx = \frac{1}{12}kb^2h + \frac{1}{6}kb^2h = \frac{1}{4}kb^2h$$

$$M_x = \int_0^{b/2} \int_0^{2hx/b} kxy \, dy \, dx + \int_{b/2}^b \int_0^{-2h(x-b)/b} kxy \, dy \, dx = \frac{1}{32}kh^2b^2 + \frac{5}{96}kh^2b^2 = \frac{1}{12}kh^2b^2$$

$$M_y = \int_0^{b/2} \int_0^{2hx/b} kx^2 \, dy \, dx + \int_{b/2}^b \int_0^{-2h(x-b)/b} kx^2 \, dy \, dx = \frac{1}{32}kb^3h + \frac{11}{96}kb^3h = \frac{7}{48}kb^3h$$

$$\bar{x} = \frac{M_y}{m} = \frac{7kb^3h/48}{kb^2h/4} = \frac{7}{12}b$$

$$\bar{y} = \frac{M_x}{m} = \frac{kh^2b^2/12}{kb^2h/4} = \frac{h}{3}$$

5. (a) The x-coordinate changes by 5: $(\bar{x}, \bar{y}) = \left(\dfrac{a}{2} + 5, \dfrac{b}{2}\right)$

(b) The x-coordinate changes by 5: $(\bar{x}, \bar{y}) = \left(\dfrac{a}{2} + 5, \dfrac{2b}{3}\right)$

(c) $m = \displaystyle\int_5^{a+5} \int_0^b kx \, dy \, dx = \frac{1}{2}k(a+5)^2 b^2 - \frac{25}{4}kb^2$

$M_x = \displaystyle\int_5^{a+5} \int_0^b kxy \, dy \, dx = \frac{1}{4}k(a+5)^2 b^2 - \frac{25}{4}kb^2$

$M_y = \displaystyle\int_5^{a+5} \int_0^b kx^2 \, dy \, dx = \frac{1}{3}k(a+5)^3 b - \frac{125}{3}kb$

$\bar{x} = \dfrac{M_y}{m} = \dfrac{2(a^2 + 15a + 75)}{3(a+10)}$

$\bar{y} = \dfrac{M_x}{m} = \dfrac{b}{2}$

7. The semicircular lamina is shown in the figure.

(a) Since the density is uniform ($\rho = k$) and the lamina is symmetric to the y-axis, $\bar{x} = 0$.

$m = \dfrac{\pi a^2 k}{2}$

$M_x = \displaystyle\int_{-a}^a \int_0^{\sqrt{a^2-x^2}} ky \, dy \, dx = \frac{2a^3 k}{3}$

$\bar{y} = \dfrac{M_x}{m} = \dfrac{2a^3 k/3}{\pi a^2 k/2} = \dfrac{4a}{3\pi}$

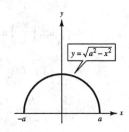

(b) When the lamina has density $\rho = k(a - y)y$, we have the following.

$m = \displaystyle\int_{-a}^a \int_0^{\sqrt{a^2-x^2}} k(a-y)y \, dy \, dx = \frac{a^4 k}{24}(16 - 3\pi)$

$M_x = \displaystyle\int_{-a}^a \int_0^{\sqrt{a^2-x^2}} k(a-y)y^2 \, dy \, dx = \frac{a^5 k}{120}(15\pi - 32)$

$M_y = \displaystyle\int_{-a}^a \int_0^{\sqrt{a^2-x^2}} kx(a-y)y \, dy \, dx = 0$

$\bar{x} = \dfrac{M_y}{m} = 0$

$\bar{y} = \dfrac{M_x}{m} = \dfrac{a^5 k(15\pi - 32)/120}{a^4 k(16 - 3\pi)/24} = \dfrac{a}{5}\left(\dfrac{15\pi - 32}{16 - 3\pi}\right)$

9. $m = \displaystyle\int_0^4 \int_0^{\sqrt{x}} kxy \, dy \, dx = \frac{32k}{3}$

$M_x = \displaystyle\int_0^4 \int_0^{\sqrt{x}} kxy^2 \, dy \, dx = \frac{256k}{21}$

$M_y = \displaystyle\int_0^4 \int_0^{\sqrt{x}} kx^2 y \, dy \, dx = 32k$

$\bar{x} = \dfrac{M_y}{m} = \dfrac{32k}{1} \cdot \dfrac{3}{32k} = 3$

$\bar{y} = \dfrac{M_x}{m} = \dfrac{256k}{21} \cdot \dfrac{3}{32k} = \dfrac{8}{7}$

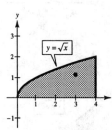

11. $\bar{x} = 0$ by symmetry

$m = \displaystyle\int_{-1}^1 \int_0^{1/(1+x^2)} k \, dy \, dx = \frac{k\pi}{2}$

$M_x = \displaystyle\int_{-1}^1 \int_0^{1/(1+x^2)} ky \, dy \, dx = \frac{k}{8}(2 + \pi)$

$\bar{y} = \dfrac{M_x}{m} = \dfrac{k}{8}(2 + \pi) \cdot \dfrac{2}{k\pi} = \dfrac{2 + \pi}{4\pi}$

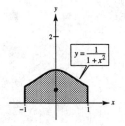

13. $\bar{y} = 0$ by symmetry

$$m = \int_{-4}^{4}\int_{0}^{16-y^2} kx\,dx\,dy = \frac{8192k}{15}$$

$$M_y = \int_{-4}^{4}\int_{0}^{16-y^2} kx^2\,dx\,dy = \frac{524{,}288k}{105}$$

$$\bar{x} = \frac{M_y}{m} = \frac{524{,}288k}{105}\cdot\frac{15}{8192k} = \frac{64}{7}$$

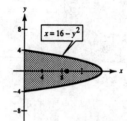

15. By symmetry, we have $\bar{x} = L/2$.

$$m = \int_{0}^{L}\int_{0}^{\sin(\pi x/L)} ky\,dy\,dx$$

$$= \frac{k}{2}\int_{0}^{L}\sin^2\left(\frac{\pi x}{L}\right) dx$$

$$= \frac{k}{4}\int_{0}^{L}\left[1 - \cos\left(\frac{2\pi x}{L}\right)\right] dx$$

$$= \frac{k}{4}\left[x - \frac{L}{2\pi}\sin\left(\frac{2\pi x}{L}\right)\right]_{0}^{L} = \frac{kL}{4}$$

$$M_x = \int_{0}^{L}\int_{0}^{\sin(\pi x/L)} ky^2\,dy\,dx$$

$$= \frac{k}{3}\int_{0}^{L}\sin^3\left(\frac{\pi x}{L}\right) dx$$

$$= \frac{k}{3}\int_{0}^{L}\left[\sin\left(\frac{\pi x}{L}\right) - \cos^2\left(\frac{\pi x}{L}\right)\sin\left(\frac{\pi x}{L}\right)\right] dx$$

$$= \frac{kL}{3\pi}\left[-\cos\left(\frac{\pi x}{L}\right) + \frac{1}{3}\cos^3\left(\frac{\pi x}{L}\right)\right]_{0}^{L} = \frac{4kL}{9\pi}$$

$$\bar{y} = \frac{M_x}{m} = \frac{4kL/9\pi}{kL/4} = \frac{16}{9\pi}$$

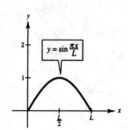

17. $m = \dfrac{\pi a^2 k}{8}$

$$M_x = \iint_R ky\,dA = \int_0^{\pi/4}\int_0^a kr^2\sin\theta\,dr\,d\theta = \frac{ka^3(2-\sqrt{2})}{6}$$

$$M_y = \iint_R kx\,dA = \int_0^{\pi/4}\int_0^a kr^2\cos\theta\,dr\,d\theta = \frac{ka^3\sqrt{2}}{6}$$

$$\bar{x} = \frac{M_y}{m} = \frac{ka^3\sqrt{2}}{6}\cdot\frac{8}{\pi a^2 k} = \frac{4a\sqrt{2}}{3\pi}$$

$$\bar{y} = \frac{M_x}{m} = \frac{ka^3(2-\sqrt{2})}{6}\cdot\frac{8}{\pi a^2 k} = \frac{4a(2-\sqrt{2})}{3\pi}$$

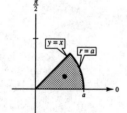

19. $m = \displaystyle\int_0^2\int_0^{e^{-x}} ky\,dy\,dx = \frac{k}{4}(1 - e^{-4})$

$$M_x = \int_0^2\int_0^{e^{-x}} ky^2\,dy\,dx = \frac{k}{9}(1 - e^{-6})$$

$$M_y = \int_0^2\int_0^{e^{-x}} kxy\,dy\,dx = \frac{k(1 - 5e^{-4})}{8}$$

$$\bar{x} = \frac{M_y}{m} = \frac{k(e^4-5)}{8e^4}\cdot\frac{4e^4}{k(e^4-1)} = \frac{e^4-5}{2(e^4-1)} \approx 0.46$$

$$\bar{y} = \frac{M_x}{m} = \frac{k(e^6-1)}{9e^6}\cdot\frac{4e^4}{k(e^4-1)} = \frac{4}{9}\left[\frac{e^6-1}{e^6-e^2}\right] \approx 0.45$$

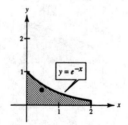

21. Since the lamina is of uniform density and symmetric to the polar axis (see figure) you have $\bar{y} = 0$.

$$m = \iint_R k\,dA$$

$$= \int_{-\pi/6}^{\pi/6} \int_0^{2\cos 3\theta} kr\,dr\,d\theta \qquad \text{(polar coordinates)}$$

$$= \frac{k\pi}{3}$$

$$M_y = \iint_R kx\,dA$$

$$= k\int_{-\pi/6}^{\pi/6} \int_0^{2\cos 3\theta} (r\cos\theta)r\,dr\,d\theta \qquad \text{(polar coordinates)}$$

$$= \frac{27\sqrt{3}}{40}$$

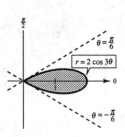

Therefore,

$$\bar{x} = \frac{M_y}{m} = \frac{27\sqrt{3}k/40}{k\pi/3} = \frac{81\sqrt{3}}{40\pi} \approx 1.12.$$

23. $e(x, y) = ky$. $\bar{y}$ will increase.

25. $\rho(x, y) = kxy$. Both $\bar{x}$ and $\bar{y}$ will increase.

27. $m = bh$

$$I_x = \int_0^b \int_0^h y^2\,dy\,dx = \frac{bh^3}{3}$$

$$I_y = \int_0^b \int_0^h x^2\,dy\,dx = \frac{b^3h}{3}$$

$$\bar{\bar{x}} = \sqrt{\frac{I_y}{m}} = \sqrt{\frac{b^3h}{3} \cdot \frac{1}{bh}} = \sqrt{\frac{b^2}{3}} = \frac{b}{\sqrt{3}}$$

$$\bar{\bar{y}} = \sqrt{\frac{I_x}{m}} = \sqrt{\frac{bh^3}{3} \cdot \frac{1}{bh}} = \sqrt{\frac{h^2}{3}} = \frac{h}{\sqrt{3}}$$

29. Recall that a relationship between polar and rectangular coordinates is $x = r\cos\theta$ and $y = r\sin\theta$.

$$m = \pi a^2$$

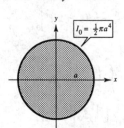

$$I_x = \iint_R y^2\rho(x, y)\,dA = \int_0^{2\pi}\int_0^a (r\sin\theta)^2\,r\,dr\,d\theta$$

$$= \int_0^{2\pi} \sin^2\theta\left[\frac{r^4}{4}\right]_0^a\,d\theta = \frac{1}{8}a^4\int_0^{2\pi}(1-\cos 2\theta)\,d\theta$$

$$= \frac{1}{8}a^4\left[\theta - \frac{1}{2}\sin 2\theta\right]_0^{2\pi} = \frac{1}{4}\pi a^4$$

$$I_y = \iint_R x^2\rho(x, y)\,dA = \int_0^{2\pi}\int_0^a (r\cos\theta)^2\,r\,dr\,d\theta$$

$$= \int_0^{2\pi} \cos^2\theta\left[\frac{r^4}{4}\right]_0^a\,d\theta = \frac{1}{8}a^4\int_0^{2\pi}(1+\cos 2\theta)\,d\theta$$

$$= \frac{1}{8}a^4\left[\theta + \frac{1}{2}\sin 2\theta\right]_0^{2\pi} = \frac{1}{4}\pi a^4$$

$$I_0 = I_x + I_y = \frac{1}{2}\pi a^4$$

$$\bar{x} = \sqrt{\frac{I_x}{m}} = \sqrt{\frac{(\pi a^4)/4}{\pi a^2}} = \frac{a}{2} = \bar{y}$$

31. $m = \dfrac{\pi a^2}{4}$

$$I_x = \iint_R y^2\, dA = \int_0^{\pi/2}\int_0^a r^3 \sin^2\theta\, dr\, d\theta = \frac{\pi a^4}{16}$$

$$I_y = \iint_R x^2\, dA = \int_0^{\pi/2}\int_0^a r^3 \cos^2\theta\, dr\, d\theta = \frac{\pi a^4}{16}$$

$$I_0 = I_x + I_y = \frac{\pi a^4}{16} + \frac{\pi a^4}{16} = \frac{\pi a^4}{8}$$

$$\bar{\bar{x}} = \bar{\bar{y}} = \sqrt{\frac{I_x}{m}} = \sqrt{\frac{\pi a^4}{16}\cdot\frac{4}{\pi a^4}} = \frac{a}{2}$$

33. $\rho = ky$

$$m = k\int_0^a\int_0^b y\, dy\, dx = \frac{kab^2}{2}$$

$$I_x = k\int_0^a\int_0^b y^3\, dy\, dx = \frac{kab^4}{4}$$

$$I_y = k\int_0^a\int_0^b x^2 y\, dy\, dx = \frac{ka^3 b^2}{6}$$

$$I_0 = I_x + I_y = \frac{3kab^4 + 2kb^2 a^3}{12}$$

$$\bar{\bar{x}} = \sqrt{\frac{I_y}{m}} = \sqrt{\frac{ka^3 b^2/6}{kab^2/2}} = \sqrt{\frac{a^2}{3}} = \frac{a}{\sqrt{3}}$$

$$\bar{\bar{y}} = \sqrt{\frac{I_x}{m}} = \sqrt{\frac{kab^4/4}{kab^2/2}} = \sqrt{\frac{b^2}{2}} = \frac{b}{\sqrt{2}}$$

35. $y = 4 - x^2,\ y = 0,\ x > 0,$ and $\rho = kx$

Since $\rho = kx$, we have

$$m = \int_0^2\int_0^{4-x^2} kx\, dy\, dx$$

$$= k\int_0^2 xy\Big]_0^{4-x^2} dx$$

$$= k\int_0^2 x(4-x^2)\, dx = \left[-\frac{k}{4}(4-x^2)^2\right]_0^2 = 4k.$$

Furthermore,

$$I_x = \iint_R y^2\rho\, dA = \int_0^2\int_0^{4-x^2} kxy^2\, dy\, dx$$

$$= \frac{k}{3}\int_0^2 xy^3\Big]_0^{4-x^2} dx$$

$$= \frac{k}{3}\int_0^2 x(4-x^2)^3\, dx$$

$$= \left[-\frac{k}{24}(4-x^2)^4\right]_0^2 = \frac{32k}{3}$$

and

$$I_y = \iint_R x^2\rho\, dA = \int_0^2\int_0^{4-x^2} kx^3\, dy\, dx$$

$$= k\int_0^2 \left[x^3 y\right]_0^{4-x^2} dx$$

$$= k\int_0^2 (4x^3 - x^5)\, dx$$

$$= k\left[x^4 - \frac{1}{6}x^6\right]_0^2 = \frac{16k}{3}.$$

Therefore, $I_0 = I_x + I_y = 16k$. Finally,

$$\bar{\bar{x}} = \sqrt{\frac{I_y}{m}} = \sqrt{\frac{16k/3}{4k}} = \frac{2}{\sqrt{3}} = \frac{2\sqrt{3}}{3}$$

$$\bar{\bar{y}} = \sqrt{\frac{I_x}{m}} = \sqrt{\frac{32k/3}{4k}} = \frac{4}{\sqrt{6}} = \frac{2\sqrt{6}}{3}$$

37. $\rho = kxy$

$$m = \int_0^4\int_0^{\sqrt{x}} kxy\, dy\, dx = \frac{32k}{3}$$

$$I_x = \int_0^4\int_0^{\sqrt{x}} kxy^3\, dy\, dx = 16k$$

$$I_y = \int_0^4\int_0^{\sqrt{x}} kx^3 y\, dy\, dx = \frac{512k}{5}$$

$$I_0 = I_x + I_y = \frac{592k}{5}$$

$$\bar{\bar{x}} = \sqrt{\frac{I_y}{m}} = \sqrt{\frac{512k}{5}\cdot\frac{3}{32k}} = \sqrt{\frac{48}{5}} = \frac{4\sqrt{15}}{5}$$

$$\bar{\bar{y}} = \sqrt{\frac{I_x}{m}} = \sqrt{\frac{16k}{1}\cdot\frac{3}{32k}} = \sqrt{\frac{3}{2}} = \frac{\sqrt{6}}{2}$$

39. $\rho = kx$

$$m = \int_0^1 \int_{x^2}^{\sqrt{x}} kx \, dy \, dx = \frac{3k}{20}$$

$$I_x = \int_0^1 \int_{x^2}^{\sqrt{x}} kxy^2 \, dy \, dx = \frac{3k}{56}$$

$$I_y = \int_0^1 \int_{x^2}^{\sqrt{x}} kx^3 \, dy \, dx = \frac{k}{18}$$

$$I_0 = I_x + I_y = \frac{55k}{504}$$

$$\bar{\bar{x}} = \sqrt{\frac{I_y}{m}} = \sqrt{\frac{k}{18} \cdot \frac{20}{3k}} = \frac{\sqrt{30}}{9}$$

$$\bar{\bar{y}} = \sqrt{\frac{I_x}{m}} = \sqrt{\frac{3k}{56} \cdot \frac{20}{3k}} = \frac{\sqrt{70}}{14}$$

41. $x^2 + y^2 = b^2,\ x = a (a > b)$, and $\rho = k$

$$I = \int\int_R (\text{distance})^2 \, \text{mass}$$

$$= \int_{-r}^{r} \int_{-\sqrt{b^2-x^2}}^{\sqrt{b^2-x^2}} (x - a)^2 (k) \, dy \, dx$$

$$= 2k \int_0^\pi \int_0^b (r \cos \theta - a)^2 \, r \, dr \, d\theta \quad \text{(polar coordinates)}$$

$$= \frac{kb^2\pi}{4}(b^2 + 4a^2)$$

43. $I = \int_0^4 \int_0^{\sqrt{x}} kx(x - 6)^2 \, dy \, dx = \int_0^4 kx\sqrt{x}(x^2 - 12x + 36) \, dx = k\left[\frac{2}{9}x^{9/2} - \frac{24}{7}x^{7/2} + \frac{72}{5}x^{5/2}\right]_0^4 = \frac{42,752k}{315}$

45. $I = \int_0^a \int_0^{\sqrt{a^2-x^2}} k(a - y)(y - a)^2 \, dy \, dx = \int_0^a \int_0^{\sqrt{a^2-x^2}} k(a - y)^3 \, dy \, dx = \int_0^a \left[-\frac{k}{a}(a - y)^4\right]_0^{\sqrt{a^2-x^2}} dx$

$$= -\frac{k}{a}\int_0^a \left[a^4 - 4a^3y + 4ay^3 + y^4\right]_0^{\sqrt{a^2-x^2}} dx$$

$$= -\frac{k}{4}\int_0^a \left[a^4 - 4a^3\sqrt{a^2 - x^2} + 6a^2(a^2 - x^2) - 4a(a^2 - x^2)\sqrt{a^2 - x^2} + (a^4 - 2a^2x^2 + x^4) - a^4\right] dx$$

$$= -\frac{k}{a}\int_0^a \left[a^4 - 8a^2x^2 + x^4 - 8a^3\sqrt{a^2 - x^2} + 4ax^2 = \sqrt{a^2 - x^2}\right] dx$$

$$= -\frac{k}{a}\left[7a^4x - \frac{8a^2}{3}x^3 + \frac{x^5}{5} - 4a^3\left(x\sqrt{a^2 - x^2} + a^2 \arcsin\frac{x}{a}\right) + \frac{a}{2}\left(x(2x^2 - a^2)\sqrt{a^2 - x^2} + a^4 \arcsin\frac{x}{a}\right)\right]_0^a$$

$$= -\frac{k}{a}\left(7a^5 - \frac{8}{3}a^5 + \frac{1}{5}a^5 - 2a^5\pi + \frac{1}{4}a^5\pi\right) = a^5k\left(\frac{7\pi}{16} - \frac{17}{15}\right)$$

47. Orient the xy-coordinate system so that L is along the y-axis and R is in the first quadrant. Then the volume of the solid is

$$V = \int\int_R 2\pi x \, dA$$

$$= 2\pi \int\int_R x \, dA$$

$$= 2\pi \left(\frac{\int\int_R x \, dA}{\int\int_R dA}\right) \int\int_R dA$$

$$= 2\pi \bar{x} A.$$

By our positioning, $\bar{x} = r$. Therefore, $V = 2\pi rA$.

49. The gate is shown in the figure. The y-coordinate of the centroid of the gate is $\bar{y} = a/2$, the area of the gate is $A = ab$, and the depth of the centroid below the surface of the water is $h = L - a/2$. The moment of inertia of the gate about $\bar{y}$ is

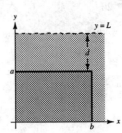

$$I_{\bar{y}} = \int_0^b \int_0^a \left(y - \frac{a}{2}\right)^2 dy\, dx$$

$$= \int_0^b \frac{1}{3}\left[\left(y - \frac{a}{2}\right)^3\right]_0^a dx$$

$$= \frac{a^3}{12}\int_0^b dx = \frac{a^3 b}{12}$$

$$y_a = \bar{y} - \frac{I_{\bar{y}}}{hA}$$

$$= \frac{a}{2} - \frac{a^3 b/12}{[L - (a/2)](ab)} = \frac{a(3L - 2a)}{3(2L - a)}$$

51. $\bar{y} = 0, A = \pi a^2, h = L$

$$I_{\bar{y}} = \int_{-a}^a \int_{-\sqrt{a^2-x^2}}^{\sqrt{a^2-x^2}} y^2\, dy\, dx = \int_0^{2\pi}\int_0^a r^3 \sin^2\theta\, dr\, d\theta = \int_0^{2\pi} \frac{a^4}{4}\sin^2\theta\, d\theta = \frac{a^4\pi}{4}$$

$$y_a = -\frac{(a^4\pi/4)}{L\pi a^2} = -\frac{a^2}{4L}$$

Section 13.5   Surface Area

1. $f(x, y) = 2x + 2y$

R = triangle with vertices $(0, 0), (2, 0), (0, 2)$

$f_x = 2, f_y = 2$

$\sqrt{1 + (f_x)^2 + (f_y)^2} = 3$

$$S = \int_0^2\int_0^{2-x} 3\, dy\, dx = 3\int_0^2 (2 - x)\, dx = \left[3\left(2x - \frac{x^2}{2}\right)\right]_0^2 = 6$$

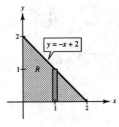

3. $f(x, y) = 8 + 2x + 2y, R = \{(x, y): x^2 + y^2 \le 4\}$

The first partial derivatives of f are $f_x(x, y) = 2$ and $f_y(x, y) = 2$, and from the formula for surface area it follows that

$$\sqrt{1 + [f_x(x, y)]^2 + [f_y(x, y)]^2} = 3.$$

Therefore, the surface area is given by

$$S = \int\int_R 3\, dA = 3\int\int_R dA = 3(\text{area of } R) = 3(4\pi) = 12\pi.$$

5. $f(x, y) = 9 - x^2$

R = square with vertices, $(0, 0), (3, 0), (0, 3), (3, 3)$

$f_x = -2x, f_y = 0$

$\sqrt{1 + (f_x)^2 + (f_y)^2} = \sqrt{1 + 4x^2}$

$$S = \int_0^3\int_0^3 \sqrt{1 + 4x^2}\, dy\, dx = \int_0^3 3\sqrt{1 + 4x^2}\, dx$$

$$= \left[\frac{3}{4}\left(2x\sqrt{1 + 4x^2} + \ln|2x + \sqrt{1 + 4x^2}|\right)\right]_0^3 = \frac{3}{4}(6\sqrt{37} + \ln|6 + \sqrt{37}|)$$

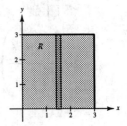

7. $f(x, y) = 2 + x^{3/2}$

R = rectangle with vertices $(0, 0)$, $(0, 4)$, $(3, 4)$, $(3, 0)$

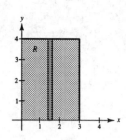

$f_x = \dfrac{3}{2}x^{1/2}$, $f_y = 0$

$$\sqrt{1 + (f_x)^2 + (f_y)^2} = \sqrt{1 + \left(\frac{9}{4}\right)x} = \frac{\sqrt{4 + 9x}}{2}$$

$$S = \int_0^3 \int_0^4 \frac{\sqrt{4 + 9x}}{2}\, dy\, dx = \int_0^3 4\left(\frac{\sqrt{4 + 9x}}{2}\right) dx$$

$$= \left[\frac{4}{27}(4 + 9)^{3/2}\right]_0^3 = \frac{4}{27}(3\sqrt{31} - 8)$$

9. $f(x, y) = \ln|\sec x|$

$$R = \left\{(x, y): 0 \leq x \leq \frac{\pi}{4},\ 0 \leq y \leq \tan x\right\}$$

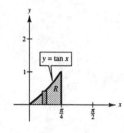

$f_x = \tan x$, $f_y = 0$

$$\sqrt{1 + (f_x)^2 + (f_y)^2} = \sqrt{1 + \tan^2 x} = \sec x$$

$$S = \int_0^{\pi/4} \int_0^{\tan x} \sec x\, dy\, dx = \int_0^{\pi/4} \sec x \tan x\, dx = \Big[\sec x\Big]_0^{\pi/4} = \sqrt{2} - 1$$

11. $f(x, y) = \sqrt{x^2 + y^2}$, $R = \{(x, y): 0 \leq f(x, y) \leq 1\}$

Observe that we are to find the surface area of that part of the cone $f(x, y) = \sqrt{x^2 + y^2}$ inside the cylinder $x^2 + y^2 = 1$. Therefore, the region R in the xy-plane is a circle of radius 1 centered at the origin. Furthermore, the first partial derivatives of f are

$$f_x(x, y) = \frac{x}{\sqrt{x^2 + y^2}} \quad \text{and} \quad f_y(x, y) = \frac{y}{\sqrt{x^2 + y^2}}$$

and from the formula for surface area, we have

$$\sqrt{1 + [f_x(x, y)]^2 + [f_y(x, y)]^2} = \sqrt{1 + \frac{x^2 + y^2}{x^2 + y^2}} = \sqrt{2}.$$

Therefore, the surface area is given by

$$S = \iint_R \sqrt{2}\, dA = \sqrt{2} \iint_R dA = \sqrt{2}(\text{area of } R) = \sqrt{2}\pi.$$

13. $f(x, y) = \sqrt{a^2 - x^2 - y^2}$

$R = \{(x, y): x^2 + y^2 \leq b^2, b < a\}$

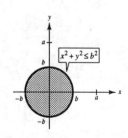

$$f_x = \frac{-x}{\sqrt{a^2 - x^2 - y^2}},\ f_y = \frac{-y}{\sqrt{a^2 - x^2 - y^2}}$$

$$\sqrt{1 + (f_x)^2 + (f_y)^2} = \sqrt{1 + \frac{x^2}{a^2 - x^2 - y^2} + \frac{y^2}{a^2 - x^2 - y^2}} = \frac{a}{\sqrt{a^2 - x^2 - y^2}}$$

$$S = \int_{-b}^b \int_{-\sqrt{b^2 - x^2}}^{\sqrt{b^2 - x^2}} \frac{a}{\sqrt{a^2 - x^2 - y^2}}\, dy\, dx = \int_0^{2\pi} \int_0^b \frac{a}{\sqrt{a^2 - r^2}} r\, dr\, d\theta = 2\pi a(a - \sqrt{a^2 - b^2})$$

15. $z = 24 - 3x - 2y$

$\sqrt{1 + (f_x)^2 + (f_y)^2} = \sqrt{14}$

$S = \int_0^8 \int_0^{-(3/2)x+12} \sqrt{14} \, dy \, dx = 48\sqrt{14}$

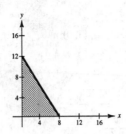

17. $z = \sqrt{25 - x^2 - y^2}$

$\sqrt{1 + (f_x)^2 + (f_y)^2} = \sqrt{1 + \dfrac{x^2}{25 - x^2 - y^2} + \dfrac{y^2}{25 - x^2 - y^2}} = \dfrac{5}{\sqrt{25 - x^2 - y^2}}$

$S = 2 \int_{-3}^{3} \int_{-\sqrt{9-x^2}}^{\sqrt{9-x^2}} \dfrac{5}{\sqrt{25 - (x^2 + y^2)}} \, dy \, dx$

$= 2 \int_0^{2\pi} \int_0^3 \dfrac{5}{\sqrt{25 - r^2}} r \, dr \, d\theta = 20\pi$

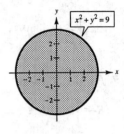

19. $f(x, y) = 2y + x^2$

R = triangle with vertices $(0, 0)$, $(1, 0)$, $(1, 1)$

$\sqrt{1 + (f_x)^2 + (f_y)^2} = \sqrt{5 + 4x^2}$

$S = \int_0^1 \int_0^x \sqrt{5 + 4x^2} \, dy \, dx = \dfrac{1}{12}\left(27 - 5\sqrt{5}\right)$

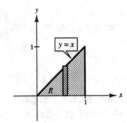

21. $f(x, y) = 4 - x^2 - y^2$, $R = \{(x, y): \ 0 \le f(x, y)\}$

$0 \le f(x, y) = 4 - x^2 - y^2 \implies x^2 + y^2 \le 4$

Therefore, we must find the surface area of that part of the paraboloid inside the cylinder $x^2 + y^2 = 4$. The first partial derivatives of f are

$f_x(x, y) = -2x \quad$ and $\quad f_y(x, y) = -2y$

and from the formula for surface area, we have

$\sqrt{1 + [f_x(x, y)]^2 + [f_y(x, y)]^2} = \sqrt{1 + 4x^2 + 4y^2}.$

Using the symmetry of the surface, the surface area is

$S = 4 \int_0^2 \int_0^{\sqrt{4-x^2}} \sqrt{1 + 4x^2 + 4y^2} \, dy \, dx$

$= 4 \int_0^{\pi/2} \int_0^2 \sqrt{1 + 4r^2} \, r \, dr \, d\theta \quad \text{(polar coordinates)}$

$= 4\left(\dfrac{1}{8}\right)\left(\dfrac{2}{3}\right) \int_0^{\pi/2} \left[(1 + 4r^2)^{3/2} \right]_0^2 \, d\theta$

$= \dfrac{1}{3} \int_0^{\pi/2} \left(17\sqrt{17} - 1\right) d\theta$

$= \dfrac{17\sqrt{17} - 1}{3} \left[\theta \right]_0^{\pi/2} = \dfrac{\left(17\sqrt{17} - 1\right)\pi}{6}.$

23. $f(x, y) = 4 - x^2 - y^2$

$R = \{(x, y): 0 \le x \le 1, 0 \le y \le 1\}$

$f_x = -2x, f_y = -2y$

$\sqrt{1 + (f_x)^2 + (f_y)^2} = \sqrt{1 + 4x^2 + 4y^2}$

$S = \int_0^1 \int_0^1 \sqrt{(1 + 4x^2) + 4y^2}\, dy\, dx \approx 1.81616$

25. Surface area $> (4) \cdot (6) = 24.$

Matches (e)

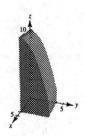

27. $f(x, y) = e^x$

$R = \{(x, y): 0 \le x \le 1, 0 \le y \le 1\}$

$f_x = e^x, f_y = 0$

$\sqrt{1 + (f_x)^2 + (f_y)^2} = \sqrt{1 + e^{2x}}$

$S = \int_0^1 \int_0^1 \sqrt{1 + e^{2x}}\, dy\, dx = \int_0^1 \sqrt{1 + e^{2x}} \approx 2.0035$

29. $f(x, y) = x^3 - 3xy^3 + y^3$

$R =$ square with vertices $(1, 1), (-1, 1), (-1, -1), (1, -1)$

$f_x = 3x^2 - 3y = 3(x^2 - y), f_y = -3x + 3y^2 = 3(y^2 - x)$

$S = \int_{-1}^1 \int_{-1}^1 \sqrt{1 + 9(x^2 - y)^2 + 9(y^2 - x)^2}\, dy\, dx$

31. $f(x, y) = e^{-x} \sin y, R = \{(x, y): x^2 + y^2 \le 4\}$

The first partial derivatives of f are $f_x(x, y) = -e^{-x} \sin y$ and $f_y(x, y) = e^{-x} \cos y$ and from the formula for surface area, we have

$\sqrt{1 + [f_x(x, y)]^2 + [f_y(x, y)]^2} = \sqrt{1 + e^{-2x} \sin^2 y + e^{-2x} \cos^2 y} = \sqrt{1 + e^{-2x}}.$

We integrate over the circle $x^2 + y^2 = 4$.

Constant bounds for x: $-2 \le x \le 2$

Variable bounds for y: $-\sqrt{4 - x^2} \le y \le \sqrt{4 - x^2}$

Therefore,

$S = \int_{-2}^2 \int_{-\sqrt{4-x^2}}^{\sqrt{4-x^2}} \sqrt{1 + e^{-2x}}\, dy\, dx.$

33. $f(x, y) = e^{xy}$

$R = \{(x, y): 0 \le x \le 4, 0 \le y \le 10\}$

$f_x = ye^{xy}, f_y = xe^{xy}$

$\sqrt{1 + (f_x)^2 + (f_y)^2} = \sqrt{1 + y^2 e^{2xy} + x^2 e^{2xy}} = \sqrt{1 + e^{2xy}(x^2 + y^2)}$

$S = \int_0^4 \int_0^{10} \sqrt{1 + e^{2xy}(x^2 + y^2)}\, dy\, dx$

35. $x^2 + z^2 = 1, \ y^2 + z^2 = 1$

The figure shows the surface in the first octant. We divide this surface into two equal parts by the plane $y = x$ and thus find $\frac{1}{16}$ of the total surface area. Therefore, find the area of the surface $z = \sqrt{1 - x^2}$ over the triangle bounded by $y = 0, y = x,$ and $x = 1$.

$\dfrac{\partial z}{\partial x} = \dfrac{-x}{\sqrt{1 - x^2}}$ and $\dfrac{\partial z}{\partial y} = 0$

Therefore,

$S = 16 \int_0^1 \int_0^x \sqrt{1 + \left(\dfrac{\partial z}{\partial x}\right)^2 + \left(\dfrac{\partial z}{\partial y}\right)^2}\, dy\, dx$

$= 16 \int_0^1 \int_0^x \sqrt{1 + \dfrac{x^2}{1 - x^2}}\, dy\, dx$

$= 16 \int_0^1 \int_0^x \dfrac{1}{\sqrt{1^2 - x^2}}\, dy\, dx$

$= 16 \int_0^1 \dfrac{x}{\sqrt{1 - x^2}}\, dx = \left[-16\sqrt{1 - x^2}\right]_0^1 = 16.$

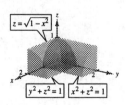

37. $z = \dfrac{x + y}{5}$ Floor: incline plane

$z = 20 + \dfrac{xy}{100}$,   Ceiling

$R = \{(x, y): x^2 + y^2 \le 50^2, x \ge 0, y \ge 0\}$

(a) $V = \displaystyle\int_0^{50} \int_0^{\sqrt{50^2 - x^2}} \left[\left(20 + \dfrac{xy}{100}\right) - \left(\dfrac{x + y}{5}\right)\right] dy\, dx$

$= \displaystyle\int_0^{\pi/2} \int_0^{50} \left[20 + \dfrac{1}{100}r^2 \sin\theta \cos\theta - \dfrac{1}{5}(r \sin\theta + r \cos\theta)\right] r\, dr\, d\theta$

$\approx 30{,}416$ cubic feet

(b) From the equation for the ceiling we have

$\dfrac{\partial z}{\partial x} = \dfrac{y}{100}$ and $\dfrac{\partial z}{\partial y} = \dfrac{x}{100}$.

$S = \displaystyle\int_0^{50} \int_0^{\sqrt{50^2 - x^2}} \sqrt{1 + \left(\dfrac{y}{100}\right)^2 + \left(\dfrac{x}{100}\right)^2}\, dy\, dx$

$= \displaystyle\int_0^{\pi/2} \int_0^{50} \sqrt{1 + \dfrac{r^2}{100}}\, r\, dr\, d\theta \approx 2082$ square feet.

39. The greater the angle between the given plane and the xy-plane, the greater the surface area. Hence, $z_2 < z_1 < z_4 < z_3$.

41. False. The surface area will remain the same for any vertical translation.

Section 13.6   Triple Integrals and Applications

1. $\displaystyle\int_0^3 \int_0^2 \int_0^1 (x + y + z)\, dx\, dy\, dx = \int_0^3 \int_0^2 \left[\dfrac{1}{2}x^2 + xy + xz\right]_0^1 dy\, dx$

$= \displaystyle\int_0^3 \int_0^2 \left(\dfrac{1}{2} + y + z\right) dy\, dz = \int_0^3 \left[\dfrac{1}{2}y + \dfrac{1}{2}y^2 + yz\right]_0^2 dz = \left[3z + z^2\right]_0^3 = 18$

3. $\displaystyle\int_0^1 \int_0^x \int_0^{xy} x\, dz\, dy\, dx = \int_0^1 \int_0^x \left[xy\right]_0^{xy} dy\, dx$

$= \displaystyle\int_0^1 \int_0^x x^2 y\, dy\, dx = \int_0^1 \left[\dfrac{x^2 y^2}{2}\right]_0^x dx = \int_0^1 \dfrac{x^4}{2}\, dx = \left[\dfrac{x^5}{10}\right]_0^1 = \dfrac{1}{10}$

5. $\displaystyle\int_1^4 \int_0^1 \int_0^x 2ze^{-x^2}\, dy\, dx\, dz = \int_1^4 \int_0^1 \left[(2ze^{-x^2})y\right]_0^x dx\, dz = \int_1^4 \int_0^1 2zxe^{-x^2}\, dx\, dz$

$= \displaystyle\int_1^4 \left[-ze^{-x^2}\right]_0^1 dz = \int_1^4 z(1 - e^{-1})\, dz = \left[(1 - e^{-1})\dfrac{z^2}{2}\right]_1^4 = \dfrac{15}{2}\left(1 - \dfrac{1}{e}\right)$

7. $\displaystyle\int_0^9 \int_0^{y/3} \int_0^{\sqrt{y^2 - 9x^2}} z\, dz\, dx\, dy = \int_0^9 \int_0^{y/3} \left[\dfrac{1}{2}z^2\right]_0^{\sqrt{y^2 - 9x^2}} dx\, dy$

$= \dfrac{1}{2}\displaystyle\int_0^9 \int_0^{y/3} (y^2 - 9x^2)\, dx\, dy = \dfrac{1}{2}\int_0^9 \left[xy^2 - 3x^3\right]_0^{y/3} dy = \dfrac{1}{9}\int_0^9 y^3\, dy = \dfrac{1}{36}\left[y^4\right]_0^9 = \dfrac{729}{4}$

9. $\int_0^2 \int_{-\sqrt{4-x^2}}^{\sqrt{4-x^2}} \int_0^{x^2} x \, dz \, dy \, dx = \int_0^2 \int_{-\sqrt{4-x^2}}^{\sqrt{4-x^2}} x^3 \, dy \, dx = \dfrac{128}{15}$

11. $\int_0^2 \int_0^{\sqrt{4-x^2}} \int_1^4 \dfrac{x^2 \sin y}{z} \, dz \, dy \, dx = \int_0^2 \int_0^{\sqrt{4-x^2}} \left[x^2 \sin y \ln|z| \right]_1^4 \, dy \, dx$

$$= \int_0^2 \left[x^2 \ln 4(-\cos y) \right]_0^{\sqrt{4-x^2}} \, dx = \int_0^2 x^2 \ln 4 \left[1 - \cos\sqrt{4-x^2} \right] dx \approx 2.44167$$

13. Plane: $3x + 6y + 4z = 12$

$\int_0^3 \int_0^{(12-4z)/3} \int_0^{(12-4z-3x)/6} dy \, dx \, dz$

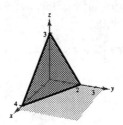

15. $\int_0^1 \int_y^1 \int_0^{\sqrt{1-y^2}} dz \, dx \, dy$

We have

    Constant bounds on y: $0 \le y \le 1$

    Variable bounds on x: $y \le x \le 1$

    Variable bounds on z: $0 \le z \le \sqrt{1-y^2}$.

From the upper bound on z, we have

    $z = \sqrt{1-y^2}$ or $y^2 + z^2 = 1$

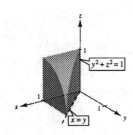

a cylinder of radius 1 with the x-axis as its axis. Therefore, the triple integral gives the volume of the solid in the first octant bounded by the graphs of $z = \sqrt{1-y^2}$, $z = 0$, $x = y$, and $x = 1$. From the sketch of the solid we observe the following bounds when the order of integration is $dz \, dy \, dx$

    Constant bounds on x: $0 \le x \le 1$

    Variable bounds on y: $0 \le y \le x$

    Variable bounds on z: $0 \le z \le \sqrt{1-y^2}$.

Therefore, the integral is $\int_0^1 \int_0^x \int_0^{\sqrt{1-y^2}} dz \, dy \, dx$.

17. $Q = \{(x, y, z) : 0 \le x \le 1, 0 \le y \le x, 0 \le z \le 3\}$

$\displaystyle\iiint_Q xyz \, dV = \int_0^3 \int_0^1 \int_y^1 xyz \, dx \, dy \, dz = \int_0^3 \int_0^1 \int_0^x xyz \, dy \, dx \, dz$

$$= \int_0^1 \int_0^3 \int_y^1 xyz \, dx \, dz \, dy$$

$$= \int_0^1 \int_0^3 \int_0^x xyz \, dy \, dz \, dx$$

$$= \int_0^1 \int_y^1 \int_0^3 xyz \, dz \, dx \, dy$$

$$= \int_0^1 \int_0^x \int_0^3 xyz \, dz \, dy \, dx \left(= \dfrac{9}{16} \right)$$

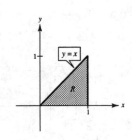

19. $\displaystyle\int_{-2}^{2}\int_{0}^{4-y^2}\int_{0}^{x} dz\, dx\, dy = \int_{-2}^{2}\int_{0}^{4-y^2} x\, dx\, dy$

$$= \frac{1}{2}\int_{-2}^{2}(4-y^2)^2\, dy = \int_{0}^{2}(16 - 8y^2 + y^4)\, dy = \left[16y - \frac{8}{3}y^3 + \frac{1}{5}y^5\right]_{0}^{2} = \frac{256}{15}$$

21. $\displaystyle 8\int_{0}^{a}\int_{0}^{\sqrt{a^2-x^2}}\int_{0}^{\sqrt{a^2-x^2-y^2}} dz\, dy\, dx = 8\int_{0}^{a}\int_{0}^{\sqrt{a^2-x^2}}\sqrt{a^2 - x^2 - y^2}\, dy\, dx$

$$= 4\int_{0}^{a}\left[y\sqrt{a^2 - x^2 - y^2} + (a^2 - x^2)\arcsin\left(\frac{y}{\sqrt{a^2 - x^2}}\right)\right]_{0}^{\sqrt{a^2-x^2}} dx$$

$$= 4\left(\frac{\pi}{2}\right)\int_{0}^{a}(a^2 - x^2)\, dx = \left[2\pi\left(a^2 x - \frac{1}{3}x^3\right)\right]_{0}^{a} = \frac{4}{3}\pi a^3$$

23. In the first octant, we have $0 \le z \le 4 - x^2$, $0 \le y \le 4 - x^2$, and $0 \le x \le 2$. Therefore, the volume is

$$V = \int_{0}^{2}\int_{0}^{4-x^2}\int_{0}^{4-x^2} dz\, dy\, dx = \int_{0}^{2}\int_{0}^{4-x^2}(4 - x^2)\, dy\, dx$$

$$= \int_{0}^{2}(4 - x^2)^2\, dx = \int_{0}^{2}(16 - 8x^2 + x^4)\, dx$$

$$= \left[16x - \frac{8x^3}{3} + \frac{x^5}{5}\right]_{0}^{2} = 32 - \frac{64}{3} + \frac{32}{5} = \frac{256}{15}.$$

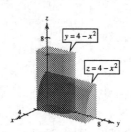

25. $\displaystyle m = k\int_{0}^{6}\int_{0}^{4-(2x/3)}\int_{0}^{2-(y/2)-(x/3)} dz\, dy\, dx$

$$= 8k$$

$$M_{yz} = k\int_{0}^{6}\int_{0}^{4-(2x/3)}\int_{0}^{2-(y/2)-(x/3)} x\, dz\, dy\, dx$$

$$= 12k$$

$$\bar{x} = \frac{M_{yz}}{m} = \frac{12k}{8k} = \frac{3}{2}$$

27. $\displaystyle m = k\int_{0}^{4}\int_{0}^{4}\int_{0}^{4-x} x\, dz\, dy\, dx = k\int_{0}^{4}\int_{0}^{4} x(4 - x)\, dy\, dx$

$$= 4k\int_{0}^{4}(4x - x^2)\, dx = \frac{128k}{3}$$

$$M_{xy} = k\int_{0}^{4}\int_{0}^{4}\int_{0}^{4-x} xz\, dz\, dy\, dx = k\int_{0}^{4}\int_{0}^{4} x\frac{(4 - x)^2}{2}\, dy\, dx$$

$$= 2k\int_{0}^{4}(16x - 8x^2 + x^3)\, dx = \frac{128k}{3}$$

$$\bar{z} = \frac{M_{xy}}{m} = 1$$

29. $x = 0$, $x = b$, $y = 0$, $y = b$, $z = 0$, $z = b$, $\rho(x, y, z) = kxy$

The mass of the cube is

$$m = \int_{0}^{b}\int_{0}^{b}\int_{0}^{b} kxy\, dz\, dy\, dx = k\int_{0}^{b}\int_{0}^{b} bxy\, dy\, dx$$

$$= kb\int_{0}^{b}\left[\frac{xy^2}{2}\right]_{0}^{b} dx = \frac{kb^3}{2}\int_{0}^{b} x\, dx = \frac{kb^3}{4}\left[x^2\right]_{0}^{b} = \frac{kb^5}{4}.$$

Furthermore,

$$M_{yz} = \int_{0}^{b}\int_{0}^{b}\int_{0}^{b} x(kxy)\, dz\, dy\, dx = k\int_{0}^{b}\int_{0}^{b} x^2 y(b)\, dy\, dx$$

$$= kb\int_{0}^{b}\left[\frac{x^2 y^2}{2}\right]_{0}^{b} dx = \frac{kb^3}{2}\int_{0}^{b} x^2\, dx = \frac{kb^3}{6}\left[x^3\right]_{0}^{b} = \frac{kb^6}{6}.$$

—CONTINUED—

29. By the symmetry of the cube and of $\rho = kxy$, we have $M_{xz} = M_{yz} = kb^6/6$. Moreover,

$$M_{xy} = \int_0^b \int_0^b \int_0^b z(kxy)\, dz\, dy\, dx = k\int_0^b \int_0^b \left[\frac{xyz^2}{2}\right]_0^b dy\, dx$$

$$= \frac{kb^2}{2}\int_0^b \int_0^b xy\, dy\, dx = \frac{kb^2}{2}\int_0^b \left[\frac{xy^2}{2}\right]_0^b dx$$

$$= \frac{kb^4}{4}\int_0^b x\, dx = \frac{kb^4}{4}\left[\frac{x^2}{2}\right]_0^b = \frac{kb^6}{8}.$$

Finally,

$$\bar{x} = \frac{M_{yz}}{m} = \frac{kb^6/6}{kb^5/4} = \frac{2b}{3}$$

$$\bar{y} = \bar{x} = \frac{2b}{3}$$

$$\bar{z} = \frac{M_{xy}}{m} = \frac{kb^6/8}{kb^5/4} = \frac{b}{2}.$$

31. $\bar{x}$ will be greater than 2, whereas $\bar{y}$ and $\bar{z}$ will be unchanged.

33. $\bar{y}$ will be greater than 0, whereas $\bar{x}$ and $\bar{z}$ will be unchanged.

35. Without loss of generality, position the cone with the vertex at the origin as shown in the figure. Assuming uniform density $\rho(x, y) = k$, the mass of the cone is $m = k(\text{volume}) = \frac{1}{3}k\pi r^2 h$. By symmetry we have $\bar{x} = \bar{y} = 0$, and

$$M_{xy} = 4k\int_0^r \int_0^{\sqrt{r^2-x^2}} \int_{h\sqrt{x^2+y^2}/r}^h z\, dz\, dy\, dx.$$

Using a symbolic integration utility to evaluate the triple integral produces

$$M_{xy} = \frac{k\pi r^2 h^2}{4}.$$

Therefore, the z-coordinate of the centroid of the cone is

$$\bar{z} = \frac{M_{xy}}{m} = \frac{k\pi r^2 h/4}{k\pi r^2 h/3} = \frac{3h}{4}.$$

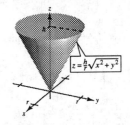

$z = \frac{h}{r}\sqrt{x^2+y^2}$

37. $m = \dfrac{128k\pi}{3}$

$\bar{x} = \bar{y} = 0$ by symmetry

$z = \sqrt{4^2 - x^2 - y^2}$

$$M_{xy} = 4k\int_0^4 \int_0^{\sqrt{4^2-x^2}} \int_0^{\sqrt{4^2-x^2-y^2}} z\, dz\, dy\, dx$$

$$= 2k\int_0^4 \int_0^{\sqrt{4^2-x^2}} (4^2 - x^2 - y^2)\, dy\, dx = 2k\int_0^4 \left[16y - x^2y - \frac{1}{3}y^3\right]_0^{\sqrt{4^2-x^2}} dx = \frac{4k}{3}\int_0^4 (4^2 - x^2)^{3/2}\, dx$$

$$= \frac{1024k}{3}\int_0^{\pi/2} \cos^4 \theta\, d\theta \qquad (\text{let } x = 4\sin\theta)$$

$$= 64\pi k \qquad \text{by Wallis's Formula}$$

$$\bar{z} = \frac{M_{xy}}{m} = \frac{64k\pi}{1} \cdot \frac{3}{128k\pi} = \frac{3}{2}$$

39. $f(x, y) = \dfrac{5}{12} y$

$$m = k \int_0^{20} \int_0^{-(3/5)x+12} \int_0^{(5/12)y} dz\, dy\, dx = 200k$$

$$M_{yz} = k \int_0^{20} \int_0^{-(3/5)x+12} \int_0^{(5/12)y} x\, dz\, dy\, dx = 1000k$$

$$M_{xz} = k \int_0^{20} \int_0^{-(3/5)+x+12} \int_0^{(5/12)y} y\, dz\, dy\, dx = 1200k$$

$$M_{xy} = k \int_0^{20} \int_0^{-(3/5)x+12} \int_0^{(5/12)y} z\, dz\, dy\, dx = 250k$$

$$\bar{x} = \frac{M_{yz}}{m} = \frac{1000k}{200k} = 5$$

$$\bar{y} = \frac{M_{xz}}{m} = \frac{1200k}{200k} = 6$$

$$\bar{z} = \frac{M_{xy}}{m} = \frac{250k}{200k} = \frac{5}{4}$$

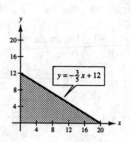

$y = -\dfrac{3}{5}x + 12$

41. (a) $I_x = k \displaystyle\int_0^a \int_0^a \int_0^a (y^2 + z^2)\, dx\, dy\, dz = ka \int_0^a \int_0^a (y^2 + z^2)\, dy\, dz$

$$= ka \int_0^a \left[\frac{1}{3}y^3 + z^2 y \right]_0^a dz = ka \int_0^a \left(\frac{1}{3}a^3 + az^2 \right) dz = \left[ka\left(\frac{1}{3}a^3 k + \frac{1}{3}az^3 \right) \right]_0^a = \frac{2ka^5}{3}$$

$$I_x = I_y = I_z = \frac{2ka^5}{3} \text{ by symmetry}$$

(b) $I_x = k \displaystyle\int_0^a \int_0^a \int_0^a (y^2 + z^2)xyz\, dx\, dy\, dz = \frac{ka^2}{a} \int_0^a \int_0^a (y^3 z + yz^3)\, dy\, dz$

$$= \frac{ka^2}{2} \int_0^a \left[\frac{y^4 a}{4} + \frac{y^2 z^3}{2} \right]_0^a dz = \frac{ka^4}{8} \int_0^a (a^2 z + 2z^3)\, dz = \left[\frac{ka^4}{8} \left(\frac{a^2 z^2}{2} + \frac{2z^4}{4} \right) \right]_0^a = \frac{ka^8}{8}$$

$$I_x = I_y = I_z = \frac{ka^8}{8} \text{ by symmetry}$$

43. (a) $I_x = k \displaystyle\int_0^4 \int_0^4 \int_0^{4-x} (y^2 + z^2)\, dz\, dy\, dx = k \int_0^4 \int_0^4 \left[y^2(4 - x) + \frac{1}{3}(4 - x)^3 \right] dy\, dx$

$$= k \int_0^4 \left[\frac{y^3}{3}(4 - x) + \frac{y}{3}(4 - x)^3 \right]_0^4 dx = k \int_0^4 \left[\frac{64}{3}(4 - x) + \frac{4}{3}(4 - x)^3 \right] dx$$

$$= k \left[-\frac{32}{3}(4 - x)^2 - \frac{1}{3}(4 - x)^4 \right]_0^4 = 256k$$

$$I_y = k \int_0^4 \int_0^4 \int_0^{4-x} (x^2 + z^2)\, dz\, dy\, dx = k \int_0^4 \int_0^4 \left[x^2(4 - x) + \frac{1}{3}(4 - x)^3 \right] dy\, dx$$

$$= 4k \int_0^4 \left[4x^2 - x^3 + \frac{1}{3}(4 - x)^3 \right] dx = 4k \left[\frac{4}{3}x^3 - \frac{1}{4}x^4 - \frac{1}{12}(4 - x)^4 \right]_0^4 = \frac{512k}{3}$$

$$I_z = k \int_0^4 \int_0^4 \int_0^{4-x} (x^2 + y^2)\, dz\, dy\, dx = k \int_0^4 \int_0^4 (x^2 + y^2)(4 - x)\, dy\, dx$$

$$= k \int_0^4 \left[\left(x^2 y + \frac{y^3}{3} \right)(4 - x) \right]_0^4 dx = k \int_0^4 \left(4x^2 + \frac{64}{3} \right)(4 - x)\, dx = 256k$$

—CONTINUED—

43. —CONTINUED—

(b) $I_x = k \int_0^4 \int_0^4 \int_0^{4-x} y(y^2 + z^2)\, dz\, dy\, dx = k \int_0^4 \int_0^4 \left[y^3(4-x) + \frac{1}{3}y(4-x)^3 \right] dy\, dx$

$\qquad = k \int_0^4 \left[\frac{y^4}{4}(4-x) + \frac{y^2}{6}(4-x)^3 \right]_0^4 dx = k \int_0^4 \left[64(4-x) + \frac{8}{3}(4-x)^3 \right] dx$

$\qquad = k \left[-32(4-x)^2 - \frac{2}{3}(4-x)^4 = \frac{2048k}{3} \right.$

$I_y = k \int_0^4 \int_0^4 \int_0^{4-x} y(x^2 + z^2)\, dz\, dy\, dx = k \int_0^4 \int_0^4 \left[x^2 y(4-x) + \frac{1}{3}y(4-x)^3 \right] dy\, dx$

$\qquad = 8k \int_0^4 \left[4x^2 - x^3 + \frac{1}{3}(4-x)^3 \right] dx = 8k \left[\frac{4}{3}x^3 - \frac{1}{4}x^4 - \frac{1}{12}(4-x)^4 \right]_0^4 = \frac{1024k}{3}$

$I_z = k \int_0^4 \int_0^4 \int_0^{4-x} y(x^2 + y^2)\, dz\, dy\, dx = k \int_0^4 \int_0^4 (x^2 y + y^3)(4-x)\, dx$

$\qquad = k \int_0^4 \left[\left(\frac{x^2 y^2}{2} + \frac{y^4}{4} \right)(4-x) \right]_0^4 dx = k \int_0^4 (8x^2 + 64)(4-x)\, dx$

$\qquad = 8k \int_0^4 (32 - 8x + 4x^2 - x^3)\, dx = \left[8k \left(32x - 4x^2 + \frac{4}{3}x^3 - \frac{1}{4}x^4 \right) \right]_0^4 = \frac{2048k}{3}$

45. The solid is a right circular of radius a, length L, and uniform density $\rho(x, y, z) = k$. Thus the mass of the cylinder is

$\qquad m = k(\text{volume}) = k\pi a^2 L.$

Now,

$\qquad I_x = \int_{-a}^a \int_{-\sqrt{a^2-x^2}}^{\sqrt{a^2-x^2}} \int_{-L/2}^{L/2} (y^2 + z^2)k\, dy\, dz\, dx$

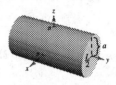

$\qquad = 8k \int_0^a \int_0^{\sqrt{a^2-x^2}} \int_0^{L/2} (y^2 + z^2)\, dy\, dz\, dx \quad \text{(by symmetry)}$

$\qquad = \frac{kL}{3} \int_0^a \int_0^{\sqrt{a^2-x^2}} (L^2 + 12z^2)\, dz\, dx$

$\qquad = \frac{kL}{3} \int_0^a \left[L^2 \sqrt{a^2 - x^2} + 4(a^2 - x^2)^{3/2} \right] dx$

Now let $x = a\sin\theta$. Then $\sqrt{a^2 - x^2} = a\cos\theta$, $dx = a\cos\theta\, d\theta$, and

$\qquad I_x = \frac{ka^2 L^3}{3} \int_0^{\pi/2} \cos^2\theta\, d\theta + \frac{4ka^4 L}{3} \int_0^{\pi/2} \cos^4\theta\, d\theta.$

By Wallis's Formula we have

$\qquad I_x = \frac{ka^2 L^3}{3} \left(\frac{1}{2} \right)\left(\frac{\pi}{2} \right) + \frac{4ka^4 L}{3} \left(\frac{1}{2} \right)\left(\frac{3}{4} \right)\left(\frac{\pi}{2} \right)$

$\qquad = \frac{k\pi a^2 L}{12}(L^2 + 3a^2) = \frac{1}{12}m(3a^2 + L^2).$

By symmetry $I_x = I_z$. To find I_y, change only the integrand in the triple integral given above and obtain

$\qquad I_y = 8k \int_0^a \int_0^{\sqrt{a^2-x^2}} \int_0^{L/2} (x^2 + z^2) = dy\, dz\, dx.$

Proceeding with integrations similar to those given above yields

$\qquad I_y = \frac{k\pi a^4 L}{2} = k\pi a^2 L \left(\frac{a^2}{2} \right) = \frac{1}{2}ma^2.$

47. $\displaystyle\int_{-1}^{1}\int_{-1}^{1}\int_{0}^{1-x}(x^2+y^2)\sqrt{x^2+y^2+z^2}\,dz\,dy\,dx$

49. Because the density increases as you move away from the axis of symmetry, the moment of inertia will increase.

Section 13.7   Triple Integrals in Cylindrical and Spherical Coordinates

1. $\displaystyle\int_{0}^{4}\int_{0}^{\pi/2}\int_{0}^{2} r\cos\theta\,dr\,d\theta\,dz = \int_{0}^{4}\int_{0}^{\pi/2}\left[\frac{r^2}{2}\cos\theta\right]_{0}^{2}d\theta\,dz$

$\displaystyle\qquad = \int_{0}^{4}\int_{0}^{\pi/2} 2\cos\theta\,d\theta\,dz = \int_{0}^{4}\left[2\sin\theta\right]_{0}^{\pi/2}dz = \int_{0}^{4} 2\,dz = 8$

3. $\displaystyle\int_{0}^{\pi/2}\int_{0}^{2\cos^2\theta}\int_{0}^{4-r^2} r\sin\theta\,dz\,dr\,d\theta = \int_{0}^{\pi/2}\int_{0}^{2\cos^2\theta}\left[rz\sin\theta\right]_{0}^{4-r^2}dr\,d\theta$

$\displaystyle\qquad = \int_{0}^{\pi/2}\int_{0}^{2\cos^2\theta} r(4-r^2)\sin\theta\,dr\,d\theta$

$\displaystyle\qquad = \int_{0}^{\pi/2}\left[-\frac{1}{4}(4-r^2)^2\sin\theta\right]_{0}^{2\cos^2\theta}d\theta$

$\displaystyle\qquad = \int_{0}^{\pi/2}(8\cos^4\theta - 4\cos^8\theta)\sin\theta\,d\theta$

$\displaystyle\qquad = \left[-\frac{8}{5}\cos^5\theta + \frac{4}{9}\cos^9\theta\right]_{0}^{\pi/2} = \frac{52}{45}$

5. $\displaystyle\int_{0}^{2\pi}\int_{0}^{\pi/4}\int_{0}^{\cos\phi}\rho^2\sin\phi\,d\rho\,d\phi\,d\theta = \frac{1}{3}\int_{0}^{2\pi}\int_{0}^{\pi/4}\cos^3\phi\sin\phi\,d\phi\,d\theta = -\frac{1}{12}\int_{0}^{2\pi}\left[\cos^4\phi\right]_{0}^{\pi/4}d\theta = \frac{\pi}{8}$

7. $\displaystyle\int_{0}^{4}\int_{0}^{z}\int_{0}^{\pi/2} re^{r}\,d\theta\,dr\,dz = \pi(e^4+3)$

9. $\displaystyle\int_{0}^{\pi/2}\int_{0}^{3}\int_{0}^{e^{-r^2}} r\,dz\,dr\,d\theta$

We first observe that the triple integral is written in terms of cylindrical coordinates. From the limits of integration we have

Constant bounds on θ: $0 \le \theta \le \pi/2$

Constant bounds on r: $0 \le r \le 3$

Variable bounds on z: $0 \le z \le e^{-r^2}$.

The limits on r determine a circular cylinder of radius 3 having the z-axis as its axis. The limits on θ and z restrict us to the first-octant portion of the cylinder bounded by the surface

$$z = e^{-r^2} = e^{-(x^2+y^2)}.$$

The solid is shown in the figure. The value of the integral is given by

$$\int_{0}^{\pi/2}\int_{0}^{3}\int_{0}^{e^{-r^2}} r\,dz\,dr\,d\theta = \int_{0}^{\pi/2}\int_{0}^{3} re^{-r^2}\,dr\,d\theta$$

$$= -\frac{1}{2}(e^{-9}-1)\int_{0}^{\pi/2}d\theta = \frac{\pi}{4}(1-e^{-9}).$$

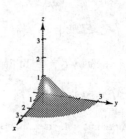

11. $\displaystyle\int_0^{2\pi}\int_{\pi/6}^{\pi/2}\int_0^4 \rho^2\sin\phi\,d\rho\,d\phi\,d\theta = \frac{64}{3}\int_0^{2\pi}\int_{\pi/6}^{\pi/2}\sin\phi\,d\phi\,d\theta$

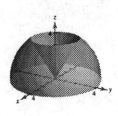

$\displaystyle\qquad\qquad\qquad\qquad\qquad = \frac{64}{3}\int_0^{2\pi}\Big[-\cos\phi\Big]_{\pi/6}^{\pi/2}d\theta$

$\displaystyle\qquad\qquad\qquad\qquad\qquad = \frac{32\sqrt{3}}{3}\int_0^{2\pi}d\theta$

$\displaystyle\qquad\qquad\qquad\qquad\qquad = \frac{64\sqrt{3}\,\pi}{3}$

13. (a) $\displaystyle\int_0^{2\pi}\int_0^2\int_{r^2}^4 r^2\cos\theta\,dz\,dr\,d\theta = 0$

(b) $\displaystyle\int_0^{2\pi}\int_0^{\arctan(1/2)}\int_0^{4\sec\phi}\rho^3\sin^2\phi\cos\theta\,d\rho\,d\phi\,d\theta + \int_0^{2\pi}\int_{\arctan(1/2)}^{\pi/2}\int_0^{\cot\phi\csc\phi}\rho^3\sin^2\phi\cos\theta\,d\rho\,d\phi\,d\theta = 0$

15. 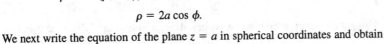 $\displaystyle\int_{-a}^{a}\int_{-\sqrt{a^2-x^2}}^{\sqrt{a^2-x^2}}\int_a^{a+\sqrt{a^2-x^2-y^2}} x\,dz\,dy\,dx$

Observe that the solid S over which we are integrating is the top half of the sphere of radius a and center $(0,0,a)$. Projecting the solid onto the xy-plane forms a circle of radius a. Thus, we have

Constant bounds on θ: $0 \le \theta \le 2\pi$

Constant bounds on r: $0 \le r \le a$

Variable bounds on z: $a \le z \le a + \sqrt{a^2 - x^2 - y^2} = a + \sqrt{a^2 - r^2}$.

Finally, since $x = r\cos\theta$, we obtain the integral in cylindrical coordinates:

$$\int_0^{2\pi}\int_0^a\int_a^{a+\sqrt{a^2-r^2}}(r\cos\theta)r\,dz\,dr\,d\theta = \int_0^{2\pi}\int_0^a\int_a^{a+\sqrt{a^2-r^2}} r^2\cos\theta\,dz\,dr\,d\theta.$$

To write the integral in spherical coordinates, first write the equation of the sphere in spherical coordinates:

$$z = a + \sqrt{a^2 - x^2 - y^2}$$
$$x^2 + y^2 + (z-a)^2 = a^2$$
$$x^2 + y^2 + z^2 - 2az + a^2 = a^2$$
$$\rho^2 - 2a(\rho\cos\phi) = 0 \qquad \text{(Since } z = \rho\cos\phi\text{)}$$
$$\rho = 2a\cos\phi.$$

We next write the equation of the plane $z = a$ in spherical coordinates and obtain

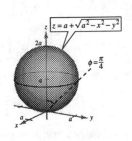

$$z = a$$
$$\rho\cos\phi = a$$
$$\rho = a\sec\phi.$$

From the figure it follows that the bounds on ϕ are $0 \le \phi \le \pi/4$. Since $x = \rho\sin\phi\cos\theta$, we can write the integral in spherical coordinates.

$$\int_0^{\pi/4}\int_0^{2\pi}\int_{a\sec\phi}^{2a\cos\phi}(\rho\sin\phi\cos\theta)(\rho^2\sin\phi)\,d\rho\,d\theta\,d\phi = \frac{1}{4}\int_0^{\pi/4}\int_0^{2\pi}\sin^2\phi\cos\theta[(2a\cos\phi)^4 - (a\sec\phi)^4]\,d\theta\,d\phi$$

$$= \frac{a^4}{4}\int_0^{\pi/4}\Big[(16\sin^2\phi\cos^4\phi - \sin^2\phi\sec^4\phi)\sin\theta\Big]_0^{2\pi}d\phi$$

$$= \frac{a^4}{4}\int_0^{\pi/4} 0\,d\phi = 0.$$

17. $z = h - \dfrac{h}{r_0}\sqrt{x^2 + y^2} = \dfrac{h}{r_0}(r_0 - r)$

$$V = 4\int_0^{\pi/2}\int_0^{r_0}\int_0^{h(r_0-r)/r_0} r\, dz\, dr\, d\theta$$

$$= \frac{4h}{r_0}\int_0^{\pi/2}\int_0^{r_0}(r_0 r - r^2)\, dr\, d\theta$$

$$= \frac{4h}{r_0}\int_0^{\pi/2}\frac{r_0^3}{6}\, d\theta$$

$$= \frac{4h}{r_0}\left(\frac{r_0^3}{6}\right)\left(\frac{\pi}{2}\right) = \frac{1}{3}\pi r_0^2 h$$

19. $\rho = k\sqrt{x^2 + y^2} = kr$

$\bar{x} = \bar{y} = 0$ by symmetry

$$m = 4k\int_0^{\pi/2}\int_0^{r_0}\int_0^{h(r_0-r)/r_0} r^2\, dz\, dr\, d\theta$$

$$= \frac{1}{6}k\pi r_0^3 h$$

$$M_{xy} = 4k\int_0^{\pi/2}\int_0^{r_0}\int_0^{h(r_0-r)/r_0} r^2 z\, dz\, dr\, d\theta$$

$$= \frac{1}{30}k\pi r_0^3\, h^2$$

$$\bar{z} = \frac{M_{xy}}{m} = \frac{k\pi r_0^3 h^2/30}{k\pi r_0^3 h/6} = \frac{h}{5}$$

21. $I_z = 4k\int_0^{\pi/2}\int_0^{r_0}\int_0^{h(r_0-r)/r_0} r^3\, dz\, dr\, d\theta$

$$= \frac{4kh}{r_0}\int_0^{\pi/2}\int_0^{r_0}(r_0 r^3 - r^4)\, dr\, d\theta$$

$$= \frac{4kh}{r_0}\left(\frac{r_0^5}{20}\right)\left(\frac{\pi}{2}\right)$$

$$= \frac{1}{10}k\pi r_0^4 h$$

$$= \left(\frac{1}{3}k\pi r_0^2 h\right)\left(\frac{3}{10}r_0^2\right)$$

$$= \frac{3}{10}m r_0^2$$

23. $m = k(\pi b^2 h - \pi a^2 h) = k\pi h(b^2 - a^2)$

$$I_z = 4k\int_0^{\pi/2}\int_a^b\int_0^h r^3\, dz\, dr\, d\theta$$

$$= 4kh\int_0^{\pi/2}\int_a^b r^3\, dr\, d\theta$$

$$= kh\int_0^{\pi/2}(b^4 - a^4)\, d\theta$$

$$= \frac{k\pi(b^4 - a^4)h}{2}$$

$$= \frac{k\pi(b^2 - a^2)(b^2 + a^2)}{2}$$

$$= \frac{1}{2}m(a^2 + b^2)$$

25. $x^2 + y^2 + z^2 = a^2,\ \left(x - \dfrac{a}{2}\right)^2 + y^2 = \left(\dfrac{a}{2}\right)^2$

The figure shows the sphere and cylinder. Using the cylindrical coordinate system, the equation of the cylinder is given by

$$r = a\cos\theta,\ \left(-\frac{\pi}{2}\le\theta\le\frac{\pi}{2}\right)$$

and the equation of the sphere is given by

$$r^2 + z^2 = a^2 \quad\text{or}\quad z = \pm\sqrt{a^2 - r^2}.$$

Therefore, the volume is

$$V = \int_{-\pi/2}^{\pi/2}\int_0^{a\cos\theta}\int_{-\sqrt{a^2-r^2}}^{\sqrt{a^2-r^2}} r\, dz\, dr\, d\theta$$

$$= 4\int_0^{\pi/2}\int_0^{a\cos\theta} r\sqrt{a^2 - r^2}\, dr\, d\theta$$

$$= -\frac{4}{3}\int_0^{\pi/2}[(a^2 - a^2\cos^2\theta)^{3/2} - a^3]\, d\theta$$

$$= \frac{4a^3}{3}\int_0^{\pi/2}(1 - \sin^3\theta)\, d\theta = \frac{4a^3}{3}\left(\frac{\pi}{2} - \frac{2}{3}\right).$$

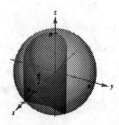

27. $V = 2\displaystyle\int_0^\pi \int_0^{a\cos\theta} \int_0^{\sqrt{a^2-r^2}} r\,dz\,dr\,d\theta$

$= 2\displaystyle\int_0^\pi \int_0^{a\cos\theta} r\sqrt{a^2-r^2}\,dr\,d\theta$

$= 2\displaystyle\int_0^\pi \left[-\frac{1}{3}(a^2-r^2)^{3/2} \right]_0^{a\cos\theta} d\theta$

$= \dfrac{2a^3}{3}\displaystyle\int_0^\pi (1 - \sin^3\theta)\,d\theta$

$= \dfrac{2a^3}{3}\left[\theta + \cos\theta - \dfrac{\cos^3\theta}{3} \right]_0^\pi$

$= \dfrac{2a^3}{9}(3\pi - 4)$

29. $V = \displaystyle\int_0^{2\pi} \int_0^\pi \int_0^{4\sin\phi} \rho^2 \sin\phi\,d\rho\,d\phi\,d\theta = 16\pi^2$

31. $m = 8k\displaystyle\int_0^{\pi/2} \int_0^{\pi/2} \int_0^a \rho^3 \sin\phi\,d\rho\,d\theta\,d\phi$

$= 2ka^4\displaystyle\int_0^{\pi/2} \int_0^{\pi/2} \sin\phi\,d\theta\,d\phi$

$= k\pi a^4\displaystyle\int_0^{\pi/2} \sin\phi\,d\phi$

$= \left[k\pi a^4(-\cos\phi) \right]_0^{\pi/2}$

$= k\pi a^4$

33. Without loss of generality, position the hemisphere with its center at the origin and base on the xy-coordinate plane. Then, by symmetry, $\bar{x} = \bar{y} = 0$. Since the solid has uniform density k, the mass is given by

$$m = k(\text{volume}) = \frac{2}{3}k\pi r^3.$$

Using symmetry, we have

$M_{xy} = \displaystyle\iiint_Q z(\text{density})\,dV$

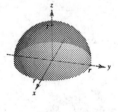

$= 4k\displaystyle\int_0^{\pi/2} \int_0^{\pi/2} \int_0^r \rho^3 \cos\phi \sin\phi\,d\rho\,d\theta\,d\phi$

$= \dfrac{1}{2}kr^4 \displaystyle\int_0^{\pi/2} \int_0^{\pi/2} \sin 2\phi\,d\theta\,d\phi$

$= \dfrac{1}{4}kr^4 \pi \displaystyle\int_0^{\pi/2} \sin 2\phi\,d\phi$

$= -\dfrac{1}{8}k\pi r^4 \left[\cos 2\phi \right]_0^{\pi/2} = \dfrac{1}{4}k\pi r^4.$

Therefore, $\bar{z} = \dfrac{M_{xy}}{m} = \dfrac{k\pi r^4/4}{2k\pi r^3/3} = \dfrac{3r}{8}.$

35. $I_z = 4k \int_{\pi/4}^{\pi/2} \int_0^{\pi/2} \int_0^{\cos \phi} \rho^4 \sin^3 \phi \, d\rho \, d\theta \, d\phi$

$= \frac{4}{5} k \int_{\pi/4}^{\pi/2} \int_0^{\pi/2} \cos^5 \phi \sin^3 \phi \, d\theta \, d\phi$

$= \frac{2}{5} k\pi \int_{\pi/4}^{\pi/2} \cos^5 \phi (1 - \cos^2 \phi) \sin \phi \, d\phi$

$= \left[\frac{2}{5} k\pi \left(-\frac{1}{6} \cos^6 \phi + \frac{1}{8} \cos^8 \phi \right) \right]_{\pi/4}^{\pi/2}$

$= \frac{k\pi}{192}$

37. (a) $r = r_0$: right circular cylinder about z-axis

$\theta = \theta_0$: plane parallel to z-axis

$z = z_0$: plane parallel to xy-plane

(b) $\rho = \rho_0$: sphere of radius ρ_0

$\theta = \theta_0$: plane parallel to z-axis

$\phi = \phi_0$: cone

39. $16 \int_0^a \int_0^{\sqrt{a^2-x^2}} \int_0^{\sqrt{a^2-x^2-y^2}} \int_0^{\sqrt{a^2-x^2-y^2-z^2}} dw \, dz \, dy \, dx$

$= 16 \int_0^a \int_0^{\sqrt{a^2-x^2}} \int_0^{\sqrt{a^2-x^2-y^2}} \sqrt{a^2 - x^2 - y^2 - z^2} \, dz \, dy \, dx$

$= 16 \int_0^{\pi/2} \int_0^a \int_0^{\sqrt{a^2-r^2}} \sqrt{(a^2 - r^2) - z^2} \, dz(r \, dr \, d\theta)$

$= 16 \int_0^{\pi/2} \int_0^a \frac{1}{2} \left[z\sqrt{(a^2 - r^2) - z^2} + (a^2 - r^2) \arcsin \frac{z}{\sqrt{a^2 - r^2}} \right]_0^{\sqrt{a^2-r^2}} r \, dr \, d\theta$

$= 8 \int_0^{\pi/2} \int_0^a \frac{\pi}{2}(a^2 - r^2) r \, dr \, d\theta$

$= 4\pi \int_0^{\pi/2} \left[\frac{a^2 r^2}{2} - \frac{r^4}{4} \right]_0^a d\theta$

$= a^4 \pi \int_0^{\pi/2} d\theta = \frac{a^4 \pi^2}{2}$

Section 13.8   Change of Variables: Jacobians

1. $x = -\frac{1}{2}(u - v)$

$y = \frac{1}{2}(u + v)$

$\frac{\partial x}{\partial u} \frac{\partial y}{\partial v} - \frac{\partial y}{\partial u} \frac{\partial x}{\partial v} = \left(-\frac{1}{2} \right) \left(\frac{1}{2} \right) - \left(\frac{1}{2} \right) \left(\frac{1}{2} \right) = -\frac{1}{2}$

3. $x = u - v^2$

$y = u + v$

$\frac{\partial x}{\partial u} \frac{\partial y}{\partial v} - \frac{\partial y}{\partial u} \frac{\partial x}{\partial v} = (1)(1) - (1)(-2v) = 1 + 2v$

5. $x = u \cos \theta - v \sin \theta$

$y = u \sin \theta + v \cos \theta$

$\frac{\partial x}{\partial u} \frac{\partial y}{\partial v} - \frac{\partial y}{\partial u} \frac{\partial x}{\partial v} = \cos^2 \theta + \sin^2 \theta = 1$

7. Using the definition the Jacobian, we have

$\frac{\partial(x, y)}{\partial(u, v)} = \begin{vmatrix} \dfrac{\partial x}{\partial u} & \dfrac{\partial y}{\partial u} \\ \dfrac{\partial x}{\partial v} & \dfrac{\partial y}{\partial v} \end{vmatrix} = \begin{vmatrix} e^u \sin v & e^u \cos v \\ e^u \cos c & -e^u \sin v \end{vmatrix} = -e^{2u} \sin^2 v - e^{2u} \cos^2 v = -e^{2u}.$

9. $x = 3u + 2v$

$y = 3v$

$v = \dfrac{y}{3}$

$u = \dfrac{x - 2v}{3} = \dfrac{x - 2(y/3)}{3} = \dfrac{x}{3} - \dfrac{2y}{9}$

(x, y)	(u, v)
$(0, 0)$	$(0, 0)$
$(3, 0)$	$(1, 0)$
$(2, 3)$	$(0, 1)$

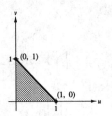

11. $x = \dfrac{1}{2}(u + v)$

$y = \dfrac{1}{2}(u - v)$

$\dfrac{\partial x}{\partial u}\dfrac{\partial y}{\partial v} - \dfrac{\partial y}{\partial u}\dfrac{\partial x}{\partial v} = \left(\dfrac{1}{2}\right)\left(-\dfrac{1}{2}\right) - \left(\dfrac{1}{2}\right)\left(\dfrac{1}{2}\right) = -\dfrac{1}{2}$

$\displaystyle\int_R\!\!\int 4(x^2 + y^2)\,dx\,dy = \int_{-1}^{1}\!\!\int_{-1}^{1} 4\left[\dfrac{1}{4}(u + v)^2 + \dfrac{1}{4}(u - v)^2\right]\!\left(\dfrac{1}{2}\right)dv\,du$

$\qquad = \int_{-1}^{1}\!\!\int_{-1}^{1} (u^2 + v^2)\,dv\,du = \int_{-1}^{1} 2\left(u^2 + \dfrac{1}{3}\right)du = \left[2\left(\dfrac{u^3}{3} + \dfrac{u}{3}\right)\right]_{-1}^{1} = \dfrac{8}{3}$

13. $x = u + v$

$y = u$

$\dfrac{\partial x}{\partial u}\dfrac{\partial y}{\partial v} - \dfrac{\partial y}{\partial u}\dfrac{\partial x}{\partial v} = (1)(0) = (1)(1) = -1$

$\displaystyle\int_R\!\!\int y(x - y)\,dx\,dy = \int_0^3\!\!\int_0^4 uv(1)\,dv\,du = \int_0^3 8u\,du = 36$

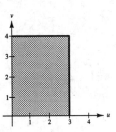

15. The region R is shown in the figure. Solving for u and v in the equations

$$x = \sqrt{\dfrac{v}{u}} \quad\text{and}\quad y = \sqrt{uv}$$

produces $u = y/x$ and $v = xy$.

Bounds in the xy-plane		Bounds in the uv-plane
$\dfrac{y}{x} = \dfrac{1}{4}$	$\rightarrow$	$u = \dfrac{1}{4}$
$\dfrac{y}{x} = 2$	$\rightarrow$	$u = 2$
$xy = 1$	$\rightarrow$	$v = 1$
$xy = 4$	$\rightarrow$	$v = 4$

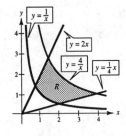

The region S is shown in the figure and the Jacobian for the transformation is

$$\dfrac{\partial(x, y)}{\partial(u, v)} = \begin{vmatrix} \dfrac{\partial x}{\partial u} & \dfrac{\partial y}{\partial u} \\[2mm] \dfrac{\partial x}{\partial v} & \dfrac{\partial y}{\partial v} \end{vmatrix} = \begin{vmatrix} -\dfrac{v^{1/2}}{2u^{3/2}} & \dfrac{v^{1/2}}{2u^{1/2}} \\[2mm] \dfrac{1}{2u^{1/2}v^{1/2}} & \dfrac{u^{1/2}}{2v^{1/2}} \end{vmatrix} = -\dfrac{1}{2u}.$$

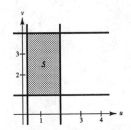

—CONTINUED—

15. —**CONTINUED**—

Therefore, we have

$$\int_R\int e^{-xy/2}\,dy\,dx = \int_S\int e^{-v/2}\left|\frac{\partial(x, y)}{\partial(u, v)}\right|\,du\,dv$$

$$= \frac{1}{2}\int_1^4\int_{1/4}^2 \frac{1}{u}e^{-v/2}\,du\,dv$$

$$= \frac{1}{2}\int_1^4 e^{-v/2}\Big[\ln|u|\Big]_{1/4}^2\,dv$$

$$= \frac{1}{2}\left(\ln 2 - \ln\frac{1}{4}\right)(-2)\int_1^4 e^{-v/2}\left(-\frac{1}{2}\right)dv$$

$$= -\ln 8\Big[e^{-v/2}\Big]_1^4$$

$$= -\ln 8(e^{-2} - e^{-1/2}) = \ln 8(e^{-1/2} - e^{-2}) \approx 0.9798.$$

17. $u = x + y = 4,$ $v = x - y = 0$

$u = x + y = 8,$ $v = x - y = 4$

$x = \frac{1}{2}(u + v)$ $y = \frac{1}{2}(u - v)$

$\dfrac{\partial(x, y)}{\partial(u, v)} = -\dfrac{1}{2}$

$$\int_R\int (x + y)e^{x-y}\,dA = \int_4^8\int_0^4 ue^v\left(\frac{1}{2}\right)dv\,du$$

$$= \frac{1}{2}\int_4^8 u(e^4 - 1)\,du = \left[\frac{1}{4}u^2(e^4 - 1)\right]_4^8 = 12(e^4 - 1)$$

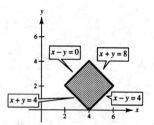

19. The region R is bounded by the graphs of $x - y = 0$, $x - y = 5$, $x + 4y = 0$, and $x + 4y = 5$ (see figure). By letting $u = x - y$ and $v = x + 4y$, we have

$$x = \frac{1}{5}(4u + v) \quad\text{and}\quad y = -\frac{1}{5}(u - v).$$

Thus, the Jacobian is

$$\frac{\partial(x, y)}{\partial(u, v)} = \begin{vmatrix} \dfrac{\partial x}{\partial u} & \dfrac{\partial y}{\partial u} \\[6pt] \dfrac{\partial x}{\partial v} & \dfrac{\partial y}{\partial v} \end{vmatrix} = \begin{vmatrix} \dfrac{4}{5} & -\dfrac{1}{5} \\[6pt] \dfrac{1}{5} & \dfrac{1}{5} \end{vmatrix} = \frac{1}{5}.$$

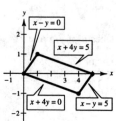

Therefore,

$$\int_R\int \sqrt{(x - y)(x + 4y)}\,dy\,dx = \int_S\int \sqrt{uv}\left|\frac{\partial(x, y)}{\partial(u, v)}\right|\,dv\,du$$

$$= \frac{1}{5}\int_0^5\int_0^5 \sqrt{uv}\,dv\,du$$

$$= \frac{2\sqrt{5}}{3}\int_0^5 \sqrt{u}\,du = \frac{100}{9}.$$

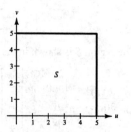

21. $u = x + y, v = x - y, x = \frac{1}{2}(u + v), y = \frac{1}{2}(u - v)$

$$\frac{\partial x}{\partial u}\frac{\partial y}{\partial v} - \frac{\partial y}{\partial u}\frac{\partial x}{\partial v} = -\frac{1}{2}$$

$$\int\int_R \sqrt{x + y}\, dA = \int_0^a \int_{-u}^u \sqrt{u}\left(\frac{1}{2}\right) dv\, du = \int_0^a u\sqrt{u}\, du = \left[\frac{2}{5}u^{5/2}\right]_0^a = \frac{2}{5}a^{5/2}$$

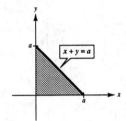
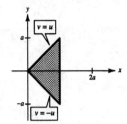

23. $\quad \frac{x^2}{a^2} + \frac{y^2}{b^2} = 1, x = au, y = bv$

$$\frac{(au)^2}{a^2} + \frac{(bv)^2}{b^2} = 1$$

$$u^2 + v^2 = 1$$

(a) $\frac{x^2}{a^2} + \frac{y^2}{b^2} = 1$ $\qquad\qquad u^2 + v^2 = 1$

(b) $\frac{\partial(x, y)}{\partial(u, v)} = \frac{\partial x}{\partial u}\frac{\partial y}{\partial v} - \frac{\partial y}{\partial u}\frac{\partial x}{\partial v}$

$= (a)(b) - (0)(0) = ab$

(c) $A = \int\int_S ab\, du\, dv$

$= ab(\pi(1)^2) = \pi ab$

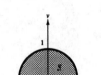

25. $x = u(1 - v), \quad y = uv(1 - w), \quad z = uvw$

$$\frac{\partial(x, y, z)}{\partial(u, v, w)} = \begin{vmatrix} 1 - v & -u & 0 \\ v(1 - w) & u(1 - w) & -uv \\ vw & uw & uv \end{vmatrix} = 1(1 - v)[u^2v(1 - w) + u^2vw] + u[uv^2(1 - w) + uv^2w]$$

$$= (1 - v)(u^2v) + u(uv^2)$$

$$= u^2v$$

27. $x = \rho \sin \phi \cos \theta, \quad y = \rho \sin \sin \theta, \quad z = \rho \cos \phi$

$$\frac{\partial(x, y, z)}{\partial(\rho, \theta, \phi)} = \begin{vmatrix} \sin \phi \cos \theta & -\rho \sin \phi \sin \theta & \rho \cos \phi \cos \theta \\ \sin \phi \sin \theta & \rho \sin \phi \cos \theta & \rho \cos \phi \sin \theta \\ \cos \phi & 0 & -\rho \sin \phi \end{vmatrix}$$

$$= \cos \phi[-\rho^2 \sin \phi \cos \phi \sin^2 \theta - \rho^2 \sin \phi \cos \phi \cos^2 \theta] - \rho \sin \phi[\rho \sin^2 \phi \cos^2\theta + \rho \sin^2 \phi \sin^2 \theta]$$

$$= \cos \phi[-\rho^2 \sin \phi \cos \phi(\sin^2 \theta + \cos^2 \theta)] - \rho \sin \phi[\rho \sin^2 \phi(\cos^2 \theta + \sin^2 \theta)]$$

$$= -\rho^2 \sin \phi \cos^2 \phi - \rho^2 \sin^3 \phi$$

$$= -\rho^2 \sin \phi(\cos^2 \phi + \sin^2 \theta)$$

$$= -\rho^2 \sin \phi$$

Review Exercises for Chapter 13

1. $\displaystyle\int_1^{x^2} x \ln y \, dy = \left[xy(-1 + \ln y) \right]_0^{x^2}$

$\qquad\qquad = x^3(-1 + \ln x^2) + x$

$\qquad\qquad = x - x^3 + x^3 \ln x^2$

3. $\displaystyle\int_0^1 \int_0^{1+x} (3x + 2y) \, dy \, dx = \int_0^1 \left[3xy + y^2 \right]_0^{1+x} dx$

$\qquad\qquad = \int_0^1 (4x^2 + 5x + 1) \, dx$

$\qquad\qquad = \left[\frac{4}{3}x^3 + \frac{5}{2}x^2 + x \right]_0^1 = \frac{29}{6}$

5. $\displaystyle\int_0^3 \int_0^{\sqrt{9-x^2}} 4x \, dy \, dx = \int_0^3 4x\sqrt{9 - x^2} \, dx = \left[-\frac{4}{3}(9 - x^2)^{3/2} \right]_0^3 = 36$

7. $\displaystyle\int_0^h \int_0^x \sqrt{x^2 + y^2} \, dy \, dx$

We choose to use polar coordinates since $r = \sqrt{x^2 + y^2}$. To rewrite the limits, we first find the equation of the line $x = h$ in polar coordinates.

$\qquad x = h$

$\qquad r \cos \theta = h$

$\qquad r = h\left(\frac{1}{\cos \theta} \right) = h \sec \theta$

Therefore,

$\displaystyle\int_0^h \int_0^x \sqrt{x^2 + y^2} \, dy \, dx = \int_0^{\pi/4} \int_0^{h \sec \theta} (r)r \, dr \, d\theta$

$\qquad\qquad = \frac{h^3}{3} \int_0^{\pi/4} \sec^3 \theta \, d\theta$

$\qquad\qquad = \frac{h^3}{3} \left[\frac{\sec \theta \tan \theta}{2} + \frac{1}{2} \ln|\sec \theta + \tan \theta| \right]_0^{\pi/4}$

$\qquad\qquad = \frac{h^3}{6} \left[\sqrt{2} + \ln(\sqrt{2} + 1) \right].$

9. $\displaystyle\int_{-3}^3 \int_{-\sqrt{9-x^2}}^{\sqrt{9-x^2}} \int_{x^2+y^2}^9 \sqrt{x^2 + y^2} \, dz \, dy \, dx = \int_0^{2\pi} \int_0^3 \int_{r^2}^9 r^2 \, dz \, dr \, d\theta$

$\qquad\qquad = \int_0^{2\pi} \int_0^3 (9r^2 - r^4) \, dr \, d\theta = \int_0^{2\pi} \left[3r^3 - \frac{r^5}{5} \right]_0^3 d\theta = \frac{162}{5} \int_0^{2\pi} d\theta = \frac{324\pi}{5}$

11. $\displaystyle\int_0^a \int_0^b \int_0^c (x^2 + y^2 + z^2) \, dx \, dy \, dz = \int_0^a \int_0^b \left(\frac{1}{3}c^3 + cy^2 + cz^2 \right) dy \, dz$

$\qquad\qquad = \int_0^a \left(\frac{1}{3}bc^3 + \frac{1}{3}b^3c + bcz^2 \right) dz = \frac{1}{3}abc^3 + \frac{1}{3}ab^3c + \frac{1}{3}a^3bc = \frac{1}{3}abc(a^2 + b^2 + c^2)$

13. $\displaystyle\int_{-2}^4 \int_{y^2/4}^{(4+y)/2} (x - y) \, dx \, dy = \frac{27}{5}$

15. $\displaystyle\int_{-\sqrt{1-x^2}}^{\sqrt{1-x^2}} \int_{-\sqrt{1-x^2-y^2}}^{\sqrt{1-x^2-y^2}} (x^2 + y^2) \, dz \, dy \, dx = \int_0^{2\pi} \int_0^1 \int_{-\sqrt{1-r^2}}^{\sqrt{1-r^2}} r^3 \, dz \, dr \, d\theta = \frac{8\pi}{15}$

17. $\displaystyle\int_0^3 \int_0^{(3-x)/3} dy\, dx = \int_0^1 \int_0^{3-3y} dx\, dy$

$$A = \int_0^1 \int_0^{3-3y} dx\, dy = \int_0^1 (3 - 3y)\, dy = \left[3y - \frac{3}{2}y^2 \right]_0^1 = \frac{3}{2}$$

19. $\displaystyle\iint_R f(x, y)\, dA = \int_{-5}^3 \int_{-\sqrt{25-x^2}}^{\sqrt{25-x^2}} f(x, y)\, dy\, dx$

$$= \int_{-5}^{-4} \int_{-\sqrt{25-y^2}}^{\sqrt{25-y^2}} f(x, y)\, dx\, dy + \int_{-4}^4 \int_{-\sqrt{25-y^2}}^3 f(x, y)\, dx\, dy + \int_4^5 \int_{-\sqrt{25-y^2}}^{\sqrt{25-y^2}} f(x, y)\, dx\, dy$$

The area of R is

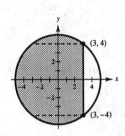

$$A = 2\int_{-5}^3 \int_0^{\sqrt{25-x^2}} dy\, dx$$

$$= 2\int_{-5}^3 \sqrt{25 - x^2}\, dx$$

$$= 2\left(\frac{1}{2}\right)\left[x\sqrt{25 - x^2} + 25\arcsin\left(\frac{x}{5}\right) \right]_{-5}^3$$

$$= 3(4) + 25\arcsin\left(\frac{3}{5}\right) - 0 - 25\left(-\frac{\pi}{2}\right)$$

$$= 12 + \frac{25\pi}{2} + 25\arcsin\left(\frac{3}{5}\right) \approx 67.36.$$

(*Note:* The area of the entire circle is $25\pi \approx 78.54$.)

21. $\displaystyle A = 4\int_0^1 \int_0^{x\sqrt{1-x^2}} dy\, dx = 4\int_0^1 x\sqrt{1 - x^2}\, dx = \left[-\frac{4}{3}(1 - x^2)^{3/2} \right]_0^1 = \frac{4}{3}$

$$A = 4\int_0^{1/2} \int_{\sqrt{(1-\sqrt{1-4y^2})/2}}^{\sqrt{(1+\sqrt{1-4y^2})/2}} dx\, dy$$

23. $\displaystyle A = \int_2^5 \int_{x-3}^{\sqrt{x-1}} dy\, dx + 2\int_1^2 \int_0^{\sqrt{x-1}} dy\, dx = \int_{-1}^2 \int_{y^2+1}^{y+3} dx\, dy = \frac{9}{2}$

25. Both integrations are over the common region R shown in the figure. Analytically,

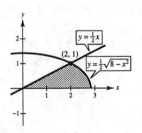

$$\int_0^1 \int_{2y}^{2\sqrt{2-y^2}} (x + y)\, dx\, dy = \frac{4}{3} + \frac{4}{3}\sqrt{2}$$

$$\int_0^2 \int_0^{x/2} (x + y)\, dy\, dx + \int_2^{2\sqrt{2}} \int_0^{\sqrt{8-x^2}/2} (x + y)\, dy\, dx = \frac{5}{3} + \left(\frac{4}{3}\sqrt{2} - \frac{1}{3}\right) = \frac{4}{3} + \frac{4}{3}\sqrt{2}.$$

27. $\displaystyle V = \int_0^4 \int_0^{x^2+4} (x^2 - y + 4)\, dy\, dx$

$$= \int_0^4 \left[x^2 y - \frac{1}{2}y^2 + 4y \right]_0^{x^2+4} dx = \int_0^4 \left(\frac{1}{2}x^4 + 4x^2 + 8\right) dx = \left[\frac{1}{10}x^5 + \frac{4}{3}x^3 + 8x \right]_0^4 = \frac{3296}{15}$$

29. The solid is outside the cylinder $x^2 + y^2 = 1$, inside the hyperboloid of one sheet $x^2 + y^2 - z^2 = 1$, above the xy-plane, and below the plane $z = h$ as shown in the figure. At a given height z_0 in cylindrical coordinates r is bounded by 1 and

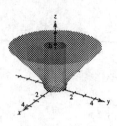

$$x^2 + y^2 - z_0{}^2 = 1$$
$$r^2 = 1 + z_0{}^2$$
$$r = \sqrt{1 + z_0{}^2}$$

Therefore, by symmetry we have

$$V = 4 \int_0^h \int_0^{\pi/2} \int_1^{\sqrt{1+z^2}} r \, dr \, d\theta \, dz$$

$$= 2 \int_0^h \int_0^{\pi/2} (1 + z^2 - 1) \, d\theta \, dz$$

$$= \pi \int_0^h z^2 \, dz = \left[\pi \left(\frac{1}{3} z^3 \right) \right]_0^h = \frac{\pi h^3}{3}.$$

31. $V = 4 \int_0^{\pi/2} \int_0^{2\cos\theta} \int_0^{\sqrt{4-r^2}} r \, dz \, dr \, d\theta$

$$= 4 \int_0^{\pi/2} \int_0^{2\cos\theta} r\sqrt{4 - r^2} \, dr \, d\theta$$

$$= -\int_0^{\pi/2} \left[\frac{4}{3}(4 - r^2)^{3/2} \right]_0^{2\cos\theta} d\theta$$

$$= \frac{32}{3} \int_0^{\pi/2} (1 - \sin^3\theta) \, d\theta$$

$$= \frac{32}{3} \left[\theta + \cos\theta - \frac{1}{3}\cos^3\theta \right]_0^{\pi/2} = \frac{32}{3}\left(\frac{\pi}{2} - \frac{2}{3} \right)$$

33. Volume $\approx$ (base)(height)

$$\approx \frac{9}{2}(3) = \frac{27}{2}$$

Matches (c)

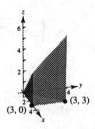

35. $f(x, y) = \begin{cases} kxye^{-(x+y)}, & x \ge 0, y \ge 0 \\ 0, & \text{elsewhere} \end{cases}$

If f is a joint density function, then $f(x, y) \ge 0$ for all (x, y), and

$$\int_{-\infty}^{\infty} \int_{-\infty}^{\infty} f(x, y) \, dA = 1.$$

Use Integration by Parts to evaluate the improper integral.

$$\int_{-\infty}^{\infty} \int_{-\infty}^{\infty} f(x, y) \, dA = \int_0^{\infty} \int_0^{\infty} kxye^{-(x+y)} \, dy \, dx$$

$$= \int_0^{\infty} \left[-kxe^{-(x+y)}(y + 1) \right]_0^{\infty} dx$$

$$= \int_0^{\infty} kxe^{-x} \, dx$$

$$= \left[-k(x + 1)e^{-x} \right]_0^{\infty} = k$$

Therefore, $k = 1$. Use the same integration steps shown above to find the required probability.

$$P(0 \le x \le 1, 0 \le y \le 1) = \int_0^1 \int_0^1 kxye^{-(x+y)} \, dy \, dx$$

$$\approx 0.070$$

37. (a) $(x^2 + y^2) = 9(x^2 - y^2)$

$$(r^2)^2 = 9(r^2\cos^2\theta - r^2\sin^2\theta)$$

$$r^2 = 9(\cos^2\theta - \sin^2\theta) = 9\cos 2\theta$$

$$r = 3\sqrt{\cos 2\theta}$$

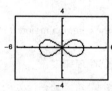

(b) $A = 4 \int_0^{\pi/4} \int_0^{3\sqrt{\cos 2\theta}} r \, dr \, d\theta = 9$

(c) $V = 4 \int_0^{\pi/4} \int_0^{3\sqrt{\cos 2\theta}} \sqrt{9 - r^2}\, r \, dr \, d\theta \approx 20.392$

39. (a) $m = k\displaystyle\int_0^1\int_{2x^3}^{2x} xy\, dy\, dx = \dfrac{k}{4}$

$M_x = k\displaystyle\int_0^1\int_{2x^3}^{2x} xy^2\, dy\, dx = \dfrac{16k}{55}$

$M_y = k\displaystyle\int_0^1\int_{2x^3}^{2x} x^2y\, dy\, dx = \dfrac{8k}{45}$

$\bar{x} = \dfrac{M_y}{m} = \dfrac{32}{45}$

$\bar{y} = \dfrac{M_x}{m} = \dfrac{64}{55}$

(b) $m = k\displaystyle\int_0^1\int_{2x^3}^{2x} (x^2 + y^2)dy\, dx = \dfrac{17k}{30}$

$M_x = k\displaystyle\int_0^1\int_{2x^3}^{2x} y(x^2 + y^2)dy\, dx = \dfrac{392k}{585}$

$M_y = k\displaystyle\int_0^1\int_{2x^3}^{2x} x(x^2 + y^2)dy\, dx = \dfrac{156k}{385}$

$\bar{x} = \dfrac{M_y}{m} = \dfrac{936}{1309}$

$\bar{y} = \dfrac{M_x}{m} = \dfrac{784}{663}$

41. $f(x, y) = 16 - x^2 - y^2,\ R\{(x, y): x^2 + y^2 \leq 16\}$

Since $z = 16 - x^2 - y^2$,

$$\frac{\partial z}{\partial x} = -2x \quad \text{and} \quad \frac{\partial z}{\partial y} = -2y.$$

$$S = \int_R\int \sqrt{1 + \left(\frac{\partial z}{\partial x}\right)^2 + \left(\frac{\partial z}{\partial y}\right)^2}\, dy\, dx$$

$$= \int_{-4}^{4}\int_{-\sqrt{16-x^2}}^{\sqrt{16-x^2}} \sqrt{1 + 4x^2 + 4y^2}\, dy\, dx$$

$$= 4\int_0^4\int_0^{\sqrt{16-x^2}} \sqrt{1 + 4(x^2 + y^2)}\, dy\, dx$$

$$= \frac{1}{2}\int_0^{\pi/2}\int_0^4 \sqrt{1 + 4r^2}(8r)\, dr\, d\theta$$

$$= \frac{1}{3}\int_0^{\pi/2} (65^{3/2} - 1)\, d\theta = \frac{\pi}{6}\left(65\sqrt{65} - 1\right)$$

43. $f(x, y) = 9 - y^2$

$f_x = 0,\ f_y = -2y$

$$S = \int_R\int \sqrt{1 + f_x^2 + f_y^2}\, dA$$

$$= \int_0^3\int_{-y}^{y} \sqrt{1 + 4y^2}\, dx\, dy$$

$$= \int_0^3\left[\sqrt{1 + 4y^2}\, x\right]_{-y}^{y} dy$$

$$= \int_0^3 2\sqrt{1 + 4y^2}\, dy = \frac{1}{4}\frac{2}{3}(1 + 4y^2)\Bigg]_0^3$$

$$= \frac{1}{6}\left[(37)^{3/2} - 1\right]$$

45. $m = 4k\displaystyle\int_{\pi/4}^{\pi/2}\int_0^{\pi/2}\int_0^{\cos\phi} \rho^2 \sin\phi\, d\rho\, d\theta\, d\phi$

$= \dfrac{4}{3}k\displaystyle\int_{\pi/4}^{\pi/2}\int_0^{\pi/2} \cos^3\phi \sin\phi\, d\theta\, d\phi = \dfrac{2}{3}k\pi\int_{\pi/4}^{\pi/2} \cos^3\phi \sin\phi\, d\phi = \left[-\dfrac{2}{3}k\pi\left(\dfrac{1}{4}\cos^4\phi\right)\right]_{\pi/4}^{\pi/2} = \dfrac{k\pi}{24}$

$M_{xy} = 4k\displaystyle\int_{\pi/4}^{\pi/2}\int_0^{\pi/2}\int_0^{\cos\phi} \rho^3 \cos\phi\, d\rho\, \sin\phi\, d\theta\, d\phi$

$= k\displaystyle\int_{\pi/4}^{\pi/2}\int_0^{\pi/2} \cos^5\phi \sin\phi\, d\rho\, d\theta\, d\phi = \dfrac{1}{2}k\pi\int_{\pi/4}^{\pi/2} \cos^5\phi \sin\phi\, d\phi = \left[-\dfrac{1}{12}k\pi\cos^6\phi\right]_{\pi/4}^{\pi/2} = \dfrac{k\pi}{96}$

$\bar{z} = \dfrac{M_{xy}}{m} = \dfrac{k\pi/96}{k\pi/24} = \dfrac{1}{4}$

$\bar{x} = \bar{y} = 0$ by symmetry

47. $x^2 + y^2 + z^2 = a^2$ (first octant)

Because of its symmetry, the coordinates of the center of mass are equal. Let k be the constant density; then the mass is

$$m = k(\text{volume}) = k\left(\frac{1}{8}\right)\left(\frac{4}{3}\pi a^3\right) = \frac{k}{6}\pi a^3.$$

Now,

$$M_{xy} = \iiint_S z(\text{density})\, dS \qquad \text{(rectangular coordinates)}$$

$$= k\int_0^{\pi/2}\int_0^{\pi/2}\int_0^a (\rho\cos\phi)(\rho^2\sin\phi)\, d\rho\, d\theta\, d\phi \qquad \text{(spherical coordinates)}$$

$$= \frac{ka^4}{4}\int_0^{\pi/2}\int_0^{\pi/2}\cos\phi\sin\phi\, d\theta\, d\phi$$

$$= \frac{k\pi a^4}{8}\int_0^{\pi/2}\cos\phi\sin\phi\, d\phi$$

$$= \frac{k\pi a^4}{8}\left[\frac{1}{2}\sin^2\phi\right]_0^{\pi/2} = \frac{k\pi a^4}{16}.$$

Therefore,

$$\bar{x} = \bar{y} = \bar{z} = \frac{M_{xy}}{m} = \frac{k\pi a^4/16}{k\pi a^3/6} = \frac{3a}{8}.$$

49. $I_z = 4k\int_0^{\pi/2}\int_3^4\int_0^{16-r^2} r^3\, dz\, dr\, d\theta = 4k\int_0^{\pi/2}\int_3^4 (16r^3 - r^5)\, dr\, d\theta = \frac{833\pi k}{3}$

51. $z = f(x, y) = \sqrt{a^2 - x^2 - y^2}$

$$= \sqrt{a^2 - r^2}$$

$$0 \le r \le \sqrt{2ah - h^2}$$

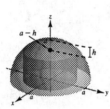

(a) Disc Method

$$V = \pi\int_{a-h}^a (a^2 - y^2)\, dy$$

$$= \pi\left[a^2 y - \frac{y^3}{3}\right]_{a-h}^a = \pi\left[\left(a^3 - \frac{a^3}{3}\right) - \left(a^2(a-h) - \frac{(a-h)^3}{3}\right)\right]$$

$$= \pi\left[a^3 - \frac{a^3}{3} - a^3 + a^2 h + \frac{a^3}{3} - a^2 h + ah^2 - \frac{h^3}{3}\right]$$

$$= \pi\left[ah^2 - \frac{h^3}{3}\right] = \frac{1}{3}\pi h^2[3a - h]$$

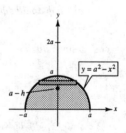

Equivalently, use spherical coordinates $V = \int_0^{2\pi}\int_0^{\cos^{-1}(a-h/a)}\int_{(a-h)\sec\phi}^a \rho^2\sin\phi\, d\rho\, d\phi\, d\theta.$

(b) $M_{xy} = \int_0^{2\pi}\int_0^{\cos^{-1}(a-h/a)}\int_{(a-h)\sec\phi}^a (\rho\cos\phi)\rho^2\sin\phi\, d\rho\, d\phi\, d\theta = \frac{1}{4}h^2\pi(2a-h)^2$

$$\bar{z} = \frac{M_{xy}}{V} = \frac{(1/4)h^2\pi(2a-h)^2}{(1/3)h^2\pi(3a-h)} = \frac{3}{4}\frac{(2a-h)^2}{3a-h}$$

centroid: $\left(0, 0, \dfrac{3(2a-h)^2}{4(3a-h)}\right)$

—CONTINUED—

51. **—CONTINUED—**

(c) If $h = a$, $\bar{z} = \dfrac{3(a)^2}{4(2a)} = \dfrac{3}{8}a$

centroid of hemisphere: $\left(0, 0, \dfrac{3}{8}a\right)$

(d) $\displaystyle\lim_{h \to 0} \bar{z} = \lim_{h \to 0} \dfrac{3(2a - h)^2}{4(3a - h)} = \dfrac{3(4a^2)}{12a} = a$

(e) $x^2 + y^2 = \rho^2 \sin^2 \phi$

$$I_z = \int_0^{2\pi} \int_0^{\cos^{-1}(a-h/a)} \int_{(a-h)\,\sec\,\phi}^{a} (\rho^2 \sin^2 \phi)\rho^2 \sin \phi \, d\rho \, d\phi \, d\theta$$

$$= \dfrac{h^3}{30}(20a^2 - 15ah + 3h^2)\pi$$

(f) If $h = a$, $I_z = \dfrac{a^3 \pi}{30}(20a^2 - 15a^2 + 3a^2) = \dfrac{4}{15}a^5 \pi$

53. $\displaystyle\int_0^{2\pi} \int_0^{\pi} \int_0^{6 \sin \phi} \rho^2 \sin \phi \, d\rho \, d\phi \, d\theta$

Since $\rho = 6 \sin \phi$ represents (in the yz-plane) a circle of radius 3 centered at $(0, 3, 0)$, the integral represents the volume of the torus formed by revolving $(0 < \theta < 2\pi)$ this circle about the z-axis.

55. True

57. True

C H A P T E R   14
Vector Analysis

C H A P T E R 14
Vector Analysis

Section 14.1   Vector Fields
Solutions to Odd-Numbered Exercises

1. All vectors are parallel to y-axis.
Matches (c)

3. All vectors point outwards.
Matches (b)

5. Vectors are parallel to x-axis for $y = n\pi$. Matches (a)

7. $\mathbf{F}(x, y) = \mathbf{i} + \mathbf{j}$

$\|\mathbf{F}\| = \sqrt{2}$

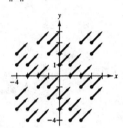

9. $\mathbf{F}(x, y) = x\mathbf{i} + y\mathbf{i}$

We will plot vectors of equal magnitude and, in this case, they lie along circles given by

$$\|\mathbf{F}(x, y)\| = \sqrt{x^2 + y^2} = c \implies x^2 + y^2 = c^2$$

For $c = 1$, sketch several vectors $x\mathbf{i} + y\mathbf{j}$ of magnitude 1 on the circle given $x^2 + y^2 = 1$.
For $c = 4$, sketch several vectors $x\mathbf{i} + y\mathbf{j}$ of magnitude 2 on the circle given by $x^2 + y^2 = 4$ (see figure).

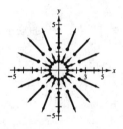

11. $\mathbf{F}(x, y, z) = 3y\mathbf{j}$

$\|\mathbf{F}\| = 3|y| = c$

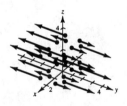

13. $\mathbf{F}(x, y) = 4x\mathbf{i} + y\mathbf{j}$

$\|\mathbf{F}\| = \sqrt{16x^2 + y^2} = c$

$\dfrac{x^2}{c^2/16} + \dfrac{y^2}{c^2} = 1$

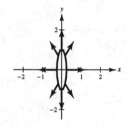

15. $\mathbf{F}(x, y, z) = \mathbf{i} + \mathbf{j} + \mathbf{k}$

$\|\mathbf{F}\| = \sqrt{3}$

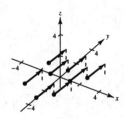

17.

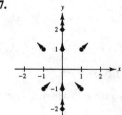

19.

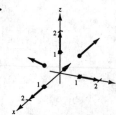

21. $f(x, y) = 5x^2 + 3xy + 10y^2$

$f_x(x, y) = 10x + 3y$

$f_y(x, y) = 3x + 20y$

$\mathbf{F}(x, y) = (10x + 3y)\mathbf{i} + (3x + 20y)\mathbf{j}$

23. $f(x, y, z) = a - ye^{x^2}$

The gradient vector field for f is

$$\mathbf{F}(x, y, z) = f_x(x, y, y)\mathbf{i} + f_y(x, y, z)\mathbf{j} + f_z(x, y, z)\mathbf{k}$$
$$= -2xye^{x^2}\mathbf{i} - e^{x^2}\mathbf{j} + \mathbf{k}.$$

25. $g(x, y, z) = xy \ln(x + y)$

$g_x(x, y, z) = y \ln(x + y) + \dfrac{xy}{x + y}$

$g_y(x, y, z) = x \ln(x + y) + \dfrac{xy}{x + y}$

$g_z(x, y, z) = 0$

$\mathbf{G}(x, y, z) = \left[\dfrac{xy}{x + y} + y \ln(x + y)\right]\mathbf{i} + \left[\dfrac{xy}{x + y} + x \ln(x + y)\right]\mathbf{j}$

27. $\mathbf{F}(x, y) = 2xy\mathbf{i} + x^2\mathbf{j}$

$\dfrac{\partial}{\partial y}[2xy] = 2x$

$\dfrac{\partial}{\partial x}[x^2] = 2x$

Conservative

$f_x(x, y) = 2xy$

$f_y(x, y) = 2x$

$f(x, y) = x^2y + K$

29. Since $\mathbf{F}(x, y) = 2xye^{x^2y}\mathbf{i} + x^2e^{x^2y}\mathbf{j}$, it follows that $\mathbf{F}$ is conservative since

$$\dfrac{\partial}{\partial y}[2xye^{x^2y}] = 2x^3ye^{x^2y} + 2xe^{x^2y} = \dfrac{\partial}{\partial x}[x^2e^{x^2y}].$$

If f is a function such that $\nabla f(x, y) = f_x(x, y)\mathbf{i} + f_y(x, y)\mathbf{j}$, then we have

$f_x(x, y) = 2xye^{x^2y}$ and $f_y(x, y) = x^2e^{x^2y}$.

To reconstruct the function f from these two partial derivatives, integrate $f_x(x, y)$ with respect to x and $f_y(x, y)$ with respect to y as follows.

$$f(x, y) = \int f_x(x, y)\, dx = \int 2xye^{x^2y}\, dx = e^{x^2y} + g(y) + K$$

$$f(x, y) = \int f_y(x, y)\, dy = \int x^2e^{x^2y}\, dy = e^{x^2y} + h(x) + K$$

These two expressions for $f(x, y)$ are the same if $g(y) = h(x) = 0$. Therefore, we have

$$f(x, y) = e^{x^2y} + K.$$

31. $\mathbf{F}(x, y) = \dfrac{x}{x^2 + y^2}\mathbf{i} + \dfrac{y}{x^2 + y^2}\mathbf{j}$

$\dfrac{\partial}{\partial y}\left[\dfrac{x}{x^2 + y^2}\right] = -\dfrac{2xy}{(x^2 + y^2)^2}$

$\dfrac{\partial}{\partial x}\left[\dfrac{y}{x^2 + y^2}\right] = -\dfrac{2xy}{(x^2 + y^2)^2}$

Conservative

$f_x(x, y) = \dfrac{x}{x^2 + y^2}$

$f_y(x, y) = \dfrac{y}{x^2 + y^2}$

$f(x, y) = \dfrac{1}{2}\ln(x^2 + y^2) + K$

33. $\mathbf{F}(x, y) = e^x(\cos y\mathbf{i} + \sin y\mathbf{j})$

$\dfrac{\partial}{\partial y}[e^x \cos y] = -e^x \sin y$

$\dfrac{\partial}{\partial x}[e^x \sin y] = e^x \sin y$

Not conservative

35. $\mathbf{F}(x, y, z) = xyz\mathbf{i} + y\mathbf{j} + z\mathbf{k}$

It follows from the definition of the curl that

$$\operatorname{curl}\mathbf{F}(x, y, z) = \begin{vmatrix} \mathbf{i} & \mathbf{j} & \mathbf{k} \\ \dfrac{\partial}{\partial x} & \dfrac{\partial}{\partial y} & \dfrac{\partial}{\partial z} \\ xyz & y & z \end{vmatrix} = \begin{vmatrix} \dfrac{\partial}{\partial y} & \dfrac{\partial}{\partial z} \\ y & z \end{vmatrix}\mathbf{i} - \begin{vmatrix} \dfrac{\partial}{\partial x} & \dfrac{\partial}{\partial z} \\ xyz & z \end{vmatrix}\mathbf{j} + \begin{vmatrix} \dfrac{\partial}{\partial x} & \dfrac{\partial}{\partial y} \\ xyz & y \end{vmatrix}\mathbf{k}$$

$$= (0 - 0)\mathbf{i} - (0 - xy)\mathbf{j} + (0 - xz)\mathbf{k} = xy\mathbf{j} - xz\mathbf{k}.$$

Therefore, $\operatorname{curl}\mathbf{F}(1, 2, 1) = 2\mathbf{j} - \mathbf{k}$.

37. $\mathbf{F}(x, y, z) = e^x \sin y\mathbf{i} - e^x \cos y\mathbf{j}, \quad (0, 0, 3)$

$$\operatorname{curl}\mathbf{F} = \begin{vmatrix} \mathbf{i} & \mathbf{j} & \mathbf{k} \\ \dfrac{\partial}{\partial x} & \dfrac{\partial}{\partial y} & \dfrac{\partial}{\partial z} \\ e^x \sin y & -e^x \cos y & 0 \end{vmatrix} = -2e^x \cos y\mathbf{k}$$

$\operatorname{curl}\mathbf{F}(0, 0, 3) = -2\mathbf{k}$

39. $\mathbf{F}(x, y, z) = \left(\arctan\dfrac{x}{y}\right)\mathbf{i} + \left(\ln\sqrt{x^2 + y^2}\right)\mathbf{j} + \mathbf{k}$

$$\operatorname{curl}\mathbf{F}(x, y, z) = \begin{vmatrix} \mathbf{i} & \mathbf{j} & \mathbf{k} \\ \dfrac{\partial}{\partial x} & \dfrac{\partial}{\partial y} & \dfrac{\partial}{\partial z} \\ \arctan\dfrac{x}{y} & \ln\sqrt{x^2 + y^2} & 1 \end{vmatrix} = (0 - 0)\mathbf{i} - (0 - 0)\mathbf{j} + \left[\dfrac{x}{x^2 + y^2} - \dfrac{-x/y^2}{1 + (x^2/y^2)}\right]\mathbf{k} = \dfrac{2x}{x^2 + y^2}\mathbf{k}$$

41. $\mathbf{F}(x, y, z) = \sin(x - y)\mathbf{i} + \sin(y - z)\mathbf{j} + \sin(z - x)\mathbf{k}$

$$\operatorname{curl}\mathbf{F} = \begin{vmatrix} \mathbf{i} & \mathbf{j} & \mathbf{k} \\ \dfrac{\partial}{\partial x} & \dfrac{\partial}{\partial y} & \dfrac{\partial}{\partial z} \\ \sin(x - y) & \sin(y - z) & \sin(z - x) \end{vmatrix} = \cos(y - z)\mathbf{i} + \cos(z - x)\mathbf{j} + \cos(x - y)\mathbf{k}$$

43. $F(x, y, z) = \sin y\mathbf{i} - x\cos y\mathbf{j} + \mathbf{k} = M\mathbf{i} + N\mathbf{j} + P\mathbf{k}$

Since

$$\frac{\partial}{\partial y} = 0 = \frac{\partial N}{\partial z}, \frac{\partial P}{\partial x} = 0 = \frac{\partial M}{\partial z},$$

and

$$\frac{\partial N}{\partial x} = -\cos y \neq \cos y = \frac{\partial M}{\partial y},$$

it follows that $\mathbf{F}$ is not conservative.

45. $F(x, y, z) = e^z(y\mathbf{i} + x\mathbf{j} + xy\mathbf{k})$

$$\text{curl } \mathbf{F} = \begin{vmatrix} \mathbf{i} & \mathbf{j} & \mathbf{k} \\ \dfrac{\partial}{\partial x} & \dfrac{\partial}{\partial y} & \dfrac{\partial}{\partial z} \\ ye^z & xe^z & xye^z \end{vmatrix} = \mathbf{0}$$

Conservative

$$f_x(x, y, z) = ye^z$$

$$f_y(x, y, z) = xe^z$$

$$f_z(x, y, z) = xye^z$$

$$f(x, y, z) = xye^z + K$$

47. $F(x, y, z) = \dfrac{1}{y}\mathbf{i} - \dfrac{x}{y^2}\mathbf{j} + (2x - 1)\mathbf{k} = M\mathbf{i} + N\mathbf{j} + P\mathbf{k}$

Since

$$\frac{\partial P}{\partial y} = 0 = \frac{\partial N}{\partial z}, \frac{\partial P}{\partial x} = 0 = \frac{\partial M}{\partial z}, \frac{\partial N}{\partial x} = -\frac{1}{y^2} = \frac{\partial M}{\partial y},$$

it follows that $\mathbf{F}$ is conservative. Now, if f is a function such that $F(x, y, z) = \nabla f(x, y, z)$, then

$$f_x(x, y, z) = \frac{1}{y}, f_y(x, y, z) = -\frac{x}{y^2}, f_z(x, y, z) = 2z - 1,$$

and by integrating with respect to x, y, and z respectively, we obtain

$$f(x, y, z) = \int M \, dx = \int \frac{1}{y} \, dx = \frac{x}{y} + g(y, z) + K$$

$$f(x, y, z) = \int N \, dy = \int -\frac{x}{y^2} \, dy = \frac{x}{y} + h(x, z) + K$$

$$f(x, y, z) = \int P \, dz = \int (2z - 1) \, dz = z^2 - z + k(x, y) + K.$$

By comparing these three versions of f, we can conclude that

$$g(y, z) = z^2 - z, \ h(x, z) = z^2 - z, \text{ and } k(x, y) = \frac{x}{y}.$$

Therefore,

$$f(x, y, z) = \frac{x}{y} + z^2 - z + K.$$

49. $F(x, y, z) = \mathbf{i} + 2x\mathbf{j} + 3y\mathbf{k}$

$G(x, y, z) = x\mathbf{i} - y\mathbf{j} + z\mathbf{k}$

$$F \times G = \begin{vmatrix} \mathbf{i} & \mathbf{j} & \mathbf{k} \\ 1 & 2x & 3y \\ x & -y & z \end{vmatrix} = (2xz + 3y^2)\mathbf{i} - (z - 3xy)\mathbf{j} + (-y - 2x^2)\mathbf{k}$$

$$\text{curl}(F \times G) = \begin{vmatrix} \mathbf{i} & \mathbf{j} & \mathbf{k} \\ \dfrac{\partial}{\partial x} & \dfrac{\partial}{\partial y} & \dfrac{\partial}{\partial z} \\ 2xz + 3y^2 & 3xy - z & -y - 2x^2 \end{vmatrix} = (-1 + 1)\mathbf{i} - (-4x - 2x)\mathbf{j} + (3y - 6y)\mathbf{k} = 6x\mathbf{j} - 3y\mathbf{k}$$

51. $\mathbf{F}(x, y, z) = xyz\mathbf{i} + y\mathbf{j} + z\mathbf{k}$

From Exercise 35 we have **curl** $\mathbf{F}(x, y, z) = xy\mathbf{j} - xz\mathbf{k}$. Thus,

$$\mathbf{curl}[(\mathbf{curl\ F})(x, y, z)] = \begin{vmatrix} \mathbf{i} & \mathbf{j} & \mathbf{k} \\ \dfrac{\partial}{\partial x} & \dfrac{\partial}{\partial y} & \dfrac{\partial}{\partial z} \\ 0 & xy & -xz \end{vmatrix} = (0 - 0)\mathbf{i} - (-z - 0)\mathbf{j} + (y - 0)\mathbf{k} = z\mathbf{j} + y\mathbf{k}.$$

53. $\mathbf{F}(x, y) = 6x^2\mathbf{i} - xy^2\mathbf{j}$

$\text{div } \mathbf{F}(x, y) = \dfrac{\partial}{\partial x}[6x^2] + \dfrac{\partial}{\partial y}[-xy^2]$

$\qquad = 12x - 2xy$

55. $\mathbf{F}(x, y, z) = \sin x\mathbf{i} + \cos y\mathbf{j} + z^2\mathbf{k}$

By definition,

$$\text{div } \mathbf{F}(x, y, z) = \frac{\partial}{\partial x}[\sin x] + \frac{\partial}{\partial y}[\cos y] + \frac{\partial}{\partial z}[z^2]$$

$$= \cos x - \sin y + 2z.$$

57. $\mathbf{F}(x, y, z) = xyz\mathbf{i} + y\mathbf{j} + z\mathbf{k}$

$\text{div } \mathbf{F}(x, y, z) = yz + 1 + 1 = yz + 2$

$\text{div } \mathbf{F}(1, 2, 1) = 4$

59. $\mathbf{F}(x, y, z) = e^x \sin y\mathbf{i} - e^x \cos y\mathbf{j}$

$\text{div } \mathbf{F}(x, y, z) = e^x \sin y + e^x \sin y$

$\text{div } \mathbf{F}(0, 0, 3) = 0$

61. $\mathbf{F}(x, y, z) = \mathbf{i} + 2x\mathbf{j} + 3y\mathbf{k}$

$\mathbf{G}(x, y, z) = x\mathbf{i} - y\mathbf{j} + z\mathbf{k}$

$$\mathbf{F} \times \mathbf{G} = \begin{vmatrix} \mathbf{i} & \mathbf{j} & \mathbf{k} \\ 1 & 2x & 3y \\ x & -y & z \end{vmatrix}$$

$$= (2xz + 3y^2)\mathbf{i} - (z - 3xy)\mathbf{j} + (-y - 2x^2)\mathbf{k}$$

$\text{div}(\mathbf{F} \times \mathbf{G}) = 2z + 3x$

63. $\mathbf{F}(x, y, z) = xyz\mathbf{i} + y\mathbf{j} + z\mathbf{k}$

From Exercise 35 we have **curl** $\mathbf{F}(x, y, z) = xy\mathbf{j} - xz\mathbf{k}$.
By definition,

$$\text{div}(\mathbf{curl\ F}) = \frac{\partial}{\partial x}[0] + \frac{\partial}{\partial y}[xy] + \frac{\partial}{\partial z}[-xz]$$

$$= x - x = 0.$$

65. Let $\mathbf{F} = M\mathbf{i} + N\mathbf{j} + P\mathbf{k}$ and $\mathbf{G} = Q\mathbf{i} + R\mathbf{j} + S\mathbf{k}$ where $M, N, P, Q, R,$ and S have continuous partial derivatives.

$\mathbf{F} + \mathbf{G} = (M + Q)\mathbf{i} + (N + R)\mathbf{j} + (P + S)\mathbf{k}$

$$\mathbf{curl}(\mathbf{F} + \mathbf{G}) = \begin{vmatrix} \mathbf{i} & \mathbf{j} & \mathbf{k} \\ \dfrac{\partial}{\partial x} & \dfrac{\partial}{\partial y} & \dfrac{\partial}{\partial z} \\ M + Q & N + R & P + S \end{vmatrix}$$

$$= \left[\frac{\partial}{\partial y}(P + S) - \frac{\partial}{\partial z}(N + R)\right]\mathbf{i} - \left[\frac{\partial}{\partial x}(P + S) - \frac{\partial}{\partial z}(M + Q)\right]\mathbf{j} + \left[\frac{\partial}{\partial x}(N + R) - \frac{\partial}{\partial y}(M + Q)\right]\mathbf{k}$$

$$= \left(\frac{\partial P}{\partial y} - \frac{\partial N}{\partial z}\right)\mathbf{i} - \left(\frac{\partial P}{\partial x} - \frac{\partial M}{\partial z}\right)\mathbf{j} + \left(\frac{\partial N}{\partial x} - \frac{\partial M}{\partial y}\right)\mathbf{k} + \left(\frac{\partial S}{\partial y} - \frac{\partial R}{\partial z}\right)\mathbf{i} - \left(\frac{\partial S}{\partial x} - \frac{\partial Q}{\partial z}\right)\mathbf{j} + \left(\frac{\partial R}{\partial x} - \frac{\partial Q}{\partial y}\right)\mathbf{k}$$

$$= \mathbf{curl\ F} + \mathbf{curl\ G}$$

67. Let $\mathbf{F} = M\mathbf{i} + N\mathbf{j} + P\mathbf{k}$ and $\mathbf{G} = R\mathbf{i} + S\mathbf{j} + T\mathbf{k}$.

$$\text{div}(\mathbf{F} + \mathbf{G}) = \frac{\partial}{\partial x}(M + R) + \frac{\partial}{\partial y}(N + S) + \frac{\partial}{\partial z}(P + T) = \frac{\partial M}{\partial x} + \frac{\partial R}{\partial x} + \frac{\partial N}{\partial y} + \frac{\partial S}{\partial y} + \frac{\partial P}{\partial z} + \frac{\partial T}{\partial z}$$

$$= \left[\frac{\partial M}{\partial x} + \frac{\partial N}{\partial y} + \frac{\partial P}{\partial z}\right] + \left[\frac{\partial R}{\partial x} + \frac{\partial S}{\partial y} + \frac{\partial T}{\partial z}\right]$$

$$= \text{div } \mathbf{F} + \text{div } \mathbf{G}$$

69. $\mathbf{F} = M\mathbf{i} + N\mathbf{j} + P\mathbf{k}$

$$\nabla \times [\nabla f + (\nabla \times \mathbf{F})] = \mathbf{curl}(\nabla f + (\nabla \times \mathbf{F}))$$

$$= \mathbf{curl}(\nabla f) + \mathbf{curl}(\nabla \times \mathbf{F}) \quad \text{(Exercise 65)}$$

$$= \mathbf{curl}(\nabla \times \mathbf{F}) \quad \text{(Exercise 66)}$$

$$= \nabla \times (\nabla \times \mathbf{F})$$

71. Let $\mathbf{F} = M\mathbf{i} + N\mathbf{j} + P\mathbf{k}$, then $f\mathbf{F} = fM\mathbf{i} + fN\mathbf{j} + fP\mathbf{k}$.

$$\text{div}(f\mathbf{F}) = \frac{\partial}{\partial x}(fM) + \frac{\partial}{\partial y}(fN) + \frac{\partial}{\partial z}(fP) = f\frac{\partial M}{\partial x} + M\frac{\partial f}{\partial x} + f\frac{\partial N}{\partial y} + N\frac{\partial f}{\partial y} + f\frac{\partial P}{\partial z} + P\frac{\partial f}{\partial z}$$

$$= f\left(\frac{\partial M}{\partial x} + \frac{\partial N}{\partial y} + \frac{\partial N}{\partial z}\right) + \left(\frac{\partial f}{\partial x}M + \frac{\partial f}{\partial y}N + \frac{\partial f}{\partial z}P\right)$$

$$= f\,\text{div}\,\mathbf{F} + \nabla f \cdot \mathbf{F}$$

In Exercises 73–77, $\mathbf{F}(x, y, z) = x\mathbf{i} + y\mathbf{j} + z\mathbf{k}$ and $f(x, y, z) = \|\mathbf{F}(x, y, z)\| = \sqrt{x^2 + y^2 + z^2}$.

73. $\quad \ln f = \frac{1}{2}\ln(x^2 + y^2 + z^2)$

$$\nabla(\ln f) = \frac{x}{x^2 + y^2 + z^2}\mathbf{i} + \frac{y}{x^2 + y^2 + z^2}\mathbf{j} + \frac{z}{x^2 + y^2 + z^2}\mathbf{k} = \frac{x\mathbf{i} + y\mathbf{j} + z\mathbf{k}}{x^2 + y^2 + z^2} = \frac{\mathbf{F}}{f^2}$$

75. $f^n = \left(\sqrt{x^2 + y^2 + z^2}\right)^n$

$$\nabla f^n = n\left(\sqrt{x^2 + y^2 + z^2}\right)^{n-1}\frac{x}{\sqrt{x^2 + y^2 + z^2}}\mathbf{i} + n\left(\sqrt{x^2 + y^2 + z^2}\right)^{n-1}\frac{y}{\sqrt{x^2 + y^2 + z^2}}\mathbf{j}$$

$$+ n\left(\sqrt{x^2 + y^2 + z^2}\right)^{n-1}\frac{z}{\sqrt{x^2 + y^2 + z^2}}\mathbf{k}$$

$$= n\left(\sqrt{x^2 + y^2 + z^2}\right)^{n-2}(x\mathbf{i} + y\mathbf{j} + z\mathbf{k}) = nf^{n-2}\mathbf{F}$$

77. $\mathbf{F}(x, y) = M(x, y)\mathbf{i} + N(x, y)\mathbf{j} = \frac{m}{(x^2 + y^2)^{5/2}}[3xy\mathbf{i} + (2y^2 - x^2)\mathbf{j}]$

$$M = \frac{3mxy}{(x^2 + y^2)^{5/2}} = 3mxy(x^2 + y^2)^{-5/2}$$

$$\frac{\partial M}{\partial y} = 3mxy\left[-\frac{5}{2}(x^2 + y^2)^{-7/2}(2y)\right] + (x^2 + y^2)^{-5/2}(3mx)$$

$$= 3mx(x^2 + y^2)^{-7/2}[-5y^2 + (x^2 + y^2)] = \frac{3mx(x^2 - 4y^2)}{(x^2 + y^2)^{7/2}}$$

$$N = \frac{m(2y^2 - x^2)}{(x^2 + y^2)^{5/2}} = m(2y^2 - x^2)(x^2 + y^2)^{-5/2}$$

$$\frac{\partial N}{\partial x} = m(2y^2 - x^2)\left[-\frac{5}{2}(x^2 + y^2)^{-7/2}(2x)\right] + (x^2 + y^2)^{-5/2}(-2mx)$$

$$= mx(x^2 + y^2)^{-7/2}[(2y^2 - x^2)(-5) + (x^2 + y^2)(-2)]$$

$$= mx(x^2 + y^2)^{-7/2}(3x^2 - 12y^2) = \frac{3mx(x^2 - 4y^2)}{(x^2 + y^2)^{7/2}}$$

Therefore, $\dfrac{\partial N}{\partial x} = \dfrac{\partial M}{\partial y}$ and $\mathbf{F}$ is conservative.

Section 14.2   Line Integrals

1. $x^2 + y^2 = 9$

$$\frac{x^2}{9} + \frac{y^2}{9} = 1$$

$$\cos^2 t + \sin^2 t = 1$$

$$\cos^2 t = \frac{x^2}{9}$$

$$\sin^2 t = \frac{y^2}{9}$$

$$x = 3 \cos t$$

$$y = 3 \sin t$$

$$\mathbf{r}(t) = 3 \cos t\mathbf{i} + 3 \sin t\mathbf{j}$$

$$0 \le t \le 2\pi$$

3. $\mathbf{r}(t) = \begin{cases} t\mathbf{i}, & 0 \le t \le 3 \\ 3\mathbf{i} + (t-3)\mathbf{j}, & 3 \le t \le 6 \\ (9-t)\mathbf{i} + 3\mathbf{j}, & 6 \le t \le 9 \\ (12-t)\mathbf{j}, & 9 \le t \le 12 \end{cases}$

5. $\mathbf{r}(t) = \begin{cases} t\mathbf{i} + \sqrt{t}\mathbf{j}, & 0 \le t \le 1 \\ (2-t)\mathbf{i} + (2-t)\mathbf{j}, & 1 \le t \le 2 \end{cases}$

7. $\mathbf{r}(t) = 4t\mathbf{i} + 3t\mathbf{j}, \ 0 \le t \le 2; \ \mathbf{r}'(t) = 4\mathbf{i} + 3\mathbf{j}$

$$\int_C (x - y)\, ds = \int_0^2 (4t - 3t)\sqrt{(4)^2 + (3)^2}\, dt$$

$$= \int_0^2 5t\, dt = \left[\frac{5t^2}{2} \right]_0^2 = 10$$

9. $\displaystyle\int_C (x^2 + y^2 + z^2)\, ds$

$C: \mathbf{r}(t) = \sin t\mathbf{i} + \cos t\mathbf{j} + 8t\mathbf{k}, 0 \le t \le \dfrac{\pi}{2}$

Since $r'(t) = \cos t\mathbf{i} - \sin t\mathbf{j} + 8\mathbf{k}$, we have

$$ds = \|\mathbf{r}'(t)\|\, dt = \sqrt{[x'(t)]^2 + [y'(t)]^2 + [z'(t)]^2}\, dt$$

$$= \sqrt{\cos^2 t + (-\sin t)^2 + 8^2}\, dt = \sqrt{65}\, dt.$$

It follows that

$$\int_C (x^2 + y^2 + z^2)\, ds = \int_0^{\pi/2} (\sin^2 t + \cos^2 t + 64t^2)\sqrt{65}\, dt$$

$$= \sqrt{65} \int_0^{\pi/2} (1 + 64t^2)\, dt = \sqrt{65}\left[t + \frac{64}{3}t^3 \right]_0^{\pi/2}$$

$$= \frac{\sqrt{65}\pi}{6}(3 + 16\pi^2).$$

11. $\mathbf{r}(t) = t\mathbf{i}, 0 \le t \le 3$

$$\int_C (x^2 + y^2)\, ds = \int_0^3 [t^2 + 0^2]\sqrt{1 + 0}\, dt$$

$$= \int_0^3 t^2\, dt$$

$$= \left[\frac{1}{3}t^3 \right]_0^3 = 9$$

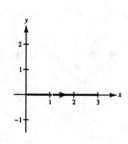

13. $\int_C (x^2 + y^2)\, ds$

$C: x^2 + y^2 = 1$ from $(1, 0)$ counterclockwise to $(0, 1)$.

Since the path is one-fourth the unit circle, it can be represented by $\mathbf{r}(t) = \cos t\mathbf{i} + \sin t\mathbf{j}$ for $0 \le t \le \pi/2$. Therefore,

$$\mathbf{r}'(t) = -\sin t\mathbf{i} + \cos t\mathbf{j}$$

$$ds = \|\mathbf{r}'(t)\|\, dt = \sqrt{(-\sin t)^2 + (\cos t)^2}\, dt = dt.$$

It follows that

$$\int_C (x^2 + y^2)\, ds = \int_0^{\pi/2} (\cos^2 t + \sin^2 t)\, dt = \int_0^{\pi/2} dt = \frac{\pi}{2}.$$

15. $\mathbf{r}(t) = t\mathbf{i} + t\mathbf{j},\ 0 \le t \le 1$

$$\int_C \left(x + 4\sqrt{y}\right) ds = \int_0^1 \left(t + 4\sqrt{t}\right)\sqrt{1 + 1}\, dt$$

$$= \left[\sqrt{2}\left(\frac{t^2}{2} + \frac{8}{3}t^{3/2}\right)\right]_0^1 = \frac{19\sqrt{2}}{6}$$

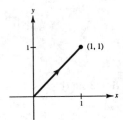

17. $\int_C \left(x + 4\sqrt{y}\right) ds$

$C:$ counterclockwise around the triangle with vertices $(0, 0)$, $(1, 0)$, and $(0, 1)$.

Path C has parts as shown in the figure.

$C_1: x = t, \qquad y = 0, \qquad 0 \le t \le 1,\ ds = \sqrt{1 + 0}\, dt = dt$

$C_2: x = 1 - t,\ \ y = t, \qquad 0 \le t \le 1,\ ds = \sqrt{1 + 1}\, dt = \sqrt{2}\, dt$

$C_3: x = 0, \qquad\ \ y = 1 - t,\ \ 0 \le t \le 1,\ ds = \sqrt{0 + 1}\, dt = dt$

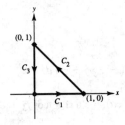

Therefore,

$$\int_C \left(x + 4\sqrt{y}\right) dx = \int_0^1 t\, dt + \int_0^1 \left[(1 - t) + 4\sqrt{t}\right]\sqrt{2}\, dt + \int_0^1 4\sqrt{1 - t}\, dt$$

$$= \left[\frac{t^2}{2}\right]_0^1 + \sqrt{2}\left[t - \frac{t^2}{2} + \frac{8}{3}t^{3/2}\right]_0^1 - \left[\frac{8}{3}(1 - t)^{3/2}\right]_0^1$$

$$= \frac{1}{2} + \sqrt{2}\left(\frac{19}{6}\right) + \frac{8}{3} = \frac{19}{6}(1 + \sqrt{2}).$$

19. $\rho(x, y, z) = \frac{1}{2}(x^2 + y^2 + z^2)$

$\mathbf{r}(t) = 3\cos t\mathbf{i} + 3\sin t\mathbf{j} + 2t\mathbf{k},\ \ 0 \le t \le 4\pi$

$\mathbf{r}'(t) = -3\sin t\mathbf{i} + 3\cos t\mathbf{j} + 2\mathbf{k}$

$\|\mathbf{r}'(t)\| = \sqrt{(-3\sin t)^2 + (3\cos t)^2 + (2)^2} = \sqrt{13}$

$$\text{Mass} = \int_C \rho(x, y, z)\, ds = \int_0^{4\pi} \frac{1}{2}\left[(3\cos t)^2 + (3\sin t)^2 + (2t)^2\right]\sqrt{13}\, dt$$

$$= \frac{\sqrt{13}}{2}\int_0^{4\pi} (9 + 4t^2)\, dt = \left[\frac{\sqrt{13}}{2}\left(9t + \frac{4t^3}{3}\right)\right]_0^{4\pi}$$

$$= \frac{2\sqrt{13}\pi}{3}(27 + 64\pi^2) \approx 4973.8$$

21. $\mathbf{F}(x, y) = xy\mathbf{i} + y\mathbf{j}$

　　$C: \mathbf{r}(t) = 4t\mathbf{i} + t\mathbf{j}, \ 0 \le t \le 1$

　　$\mathbf{F}(t) = 4t^2\mathbf{i} + t\mathbf{j}$

　　$\mathbf{r}'(t) = 4\mathbf{i} + \mathbf{j}$

$$\int_C \mathbf{F} \cdot d\mathbf{r} = \int_0^1 (16t^2 + t) \, dt$$

$$= \left[\frac{16}{3}t^3 + \frac{1}{2}t^2 \right]_0^1 = \frac{35}{6}$$

23. $\mathbf{F}(x, y) = 3x\mathbf{i} + 4y\mathbf{j}$

　　$C: \mathbf{r}(t) = (2 \cos t)\mathbf{i} + (2 \sin t)\mathbf{j}, 0 \le t \le \dfrac{\pi}{2}$

Since $x(t) = 2 \cos t$ and $y(t) = 2 \sin t$, the vector field can be written $\mathbf{F}(x, y) = 6 \cos t\mathbf{i} + 8 \sin t\mathbf{j}$. Use the fact that $\mathbf{r}'(t) = -2 \sin t\mathbf{i} + 2 \cos t\mathbf{j}$ and write the following.

$$\int_C \mathbf{F} \cdot d\mathbf{r} = \int_a^b \mathbf{F}(x(t), y(t)) \cdot \mathbf{r}'(t) \, dt$$

$$= \int_0^{\pi/2} (-12 \sin t \cos t + 16 \sin t \cos t) \, dt$$

$$= 4\int_0^{\pi/2} \sin t \cos t \, dt = 4\left[\frac{\sin^2 t}{2} \right]_0^{\pi/2} = 2$$

25. $\mathbf{F}(x, y, z) = x^2 y\mathbf{i} + (x - z)\mathbf{j} + xyz\mathbf{k}$

　　$C: \mathbf{r}(t) = t\mathbf{i} + t^2\mathbf{j} + 2\mathbf{k}, \ 0 \le t \le 1$

　　$\mathbf{F}(t) = t^4\mathbf{i} + (t - 2)\mathbf{j} + 2t^3\mathbf{k}$

　　$\mathbf{r}'(t) = \mathbf{i} + 2t\mathbf{j}$

$$\int_C \mathbf{F} \cdot d\mathbf{r} = \int_0^1 [t^4 + 2t(t - 2)] \, dt$$

$$= \left[\frac{t^5}{5} + \frac{2t^3}{3} - 2t^2 \right]_0^1 = -\frac{17}{15}$$

27. $\mathbf{F}(x, y, z) = x^2 z\mathbf{i} + 6y\mathbf{j} + yz^2\mathbf{k}$

　　$\mathbf{r}(t) = t\mathbf{i} + t^2\mathbf{j} + \ln t\mathbf{k}, \ 1 \le t \le 3$

　　$\mathbf{F}(t) = t^2 \ln t\mathbf{i} + 6t^2\mathbf{j} + t^2 \ln^2 t\mathbf{k}$

$$d\mathbf{r} = \left(\mathbf{i} + 2t\mathbf{j} + \frac{1}{t}\mathbf{k} \right) dt$$

$$\int_C \mathbf{F} \cdot d\mathbf{r} = \int_1^3 [t^2 \ln t + 12t^3 + t(\ln t)^2] \, dt$$

$$\approx 249.49$$

29. $\mathbf{F}(x, y) = -x\mathbf{i} - 2y\mathbf{j}$

　　$C: y = x^3$ from $(0, 0)$ to $(2, 8)$

Since the path of C is given by $x = t$ and $y = t^3$, with $0 \le t \le 2$, we have $\mathbf{F}(t) = -t\mathbf{i} - 2t^3\mathbf{j}$ and $\mathbf{r}'(t) = \mathbf{i} + 3t^2\mathbf{j}$. Therefore,

$$W = \int_C \mathbf{F}(t) \cdot \mathbf{r}'(t) \, dt = \int_0^2 (-t - 6t^5) \, dt = \left[-\frac{t^2}{2} - t^6 \right]_0^2 = -66.$$

31. $\mathbf{F}(x, y) = 2x\mathbf{i} + y\mathbf{j}$

　　$C:$ counterclockwise around the triangle whose vertices are $(0, 0), (1, 0), (1, 1)$

$$\mathbf{r}(t) = \begin{cases} t\mathbf{i}, & 0 \le t \le 1 \\ \mathbf{i} + (t - 1)\mathbf{j}, & 1 \le t \le 2 \\ (3 - t)\mathbf{i} + (3 - t)\mathbf{j}, & 2 \le t \le 3 \end{cases}$$

On C_1:　$\mathbf{F}(t) = 2t\mathbf{i}, \ \mathbf{r}'(t) = \mathbf{i}$

$$\text{Work} = \int_{C_1} \mathbf{F} \cdot d\mathbf{r} = \int_0^1 2t \, dt = 1$$

On C_2:　$\mathbf{F}(t) = 2\mathbf{i} + (t - 1)\mathbf{j}, \ \mathbf{r}'(t) = \mathbf{j}$

$$\text{Work} = \int_{C_2} \mathbf{F} \cdot d\mathbf{r} = \int_1^2 (t - 1) \, dt = \frac{1}{2}$$

On C_3:　$\mathbf{F}(t) = 2(3 - t)\mathbf{i} + (3 - t)\mathbf{j}, \ \mathbf{r}'(t) = -\mathbf{i} - \mathbf{j}$

$$\text{Work} = \int_{C_3} \mathbf{F} \cdot d\mathbf{r} = \int_2^3 [-2(3 - t) - (3 - t)] \, dt = -\frac{3}{2}$$

Total work $= \displaystyle\int_C \mathbf{F} \cdot d\mathbf{r} = 1 + \frac{1}{2} - \frac{3}{2} = 0$

33. $\mathbf{F}(x, y, z) = x\mathbf{i} + y\mathbf{j} - 5z\mathbf{k}$

  $C:$ $\mathbf{r}(t) = 2\cos t\mathbf{i} + 2\sin t\mathbf{j} + t\mathbf{k}, \ 0 \le t \le 2\pi$

   $\mathbf{r}'(t) = -2\sin t\mathbf{i} + 2\cos t\mathbf{j} + \mathbf{k}$

   $\mathbf{F}(t) = 2\cos t\mathbf{i} + 2\sin t\mathbf{j} - 5t\mathbf{k}$

   $\mathbf{F} \cdot \mathbf{r}' = -5t$

  Work $= \displaystyle\int_C \mathbf{F} \cdot d\mathbf{r} = \int_0^{2\pi} -5t \, dt = -10\pi^2$

35. $\mathbf{r}(t) = 3\sin t\mathbf{i} + 3\cos t\mathbf{j} + \dfrac{10}{2\pi}t\mathbf{k}, \ 0 \le t \le 2\pi$

  $\mathbf{F} = 150\mathbf{k}$

  $d\mathbf{r} = \left(3\cos t\mathbf{i} - 3\sin t\mathbf{j} + \dfrac{10}{2\pi}\mathbf{k}\right) dt$

  $\displaystyle\int_C \mathbf{F} \cdot d\mathbf{r} = \int_0^{2\pi} \dfrac{1500}{2\pi} \, dt = \left[\dfrac{1500}{2\pi}t\right]_0^{2\pi} = 1500 \text{ ft} \cdot \text{lb}$

37. $\mathbf{F}(x, y) = y\mathbf{i} - x\mathbf{j}$

  $C:$ $\mathbf{r}(t) = t\mathbf{i} - 2t\mathbf{j}$

   $\mathbf{r}'(t) = \mathbf{i} - 2\mathbf{j}$

   $\mathbf{F}(t) = -2t\mathbf{i} - t\mathbf{j}$

   $\mathbf{F} \cdot \mathbf{r}' = -2t + 2t = 0$

  Thus, $\displaystyle\int_C \mathbf{F} \cdot d\mathbf{r} = 0.$

39. $\mathbf{F}(x, y) = (x^3 - 2x^2)\mathbf{i} + \left(x - \dfrac{y}{2}\right)\mathbf{j}$

  $C:$ $\mathbf{r}(t) = t\mathbf{i} + t^2\mathbf{j}$

  Since the path of C is given by $x = t$ and $y = t^2$, we have

   $\mathbf{F}(x, y) = (t^3 - 2t^2)\mathbf{i} + \left(t - \dfrac{t^2}{2}\right)\mathbf{j}$

  and $\mathbf{r}'(t) = \mathbf{i} + 2t\mathbf{j}$. Therefore,

   $\displaystyle\int_C \mathbf{F} \cdot d\mathbf{r} = \int_a^b \mathbf{F}(x(t), y(t)) \cdot \mathbf{r}'(t) \, dt$

   $= \displaystyle\int_a^b (t^3 - 2t^2 + 2t^2 - t^3) \, dt = \int_a^b 0 \, dt = 0.$

41. $W = \displaystyle\int_C \mathbf{F} \cdot d\mathbf{r} = \int_C M \, dx + N \, dy$

  $M = 15(4 - x^2y) = 60 - 15x^2(c - cx^2)$

  $N = -15xy = -15x(c - cx^2)$

  $dx = dx, \ dy = -2cx \, dx$

  $W = \displaystyle\int_{-1}^1 [60 - 15x^2(c - cx^2) + (-15x(c - cx^2))(-2\,cx)] \, dx$

   $= 120 - 4c + 8c^2 \quad \text{(parabola)}$

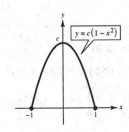

$y = c(1 - x^2)$

  $w' = 16c - 4 = 0 \implies c = \frac{1}{4}$ yields the minimum work, 119.5. Along the straight line path, $y = 0$, the work is 120.

43. $x = 2t, \ y = 10t, \ 0 \le t \le 1 \implies y = 5x$ or $x = \dfrac{y}{5}, \ 0 \le y \le 10$

  $\displaystyle\int_C (x + 3y^2) \, dy = \int_0^{10} \left(\dfrac{y}{5} + 3y^2\right) dy = \left[\dfrac{y^2}{10} + y^3\right]_0^{10} = 1010$

45. $x = 2t, \ y = 10t, \ 0 \le t \le 1 \implies x = \dfrac{y}{5}, \ 0 \le y \le 10, \ dx = \dfrac{1}{5} \, dy$

  $\displaystyle\int_C xy \, dx + y \, dy = \int_0^{10} \left(\dfrac{y^2}{25} + y\right) dy = \left[\dfrac{y^3}{75} + \dfrac{y^2}{2}\right]_0^{10} = \dfrac{190}{3}$ OR

  $y = 5x, \ dy = 5 \, dx, \ 0 \le x \le 2$

  $\displaystyle\int_C xy \, dx + y \, dy = \int_0^2 (5x^2 + 25x) \, dx = \left[\dfrac{5x^3}{3} + \dfrac{25x^2}{2}\right]_0^2 = \dfrac{190}{3}$

47. $\mathbf{r}(t) = t\mathbf{i}, \ 0 \le t \le 5$

$x(t) = t, \quad y(t) = 0$

$dx = dt, \quad dy = 0$

$\displaystyle\int_C (2x - y)\,dx + (x + 3y)\,dy = \int_0^5 2t\,dt = 25$

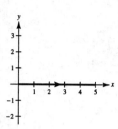

49. $\mathbf{r}(t) = \begin{cases} t\mathbf{i}, & 0 \le t \le 3 \\ 3\mathbf{i} + (t - 3)\mathbf{j}, & 3 \le t \le 6 \end{cases}$

$C_1: \quad x(t) = t, \ y(t) = 0,$

$\qquad dx = dt, \ dy = 0$

$\displaystyle\int_{C_1} (2x - y)\,dx + (x + 3y)\,dy = \int_0^3 2t\,dt = 9$

$C_2: \quad x(t) = 3, \ y = t - 3$

$\qquad dx = 0, \ dy = dt$

$\displaystyle\int_{C_2} (2x - y)\,dx + (x + 3y)\,dy = \int_3^6 [3 + 3(t - 3)]\,dt = \left[\dfrac{3t^2}{2} - 6t\right]_3^6 = \dfrac{45}{2}$

$\displaystyle\int_C (2x - y)\,dx + (x + 3y)\,dy = 9 + \dfrac{45}{2} = \dfrac{63}{2}$

51. $\displaystyle\int_C (2x - y)\,dx + (x + 3y)\,dy$

$C: x = t$ and $y = 2t^2$ from $(0, 0)$ to $(2, 8)$

The path C is given by $x = t$, $y = 2t^2$, with $0 \le t \le 2$, $dx = dt$, and $dy = 4t\,dt$. Therefore,

$$\int_C (2x - y)\,dx + (x + 3y)\,dy = \int_0^2 (2t - 2t^2)\,dt + (t + 6t^2)4t\,dt$$

$$= \int_0^2 (2t + 2t^2 + 24t^3)\,dt$$

$$= \left[t^2 + \dfrac{2t^3}{3} + 6t^4\right]_0^2$$

$$= 4 + \dfrac{16}{3} + 96 = \dfrac{316}{3}.$$

53. $f(x, y) = h$

$C:$ line from $(0, 0)$ to $(3, 4)$

$\qquad \mathbf{r} = 3t\mathbf{i} + 4t\mathbf{j}, \ 0 \le t \le 1$

$\qquad \mathbf{r}'(t) = 3\mathbf{i} + 4\mathbf{j}$

$\qquad \|\mathbf{r}'(t)\| = 5$

Lateral surface area:

$$\int_C f(x, y)\,ds = \int_0^1 5h\,dt = 5h$$

55. $f(x, y) = xy$

$C: x^2 + y^2 = 1$ from $(1, 0)$ to $(0, 1)$

We represent C parametrically as $x = \cos t$ and $y = \sin t$ for $0 \le t \le \pi/2$. Then $f(x, y) = xy = \cos t \sin t$ and

$$ds = \sqrt{[x'(t)]^2 + [y'(t)]^2}\,dt$$

$$= \sqrt{(-\sin t)^2 + (\cos t)^2}\,dt = dt.$$

Therefore,

$$\text{area} = \int_C f(x, y)\,ds$$

$$= \int_0^{\pi/2} \cos t \sin t\,dt = \left[\dfrac{1}{2}\sin^2 t\right]_0^{\pi/2} = \dfrac{1}{2}.$$

57. $f(x, y) = h$

$C: y = 1 - x^2$ from $(1, 0)$ to $(0, 1)$

$\mathbf{r}(t) = (1 - t)\mathbf{i} + [1 - (1 - t)^2]\mathbf{j}, \ 0 \le t \le 1$

$\mathbf{r}'(t) = -\mathbf{i} + 2(1 - t)\mathbf{j}$

$\|\mathbf{r}'(t)\| = \sqrt{1 + 4(1 - t)^2}$

Lateral surface area:

$$\int_C f(x, y) \, ds = \int_0^1 h\sqrt{1 + 4(1 - t)^2} \, dt$$

$$= -\frac{h}{4}\left[2(1 - t)\sqrt{1 + 4(1 - t)^2} + \ln|2(1 - t) + \sqrt{1 + 4(1 - t)^2}| \right]_0^1$$

$$= \frac{h}{4}\left[2\sqrt{5} + \ln(2 + \sqrt{5})\right] \approx 1.4789h$$

59. $f(x, y) = xy$

$C: y = 1 - x^2$ from $(1, 0)$ to $(0, 1)$

You could parameterize the curve C as in Exercises 57 and 58. Alternatively, let $x = \cos t$, then:

$y = 1 - \cos^2 t = \sin^2 t$

$\mathbf{r}(t) = \cos t\mathbf{i} + \sin^2 t\mathbf{j}, \ 0 \le t \le \dfrac{\pi}{2}$

$\mathbf{r}'(t) = -\sin t\mathbf{i} + 2\sin t \cos t\mathbf{j}$

$\|\mathbf{r}'(t)\| = \sqrt{\sin^2 t + 4\sin^2 t \cos^2 t} = \sin t\sqrt{1 + 4\cos^2 t}$

Lateral surface area:

$$\int_C f(x, y) \, dx \int_0^{\pi/2} \cos t \sin^2 t\left(\sin t\sqrt{1 + 4\cos^2 t}\right) dt = \int_0^{\pi/2} \sin^2 t[(1 + 4\cos^2 t)^{1/2}\sin t \cos t] \, dt$$

Let $u = \sin^2 t$ and $dv = (1 + 4\cos^2 t)^{1/2}\sin t \cos t$, then $du = 2\sin t \cos t \, dt$ and $v = -\frac{1}{12}(1 + 4\cos^2 t)^{3/2}$.

$$\int_C f(x, y) \, ds = \left[-\frac{1}{2}\sin^2 t(1 + 4\cos^2 t)^{3/2}\right]_0^{\pi/2} + \frac{1}{6}\int_0^{\pi/2}(1 + 4\cos^2 t)^{3/2}\sin t \cos t \, dt$$

$$= \left[-\frac{1}{12}\sin^2 t(1 + 4\cos^2 t)^{3/2} - \frac{1}{120}(1 + 4\cos^2 t)^{5/2}\right]_0^{\pi/2}$$

$$= \left(-\frac{1}{12} - \frac{1}{120}\right) + \frac{1}{120}(5)^{5/2} = \frac{1}{120}(25\sqrt{5} - 11) \approx 0.3742$$

61. (a) $z = f(x, y) = 1 + y^2$

$\mathbf{r}(t) = 2\cos t\mathbf{i} + 2\sin t\mathbf{j}$

$\mathbf{r}'(t) = -2\sin t\mathbf{i} + 2\cos t\mathbf{j}$

$\|\mathbf{r}'(t)\| = \sqrt{(-2\sin t)^2 + (2\cos t)^2} = 2$

$$S = \int_C f(x, y) \, ds$$

$$= \int_a^b f(x(t), y(t))\|\mathbf{r}'(t)\| \, dt$$

$$= \int_0^{2\pi}(1 + 4\sin^2 t)(2) \, dt$$

$$= \int_0^{2\pi}(6 - 4\cos 2t) \, dt$$

$$= \left[6t - 2\sin 2t\right]_0^{2\pi} = 12\pi \approx 37.70 \text{ sq cm}$$

(b) The volume of steel is approximated by the product of the thickness of the steel and the surface area of the component.

$$0.2(12\pi) = \frac{12\pi}{5} \approx 7.54 \text{ cu cm}$$

(c) A sketch of the component is shown in the figure.

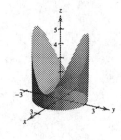

63. The greater the height of the surface over the curve, the greater the lateral surface area. Hence,

$$z_3 < z_1 < z_2 < z_4.$$

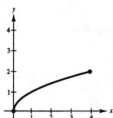

65. $S \approx 25$

Matches b

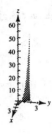

67. False

$$\int_C xy \, ds = \sqrt{2} \int_0^1 t^2 \, dt$$

69. False, the orientations are different.

Section 14.3   Conservative Vector Fields and Independence of Path

1. $\mathbf{F}(x, y) = x^2\mathbf{i} + xy\mathbf{j}$

(a) $\mathbf{r}_1(t) = t\mathbf{i} + t^2\mathbf{j}, \ 0 \le t \le 1$

$\mathbf{r}_1{}'(t) = \mathbf{i} + 2t\,\mathbf{j}$

$\mathbf{F}(t) = t^2\mathbf{i} + t^3\mathbf{j}$

$$\int_C \mathbf{F} \cdot d\mathbf{r} = \int_0^1 (t^2 + 2t^4) \, dt = \frac{11}{15}$$

(b) $\mathbf{r}_2(\theta) = \sin\theta\mathbf{i} + \sin^2\theta\mathbf{j}, \ 0 \le \theta \le \dfrac{\pi}{2}$

$\mathbf{r}_2{}'(\theta) = \cos\theta\mathbf{i} + 2\sin\theta\cos\theta\mathbf{j}$

$\mathbf{F}(t) = \sin^2\theta\mathbf{i} + \sin^3\theta\mathbf{j}$

$$\int_C \mathbf{F} \cdot d\mathbf{r} = \int_0^{\pi/2} (\sin^2\theta\cos\theta + 2\sin^4\theta\cos\theta) \, d\theta$$

$$= \left[\frac{\sin^3\theta}{3} + \frac{2\sin^5\theta}{5}\right]_0^{\pi/2} = \frac{11}{15}$$

3. $\mathbf{F}(x, y) = y\mathbf{i} - x\mathbf{j}$

(a) For $\mathbf{r}_1(\theta) = \sec\theta\mathbf{i} + \tan\theta\mathbf{j}$, we have $\mathbf{F}(x, y) = \tan\theta\mathbf{i} - \sec\theta\mathbf{j}$ and $\mathbf{r}'(\theta) = \sec\theta\tan\theta\mathbf{i} + \sec^2\theta\mathbf{j}$. Therefore,

$$\int_C \mathbf{F} \cdot d\mathbf{r}_1 = \int_0^{\pi/3} \mathbf{F} \cdot \mathbf{r}_1{}' \, d\theta = \int_0^{\pi/3} (\sec\theta\tan^2\theta - \sec^3\theta) \, d\theta$$

$$= -\int_0^{\pi/3} \sec\theta \, d\theta = \left[-\ln|\sec\theta + \tan\theta|\right]_0^{\pi/3} = -\ln(2 + \sqrt{3})$$

(b) For $\mathbf{r}_2(t) = \sqrt{t + 1}\,\mathbf{i} + \sqrt{t}\,\mathbf{j}$, we have $\mathbf{F}(t)\sqrt{t}\,\mathbf{i} - \sqrt{t + 1}\,\mathbf{j}$ and $\mathbf{r}_2{}'(t) = \dfrac{1}{2\sqrt{t + 1}}\mathbf{i} + \dfrac{1}{2\sqrt{t}}\mathbf{j}$. Therefore,

$$\int_C \mathbf{F} \cdot d\mathbf{r}_2 = \int_0^3 \mathbf{F} \cdot \mathbf{r}_2{}' \, dt$$

$$= \int_0^3 \left(\frac{\sqrt{t}}{2\sqrt{t + 1}} - \frac{\sqrt{t + 1}}{2\sqrt{t}}\right) dt = \frac{1}{2}\int_0^3 \frac{-1}{\sqrt{t + 1}\sqrt{t}} \, dt.$$

If $u = \sqrt{t + 1}$, then $u^2 = t + 1$, $u^2 - 1 = t$, $2u \, du = dt$, and $\sqrt{u^2 - 1} = \sqrt{t}$. Thus,

$$\frac{1}{2}\int_0^3 \frac{-1}{\sqrt{t + 1}\sqrt{t}} \, dt = -\int_1^2 \frac{du}{\sqrt{u^2 - 1}} = \left[-\ln|u + \sqrt{u^2 + 1}|\right]_1^2 = -\ln(2 + \sqrt{3}).$$

5. $\mathbf{F}(x, y) = e^x \sin y\mathbf{i} + e^x \cos y\mathbf{j}$

$\dfrac{\partial N}{\partial x} = e^x \cos y \qquad \dfrac{\partial M}{\partial y} = e^x \cos y$

Since $\dfrac{\partial N}{\partial x} = \dfrac{\partial M}{\partial y}$, $\mathbf{F}$ is conservative.

7. $\mathbf{F}(x, y) = \dfrac{1}{y}\mathbf{i} + \dfrac{x}{y^2}\mathbf{j}$

$\dfrac{\partial N}{\partial x} = \dfrac{1}{y^2} \qquad \dfrac{\partial M}{\partial y} = -\dfrac{1}{y^2}$

Since $\dfrac{\partial N}{\partial x} \neq \dfrac{\partial M}{\partial y}$, $\mathbf{F}$ is not conservative.

9. The vector field $\mathbf{F}(x, y, z) = M\mathbf{i} + N\mathbf{j} + P\mathbf{k}$ is conservative if and only if

$$\dfrac{\partial P}{\partial y} = \dfrac{\partial N}{\partial z}, \dfrac{\partial P}{\partial x} = \dfrac{\partial M}{\partial z}, \text{ and } \dfrac{\partial N}{\partial x} = \dfrac{\partial M}{\partial y}.$$

For the vector field $\mathbf{F}(x, y, z) = y^2 z\mathbf{i} + 2xyz\mathbf{j} + xy^2\mathbf{k}$, we have

$$\dfrac{\partial P}{\partial y} = 2xy = \dfrac{\partial N}{\partial z}$$

$$\dfrac{\partial P}{\partial x} = y^2 = \dfrac{\partial M}{\partial z}$$

$$\dfrac{\partial N}{\partial x} = 2yz = \dfrac{\partial M}{\partial y}.$$

Therefore, $\mathbf{F}$ is conservative. A second method for determining whether $\mathbf{F}$ is conservative is to find **curl** $\mathbf{F}(x, y, z)$. $\mathbf{F}$ is conservative if and only if **curl** $\mathbf{F}(x, y, z) = \mathbf{0}$.

11. $\mathbf{F}(x, y) = 2xy\mathbf{i} + x^2\mathbf{j}$

(a) $\mathbf{r}_1(t) = t\mathbf{i} + t^2\mathbf{j}, \ 0 \leq t \leq 1$

$\mathbf{r}_1'(t) = \mathbf{i} + 2t\mathbf{j}$

$\mathbf{F}(t) = 2t^3\mathbf{i} + t^2\mathbf{j}$

$\displaystyle\int_C \mathbf{F} \cdot d\mathbf{r} = \int_0^1 4t^3 \, dt = 1$

(b) $\mathbf{r}_2(t) = t\mathbf{i} + t^3\mathbf{j}, \ 0 \leq t \leq 1$

$\mathbf{r}_2'(t) = \mathbf{i} + 3t^2\mathbf{j}$

$\mathbf{F}(t) = 2t^4\mathbf{i} + t^2\mathbf{j}$

$\displaystyle\int_C \mathbf{F} \cdot d\mathbf{r} = \int_0^1 5t^4 \, dt = 1$

13. $\mathbf{F}(x, y) = y\mathbf{i} - x\mathbf{j}$

(a) $\mathbf{r}_1(t) = t\mathbf{i} + t\mathbf{j}, \ 0 \leq t \leq 1$

$\mathbf{r}_1'(t) = \mathbf{i} + \mathbf{j}$

$\mathbf{F}(t) = t\mathbf{i} - t\mathbf{j}$

$\displaystyle\int_C \mathbf{F} \cdot d\mathbf{r} = 0$

(b) $\mathbf{r}_2(t) = t\mathbf{i} + t^2\mathbf{j}, \ 0 \leq t \leq 1$

$\mathbf{r}_2'(t) = \mathbf{i} + 2t\mathbf{j}$

$\mathbf{F}(t) = t^2\mathbf{i} - t\mathbf{j}$

$\displaystyle\int_C \mathbf{F} \cdot d\mathbf{r} = \int_0^1 -t^2 \, dt = -\dfrac{1}{3}$

(c) $\mathbf{r}_3(t) = t\mathbf{i} + t^3\mathbf{j}, \ 0 \leq t \leq 1$

$\mathbf{r}_3'(t) = \mathbf{i} + 3t^2\mathbf{j}$

$\mathbf{F}(t) = t^3\mathbf{i} - t\mathbf{j}$

$\displaystyle\int_C \mathbf{F} \cdot d\mathbf{r} = \int_0^1 -2t^3 \, dt = -\dfrac{1}{2}$

15. $\displaystyle\int_C y^2 \, dx + 2xy \, dy$

Since $\partial M/\partial y = \partial N/\partial x = 2y$, $\mathbf{F}(x, y) = y^2\mathbf{i} + 2xy\mathbf{j}$ is conservative. The potential function is $f(x, y) = xy^2 + k$. Therefore, we can use the Fundamental Theorem of Line Integrals.

(a) $\displaystyle\int_C y^2 \, dx + 2xy \, dy = \Big[x^2 y\Big]_{(0, 0)}^{(4, 4)} = 64$

(b) $\displaystyle\int_C y^2 \, dx + 2xy \, dy = \Big[x^2 y\Big]_{(-1, 0)}^{(1, 0)} = 0$

(c) and (d) Since C is a closed curve, $\displaystyle\int_C y^2 \, dx + 2xy \, dy = 0$.

17. $\displaystyle\int_C 2xy\,dx + (x^2 + y^2)\,dy$

(a) C: ellipse $\left(\dfrac{x^2}{25}\right) + \left(\dfrac{y^2}{16}\right) = 1$ from $(5, 0)$ to $(0, 4)$

Observe that the vector field $\mathbf{F}(x, y) = 2xy\mathbf{i} + (x^2 + y^2)\mathbf{j}$ is conservative, since

$$\frac{\partial}{\partial y}[2xy] = 2x = \frac{\partial}{\partial x}[x^2 + y^2].$$

Therefore, the line integral is independent of the path and we can replace the path along the ellipse from $(5, 0)$ to $(0, 4)$ with a path which will simplify the integration. One possibility is the path along the coordinate axes from $(5, 0)$ to $(0, 0)$ and then from $(0, 0)$ to $(0, 4)$. Along the path from $(5, 0)$ to $(0, 0)$ we have $y = 0$ and $dy = 0$. On the path from $(0, 0)$ to $(0, 4)$ we have $x = 0$ and $dx = 0$. Hence,

$$\int_C 2xy\,dx + (x^2 + y^2)\,dy = \int_5^0 0\,dx + (x^2)0 + \int_0^4 (0)(0) + (0 + y^2)\,dy = \left[\frac{y^3}{3}\right]_0^4 = \frac{64}{3}.$$

(b) C: parabola $y = 4 - x^2$ from $(2, 0)$ to $(0, 4)$

Using the same method as in part (a) replace the path along the parabola by the path along the axes from $(2, 0)$ to $(0, 0)$ and then from $(0, 0)$ to $(0, 4)$. Thus,

$$\int_C 2xy\,dx + (x^2 + y^2)\,dy = \int_2^0 0\,dx + (x^2 + 0)(0) + \int_0^4 (0)(0) + (0 + y^2)\,dy = \left[\frac{y^3}{3}\right]_0^4 = \frac{64}{3}.$$

(Since the line integral is path-independent, we could have used the Fundamental Theorem.)

19. $\mathbf{F}(x, y, z) = yz\mathbf{i} + xz\mathbf{j} + xy\mathbf{k}$

Since $\mathbf{curl\ F} = \mathbf{0}$, $\mathbf{F}(x, y, z)$ is conservative. The potential function is $f(x, y, z) = xyz + k$.

(a) $\mathbf{r}_1(t) = t\mathbf{i} + 2\mathbf{j} + t\mathbf{k}, \ 0 \le t \le 4$

$$\int_C \mathbf{F}\cdot d\mathbf{r} = \Big[xyz\Big]_{(0, 2, 0)}^{(4, 2, 4)} = 32$$

(b) $\mathbf{r}_2(t) = t^2\mathbf{i} + t\mathbf{j} + t^2\mathbf{k}, \ 0 \le t \le 2$

$$\int_C \mathbf{F}\cdot d\mathbf{r} = \Big[xyz\Big]_{(0, 0, 0)}^{(4, 2, 4)} = 32$$

21. $\mathbf{F}(x, y, z) = (2y + x)\mathbf{i} + (x^2 - z)\mathbf{j} + (2y - 4z)\mathbf{k}$

(a) $\mathbf{r}_1(t) = t\mathbf{i} + t^2\mathbf{j} + \mathbf{k}, 0 \le t \le 1$

Along the path of $\mathbf{r}_1(t)$, we have $\mathbf{F}(x, y, z) = (2t^2 + t)\mathbf{i} + (t^2 - 1)\mathbf{j} + (2t^2 - 4)\mathbf{k}$ and $\mathbf{r}_1' = \mathbf{i} + 2t\mathbf{j}$. Therefore,

$$\int_C \mathbf{F}\cdot d\mathbf{r}_1 = \int_a^b \mathbf{F}(x(t), y(t), z(t))\cdot \mathbf{r}_1'(t)\,dt$$

$$= \int_0^1 (2t^3 + 2t^2 - t)\,dt = \frac{2}{3}.$$

(b) $\mathbf{r}_2(t) = t\mathbf{i} + t\mathbf{j} + (2t - 1)^2\mathbf{k}$

Along the path of $\mathbf{r}_2(t)$, we have

$$\mathbf{F}(x, y, z) = (2t + t)\mathbf{i} + [t^2 - (2t - 1)^2]\mathbf{j} + [2t - 4(2t - 1)^2]\mathbf{k}$$

$$= 3t\mathbf{i} + (-3t^2 + 4t - 1)\mathbf{j} + (-16t^2 + 18t - 4)\mathbf{k}$$

and $\mathbf{r}_2'(t) = \mathbf{i} + \mathbf{j} + 4(2t - 1)\mathbf{k}$. Therefore,

$$\int_C \mathbf{F}\cdot d\mathbf{r}_2 = \int_a^b \mathbf{F}(x(t), y(t), z(t))\cdot \mathbf{r}_2'(t)\,dt$$

$$= \int_0^1 (-128t^3 + 205t^2 - 97t + 15)\,dt = \frac{17}{6}.$$

23. $\mathbf{F}(x, y, z) = e^z(y\mathbf{i} + x\mathbf{j} + xy\mathbf{k})$

$\mathbf{F}(x, y, z)$ is conservative. The potential function is $f(x, y, z) = xye^z + k$.

(a) $\mathbf{r}_1(t) = 4\cos t\,\mathbf{i} + 4\sin t\,\mathbf{j} + 3\mathbf{k},\ 0 \le t \le \pi$

$$\int_C \mathbf{F} \cdot d\mathbf{r} = \left[xye^z\right]_{(4, 0, 3)}^{(-4, 0, 3)} = 0$$

(b) $\mathbf{r}_2(t) = (4 - 8t)\mathbf{i} + 3\mathbf{k},\ 0 \le t \le 1$

$$\int_C \mathbf{F} \cdot d\mathbf{r} = \left[xye^z\right]_{(4, 0, 3)}^{(-4, 0, 3)} = 0$$

25. $\displaystyle\int_C (y\mathbf{i} + x\mathbf{j}) \cdot d\mathbf{r} = \left[xy\right]_{(0, 0)}^{(3, 8)} = 24$

27. $\displaystyle\int_C \cos x \sin y\,dx + \sin x \cos y\,dy = \left[\sin x \sin y\right]_{(0, -\pi)}^{(3\pi/2, \pi/2)}$
$$= -1$$

29. $\displaystyle\int_C e^x \sin y\,dx + e^x \cos y\,dy$

$C: x = \theta - \sin\theta,\ y = 1 - \cos\theta$ from $(0, 0)$ to $(2\pi, 0)$

Since

$$\frac{\partial}{\partial y}[e^x \sin y] = e^x \cos y = \frac{\partial}{\partial x}[e^x \cos y],$$

the integral is path-independent. Therefore, we can evaluate the line integral by using the Fundamental Theorem. We begin by finding the potential function for the vector field $\mathbf{F}(x, y) = e^x \sin y\,\mathbf{i} + e^x \cos y\,\mathbf{j}$. If f is a potential function of $\mathbf{F}$, then

$$f_x(x, y) = e^x \sin y \quad \text{and} \quad f_y(x, y) = e^x \cos y$$

and we have

$$f(x, y) = \int f_x(x, y)\,dx = \int e^x \sin y\,dx = e^x \sin y + g(y) + K$$

$$f(x, y) = \int f_y(x, y)\,dy = \int e^x \cos y\,dy = e^x \sin y + h(x) + K$$

These two expressions for $f(x, y)$ are the same if $g(y) = h(x) = 0$. Therefore, we have

$$f(x, y) = e^x \sin y + K$$

and

$$\int_C e^x \sin y\,dx + e^x \cos y\,dy = f(2\pi, 0) - f(0, 0) = e^{2\pi}(0) - e^0(0) = 0.$$

[Since this line integral is path-independent, we could have integrated along the x-axis from $(0, 0)$ to $(2\pi, 0)$ with $y = 0$ and $dy = 0$. This would have given the result of zero immediately.]

31. $\displaystyle\int_C (z + 2y)\,dx + (2x - z)\,dy + (x - y)\,dz$

Note: Since $\mathbf{F}(x, y, z) = (z + 2y)\mathbf{i} + (2x - z)\mathbf{j} + (x - y)\mathbf{k}$ is conservative and the potential function is $f(x, y, z) = xz + 2xy - yz + k$, the integral is independent of path as illustrated below.

(a) $\left[xz + 2xy - yz\right]_{(0, 0, 0)}^{(1, 1, 1)} = 2$

(b) $\left[xz + 2xy - yz\right]_{(0, 0, 0)}^{(0, 0, 1)} + \left[xz + 2xy - yz\right]_{(0, 0, 1)}^{(1, 1, 1)} = 0 + 2 = 2$

(c) $\left[xz + 2xy - yz\right]_{(0, 0, 0)}^{(1, 0, 0)} + \left[xz + 2xy - yz\right]_{(1, 0, 0)}^{(1, 1, 0)} + \left[xz + 2xy - yz\right]_{(1, 1, 0)}^{(1, 1, 1)} = 0 + 2 + 0 = 2$

33. $\displaystyle\int_C -\sin x\,dx + z\,dy + y\,dz = \left[\cos x + yz\right]_{(0, 0, 0)}^{(\pi/2, 3, 4)} = 12 - 1 = 11$

35. $\mathbf{F}(x, y) = 9x^2y^2\mathbf{i} + (6x^3y - 1)\mathbf{j}$

    $\mathbf{F}$ is conservative because

$$\frac{\partial}{\partial y}[9x^2y^2] = 18x^2y \quad \text{and} \quad \frac{\partial}{\partial x}[6x^3y - 1] = 18x^2y.$$

    If f is a function such that $\nabla f = \mathbf{F}$, then

$$f_x(x, y) = 9x^2y^2 \quad \text{and} \quad f_y(x, y) = 6x^3y - 1.$$

$$f(x, y) = \int f_x(x, y)\, dx = \int 9x^2y^2\, dx = 3x^3y + g(y)$$

$$f(x, y) = \int f_y(x, y)\, dy = \int (6x^3y - 1)\, dx = 3x^3y^2 - y + h(x)$$

    It follows that

$$g(y) = -y + K, h(x) = K, \text{ and } f(x, y) = 3x^3y^2 - y + K.$$

    Therefore, the work done by $\mathbf{F}$ in moving an object from $P(0, 0)$ to $Q(5, 9)$ along any path C is

$$W = \int_C \mathbf{F} \cdot d\mathbf{r} = f(5, 9) - f(0, 0) = 30{,}366.$$

37. $\mathbf{r}(t) = 2\cos 2\pi t\mathbf{i} + 2\sin 2\pi t\mathbf{j}$

    $\mathbf{r}'(t) = -4\pi\sin 2\pi t\mathbf{i} + 4\pi\cos 2\pi t\mathbf{j}$

    $\mathbf{a}(t) = -8\pi^2\cos 2\pi t\mathbf{i} - 8\pi^2\sin 2\pi t\mathbf{j}$

    $\mathbf{F}(t) = m \cdot \mathbf{a}(t) = \dfrac{1}{32}\mathbf{a}(t) = -\dfrac{\pi^2}{4}(\cos 2\pi t\mathbf{i} + \sin 2\pi t\mathbf{j})$

$$W = \int_C \mathbf{F} \cdot d\mathbf{r} = \int_C -\frac{\pi^2}{4}(\cos 2\pi t\mathbf{i} + \sin 2\pi t\mathbf{j}) \cdot 4\pi(-\sin 2\pi t\mathbf{i} + \cos 2\pi t\mathbf{j})\, dt = -\pi^3\int_C 0\, dt = 0$$

39. Since the sum of the potential and kinetic energies remains constant from point to point, if the kinetic energy is decreasing at a rate of 10 units per minute, then the potential energy is increasing at a rate of 10 units per minute.

41. No. The force field is conservative.

43. False, it would be true if $\mathbf{F}$ were conservative.   **45.** True

47. Let

$$\mathbf{F} = M\mathbf{i} + N\mathbf{j} = \frac{\partial f}{\partial y}\mathbf{i} - \frac{\partial f}{\partial x}\mathbf{j}.$$

    Then $\dfrac{\partial M}{\partial y} = \dfrac{\partial}{\partial y}\left(\dfrac{\partial f}{\partial y}\right) = \dfrac{\partial^2 f}{\partial y^2}$ and $\dfrac{\partial N}{\partial x} = \dfrac{\partial}{\partial x}\left(-\dfrac{\partial f}{\partial x}\right) = -\dfrac{\partial^2 f}{\partial x^2}.$ Since

    $\dfrac{\partial^2 f}{\partial x^2} + \dfrac{\partial^2 f}{\partial y^2} = 0$ we have $\dfrac{\partial M}{\partial y} = \dfrac{\partial N}{\partial x}.$

    Thus, $\mathbf{F}$ is conservative. Therefore, by Theorem 14.7, we have

$$\int_C \left(\frac{\partial f}{\partial y}\, dx - \frac{\partial f}{\partial x}\, dy\right) = \int_C (M\, dx + N\, dy) = \int_C \mathbf{F} \cdot d\mathbf{r} = 0$$

    for every closed curve in the plane.

49. No, the amount of fuel required depends on the flight path. Fuel consumption is dependent on wind speed and direction. The vector field is not conservative.

Section 14.4   Green's Theorem

1. $r(t) = \begin{cases} t\mathbf{i}, & 0 \le t \le 4 \\ 4\mathbf{i} + (t-4)\mathbf{j}, & 4 \le t \le 8 \\ (12-t)\mathbf{i} + 4\mathbf{j}, & 8 \le t \le 12 \\ (16-t)\mathbf{j}, & 12 \le t \le 16 \end{cases}$

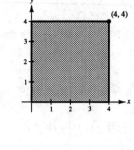

$$\int_C y^2\, dx + x^2\, dy = \int_0^4 [0\, dt + t^2(0)] + \int_4^8 [(t-4)^2(0) + 16\, dt]$$

$$+ \int_8^{12} [16(-dt) + (12-t)^2(0)] + \int_{12}^{16} [(16-t)^2(0) + 0(-dt)]$$

$$= 0 + 64 - 64 + 0 = 0$$

By Green's Theorem, $\displaystyle\int\!\!\!\int_R \left(\frac{\partial N}{\partial x} - \frac{\partial M}{\partial y}\right) dA = \int_0^4\!\!\int_0^4 (2x - 2y)\, dy\, dx = \int_0^4 (8x - 16)\, dx = 0.$

3. $\displaystyle\int_C y^2\, dx + x^2\, dy$

C: boundary of the region lying between $y = x$ and $x = \dfrac{x^2}{4}$

(a) As a line integral define C_1 and C_2 as shown in the figure.

$$C_1: x = t, \; y = \frac{t^2}{4}, \; dx = dt, \, dy = \frac{t}{2}\, dt, \, 0 \le t \le 4$$

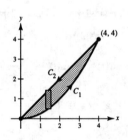

$$C_2: x = 4 - t, \; y = 4 - t, \; dx = dy = -dt, \, 0 \le t \le 4$$

Thus,

$$\int_C y^2\, dx + x^2\, dy = \int_{C_1} \left(\frac{t^4}{16} + \frac{t^3}{2}\right) dt + \int_{C_2} 2(4-t)^2(-dt)$$

$$= \int_0^4 \left(\frac{t^4}{16} + \frac{t^3}{2}\right) dt + 2\int_0^4 (4-t)^2(-1)\, dt$$

$$= \left[\frac{t^5}{5(16)} + \frac{t^4}{2(4)} + \frac{2(4-t)^3}{3}\right]_0^4$$

$$= \frac{64}{5} + 32 - \frac{128}{3} = \frac{32}{15}.$$

(b) By Green's Theorem we have

$$\int\!\!\!\int_R \left(\frac{\partial N}{\partial x} - \frac{\partial M}{\partial y}\right) dA = \int\!\!\!\int_R (2x - 2y)\, dy\, dx$$

$$= \int_0^4\!\!\int_{x^2/4}^x (2x - 2y)\, dy\, dx = \int_0^4 \left[2xy - y^2\right]_{x^2/4}^x dx$$

$$= \int_0^4 \left(x^2 - \frac{x^3}{2} + \frac{x^4}{16}\right) dx = \left[\frac{x^3}{3} - \frac{x^4}{8} + \frac{x^5}{80}\right]_0^4$$

$$= \frac{63}{3} - 32 + \frac{64}{5} = \frac{32}{15}.$$

5. C: $x^2 + y^2 = 4$

Let $x = 2 \cos t$ and $y = 2 \sin t$, $0 \le t \le 2\pi$.

$$\int_C xe^y \, dx + e^x \, dy = \int_0^{2\pi} [2 \cos t e^{2 \sin t} (-2 \sin t) + e^{2 \cos t}(2 \cos t)] \, dt \approx 19.99$$

$$\iint_R \left(\frac{\partial N}{\partial x} - \frac{\partial M}{\partial y} \right) dA = \int_{-2}^2 \int_{-\sqrt{4-x^2}}^{\sqrt{4-x^2}} (e^x - xe^y) \, dy \, dx = \int_{-2}^2 \left[2\sqrt{4 - x^2}\, e^x - xe^{\sqrt{4-x^2}} + xe^{-\sqrt{4-x^2}} \right] dx \approx 19.99$$

7.
$$\int_C (y - x) \, dx + (2x - y) \, dy = \int_0^2 \int_{x^2-x}^x dy \, dx$$
$$= \int_0^2 (2x - x^2) \, dx$$
$$= \frac{4}{3}$$

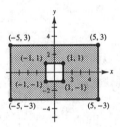

9.
$$\int_C (y - x) \, dx + (2x - y) \, dy$$

C: boundary of the region lying inside the rectangle with vertices

$(5, 3)$, $(-5, 3)$, $(-5, -3)$, and $(5, -3)$

and outside the square with vertices

$(1, 1)$, $(-1, 1)$, $(-1, -1)$, and $(1, -1)$.

Using $M(x, y) = y - x$, $N(x, y) = 2x - y$, and the figure, we have

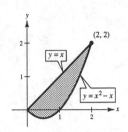

$$\int_C (y - x) \, dx + (2x - y) \, dy = \iint_R \left(\frac{\partial N}{\partial x} - \frac{\partial M}{\partial y} \right) dA$$
$$= \iint_R (2 - 1) \, dA$$
$$= \text{area of region}$$
$$= (\text{area of rectangle}) - (\text{area of square})$$
$$= 6(10) - 2(2) = 56.$$

11. Since the curves $y = 0$ and $y = 4 - x^2$ intersect at $(-2, 0)$ and $(2, 0)$, Green's Theorem yields

$$\int_C 2xy \, dx + (x + y) \, dy = \iint_R (1 - 2x) \, dA = \int_{-2}^2 \int_0^{4-x^2} (1 - 2x) \, dy \, dx$$
$$= \int_{-2}^2 \left[y - 2xy \right]_0^{4-x^2} dx$$
$$= \int_{-2}^2 (4 - 8x - x^2 + 2x^3) \, dx$$
$$= \left[4x - 4x^2 - \frac{x^3}{3} + \frac{x^4}{2} \right]_{-2}^2$$
$$= -\frac{8}{3} - \frac{8}{3} + 16 = \frac{32}{3}.$$

13. Since R is the interior of the circle $x^2 + y^2 = a^2$, Green's Theorem yields:

$$\int_C (x^2 - y^2)\,dx + 2xy\,dy = \iint_R (2y + 2y)\,dA$$

$$= \int_{-a}^{a}\int_{-\sqrt{a^2-x^2}}^{\sqrt{a^2-x^2}} 4y\,dy\,dx$$

$$= 4\int_{-a}^{a} 0\,dx = 0$$

15. $\displaystyle\int_C 2\arctan\frac{y}{x}\,dx + \ln(x^2 + y^2)\,dy$

$C: x = 4 + 2\cos\theta, y = 4 + \sin\theta$

By Green's Theorem, we have

$$\int_C M\,dx + N\,dy = \int_C 2\arctan\frac{y}{x}\,dx + \ln(x^2 + y^2)\,dy$$

$$= \iint_R \left(\frac{\partial N}{\partial x} - \frac{\partial M}{\partial y}\right)dA$$

$$= \iint_R \left[\frac{2x}{x^2 + y^2} - \frac{2(1/x)}{1 + (y/x)^2}\right]dA$$

$$= \iint_R \left[\frac{2x}{x^2 + y^2} - \frac{2}{x^2 + y^2}\right]dA = 0.$$

17. By Green's Theorem,

$$\int_C \sin x \cos y\,dx + (xy + \cos x \sin y)\,dy = \iint_R [(y - \sin x \sin y) - (-\sin x \sin y)]\,dA$$

$$= \int_0^1\int_x^{\sqrt{x}} y\,dy\,dx = \frac{1}{2}\int_0^1 (x - x^2)\,dx = \frac{1}{2}\left[\frac{x^2}{2} - \frac{x^3}{3}\right]_0^1 = \frac{1}{12}.$$

19. By Green's Theorem,

$$\int_C xy\,dx + (x + y)\,dy = \iint_R (1 - x)\,dA$$

$$= \int_0^{2\pi}\int_1^3 (1 - r\cos\theta)r\,dr\,d\theta = \int_0^{2\pi}\left(4 - \frac{26}{3}\cos\theta\right)d\theta = 8\pi.$$

21. $\mathbf{F}(x, y) = xy\mathbf{i} + (x + y)\mathbf{j}$

$C: x^2 + y^2 = 4$

$$\text{Work} = \int_C xy\,dx + (x + y)\,dy$$

$$= \iint_R \left(\frac{\partial N}{\partial x} - \frac{\partial M}{\partial y}\right)dA = \iint_R (1 - x)\,dA$$

$$= \int_0^{2\pi}\int_0^2 (1 - r\cos\theta)r\,dr\,d\theta$$

$$= \int_0^{2\pi}\left[\frac{1}{2}r^2 - \frac{1}{3}r^3\cos\theta\right]_0^2 d\theta$$

$$= \int_0^{2\pi}\left(2 - \frac{8}{3}\cos\theta\right)d\theta = \left[2\theta - \frac{8}{3}\sin\theta\right]_0^{2\pi} = 4\pi$$

23. $\mathbf{F}(x, y) = (x^{3/2} - 3y)\mathbf{i} + (6x + 5\sqrt{y})\mathbf{j}$

$C:$ boundary of the triangle with vertices $(0, 0), (5, 0), (0, 5)$

$$\text{Work} = \int_C (x^{3/2} - 3y)\,dx + (6x + 5\sqrt{y})\,dy = \iint_R 9\,dA = 9\left(\frac{1}{2}\right)(5)(5) = \frac{225}{2}$$

25. C: let $x = a \cos t$, $y = a \sin t$, $0 \leq t \leq 2\pi$. By Theorem 14.9, we have

$$A = \frac{1}{2}\int_C x\,dy - y\,dx = \frac{1}{2}\int_0^{2\pi}[a\cos t(a\cos t) - a\sin t(-a\sin t)]\,dt = \frac{1}{2}\int_0^{2\pi} a^2\,dt = \left[\frac{a^2}{2}t\right]_0^2 = \pi a^2.$$

27. R: $y = 2x + 1$ and $y = 4 - x^2$

The region R (see figure) is enclosed by the path C given by

$$C_1: x = t, y = 2t + 1, \qquad\qquad dx = dt, dy = 2\,dt, \qquad -3 \leq t \leq 1$$

$$C_2: x = 1 - t, y = 4 - (1-t)^2 = 3 + 2t - t^2, \quad dx = -dt, dy = (2 - 2t)\,dt, \quad 0 \leq t \leq 4.$$

Therefore, the area of R is

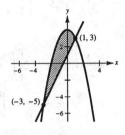

$$A = \frac{1}{2}\int_C x\,dy - y\,dx$$

$$= \frac{1}{2}\int_{C_1} t(2\,dt) - (2t - 1)\,dt + \frac{1}{2}\int_{C_2}(1 - t)(2 - 2t)\,dt - (3 + 2t - t^2)(-dt)$$

$$= \frac{1}{2}\int_{-3}^{1}(-1)\,dt + \frac{1}{2}\int_0^4 (5 - 2t + t^2)\,dt$$

$$= \left[-\frac{t}{2}\right]_{-3}^{1} + \frac{1}{2}\left[5t - t^2 + \frac{t^3}{3}\right]_0^4$$

$$= -2 + \frac{1}{2}\left(20 - 16 + \frac{64}{3}\right) = \frac{32}{3}.$$

29. For the moment about the x-axis, $M_x = \displaystyle\int\int_R y\,dA$. Let $N = 0$ and $M = -y^2/2$. By Green's Theorem,

$$M_x = \int_C -\frac{y^2}{2}\,dx = -\frac{1}{2}\int_C y^2\,dx \text{ and } \bar{y} = \frac{M_x}{2A} = -\frac{1}{2A}\int_C y^2\,dx.$$

For the moment about the y-axis, $M_y = \displaystyle\int\int_R x\,dA$. Let $N = x^2/2$ and $M = 0$. By Green's Theorem,

$$M_y = \int_C \frac{x^2}{2}\,dy = \frac{1}{2}\int_C x^2\,dy \text{ and } \bar{x} = \frac{M_y}{2A} = \frac{1}{2A}\int_C x^2\,dy.$$

31. $A = \displaystyle\int_{-2}^{2}(4 - x^2)\,dx = \left[4x - \frac{x^3}{3}\right]_{-2}^{2} = \frac{32}{3}$

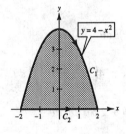

$$\bar{x} = \frac{1}{2A}\int_{C_1} x^2\,dy + \frac{1}{2A}\int_{C_2} x^2\,dy$$

For C_1, $dy = -2x\,dx$ and for C_2, $dy = 0$. Thus,

$$\bar{x} = \frac{1}{2(32/3)}\int_2^{-2} x^2(-2x\,dx) = \left[\frac{3}{64}\left(-\frac{x^4}{2}\right)\right]_2^{-2} = 0.$$

To calculate $\bar{y}$, note that $y = 0$ along C_2. Thus,

$$\bar{y} = \frac{-1}{2(32/3)}\int_2^{-2}(4 - x^2)^2\,dx = \frac{3}{64}\int_{-2}^{2}(16 - 8x^2 + x^4)\,dx = \frac{3}{64}\left[16x - \frac{8x^3}{3} + \frac{x^5}{5}\right]_{-2}^{2} = \frac{8}{5}.$$

33. $R: y = x^3, y = x, 0 \le x \le 1$

The region R (see figure) enclosed by the path C given by

$C_1:$ $x = t, y = t^3,$ $dx = dt, dy = 3t^2\, dy,$ $0 \le t \le 1$

$C_2:$ $x = 1 - t, y = 1 - t,$ $dx = -dt, dy = -dt,$ $0 \le t \le 1.$

Therefore, the area of R is

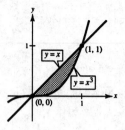

$$A = \frac{1}{2}\int_C x\, dy - y\, dx$$

$$= \frac{1}{2}\int_{C_1} t(3t^2)\, dt - t^3\, dt + \frac{1}{2}\int_{C_2} (1 - t)(-dt) - (1 - t)(-dt)$$

$$= \frac{1}{2}\int_0^1 2t^3\, dt = \left[\frac{1}{4}t^4\right]_0^1 = \frac{1}{4}.$$

Thus,

$$\bar{x} = \frac{1}{2A}\int_C x^2\, dy = 2\left[\int_{C_1} t^2(3t^2)\, dt + \int_{C_2}(1 - t)^2(-dt)\right] = 2\int_0^1 [3t^4 - (1 - t)^2]\, dt$$

$$= 2\left[\frac{3}{5}t^5 + \frac{1}{3}(1 - t)^3\right]_0^1 = 2\left[\frac{3}{5} - \frac{1}{3}\right] = \frac{8}{15}$$

and

$$\bar{y} = -\frac{1}{2A}\int_C y^2\, dx = -2\left[\int_{C_1} t^6\, dt + \int_{C_2}(1 - t)^2(-dt)\right] = -2\int_0^1 [t^6 - (1 - t)^2]\, dt$$

$$= -2\left[\frac{1}{7}t^7 + \frac{1}{3}(1 - t)^3\right]_0^1 = -2\left[\frac{1}{7} - \frac{1}{3}\right] = \frac{8}{21}.$$

35. $A = \dfrac{1}{2}\displaystyle\int_0^{2\pi} a^2(1 - \cos\theta)^2\, d\theta$

$$= \frac{a^2}{2}\int_0^{2\pi}\left(1 - 2\cos\theta + \frac{1}{2} + \frac{\cos 2\theta}{2}\right) d\theta = \frac{a^2}{2}\left[\frac{3\theta}{2} - 2\sin\theta + \frac{1}{2}\sin 2\theta\right]_0^{2\pi} = \frac{a^2}{2}(3\pi) = \frac{3\pi a^2}{2}$$

37. $R:\ r = 1 + 2\cos\theta$ (inner loop)

The inner loop of $r = 1 + 2\cos\theta$ starts at $\theta = 2\pi/3$ and ends at $\theta = 4\pi/3$ (see figure). Hence the area enclosed by this inner loop is

$$A = \frac{1}{2}\int_{2\pi/3}^{4\pi/3} (1 + 2\cos\theta)^2\, d\theta$$

$$= \frac{1}{2}\int_{2\pi/3}^{4\pi/3}\left[1 + 4\cos\theta + 4\left(\frac{1 + \cos 2\theta}{2}\right)\right] d\theta$$

$$= \frac{1}{2}\int_{2\pi/3}^{4\pi/3} (3 + 4\cos\theta + 2\cos 2\theta)\, d\theta$$

$$= \frac{1}{2}\left[3\theta + 4\sin\theta + \sin 2\theta\right]_{2\pi/3}^{4\pi/3} = \pi - \frac{3\sqrt{3}}{2}.$$

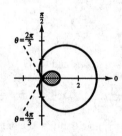

39. $I = \displaystyle\int_C \dfrac{y\,dx - x\,dy}{x^2 + y^2}$

(a) Let $\mathbf{F} = \dfrac{y}{x^2 + y^2}\mathbf{i} - \dfrac{x}{x^2 + y^2}\mathbf{j}$.

F is conservative since $\dfrac{\partial N}{\partial x} = \dfrac{\partial M}{\partial y} = \dfrac{x^2 - y^2}{(x^2 + y^2)^2}$.

F is defined and has continuous first partials everywhere except at the origin. If C is a circle (a closed path) that does not contain the origin, then

$$\int_C \mathbf{F} \cdot d\mathbf{r} = \int_C M\,dx + N\,dy = \iint_R \left(\dfrac{\partial N}{\partial x} - \dfrac{\partial M}{\partial y}\right) dA = 0.$$

(b) Let $\mathbf{r} = a\cos t\,\mathbf{i} - a\sin t\,\mathbf{j}$, $0 \le t \le 2\pi$ be a circle C_1 oriented clockwise inside C (see figure). Introduce line segments C_2 and C_3 as illustrated in Example 6 of this section in the text. For the region inside C and outside C_1, Green's Theorem applies. Note that since C_2 and C_3 have opposite orientations, the line integrals over them cancel. Thus, $C_4 = C_1 + C_2 + C + C_3$ and

$$\int_{C_4} \mathbf{F} \cdot d\mathbf{r} = \int_{C_1} \mathbf{F} \cdot d\mathbf{r} + \int_C \mathbf{F} \cdot d\mathbf{r} = 0.$$

But,

$$\int_{C_1} \mathbf{F} \cdot d\mathbf{r} = \int_0^{2\pi} \left[\dfrac{(-a\sin t)(-a\sin t)}{a^2\cos^2 t + a^2\sin^2 t} + \dfrac{(-a\cos t)(-a\cos t)}{a^2\cos^2 t + a^2\sin^2 t}\right] dt$$

$$= \int_0^{2\pi} (\sin^2 t + \cos^2 t)\,dt = \left[t\right]_0^{2\pi} = 2\pi.$$

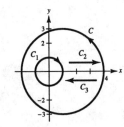

Finally, $\displaystyle\int_C \mathbf{F} \cdot d\mathbf{r} = -\int_{C_1} \mathbf{F} \cdot d\mathbf{r} = -2\pi$.

Note: If C were orientated clockwise, then the answer would have been 2π.

41. Pentagon: $(0,0)$, $(2,0)$, $(3,2)$, $(1,4)$, $(-1,1)$

$A = \frac{1}{2}[(0-0) + (4-0) + (12-2) + (1+4) + (0-0)] = \frac{19}{2}$

43. $\displaystyle\int_C y^n\,dx + x^n\,dy = \iint_R \left(\dfrac{\partial N}{\partial x} - \dfrac{\partial M}{\partial y}\right) dA$

For the line integral, use the two paths

C_1: $\mathbf{r}_1(x) = x\mathbf{i}$, $-a \le x \le a$

C_2: $\mathbf{r}_2(x) = x\mathbf{i} + \sqrt{a^2 - x^2}\,\mathbf{j}$, $x = a$ to $x = -a$

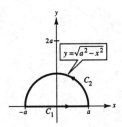

$\displaystyle\int_{C_1} y^n\,dx + x^n\,dy = 0$

$\displaystyle\int_{C_2} y^n\,dx + x^n\,dy = \int_a^{-a} \left[(a^2 - x^2)^{n/2} + x^n\dfrac{-x}{\sqrt{a^2 - x^2}}\right] dx$

$\displaystyle\iint_R \left(\dfrac{\partial N}{\partial x} - \dfrac{\partial M}{\partial y}\right) dA = \int_{-a}^a \int_0^{\sqrt{a^2 - x^2}} \left[nx^{n-1} - ny^{n-1}\right] dy\,dx$

(a) For $n = 1, 3, 5, 7$, both integrals give 0.

(b) For n even, you obtain:

     $n = 2: -\frac{4}{3}a^3$ $n = 4: -\frac{16}{15}a^5$ $n = 6: -\frac{32}{35}a^7$ $n = 8: -\frac{256}{315}a^9$

(c) If n is odd and $0 < a < 1$, then the integral equals 0.

45. $\displaystyle\int_C (fD_N g - gD_N f)\,ds = \int_C fD_N g\,ds - \int_C gD_N f\,ds$

$$= \iint_R (f\nabla^2 g + \nabla f \cdot \nabla g)\,dA - \iint_R (g\nabla^2 f + \nabla g \cdot \nabla f)\,dA = \iint_R (f\nabla^2 g - g\nabla^2 f)\,dA$$

47. F = M**i** + N**j**

$$\text{curl } \mathbf{F} = \left(\frac{\partial N}{\partial x} - \frac{\partial M}{\partial y}\right)\mathbf{k} = 0 \implies \frac{\partial N}{\partial x} = \frac{\partial M}{\partial y}$$

$$\int_C \mathbf{F} \cdot d\mathbf{r} = \int_C M\,dx + N\,dy = \iint_R \left(\frac{\partial N}{\partial x} - \frac{\partial M}{\partial y}\right)dA = \iint_R (0)\,dA = 0$$

Section 14.5   Parametric Surfaces

1. $\mathbf{r}(u, v) = u\mathbf{i} + v\mathbf{j} + uv\mathbf{k}$

$z = xy$

Matches c.

3. $\mathbf{r}(u, v) = 2\cos v \cos u\mathbf{i} + 2\cos v \sin u\mathbf{j} + 2\sin v\mathbf{k}$

$x^2 + y^2 + z^2 = 4$

Matches b.

5. $\mathbf{r}(u, v) = u\mathbf{i} + v\mathbf{j} + \dfrac{v}{2}\mathbf{k}$

$y - 2z = 0$

Plane

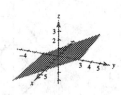

7. $\mathbf{r}(u, v) = 2\cos u\mathbf{i} + v\mathbf{j} + 2\sin u\mathbf{k}$

To identify the surface, we can use the trigonometric identity $\sin^2 \theta + \cos^2 \theta = 1$ to eliminate the parameter u and obtain $x^2 + z^2 = (2\cos u)^2 + (2\sin u)^2 = 4$. Since $y = v$ can be any real number, the surface is a circular cylinder of radius 2 and rulings parallel to the y-axis.

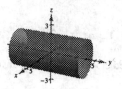

For Exercises 9 and 11,

$$\mathbf{r}(u, v) = u\cos v\mathbf{i} + u\sin v\mathbf{j} + u^2\mathbf{k}, \ 0 \le u \le 2, \ 0 \le v \le 2\pi.$$

Eliminating the parameter yields

$$z = x^2 + y^2, \ 0 \le z \le 4.$$

9. $\mathbf{s}(u, v) = u\cos v\mathbf{i} + u\sin v\mathbf{j} - u^2\mathbf{k}, \ 0 \le u \le 2, \ 0 \le v \le 2\pi$

$z = -(x^2 + y^2)$

The paraboloid is reflected (inverted) through the xy-plane.

11. $\mathbf{s}(u, v) = u\cos v\mathbf{i} + u\sin v\mathbf{j} + u^2\mathbf{k}$

$0 \le u \le 3, 0 \le v \le 2\pi$

For a specific value of u in the interval $0 \le u \le 3$, we have a circular trace of radius u located u^2 units above the xy-plane. Therefore, **s** differs from **R** in that the height of the paraboloid is increased from 4 to 9.

13. $\mathbf{r}(u, v) = 2u\cos v\mathbf{i} + 2u\sin v\mathbf{j} + u^4\mathbf{k}$,

   $0 \le u \le 1, 0 \le v \le 2\pi$

   $z = \dfrac{(x^2 + y^2)^2}{16}$

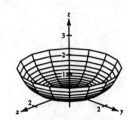

15. $\mathbf{r}(u, v) = 2\sinh u\cos v\mathbf{i} + \sinh u\sin v\mathbf{j} + \cosh u\mathbf{k}$,

   $0 \le u \le 2, 0 \le v \le 2\pi$

   $\dfrac{z^2}{1} - \dfrac{x^2}{4} - \dfrac{y^2}{1} = 1$

17. $\mathbf{r}(u, v) = (u - \sin u)\cos v\mathbf{i} + (1 - \cos u)\sin v\mathbf{j} + u\mathbf{k}$,

   $0 \le u \le \pi, 0 \le v \le 2\pi$

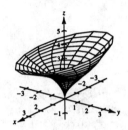

19. (a) From $(-10, 10, 0)$

   (b) From $(10, 10, 10)$

   (c) From $(0, 10, 0)$

   (d) From $(10, 0, 0)$

21. (a) $\mathbf{r}(u, v) = (4 + \cos v)\cos u\mathbf{i} + (4 + \cos v)\sin u\mathbf{j} + \sin v\mathbf{k}$

   $0 \le u \le 2\pi, 0 \le v \le 2\pi$

   (b) $\mathbf{r}(u, v) = (4 + 2\cos v)\cos u\mathbf{i} + (4 + 2\cos v)\sin u\mathbf{j} + 2\sin v\mathbf{k}$

   $0 \le u \le 2\pi, 0 \le v \le 2\pi$

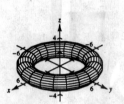

   (c) $\mathbf{r}(u, v) = (8 + \cos v)\cos u\mathbf{i} + (8 + \cos v)\sin u\mathbf{j} + \sin v\mathbf{k}$

   $0 \le u \le 2\pi, 0 \le v \le 2\pi$

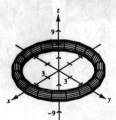

   (d) $\mathbf{r}(u, v) = (8 + 3\cos v)\cos u\mathbf{i} + (8 + 3\cos v)\sin u\mathbf{j} + 3\sin v\mathbf{k}$

   $0 \le u \le 2\pi, 0 \le v \le 2\pi$

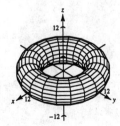

23. $z = y$

$\mathbf{r}(u, v) = u\mathbf{i} + v\mathbf{j} + v\mathbf{k}$

25. $x^2 + y^2 = 16$

$\mathbf{r}(u, v) = 4 \cos u\mathbf{i} + 4 \sin u\mathbf{j} + v\mathbf{k}$

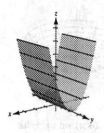

27. The graph is a cylinder whose generating curve, $z = x^2$, is a parabola in the xz-plane. The rulings of the cylinder are parallel to the y-axis (see figure). Therefore, if $x = u$, then $z = u^2$. Since there is no restriction on y, we let $y = v$. Thus, the vector-valued function is

$$\mathbf{r}(u, v) = u\mathbf{i} + v\mathbf{j} + u^2\mathbf{k}.$$

29. $z = 4$ inside $x^2 + y^2 = 9$.

$\mathbf{r}(u, v) = v \cos u\mathbf{i} + v \sin u\mathbf{j} + 4\mathbf{k}, \ 0 \leq v \leq 3$

31. Function: $y = \dfrac{x}{2}, \ 0 \leq x \leq 6$

Axis of revolution: x-axis

$x = u, \ y = \dfrac{u}{2} \cos v, \ z = \dfrac{u}{2} \sin v$

$0 \leq u \leq 6, \ 0 \leq v \leq 2\pi$

33. Surface: $x = f(z) = \sin z, \ 0 \leq z \leq \pi$ revolved about the z-axis. If we use the parameters u and v and let $x = f(u) \cos v$ and $y = f(u) \sin v$, then

$$x^2 + y^2 = [f(u) \cos v]^2 + [f(u) \sin v]^2 = [f(u)]^2.$$

Therefore, a parametric representation of the surface of revolution is

$$x = \sin u \cos v, \ y = \sin u \sin v, \text{ and } z = u$$

where $0 \leq u \leq \pi$ and $0 \leq v \leq 2\pi$.

35. $\mathbf{r}(u, v) = (u + v)\mathbf{i} + (u - v)\mathbf{j} + v\mathbf{k}, \ (1, -1, 1)$

$\mathbf{r}_u(u, v) = \mathbf{i} + \mathbf{j}, \ \mathbf{r}_v(u, v) = \mathbf{i} - \mathbf{j} + \mathbf{k}$

At $(1, -1, 1), \ u = 0$ and $v = 1$.

$\mathbf{r}_u(0, 1) = \mathbf{i} + \mathbf{j}, \ \mathbf{r}_v(0, 1) = \mathbf{i} - \mathbf{j} + \mathbf{k}$

$$\mathbf{N} = \mathbf{r}_u(0, 1) \times \mathbf{r}_v(0, 1) = \begin{vmatrix} \mathbf{i} & \mathbf{j} & \mathbf{k} \\ 1 & 1 & 0 \\ 1 & -1 & 1 \end{vmatrix} = \mathbf{i} - \mathbf{j} - 2\mathbf{k}$$

Tangent plane: $(x - 1) - (y + 1) - 2(z - 1) = 0$

$$x - y - 2z = 0$$

(The original plane!)

37. $\mathbf{r}(u, v) = 2u \cos v\mathbf{i} + 3u \sin v\mathbf{j} + u^2\mathbf{k}$

The point in the uv-plane that is mapped to the point $(x, y, z) = (0, 6, 4)$ is $(u, v) = (2, \pi/2)$. The partial derivatives of $\mathbf{r}$ are $\mathbf{r}_u = 2 \cos v\mathbf{i} + 3 \sin v\mathbf{j} + 2u\mathbf{k}$ and $\mathbf{r}_v = -2u \sin v\mathbf{i} + 3u \cos v\mathbf{j}$. Therefore,

$$\mathbf{r}_u\left(2, \frac{\pi}{2}\right) = 3\mathbf{j} + 4\mathbf{k} \quad \text{and} \quad \mathbf{r}_v\left(2, \frac{\pi}{2}\right) = -4\mathbf{i}.$$

The normal vector at the point $(0, 6, 4)$ on the surface is

$$\mathbf{r}_u \times \mathbf{r}_v = \begin{vmatrix} \mathbf{i} & \mathbf{j} & \mathbf{k} \\ 0 & 3 & 4 \\ -4 & 0 & 0 \end{vmatrix} = -16\mathbf{j} + 12\mathbf{k}.$$

Thus, an equation of the tangent plane at $(0, 6, 4)$ is

$$0(x - 0) - 16(y - 6) + 12(z - 4) = 0$$

$$4y - 3z = 12.$$

39. $\mathbf{r}(u, v) = 2u\mathbf{i} - \dfrac{v}{2}\mathbf{j} + \dfrac{v}{2}\mathbf{k}, \ 0 \le u \le 2, \ 0 \le v \le 1$

$\mathbf{r}_u(u, v) = 2\mathbf{i}, \ \mathbf{r}_v(u, v) = -\dfrac{1}{2}\mathbf{j} + \dfrac{1}{2}\mathbf{k}$

$\mathbf{r}_u \times \mathbf{r}_v = \begin{vmatrix} \mathbf{i} & \mathbf{j} & \mathbf{k} \\ 2 & 0 & 0 \\ 0 & -\frac{1}{2} & \frac{1}{2} \end{vmatrix} = -\mathbf{j} - \mathbf{k}$

$\|\mathbf{r}_u \times \mathbf{r}_v\| = \sqrt{2}$

$A = \displaystyle\int_0^1 \int_0^2 \sqrt{2} \, du \, dv = 2\sqrt{2}$

41. $\mathbf{r}(u, v) = a \cos u\mathbf{i} + a \sin u\mathbf{j} + v\mathbf{k},$

$0 \le u \le 2\pi, \ 0 \le v \le b$

$\mathbf{r}_u(u, v) = -a \sin u\mathbf{i} + a \cos u\mathbf{j}$

$\mathbf{r}_v(u, v) = \mathbf{k}$

$\mathbf{r}_u \times \mathbf{r}_v = \begin{vmatrix} \mathbf{i} & \mathbf{j} & \mathbf{k} \\ -a \sin u & a \cos u & 0 \\ 0 & 0 & 1 \end{vmatrix} = a \cos u\mathbf{i} + a \sin u\mathbf{j}$

$\|\mathbf{r}_u \times \mathbf{r}_v\| = a$

$A = \displaystyle\int_0^b \int_0^{2\pi} a \, du \, dv = 2\pi ab$

43. $\mathbf{r}(u, v) = au \cos v\mathbf{i} + au \sin v\mathbf{j} + u\mathbf{k}, \ 0 \le u \le b, \ 0 \le v \le 2\pi$

Begin by calculating $\mathbf{r}_u$ and $\mathbf{r}_v$.

$\mathbf{r}_u = a \cos v\mathbf{i} + a \sin v\mathbf{j} + \mathbf{k}$

$\mathbf{r}_v = -au \sin v\mathbf{i} + au \cos v\mathbf{j}$

The cross product of these two vectors is

$\mathbf{r}_u \times \mathbf{r}_v = \begin{vmatrix} \mathbf{i} & \mathbf{j} & \mathbf{k} \\ a \cos v & a \sin v & 1 \\ -au \sin v & au \cos v & 0 \end{vmatrix} = -au \cos v\mathbf{i} - au \sin v\mathbf{j} + a^2 u\mathbf{k}$

which implies that

$\begin{aligned} \|\mathbf{r}_u \times \mathbf{r}_v\| &= \sqrt{(-au \cos v)^2 + (-au \sin v)^2 + (a^2 u)^2} \\ &= \sqrt{a^2 u^2 + a^4 u^2} \\ &= au\sqrt{1 + a^2} \quad (0 < a, 0 \le u). \end{aligned}$

Finally, the surface area of the specified portion of the cone is

$\begin{aligned} A &= \iint_R \|\mathbf{r}_u \times \mathbf{r}_v\| = \int_0^{2\pi} \int_0^b au\sqrt{1 + a^2} \, du \, dv \\ &= a\sqrt{1 + a^2} \int_0^{2\pi} \frac{b^2}{2} \, dv \\ &= \pi ab^2 \sqrt{1 + a^2}. \end{aligned}$

45. $\mathbf{r}(u, v) = \sqrt{u} \cos v\mathbf{i} + \sqrt{u} \sin v\mathbf{j} + u\mathbf{k}, \ 0 \le u \le 4, \ 0 \le v \le 2\pi$

$\mathbf{r}_u(u, v) = \dfrac{\cos v}{2\sqrt{u}}\mathbf{i} + \dfrac{\sin v}{2\sqrt{u}}\mathbf{j} + \mathbf{k}$

$\mathbf{r}_v(u, v) = -\sqrt{u} \sin v\mathbf{i} + \sqrt{u} \cos v\mathbf{j}$

$\mathbf{r}_u \times \mathbf{r}_v = \begin{vmatrix} \mathbf{i} & \mathbf{j} & \mathbf{k} \\ \dfrac{\cos v}{2\sqrt{u}} & \dfrac{\sin v}{2\sqrt{u}} & 1 \\ -\sqrt{u} \sin v & \sqrt{u} \cos v & 0 \end{vmatrix} = -\sqrt{u} \cos v\mathbf{i} - \sqrt{u} \sin v\mathbf{j} + \dfrac{1}{2}\mathbf{k}$

$\|\mathbf{r}_u \times \mathbf{r}_v\| = \sqrt{u + \dfrac{1}{4}}$

$A = \displaystyle\int_0^{2\pi} \int_0^4 \sqrt{u + \dfrac{1}{4}} \, du \, dv = \dfrac{\pi}{6}\left(17\sqrt{17} - 1\right) \approx 36.177$

47. $\mathbf{r}(u, v) = 20 \sin(u) \cos(v)\mathbf{i} + 20 \sin(u) \sin(v)\mathbf{j} + 20 \cos(u)\mathbf{k}, \; 0 \le u \le \pi/3, \; 0 \le v \le 2\pi$

$\mathbf{r}_u = 20 \cos u \cos v \mathbf{i} + 20 \cos u \sin v \mathbf{j} - 20 \sin u \mathbf{k}$

$\mathbf{r}_v = -20 \sin u \sin v \mathbf{i} + 20 \sin u \cos v \mathbf{j}$

$\mathbf{r}_u \times \mathbf{r}_v = \begin{vmatrix} \mathbf{i} & \mathbf{j} & \mathbf{k} \\ 20 \cos u \cos v & 20 \cos u \sin v & -20 \sin u \\ -20 \sin u \sin v & 20 \sin u \cos v & 0 \end{vmatrix}$

$\phantom{\mathbf{r}_u \times \mathbf{r}_v} = 400 \sin^2 u \cos v \mathbf{i} + 400 \sin^2 u \sin v \mathbf{j} + 400(\cos u \sin u \cos^2 v + \cos u \sin u \sin^2 v)\mathbf{k}$

$\phantom{\mathbf{r}_u \times \mathbf{r}_v} = 400[\sin^2 u \cos v \mathbf{i} + \sin^2 u \sin v \mathbf{j} + \cos u \sin u \mathbf{k}]$

$\|\mathbf{r}_u \times \mathbf{r}_v\| = 400\sqrt{\sin^4 u \cos^2 v + \sin^4 u \sin^2 v + \cos^2 u \sin^2 u}$

$\phantom{\|\mathbf{r}_u \times \mathbf{r}_v\|} = 400\sqrt{\sin^4 u + \cos^2 u \sin^2 u}$

$\phantom{\|\mathbf{r}_u \times \mathbf{r}_v\|} = 400\sqrt{\sin^2 u} = 400 \sin u$

$S = \iint_S dS = \int_0^{2\pi} \int_0^{\pi/3} 400 \sin u \, du \, dv = \int_0^{2\pi} \left[-400 \cos u \right]_0^{\pi/3} dv = \int_0^{2\pi} 200 \, dv = 400\pi \; \mathrm{m}^2$

49. $\mathbf{r}(u, v) = u \cos v \mathbf{i} + u \sin v \mathbf{j} + 2v\mathbf{k}, \; 0 \le u \le 3, \; 0 \le v \le 2\pi$

$\mathbf{r}_u(u, v) = \cos v \mathbf{i} + \sin v \mathbf{j}$

$\mathbf{r}_v(u, v) = -u \sin v \mathbf{i} + u \cos v \mathbf{j} + 2\mathbf{k}$

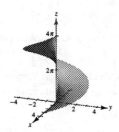

$\mathbf{r}_u \times \mathbf{r}_v = \begin{vmatrix} \mathbf{i} & \mathbf{j} & \mathbf{k} \\ \cos v & \sin v & 0 \\ -u \sin v & u \cos v & 2 \end{vmatrix} = 2 \sin v \mathbf{i} - 2 \cos v \mathbf{j} + u\mathbf{k}$

$\|\mathbf{r}_u \times \mathbf{r}_v\| = \sqrt{4 + u^2}$

$A = \int_0^{2\pi} \int_0^3 \sqrt{4 + u^2} \, du \, dv = \pi\left[3\sqrt{13} + 4 \ln\left(\frac{3 + \sqrt{13}}{2} \right) \right]$

51. Essay

Section 14.6   Surface Integrals

1. $S: z = 4 - x, \; 0 \le x \le 4, \; 0 \le y \le 4, \; \dfrac{\partial z}{\partial x} = -1, \; \dfrac{\partial z}{\partial y} = 0$

$\iint_S (x - 2y + z) \, dS = \int_0^4 \int_0^4 (x - 2y + 4 - x)\sqrt{1 + (-1)^2 + (0)^2} \, dy \, dx$

$ = \sqrt{2} \int_0^4 \int_0^4 (4 - 2y) \, dy \, dx = 0$

3. $S: z = 10, \; x^2 + y^2 \le 1, \; \dfrac{\partial z}{\partial x} = \dfrac{\partial z}{\partial y} = 0$

$\iint_S (x - 2y + z) \, dS = \int_{-1}^1 \int_{-\sqrt{1-x^2}}^{\sqrt{1-x^2}} (x - 2y + 10)\sqrt{1 + (0)^2 + (0)^2} \, dy \, dx$

$ = \int_0^{2\pi} \int_0^1 (r \cos \theta - 2r \sin \theta + 10)r \, dr \, d\theta$

$ = \int_0^{2\pi} \left(\frac{1}{3} \cos \theta - \frac{2}{3} \sin \theta + 5 \right) d\theta$

$ = \left[\frac{1}{3} \sin \theta + \frac{2}{3} \cos \theta + 5\theta \right]_0^{2\pi} = 10\pi$

5. S: $z = 6 - x - 2y$, (first octant) $\dfrac{\partial z}{\partial x} = -1$, $\dfrac{\partial z}{\partial y} = -2$

$$\iint_S xy \, dS = \int_0^6 \int_0^{3-(x/2)} xy\sqrt{1 + (-1)^2 + (-2)^2} \, dy \, dx$$

$$= \sqrt{6}\int_0^6 \left[\frac{xy^2}{2}\right]_0^{3-(x/2)} dx$$

$$= \frac{\sqrt{6}}{2}\int_0^6 x\left(9 - 3x + \frac{1}{4}x^2\right) dx$$

$$= \frac{\sqrt{6}}{2}\left[\frac{9x^2}{2} - x^3 + \frac{x^4}{16}\right]_0^6 = \frac{27\sqrt{6}}{2}$$

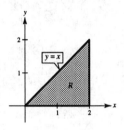

7. $\displaystyle\iint_S xy \, dS$

S: $z = 9 - x^2$ for $0 \le x \le 2$, and $0 \le y \le x$

Begin by writing the equation for the surface S as $z = g(x, y) = 9 - x^2$ so that $g_x(x, y) = -2x$ and $g_y(x, y) = 0$, to obtain

$$\sqrt{1 + [g_x(x, y)]^2 + [g_y(x, y)]^2} = \sqrt{1 + 4x^2}.$$

Using the figure, we have

$$\iint_S xy \, dS = \iint_R f(x, y, g(x, y))\sqrt{1 + [g_x(x, y)]^2 + [g_y(x, y)]^2}\, dA$$

$$= \int_0^2 \int_0^x xy\sqrt{1 + 4x^2}\, dy \, dx$$

$$= \frac{1}{2}\int_0^2 x^3\sqrt{1 + 4x^2}\, dx.$$

Using a symbolic integration utility to evaluate the last integral yields

$$\iint_S xy \, dS = \frac{391\sqrt{17} + 1}{240}.$$

If we do not have access to a symbolic integration utility, use trigonometric substitution letting $2x = \tan\theta$ and $2\, dx = \sec^2\theta\, d\theta$ to obtain

$$\iint_S xy \, dS = \frac{1}{32}\int_0^{\arctan 4} \tan^3\theta \sec^3\theta\, d\theta$$

$$= \frac{1}{32}\left[\frac{1}{5}\sec^5\theta - \frac{1}{3}\sec^3\theta\right]_0^{\arctan 4} = \frac{391\sqrt{17} + 1}{240}.$$

9. S: $z = 10 - x^2 - y^2$, $0 \le x \le 2$, $0 \le y \le 2$

$$\iint_S (x^2 - 2xy) \, dS = \int_0^2 \int_0^2 (x^2 - 2xy)\sqrt{1 + 4x^2 + 4y^2}\, dy\, dx \approx -11.47$$

11. S: $\mathbf{r}(u, v) = u\mathbf{i} + v\mathbf{j} + \dfrac{v}{2}\mathbf{k}$, $0 \le u \le 1$, $0 \le v \le 2$

$$\|\mathbf{r}_u \times \mathbf{r}_v\| = \left\| -\frac{1}{2}\mathbf{j} + \mathbf{k} \right\| = \frac{\sqrt{5}}{2}$$

$$\iint_S (y + 5) \, dS = \int_0^2 \int_0^1 (v + 5)\frac{\sqrt{5}}{2}\, du\, dv = 6\sqrt{5}$$

13. S: $\mathbf{r}(u, v) = 2 \cos u \mathbf{i} + 2 \sin u \mathbf{j} + v \mathbf{k}$, $0 \leq u \leq \dfrac{\pi}{2}$, $0 \leq v \leq 2$

$\|\mathbf{r}_u \times \mathbf{r}_v\| = \|2 \cos u \mathbf{i} + 2 \sin u \mathbf{j}\| = 2$

$$\iint_S xy \, dS = \int_0^2 \int_0^{\pi/2} 8 \cos u \sin u \, du \, dv = 8$$

15. $f(x, y, z) = x^2 + y^2 + z^2$

S: $z = x + 2$, $x^2 + y^2 \leq 1$

$$\iint_S f(x, y, z) \, dS = \int_{-1}^1 \int_{-\sqrt{1-x^2}}^{\sqrt{1-x^2}} [x^2 + y^2 + (x + 2)^2] \sqrt{1 + (1)^2 + (0)^2} \, dy \, dx$$

$$= \sqrt{2} \int_0^{2\pi} \int_0^1 [r^2 + (r \cos \theta + 2)^2] r \, dr \, d\theta$$

$$= \sqrt{2} \int_0^{2\pi} \int_0^1 [r^2 + r^2 \cos^2 \theta + 4r \cos \theta + 4] r \, dr \, d\theta$$

$$= \sqrt{2} \int_0^{2\pi} \left[\frac{r^4}{4} + \frac{r^4}{4} \cos^2 \theta + \frac{4r^3}{3} \cos \theta + 2r^2 \right]_0^1 d\theta$$

$$= \sqrt{2} \int_0^{2\pi} \left[\frac{9}{4} + \left(\frac{1}{4}\right) \frac{1 + \cos 2\theta}{2} + \frac{4}{3} \cos \theta \right] d\theta$$

$$= \sqrt{2} \left[\frac{9}{4}\theta + \frac{1}{8}\left(\theta + \frac{1}{2} \sin 2\theta\right) + \frac{4}{3} \sin \theta \right]_0^{2\pi} = \sqrt{2} \left[\frac{18\pi}{4} + \frac{\pi}{4} \right] = \frac{19\sqrt{2}\pi}{4}$$

17. $\displaystyle\iint_S \sqrt{x^2 + y^2 + z^2} \, dS$

S: $z = \sqrt{x^2 + y^2}$ for $x^2 + y^2 \leq 4$

Begin by writing the equation of the surface S as $z = g(x, y) = \sqrt{x^2 + y^2}$, so that

$$g_x(x, y) = \frac{x}{\sqrt{x^2 + y^2}} \quad \text{and} \quad g_y(x, y) = \frac{y}{\sqrt{x^2 + y^2}}$$

to obtain

$$\sqrt{1 + [g_x(x, y)]^2 + [g_y(x, y)]^2} = \sqrt{1 + \frac{x^2}{x^2 + y^2} + \frac{y^2}{x^2 + y^2}} = \sqrt{2}.$$

Using the figure, we have

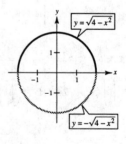

$$\iint_S \sqrt{x^2 + y^2 + z^2} \, dS = \iint_R f(x, y, g(x, y)) \sqrt{1 + [g_x(x, y)]^2 + [g_y(x, y)]^2} \, dA$$

$$= \int_{-2}^2 \int_{-\sqrt{4-x^2}}^{\sqrt{4-x^2}} \sqrt{x^2 + y^2 + \left(\sqrt{x^2 + y^2}\right)^2} \sqrt{2} \, dy \, dx$$

$$= 2 \int_{-2}^2 \int_{-\sqrt{4-x^2}}^{\sqrt{4-x^2}} \sqrt{x^2 + y^2} \, dy \, dx$$

$$= 2 \int_0^{2\pi} \int_0^2 r(r \, dr \, d\theta) \quad \text{(polar coordinates)}$$

$$= 2 \int_0^{2\pi} \left[\frac{r^3}{3} \right]_0^2 d\theta = \frac{16}{3} \int_0^{2\pi} d\theta = \frac{32\pi}{3}.$$

19. $f(x, y, z) = x^2 + y^2 + z^2$

$S: x^2 + y^2 = 9, \ 0 \leq x \leq 3, \ 0 \leq y \leq 3, 0 \leq z \leq 9$

Project the solid onto the yz-plane; $x = \sqrt{9 - y^2}, \ 0 \leq y \leq 3, \ 0 \leq z \leq 9$.

$$\iint_S f(x, y, z) \, dS = \int_0^3 \int_0^9 [(9 - y^2) + y^2 + z^2] \sqrt{1 + \left(\frac{y}{\sqrt{9 - y^2}}\right)^2 + (0)^2} \, dz \, dy$$

$$= \int_0^3 \int_0^9 (9 + z^2) \frac{3}{\sqrt{9 - y^2}} \, dz \, dy = \int_0^3 \left[\frac{3}{\sqrt{9 - y^2}}\left(9z + \frac{z^3}{3}\right)\right]_0^9 dy$$

$$= 324 \int_0^3 \frac{3}{\sqrt{9 - y^2}} \, dy = \left[972 \arcsin\left(\frac{y}{3}\right)\right]_0^3 = 972\left(\frac{\pi}{2} - 0\right) = 486\pi$$

21. $\mathbf{F}(x, y, z) = 3z\mathbf{i} - 4\mathbf{j} + y\mathbf{k}$

$\quad S: x + y + z = 1$ (first octant)

$\quad G(x, y, z) = x + y + z - 1$

$\quad \nabla G(x, y, z) = \mathbf{i} + \mathbf{j} + \mathbf{k}$

$$\iint_S \mathbf{F} \cdot \mathbf{N} \, dS = \iint_R \mathbf{F} \cdot \nabla G \, dA = \int_0^1 \int_0^{1-x} (3z - 4 + y) \, dy \, dx$$

$$= \int_0^1 \int_0^{1-x} [3(1 - x - y) - 4 + y] \, dy \, dx$$

$$= \int_0^1 \int_0^{1-x} (-1 - 3x - 2y) \, dy \, dx$$

$$= \int_0^1 \left[-y - 3xy - y^2\right]_0^{1-x} dx$$

$$= -\int_0^1 [(1 - x) + 3x(1 - x) + (1 - x)^2] \, dx$$

$$= -\int_0^1 (2 - 2x^2) \, dx = -\frac{4}{3}$$

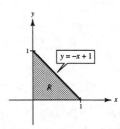

23. $\mathbf{F}(x, y, z) = x\mathbf{i} + y\mathbf{j} + z\mathbf{k}$

$\quad S: z = 9 - x^2 - y^2, 0 \leq z$

The vector field $\mathbf{F}$, over the surface S, is given by

$$\mathbf{F}(x, y, z) = x\mathbf{i} + y\mathbf{j} + z\mathbf{k} = x\mathbf{i} + y\mathbf{j} + (9 - x^2 - y^2)\mathbf{k}.$$

We write the equation for the surface S as $z = g(x, y) = 9 - x^2 - y^2$ so that

$$g_x(x, y) = -2x \quad \text{and} \quad g_y(x, y) = -2y.$$

$$\iint_S \mathbf{F} \cdot \mathbf{N} \, dS = \iint_R \mathbf{F} \cdot [-g_x(x, y)\mathbf{i} - g_y(x, y)\mathbf{j} + \mathbf{k}] \, dA$$

$$= \iint_R [x\mathbf{i} + y\mathbf{j} + (9 - x^2 - y^2)\mathbf{k}] \cdot (2x\mathbf{i} + 2y\mathbf{j} + \mathbf{k}) \, dA$$

$$= \iint_R (9 + x^2 + y^2) \, dA$$

$$= 4 \int_0^{\pi/2} \int_0^3 (9 + r^2) r \, dr \, d\theta \quad \text{(polar coordinates)}$$

$$= \frac{243\pi}{2}$$

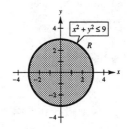

25. $\mathbf{F}(x, y, z) = 4\mathbf{i} - 3\mathbf{j} + 5\mathbf{k}$

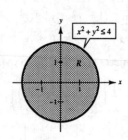

$S: z = x^2 + y^2,\ x^2 + y^2 \le 4$

$G(x, y, z) = -x^2 - y^2 + z$

$\nabla G(x, y, z) = -2x\mathbf{i} - 2y\mathbf{j} + \mathbf{k}$

$$\iint_S \mathbf{F} \cdot \mathbf{N}\, dS = \iint_R \mathbf{F} \cdot \nabla G\, dA = \iint_R (-8x + 6y + 5)\, dA$$

$$= \int_0^{2\pi} \int_0^2 [-8r\cos\theta + 6r\sin\theta + 5]r\, dr\, d\theta$$

$$= \int_0^{2\pi} \left[-\frac{8}{3}r^3\cos\theta + 2r^3\sin\theta + \frac{5}{2}r^2 \right]_0^2 d\theta$$

$$= \int_0^{2\pi} \left[-\frac{64}{3}\cos\theta + 16\sin\theta + 10 \right] d\theta$$

$$= \left[-\frac{64}{3}\sin\theta - 16\cos\theta + 10\theta \right]_0^{2\pi} = 20\pi$$

27. $\mathbf{F}(x, y, z) = 4xy\mathbf{i} + z^2\mathbf{j} + yz\mathbf{k}$

$S:$ unit cube bounded by $x = 0,\ x = 1,\ y = 0,\ y = 1,\ z = 0,\ z = 1$

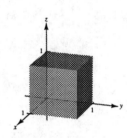

$S_1:$ The top of the cube

$\mathbf{N} = \mathbf{k},\ z = 1$

$$\iint_{S_1} \mathbf{F} \cdot \mathbf{N}\, dS = \int_0^1 \int_0^1 y(1)\, dy\, dx = \frac{1}{2}$$

$S_2:$ The bottom of the cube

$\mathbf{N} = -\mathbf{k},\ z = 0$

$$\iint_{S_2} \mathbf{F} \cdot \mathbf{N}\, dS = \int_0^1 \int_0^1 -y(0)\, dy\, dx = 0$$

$S_4:$ The back of the cube

$\mathbf{N} = -\mathbf{i},\ x = 0$

$$\iint_{S_4} \mathbf{F} \cdot \mathbf{N}\, dS = \int_0^1 \int_0^1 -4(0)y\, dy\, dx = 0$$

$S_6:$ The left side of the cube

$\mathbf{N} = -\mathbf{j},\ y = 0$

$$\iint_{S_6} \mathbf{F} \cdot \mathbf{N}\, dS = \int_0^1 \int_0^1 -z^2\, dz\, dx = -\frac{1}{3}$$

$S_3:$ The front of the cube

$\mathbf{N} = \mathbf{i},\ x = 1$

$$\iint_{S_3} \mathbf{F} \cdot \mathbf{N}\, dS = \int_0^1 \int_0^1 4(1)y\, dy\, dz = 2$$

$S_5:$ The right side of the cube

$\mathbf{N} = \mathbf{j},\ y = 1$

$$\iint_{S_5} \mathbf{F} \cdot \mathbf{N}\, dS = \int_0^1 \int_0^1 z^2\, dz\, dx = \frac{1}{3}$$

$$\iint_S \mathbf{F} \cdot \mathbf{N}\, dS = \frac{1}{2} + 0 + 2 + 0 + \frac{1}{3} - \frac{1}{3} = \frac{5}{2}$$

29. $S: 2x + 3y + 6z = 12$ (first octant) $\implies z = 2 - \frac{1}{3}x - \frac{1}{2}y$

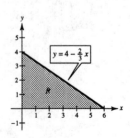

$\rho(x, y, z) = x^2 + y^2$

$$m = \iint_R (x^2 + y^2)\sqrt{1 + \left(-\frac{1}{3}\right)^3 + \left(-\frac{1}{2}\right)^2}\, dA$$

$$= \frac{7}{6} \int_0^6 \int_0^{4-(2x/3)} (x^2 + y^2)\, dy\, dx$$

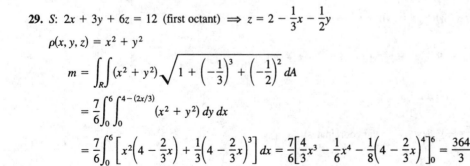

$$= \frac{7}{6} \int_0^6 \left[x^2\left(4 - \frac{2}{3}x\right) + \frac{1}{3}\left(4 - \frac{2}{3}x\right)^3 \right] dx = \frac{7}{6}\left[\frac{4}{3}x^3 - \frac{1}{6}x^4 - \frac{1}{8}\left(4 - \frac{2}{3}x\right)^4 \right]_0^6 = \frac{364}{3}$$

31. $z = \sqrt{x^2 + y^2}$, $0 \le z \le a$

$$m = \iint_S k \, dS = k \iint_R \sqrt{1 + \left(\frac{x}{\sqrt{x^2 + y^2}}\right)^2 + \left(\frac{y}{\sqrt{x^2 + y^2}}\right)^2} \, dA = k \iint_R \sqrt{2} \, dA = \sqrt{2} \, k\pi a^2$$

$$I_z = \iint_S k(x^2 + y^2) \, dS = \iint_R k(x^2 + y^2)\sqrt{2} \, dA$$

$$= \sqrt{2} k \int_0^{2\pi} \int_0^a r^3 \, dr \, d\theta = \frac{\sqrt{2}ka^4}{4}(2\pi)$$

$$= \frac{\sqrt{2}k\pi a^4}{2} = \frac{a^2}{2}(\sqrt{2}k\pi a^2) = \frac{a^2 m}{2}$$

33. $S: x^2 + y^2 = a^2 (0 \le z \le h)$

Note that S does not define z as a function of x and y. Hence, project onto the xz-plane, so that $y = \sqrt{a^2 - x^2} = g(x, z)$ and obtain

$$\sqrt{1 + [g_x(x, z)]^2 + [g_z(x, z)]^2} = \sqrt{1 + \frac{x^2}{a^2 - x^2}} = \frac{a}{\sqrt{a^2 - x^2}}.$$

$$I_z = \iint_S (x^2 + y^2)(1) \, dS$$

$$= \iint_R a^2 \sqrt{1 + [g_x(x, z)]^2 + [g_z(x, z)]^2} \, dA$$

$$= 4a^2 \int_0^a \int_0^h \frac{a}{\sqrt{a^2 - x^2}} \, dz \, dx$$

$$= 4a^3 h \int_0^a \frac{1}{\sqrt{a^2 - x^2}} \, dx$$

$$= 4a^3 h \left[\arcsin \frac{x}{a} \right]_0^a = 2\pi a^3 h$$

35. $S: z = 16 - x^2 - y^2$, $z \ge 0$

$\mathbf{F}(x, y, z) = 0.5z\mathbf{k}$

$$\iint_S \rho \mathbf{F} \cdot \mathbf{N} \, dS = \iint_R \rho \mathbf{F} \cdot (-g_x(x, y)\mathbf{i} - g_y(x, y)\mathbf{j} + \mathbf{k}) \, dA = \iint_R 0.5\rho z\mathbf{k} \cdot (2x\mathbf{i} + 2y\mathbf{j} + \mathbf{k}) \, dA$$

$$= \iint_R 0.5\rho z \, dA = \iint_R 0.5\rho(16 - x^2 - y^2) \, dA$$

$$= 0.5\rho \int_0^{2\pi} \int_0^4 (16 - r^2)r \, dr \, d\theta = 0.5\rho \int_0^{2\pi} 64 \, d\theta = 64\pi\rho$$

37. (a)

(b) If a normal vector at a point P on the surface is moved around the Möbius strip once, it will point in the opposite direction.

(d) (construction)

(c) $\mathbf{r}(u, 0) = 4 \cos(2u)\mathbf{i} + 4 \sin(2u)\mathbf{j}$

This is a circle.

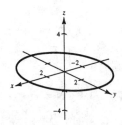

(e) You obtain a strip with a double twist and twice as long as the original Möbius strip.

39. E $= yz\mathbf{i} + xz\mathbf{j} + xy\mathbf{k}$

   $S: z = \sqrt{1 - x^2 - y^2}$

$$\iint_S \mathbf{E} \cdot \mathbf{N}\, dS = \iint_R \mathbf{E} \cdot (-g_x(x, y)\mathbf{i} - g_y(x, y)\mathbf{j} + \mathbf{k})\, dA$$

$$= \iint_R (yz\mathbf{i} + xz\mathbf{j} + xy\mathbf{k}) \cdot \left(\frac{x}{\sqrt{1 - x^2 - y^2}}\mathbf{i} + \frac{y}{\sqrt{1 - x^2 - y^2}}\mathbf{j} + \mathbf{k} \right) dA$$

$$= \iint_R \left(\frac{2xyz}{\sqrt{1 - x^2 - y^2}} + xy \right) dA = \iint_R 3xy\, dA = \int_{-1}^{1} \int_{-\sqrt{1-x^2}}^{\sqrt{1-x^2}} 3xy\, dy\, dx = 0$$

Section 14.7   Divergence Theorem

1. Surface Integral: There are six surfaces to the cube, each with $dS = \sqrt{1}\, dA$.

$$z = 0, \quad \mathbf{N} = -\mathbf{k}, \quad \mathbf{F} \cdot \mathbf{N} = -z^2, \quad \iint_{S_1} 0\, dA = 0$$

$$z = a, \quad \mathbf{N} = \mathbf{k}, \quad \mathbf{F} \cdot \mathbf{N} = z^2, \quad \iint_{S_2} a^2\, dA = \int_0^a \int_0^a a^2\, dx\, dy = a^4$$

$$x = 0, \quad \mathbf{N} = -\mathbf{i}, \quad \mathbf{F} \cdot \mathbf{N} = -2x, \quad \iint_{S_3} 0\, dA = 0$$

$$x = a, \quad \mathbf{N} = \mathbf{i}, \quad \mathbf{F} \cdot \mathbf{N} = 2x, \quad \iint_{S_4} 2a\, dy\, dz = \int_0^a \int_0^a 2a\, dy\, dz = 2a^3$$

$$y = 0, \quad \mathbf{N} = -\mathbf{j}, \quad \mathbf{F} \cdot \mathbf{N} = 2y, \quad \iint_{S_5} 0\, dA = 0$$

$$y = a, \quad \mathbf{N} = \mathbf{j}, \quad \mathbf{F} \cdot \mathbf{N} = -2y, \quad \iint_{S_6} -2a\, dA = \int_0^a \int_0^a -2a\, dz\, dx = -2a^3$$

Therefore, $\iint_S \mathbf{F} \cdot \mathbf{N}\, dS = a^4 + 2a^3 - 2a^3 = a^4$.

Divergence Theorem: Since div $\mathbf{F} = 2z$, the Divergence Theorem yields

$$\iiint_Q \text{div } \mathbf{F}\, dV = \int_0^a \int_0^a \int_0^a 2z\, dz\, dy\, dx = \int_0^a \int_0^a a^2\, dy\, dx = a^4.$$

3. F$(x, y, z) = (2x - y)\mathbf{i} - (2y - z)\mathbf{j} + z\mathbf{k}$

Surface Integral: There are four surfaces to this solid.

As shown in the figure, there are four surfaces to the solid bounded by the coordinate planes and $2x + 4y + 2z = 12$.

$z = 0, \mathbf{N} = -\mathbf{k}, \mathbf{F} \cdot \mathbf{N} = -z$

$$\iint_{S_1} 0\, dS = 0$$

$y = 0, \mathbf{N} = -\mathbf{j}, \mathbf{F} \cdot \mathbf{N} = 2y - z, dS = dA = dx\, dz$

$$\iint_{S_2} -z\, dS = \int_0^6 \int_0^{6-z} -z\, dx\, dz = \int_0^6 (z^2 - 6z)\, dx = -36$$

$x = 0, \mathbf{N} = -\mathbf{i}, \mathbf{F} \cdot \mathbf{N} = y - 2x, dS = dA = dz\, dy$

$$\iint_{S_3} y\, dS = \int_0^3 \int_0^{6-2y} y\, dz\, dy = \int_0^3 (6y - 2y^2)\, dy = 9$$

—CONTINUED—

3. —CONTINUED—

$$x + 2y + z = 6, \mathbf{N} = \frac{\mathbf{i} + 2\mathbf{j} + \mathbf{k}}{\sqrt{6}}, \mathbf{F} \cdot \mathbf{N} = \frac{2x - 5y + 3z}{\sqrt{6}}, dS = \sqrt{6}\, dA$$

$$\iint_{S_4} (2x - 5y + 3z)\, dz\, dy = \int_0^3 \int_0^{6-2y} (18 - x - 11y)\, dx\, dy = \int_0^3 (90 - 90y + 20y^2)\, dy = 45$$

Therefore, $\displaystyle\iint_S \mathbf{F} \cdot \mathbf{N}\, dS = 0 - 36 + 9 + 45 = 18.$

Divergence Theorem: Since div $\mathbf{F} = 1$, we have

$$\iiint_Q dV = (\text{Volume of solid}) = \frac{1}{3}(\text{Area of base}) \times (\text{Height}) = \frac{1}{3}(9)(6) = 18.$$

5. Since div $\mathbf{F} = 2x + 2y + 2z$, we have

$$\iiint_Q \text{div } \mathbf{F}\, dV = \int_0^a \int_0^a \int_0^a (2x + 2y + 2z)\, dz\, dy\, dx$$

$$= \int_0^a \int_0^a (2ax + 2ay + a^2)\, dy\, dx = \int_0^a (2a^2x + 2a^3)\, dx = \left[a^2x^2 + 2a^3x \right]_0^a = 3a^4.$$

7. Since div $\mathbf{F} = 2x - 2x + 2xyz = 2xyz$

$$\iiint_Q \text{div } \mathbf{F}\, dV = \iiint_Q 2xyz\, dV = \int_0^a \int_0^{2\pi} \int_0^{\pi/2} 2(\rho \sin\phi \cos\theta)(\rho \sin\phi \sin\theta)(\rho \cos\phi)\rho^2 \sin\phi\, d\phi\, d\theta\, d\rho$$

$$= \int_0^a \int_0^{2\pi} \int_0^{\pi/2} 2\rho^5 (\sin\theta \cos\theta)(\sin^3\phi \cos\phi)\, d\phi\, d\theta\, d\rho$$

$$= \int_0^a \int_0^{2\pi} \frac{1}{2}\rho^5 \sin\theta \cos\theta\, d\theta\, d\rho = \int_0^a \left[\left(\frac{\rho^5}{2} \right) \frac{\sin^2\theta}{2} \right]_0^{2\pi} d\rho = 0.$$

9. $\mathbf{F}(x, y, z) = x\mathbf{i} + y\mathbf{j} + z\mathbf{k}$

$S:\ x^2 + y^2 + z^2 = 4$

Since div $\mathbf{F}(x, y, z) = 1 + 1 + 1 = 3$, it follows that

$$\iiint_Q \text{div } \mathbf{F}\, dV = 3 \iiint_Q dV = 3(\text{volume of sphere of radius 2}) = 3\left[\frac{4\pi 2^3}{3} \right] = 32\pi.$$

11. Since div $\mathbf{F} = 1 + 2y - 1 = 2y$, we have

$$\iiint_Q 2y\, dV = \int_0^4 \int_{-3}^3 \int_{-\sqrt{9-y^2}}^{\sqrt{9-y^2}} 2y\, dx\, dy\, dz = \int_0^4 \int_{-3}^3 4y\sqrt{9 - y^2}\, dy\, dz = \int_0^4 \left[-\frac{4}{3}(9 - y^2)^{3/2} \right]_{-3}^3 dz = 0.$$

13. Since div $\mathbf{F} = 3x^2 + x^2 + 0 = 4x^2$, we have

$$\iiint_Q 4x^2\, dV = \int_0^6 \int_0^4 \int_0^{4-y} 4x^2\, dz\, dy\, dx = \int_0^6 \int_0^4 4x^2(4 - y)\, dy\, dx = \int_0^6 32x^2\, dx = 2304.$$

15. $\mathbf{F}(x, y, z) = xy\mathbf{i} + 4y\mathbf{j} + xz\mathbf{k}$

$\text{div } \mathbf{F} = y + 4 + x$

$$\iint_S \mathbf{F} \cdot \mathbf{N} \, dS = \iiint_Q \text{div } \mathbf{F} \, dV = \iiint_Q (y + x + 4) \, dV$$

$$= \int_0^2 \int_0^\pi \int_0^{2\pi} (\rho \sin \phi \sin \theta + \rho \sin \phi \cos \theta + 4)\rho^2 \sin \phi \, d\theta \, d\phi \, d\rho$$

$$= \int_0^2 \int_0^\pi \int_0^{2\pi} [\rho^3 \sin^2 \phi \sin \theta + \rho^3 \sin^2 \phi \cos \theta + 4\rho^2 \sin \phi] \, d\theta \, d\phi \, d\rho$$

$$= \int_0^2 \int_0^\pi \left[-\rho^3 \sin^2 \phi \cos \theta + \rho^3 \sin^2 \phi \sin \theta + 4\rho^2 \sin \phi \cdot \theta \right]_0^{2\pi} d\phi \, d\rho$$

$$= \int_0^2 \int_0^\pi 8\pi\rho^2 \sin \phi \, d\phi \, d\rho$$

$$= \int_0^2 \left[-8\pi\rho^2 \cos \phi \right]_0^\pi d\rho$$

$$= \int_0^2 16\pi\rho^2 \, d\rho = \left[\frac{16\pi\rho^3}{3} \right]_0^2 = \frac{128\pi}{3}.$$

17. Using the triple integral to find volume, we need $\mathbf{F}$ so that

$$\text{div } \mathbf{F} = \frac{\partial M}{\partial x} + \frac{\partial N}{\partial y} + \frac{\partial P}{\partial z} = 1.$$

Hence, we could have $\mathbf{F} = x\mathbf{i}$, $\mathbf{F} = y\mathbf{j}$, or $\mathbf{F} = z\mathbf{k}$.

For $dA = dy \, dz$ consider $\mathbf{F} = x\mathbf{i}$, $x = f(y, z)$, then $\mathbf{N} = \dfrac{\mathbf{i} + f_y\mathbf{j} + f_z\mathbf{k}}{\sqrt{1 + f_y^2 + f_z^2}}$ and $dS = \sqrt{1 + f_y^2 + f_z^2} \, dy \, dz$.

For $dA = dz \, dx$ consider $\mathbf{F} = y\mathbf{j}$, $y = f(x, z)$, then $\mathbf{N} = \dfrac{f_x\mathbf{i} + \mathbf{j} + f_z\mathbf{k}}{\sqrt{1 + f_x^2 + f_z^2}}$ and $dS = \sqrt{1 + f_x^2 + f_z^2} \, dz \, dx$.

For $dA = dx \, dy$ consider $\mathbf{F} = z\mathbf{k}$, $z = f(x, y)$, then $\mathbf{N} = \dfrac{f_x\mathbf{i} + f_y\mathbf{j} + \mathbf{k}}{\sqrt{1 + f_x^2 + f_y^2}}$ and $dS = \sqrt{1 + f_x^2 + f_y^2} \, dx \, dy$.

Correspondingly, we then have $V = \iint_S \mathbf{F} \cdot \mathbf{N} \, dS = \iint_S x \, dy \, dz = \iint_S y \, dz \, dx = \iint_S z \, dx \, dy$.

19. $\mathbf{F}(x, y, z) = (4xy + z^2)\mathbf{i} + (2x^2 + 6yz)\mathbf{j} + 2xz\mathbf{k}$

S: The closed surface of the solid bounded by the graphs of $x = 4$, $z = 9 - y^2$, and the coordinate planes.

Using the Divergence Theorem, we have

$$\iint_S \text{curl } \mathbf{F} \cdot \mathbf{N} \, dS = \iiint_Q \text{div(curl } \mathbf{F}) \, dV.$$

$$\text{curl } \mathbf{F}(x, y, z) = \begin{vmatrix} \mathbf{i} & \mathbf{j} & \mathbf{k} \\ \dfrac{\partial}{\partial x} & \dfrac{\partial}{\partial y} & \dfrac{\partial}{\partial z} \\ 4xy + z^2 & 2x^2 + 6yz & 2xz \end{vmatrix} = -6y\mathbf{i} - (2z - 2z)\mathbf{j} + (4x - 4x)\mathbf{k} = -6y\mathbf{i}.$$

Therefore, $\text{div(curl } \mathbf{F}(x, y, z)) = 0$ and

$$\iint_S \text{curl } \mathbf{F} \cdot \mathbf{N} \, dS = \iiint_Q \text{div(curl } \mathbf{F}) \, dV = 0.$$

21. Using the Divergence Theorem, we have $\displaystyle\iint_S \text{curl } \mathbf{F} \cdot \mathbf{N} \, dS = \iiint_Q \text{div(curl } \mathbf{F}) \, dV$. Let

$$\mathbf{F}(x, y, z) = M\mathbf{i} + N\mathbf{j} + P\mathbf{k}$$

$$\text{curl } \mathbf{F} = \left(\frac{\partial P}{\partial y} - \frac{\partial N}{\partial z}\right)\mathbf{i} - \left(\frac{\partial P}{\partial x} - \frac{\partial M}{\partial z}\right)\mathbf{j} + \left(\frac{\partial N}{\partial x} - \frac{\partial M}{\partial y}\right)\mathbf{k}$$

$$\text{div(curl } \mathbf{F}) = \frac{\partial^2 P}{\partial x \partial y} - \frac{\partial^2 N}{\partial x \partial z} - \frac{\partial^2 P}{\partial y \partial x} + \frac{\partial^2 M}{\partial y \partial z} + \frac{\partial^2 N}{\partial z \partial x} - \frac{\partial^2 M}{\partial z \partial y} = 0.$$

Therefore, $\displaystyle\iint_S \text{curl } \mathbf{F} \cdot \mathbf{N} \, dS = \iiint_Q 0 \, dV = 0.$

23. If $\mathbf{F}(x, y, z) = x\mathbf{i} + y\mathbf{j} + z\mathbf{k}$, then div $\mathbf{F} = 3$.

$$\iint_S \mathbf{F} \cdot \mathbf{N} \, dS = \iiint_Q \text{div } \mathbf{F} \, dV = \iiint_Q 3 \, dV = 3V.$$

25. $\displaystyle\iint_S f D_{\mathbf{N}} g \, dS = \iint_S f \nabla g \cdot \mathbf{N} \, dS$

$$= \iiint_Q \text{div}(f \nabla g) \, dV = \iiint_Q (f \text{ div } \nabla g + \nabla f \cdot \nabla g) \, dV = \iiint_Q (f \nabla^2 g + \nabla f \cdot \nabla g) \, dV$$

Section 14.8   Stokes's Theorem

1. $\mathbf{F}(x, y, z) = (2y - z)\mathbf{i} + xyz\mathbf{j} + e^z\mathbf{k}$

$$\text{curl } \mathbf{F} = \begin{vmatrix} \mathbf{i} & \mathbf{j} & \mathbf{k} \\ \dfrac{\partial}{\partial x} & \dfrac{\partial}{\partial y} & \dfrac{\partial}{\partial z} \\ 2y - z & xyz & e^z \end{vmatrix} = -xy\mathbf{i} - \mathbf{j} + (yz - 2)\mathbf{k}$$

3. $\mathbf{F}(x, y, z) = 2z\mathbf{i} - 4x^2\mathbf{j} + \arctan x\mathbf{k}$

$$\text{curl } \mathbf{F} = \begin{vmatrix} \mathbf{i} & \mathbf{j} & \mathbf{k} \\ \dfrac{\partial}{\partial x} & \dfrac{\partial}{\partial y} & \dfrac{\partial}{\partial z} \\ 2z & -4x^2 & \arctan x \end{vmatrix}$$

$$= \left(2 - \frac{1}{1 + x^2}\right)\mathbf{j} - 8x\mathbf{k}$$

5. $\mathbf{F}(x, y, z) = e^{x^2 + y^2}\mathbf{i} + e^{y^2 + z^2}\mathbf{j} + xyz\mathbf{k}$

$$\text{curl } \mathbf{F} = \begin{vmatrix} \mathbf{i} & \mathbf{j} & \mathbf{k} \\ \dfrac{\partial}{\partial x} & \dfrac{\partial}{\partial y} & \dfrac{\partial}{\partial z} \\ e^{x^2 + y^2} & e^{y^2 + z^2} & xyz \end{vmatrix}$$

$$= (xz - 2ze^{y^2 + z^2})\mathbf{i} - yz\mathbf{j} - 2ye^{x^2 + y^2}\mathbf{k}$$

$$= z(x - 2e^{y^2 + z^2})\mathbf{i} - yz\mathbf{j} - 2ye^{x^2 + y^2}\mathbf{k}$$

7. In this case, $M = -y + z$, $N = x - z$, $P = x - y$ and C is the circle $x^2 + y^2 = 1$, $z = 0$, $dz = 0$.

Line Integral: $\displaystyle\int_C \mathbf{F} \cdot d\mathbf{r} = \int_C -y \, dx + x \, dy$

Letting $x = \cos t$, $y = \sin t$, we have $dx = -\sin t \, dt$, $dy = \cos t \, dt$ and

$$\int_C -y \, dx + x \, dy = \int_0^{2\pi} (\sin^2 t + \cos^2 t) \, dt = 2\pi.$$

—CONTINUED—

7. —CONTINUED—

Double Integral: Consider $F(x, y, z) = x^2 + y^2 + z^2 - 1$. Then

$$N = \frac{\nabla F}{\|\nabla F\|} = \frac{2x\mathbf{i} + 2y\mathbf{j} + 2z\mathbf{k}}{2\sqrt{x^2 + y^2 + z^2}} = x\mathbf{i} + y\mathbf{j} + z\mathbf{k}.$$

Since

$$z^2 = 1 - x^2 - y^2, \quad z_x = \frac{-2x}{2z} = \frac{-x}{z}, \text{ and } z_y = \frac{-y}{z}, \quad dS = \sqrt{1 + \frac{x^2}{z^2} + \frac{y^2}{z^2}}\, dA = \frac{1}{z}\, dA.$$

Now, since **curl F** $= 2\mathbf{k}$, we have

$$\int_S \int (\text{curl } \mathbf{F}) \cdot \mathbf{N}\, dS = \int_R \int 2z\left(\frac{1}{z}\right) dA = \int_R \int 2\, dA = 2(\text{Area of circle of radius } 1) = 2\pi.$$

9. $\mathbf{F}(x, y, z) = xyz\mathbf{i} + y\mathbf{j} + z\mathbf{k}$

S: $3x + 4y + 2z = 12$ first octant

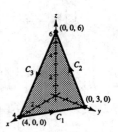

As a *line integral*, integrate along the three paths shown in the figure and obtain

$$\int_{C_1} \mathbf{F} \cdot \mathbf{T}\, ds = \int_C xyz\, dx + y\, dy + z\, dz$$

$$= \int_{C_1} 0\, dx + y\, dy + 0\, dz + \int_{C_2} 0\, dx + y\, dy + z\, dz + \int_{C_3} 0\, dx + 0\, dy + z\, dz$$

$$= \int_0^3 y\, dy + \int_3^0 y\, dy + \int_0^6 z\, dz + \int_6^0 z\, dz = 0.$$

As a *double integral*, begin by finding **curl F**.

$$\text{curl } \mathbf{F}(x, y, z) = \begin{vmatrix} \mathbf{i} & \mathbf{j} & \mathbf{k} \\ \dfrac{\partial}{\partial x} & \dfrac{\partial}{\partial y} & \dfrac{\partial}{\partial z} \\ xyz & y & z \end{vmatrix} = xy\mathbf{j} - xz\mathbf{k}.$$

The upward normal is $\mathbf{N} = 3\mathbf{i} + 4\mathbf{j} + 2\mathbf{k}$.

$$\int_S \int (\text{curl } \mathbf{F}) \cdot \mathbf{N}\, dS = \int_R \int (xy\mathbf{j} - xz\mathbf{k}) \cdot (3\mathbf{i} + 4\mathbf{j} + 2\mathbf{k})\, dA$$

$$= \int_R \int (4xy - 2xz)\, dA$$

$$= \int_0^4 \int_0^{3(4-x)/4} \left[4xy - 2x\left(6 - 2y - \frac{3x}{2}\right)\right] dy\, dx$$

$$= \int_0^4 \int_0^{3(4-x)/4} (8xy + 3x^2 - 12x)\, dy\, dx$$

$$= \int_0^4 \left(36x - 18x^2 + \frac{9x^3}{4} + 9x^2 - \frac{9x^3}{4} - 36x + 9x^2\right) dx$$

$$= \int_0^4 (0)\, dx = 0.$$

11. $\mathbf{F}(x, y, z) = 2y\mathbf{i} + 3z\mathbf{j} - x\mathbf{k}$

C: triangle with vertices $(0, 0, 0)$, $(0, 2, 0)$, and $(1, 1, 1)$

$$\text{curl } \mathbf{F} = \begin{vmatrix} \mathbf{i} & \mathbf{j} & \mathbf{k} \\ \dfrac{\partial}{\partial x} & \dfrac{\partial}{\partial y} & \dfrac{\partial}{\partial z} \\ 2y & 3z & -x \end{vmatrix} = (0 - 3)\mathbf{i} - (-1 - 0)\mathbf{j} + (0 - 2)\mathbf{k} = -3\mathbf{i} + \mathbf{j} - 2\mathbf{k}$$

Using the coordinates of the vertices of the triangle we obtain the vectors $\mathbf{u}$ and $\mathbf{v}$ forming two of its edges. They are $\mathbf{u} = \mathbf{i} + \mathbf{j} + \mathbf{k}$ and $\mathbf{v} = 0\mathbf{i} + 2\mathbf{j} + 0\mathbf{k} = 2\mathbf{j}$. Therefore, a vector normal to the surface is given by

$$\mathbf{u} \times \mathbf{v} = \begin{vmatrix} \mathbf{i} & \mathbf{j} & \mathbf{k} \\ 1 & 1 & 1 \\ 0 & 2 & 0 \end{vmatrix} = -2\mathbf{i} + 2\mathbf{k},$$

and a unit vector normal to the surface is

$$\mathbf{N} = \frac{\mathbf{u} \times \mathbf{v}}{\|\mathbf{u} \times \mathbf{v}\|} = \frac{-2\mathbf{i} + 2\mathbf{k}}{2\sqrt{2}} = \frac{-\mathbf{i} + \mathbf{k}}{\sqrt{2}}.$$

Thus, the surface (plane) is given by $f(x, y, z) = -x + z$, and we have $dS = \sqrt{1 + 1}\, dA = \sqrt{2}\, dA$. We conclude that

$$\int_C \mathbf{F} \cdot d\mathbf{r} = \iint_S (\text{curl } \mathbf{F}) \cdot \mathbf{N}\, dS$$

$$= \iint_R \frac{(3 - 2)}{\sqrt{2}} \sqrt{2}\, dA$$

$$= \iint_R dA = \text{area of triangle}$$

$$= \left(\frac{1}{2}\right)(2)(1) = 1.$$

13. $\mathbf{F}(x, y, z) = z^2\mathbf{i} + x^2\mathbf{j} + y^2\mathbf{k}$, $S: z = 4 - x^2 - y^2$, $0 \le z$

$$\text{curl } \mathbf{F} = \begin{vmatrix} \mathbf{i} & \mathbf{j} & \mathbf{k} \\ \dfrac{\partial}{\partial x} & \dfrac{\partial}{\partial y} & \dfrac{\partial}{\partial z} \\ z^2 & x^2 & y^2 \end{vmatrix} = 2y\mathbf{i} + 2z\mathbf{j} + 2x\mathbf{k}$$

$G(x, y, z) = x^2 + y^2 + z - 4$

$\nabla G(x, y, z) = 2x\mathbf{i} + 2y\mathbf{j} + \mathbf{k}$

$$\iint_S (\text{curl } \mathbf{F}) \cdot \mathbf{N}\, dS = \iint_R (4xy + 4yz + 2x)\, dA$$

$$= \int_{-2}^{2} \int_{-\sqrt{4-x^2}}^{\sqrt{4-x^2}} [4xy + 4y(4 - x^2 - y^2) + 2x]\, dy\, dx$$

$$= \int_{-2}^{2} \int_{-\sqrt{4-x^2}}^{\sqrt{4-x^2}} [4xy + 16y - 4x^2y - 4y^3 + 2x]\, dy\, dx$$

$$= \int_{-2}^{2} 4x\sqrt{4 - x^2}\, dx = 0$$

15. $\mathbf{F}(x, y, z) = z^2\mathbf{i} + y\mathbf{j} + xz\mathbf{k}$, $S: z = \sqrt{4 - x^2 - y^2}$

$$\text{curl } \mathbf{F} = \begin{vmatrix} \mathbf{i} & \mathbf{j} & \mathbf{k} \\ \dfrac{\partial}{\partial x} & \dfrac{\partial}{\partial y} & \dfrac{\partial}{\partial z} \\ z^2 & y & xz \end{vmatrix} = z\mathbf{j}$$

$$G(x, y, z) = z - \sqrt{4 - x^2 - y^2}$$

$$\nabla G(x, y, z) = \frac{x}{\sqrt{4 - x^2 - y^2}}\mathbf{i} + \frac{y}{\sqrt{4 - x^2 - y^2}}\mathbf{j} + \mathbf{k}$$

$$\iint_S (\text{curl } \mathbf{F}) \cdot \mathbf{F} \, dS = \iint_R \frac{yz}{\sqrt{4 - x^2 - y^2}} \, dA = \iint_R \frac{y\sqrt{4 - x^2 - y^2}}{\sqrt{4 - x^2 - y^2}} \, dA = \int_{-2}^{2} \int_{-\sqrt{4-x^2}}^{\sqrt{4-x^2}} y \, dy \, dx = 0$$

17. $\mathbf{F}(x, y, z) = -\ln\sqrt{x^2 + y^2}\,\mathbf{i} + \arctan\dfrac{x}{y}\mathbf{j} + \mathbf{k}$

S: first octant portion of the plane $z = 9 - 2x - 3y$ over one petal of the rose curve $r = 2\sin 2\theta$

$$\text{curl } \mathbf{F} = \begin{vmatrix} \mathbf{i} & \mathbf{j} & \mathbf{k} \\ \dfrac{\partial}{\partial x} & \dfrac{\partial}{\partial y} & \dfrac{\partial}{\partial z} \\ -\ln\sqrt{x^2 + y^2} & \arctan\dfrac{x}{y} & 1 \end{vmatrix} = \left[\frac{1/y}{1 + (x^2/y^2)} + \frac{y}{x^2 + y^2}\right]\mathbf{k} = \left[\frac{2y}{x^2 + y^2}\right]\mathbf{k}.$$

Since S is the first octant portion of the plane $z = 9 - 2x - 3y$ over one petal of $r = 2\sin 2\theta$, we have
$\mathbf{N} = (2\mathbf{i} + 3\mathbf{j} + \mathbf{k})/\sqrt{14}$ and $dS = \sqrt{1 + (-2)^2 + (-3)^2}\,dA = \sqrt{14}\,dA$. Therefore,

$$\iint_S \text{curl } \mathbf{F} \cdot \mathbf{N}\, dS = \iint_R \frac{2y}{x^2 + y^2} \frac{1}{\sqrt{14}}\sqrt{14}\, dA$$

$$= \iint_R \frac{2y}{x^2 + y^2}\, dA$$

$$= \int_0^{\pi/2} \int_0^{2\sin 2\theta} \frac{2r\sin\theta}{r^2} r\, dr\, d\theta \quad \text{(polar coordinates)}$$

$$= \int_0^{\pi/2} \int_0^{4\sin\theta\cos\theta} 2\sin\theta\, dr\, d\theta$$

$$= \int_0^{\pi/2} 8\sin^2\theta\cos\theta\, d\theta = \left[\frac{8\sin^3\theta}{3}\right]_0^{\pi/2} = \frac{8}{3}.$$

19. From Exercise 10, we have $\mathbf{N} = \dfrac{2x\mathbf{i} - \mathbf{k}}{\sqrt{1 + 4x^2}}$ and $dS = \sqrt{1 + 4x^2}\, dA$. Since $\text{curl } \mathbf{F} = xy\mathbf{j} - xz\mathbf{k}$, we have

$$\iint_S (\text{curl } \mathbf{F}) \cdot \mathbf{N}\, dS = \iint_R xz\, dA = \int_0^a \int_0^a x^3\, dy\, dx = \int_0^a ax^3\, dx = \left[\frac{ax^4}{4}\right]_0^a = \frac{a^5}{4}.$$

21. $\mathbf{F}(x, y, z) = \mathbf{i} + \mathbf{j} - 2\mathbf{k}$

$$\text{curl } \mathbf{F} = \begin{vmatrix} \mathbf{i} & \mathbf{j} & \mathbf{k} \\ \dfrac{\partial}{\partial x} & \dfrac{\partial}{\partial y} & \dfrac{\partial}{\partial z} \\ 1 & 1 & -2 \end{vmatrix} = \mathbf{0}$$

Letting $\mathbf{N} = \mathbf{k}$, we have $\displaystyle\iint_S (\text{curl } \mathbf{F}) \cdot \mathbf{N}\, dS = 0.$

23. (a) $\int_C f\nabla g \cdot d\mathbf{r} = \int\int_S \mathbf{curl}[f\nabla g] \cdot \mathbf{N}\, dS$ (Stoke's Theorem)

$$f\nabla g = f\frac{\partial g}{\partial x}\mathbf{i} + f\frac{\partial g}{\partial y}\mathbf{j} + f\frac{\partial g}{\partial z}\mathbf{k}$$

$$\mathbf{curl}(f\nabla g) = \begin{vmatrix} \mathbf{i} & \mathbf{j} & \mathbf{k} \\ \frac{\partial}{\partial x} & \frac{\partial}{\partial y} & \frac{\partial}{\partial z} \\ f(\partial g/\partial x) & f(\partial g/\partial y) & f(\partial g/\partial z) \end{vmatrix}$$

$$= \left[\left[f\left(\frac{\partial^2 g}{\partial y\partial z}\right) + \left(\frac{\partial f}{\partial y}\right)\left(\frac{\partial g}{\partial z}\right)\right] - \left[f\left(\frac{\partial^2 g}{\partial z\partial y}\right) + \left(\frac{\partial f}{\partial z}\right)\left(\frac{\partial g}{\partial y}\right)\right]\right]\mathbf{i}$$

$$- \left[\left[f\left(\frac{\partial^2 g}{\partial x\partial z}\right) + \left(\frac{\partial f}{\partial x}\right)\left(\frac{\partial g}{\partial z}\right)\right] - \left[f\left(\frac{\partial^2 g}{\partial z\partial x}\right) + \left(\frac{\partial f}{\partial z}\right)\left(\frac{\partial g}{\partial x}\right)\right]\right]\mathbf{j}$$

$$+ \left[\left[f\left(\frac{\partial^2 g}{\partial x\partial y}\right) + \left(\frac{\partial f}{\partial x}\right)\left(\frac{\partial g}{\partial y}\right)\right] - \left[f\left(\frac{\partial^2 g}{\partial y\partial x}\right) + \left(\frac{\partial f}{\partial y}\right)\left(\frac{\partial g}{\partial x}\right)\right]\right]\mathbf{k}$$

$$= \left[\left(\frac{\partial f}{\partial y}\right)\left(\frac{\partial g}{\partial z}\right) - \left(\frac{\partial f}{\partial z}\right)\left(\frac{\partial g}{\partial y}\right)\right]\mathbf{i} - \left[\left(\frac{\partial f}{\partial x}\right)\left(\frac{\partial g}{\partial z}\right) - \left(\frac{\partial f}{\partial z}\right)\left(\frac{\partial g}{\partial x}\right)\right]\mathbf{j} + \left[\left(\frac{\partial f}{\partial x}\right)\left(\frac{\partial g}{\partial y}\right) - \left(\frac{\partial f}{\partial y}\right)\left(\frac{\partial g}{\partial x}\right)\right]\mathbf{k}$$

$$= \begin{vmatrix} \mathbf{i} & \mathbf{j} & \mathbf{k} \\ \frac{\partial f}{\partial x} & \frac{\partial f}{\partial y} & \frac{\partial f}{\partial z} \\ \frac{\partial g}{\partial x} & \frac{\partial g}{\partial y} & \frac{\partial g}{\partial z} \end{vmatrix} = \nabla f \times \nabla g$$

Therefore, $\int_C f\nabla g \cdot d\mathbf{r} = \int\int_S \mathbf{curl}[f\nabla g] \cdot \mathbf{N}\, dS = \int\int_S [\nabla f \times \nabla g] \cdot \mathbf{N}\, dS.$

(b) $\int_C (f\nabla f) \cdot d\mathbf{r} = \int\int_S (\nabla f \times \nabla f) \cdot \mathbf{N}\, dS$ (using part a.)

$$= 0 \text{ since } \nabla f \times \nabla f = 0.$$

(c) $\int_C (f\nabla g + g\nabla f) \cdot d\mathbf{r} = \int_C (f\nabla g) \cdot d\mathbf{r} + \int_C (g\nabla f) \cdot d\mathbf{r}$

$$= \int\int_S (\nabla f \times \nabla g) \cdot \mathbf{N}\, dS + \int\int_S (\nabla g \times \nabla f) \cdot \mathbf{N}\, dS \text{ (using part a.)}$$

$$= \int\int_S (\nabla f \times \nabla g) \cdot \mathbf{N}\, dS + \int\int_S -(\nabla f \times \nabla g) \cdot \mathbf{N}\, dS = 0$$

25. Let $\mathbf{C} = a\mathbf{i} + b\mathbf{j} + c\mathbf{k}$, then

$$\frac{1}{2}\int_C (\mathbf{C} \times \mathbf{r}) \cdot d\mathbf{r} = \frac{1}{2}\int\int_S \mathbf{curl}(\mathbf{C} \times \mathbf{r}) \cdot \mathbf{N}\, dS = \frac{1}{2}\int\int_S 2\mathbf{C} \cdot \mathbf{N}\, dS = \int\int_S \mathbf{C} \cdot \mathbf{N}\, dS$$

since

$$\mathbf{C} \times \mathbf{r} = \begin{vmatrix} \mathbf{i} & \mathbf{j} & \mathbf{k} \\ a & b & c \\ x & y & z \end{vmatrix} = (bz - cy)\mathbf{i} - (az - cx)\mathbf{j} + (ay - bx)\mathbf{k}$$

and

$$\mathbf{curl}(\mathbf{C} \times \mathbf{r}) = \begin{vmatrix} \mathbf{i} & \mathbf{j} & \mathbf{k} \\ \frac{\partial}{\partial x} & \frac{\partial}{\partial y} & \frac{\partial}{\partial z} \\ bz - cy & cx - az & ay - bx \end{vmatrix} = 2(a\mathbf{i} + b\mathbf{j} + c\mathbf{k}) = 2\mathbf{C}.$$

Review Exercises for Chapter 14

1. $F(x, y, z) = x\mathbf{i} + \mathbf{j} + 2\mathbf{k}$

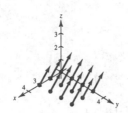

3. $f(x, y, z) = 8x^2 + xy + z^2$

$$F(x, y, z) = (16x + y)\mathbf{i} + x\mathbf{j} + 2z\mathbf{k}$$

5. Since $\partial M/\partial y = -1/y^2 \neq \partial N/\partial x$, $\mathbf{F}$ is not conservative.

7. Since $\partial M/\partial y = 12xy = \partial N/\partial x$, $\mathbf{F}$ is conservative. From $M = \partial U/\partial x = 6xy^2 - 3x^2$ and $N = \partial U/\partial y = 6x^2y + 3y^2 - 7$, partial integration yields $U = 3x^2y^2 - x^3 + h(y)$ and $U = 3x^2y^2 + y^3 - 7y + g(x)$ which suggests $h(y) = y^3 - 7y$, $g(x) = -x^3$, and $U(x, y) = 3x^2y^2 - x^3 + y^3 - 7y + C$.

9. Since $\dfrac{\partial M}{\partial y} = 4x = \dfrac{\partial N}{\partial x}$, $\dfrac{\partial M}{\partial z} = 1 \neq \dfrac{\partial P}{\partial x}$. $\mathbf{F}$ is not conservative.

11. $\mathbf{F}(x, y, z) = \dfrac{yz\mathbf{i} - xz\mathbf{j} - xy\mathbf{k}}{y^2z^2}$

$$\mathbf{curl}\ \mathbf{F}(x, y, z) = \begin{vmatrix} \mathbf{i} & \mathbf{j} & \mathbf{k} \\ \dfrac{\partial}{\partial x} & \dfrac{\partial}{\partial y} & \dfrac{\partial}{\partial z} \\ \dfrac{1}{yz} & \dfrac{-x}{y^2z} & \dfrac{-x}{yz^2} \end{vmatrix} = \left(\dfrac{x}{y^2z^2} - \dfrac{x}{y^2z^2} \right)\mathbf{i} - \left(\dfrac{-1}{yz^2} - \dfrac{-1}{yz^2} \right)\mathbf{j} + \left(\dfrac{-1}{y^2z} - \dfrac{-1}{y^2z} \right)\mathbf{k} = \mathbf{0}$$

Therefore, $\mathbf{F}$ is conservative. Now, if f is a function such that $\mathbf{F}(x, y, z) = \nabla f(x, y, z)$, then

$$f_x(x, y, z) = \dfrac{1}{yz},\ f_y(x, y, z) = -\dfrac{x}{y^2z},\ \text{and}\ f_z(x, y, z) = -\dfrac{x}{yz^2}$$

and by integrating with respect to x, y, and z separately, we obtain

$$f(x, y, z) = \int \dfrac{1}{yz}\, dx = \dfrac{x}{yz} + g(y, z) + K$$

$$f(x, y, z) = \int -\dfrac{x}{y^2z}\, dy = \dfrac{x}{yz} + h(x, z) + K$$

$$f(x, y, z) = \int -\dfrac{x}{yz^2}\, dz = \dfrac{x}{yz} + k(x, y) + K.$$

By comparing these three versions of $f(x, y, z)$, we can conclude that $g(y, z) = h(x, z) = k(x, y) = 0$, and

$$f(x, y, z) = \dfrac{x}{yz} + K.$$

13. Since $\mathbf{F} = x^2\mathbf{i} + y^2\mathbf{j} + z^2\mathbf{k}$:

(a) $\text{div}\ \mathbf{F} = 2x + 2y + 2z$

(b) $\mathbf{curl}\ \mathbf{F} = \left(\dfrac{\partial P}{\partial y} - \dfrac{\partial N}{\partial z} \right)\mathbf{i} - \left(\dfrac{\partial P}{\partial x} - \dfrac{\partial M}{\partial z} \right)\mathbf{j} + \left(\dfrac{\partial N}{\partial x} - \dfrac{\partial M}{\partial y} \right)\mathbf{k} = 0\mathbf{i} - 0\mathbf{j} + 0\mathbf{k} = \mathbf{0}$

15. $\mathbf{F}(x, y, z) = (\cos y + y \cos x)\mathbf{i} + (\sin x - x \sin y)\mathbf{j} + xyz\mathbf{k}.$

(a) div $\mathbf{F}(x, y, z) = \dfrac{\partial}{\partial x}[\cos y + y \cos x] + \dfrac{\partial}{\partial y}[\sin x - x \sin y] + \dfrac{\partial}{\partial z}[xyz]$

$= -y \sin x - x \cos y + xy$

(b) **curl** $\mathbf{F}(x, y, z) = \begin{vmatrix} \mathbf{i} & \mathbf{j} & \mathbf{k} \\ \dfrac{\partial}{\partial x} & \dfrac{\partial}{\partial y} & \dfrac{\partial}{\partial z} \\ \cos y + y \cos x & \sin x - x \sin y & xyz \end{vmatrix}$

$= (xz - 0)\mathbf{i} - (yz - 0)\mathbf{j} + (\cos x - \sin y + \sin y - \cos x)\mathbf{k}$

$= xz\mathbf{i} - yz\mathbf{j}$

17. Since $\mathbf{F} = \arcsin x\mathbf{i} + xy^2\mathbf{j} + yz^2\mathbf{k}$:

(a) div $\mathbf{F} = \dfrac{1}{\sqrt{1 - x^2}} + 2xy + 2yz$

(b) **curl** $\mathbf{F} = z^2\mathbf{i} + y^2\mathbf{k}$

19. Since $\mathbf{F} = \ln(x^2 + y^2)\mathbf{i} + \ln(x^2 + y^2)\mathbf{j} + z\mathbf{k}$:

(a) div $\mathbf{F} = \dfrac{2x}{x^2 + y^2} + \dfrac{2y}{x^2 + y^2} + 1$

$= \dfrac{2x + 2y}{x^2 + y^2} + 1$

(b) **curl** $\mathbf{F} = \dfrac{2x - 2y}{x^2 + y^2}\mathbf{k}$

21. (a) Let $x = t, y = t, -1 \le t \le 2$, then $ds = \sqrt{2}\, dt$.

$\displaystyle\int_C (x^2 + y^2)\, ds = \int_{-1}^{2} 2t^2\sqrt{2}\, dt = \left[2\sqrt{2}\left(\dfrac{t^3}{3}\right)\right]_{-1}^{2} = 6\sqrt{2}$

(b) Let $x = 4 \cos t, y = 4 \sin t, 0 \le t \le 2\pi$, then $ds = 4\, dt$.

$\displaystyle\int_C (x^2 + y^2)\, ds = \int_0^{2\pi} 16(4\, dt) = 128\pi$

23. $x = \cos t + t \sin t, y = \sin t - t \cos t, 0 \le t \le 2\pi, \dfrac{dx}{dt} = t \cos t, \dfrac{dy}{dt} = t \sin t$

$\displaystyle\int_C (x^2 + y^2)\, ds = \int_0^{2\pi} [(\cos t + t \sin t)^2 + (\sin t - t \cos t)^2]\sqrt{t^2 \cos^2 t + t^2 \sin^2 t}\, dt$

$= \displaystyle\int_0^{2\pi} (1 + t^2)t\, dt = \left[\dfrac{t^2}{2} + \dfrac{t^4}{4}\right]_0^{2\pi} = 2\pi^2 + 4\pi^4 = 2\pi^2(1 + 2\pi^2)$

25. $\displaystyle\int_C (2x - y)\, dx + (x + 3y)\, dy$

(a) C is the line segment from $(0, 0)$ to $(2, -3)$.

$C: x = t, dx = dt, y = -\dfrac{3t}{2}, dy = \left(-\dfrac{3}{2}\right) dt, 0 \le t \le 2$

Therefore,

$\displaystyle\int_C (2x - y)\, dx + (x + 3y)\, dy = \int_0^2 \left[\dfrac{7t}{2}\, dt + \left(-\dfrac{7t}{2}\right)\left(-\dfrac{3}{2}\, dt\right)\right]$

$= \displaystyle\int_0^2 \dfrac{35}{4}t\, dt = \left[\dfrac{35}{8}t^2\right]_0^2 = \dfrac{35}{2}.$

—CONTINUED—

25. —CONTINUED—

(b) *C* is one counterclockwise revolution on the circle $x = 3 \cos t$ and $y = 3 \sin t$.

   C: $x = 3 \cos t, dx = -3 \sin t \, dt, y = 3 \sin t, dy = 3 \cos t \, dt, 0 \leq t \leq 2\pi$

   Therefore,

$$\int_C (2x - y) \, dx + (x + 3y) \, dy = \int_0^{2\pi} [(6 \cos t - 3 \sin t)(-3 \sin t) + (3 \cos t + 9 \sin t)(3 \cos t)] \, dt$$

$$= \int_0^{2\pi} (9 \sin t \cos t + 9) \, dt = \left[\frac{9 \sin^2 t}{2} + 9t \right]_0^{2\pi} = 18\pi.$$

27. $\displaystyle\int_C (2x + y) \, ds, \mathbf{r}(t) = a \cos^3 t \, \mathbf{i} + a \sin^3 t \, \mathbf{j}, 0 \leq t \leq \frac{\pi}{2}$

$x'(t) = -3a \cdot \cos^2 t \sin t$

$y'(t) = 3a \cdot \sin^2 t \cos t$

$$\int_C (2x + y) \, ds = \int_0^{\pi/2} (2(a \cdot \cos^3 t) + a \cdot \sin^3 t) \sqrt{x'(t)^2 + y'(t)^2} \, dt = \frac{9a^2}{5}$$

29. $f(x, y) = 5 + \sin(x + y)$

   C: $y = 3x$ from $(0, 0)$ to $(2, 6)$

   A vector-valued function for the path *C* is $\mathbf{r}(t) = t\mathbf{i} + 3t\mathbf{j}, 0 \leq t \leq 2$, and $f(x(t), y(t)) = 5 + \sin(x + y) = 5 + \sin 4t$.

$$ds = \sqrt{[x'(t)]^2 + [y'(t)]^2} \, dt = \sqrt{(1)^2 + (3)^2} = \sqrt{10}$$

   Therefore,

$$\text{area} = \int_C f(x, y) \, ds = \int_0^2 (5 + \sin 4t) \sqrt{10} \, dt = \sqrt{10} \left[5t - \frac{1}{4} \cos 4t \right]_0^2 = \frac{\sqrt{10}}{4}(41 - \cos 8) \approx 32.528.$$

31. $d\mathbf{r} = (2t\mathbf{i} + 3t^2\mathbf{j}) \, dt$

   $\mathbf{F} = t^5\mathbf{i} + t^4\mathbf{j}, 0 \leq t \leq 1$

$$\int_C \mathbf{F} \cdot d\mathbf{r} = \int_0^1 5t^6 \, dt = \frac{5}{7}$$

33. $d\mathbf{r} = [(-2 \sin t)\mathbf{i} + (2 \cos t)\mathbf{j} + \mathbf{k}] \, dt$

   $\mathbf{F} = (2 \cos t)\mathbf{i} + (2 \sin t)\mathbf{j} + t\mathbf{k}, 0 \leq t \leq 2\pi$

$$\int_C \mathbf{F} \cdot d\mathbf{r} = \int_0^{2\pi} t \, dt = 2\pi^2$$

35. $\mathbf{F}(x, y, z) = (y - z)\mathbf{i} + (z - x)\mathbf{j} + (x - y)\mathbf{k}$

   C: curve of the intersection of $z = x^2 + y^2$ and $x + y = 0$ from $(-2, 2, 8)$ to $(2, -2, 8)$

   On the curve of intersection $z = x^2 + (-x)^2 = 2x^2$. Hence, *C* is given by $x = t, y = -t, z = 2t^2, -2 \leq t \leq 2$, and we have $\mathbf{r}(t) = t\mathbf{i} - t\mathbf{j} + 2t^2\mathbf{k}$ and $\mathbf{r}'(t) = \mathbf{i} - \mathbf{j} + 4t\mathbf{k}$. Thus,

$$\mathbf{F}(x, y, z) = (y - z)\mathbf{i} + (z - x)\mathbf{j} + (x - y)\mathbf{k}$$

$$= (-t - 2t^2)\mathbf{i} + (2t^2 - t)\mathbf{j} + 2t\mathbf{k}$$

   and

$$\int_C \mathbf{F} \cdot d\mathbf{r} = \int_a^b \mathbf{F}(x(t), y(t), z(t)) \cdot \mathbf{r}'(t) \, dt$$

$$= \int_{-2}^2 (-2t^2 - t - 2t^2 + t + 8t^2) \, dt$$

$$= \int_{-2}^2 4t^2 \, dt = \frac{64}{3}.$$

37. For $y = x^2$, $\mathbf{r}_1(t) = t\mathbf{i} + t^2\mathbf{j}$, $0 \le t \le 2$

For $y = 2x$, $\mathbf{r}_2(t) = (2 - t)\mathbf{i} + (4 - 2t)\mathbf{j}$, $0 \le t \le 2$

$$\int_C xy\,dx + (x^2 + y^2)\,dy = \int_{C_1} xy\,dx + (x^2 + y^2)\,dy + \int_{C_2} xy\,dx + (x^2 + y^2)\,dy$$

$$= \frac{100}{3} + (-32) = \frac{4}{3}$$

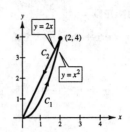

39. $\mathbf{F} = x\mathbf{i} - \sqrt{y}\mathbf{j}$ is conservative.

$$\text{Work} = \left[\frac{1}{2}x^2 - \frac{2}{3}y^{3/2}\right]_{(0,\,0)}^{(4,\,8)} = \frac{1}{2}(16) - \left(\frac{2}{3}\right)8^{3/2} = \frac{8}{3}(3 - 4\sqrt{2})$$

41. $\displaystyle\int_C 2xyz\,dx + x^2z\,dy + x^2y\,dz$

Since,

$$\frac{\partial}{\partial y}[x^2y] = x^2 = \frac{\partial}{\partial z}[x^2z]$$

$$\frac{\partial}{\partial x}[x^2y] = 2xy = \frac{\partial}{\partial z}[2xyz]$$

$$\frac{\partial}{\partial x}[x^2z] = 2xz = \frac{\partial}{\partial y}[xyz],$$

the vector field $\mathbf{F}(x, y, z) = 2xyz\mathbf{i} + x^2z\mathbf{j} + x^2y\mathbf{k}$ is conservative. Therefore,

$$f_x(x, y, z) = 2xyz \implies f(x, y, z) = \int 2xyz\,dx = x^2yz + g(y, z)$$

$$f_y(x, y, z) = x^2z \implies f(x, y, z) = \int x^2z\,dy = x^2yz + h(x, z)$$

$$f_z(x, y, z) = x^2y \implies f(x, y, z) = \int x^2y\,dz = x^2yz + k(x, y).$$

Comparing these three versions of the potential function f, we conclude that $f(x, y, z) = x^2yz + C$, and by the Fundamental Theorem we have

$$\int_C 2xyz\,dx + x^2z\,dy + x^2y\,dz = f(1, 4, 3) - f(0, 0, 0) = 12.$$

43. (a) $\displaystyle\int_C y^2\,dx + 2xy\,dy = \int_0^1 \left[(1 + t)^2(3) + 2(1 + 3t)(1 + t)\right]dt$

$$= \int_0^1 3(t^2 + 2t + 1) + 2(3t^2 + 4t + 1)]\,dt$$

$$= \int_0^1 (9t^2 + 14t + 5)\,dt$$

$$= \left[3t^3 + 7t^2 + 5t\right]_0^1 = 15$$

(b) $\displaystyle\int_C y^2\,dx + 2xy\,dy = \int_1^4 \left[t(1) + 2(t)(\sqrt{t})\frac{1}{2\sqrt{t}}\right]dt$

$$= \int_1^4 (t + t)\,dt = \left[t^2\right]_1^4 = 15$$

—CONTINUED—

43. —CONTINUED—

(c) $\mathbf{F}(x, y) = y^2\mathbf{i} + 2xy\,\mathbf{j} = \nabla f$ where $f(x, y) = xy^2$.

Hence,

$$\int_C \mathbf{F} \cdot d\mathbf{r} = 4(2)^2 - 1(1)^2 = 15$$

45. $\displaystyle\int_C y\,dx + 2x\,dy = \int_0^2\int_0^2 (2 - 1)\,dy\,dx = \int_0^2 2\,dx = 4$
47. $\displaystyle\int_C xy^2\,dx + x^2y\,dy = \int\int_R (2xy - 2xy)\,dA = 0$

49. $\displaystyle\int_C xy\,dx + x^2\,dy$

C: boundary of the region between the graphs of $y = x^2$ and $y = x$

By Green's Theorem and the figure, we have

$$\int_C M(x, y)\,dx + N(x, y)\,dy = \int_C xy\,dx + x^2\,dy$$

$$= \int\int_R \left[\frac{\partial N}{\partial x} - \frac{\partial M}{\partial y}\right] dA$$

$$= \int_0^1\int_{x^2}^x x\,dy\,dx$$

$$= \int_0^1 (x^2 - x^3)\,dx = \frac{1}{12}.$$

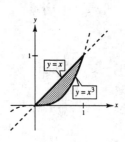

51. $\mathbf{r}(u, v) = \sec u \cos v\,\mathbf{i} + (1 + 2\tan u)\sin v\,\mathbf{j} + 2u\mathbf{k}$

$$0 \le u \le \frac{\pi}{3}, \quad 0 \le v \le 2\pi$$

53. (a)

(b)

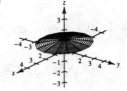

(c)

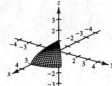

(d)

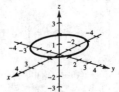

—CONTINUED—

The space curve is a circle:

$$\mathbf{r}\left(u, \frac{\pi}{4}\right) = \frac{3\sqrt{2}}{2}\cos u\mathbf{i} + \frac{3\sqrt{2}}{2}\sin u\mathbf{j} + \frac{\sqrt{2}}{2}\mathbf{k}$$

53. **—CONTINUED—**

(e) $\mathbf{r}_u = -3\cos v \sin u\,\mathbf{i} + 3\cos v \cos u\,\mathbf{j}$

$\mathbf{r}_v = -3\sin v \cos u\,\mathbf{i} - 3\sin v \sin u \sin u\,\mathbf{j} + \cos v\,\mathbf{k}$

$$\mathbf{r}_u \times \mathbf{r}_v = \begin{vmatrix} \mathbf{i} & \mathbf{j} & \mathbf{k} \\ -3\cos v \sin u & 3\cos v \cos u & 0 \\ -3\sin v \cos u & -3\sin v \sin u & \cos v \end{vmatrix}$$

$= (3\cos^2 v \cos u)\mathbf{i} + (3\cos^2 v \sin u)\mathbf{j} + 9\cos v \sin v \sin^2 u + 9\cos v \sin v \cos^2 u)\mathbf{k}$

$= (3\cos^2 v \cos u)\mathbf{i} + (3\cos^2 v \sin u)\mathbf{j} + (9\cos v \sin v)\mathbf{k}$

$\|\mathbf{r}_u \times \mathbf{r}_v\| = \sqrt{9\cos^4 v \cos^2 u + 9\cos^4 v \sin^2 u + 81\cos^2 v \sin \sin^2 v}$

$= \sqrt{9\cos^4 v + 81\cos^2 v \sin^2 v}$

Using a symbolic integration utility,

$$\int_{\pi/4}^{\pi/2}\int_0^{2\pi} \|\mathbf{r}_u \times \mathbf{r}_v\|\,dv\,du \approx 14.44$$

(f) Similarly,

$$\int_0^{\pi/4}\int_0^{\pi/2} \|\mathbf{r}_u \times \mathbf{r}_v\|\,dv\,du \approx 4.27$$

55. $S: \mathbf{r}(u, v) = u\cos v\,\mathbf{i} + u\sin v\,\mathbf{j} + (u-1)(2-u)\mathbf{k}, \quad 0 \le u \le 2, 0 \le v \le 2\pi$

$\mathbf{r}_u(u, v) = \cos v\,\mathbf{i} + \sin v\,\mathbf{j} + (3-2u)\mathbf{k}$

$\mathbf{r}_v(u, v) = -u\sin v\,\mathbf{i} + u\cos v\,\mathbf{j}$

$$\mathbf{r}_u \times \mathbf{r}_u = \begin{vmatrix} \mathbf{i} & \mathbf{j} & \mathbf{k} \\ \cos v & \sin v & 3-2u \\ -u\sin v & u\cos v & 0 \end{vmatrix} = (2v-3)u\cos v\,\mathbf{i} + (2u-3)u\sin v\,\mathbf{j} + u\mathbf{k}$$

$\|\mathbf{r}_u \times \mathbf{r}_v\| = u\sqrt{(2u-3)^2 + 1}$

$$\int_S\!\!\int (x+y)\,dS = \int_0^{2\pi}\int_0^2 (u\cos v + u\sin v)\,u\sqrt{(2u-3)^2 + 1}\,du\,dv$$

$$= \int_0^2\int_0^{2\pi} (\cos v + \sin v)u^2\sqrt{(2u-3)^2 + 1}\,dv\,du = 0$$

57. $\mathbf{F}(x, y, z) = x^2\mathbf{i} + xy\mathbf{j} + z\mathbf{k}$

Q: solid region bounded by the coordinates planes and the plane $2x + 3y + 4z = 12$

Surface Integral: There are four surfaces for this solid.

$z = 0 \quad \mathbf{N} = -\mathbf{k}, \quad \mathbf{F}\cdot\mathbf{N} = -z, \quad \int_{S_1}\!\!\int 0\,dS = 0$

$y = 0, \quad \mathbf{N} = -\mathbf{j}, \quad \mathbf{F}\cdot\mathbf{N} = -xy, \quad \int_{S_2}\!\!\int 0\,dS = 0$

$x = 0, \quad \mathbf{N} = -\mathbf{i}, \quad \mathbf{F}\cdot\mathbf{N} = -x^2, \quad \int_{S_3}\!\!\int 0\,dS = 0$

$2x + 3y + 4z = 12, \mathbf{N} = \dfrac{2\mathbf{i} + 3\mathbf{j} + 4\mathbf{k}}{\sqrt{29}}, \, dS = \sqrt{1 + \left(\dfrac{1}{4}\right) + \left(\dfrac{9}{16}\right)}dA = \dfrac{\sqrt{29}}{4}\,dA$

—CONTINUED—

57. —CONTINUED—

$$\iint_{S_4} \mathbf{F} \cdot \mathbf{N} \, dS = \frac{1}{4} \iint_R (2x^2 + 3xy + 4z) \, dA$$

$$= \frac{1}{4} \int_0^6 \int_0^{4-(2x/3)} (2x^2 + 3xy + 12 - 2x - 3y) \, dy \, dx$$

$$= \frac{1}{4} \int_0^6 \left[2x^2 \left(\frac{12 - 2x}{3} \right) + \frac{3x}{2} \left(\frac{12 - 2x}{3} \right)^2 + 12 \left(\frac{12 - 2x}{3} \right) - 2x \left(\frac{12 - 2x}{3} \right) - \frac{3}{2} \left(\frac{12 - 2x}{3} \right)^2 \right] dx$$

$$= \frac{1}{6} \int_0^6 (-x^3 + x^2 + 24x + 36) \, dx = \frac{1}{6} \left[-\frac{x^4}{4} + \frac{x^3}{3} + 12x^2 + 36x \right]_0^6 = 66$$

Divergence Theorem: Since div $\mathbf{F} = 2x + x + 1 = 3x + 1$, Divergence Theorem yields

$$\iiint_Q \text{div } \mathbf{F} \, dV = \int_0^6 \int_0^{(12-2x)/3} \int_0^{(12-2x-3y)/4} (3x + 1) \, dz \, dy \, dx$$

$$= \int_0^6 \int_0^{(12-2x)/3} (3x + 1) \left(\frac{12 - 2x - 3y}{4} \right) dy \, dx$$

$$= \frac{1}{4} \int_0^6 (3x + 1) \left[12y - 2xy - \frac{3}{2}y^2 \right]_0^{(12-2x)/3} dx$$

$$= \frac{1}{4} \int_0^6 (3x + 1) \left[4(12 - 2x) - 2x \left(\frac{12 - 2x}{3} \right) - \frac{3}{2} \left(\frac{12 - 2x}{3} \right)^2 \right] dx$$

$$= \frac{1}{4} \int_0^6 \frac{2}{3} (3x^3 - 35x^2 + 96x + 36) \, dx = \frac{1}{6} \left[\frac{3x^4}{4} - \frac{35x^3}{3} + 48x^2 + 36x \right]_0^6 = 66.$$

59. $\mathbf{F}(x, y, z) = (\cos y + y \cos x)\mathbf{i} + (\sin x - x \sin y)\mathbf{j} + xyz\mathbf{k}$

S: portion of $z = y^2$ over the square in the xy-plane with vertices $(0, 0)$, $(a, 0)$, (a, a), $(0, a)$

Line Integral: Using the line integral we have

C_1: $y = 0$, $dy = 0$

C_2: $x = 0$, $dx = 0$, $z = y^2$, $dz = 2y \, dy$

C_3: $y = a$, $dy = 0$, $z = a^2$, $dz = 0$

C_4: $x = a$, $dx = 0$, $z = y^2$, $dz = 2y \, dy$.

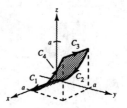

$$\int_C \mathbf{F} \cdot d\mathbf{r} = \int_C (\cos y + y \cos x) \, dx + (\sin x - x \sin y) \, dy + xyz \, dz$$

$$= \int_{C_1} dx + \int_{C_2} 0 + \int_{C_3} (\cos a + a \cos x) \, dx + \int_{C_4} (\sin a - a \sin y) \, dy + ay^3(2y \, dy)$$

$$= \int_0^a dx + \int_a^0 (\cos a + a \cos x) \, dx + \int_0^a (\sin a - a \sin y) \, dy + \int_0^a 2ay^4 \, dy$$

$$= a + \left[x \cos a + a \sin x \right]_a^0 + \left[y \sin a + a \cos y \right]_0^a + \left[2a \frac{y^5}{5} \right]_0^a$$

$$= a - a \cos a - a \sin a - a + a \sin a + a \cos a + \frac{2a^6}{5} = \frac{2a^6}{5}$$

Double Integral: Consider $f(x, y, z) = y^2 - z$, we have

$$\mathbf{N} = \frac{-\nabla f}{\|\nabla f\|} = \frac{-2y\mathbf{j} + \mathbf{k}}{\sqrt{1 + 4y^2}}, \quad dS = \sqrt{1 + 4y^2} \, dA, \text{ and } \mathbf{curl } \mathbf{F} = xz\mathbf{i} - yz\mathbf{j}.$$

Hence, $\displaystyle \iint_S (\mathbf{curl } \mathbf{F}) \cdot \mathbf{N} \, dS = \int_0^a \int_0^a 2y^2 z \, dy \, dx = \int_0^a \int_0^a 2y^4 \, dy \, dx = \int_0^a \frac{2a^5}{5} \, dx = \frac{2a^6}{5}.$

Appendix A.1

1. $0.7 = \dfrac{7}{10}$

Rational

3. $\dfrac{3\pi}{2}$

Irrational
(since π is irrational)

5. $4.3451\overline{451}$

Rational

7. Since $4^3 = 64$, it follows that $\sqrt[3]{64} = 4$ and is therefore rational.

9. $4\frac{5}{8} = \frac{45}{8}$

Rational

11. Let $x = 0.36\overline{36}$.

$$100x = 36.36\overline{36}$$
$$\underline{-x = -0.36\overline{36}}$$
$$99x = 36$$
$$x = \tfrac{36}{99} = \tfrac{4}{11}$$

13. Let $x = 0.297297\ldots$. Since the repeating pattern occurs every three decimal places, multiply both sides of the equation by 1000 and obtain

$$1000x = 297.297297\ldots$$
$$\underline{\quad x = \quad 0.297297\ldots} \quad \text{Subtract}$$
$$999x = 297$$
$$x = \tfrac{297}{999} = \tfrac{11}{37}.$$

15. Given $a < b$:

(a) $a + 2 < b + 2$; True

(b) $5b < 5a$; False

(c) $5 - a > 5 - b$; True

(d) $\dfrac{1}{a} < \dfrac{1}{b}$; False

(e) $(a - b)(b - a) > 0$; False

(f) $a^2 < b^2$; False

17. x is greater than -3 and less than 3.

The interval is bounded.

19. x is less than, or equal to, 5.

The interval is unbounded.

21. $y \geq 4$, $[4, \infty)$

23. $0.03 < r \leq 0.07$, $(0.03, 0.07]$

25. $2x - 1 \geq 0$

$$2x \geq 1$$
$$x \geq \tfrac{1}{2}$$

27. $\quad -4 < \quad 2x - 3 \quad < 4$

$$-4 + 3 < 2x - 3 + 3 < 4 + 3$$
$$-1 < \quad 2x \quad < 7$$
$$-\tfrac{1}{2} < \quad x \quad < \tfrac{7}{2}$$

29. $\dfrac{x}{2} + \dfrac{x}{3} > 5$

$$3x + 2x > 30$$
$$5x > 30$$
$$x > 6$$

31. $|x| < 1 \implies -1 < x < 1$

33. $\left| \dfrac{x - 3}{2} \right| \geq 5$

$$x - 3 \geq 10 \quad \text{or} \quad x - 3 \leq -10$$
$$x \geq 13 \qquad\qquad x \leq -7$$

35. $|x - a| < b$

$$-b < x - a < \quad b$$
$$a - b < \quad x \quad < a + b$$

37. $|2x + 1| < 5$

$$-5 < 2x + 1 < 5$$
$$-6 < \quad 2x \quad < 4$$
$$-3 < \quad x \quad < 2$$

39. $\left|1 - \dfrac{2x}{3}\right| < 1$

$$-1 < 1 - \frac{2x}{3} < 1$$
$$-2 < \quad -\frac{2x}{3} \quad < 0$$
$$3 > \quad x \quad > 0$$

41. $\qquad x^2 \le 3 - 2x$

$$x^2 + 2x - 3 \le 0$$
$$(x + 3)(x - 1) \le 0$$

Test intervals:

$$(-\infty, -3), \ (-3, 1), \ (1, \infty)$$

Solution: $-3 \le x \le 1$

43. $\qquad x^2 + x - 1 \le 5$

$$x^2 + x - 6 \le 0$$
$$(x + 3)(x - 2) \le 0$$

Critical numbers are: $x = -3$ and $x = 2$

Solution: $-3 \le x \le 2$

Interval	$-\infty < x < -3$	$-3 < x < 2$	$2 < x < \infty$
Test value	$x = -4$	$x = 0$	$x = 3$
Sign of $x + 3$	$-$	$+$	$+$
Sign of $x - 2$	$-$	$-$	$+$
Sign of $(x + 3)(x - 2)$	$+$	$-$	$+$

45. $a = -1, \ b = 3$

Directed distance from a to b: 4

Directed distance from b to a: -4

Distance between a and b: 4

47. (a) $a = 126, \ b = 75$

Directed distance from a to b: -51

Directed distance from b to a: 51

Distance between a and b: 51

(b) $a = -126, \ b = -75$

Directed distance from a to b: 51

Directed distance from b to a: -51

Distance between a and b: 51

49. $a = -1, \ b = 3$

Midpoint: $\dfrac{-1 + 3}{2} = 1$

51. (a) $[7, 21]$

Midpoint: 14

(b) $[8.6, 11.4]$

Midpoint: 10

53. $a = -2, b = 2$

Midpoint: 0

Distance between midpoint and each endpoint: 2

$$|x - 0| \le 2$$
$$|x| \le 2$$

55. From the figure we have

$$x < \quad 0 \ \text{or} \quad x > 4$$
$$x - 2 < -2 \ \text{or} \ x - 2 > 4 - 2 \quad \text{Centered at 2}$$
$$x - 2 < -2 \ \text{or} \ x - 2 > 2.$$

Therefore, the magnitude of $x - 2$ must be greater than 2 or $|x - 2| > 2$.

57. (a) All numbers that are at most 10 units from 12

$$|x - 12| \le 10$$

(b) All numbers that are at least 10 units from 12

$$|x - 12| \ge 10$$

59. Since the revenue R must be greater than the cost C for the product to return a profit, it follows that

$$R > C$$
$$115.95x > 95x + 750$$
$$115.95x - 95x > 750$$
$$20.95x > 750$$
$$x > 35.7995 \text{ or } x \geq 36 \text{ units.}$$

61. Since $\left|\dfrac{x - 50}{5}\right| \geq 1.645$, we have

$$-\dfrac{x - 50}{5} \geq 1.645 \quad \text{or} \quad \dfrac{x - 50}{5} \geq 1.645$$

$$-\dfrac{x - 50}{5}(-5) \leq 1.645(-5) \text{ or } \dfrac{x - 50}{5}(5) \geq 1.645(5)$$

$$x - 50 \leq -8.225 \quad \text{or} \quad x - 50 \geq 8.225$$

$$x \leq 41.775 \quad \text{or} \quad x \geq 58.225.$$

Therefore the coin will be declared unfair if $x \leq 41$ or $x \geq 59$.

63. (a) $\pi \approx 3.1415926535$

$\dfrac{355}{113} = 3.141592920$

$\dfrac{355}{113} > \pi$

(b) $\pi \approx 3.1415926535$

$\dfrac{22}{7} \approx 3.142857143$

$\dfrac{22}{7} > \pi$

65. Speed of light: 2.998×10^8 meters per second

Distance traveled in one year = rate × time

$$d = (2.998 \times 10^8) \times (365 \times \ 24 \ \times \ 60 \ \times \ 60 \ )$$
$$\text{days} \times \text{hours} \ \times \text{minutes} \times \text{seconds}$$

$$= (2.998 \times 10^8) \times (3.1536 \times 10^7) \approx 9.45 \times 10^{15}$$

This is best estimated by (b).

67. False; 2 is a nonzero integer and the reciprocal of 2 is $\frac{1}{2}$.

69. True

71. True; if $x < 0$, then
$$|x| = -x = \sqrt{x^2}.$$

73. Case 1: $a > 0, b > 0$, and $ab > 0$.

$$|ab| = ab = |a||b|$$

Case 2: $a < 0, b < 0$, and $ab > 0$.

$$|ab| = ab = (-a)(-b) = |a||b|$$

Case 3: $a > 0, b < 0$, and $ab < 0$.

$$|ab| = -(ab) = a(-b) = |a||b|$$

Case 4: $a < 0, b > 0$, and $ab < 0$.

$$|ab| = -(ab) = (-a)(b) = |a||b|$$

75. $\left|\dfrac{a}{b}\right| = \left|a\left(\dfrac{1}{b}\right)\right|$

$= |a|\left|\dfrac{1}{b}\right| = |a| \cdot \dfrac{1}{|b|} = \dfrac{|a|}{|b|}, \ b \neq 0$

77. $n = 1, \qquad |a| = |a|$

$n = 2, \qquad |a^2| = |a \cdot a| = |a||a| = |a|^2$

$n = 3, \qquad |a^3| = |a^2 \cdot a| = |a^2||a| = |a|^2|a| = |a|^3$

$\vdots$

$$|a^n| = |a^{n-1}a| = |a^{n-1}||a| = |a|^{n-1}|a| = |a|^n$$

79. $|a| \leq k \iff \sqrt{a^2} \leq k \iff a^2 \leq k^2 \iff a^2 - k^2 \leq 0 \iff (a + k)(a - k) \leq 0 \iff -k \leq a \leq k, \ \ k > 0$

81. $\left.\begin{array}{l} |7 - 12| = |-5| = 5 \\ |7| - |12| = 7 - 12 = -5 \end{array}\right\} |7 - 12| > |7| - |12|$

$\left.\begin{array}{l} |12 - 7| = |5| = 5 \\ |12| - |7| = 12 - 7 = 5 \end{array}\right\} |12 - 7| = |12| - |7|$

We know that $|a||b| \geq ab$. Thus, $-2|a||b| \leq -2ab$. Since $a^2 = |a|^2$ and $b^2 = |b|^2$, we have

$$|a|^2 + |b|^2 - 2|a||b| \leq a^2 + b^2 - 2ab$$

$$0 \leq (|a| - |b|)^2 \leq (a - b)^2$$

$$\sqrt{(|a| - |b|)^2} \leq \sqrt{(a - b)^2}$$

$$\bigl||a| - |b|\bigr| \leq |a - b|.$$

Since $|a| - |b| \leq \bigl||a| - |b|\bigr|$, we have $|a| - |b| \leq |a - b|$. Thus, $|a - b| \geq |a| - |b|$.

Appendix A.2

1. (a)

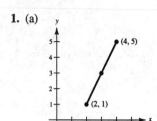

(b) Let $(2, 1) = (x_1, y_1)$ and $(4, 5) = (x_2, y_2)$. Then

$$d = \sqrt{(x_2 - x_1)^2 + (y_2 - y_1)^2}$$
$$= \sqrt{(4 - 2)^2 + (5 - 1)^2} = \sqrt{2^2 + 4^2}$$
$$= \sqrt{20} = 2\sqrt{5}.$$

(c) midpoint $= \left(\dfrac{x_1 + x_2}{2}, \dfrac{y_1 + y_2}{2}\right) = \left(\dfrac{2 + 4}{2}, \dfrac{1 + 5}{2}\right) = (3, 3)$

3. $d = \sqrt{\left(\dfrac{1}{2} + \dfrac{3}{2}\right)^2 + (1 + 5)^2}$

$\quad = \sqrt{4 + 36} = \sqrt{40} = 2\sqrt{10}$

Midpoint: $\left(\dfrac{(-3/2) + (1/2)}{2}, \dfrac{-5 + 1}{2}\right) = \left(-\dfrac{1}{2}, -2\right)$

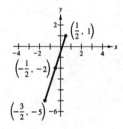

5. $d = \sqrt{(-1 - 1)^2 + \left(1 - \sqrt{3}\right)^2}$

$\quad = \sqrt{4 + 1 - 2\sqrt{3} + 3} = \sqrt{8 - 2\sqrt{3}}$

Midpoint: $\left(\dfrac{-1 + 1}{2}, \dfrac{1 + \sqrt{3}}{2}\right) = \left(0, \dfrac{1 + \sqrt{3}}{2}\right)$

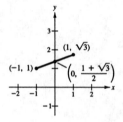

7. Let d_1 = distance between $(4, 0)$ and $(2, 1)$.

$\quad d_1^2 = (2 - 4)^2 + (1 - 0)^2 = (-2)^2 + 1^2 = 5$

Let d_2 = distance between $(2, 1)$ and $(-1, -5)$.

$\quad d_2^2 = (-1 - 2)^2 + (-5 - 1)^2 = (-3)^2 + (-6)^2 = 45$

Let d_3 = distance between $(4, 0)$ and $(-1, -5)$.

$\quad d_3^2 = (-1 - 4)^2 + (-5 - 0)^2 = (-5)^2 + (-5)^2 = 50$

Since $d_1^2 + d_2^2 = 5 + 45 = 50 = d_3^2$, the triangle is a right triangle.

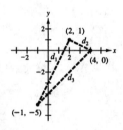

9. $d_1 = d_2 = d_3 = d_4 = \sqrt{5}$

Rhombus

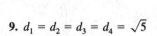

11. $x = -2 \implies$ quadrants II, III

$\quad y > 0 \implies$ quadrants I, II

Therefore, quadrant II

13. $xy > 0 \implies$ quadrants I or III

15.

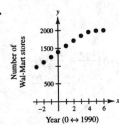

17. $d_1 = \sqrt{4 + 16} = \sqrt{20} = 2\sqrt{5}$

$d_2 = \sqrt{1 + 4} = \sqrt{5}$

$d_3 = \sqrt{9 + 36} = 3\sqrt{5}$

$d_1 + d_2 = d_3$

Collinear

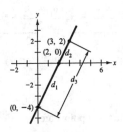

19. Let d_1 = distance between $(-2, 1)$ and $(-1, 0)$. Then

$$d_1 = \sqrt{[-1 - (-2)]^2 + (0 - 1)^2} = \sqrt{1^2 + (-1)^2} = \sqrt{2}.$$

Let d_2 = distance between $(-1, 0)$ and $(2, -2)$. Then

$$d_2 = \sqrt{[2 - (-1)]^2 + (-2 - 0)^2} = \sqrt{3^2 + (-2)^2} = \sqrt{13}.$$

Let d_3 = distance between $(-2, 1)$ and $(2, -2)$. Then

$$d_3 = \sqrt{[2 - (-2)]^2 + (-2 - 1)^2} = \sqrt{4^2 + (-3)^2} = \sqrt{25} = 5.$$

The points $(-2, 1)$, $(-1, 0)$, and $(2, -2)$ lie on a line only if $d_1 + d_2 = d_3$. Since $\sqrt{2} + \sqrt{13} \approx 5.02 \neq 5$, the points are *not* collinear.

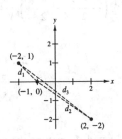

21. $5 = \sqrt{(x - 0)^2 + (-4 - 0)^2}$

$5 = \sqrt{x^2 + 16}$

$25 = x^2 + 16$

$9 = x^2$

$x = \pm 3$

23. $8 = \sqrt{(3 - 0)^2 + (y - 0)^2}$

$8 = \sqrt{9 + y^2}$

$64 = 9 + y^2$

$55 = y^2$

$y = \pm\sqrt{55}$

25. The midpoint of the line segment from (x_1, y_1) to (x_2, y_2) is $\left(\dfrac{x_1 + x_2}{2}, \dfrac{y_1 + y_2}{2}\right)$.

The midpoint between (x_1, y_1) and $\left(\dfrac{x_1 + x_2}{2}, \dfrac{y_1 + y_2}{2}\right)$ is

$$\left(\dfrac{x_1 + \dfrac{x_1 + x_2}{2}}{2}, \dfrac{y_1 + \dfrac{y_1 + y_2}{2}}{2}\right) = \left(\dfrac{1}{2}\left(\dfrac{2x_1 + x_1 + x_2}{2}\right), \dfrac{1}{2}\left(\dfrac{2y_1 + y_1 + y_2}{2}\right)\right)$$

$$= \left(\dfrac{3x_1 + x_2}{4}, \dfrac{3y_1 + y_2}{4}\right).$$

—CONTINUED—

25. —CONTINUED—

The midpoint between $\left(\dfrac{x_1 + x_2}{2}, \dfrac{y_1 + y_2}{2}\right)$ and (x_2, y_2) is

$$\left(\frac{\frac{x_1 + x_2}{2} + x_2}{2}, \frac{\frac{y_1 + y_2}{2} + y_2}{2}\right) = \left(\frac{1}{2}\left(\frac{x_1 + x_2 + 2x_2}{2}\right), \frac{1}{2}\left(\frac{y_1 + y_2 + 2y_2}{2}\right)\right)$$

$$= \left(\frac{x_1 + 3x_2}{4}, \frac{y_1 + 3y_2}{4}\right)$$

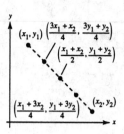

Thus the three points are

$$\left(\frac{3x_1 + x_2}{4}, \frac{3y_1 + y_2}{4}\right), \left(\frac{x_1 + x_2}{2}, \frac{y_1 + y_2}{2}\right), \left(\frac{x_1 + 3x_2}{4}, \frac{y_1 + 3y_2}{4}\right).$$

27. Center: $(0, 0)$

Radius: 1

Matches graph (c)

29. Center: $(1, 0)$

Radius: 0

Matches graph (a)

31. $(x - 0)^2 + (y - 0)^2 = (3)^2$

$$x^2 + y^2 - 9 = 0$$

33. Let $(2, -1) = (h, k)$ and $r = 4$. Then using the standard form of the equation of a circle, we have

$$(x - h)^2 + (y - k)^2 = r^2$$

$$(x - 2)^2 + [y - (-1)]^2 = 4^2$$

$$x^2 - 4x + 4 + y^2 + 2y + 1 = 16$$

$$x^2 + y^2 - 4x + 2y - 11 = 0.$$

35. Radius $= \sqrt{(-1 - 0)^2 + (2 - 0)^2} = \sqrt{5}$

$$(x + 1)^2 + (y - 2)^2 = 5$$

$$x^2 + 2x + 1 + y^2 - 4y + 4 = 5$$

$$x^2 + y^2 + 2x - 4y = 0$$

37. Center $=$ Midpoint $= (3, 2)$

Radius $= \sqrt{10}$

$$(x - 3)^2 + (y - 2)^2 = \left(\sqrt{10}\right)^2$$

$$x^2 - 6x + 9 + y^2 - 4y + 4 = 10$$

$$x^2 + y^2 - 6x - 4y + 3 = 0$$

39. Place the center of the earth at the origin. Then we have

$$x^2 + y^2 = (22,000 + 4,000)^2$$

$$x^2 + y^2 = 26,000^2.$$

41. $$x^2 + y^2 - 2x + 6y + 6 = 0$$

$$(x^2 - 2x + 1) + (y^2 + 6y + 9) = -6 + 1 + 9$$

$$(x - 1)^2 + (y + 3)^2 = 4$$

Center: $(1, -3)$

Radius: 2

43. $$x^2 + y^2 - 2x + 6y + 10 = 0$$

$$(x^2 - 2x + \_\_) + (y^2 + 6y + \_\_) = -10$$

$$(x^2 - 2x + 1) + (y^2 + 6y + 9) = -10 + 1 + 9$$

$$(x - 1)^2 + (y + 3)^2 = 0$$

The only solution point of the equation is $(1, -3)$.

45.
$$2x^2 + 2y^2 - 2x - 2y - 3 = 0$$

$$2\left(x^2 - x + \frac{1}{4}\right) + 2\left(y^2 - y + \frac{1}{4}\right) = 3 + \frac{1}{2} + \frac{1}{2}$$

$$\left(x - \frac{1}{2}\right)^2 - \left(y - \frac{1}{2}\right)^2 = 2$$

Center: $\left(\dfrac{1}{2}, \dfrac{1}{2}\right)$

Radius: $\sqrt{2}$

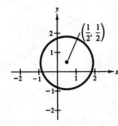

47.
$$16x^2 + 16y^2 + 16x + 40y - 7 = 0$$

$$16\left(x^2 + x + \frac{1}{4}\right) + 16\left(y^2 + \frac{5y}{2} + \frac{25}{16}\right) = 7 + 4 + 25$$

$$16\left(x + \frac{1}{2}\right)^2 + 16\left(y + \frac{5}{4}\right)^2 = 36$$

$$\left(x + \frac{1}{2}\right)^2 + \left(y + \frac{5}{4}\right)^2 = \frac{9}{4}$$

Center: $\left(-\dfrac{1}{2}, -\dfrac{5}{4}\right)$

Radius: $\dfrac{3}{2}$

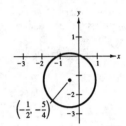

49. (a) $4x^2 + 4y^2 - 4x + 24y - 63 = 0$

$$x^2 + y^2 - x + 6y = \frac{63}{4}$$

$$\left(x^2 - x + \frac{1}{4}\right) + (y^2 + 6y + 9) = \frac{63}{4} + \frac{1}{4} + 9$$

$$\left(x - \frac{1}{2}\right)^2 + (y + 3)^2 = 25$$

$$(y + 3)^2 = 25 - \left(x - \frac{1}{2}\right)^2$$

$$y + 3 = \pm\sqrt{25 - \left(x - \frac{1}{2}\right)^2}$$

$$y = -3 \pm \sqrt{25 - \left(x - \frac{1}{2}\right)^2}$$

$$= \frac{-6 \pm \sqrt{99 + 4x - 4x^2}}{2}$$

(b)

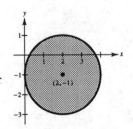

51.
$$x^2 + y^2 - 4x + 2y + 1 \le 0$$

$$(x^2 - 4x + 4) + (y^2 + 2y + 1) \le -1 + 4 + 1$$

$$(x - 2)^2 + (y + 1)^2 \le 4$$

Therefore, the inequality is satisfied by the set of all points lying on the boundary and in the interior of the circle with center $(2, -1)$ and radius 2.

53. The distance between (x_1, y_1) and $\left(\dfrac{2x_1 + x_2}{3}, \dfrac{2y_1 + y_2}{3}\right)$ is

$$d = \sqrt{\left(x_1 - \dfrac{2x_1 + x_2}{3}\right)^2 + \left(y_1 - \dfrac{2y_1 + y_2}{3}\right)^2}$$

$$= \sqrt{\left(\dfrac{x_1 - x_2}{3}\right)^2 + \left(\dfrac{y_1 - y_2}{3}\right)^2}$$

$$= \sqrt{\dfrac{1}{9}[(x_1 - x_2)^2 + (y_1 - y_2)^2]} = \dfrac{1}{3}\sqrt{(x_1 - x_2)^2 + (y_1 - y_2)^2}$$

which is $\frac{1}{3}$ of the distance between (x_1, y_1) and (x_2, y_2).

$$\left(\dfrac{\left(\dfrac{2x_1 + x_2}{3}\right) + x_2}{2}, \dfrac{\left(\dfrac{2y_1 + y_2}{3}\right) + y_2}{2}\right) = \left(\dfrac{x_1 + 2x_2}{3}, \dfrac{y_1 + 2y_2}{3}\right)$$

is the second point of trisection.

55. True; if $ab < 0$ then either a is positive and b is negative (Quadrant IV) or a is negative and b is positive (Quadrant II).

57. True

59. Let one vertex be at $(0, 0)$ and another at $(a, 0)$.

Midpoint of $(0, 0)$ and (d, e) is $\left(\dfrac{d}{2}, \dfrac{e}{2}\right)$.

Midpoint of (b, c) and $(a, 0)$ is $\left(\dfrac{a + b}{2}, \dfrac{c}{2}\right)$.

Midpoint of $(0, 0)$ and $(a, 0)$ is $\left(\dfrac{a}{2}, 0\right)$.

Midpoint of (b, c) and (d, e) is $\left(\dfrac{b + d}{2}, \dfrac{c + e}{2}\right)$.

Midpoint of line segment joining $\left(\dfrac{d}{2}, \dfrac{e}{2}\right)$ and $\left(\dfrac{a + b}{2}, \dfrac{c}{2}\right)$ is $\left(\dfrac{a + b + d}{4}, \dfrac{c + e}{4}\right)$.

Midpoint of line segment joining $\left(\dfrac{a}{2}, 0\right)$ and $\left(\dfrac{b + d}{2}, \dfrac{c + e}{2}\right)$ is $\left(\dfrac{a + b + d}{4}, \dfrac{c + e}{4}\right)$.

Therefore the line segments intersect at their midpoints.

61. For simplicity, assume the semicircle is centered at the origin with a radius r (see figure). If (a, b) is a point on the semicircle, then it must satisfy the equation $a^2 + b^2 = r^2$. To verify that the angle at (a, b) is a right angle, it is sufficient to show that $d_1^2 + d_2^2 = d_3^2$.

$$d_1^2 = [a - (-r)]^2 + (b - 0)^2$$

$$d_2^2 = (a - r)^2 + (b - 0)^2$$

$$d_1^2 + d_2^2 = (a^2 + 2ar + r^2 + b^2) + (a^2 - 2ar + r^2 + b^2)$$

$$= 2a^2 + 2b^2 + 2r^2$$

$$= 2(a^2 + b^2) + 2r^2$$

$$= 2r^2 + 2r^2 = 4r^2 = (2r)^2 = d_3^2$$

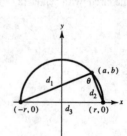

Appendix A.3

1. (a) $396°, -324°$

(b) $240°, -480°$

3. (a) $\dfrac{19\pi}{9}, -\dfrac{17\pi}{9}$

(b) $\dfrac{10\pi}{3}, -\dfrac{2\pi}{3}$

5. (a) $30\left(\dfrac{\pi}{180}\right) = \dfrac{\pi}{6} \approx 0.524$

(b) $150\left(\dfrac{\pi}{180}\right) = \dfrac{5\pi}{6} \approx 2.618$

(c) $315\left(\dfrac{\pi}{180}\right) = \dfrac{7\pi}{4} \approx 5.498$

(d) $120\left(\dfrac{\pi}{180}\right) = \dfrac{2\pi}{3} \approx 2.094$

7. Since $180° = \pi$ radians, it follows that 1 radian $= 180°/\pi$.

(a) $\dfrac{3\pi}{2}$ radians $= \left(\dfrac{3\pi}{2}\right)\left(\dfrac{180°}{\pi}\right) = 270°$

(b) $\dfrac{7\pi}{6}$ radians $= \left(\dfrac{7\pi}{6}\right)\left(\dfrac{180°}{\pi}\right) = 210°$

(c) $-\dfrac{7\pi}{12}$ radians $= \left(-\dfrac{7\pi}{12}\right)\left(\dfrac{180°}{\pi}\right) = -105°$

(d) -2.367 radians $= (-2.367)\left(\dfrac{180°}{\pi}\right) \approx -135.619°$

9.

r	8 ft	15 in.	85 cm	24 in.	$\dfrac{12963}{\pi}$ mi.
s	12 ft.	24 in.	63.72π	96 in.	8642 mi.
θ	1.5	1.6	$\dfrac{3\pi}{4}$	4	$\dfrac{2\pi}{3}$

11. (a) From the figure we have $x = 3$, $y = 4$, and $r = \sqrt{x^2 + y^2} = 5$.

$\sin\theta = \dfrac{y}{r} = \dfrac{4}{5}$ $\qquad \csc\theta = \dfrac{r}{y} = \dfrac{5}{4}$

$\cos\theta = \dfrac{x}{r} = \dfrac{3}{5}$ $\qquad \sec\theta = \dfrac{r}{x} = \dfrac{5}{3}$

$\tan\theta = \dfrac{y}{x} = \dfrac{4}{3}$ $\qquad \cot\theta = \dfrac{x}{y} = \dfrac{3}{4}$

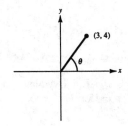

(b) From the figure we have $x = -12$, $y = -5$, and $r = \sqrt{x^2 + y^2} = 13$.

$\sin\theta = \dfrac{y}{r} = -\dfrac{5}{13}$ $\qquad \csc\theta = \dfrac{r}{y} = -\dfrac{13}{5}$

$\cos\theta = \dfrac{x}{r} = -\dfrac{12}{13}$ $\qquad \sec\theta = \dfrac{r}{x} = -\dfrac{13}{12}$

$\tan\theta = \dfrac{y}{x} = \dfrac{5}{12}$ $\qquad \cot\theta = \dfrac{x}{y} = \dfrac{12}{5}$

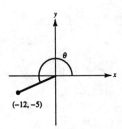

13. (a) $\sin\theta < 0 \Rightarrow \theta$ is in Quadrant III or IV.

$\cos\theta < 0 \Rightarrow \theta$ is in Quadrant II or III.

$\sin\theta < 0$ **and** $\cos\theta < 0 \Rightarrow \theta$ is in Quadrant III.

(b) $\sec\theta > 0 \Rightarrow \theta$ is in Quadrant I or IV.

$\cot\theta < 0 \Rightarrow \theta$ is in Quadrant II or IV.

$\sec\theta > 0$ **and** $\cot\theta < 0 \Rightarrow \theta$ is in Quadrant IV.

15. $x^2 + 1^2 = 2^2 \Rightarrow x = \sqrt{3}$

$\cos\theta = \dfrac{x}{2} = \dfrac{\sqrt{3}}{2}$

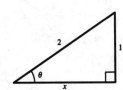

17. Using the fact that

$$\cos \theta = \frac{4}{5},$$

construct the figure and obtain

$$\cot \theta = \frac{4}{y} = \frac{4}{\sqrt{25 - 16}} = \frac{4}{3}.$$

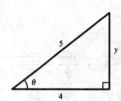

19. (a) $\sin 60° = \dfrac{\sqrt{3}}{2}$

$\cos 60° = \dfrac{1}{2}$

$\tan 60° = \sqrt{3}$

(c) $\sin \dfrac{\pi}{4} = \dfrac{\sqrt{2}}{2}$

$\cos \dfrac{\pi}{4} = \dfrac{\sqrt{2}}{2}$

$\tan \dfrac{\pi}{4} = 1$

(b) $\sin 120° = \sin 60° = \dfrac{\sqrt{3}}{2}$

$\cos 120° = -\cos 60° = -\dfrac{1}{2}$

$\tan 120° = -\tan 60° = -\sqrt{3}$

(d) $\sin \dfrac{5\pi}{4} - \sin \dfrac{\pi}{4} = -\dfrac{\sqrt{2}}{2}$

$\cos \dfrac{5\pi}{4} = \cos \dfrac{\pi}{4} = -\dfrac{\sqrt{2}}{2}$

$\tan \dfrac{5\pi}{4} = \tan \dfrac{\pi}{4} = 1$

21. (a) The angle $225°$ is in Quadrant III and the reference angle is $225° - 180° = 45°$. Therefore,

$$\sin 225° = -\sin 45° = -\frac{\sqrt{2}}{2}$$

$$\cos 225° = -\cos 45° = -\frac{\sqrt{2}}{2}$$

$$\tan 225° = \tan 45° = 1.$$

(b) The angle $-225°$ is in Quadrant II and the reference angle is $225° - 180° = 45°$. Therefore,

$$\sin (-225°) = \sin 45° = \frac{\sqrt{2}}{2}$$

$$\cos (-225°) = -\cos 45° = -\frac{\sqrt{2}}{2}$$

$$\tan (-225°) = -\tan 45° = -1.$$

(c) The angle $5\pi/3$ is in Quadrant IV and the reference angle is $2\pi - (5\pi/3) = \pi/3$. Therefore,

$$\sin \frac{5\pi}{3} = -\sin \frac{\pi}{3} = -\frac{\sqrt{3}}{2}$$

$$\cos \frac{5\pi}{3} = \cos \frac{\pi}{3} = \frac{1}{2}$$

$$\tan \frac{5\pi}{3} = -\tan \frac{\pi}{3} = -\sqrt{3}.$$

(d) The angle $11\pi/6$ is in Quadrant IV and the reference angle is $2\pi - (11\pi/6) = \pi/6$. Therefore,

$$\sin \frac{11\pi}{6} = -\sin \frac{\pi}{6} = -\frac{1}{2}$$

$$\cos \frac{11\pi}{6} = \cos \frac{\pi}{6} = \frac{\sqrt{3}}{2}$$

$$\tan \frac{11\pi}{6} = -\tan \frac{\pi}{6} = -\frac{\sqrt{3}}{3}.$$

23. (a) $\sin 10° \approx 0.1736$

(b) $\csc 10° \approx 5.759$

25. (a) $\tan \dfrac{\pi}{9} \approx 0.3640$

(b) $\tan \dfrac{10\pi}{9} \approx 0.3640$

27. (a) $\cos \theta = \dfrac{\sqrt{2}}{2}$

To solve the equation, we realize that the cosine is positive in Quadrants I and IV and that

$$\cos \frac{\pi}{4} = \frac{\sqrt{2}}{2}.$$

Therefore, the reference angle is $\pi/4$ and the required angles are

$$\theta = \frac{\pi}{4} \text{ and } \theta = 2\pi - \frac{\pi}{4} = \frac{7\pi}{4}.$$

(b) $\cos \theta = -\dfrac{\sqrt{2}}{2}$

To solve the equation, we realize that the cosine is negative in Quadrants II and III and that

$$\cos \frac{\pi}{4} = \frac{\sqrt{2}}{2}.$$

Therefore, the reference angle is $\pi/4$ and the required angles are

$$\theta = \pi - \frac{\pi}{4} = \frac{3\pi}{4} \text{ and } \theta = \pi + \frac{\pi}{4} = \frac{5\pi}{4}.$$

29. (a) $\tan \theta = 1$

$$\theta = \frac{\pi}{4}, \frac{5\pi}{4}$$

(b) $\cot \theta = -\sqrt{3}$

$$\theta = \frac{5\pi}{6}, \frac{11\pi}{6}$$

31. $2 \sin^2 \theta = 1$

$$\sin \theta = \pm \frac{\sqrt{2}}{2}$$

$$\theta = \frac{\pi}{4}, \frac{3\pi}{4}, \frac{5\pi}{4}, \frac{7\pi}{4}$$

33. $\tan^2 \theta - \tan \theta = 0, 0 \leq \theta < 2\pi$

$$\tan \theta(\tan \theta - 1) = 0$$

If $\tan \theta = 0$, then $\theta = 0$ or $\theta = \pi$. If $\tan \theta - 1 = 0$, then $\tan \theta = 1$ and $\theta = \pi/4$ or $\theta = 5\pi/4$. Thus for

$$0 \leq \theta < 2\pi,$$

there are four solutions:

$$\theta = 0, \frac{\pi}{4}, \pi, \frac{5\pi}{4}.$$

35. $\sec \theta \csc \theta - 2 \csc \theta = 0$

$$\csc \theta(\sec \theta - 2) = 0$$

$$(\csc \theta \neq 0 \text{ for any value of } \theta)$$

$$\sec \theta = 2$$

$$\theta = \frac{\pi}{3}, \frac{5\pi}{3}$$

37. $\cos^2 \theta + \sin \theta = 1$

$$1 - \sin^2 \theta + \sin \theta = 1$$

$$\sin^2 \theta - \sin \theta = 0$$

$$\sin \theta(\sin \theta - 1) = 0$$

$$\sin \theta = 0 \qquad \sin \theta = 1$$

$$\theta = 0, \pi \qquad \theta = \frac{\pi}{2}$$

39. In one minute the plane travels

$$(60 \text{ sec})(275 \text{ ft/sec}) = 16{,}500 \text{ ft.}$$

This distance is the approximate length of the hypotenuse of a right triangle whose side opposite the angle of magnitude $18°$ is the altitude h of the plane. Therefore,

$$\sin 18° \approx \frac{h}{16{,}500}$$

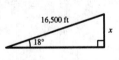

$$16{,}500 \sin 18° \approx h$$

$$h \approx 5100 \text{ ft.}$$

41. (a) Period: π

Amplitude: 2

(b) Period: 2

Amplitude: $\frac{1}{2}$

43. Period: $\frac{1}{2}$

Amplitude: 3

45. Period: $\dfrac{\pi}{2}$

47. Since the period of $y = \sec x$ is 2π, the period of $y = \sec 5x$ is $\dfrac{2\pi}{5}$.

49. (a) $f(x) = c \sin x$; changing c changes the amplitude.

When $c = -2$: $f(x) = -2 \sin x$.

When $c = -1$: $f(x) = -\sin x$.

When $c = 1$: $f(x) = \sin x$.

When $c = 2$: $f(x) = 2 \sin x$.

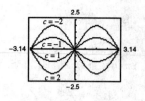

(b) $f(x) = \cos(cx)$; changing c changes the period.

When $c = -2$: $f(x) = \cos(-2x) = \cos 2x$.

When $c = -1$: $f(x) = \cos(-x) = \cos x$.

When $c = 1$: $f(x) = \cos x$.

When $c = 2$: $f(x) = \cos 2x$.

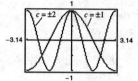

(c) $f(x) = \cos(\pi x - c)$; changing c causes a horizontal shift.

When $c = -2$: $f(x) = \cos(\pi x + 2)$.

When $c = -1$: $f(x) = \cos(\pi x + 1)$.

When $c = 1$: $f(x) = \cos(\pi x - 1)$.

When $c = 2$: $f(x) = \cos(\pi x - 2)$.

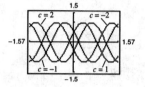

51. $y = \sin \dfrac{x}{2}$

Period: 4π

Amplitude: 1

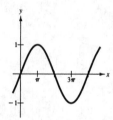

53. $y = -\sin \dfrac{2\pi x}{3}$

Period: 3

Amplitude: 1

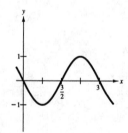

55. The graph of $y = \csc(x/2)$ has the following characteristics:

Period: $\dfrac{2\pi}{1/2} = 4\pi$

Vertical asymptote: $x = 2n\pi$, n an integer

Using the basic shape of the graph of the cosecant function, we sketch one period of the function on the interval $[0, 4\pi]$, following the pattern

minimum: $(\pi, 1)$

maximum: $(3\pi, -1)$.

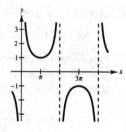

57. $y = 2 \sec 2x$

Period: π

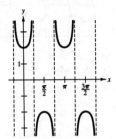

59. $y = \sin(x + \pi)$

Period: 2π

Amplitude: 1

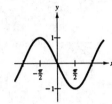

61. $y = 1 + \cos\left(x - \dfrac{\pi}{2}\right)$

Period: 2π

Amplitude: 1

63. $y = a\cos(bx - c)$

From the graph, we see that the amplitude is 3, the period is 4π and the horizontal shift is, π. Thus,

$a = 3$

$\dfrac{2\pi}{b} = 4\pi \Rightarrow b = \dfrac{1}{2}$

$\dfrac{c}{d} = \pi \Rightarrow c = \dfrac{\pi}{2}.$

Therefore, $y = 3\cos[(1/2)x - (\pi/2)]$.

65. $f(x) = \sin x$

$g(x) = |\sin x|$

$h(x) = \sin|x|$

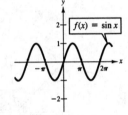 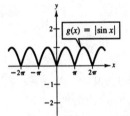 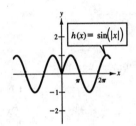

The graph of $|f(x)|$ will reflect any parts of the graph below the x-axis about the y-axis.

The graph of $f(|x|)$ will reflect the part of the graph to the left of the y-axis about the x-axis.

67. $S = 58.3 + 32.5\cos\dfrac{\pi t}{6}$

The graph of the sales function and the horizontal line $S = 75$ are shown in the figure. Using the capabilities of a graphing utility to find the points of intersection of two graphs, we find that the graphs intersect when $t = 1.97$ and $t = 10.03$. Therefore, sales exceed 75,000 during the months of January, November, and December.

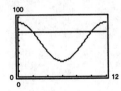

69. $f(x) = \dfrac{4}{\pi}\left(\sin \pi x + \dfrac{1}{3}\sin 3\pi x\right)$

$g(x) = \dfrac{4}{\pi}\left(\sin \pi x + \dfrac{1}{3}\sin 3\pi x + \dfrac{1}{5}\sin 5\pi x\right)$

Pattern:

$$f(x) = \dfrac{4}{\pi}\left(\sin \pi x + \dfrac{1}{3}\sin 3\pi x + \dfrac{1}{5}\sin 5\pi x + \cdots + \dfrac{1}{2n-1}\sin(2n-1)\pi x\right),\ n = 1, 2, 3 \ldots$$

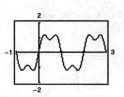

Appendix E

1. $xy + 1 = 0$

$\cot 2\theta = \dfrac{A - C}{B} = 0,\ 2\theta = \dfrac{\pi}{2} \implies \theta = \dfrac{\pi}{4}$

$x = x'\cos\dfrac{\pi}{4} - y'\sin\dfrac{\pi}{4} = \dfrac{x' - y'}{\sqrt{2}}$

$y = x'\sin\dfrac{\pi}{4} + y'\cos\dfrac{\pi}{4} = \dfrac{x' + y'}{\sqrt{2}}$

$\left(\dfrac{x' - y'}{\sqrt{2}}\right)\left(\dfrac{x' + y'}{\sqrt{2}}\right) + 1 = 0$

$\dfrac{(y')^2}{2} - \dfrac{(x')^2}{2} = 1$

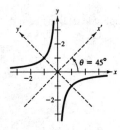

3. From the equations

$$x^2 - 10xy + y^2 + 1 = 0$$

$$Ax^2 + Bxy + Cy^2 + Dx + Ey + F = 0$$

we have $A = 1,\ B = -10,\ C = 1,\ D = 0,\ E = 0,$ and $F = 1.$ Thus

$$\cot 2\theta = \dfrac{A - C}{B} = 0 \quad \text{or} \quad 2\theta = \dfrac{\pi}{2} \quad \text{and} \quad \theta = \dfrac{\pi}{4}.$$

Therefore, $\sin \theta = \cos \theta = \dfrac{\sqrt{2}}{2}$ and

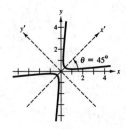

$$x = x'\cos \theta - y'\sin \theta = \dfrac{\sqrt{2}}{2}x' - \dfrac{\sqrt{2}}{2}y'$$

$$y = x'\sin \theta + y'\cos \theta = \dfrac{\sqrt{2}}{2}x' + \dfrac{\sqrt{2}}{2}y'.$$

Substitution into $x^2 - 10xy + y^2 + 1 = 0$ yields

$$\left(\dfrac{\sqrt{2}}{2}x' - \dfrac{\sqrt{2}}{2}y'\right)^2 - 10\left(\dfrac{\sqrt{2}}{2}x' - \dfrac{\sqrt{2}}{2}y'\right)\left(\dfrac{\sqrt{2}}{2}x' + \dfrac{\sqrt{2}}{2}y'\right) + \left(\dfrac{\sqrt{2}}{2}x' + \dfrac{\sqrt{2}}{2}y'\right)^2 + 1 = 0.$$

After expanding and combining like terms we have

$$-4(x')^2 + 6(y')^2 + 1 = 0 \quad \text{or} \quad \dfrac{(x')^2}{1/4} - \dfrac{(y')^2}{1/6} = 1.$$

5. $xy - 2y - 4x = 0$

$$\cot 2\theta = \frac{A - C}{B} = 0, \ 2\theta = \frac{\pi}{2} \implies \theta = \frac{\pi}{4}$$

$$x = x' \cos \frac{\pi}{4} - y' \sin \frac{\pi}{4} = \frac{x' - y'}{\sqrt{2}}$$

$$y = x' \sin \frac{\pi}{4} + y' \cos \frac{\pi}{4} = \frac{x' + y'}{\sqrt{2}}$$

$$\left(\frac{x' - y'}{\sqrt{2}}\right)\left(\frac{x' + y'}{\sqrt{2}}\right) - 2\left(\frac{x' + y'}{\sqrt{2}}\right) - 4\left(\frac{x' - y'}{\sqrt{2}}\right) = 0$$

$$\frac{1}{2}(x')^2 - \frac{1}{2}(y')^2 - 3\sqrt{2}x' + \sqrt{2}y' = 0$$

$$\frac{(x' - 3\sqrt{2})^2}{16} - \frac{(y' - \sqrt{2})^2}{16} = 1$$

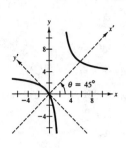

7. From the equations

$$5x^2 - 2xy + 5y^2 - 12 = 0$$

$$Ax^2 + Bxy + Cy^2 + Dx + Ey + F = 0$$

we have $A = 5$, $B = -2$, $C = 5$, $D = 0$, $E = 0$, and $F = -12$. Thus

$$\cot 2\theta = \frac{A - C}{B} = 0 \quad \text{or} \quad 2\theta = \frac{\pi}{2} \quad \text{and} \quad \theta = \frac{\pi}{4}.$$

Therefore, $\sin \theta = \cos \theta = \frac{\sqrt{2}}{2}$ and

$$x = x' \cos \theta - y' \sin \theta = \frac{\sqrt{2}}{2}x' - \frac{\sqrt{2}}{2}y'$$

$$y = x' \sin \theta + y' \cos \theta = \frac{\sqrt{2}}{2}x' + \frac{\sqrt{2}}{2}y'$$

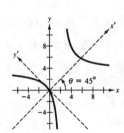

Substituting into $5x^2 - 2xy + 5y^2 - 12 = 0$ yields

$$5\left(\frac{\sqrt{2}}{2}x' - \frac{\sqrt{2}}{2}y'\right)^2 - 2\left(\frac{\sqrt{2}}{2}x' - \frac{\sqrt{2}}{2}y'\right)\left(\frac{\sqrt{2}}{2}x' + \frac{\sqrt{2}}{2}y'\right) + 5\left(\frac{\sqrt{2}}{2}x' + \frac{\sqrt{2}}{2}y'\right)^2 - 12 = 0.$$

After expanding and combining like terms we have

$$4(x')^2 + 6(y')^2 - 12 = 0$$

$$\frac{(x')^2}{3} + \frac{(y')^2}{2} = 1.$$

9. $3x^2 - 2\sqrt{3}xy + y^2 + 2x + 2\sqrt{3}y = 0$

$$\cot 2\theta = -\frac{1}{\sqrt{3}}, \ 2\theta = \frac{2\pi}{3} \implies \theta = \frac{\pi}{3}$$

$$x = x' \cos \frac{\pi}{3} - y' \sin \frac{\pi}{3} = \frac{x' - 3y'}{2}$$

$$y = x' \sin \frac{\pi}{3} + y' \cos \frac{\pi}{3} = \frac{\sqrt{3}x' + y'}{2}$$

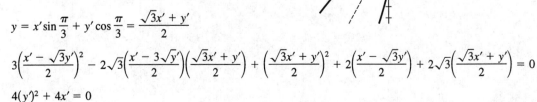

$$3\left(\frac{x' - \sqrt{3}y'}{2}\right)^2 - 2\sqrt{3}\left(\frac{x' - 3\sqrt{y'}}{2}\right)\left(\frac{\sqrt{3}x' + y'}{2}\right) + \left(\frac{\sqrt{3}x' + y'}{2}\right)^2 + 2\left(\frac{x' - \sqrt{3}y'}{2}\right) + 2\sqrt{3}\left(\frac{\sqrt{3}x' + y'}{2}\right) = 0$$

$$4(y')^2 + 4x' = 0$$

$$x' = -(y')^2$$

11. From the equations

$$9x^2 + 24xy + 16y^2 + 90x - 130y = 0$$

$$Ax^2 + Bxy + Cy^2 + Dx + Ey + F = 0$$

we have $A = 9$, $B = 24$, $C = 16$, $D = 90$, $E = -130$, and $F = 0$. Thus

$$\cot 2\theta = \frac{A - C}{B} = \frac{9 - 16}{24} = \frac{-7}{24}.$$

From the identity

$$\cot 2\theta = \frac{\cot^2 \theta - 1}{2 \cot \theta},$$

we have

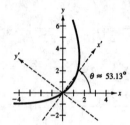

$\theta \approx 53.13°$

$$\frac{\cot^2 \theta - 1}{2 \cot \theta} = \frac{-7}{24}$$

$$24 \cot^2 \theta - 24 = -14 \cot \theta$$

$$12 \cot^2 \theta + 7 \cot \theta - 12 = 0$$

$$(4 \cot \theta - 3)(3 \cot \theta + 4) = 0$$

$$\cot \theta = \frac{3}{4} \ \text{ or } \ -\frac{4}{3}.$$

Since $0 < \theta < 90°$, choose $\cot \theta = \frac{3}{4}$ and therefore, $\theta \approx 53.13°$. Since $\cot \theta = \frac{3}{4}$, $\sin \theta = \frac{4}{5}$ and $\cos \theta = \frac{3}{5}$. Therefore, using the equations

$$x = x' \cos \theta - y' \sin \theta = \frac{3}{5}x' - \frac{4}{5}y'$$

$$y = x' \sin \theta + y' \cos \theta = \frac{4}{5}x' + \frac{3}{5}y'$$

and

$$9x^2 + 24xy + 16y^2 + 90x - 130y = 0,$$

we have

$$9\left(\frac{3}{5}x' - \frac{4}{5}y'\right)^2 + 24\left(\frac{3}{5}x' - \frac{4}{5}y'\right)\left(\frac{4}{5}x' + \frac{3}{5}y'\right) + 16\left(\frac{4}{5}x' + \frac{3}{5}y'\right)^2 + 90\left(\frac{3}{5}x' - \frac{4}{5}y'\right) - 130\left(\frac{4}{5}x' + \frac{3}{5}y'\right) = 0.$$

After expanding and combining like terms we have

$$25(x')^2 - 50x' - 150y' = 0$$

$$(x')^2 - 2x' - 6y' = 0$$

$$(x' - 1)^2 = 4\left(\frac{3}{2}\right)\left(y' + \frac{1}{6}\right).$$

13. $x^2 + xy + y^2 = 10$

$$\cot 2\theta = \frac{A - C}{B} = 0 \implies \theta = \frac{\pi}{4} = 45°$$

Solve for y in terms of x.

$$y^2 + xy + \frac{x^2}{4} = 10 - x^2 + \frac{x^2}{4}$$

$$\left(y + \frac{x}{2}\right)^2 = \frac{40 - 3x^2}{4}$$

$$y = -\frac{x}{2} \pm \frac{\sqrt{40 - 3x^2}}{2} = \frac{-x \pm \sqrt{40 - 3x^2}}{2}$$

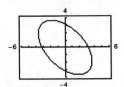

15. $17x^2 + 32xy - 7y^2 = 75$

$$\cot 2\theta = \frac{3}{4} \implies \theta = \frac{1}{2} \operatorname{arccot} \frac{3}{4} \approx 26.57°$$

Solve for y in terms of x.

$$7\left(y^2 - \frac{32}{7}xy + \frac{256}{49}x^2\right) = 17x^2 - 75 + \frac{256}{7}x^2$$

$$\left(y - \frac{16}{7}x\right)^2 = \frac{375x^2 - 525}{49}$$

$$y = \frac{16x \pm \sqrt{375x^2 - 525}}{7}$$

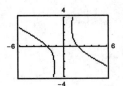

17. From the equations

$$32x^2 + 50xy + 7y^2 = 52$$

$$Ax^2 + Bxy + Cy^2 + Dx + Ey + F = 0,$$

we have $A = 32, B = 50, C = 7, D = 0, E = 0$, and $F = -52$. Therefore,

$$\cot 2\theta = \frac{A - C}{B} = \frac{1}{2}$$

$$\theta = \frac{1}{2} \operatorname{arccot} \frac{1}{2} \approx 31.72°.$$

Use the Quadratic Formula to solve for y in terms of x.

$$7y^2 + (50x)y + (32x^2 - 52) = 0$$

$$y = \frac{-50x \pm \sqrt{(50x)^2 - 4(7)(32x^2 - 52)}}{2(7)}$$

$$= \frac{-50x \pm 2\sqrt{401x^2 + 364}}{2(7)}$$

$$= \frac{-25x \pm \sqrt{401x^2 + 364}}{7}$$

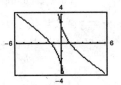

Use a graphing utility to graph the two resulting equations and obtain the hyperbola shown in the figure.

19. $B^2 - 4AC = (-24)^2 - 4(16)(9) = 0$

Parabola

21. $B^2 - 4AC = (-8)^2 - 4(13)(7) = -300$

Ellipse

23. $B^2 - 4AC = (-6)^2 - 4(1)(-5) = 56$

Hyperbola

25. From the equations

$$x^2 + 4xy + 4y^2 - 5x - y - 3 = 0$$

$$Ax^2 + Bxy + Cy^2 + Dx + Ey + F = 0$$

we have $A = 1, B = 4, C = 4, D = -5, E = -1$, and $F = -3$. The value of the discriminant is

$$B^2 - 4AC = 4^2 - 4(1)4 = 0$$

and the curve is a parabola.

27. $y^2 - 4x^2 = 0$

$y = \pm 2x$

Two intersecting lines

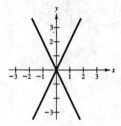

29. $x^2 + 2xy + y^2 - 1 = 0$

$(x + y)^2 = 1$

$x + y = \pm 1$

Two parallel lines

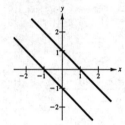

31. $(x - 2y + 1)(x + 2y - 3) = 0$

$x - 2y + 1 = 0 \qquad \text{or} \qquad x + 2y - 3 = 0$

$x - 2y = -1 \qquad\qquad\qquad x + 2y = 3$

Two intersecting lines

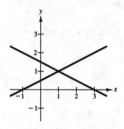

33. $(x')^2 + (y')^2 = (x \cos \theta + y \sin \theta)^2 + (y \cos \theta - x \sin \theta)^2$

$\qquad = x^2 \cos^2 \theta + 2xy \cos \theta \sin \theta + y^2 \sin^2 \theta + y^2 \cos^2 \theta - 2xy \cos \theta \sin \theta + x^2 \sin^2 \theta$

$\qquad = x^2(\cos^2 \theta + \sin^2 \theta) + y^2(\sin^2 \theta + \cos^2\theta) = x^2 + y^2 = r^2$